Biochemistry and Disease

Bridging

Basic Science and

Clinical Practice

Biochemistry and Disease

Bridging

Basic Science and

Clinical Practice

Robert M. Cohn, M.D.
Deputy Director
Clinical Laboratories
Senior Physician, Division of Metabolism
The Children's Hospital of Philadelphia
Associate Professor,
Department of Pediatrics
University of Pennsylvania
School of Medicine
Philadelphia, Pennsylvania

Karl S. Roth, M.D.
Professor and Chair
Division of Genetics, Endocrinology,
and Metabolism
Department of Pediatrics
Professor, Biochemistry and
Molecular Biophysics
Medical College of Virginia
Richmond, Virginia

Williams & Wilkins
A WAVERLY COMPANY
BALTIMORE • PHILADELPHIA • LONDON • PARIS • BANGKOK
BUENOS AIRES • HONG KONG • MUNICH • SYDNEY • TOKYO • WROCLAW
1996

Executive Editor: Carroll C. Cann
Managing Editor: Tanya Lazar
Production Coordinator: Danielle Santucci
Copy Editor: Arlene C. Sheir-Allen
Designer: Karen Klinedinst
Cover Designer: Karen Klinedinst
Typesetter: Maryland Composition Co., Inc.
Printer: Port City Press, Inc.
Binder: Port City Press, Inc.
The halftones on the cover are from O'Connor, B.H.: A Color Atlas and Instruction Manual of Peripheral Blood Cell Morphology. Baltimore: Williams and Wilkins, 1984.

351 West Camden Street
Baltimore, Maryland 21201-2436 USA

Rose Tree Corporate Center
1400 North Providence Road
Building II, Suite 5025
Media, Pennsylvania 19063-2043 USA

Accurate indications, adverse reactions and dosage schedules for drugs are provided in this book, but it is possible that they may change. The reader is urged to review the package information data of the manufacturers of the medications mentioned.

Printed in the United States of America

Library of Congress Cataloging-in-Publication Data

Cohn, Robert M.
Biochemistry and disease : bridging basic science and clinical practice / Robert M. Cohn, Karl S. Roth.
p. cm.
Includes bibliographical references and index.
ISBN 0-683-02049-8
1. Clinical biochemistry. I. Roth, Karl S. II. Title.
[DNLM: 1. Medicine. 2. Biochemistry. 3. Metabolic Diseases. WB. 100 C679b 1996]
RB112.5.C64 1996
616.07—dc20
DNLM/DLC
for Library of Congress 96-24383
CIP

The publishers have made every effort to trace the copyright holders for borrowed material. If they have inadvertently overlooked any, they will be pleased to make the necessary arrangements at the first opportunity.

96 97 98 99
1 2 3 4 5 6 7 8 9 10

Dedication

To my wife Nancy for being so nurturing and patient, and for believing in this project as much as I do. To my children Eric and Scott who now understand, through personal experience, the joy of being dedicated to a calling. To my parents Eva and Emanuel for instilling in their children a sense of wonder about the world and the values of kindness and honesty.

Robert M. Cohn

To my wife Carole whose love and support has sustained and encouraged me throughout. To my son Chris, whose keen insight helped shape my approach to difficult issues from the first- and second-year medical student's point of view. To my son Marc, whose gentleness and tolerance since infancy remain an inspiration to me. To my son Parham, who entered my life just in time to remind me that this book may help children whose parents love them as much as I love him. To my parents Victor and Ruth, who taught me how to be a good husband and father and to cherish and try to understand the world in which we all live.

Karl S. Roth

To all of those students of Medicine who work through their fatigue to learn, and thereby help their patients cope with and understand what has gone wrong with their bodies.

Robert M. Cohn
Karl S. Roth

Preface

For more than 2000 years, the history of medicine is replete with examples of men who, driven by a restless need to know, have braved the worst imaginable penalties in order to unlock puzzles, the answers to which are now common knowledge. In the 16th century, the great French mathematician René Descartes gave voice to those whose curiosity would not let them rest—"Cognito, ergo sum" (I think, therefore I am). This concept of man as a rational being who thus defines his own existence has formed the philosophical framework of western thought for centuries since. In the past decade, medical science has experienced a virtual explosion in the centuries-long quest for basic understanding of clinical phenomena. This has been brought about chiefly by the application of many new technologies in the field of molecular biology to the study of genetics. The results have enabled us, as never before, to explain disease in molecular terms. Further applications in the areas of infectious disease and pharmacology have helped us to understand acquired disease and its treatment modalities in terms unimaginable only 20 years ago. We are in the process of learning about the molecular basis of life itself. Indeed, so close are we that were Descartes to return, he might be convinced to restate his theorem as "Sum, ergo cognito" (I am, therefore I think).

This book, as originally conceived by us, was intended to help the sagging spirits of the first-year medical student by enabling him or her to understand the applicability of the basic sciences to the practice of medicine. As pedagogues who believe in the dictum that all disease is biochemical in nature, it has dismayed us over the years to watch students suffer through material that should be exciting to them. Yet, it is admittedly difficult for even the best and the brightest of students to grasp clinical relevance in the Michaelis-Menten equation, especially when inundated by massive quantities of additional, equally bewildering information. To make such relevance clear, then, became our inspiration as we conceived the format of the work. However, as we talked, it became apparent that the same work might reasonably be considered useful for the physician who has become competent in diagnosis and treatment, but has long since relegated basic science material to the catacombs of the mind. Thus, we would describe our concept as a "bidirectional" one, which should serve each end of the learning spectrum equally well, but in different fashions.

As we emerged from the early embryological stages of this book, an unexpected event occurred in American medicine—the mandate from the highest level of government that academic medicine train more generalist physicians. If this mandate is implemented, the next and following generations of physicians will have fewer and fewer resources other than their own wits upon which to rely in the face of a difficult diagnostic situation. Access to subspecialists will become increasingly difficult. To offset these impending problems in delivering optimal health care, it becomes all the more critical for students headed for primary care to achieve a profound understanding of disease mechanisms.

In a very real sense, we would hope that each of our readers comes away with the feeling that the book was helpful and written specifically for him or her, much in the same way that a teacher answers an eager student's question. We have endeavored to demystify and avoid jargon as much as possible, although in the interests of reading beyond this text, certain specific terminology was considered essential. It has been our primary aim to convey understanding, frequently at the expense of comprehensive coverage of a subject. We make claim only to accurate and understandable explanation of what are often exceedingly difficult concepts. To the extent possible, we have endeavored to deal with mechanisms of disease at a molecular level. However, in many areas of medicine, what is available as a basis for understanding does not go beyond the level of normal and abnormal physiology. In cardiovascular disease, for example, only in the past decade have investigators started delving into molecular mechanisms of myocardial function. Where such information is lacking, we have limited discussion to what is available. Thus, absence of biochemical discussion in a particular instance may be taken as a measure of the size of the information gap regarding the specific subject. For completeness, the reader in search of further information is referred to specific works listed at the end of each chapter.

Despite its rather novel nature, the organization of the book has a clear rationale. In the first part, we have provided Chapter 1 as a very brief overview and review of some of the basic biochemical concepts needed to understand the text. The second chapter, in the best tradition of medical pedagogy, is intended to demonstrate how many of these concepts and principles act together to bring about normal growth and development of the organism. Chapters 3 to 6 are prime examples of authors' privilege, wherein we have discussed what we believe to be the most global areas of biochemistry, which are basic to an understanding of the remainder of the book. For example, the fundamental biochemical function of energy production depends upon synthesis of heme (Chapter 6), a compound generally consigned by students and physicians alike to oxygen carriage in its role as a moiety of hemoglobin. Yet, this general oversight leads to huge gaps in understanding of, for example, the interplay between cyanide poisoning and membrane transport. Moreover, beyond the red blood cell, all other cell types in the body oxidatively metabolize and, therefore, require hemoproteins for electron transport. Clearly, some understanding of heme biosynthesis is generally applicable throughout the body. As for the other two chapters dealing with the liver and the kidney, these were chosen for inclusion here because disordered function in either of these two organs has ramifications for metabolism in all other organs of the body. Many will argue with this concept, yet it is clear, for example, that there may be disordered central nervous system function without any effects whatever on the rest of the organism, such as in mental retardation. In contrast, disordered renal acidification mechanisms will cause change in body fluid pH that will impact on every cell in the body. The same is the case for hepatic gluconeogenesis, for example.

From the aforementioned reasoning, then, we have derived the organization of the second part of the book, entitled "Disorders of Metabolism." We began with the view that insulin-dependent diabetes mellitus (IDDM) is the prototype of all metabolic disorders. Thus, we chose to approach this disorder by first dealing with disordered glucose, lactate, and ketone body metabolism, all of which are key partners in producing the picture of the "starvation gone wild" that is seen in IDDM. In each of these three areas, as well, the liver and kidney are key players, thus helping to marry the first six chapters with subsequent chapters, culminating in discussion of diabetes mellitus. Following the same line of reasoning, it seemed to us that with knowledge of glycolysis and glycogen metabolism derived from earlier chapters, coverage of carbohydrate disorders other than diabetes mellitus would be a logical sequence. By the same token, since catabolism of amino acids results in glucose, ketone bodies, or both, aminoacidopathies were next, followed by organic acidemias, which are defects in amino acid catabolism beyond the first step in the respective pathways. With all of this information in hand, mastery of the next subject, nutritional disorders, should be relatively easy.

We chose to discuss the subjects of chapters 15 to 17 as distinct areas of metabolism, not because they are so isolated that they could not be reasonably fit into the previous chapters, but rather because in our experience, they tend to be considered inaccessible by most students. We felt that it was possible to demystify these areas of metabolism, but that each area required lengthy enough coverage to do so that separate chapters were warranted.

The third portion of the text is divided into "Disorders of Organs," each organ system being covered separately. Where possible, we have grouped the organ discussions according to the extent of overlap in functions. This system, however, cannot be held to be as logical as what has gone before. Hence, the student can begin to perceive the basis for the "turf wars" that subspecialties have waged with one another. How, for instance, does one decide in a patient with cerebrovascular and coronary atherosclerosis whether the cardiologist or the neurologist is "more important"? Does it really matter? Our position is that it does not—certainly not to the affected organs, and most definitively not to the affected patient who simply wants relief. To the extent that our work successfully provides the basis for any physician seeking to relieve suffering, we have achieved our objective.

The principles of disease that we seek to convey herein are not those held to be the exclusive province of one or another subspecialist, nor do we hold ourselves to be experts in diabetology, neurology, or a multitude of other disciplines. Our late mentor and dear friend Dr. Alfred Bongiovanni taught us that our tools need not be elegant and complex, but only highly effective. We have tried to do for our readers what he did so often for us—make the frighteningly complicated more comprehensible. There can be no more fitting tribute to his memory than for us to have succeeded in this aim.

Acknowledgments

We wish to acknowledge Carroll Cann and Tanya Lazar, who were steadfast in their patient support and good counsel. They began as our editors and ended as our friends. We also thank our many colleagues and students past and present, who collectively contributed to the style and scope of the book through helpful advice and constructive criticism. Finally, we gratefully acknowledge our secretaries, the unsung-heroes without whose good humor and tolerance this book would never have reached completion: Cathy W. James, Maria Moreschi, and Theresa Long-Newton.

Contents

I Biochemical Foundations of Medicine

II Disorders of Metabolism

III Disorders of Organs

part I

Biochemical Foundations of Medicine

chapter **1**

The Interplay Between Biochemistry and Medicine

Living systems epitomize a level of complexity and order that is not found in the nonliving world. Despite this complexity, numerous investigators have made enormous strides in deciphering how living systems are organized and how they work; they have shown that the order depends upon two crucial phenomena: (*a*) an enormous store of genetic and catalytic information that is miniaturized at the level of biologic macromolecules and (*b*) the maintenance of this structural and functional complexity by expending energy. Thus, these investigators have shown that life's processes can be explained in terms of matter and energy. From this point of view, life can be explored in terms of transformations of chemical substrates, mediated by enzymes (organic catalysts). These myriad chemical transformations occur within the organized complex of the cell, the simplest living entity.

Mammalian cells exist in an extracellular environment in which conditions must be rigidly maintained within tight tolerances. For example, alterations of pH, temperature, and ionic concentration in the external environment would trigger the cell to respond by returning the intracellular environment to its original conditions. If the cell is unable to adjust to such changes, the normal conduct of metabolism would be disrupted, leading to disordered functioning; if widespread, this would be expressed at the level of the organism. Indeed, without the capacity of intracellular machinery to adjust to various physiologic and pathologic changes, cell damage or death is likely. Clearly, the cornerstone of life then must be the control of intermediary metabolism, which allows the cell to withstand altered intracellular and extracellular environmental changes. Seen in that light, we may say that disease begins at the level of response of intracellular components to a disturbance, be it inherited or acquired. As such, *all disease results from disordered cellular function.*

ORDER IN LIFE AND DISEASE

It is impossible to overemphasize the role control plays in the life process. Control mechanisms are found at every level of biologic function, beginning with enzymatic processes. Such mechanisms provide for the proper function of metabolic pathways, of cells within a tissue, and between the various organs, providing ultimately for the ability of the organism to adapt to its environment. Control, in the biochemical sense, connotes the ability to use *information* both from inside and outside of the cell. Because all physiologic functions depend ultimately upon biochemical function, it follows that decisive control is found at the level of enzymes, the functional entities that mediate the chemical reactions constituting intermediary metabolism. Derangement of enzyme function or control, therefore, would lead to disease or even death.

One of the major factors in establishing that *structure mandates function* in living systems was the discovery of the relationship between the sequence of bases in DNA and the sequence of amino acids in proteins. An inherited defect in the DNA code may render the code untranslatable or cause it to be translated into a protein of altered amino acid composition. If this change occurs at a site that affects the shape (highly ordered, three-dimensional structure) of the protein, enzyme activity will be modified or abolished, resulting in an inborn error of metabolism.

In living systems, enzymes provide the mechanism by which matter is consumed, supplying the energy to balance the system in its essential bio-

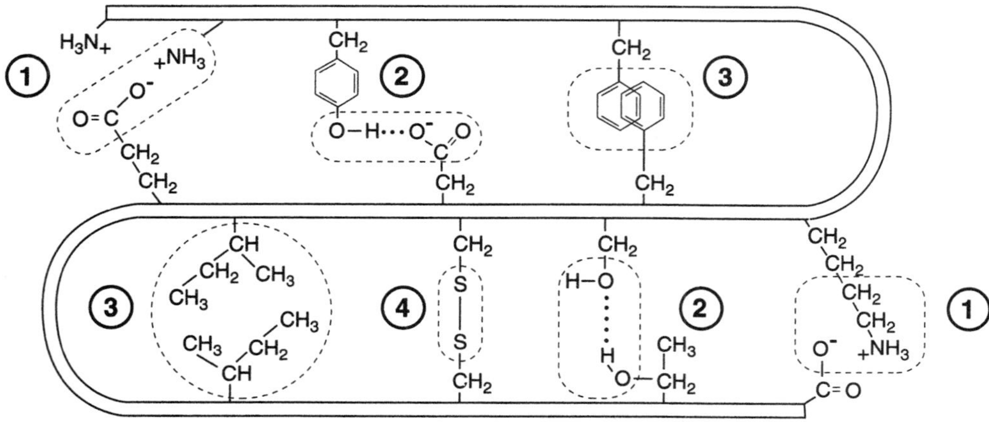

Figure 1.1. Interactive forces conferring macromolecular flexibility. Circled 1 refers to electrostatic interactions; circled 2, to hydrogen bonds; circled 3 to hydrophobic interactions; and circled 4 to disulfide bonds. Note that all are weak except the disulfide bond; yet, in aggregate, these forces exert sufficient force to ensure a predictable three-dimensional molecular conformation. Reprinted with permission from Marks DB. Biochemistry. 2nd ed. Baltimore: Williams & Wilkins, 1994: 29.

logic state, far from equilibrium. Enzymes possess tremendous specificity and prodigious efficiency, which permit them to conduct the reactions of intermediary metabolism within the rapid time frame necessary for life to continue. To sustain life, the cell must generate adenosine triphosphate (ATP) at a rate that will ensure (*a*) the synthesis of the structural and functional macromolecules of the cell, (*b*) the maintenance of the cellular hierarchy against the relentless drive toward increasing entropy, and (*c*) the maintenance of transmembrane ionic gradients. These energy-requiring processes preserve the cell in a state far from equilibrium.

How Macromolecules Work

THE NEED FOR FLEXIBILITY

Large molecules that make up supramolecular structures (eg, membranes and multienzyme complexes) are indispensable components of the cell and extracellular structures (eg, collagen fibrils). Although covalent forces, in the range of 50 to 100 kcal/mole, are essential to the structural integrity of these large cell structures, it is the weak or noncovalent forces, in the range of 1 to 5 kcal/mole, that give these macromolecules the flexibility that permits them to respond to perturbations in their environment (Figure 1.1).

Many factors disrupt the ordered state of life, and they would undermine function if left unopposed. Ultimately, all living systems age and die as they become less organized. In particular, proteins and lipids in cell membranes may become denatured or oxidized. For example, proteins may be denatured by a host of environmental factors (eg, ionizing radiation, temperature, and pH) and by their own substrates or products, and lipids may undergo peroxidative destruction.

While focusing on the impermanent nature of life, we want to emphasize the role that *noncovalent forces* play in the life process (Table 1.1). Organic chemistry, which deals with carbon and covalent bonds, provides the basis for a thorough understanding of the nature of chemical processes, occurring both in the laboratory and in the cell. Nonetheless, we must consider noncovalent bonds to achieve an understanding of the life process.

Table 1.1. Class of Weak (Noncovalent) Chemical Interactions

INTERACTION	APPROXIMATE BOND ENERGIES (KCAL/MOLE)
Electrostatic	5
Hydrogen bonds	2–5
Hydrophobic	0.3–3
Van der Waals forces	1

Table 1.2. Structures and Functions Dependent on Weak Forces

Secondary, tertiary, and quaternary protein structures
Enzyme-substrate complex
Membrane structure and membrane receptor-ligand interactions
Higher order structure of water
Nucleic acid interactions with other nucleic acids or proteins

Covalent bonds are essential to the formation of the polymers (proteins, glycosaminoglycans, and membranes) encountered in living systems, and it is because of their great strength that they are unable to flexibly respond to environmental perturbations. Substances that are predominantly held together by covalent bonds, like horn and wood, do not possess those attributes that we intuitively associate with living systems. Thus, it becomes necessary to appreciate weaker, noncovalent forces that underlie the changes in shape enzymes, receptors, and nucleic acids experience as they perform their essential tasks.

Noncovalent forces account for life's flexibility or plasticity; they are responsive to fluctuations within the environment. Enzymes act largely by virtue of these noncovalent forces, which include hydrogen bonding, electrostatic interactions, Van der Waals interactions, and hydrophobic interactions. These forces account for the high degree of organization of proteins and nucleic acids, and the binding of compounds and effectors to proteins such as enzymes, immunoglobulins, and membrane receptors (Table 1.2).

Although these weaker forces allow the living organism to flexibly respond to environmental conditions, they also introduce instability into the protein structure and, consequently, the protein function. For example, proteins may undergo denaturation by thermal agitation, with the evolution of heat then leading to the disruption of the noncovalent bonds. A short discussion on noncovalent forces will be presented. A more detailed account can be found by referring to the works listed in the suggested reading section at the end of this chapter.

The Nature of Noncovalent Bonds

Because the strength of chemical bonds correlates directly with length, two atoms bound covalently will be closer together than two bound noncovalently. Even though noncovalent bonds are weaker than covalent bonds, the cumulative effect of noncovalent interactions can be appreciable when two molecules possess structures that permit a complementary interaction (as with jigsaw puzzle pieces). This is especially so when these weaker forces enter the environment of macromolecules and supramolecules. In these cases, the cumulative contribution of noncovalent forces can be significant and decisive in determination of binding specificity.

HYDROGEN BONDING

When hydrogen forms a covalent bond with an electronegative atom like nitrogen or oxygen, the bonding electrons are attracted toward the electronegative atom (Figure 1.1). As a consequence, the proton remains at the outer end of the covalent bond with its charge unbalanced and forms a dipole in which one atom has a slight positive charge and the other a slight negative charge. The proton is able to attract an external negatively charged group on another molecule in an essentially ionic interaction that represents bond energy of about 3 to 5 kcal/mole.

Groups such as protein side chains that have the potential to participate in hydrogen bonding usually do so. Although hydrogen bonds have an important role in stabilizing the structures of proteins (through interpeptide and interside chains, and side chain-peptide hydrogen bonds) and nucleic acids (through base-pair hydrogen bonds), they are involved only after covalent forces (peptide and disulfide bonds) and noncovalent forces (hydrophobic interactions) have generated the general form of the three-dimensional structure. This is so because hydrogen bonds are highly directional in nature and, therefore, require complementary structures for their full potential to be realized. If a mutation affects the ability of a protein to assume its normal structure, then this would preclude participation in complementary interactions.

SALT BRIDGES OR ELECTROSTATIC INTERACTIONS

Fixed positive charges (eg, a positively charged amino group from the N-terminal residue of lysine or arginine) may attract and be attracted to negatively charged groups, such as the carboxylate group in the side chain of glutamic and aspartic acid residues of a protein (Figure 1.1).

VAN DER WAALS INTERACTIONS

Van der Waals interactions are relatively weak forces and often called nonbonded interactions, which exist among atoms that do not otherwise attract (Figure 1.1). These interactions are generated by the fluctuating dipole moments associated with all atoms. During the temporary moment induced, an atom can polarize another atom it comes in contact with, causing an attraction between them. Once such polarization is established, when the atoms interact as if they were dipoles, the interaction may be viewed as occurring between transient dipoles. Because the force of attraction is inversely proportional to the sixth power of the distance, van der Waals forces require close approximation for optimal attraction; like hydrogen bonds, proximity is achieved when a complementary structure exists.

HYDROPHOBIC INTERACTIONS

The essential feature of hydrophobic interaction is the inability of water to solubilize hydrophobic or nonpolar residues; thus, the interaction occurs among hydrophobic molecules rather than between hydrophobic molecules and water (Figure 1.1). By forming an oil droplet-like structure, the hydrophobic side chains avoid the increased order (unfavorable decreased entropy) that would have occurred if they had been incorporated into the water lattice. Because "likes dissolve in likes," the apolar residues avoid water and, thus, do not impose an orderly arrangement on the water molecules in their immediate vicinity. Hence, the driving force for hydrophobic interaction is essentially entropic because the disorganization (entropy) of water increases when the hydrophobic molecules coalesce; this is in conformity with the Second Law of Thermodynamics.

Hydrophobic forces contribute to the stabilization of the general three-dimensional protein structure because they are nondirectional, but they are unlikely to greatly contribute to specificity as expressed by recognition and binding. Rather, it is the van der Waals, electrostatic and hydrogen bonds, which require complementary surfaces and proximity, that control the binding of substances to proteins.

Water and Life

On earth, water is the essential ingredient for the functioning of all biologic systems. Proteins (enzymes) need an aqueous environment for their biologic activity to develop. The hydrophobic interaction discussed earlier is one of the most important forces in stabilizing the three-dimensional structures of proteins. As indicated, the driving force of these interactions appears to be based largely on the formation of oil-like enclaves by which hydrophobic side chains of amino acids within the protein coalesce. Thus, hydrophobic interactions do not create a local ordering of the surrounding water (and unfavorable decrease in entropy) that would have occurred if they had been incorporated into a water lattice. On a more macroscopic level, certain properties of water greatly contribute to the ability of organisms to prevail over harsh environmental circumstances. These properties include: high heat capacity, high heat of vaporization, wide range between freezing and boiling points, solubilizing ability, high dielectric constant, ionizing ability, and high surface tension of water. All of these properties relate to the hydrogen-bonding ability of water (Figure 1.2).

THE IMPORTANCE OF MACROMOLECULES IN LIFE

Types of Macromolecules

As noted, the structural and functional hierarchies of life depend on the special properties of certain classes of macromolecules: protein, nucleic acids, and polysaccharides, in particular. The structures of proteins and nucleic acids are precise. Proteins have a linear sequence of amino acids, which is defined by the nucleotide triplet code and specifies the three-dimensional shape that the protein will assume in an aqueous environment.

All three classes of macromolecules are chain polymers formed by a condensation process during which a molecule of water is eliminated for each two building blocks that condense (Figure 1.3). In each case, the precursors are small molecules that are intermediates of metabolic sequences. Condensation reactions between the amino and carboxyl groups of amino acids forming the *peptide*

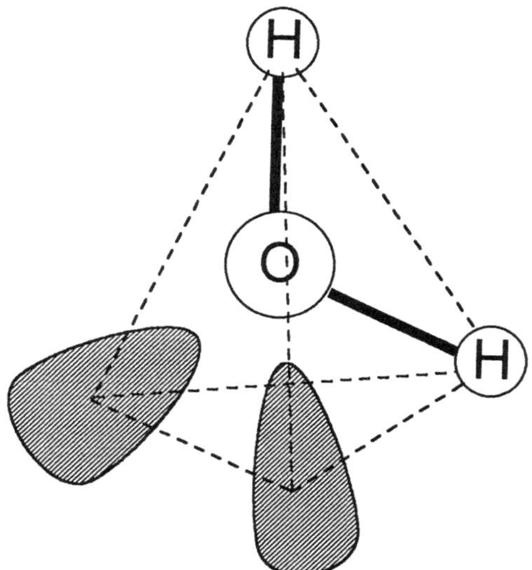

Figure 1.2. Structure of water. The general shape of the water molecule is governed by the shapes of the outer electron orbitals of the oxygen atom. These orbitals, like the bonding orbitals of carbons, are roughly tetrahedral in shape: a single hydrogen atom is placed at two corners and unshared electrons at the other two. Because the oxygen nucleus attracts electrons more than hydrogen does, the water molecule is dipolar. Thus, the hydrogen nuclei are slightly positively charged and the oxygen nucleus slightly negatively charged. Other water molecules can fleetingly join together to create a lattice of water molecules held together by hydrogen bonds. This short-lived ensemble has been called a flickering cluster.

bond create proteins. The *phosphodiester bond* is the analogous condensation product of nucleic acids, and involves the phosphate group and a hydroxyl group on the pentose of an adjacent nucleotide. There is a pentose at one end of the nucleic acid chain in which the 3′-position is free, whereas the 5′-position of a pentose at the opposite end is not involved in the condensation process.

Lastly, the polysaccharides (which will be covered in more depth when the glycogen storage diseases are considered) consist of sugar monomers that were condensed through their hydroxyl groups to form *glycosidic* linkages.

Protein Structure

The linear sequence in nucleic acids and proteins is stringently controlled by precise recognition of nucleotide base sequences by DNA polymerases, RNA polymerases, and t-RNA aminoacyl synthetases. This stereospecific recognition depends upon structural and electronic complementarities that were discussed earlier. This tight control is essential because, as previously emphasized, the relationship between structure and function is so interdependent that changes at crucial positions in the sequence will change the three-dimensional structure and, thereby, alter the biologic activity of a protein. Herein lies the essence of an inborn error of metabolism.

Proteins are the most abundant and variegated macromolecules in the body; they usually comprise hundreds of amino acids. Although the mass of individual molecules is in the range of 10,000 to 50,000 daltons, higher order structures have masses greater than 1,000,000 daltons.

The side chains, which are not chemically altered by peptide-bond formation among amino acids, are responsible for the structural and functional characteristics of the resulting protein molecule. Certain amino acids that possess either an aromatic ring or long side chain engage in hydrophobic interactions. Residues in space can be approximated by these hydrophobic interactions that are dependent on the aqueous environment, permitting individual van der Waals and other short-range forces to act. Complementary structural interactions may help form the final structure as well.

There are four main levels of protein structure. The *primary* structure is the unique linear sequence of amino acids determined by the genetic code (Figure 1.4). Because this linear sequence will direct the three-dimensional shape of the protein in an aqueous environment, the relationship between linear sequence to structure and structure to function of a protein is highlighted. In other words, changes at crucial points in the linear sequence of a protein can have significant effects on form and function. For example, changes that occur in hemoglobin S of sickle cell disease account for many inborn errors of metabolism.

The *secondary* structure is the spiral course traversed by the polypeptide chain and was first delineated by x-ray diffraction in studies undertaken by Pauling and Corey. The α-helix is a right-handed helix that has 3.6 amino acid residues per turn and owes its stability to hydrogen bonds

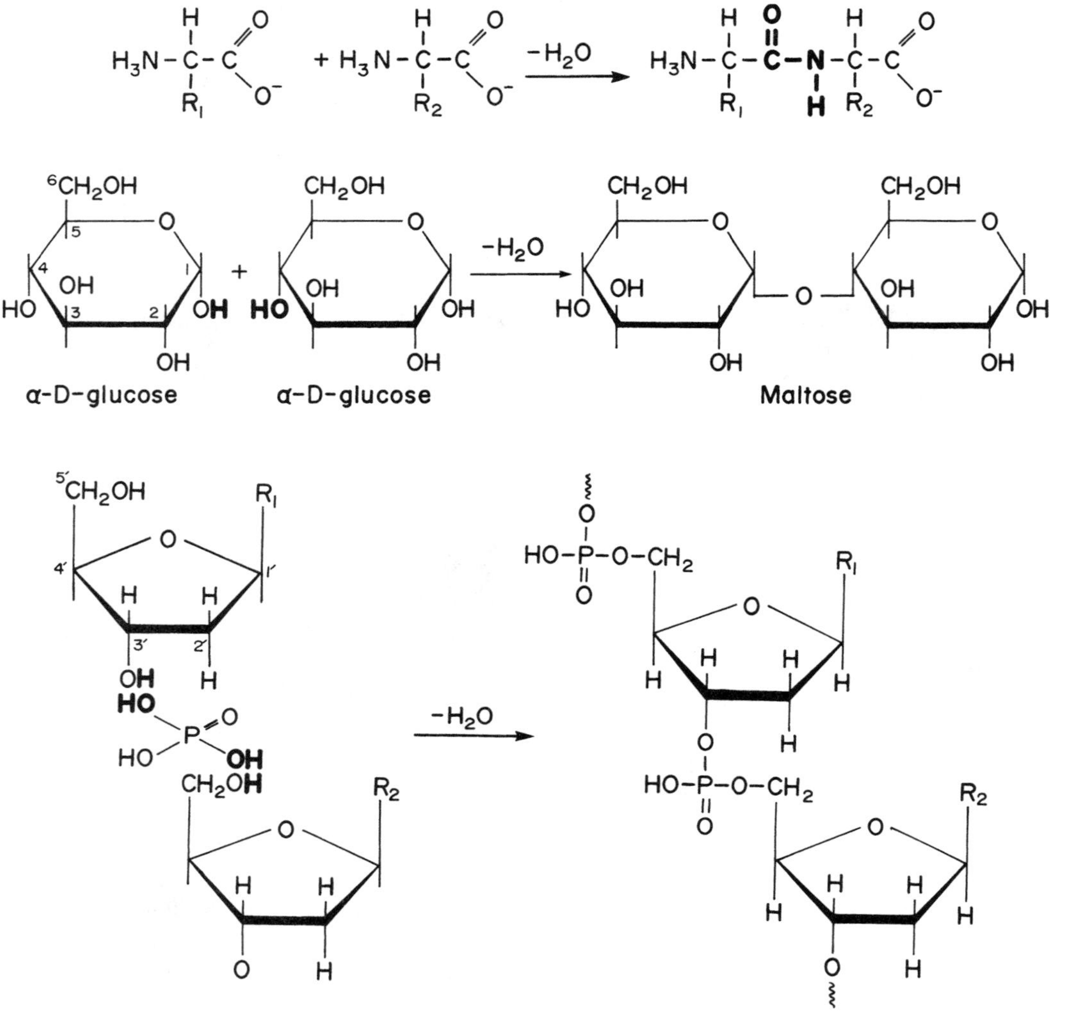

Figure 1.3. Formation of biologic polymers. A condensation process eliminates one molecule of water per bond. (A) Peptide bond. (B) Glycosidic bond. (C) Phosphodiester bond.

between a carbonyl group of one residue and an NH-group of another (Figure 1.4). Because these two groups are covalently bound and, therefore, are relatively fixed in space, it would be expected that they would generate a recurring structure such as the α-helix; other noncovalent forces may contribute as well. Another variant of secondary structure is the β-pleated sheet shown in Figure 1.4.

X-ray diffraction studies indicate that most proteins are compact and possess a structure similar to that of a tightly packed crystal. The secondary structure cannot entirely account for such a formation; recourse to a *tertiary* structure that also is stabilized by noncovalent interactions is necessary (Figure 1.4). The tertiary structure is the three-dimensional structure of a single polypeptide chain called the conformation. For example, most enzymes possess a globular tertiary structure with a polar surface and a hydrophobic interior. This is expected because of the axial role water plays in directing the hydrophobic interactions of macromolecules; thus, it is fair to state that a polypeptide (one dimension) does not become a protein (three dimensions) until placed in an aqueous environment.

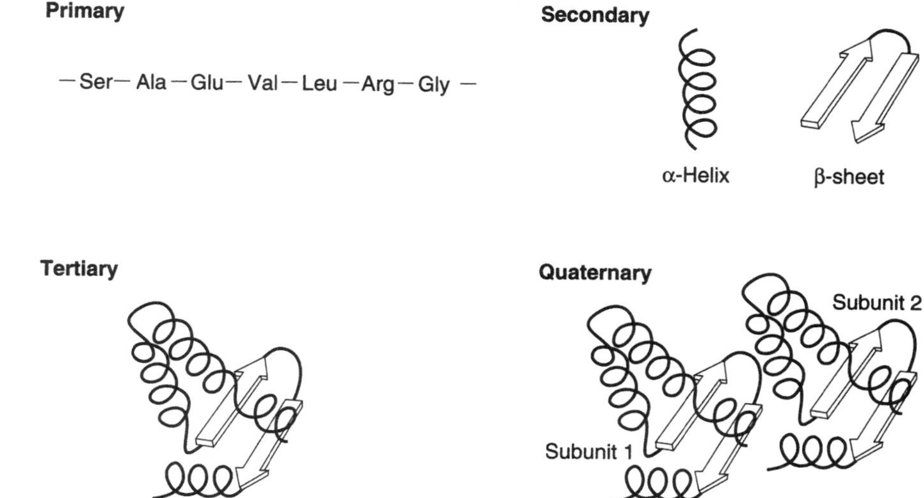

Figure 1.4. Various levels of protein structure. "Primary" refers to the simple amino acid sequence coded for by the genome. "Secondary" refers to one of two spiral configurations assumed by this linear sequence, either the α-helix or the β-pleated sheet. "Tertiary" refers to the three-dimensional folding of the molecule, stabilized by interactive forces. "Quaternary" designates the structural relationship of subunits of proteins consisting of more than one complete polypeptide chain. Reprinted with permission from Marks DB. Biochemistry. 2nd ed. Baltimore: Williams & Wilkins, 1994: 27.

The final level, the *quaternary* structure, is the interaction of individual polypeptide chains with their own tertiary structures to form a larger (polymeric) protein molecule composed of subunits. Hemoglobin, the most extensively studied protein, possesses a quaternary structure composed of two alpha and two beta chains, designated α_2, β_2 (Figure 1.5). As a rule of thumb, most proteins with molecular weights greater than 20,000 are composed of more than one polypeptide chain, but not all proteins are composed of subunits.

While the protein adopts its native or fully active form, longer range forces, particularly hydrophobic interactions, will play an early important role as water is excluded. With the general form of the protein defined by these hydrophobic interactions, disulfide bonds, hydrogen bonds, and Van der Waals interactions become involved as the interbond distances diminish.

The peptide bond, which links C-2 atoms of adjoining amino acids, is the most important covalent bond determining the linear sequence (primary structure) of a protein. However, there is another covalent bond in proteins: the disulfide bond formed by the oxidation of two cysteine residues to form cystine (Figure 1.6). This bond is found most frequently in cross-links between dif-

Figure 1.5. The quaternary structure of the hemoglobin molecule. Hemoglobin A, the normal adult molecule, is composed of two α- and two β-subunits, each containing a heme moiety. Note that the molecule adopts its conformation spontaneously and can be regenerated after separation of the alpha and beta chains by recombining them in the same solution. Thus, the association is not a result of inter-subunit bonds. Reprinted with permission from De Robertis EDP, De Robertis EMF, Jr. Cell and Molecular Biology. 8th ed. Philadelphia: Lea & Febiger, 1987: 51.

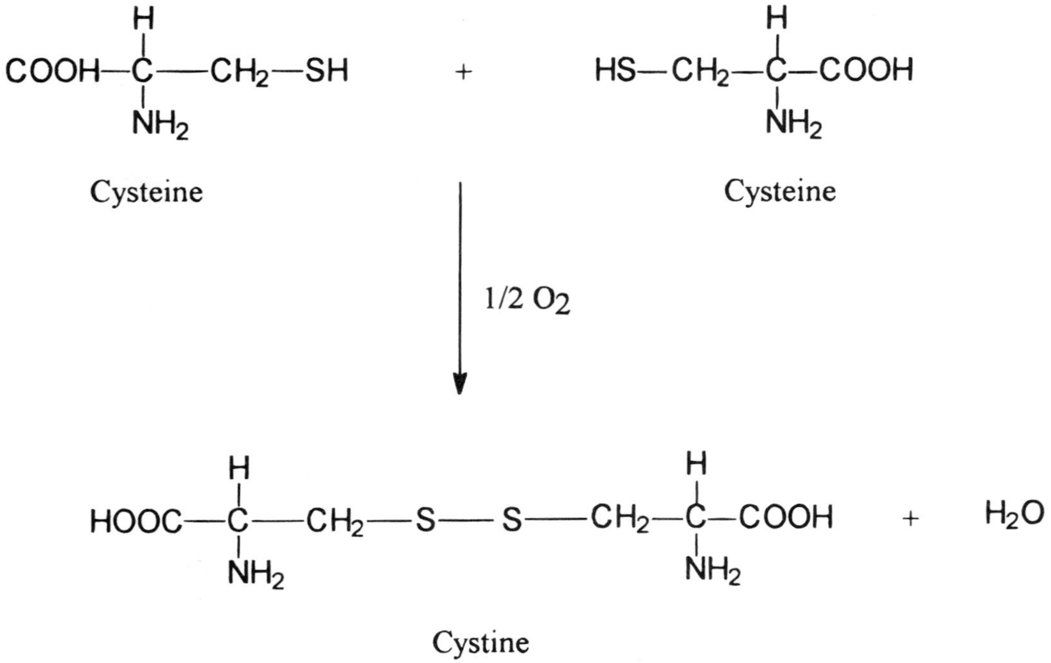

$$\mathrm{COOH{-}CH(NH_2){-}CH_2{-}SH} \quad + \quad \mathrm{HS{-}CH_2{-}CH(NH_2){-}COOH}$$

Cysteine   Cysteine

$$\xrightarrow{1/2\ O_2}$$

$$\mathrm{HOOC{-}CH(NH_2){-}CH_2{-}S{-}S{-}CH_2{-}CH(NH_2){-}COOH} \quad + \quad \mathrm{H_2O}$$

Cystine

Figure 1.6. The disulfide bond. The reduced (−SH) cysteine units in a polypeptide can be oxidized to form cystine. This covalent bond, which requires close approximation of the participants, can form between residues in loops of a single polypeptide or between residues in separate subunits or both. These bonds contribute greatly to the conformational stability of proteins.

ferent parts of the polypeptide chain and between different polypeptide chains. These covalent bridges can stabilize the three-dimensional structure (tertiary structure) because they are much stronger than noncovalent bonds. But, as with all covalent bonds, they are very short range because even a slight extension breaks them completely; hence, they will stabilize the conformation only after other interactions have generated the general three-dimensional structure that the protein will assume. Thus, the cysteine residues must be approximated by other forces before such a bond can form and act to fix the final conformation.

Nucleic Acid Structure

The four nucleotide subunits that comprise the nucleic acids are shown in Figure 1-7. A *mononucleotide* consists of a ring compound known as a base (called heterocyclic because it contains atoms other than carbon and hydrogen) linked to a sugar that is attached to a phosphate group. The nucleotide base-sugar combination without the phosphate group is a *nucleoside.*

The phosphodiester bond is analogous to the peptide bond of proteins and is formed by the esterification of two of the three hydroxyl groups of phosphoric acid with the hydroxyl groups on the pentose sugar. Because the remaining hydroxyl can donate a proton, this accounts for the designation nucleic "acids."

As with polypeptides, the hydrophobic properties of the bases play an important role in the structure assumed by nucleic acid polymers. The planar aromatic rings exclude water; instead, they seek hydrophobic interactions with other bases as they stack together. Great interest has been shown in the hydrogen-bonding properties of the bases because of their role during purine-pyrimidine interaction in forming the double helix characteristic of DNA. The carbonyl and amino groups of the bases are able to form hydrogen bonds with both water and corresponding groups on other bases.

Certainly, one way to account for the capacity

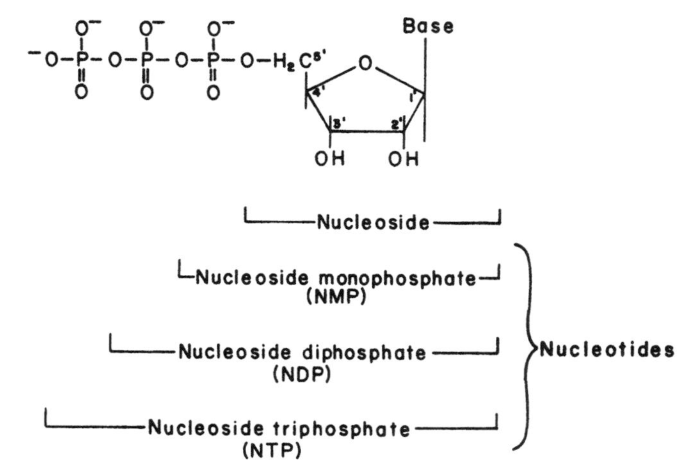

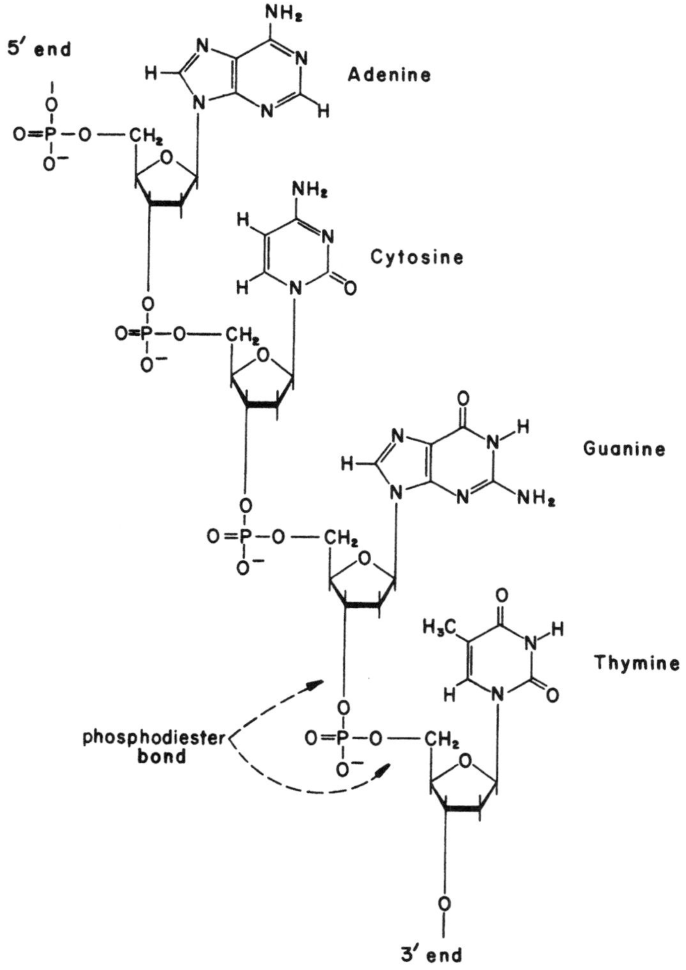

Figure 1.7. The four nucleotide subunits of DNA. The linkage of nucleotides through a phosphodiesterase bond forms the basis for the sugar backbone of the polynucleotide molecule. Reprinted with permission from Marks DB. Biochemistry. 2nd ed. Baltimore: Williams & Wilkins, 1994: 49.

of a linear sequence to direct formation of other linear sequences is to consider a helix (as in the protein α-helix). In this instance, the effects of intramolecular forces arrayed in regular sequence can be used to transmit information. Although the hydrophobic interaction accounts for the majority of the 1000 calories/mole/base pair that holds the double helix together, it is the hydrogen-bonded base pairing that ultimately determines the stability of the structure (Figure 1.8). Hydrophobic interactions first must eliminate water between the helices before the hydrogen bonds can provide the crucial contribution to the stability of the helix.

Notwithstanding the great lengths taken to store hereditary information as a helix, the double helix must unwind for this information in DNA to be expressed. This is not trivial because separation of the components of the single pair of bases requires 1000 calories/mole. Because nucleic acids may possess thousands of such pairs, unwinding them would require an enormous outlay of energy. However, this dilemma of energetics is avoided in an economic fashion: During replication and transcription, only a limited section of the helix unwinds at a time, and only a few base pairs are separated briefly and rejoin as contiguous base pairs unwind. Thus, there is propagation down the double helix of a sequential unwinding-rewinding phenomenon, which involves only a few bases at a time. In this manner, the energy required remains within tolerable limits: once unwinding begins, much of the energy necessary to separate the bases is furnished by that released through the bases reuniting. Of course, this complicated process is expedited by a number of enzymes (eg, helicases, gyrases, and unwindases) that promote unwinding and separation of the two strands while decreasing the energy of activation for the process (see the section on enzymes below).

It was stated earlier that the base pairing implicit in the double helical structure explains how DNA plays a role in reproduction. Here, hydrogen bonding provides the optimal fit of certain base pairs: a purine with a pyrimidine (G-C and A-T) so that once the sequence of one strand is specified, the complementary sequence of the other strand also is specified. In this manner, the self-replication of DNA and the transcription of the DNA-contained code into the various RNA species (ie, messenger, ribosomal, and transfer) are di-

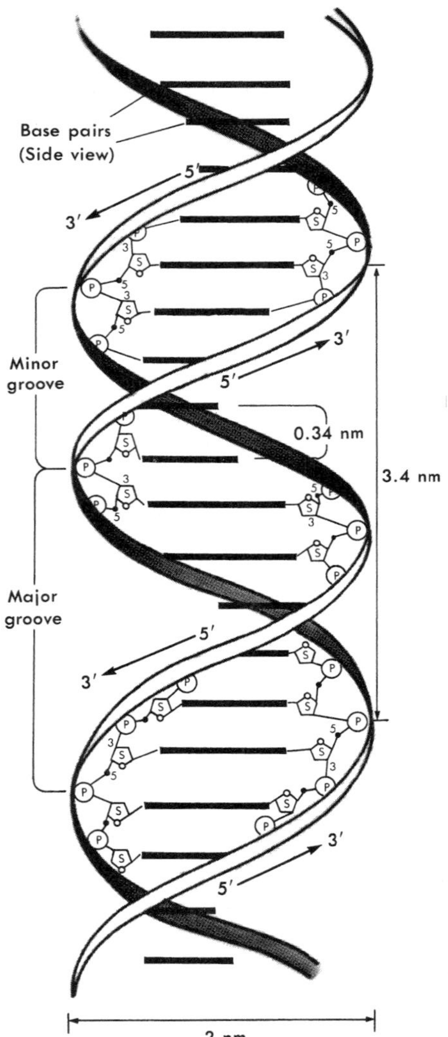

Figure 1.8. The structure of the DNA double helix. The ribbon-like structures represent the -ribose-phosphodiester-ribose-(-S-P-S-) backbone of each DNA strand. The base pairs, which normally are oriented at right angles to the helical axis, are shown as horizontal lines. The helix describes a complete turn every 10 base pairs, and each strand runs in the opposite direction from the other (3′→ 5′ versus 5′→ 3′), which permits complementary base-pairing. Reprinted with permission from De Robertis EDP, De Robertis EMF Jr. Cell and Molecular Biology. 8th ed. Philadelphia: Lea & Febiger, 1987: 34.

rected by one strand of the DNA helix. These are enzyme-mediated processes that are conducted by DNA polymerases, in the case of replication, or RNA polymerases, in the case of transcription.

Nucleic-Acid Function in Biochemical Information Transfer

As noted earlier, the term "information," used in conjunction with "nucleic acid," is synonymous with "sequence" because the double helix is functionally a linear chain that contains four major nucleotide components. The code that determines the order of amino acids and of RNA sequences resides in the order of these four units; the molecular language of the nucleic acids can be viewed as consisting of a four-letter alphabet. Perhaps a punched tape in a computer conveys the picture more vividly.

DNA must perform two functions: first, it must reproduce itself during cell division so that its information can be transmitted precisely to daughter cells; second, cellular metabolism must be controlled by expression of this information. Metabolic control is achieved by regulating the supply of enzymes. In the presence of the appropriate enzymes, chemical reactions proceed readily; in their absence, these reactions proceed very slowly. Additionally, enzymes are sites of control of the rate of chemical reactions.

Nucleic acid macromolecules acting as the repository for the genetic information emphasizes the key to transferral of information in living systems; that is, the linear sequence in the nucleic acids, present as *triplets* created from the four nucleotide bases, is amplified and diversified when it is expressed as proteins composed of 20 amino acids. This amplification of building blocks creates hydrophobic, hydrophilic, and charged environments and enables proteins to serve as enzymes or structural elements. In general, nucleic acids cannot form such complex structures, but some regions possessing single-stranded RNA and complementary base sequences can fold back on themselves, causing the molecules to adopt a secondary structure reminiscent of the higher order structure of proteins. These structures particularly are important in tRNA and rRNA, and account for the remarkable discovery that the earliest enzymes were ribonucleic acid (see the section on ribozymes below).

The linear sequence of DNA directs the linear sequence (primary structure) of proteins and, thereby, controls all of the functional and structural proteins of the cell. The amino acid sequence determines the folding characteristics of a particular protein as it assumes its higher order structure. A change in that sequence, which is caused by a mutation in the genome, can result in a protein having severely impaired functional capability if the change occurs in a position essential for this structure. This type of change is the basis for many inherited defects. The information present in the triplet code of the DNA is used to transcribe complementary (cognate) messenger RNA, ribosomal RNA, and transfer RNA molecules, which will either direct or be used in protein synthesis (Figure 1.9). Recognition and information transfer involve *codon-anticodon* pairing through hydrogen bonding.

A point mutation in the protein linear sequence can have profound effects on protein structure and, consequently, function. Such structural lability emphasizes how a defect in the genetic information (DNA) that causes the formation of an abnormal protein then may function abnormally, thus defining the biochemical basis for an inherited disease.

ENZYMES

The Nature of Catalysis

Enzymes are the catalysts of the cell. They accelerate a chemical reaction in reaching thermodynamic equilibrium by providing an alternative pathway with a lower energy of activation than the reaction that was not catalyzed. The enormous capability these catalysts have for stereospecific recognition and rate acceleration enables the brisk conduct of the thousands of chemical reactions that occur during **intermediary metabolism.** Indeed, intermediary metabolism forms the "roadways" of life's processes. In the following section, we consider how enzymes conduct their indispensable biologic activities.

Without enzymes, life as we know it would not be possible. Consider why this is so: Enzymes pos-

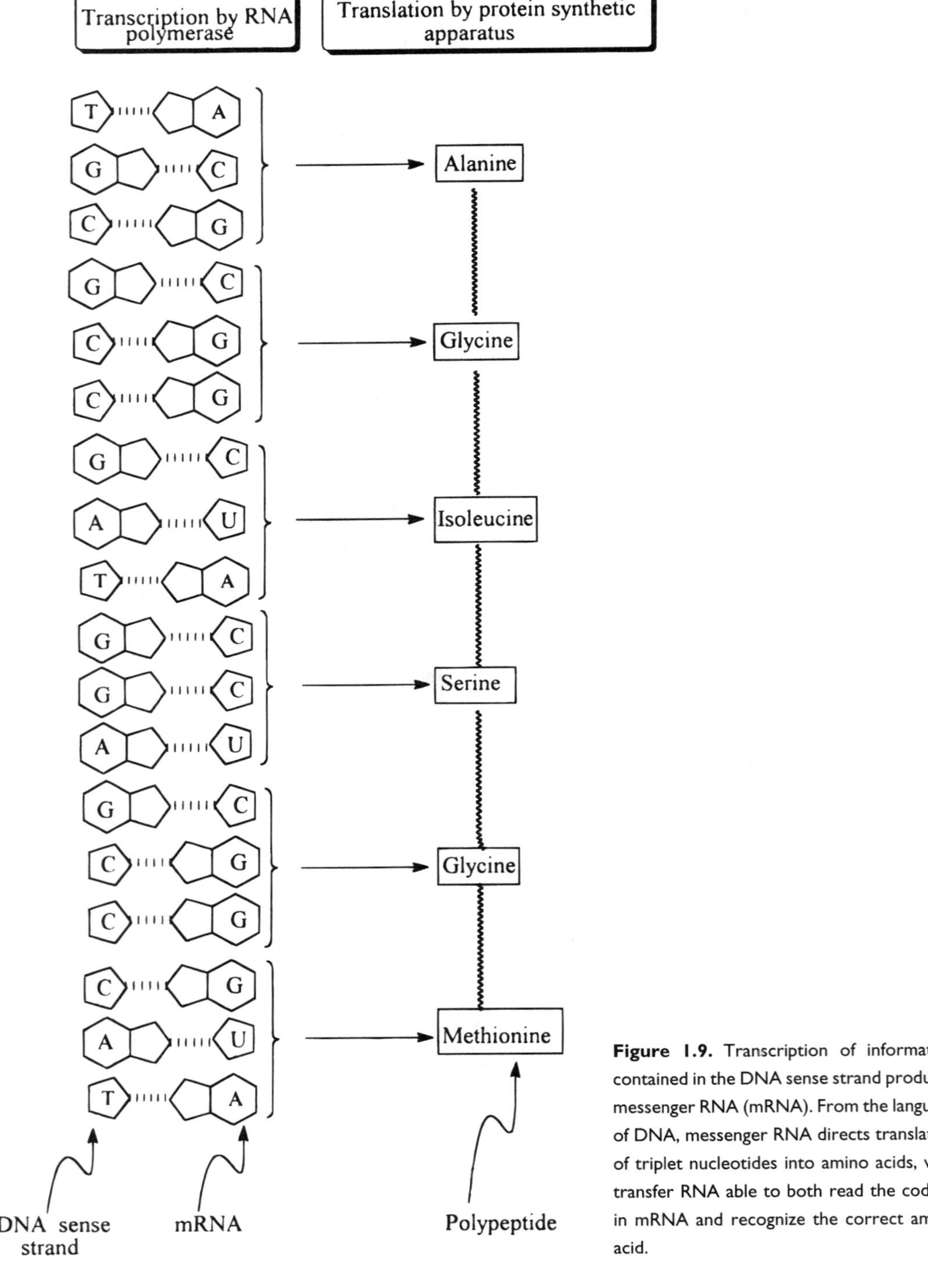

Figure 1.9. Transcription of information contained in the DNA sense strand produces messenger RNA (mRNA). From the language of DNA, messenger RNA directs translation of triplet nucleotides into amino acids, with transfer RNA able to both read the codons in mRNA and recognize the correct amino acid.

sess great stereochemical specificity that permits them to bind a compound (the substrate) to the active site. This specificity is a direct consequence of complementary surfaces between the substrate (in its transition state, see below) and the enzyme, as found between the pieces of a jigsaw puzzle. Most notably, the forces involved are noncovalent. In addition to their specificity, enzymes are able to accelerate the rate of the reaction they mediate to a degree that cannot be achieved by inorganic catalysts acting under the constraints of body temperature and ionic concentrations (particularly hydrogen ion) characteristic of living cells. In other words, living cells cannot raise their temperature appreciably or change the ionic composition of the medium, as may be done in the organic chemistry laboratory.

The tenuous balance of the living system, poised far from equilibrium, requires a brisk transport to the whole of intermediary metabolism. This can be achieved only by the ability of enzymes to accelerate the rates of the chemical reactions involved. Enzymes can mediate the transformation of anywhere from 1000 to 1 million moles of substrate per minute per mole of enzyme—an awesome ability to accelerate a chemical reaction. As shall be reported, enzymes act by lowering the energy of activation of the reaction that they catalyze (ie, they provide an alternative mechanism to achieve the formation of products from reactants). How they do this will be the major focus of this section.

Before the catalytic properties of enzymes are discussed, we note a third attribute of enzymes, one uniquely in keeping with the properties of a living system. These macromolecules can receive information by binding *effector* or *signal molecules*, which provide information to the enzymes, thereby permitting the enzymes to modify the rate of the reactions they catalyze. Defects in these binding sites can cause inborn errors of metabolism.

ENZYME MECHANISM OF ACTION

A chemical reaction involves attraction between opposite charges, with movement of electrons as bonds are broken and then formed between the participating atoms. Accordingly, it is said that a chemical reaction occurs when the electrons that maintain the structure of compound A undergo a permanent change in configuration, forming a new molecular entity that has a unique geometry, that of compound B. Because covalent forces are strong, compounds A and B usually are stable and isolatable; indeed, they often can be purchased from a biochemical supply house. The same cannot be said for noncovalent aggregates (eg, the enzyme-substrate complex that is unstable and exists only momentarily).

Early theories of enzyme function defined the interaction between enzymes and their substrates as that which occurs between a lock and its key. More recently, studies demonstrating changes in the conformation of enzymes as they bind their substrates rendered this view of enzymes simplistic, if not misleading. Nonetheless, both the static template and induced-fit flexible enzyme models assume that the *active site* of an enzyme possesses electric charges or dipoles that complement those of the reactants. This active site is located in the interior of the globular or ellipsoid enzyme and, thus, is isolated from the surrounding aqueous environment. As a result of this protected status, charged molecules are able to interact without hindrance from water, which would diminish charge attraction between charged groups in the substrate and the enzyme because of its high dielectric constant. Thus, the interior of the enzyme molecule may be considered to be "wax-like" while its exterior may be considered to be "soap-like." Consequently, the molecule has the properties of a micelle (Figure 1.10) and can exist simultaneously in aqueous and hydrophobic environments.

X-ray diffraction studies have shown that the protein's active site comprises functional groups brought together from different regions of the primary sequence. As a result, only a small percentage of the total number of amino acid side chains contribute to the catalytic or active site. Functionally, the active site represents those amino acid side chains and co-factors that are involved in the chemical transformation; these include sites that provide the actual catalytic mechanism to mediate the chemical reaction and those that provide for the specificity of the reaction through stereospecific binding of substrates. Again, by exploiting stereospecific binding, enzymes lower the free energy of activation of the reaction they catalyze, thus bringing about significant rate acceleration.

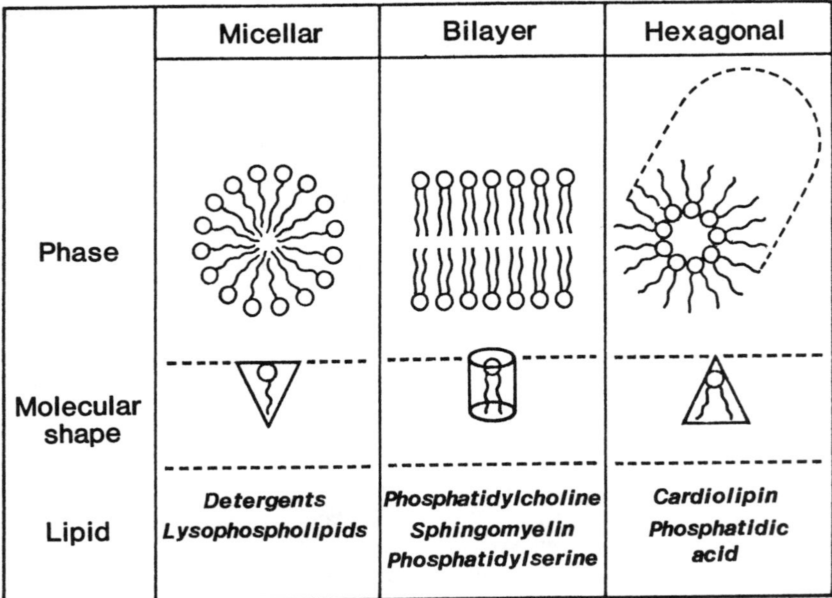

Figure 1.10. The molecular shape of lipids influences their tendency to form hydrophobic and hydrophilic regions, like detergents. Enzymes also are able to create different domains that contribute to their biologic activity. Reprinted with permission from De Robertis EDP, De Robertis EMF Jr. Cell and Molecular Biology. 8th ed. Philadelphia: Lea & Febiger, 1987, 114.

APPROXIMATION AND ORIENTATION

Approximating reactants at the active site and placing them in correct position for reactions provide the essential environment for the enzyme-mediated reaction to be successful. As noted earlier, the first step of an enzyme-mediated reaction is the binding of substrates to the enzyme in the noncovalent **enzyme substrate complex**. When the substrate binds to the enzyme, its ability to move freely is severely restricted. Hence, the degree of order of this microsystem is increased and the entropy of the enzyme substrate complex is lowered, making collision and subsequent reaction more probable. This aspect of catalysis is called *approximation* or *propinquity*. It also assumes that the catalytic groups of the active site of the enzyme are oriented precisely in regard to the substrate, allowing for key groups in the enzyme to interact with the substrate.

As a chemical reaction progresses, the reactants enter a short-lived state called the *transition state*, which represents a molecule in which covalent bonds are in the midst of being formed and destroyed (Figure 1.11). Consequently, some

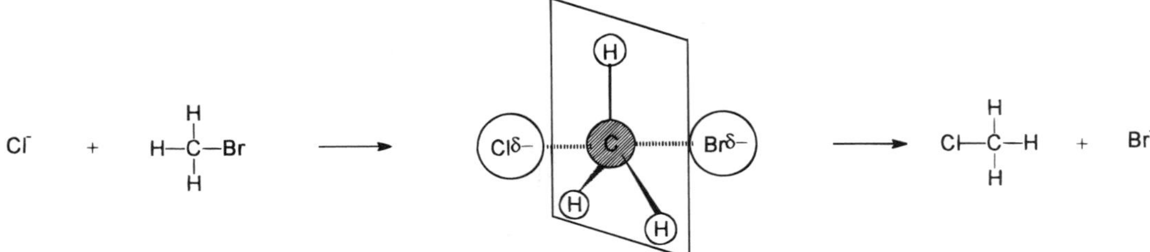

Figure 1.11. Example of a transition state in the mechanistic pathway to forming methyl chloride from chloride ion and methyl bromide. The transition state represents bonds in the midst of being broken as new ones are being formed.

bonds are stretched and the charge distribution of the molecule may be altered. Over 30 years ago, Pauling suggested that an enzyme would bind more strongly to a molecular aggregation similar to that found in the transition state than it would to either substrates or products. The reason for this affinity was the greater complementarity in structure between the transition state and the active site. This powerful insight has been supported by data that show when a substrate binds to the active site, a portion of the energy of binding is used to strain the substrate complex toward the geometry of the transition state. Accordingly, the separation between enzyme specificity and catalytic efficiency becomes artificial because a considerable enhancement of the reaction rate occurs when the enzyme binds the substrate. This explains why enzymes are large molecules: the substrates and their enzymes will interact at multiple sites to bring about complementary binding as the energy of interaction is used to coax the substrate into the molecular geometry of the transition state. Furthermore, this optimization of binding interaction characterizes the interaction of coenzymes (cofactors) as well.

GENERAL ACID BASE CATALYSIS

We have stated earlier that although an acid or base can be used in the laboratory to prepare a molecule to react, wide variations in hydrogen ions or hydroxyl ions are incompatible with life. Because the hydrogen ion is a small naked charge, it polarizes other groups easily; this is exploited readily in the laboratory. Remembering that delocalization of electrons (resonance) causes increased stability, it follows that localization of electrons can destabilize a molecule, preparing it to react further. Through the agency of general acid catalysis, a weak acid functions by inducing polarization through hydrogen bonding and, thus, acts in a manner analogous to that of the proton itself. Hence, general acid base catalysis may serve to prime a reactant for further chemical modification. The side chains of glutamic and aspartic acids, histidine, tyrosine, and cysteine have considerable acidic or basic character and are likely to function in a general acid-base role in the cell.

COVALENT CATALYSIS

Many enzymes can catalyze a chemical reaction by using a functional group in one of the limited number of side-chains remaining after formation of peptide bonds to create their primary structure. The predominant side-chain residues that can catalyze a chemical reaction are those of the amino acids histidine, serine, cysteine, lysine, glutamate, and aspartate. This catalytic strategy often involves formation of a covalent intermediate with a group in the substrate, permitting the formation of a new structure with greater reactivity than that present in the starting substrate. Such intermediates are essential to the mechanism of extracellular proteases that are necessary in digestion (chymotrypsin, trypsin, and elastase), the coagulation cascade (thrombin), and aldolases and decarboxylases.

Two types of reactive centers participate in covalent catalysis: (*a*) A nucleophile is an atomic center with a strong tendency to donate an electron pair; in nucleophilic catalysis, rate enhancement occurs when the enzyme donates an electron pair to the substrate. (*b*) An electrophile is an electron-seeking center; electrophilic catalysis involves removal of an electron pair from the substrate by a group in the enzyme. The most common electrophiles in biology are the metal ions and the coenzymes pyridoxal phosphate and thiamine. The most common type of electrophilic mechanism involves the creation of a positive nitrogen that acts as an electron "sink" or a free nitrogen that donates an electron pair. Despite the limited tendency of nitrogen to attract electrons (electronegativity), it easily is protonated, thereby facilitating its role as an electron sink.

Role of Certain Functional Groups in the Protein

From the previous discussion it should be clear that many enzymes supply the essential nucleophilic, basic, or acidic groups from the side chains of certain amino acids in the primary sequence. Hydrolytic cleavages (eg, chymotrypsin) are the best studied examples of enzymes that illustrate this role for protein functional groups. These groups include the carboxyl, thiol, and imidazole of histidine, and the serine hydroxyl. The imidazole and thiol groups can act as nucleophiles while the carboxylate anion functions in general base catalysis.

Detailed studies of the mechanism of action

of chymotrypsin, lysozyme, and ribonuclease have led to the following generalizations about enzyme catalysis:

1. Optimal energy interactions between substrate and enzyme occur when binding is closest to that of the transition state.
2. Incorrect binding will not permit key functional groups in the enzyme to adopt the complementary orientation with respect to the transition state.
3. Stabilizing the transition state is an important aspect of the catalytic mechanism of enzymes.

Further details of enzyme catalysis can be found by referring to the works listed in the Suggested Reading Section at the end of this chapter.

Coenzymes

As noted before, the active site is composed of side chains remaining from the enzyme's constituent amino acids after condensation to form peptide bonds. Although these functional groups can engage in many catalytic roles, the diversity of metabolism has led to an increase in the limited repertoire of such groups present in proteins. Vitamins contribute to the effectiveness of these diverse and expanded roles: Through conversion to coenzymes and incorporation into enzymes, either through noncovalent or covalent means, vitamins can extend the capability of the protein.

Enzymes may dramatically increase their capability for binding of substrates by attaching certain specific cofactors. In general, coenzymes are ring structures that closely resemble the purines and pyrimidines of the nucleic acids. These heterocylics can stabilize transition states by electronic delocalization, transmitting electronic perturbations over several atoms, and facilitating electron mobility. Additionally, they may promote optimal binding interaction with specific subsites on the enzymes, thereby contributing to approximation and orientation at the active site of the enzyme.

Enzymes devoid of any coenzyme or metal cofactor may conduct hydrolytic reactions exemplified by chymotrypsin. However, providing a coenzyme greatly expands the variety of reaction types susceptible to catalysis to include oxidation-reduction, decarboxylation, condensation, elimination, transamination, and carboxylation, as well as oxidation of β-keto acids (eg, pyruvate), which is a notoriously difficult reaction under conditions prevailing within the cell. Table 1.3 lists the metabolic role played by each of the coenzymes.

Most enzymes require cofactors or coenzymes to provide specific chemical properties that amino acid chains cannot attain alone. Abnormal binding of a cofactor to its enzyme may cause an inborn error of metabolism.

Ribozymes and the Evolution of Enzyme Function

In the early 1980s, working independently, Cech and Altman showed that RNA can express enzymatic activity, including the ability to self-replicate. This discovery of *ribozymes* was both unanticipated and revolutionary. Because ribose can be synthesized from formaldehyde in experiments that mimic presumed prebiotic conditions on earth, it has been believed that RNA antedates DNA. When it is recognized that deoxyribonucleotides are synthesized from ribonucleotides, it seems clear that RNA preceded DNA.

As noted earlier, single-stranded RNA can fold into higher order structures by base pairing of complementary sequences. Such tertiary conformations can deploy functional groups in an active site in a fashion similar to protein enzymes. Proteins with 20 amino acids can adopt more intricate shapes and have more functional groups at their disposal. Nevertheless, with the discovery of ribozymes, it became clear that RNA could function as a catalyst.

A self-splicing intron (intervening sequence in the linear sequence of DNA) in the ribosomal RNA gene of a protozoan was identified in 1981 as the first ribozyme. Soon thereafter, a bacterial enzyme, ribonuclease P, was shown to contain both RNA and protein. Scientists were astonished to learn that the enzymatic activity resides in the RNA and not in the protein. Thus, it is clear that RNA can fold in a manner consistent with creating a tertiary structure that brings distant functional groups together, making an enzyme active site. Biology is exciting because, as Whitehead remarked about quantum mechanics over 70 years ago, "Who

Table 1.3. Coenzyme Functions

COENZYME	FUNCTION
Coenzymes Engaged in Oxidation Reduction Reactions	
NAD	Dehydrogenases
FAD, FMN	Dehydrogenases
	Oxidation and acyl group transfer
Hemoproteins	Cytochromes, catalase, peroxidase
B_{12}	Hydrogen transfer (isomerization of L-methylmalonyl CoA to succinyl CoA)
	Methyl group-THF-homocysteine
Vitamin C	Reducing agent
Coenzymes Catalyzing Other Reactions	
Thiamine	Oxidative decarboxylation-α-keto acids (scission C-C bonds)
Pyridoxal phosphate	Transamination, racemization, decarboxylation
Folic acid	Transfer of 1-carbon units
Biotin	Carboxylation
Coenzyme A	Transfer of acyl groups by forming thiol esters
Purine and pyrimidine phosphates	Purines—driving force for biochemical reactions; pyrimidines—transfer of glycosyl groups as in glycoprotein synthesis
S-adenosylmethionine	Biological methyl donor

knows what seeming nonsense will tomorrow be proven fact?"

Summary of Enzyme Action

Enzymes, because they are macromolecules, provide specific binding and catalytic sites that recognize and interact with transition states in a precise manner based upon complementary interactions. As they bind the substrate, enzymes cause it to be strained or deformed into the conformation of the transition state (activated complex). In this way, the starting state is more labile and, therefore, more likely to react. In actuality, the conformation of the enzyme changes as well. Using somewhat simplified terms, the interaction between enzyme and substrate transfers some of the conformational energy of the enzyme to the substrate, thereby increasing the energy of the substrate so that it approaches the configuration of the transition state. In addition, the orientation effects mentioned earlier, coupled with the ability of an enzyme to create regions of unusual reactivity within the hydrophobic interior of its structure, also enhance the chemical reactions mediated by enzymes. It follows that a mutation in DNA could alter or abolish the activity of the protein it specifies by altering the folding of the protein.

REGULATION OF INTERMEDIARY METABOLISM

Levels of Control

The highly organized state of life demands tight control. A hierarchy of sites at which this control can be exercised is necessary. Enzymes not only can catalyze reactions, they can be controlled as well. Control at any level must be based on the ability to obtain information and use that information to alter metabolic phenomena appropriately. This often is accomplished by changing the rate of catalysis of a reaction. Within the cell, a remarkable multiplicity of controls allows the brisk and usually faultless conduct of intermediary metabolism. Because intermediary metabolism must provide both adequate ATP and other high energy compounds, and intermediates that are necessary to construct other molecules and macromolecules, regulation must coordinate disparate reactions and pathways. By ensuring that a proper balance of all precursors exists, synthesis of the complex structural elements of the cell (eg, membranes) can occur.

We want to concentrate on the aspects of regulation that are essential to understanding the disordered biochemistry that is the basis of disease.

The means available to the cell to regulate intermediary metabolism will be discussed on the basis of the physical or chemical transformations that the enzymes undergo and the time in which they occur. The following mechanisms may be distinguished:

1. *Noncovalent* interactions that are rapid and freely reversible, and occur within milliseconds. These cause the enzyme conformation to change when the substrate or modifier, such as H^+ or other ions, binds to key control sites or changes the state of ionization of groups that govern the conformation of the protein.
2. *Covalent modifications* (eg, protein phosphorylation), which are mediated by enzymes and change the catalytic or regulatory properties of the enzyme being acted upon. Such modifications occur over a longer period and are more definitive than noncovalent modifications, which depend on equilibrium binding. Moreover, covalent modifications either can be irreversible or reversible. In the irreversible category, an enzyme stored in an inactive state (eg, a zymogen) is not activated until it is needed. In the reversible category, a regulatory signal may be transmitted and amplified (eg, glucagon), and acts through the stimulation of cyclic adenosine monophosphate (cAMP) formation. The cAMP produced activates a protein kinase that phosphorylates key proteins in various pathways. Thus, when a hormone binds to a specific receptor on the cell membrane, it triggers a cascade of events that culminate in definitive control of a pathway. (This will be discussed further in the section on hormonal control of metabolic processes.) The first step in the information process is amplified into a cascade of subsequent enzyme reactions.
3. *De novo* synthesis, a relatively slow process compared with the other two forms of regulation, but it has greater overall effect. Because this process involves the synthesis of proteins, more energy is expended, which is consistent with the more definitive result achieved.

Noncovalent Regulatory Mechanisms

MODULATION OF ENZYME ACTIVITY BY SUBSTRATE AND PRODUCT CONCENTRATION: HYPERBOLIC KINETICS

Substrate availability is one way in which a metabolic pathway could be controlled. When substrate concentration decreases, enzyme activity also would decrease, diminishing the rate of the entire pathway. In actuality, substrate levels *in vivo* show little fluctuation; it is thought that although such a mechanism may be important for single enzymes, it is not the definitive factor that controls entire pathways in higher order life forms.

A hyperbolic response of velocity to changing substrate concentration characterizes classic Michaelis-Menten kinetics (Figure 1.12). These enzymes are most responsive to changes in substrate concentration in the range from zero to the K_m, with K_m defined as the substrate concentration at which one-half maximal velocity is achieved. A hyperbolic response system restricts the ability of the enzyme to respond to substrate concentrations outside of the K_m range. Although the enzyme still may be able to respond rapidly to a small change in substrate concentration at the K_m, when substrate levels fall far below the K_m, the catalytic ability of the enzyme would be unrealized—a wasteful situation. For enzymes to adjust reaction rates quickly, it is preferable that their substrates remain in the K_m range.

Hepatic glucokinase is an instructive example of the significance of the K_m in hyperbolic kinetic responses. For glucokinase, the K_m (10 mM) exceeds the usual glucose level, but this ability to function efficiently at a high glucose concentration permits the enzyme to respond to the episodic influx of glucose that occurs after ingestion of a meal that contains carbohydrates.

COOPERATIVITY

As we have discussed, enzymes with a hyperbolic response curve (which defines a decreasing responsiveness to increasing substrate concentration), have a limited ability to maintain substrate levels within small tolerances. Enzymes that have a role in controlling the flux through a pathway usually have greater flexibility in their response to substrate, demonstrating the phenomenon of *cooperativity*. Such enzymes often are polymeric

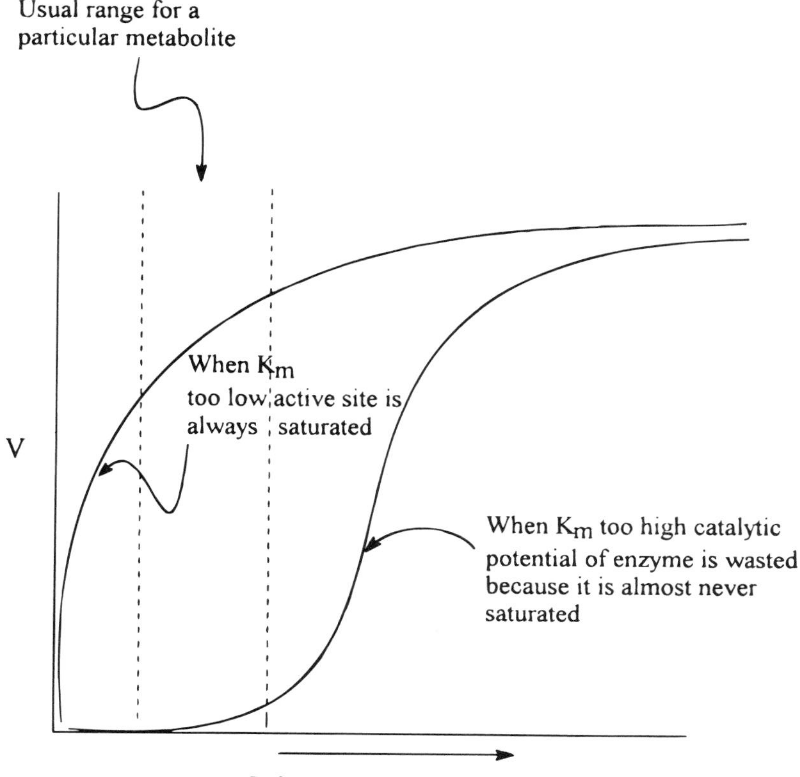

Figure 1.12. Hyperbolic and sigmoid curves plotting velocity (v) of the enzyme-catalyzed reaction as a function of substrate concentration. The Km is an approximation of the affinity of the enzyme for its substrate. When the Km is too low, the active site always will be saturated and an increase in substrate concentration will not have any effect on velocity. When the Km is too high, the active site almost is never saturated, wasting the catalytic potential of the enzyme. Thus, the Km usually is within the physiologic range of substrate concentration to exploit the ability of an enzyme to adjust the reaction rate within the physiologic range for a particular metabolite.

and have more than one catalytic site, usually located on separate polypeptides. Most importantly, these sites communicate their status to each other by provoking a conformational change in the enzyme structure. In this manner, a macromolecule composed of subunits receives and responds to information.

Two forms of cooperativity have been described, both usually found in enzymes composed of subunits (Figure 1.13). With *positive cooperativity*, when a substrate binds to one catalytic site on the enzyme, the activity of other sites is enhanced by boosting either the binding affinity for the substrate or the catalytic activity. Enzymes displaying positive cooperativity have a velocity-substrate profile that describes a sigmoid curve. As substrate concentration increases, additional sites are occupied, accentuating the activity of the remaining sites until all the sites are fully active and velocity no longer increases. In contrast to hyperbolic enzymes, when the substrate concentration permitting half maximal velocity is approached, the velocity curve becomes nearly vertical. Hence, small changes in substrate concentration in the region of the K_m cause significant rate changes.

On the other hand, *negative cooperativity* occurs when enzymes have velocity-substrate profiles that show even less variability than hyperbolic enzymes (Figure 1.13). In an example of extreme negative cooperativity, called half-of-the-sites reactivity, binding at the initial half of the

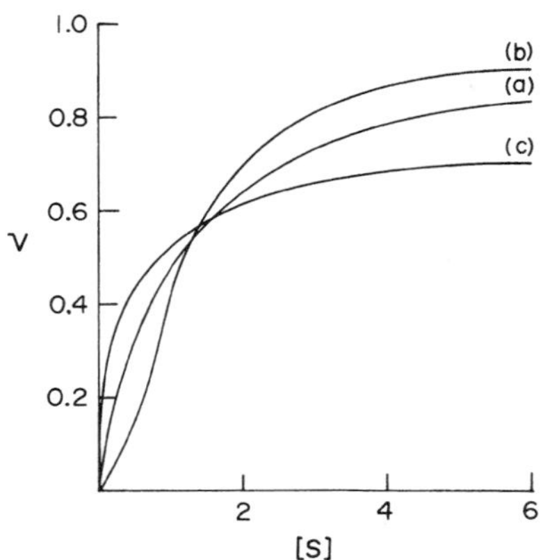

Figure 1.13. Idealized plots of velocity (v) versus substrate concentration (s) for enzyme activity. (a) Hyperbolic behavior. (b) Positive cooperativity. (c) Negative cooperativity. Reprinted with permission from Cohn RM, Yandrasitz JR. Modulation of enzyme activity. In: Herman RH, Cohn RM, McNamara PD, eds. Principles of metabolic control in mammalian systems. New York: Plenum, 1980.

sites renders the remaining half of the sites virtually inactive.

What do these control mechanisms achieve? Positive cooperativity facilitates a rapid response to increasing substrate concentration, thereby attenuating fluctuations in substrate levels. Negative cooperativity, on the other hand, permits constancy of enzyme activity (rather than substrate concentration, as with positive cooperativity) while substrate concentration fluctuates. In particular, by optimizing the binding of a cofactor (eg, NAD^+), it will be ensured that such an enzyme will get its share of substrate or cofactor when a key metabolite or coenzyme is in short supply. Once the catalytic sites are saturated, further binding is unnecessary; the enzyme binds substrate at additional sites with a low affinity.

ALLOSTERISM—MODULATION OF ENZYME ACTIVITY

We have considered modulation of enzyme activity by substrate and product interaction at the active or catalytic site of the enzyme. Enzyme activity also may be regulated by allosteric compounds, which bear no chemical resemblance to the substrate. Allosteric metabolites or modifiers have been shown to bind at sites that are distinct from the catalytic site; this phenomenon is called allostery, and the site at which the modifier binds is the *allosteric site*. The distinctive nature of the catalytic and allosteric sites can be demonstrated by chemicals that eliminate the allosteric control while catalytic activity remains unchanged (Figure 1.14).

In terms of receiving information, this binding causes a conformational change in the enzyme, which results in alteration of the enzyme activity. This capacity to be regulated by a product of a biosynthetic pathway is called *feedback inhibition*. Although it usually is the final product of the pathway that inhibits the activity of the first enzyme of that pathway, metabolites from other pathways that may share common cofactors (eg, ATP, NAD^+) also can act in such a servomechanism. Feedback inhibition must be distinguished from repression of enzyme synthesis. Feedback inhibition reversibly decreases the activity of an enzyme, and repression inhibits protein synthesis. Loss of feedback inhibition has been implicated in the pathogenesis of the porphyrias, familial hypercholesterolemia, and some forms of hyperuricemia.

Covalent Regulation of Enzyme Activity

In covalent regulation, a covalent change in the enzyme causes conformation of the enzyme to change; one form is active and the other is inactive. Such a change is mediated by another enzyme and, consequently, takes longer than equilibrium binding, the mechanism underlying noncovalent modulation. Moreover, energy (ATP) often is expended, increasing the odds, so to speak, to ensure the outcome.

MODULATION BY REVERSIBLE COVALENT ACTION

Certain key intracellular enzymes can undergo reversible phosphorylation/dephosphorylation, which stabilizes the configuration of the active site. Many examples of phosphorylation have been discovered, all of which involve the addition of phosphate to specific serine or threonine residues. Covalent modification is different from noncovalent modification because the response is persistent, even after the triggering signal has disappeared. Important mammalian systems involved in phosphorylation regulation include the pyruvate

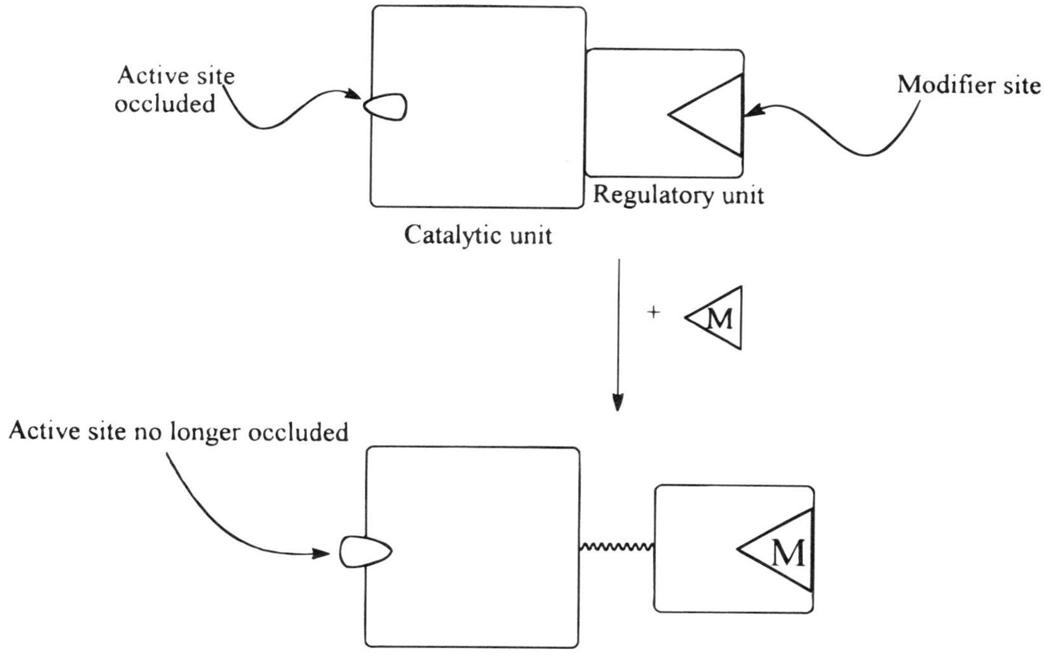

Figure 1.14. Regulatory and active sites. Many enzymes that are regulated by metabolites or other signal molecules undergo a subtle change in shape when the modifier (M) binds to the enzyme at the allosteric site. In this example, the catalytic and regulatory subunits are bound together in the absence of the modifier, suppressing the activity of the catalytic subunit. When M binds to its site, the regulatory subunit disengages from the catalytic subunit. Consequently, the active site changes its orientation so that it can bind substrate (ie, it is no longer occluded).

dehydrogenase multienzyme complex, triglyceride lipase, acetyl CoA carboxylase, and glycogen phosphorylase-glycogen synthetase. The glycogen system is the axial system involved in glycogen metabolism and the locus of several disorders resulting in the glycogen storage diseases. Covalent regulation is complicated and will be covered in the section on hormonal control of metabolism.

CONTROL BY IRREVERSIBLE COVALENT INTERCONVERSIONS

Gastrointestinal proteases exist in an inactive form (*zymogen* or *proenzyme*) that can be converted into the active form when an amino acid or small peptide group is removed (Figure 1.15). Such a system protects the mucosa of the gut from being damaged by an enzyme when no normal substrate is present. Hormone production, the coagulation cascade, fibrinolysis, and the complement cascade are examples of such irreversible conversions. These are discussed in the appropriate sections in Part III of this book.

PROTEIN SYNTHESIS

Enzyme "Death"

We have noted before that it is necessary to synthesize proteins continually because of their liability to constant degradation. Furthermore, we have observed that the enzymes that use noncovalent forces function because they can undergo conformational changes. These weak forces are used to effect substrate binding and product release, and cause the covalency changes required for chemical reactions. As a consequence of this conformability, enzymes are liable to experience de-

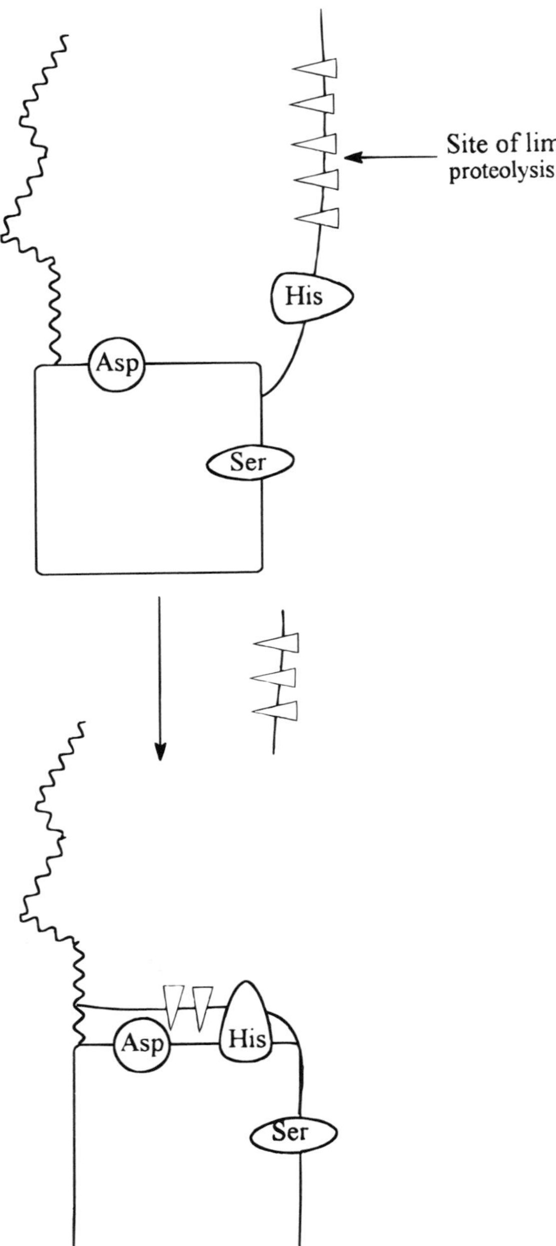

Figure 1.15. Formation of active enzyme from zymogen. Activation of the precursor enzyme (zymogen) by limited proteolysis permits the enzyme to change to the active conformation, forming the serine-histidine-aspartate (Ser-His-Asp) catalytic grouping characteristic of serine proteases.

naturation and consequent loss of function; hence, they are semistable. A balance between function and denaturation is maintained by protein synthesis on one side and degradation of denatured enzymes on the other. Because enzymes make life possible, they continually must be renewed or life would cease. Synthesis and degradation of proteins and enzymes continue incessantly, maintaining the entire metabolic network far from equilibrium—a condition that reflects its highly ordered (negative entropic) state. As emphasized earlier, this nonequilibrium state constitutes the poising of the life process.

If an enzyme was totally stable, it would have

no catalytic function because it acts by its ability to bind other molecules and respond to environmental changes. In effect, it would be a "dud." But, a highly unstable enzyme then would be too transient in its existence to act, thus blocking a particular metabolic step. Hence, enzyme catalysis requires the protein to be flexible, therefore implying inherent instability.

Overview of Protein Synthesis

Some of the information contained in the genome is expressed by the synthesis of proteins. In addition, the genes contain information for their own replication, for the synthesis of complementary nucleic acids, and for binding of informational molecules (eg, hormones), which exert a control function in protein biosynthesis. The impact of the information explosion in molecular biology has been so profound that high school students are taught that the genes are polymers of purine and pyrimidine nucleoside triphosphates arranged to form deoxyribonucleic acid (DNA). Furthermore, the double-stranded nature of DNA, with each strand joined with its partner in an anticomplementary helical fashion, now is a part of the general information taught at that level of schooling. Attached to the double-stranded DNA are histones (basic proteins) and nucleic acidic proteins that constitute the chromatin of the nucleus. These proteins are believed to play a role in the structure of the chromatin and serve to modulate transcription of DNA into RNA.

EUCARYOTIC GENES

The general sequence of protein synthesis begins with the unfolding of the double-stranded DNA in a circumscribed region (Figure 1.9). A DNA-dependent RNA polymerase uses the unfolded strand as a template to polymerize purine and pyrimidine nucleoside triphosphates into a messenger RNA (mRNA). But, when isolated DNA was hybridized to its complementary mRNA, loops of unpaired DNA were discovered. This led to an unanticipated complication of the DNA structure of eucaryotes. Whereas in prokaryotes, there is a one-to-one correspondence between the triplet base sequence in DNA and the transcribed base sequence in mRNA, this is not true for most eucaryotic genes. Rather, most eucaryotic genes are interrupted by one or more sequences of nucleotides that do not code for mRNA and, therefore, are not expressed in the final mRNA produced (Figure 1.16). But these noncoding stretches of DNA are expressed in the first transcribed product of DNA, heterogenous RNA (hnRNA), which is the unabridged copy that contains both coding and noncoding sequences. The expressed sequences are called *exons* and the noncoding are called *intervening sequences* or *introns*. Obviously, if the hnRNA contains both exons and introns and the final mRNA contains only exons, then the introns must be removed and the exons *spliced* together to produce the final mRNA. Actually, the *split-gene* organization is not limited to DNA coding for mRNA, but also characterizes DNA directing the transcription of ribosomal RNA (rRNA) and transfer RNA (tRNA).

The importance of precise excision of intervening sequences and linkage of exons in generating an mRNA molecule that is a faithful copy of the parent DNA cannot be overemphasized. In eucaryotes, the fidelity of protein synthesis depends on information carried by mRNA; therefore, it is expected that the splicing process would require some special participants to ensure that fidelity. This function is performed by a group of small nuclear RNAs and associated proteins collectively called the *spliceosome* (Figure 1.17).

It should be clear, however, that building a protein with modular pieces from within the linear sequence of DNA implies both risks and opportunities. In fact, many proteins (including immunoglobulins) are created from such alternative splicing. Of course, after mixing and matching pieces of genes to build a protein, imprecise splicing may cause mutations. Some of the thalassemias (see Chapter 18 on hematology) result from mutations that permanently transform the splice sites.

The messenger RNA formed is modified further by the addition of poly A at the 5′ and a cap at the 3′ (Figure 1.18). The purine and pyrimidine bases in messenger RNA are arrayed in a sequence that is anticomplementary to the sequence in the unwound strand of DNA. Thus, the sequence of bases in the messenger RNA mirrors the sequence of bases in the gene. Ribosomal RNA and transfer RNA are synthesized from their specific genes through the action of a DNA-dependent RNA polymerase as well. The various tRNA spe-

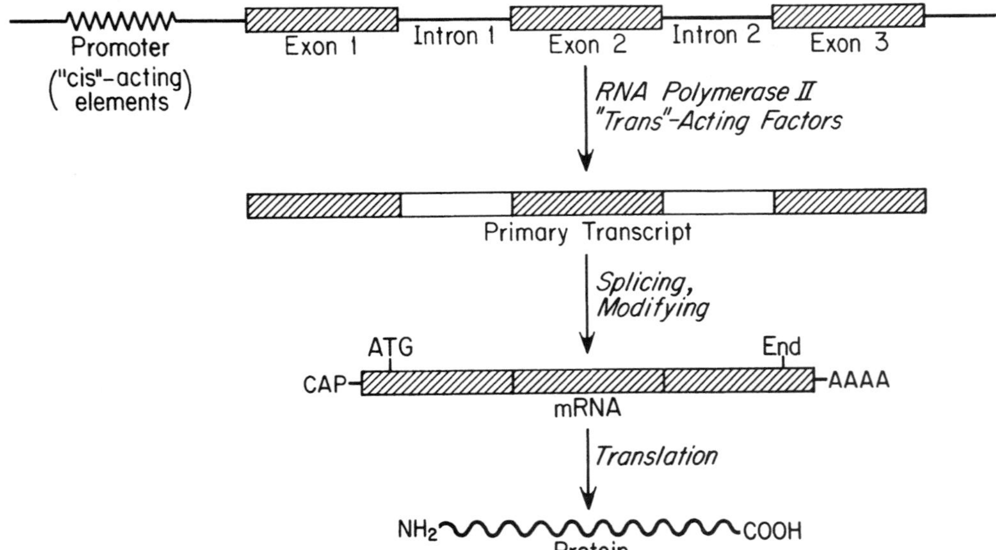

Figure 1.16. Structure of the eucaryotic gene. The DNA segment designated as a gene contains a promoter region at the 5′ end (upstream) that controls gene expression. Specific nucleotide sequences or cis-acting elements are required to initiate expression. Only certain regions (exons) of the overall nucleotide sequence that are downstream from the promoter region are transcribed into mRNA. Thus, specific proteins (trans-acting factors), acting on RNA polymerase control synthesis of the primary transcript, which includes both introns and exons, must be further modified. These intranuclear modifications occur by (*a*) removing the introns, (*b*) splicing together the exons, (*c*) adding a "cap" of modified nucleotides at the 5′ end, and (*d*) adding of a polyadenylate tail at the 3′ termination. After all of these modifications, the newly synthesized mRNA moves to the cytoplasm, where it may direct translation. Reprinted with permission from Holland JF, Frei E III, Bast RC Jr, Kufe DW, Morton DL, Weichselbaum RR. Cancer Medicine. 3rd ed. Baltimore: Williams & Wilkins, MD, 1993.

cies undergo covalent modification in a phenomenon called *processing*. These tRNAs, with their attached amino acids, are polymerized into polypeptides on the ribosomes according to the information contained in the messenger RNAs. The sequence of the amino acids in each polypeptide, therefore, depends on the order of the tRNAs in accordance with the sequential arrangement of the bases in the messenger RNAs. A multiplicity of protein factors, assumed to be enzymatic in function, controls the *initiation*, *elongation*, and *termination* of the polypeptide chain; but, as yet, it is not completely characterized or understood.

Translation from the linear sequences of mRNA to synthesize proteins is a rigidly controlled and complex process, consistent with the fidelity requirements of a process that forms the basis of life. Translation hinges upon the tRNA molecules that are akin to the Rosetta Stone. These specific adaptor molecules align the amino acids with the mRNA code and, thus, read the information in mRNA and in amino acids.

The triplet codons represent a prescription for pairing between the tRNA-amino acid moieties and the mRNA transcript of the genome. As with transcription, the code functions through antiparallel recognition between codon and its anticodon. Messenger RNA and tRNA act with a group of specific enzymes, the aminoacyl tRNA synthetases. Ribosomes are elaborate supramolecular structures in which protein synthesis occurs.

Messenger RNA attaches to the ribosomes and directs the sequence of amino acids incorporated into the protein as the various tRNA-amino acid species bring the amino acids to the synthetic apparatus. The anticodon in tRNA corresponds to a particular triplet code in mRNA; therefore, specificity for amino acid selection is provided by complementary base recognition. When the polypeptide chain is completed, it detaches from the

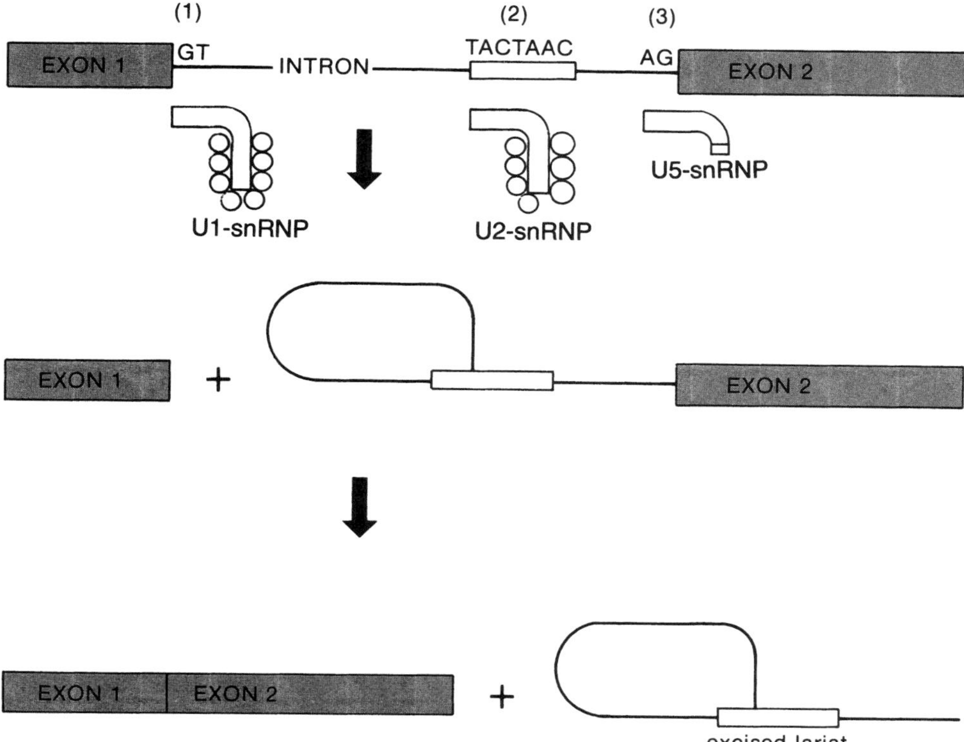

Figure 1.17. Spliceosome action. Synthesis of mRNA requires the removal of intron segments from the primary (pre-mRNA) transcript. Intron segments must be cleaved and rejoined with precision for translation of a consistently normal gene product. Numbers (1), (2), and (3) refer to the gene regions that are involved as recognition sites. Small RNA molecules functioning as enzymes (ribozymes) associate with proteins (small circles) to form small ribonucleoprotein (snRNP) complexes. Several of these complexes act together as a spliceosome. As shown, U1-snRNP attaches to (1), U2-snRNP attaches to (2), and U5-snRNP to (3), all through RNA-RNA base pairing. The 5′ end of the intron is cleaved at its guanine-thymine (GT) recognition site, and then is covalently bound to an adenine residue downstream on the intron, forming a lariat. Cleavage of the intron at the adenine-guanine (AG) recognition site, with subsequent ligation of exons 1 and 2, results in a residual, excised lariat. Reprinted with permission from De Robertis EDP, De Robertis EMF Jr. Cell and Molecular Biology. 8th ed. Philadelphia: 1987; Lea & Febiger, 1987.

ribosome and assumes its unique three-dimensional structure. At this stage, it can combine with other polypeptide chains to form a protein with quaternary structure.

This complex process is depicted in Figure 1.19. Further details may be found by referring to the biochemistry texts listed at the end of this chapter.

Mutations: Alterations in DNA

Because the information for all of the proteins of the cell is contained in the DNA sequences and because each amino acid is determined by a triplet of nucleotide bases, alteration in that sequence can have profound effects on the resulting protein synthesized. Such errors can occur through mistakes made during DNA replication, with substitution of the incorrect base, through radiation or chemical modification, or, most commonly, through errors in *crossing over*. These heritable defects are called mutations and may result in the code being *misread* because of the *deletion* of a key amino acid, a *substitution* of one amino acid for another, premature cessation of protein synthesis, or addition of amino acid sequences beyond the point of correct termination. Considering that

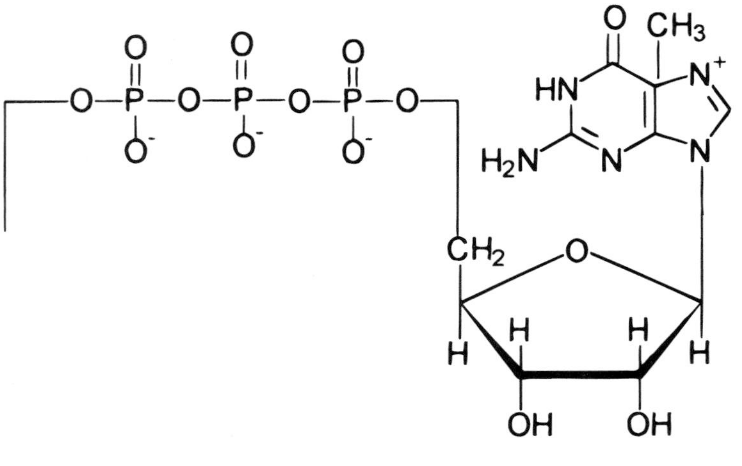

7-Methyl guanosine

Figure 1.18. The methylated cap of eucaryotic mRNA. Note 7-methylguanosine is attached at the 5′ end through a phosphodiester bond to a triphosphate group that links it to the succeeding nucleotides in the mRNA chain. The methyl cap protects the mRNA transcript from the action of some nucleases. Bacterial mRNA does not possess a methyl cap and, therefore, is vulnerable to these nucleases.

the linear sequence of amino acids directs the folding of the protein into its three-dimensional structure, any of these defects may have definitive effects on the protein structure and, therefore, its function. Nonetheless, many variations (eg, hemoglobin) are detected by laboratory techniques only and do not have uniformly deleterious effects on functions. **The key, then, lies in the location of the change in the primary structure. If the amino acid position affected is crucial in directing the folding or in forming part of a binding/catalytic site, or has increased its *in vivo* lability, then the mutation will be significant and will likely manifest as clinical disease.**

Recombinant DNA and Genetic Engineering

Six billion base pairs exist in the human genome. To demonstrate a correspondence between the nucleotide sequence in DNA and the RNA transcribed from that DNA, and to establish the relationship between the sequence in mRNA and the protein translated, it is necessary to make the size of the DNA in the genome more manageable. Without the ability to cut the DNA into well-defined pieces, it would be impossible to find those DNA sequences for a particular protein, even for one that is produced in large amounts, such as hemoglobin by reticulocytes. In most instances, however, a particular cell creates meager amounts of a protein; therefore, the amount of DNA coding for that protein must be amplified in other ways.

Fortunately, in the 1970s, a group of enzymes, the *restriction endonucleases*, were discovered and characterized—enzymes that, by their ability to cut out precise pieces of DNA from along the entire linear sequence, have revolutionized the approach to working with genes. Furthermore, another group of enzymes, the *DNA ligases*, can link two pieces of DNA from differing organisms. Combining cloning techniques (see below) to produce large amounts of specific sequences with the power of restriction enzymes and DNA ligase placed the necessary tools in the hands of investigators to fashion recombinant DNAs from these enzymatically generated fragments.

Finally, by capitalizing on the ability of DNA and RNA to hybridize to the appropriate complementary sequences in stretches of nucleic acid, it is possible to localize a gene to its exact site on a chromosome. As is the case with proteins, hydrophobic interactions are the most important weak

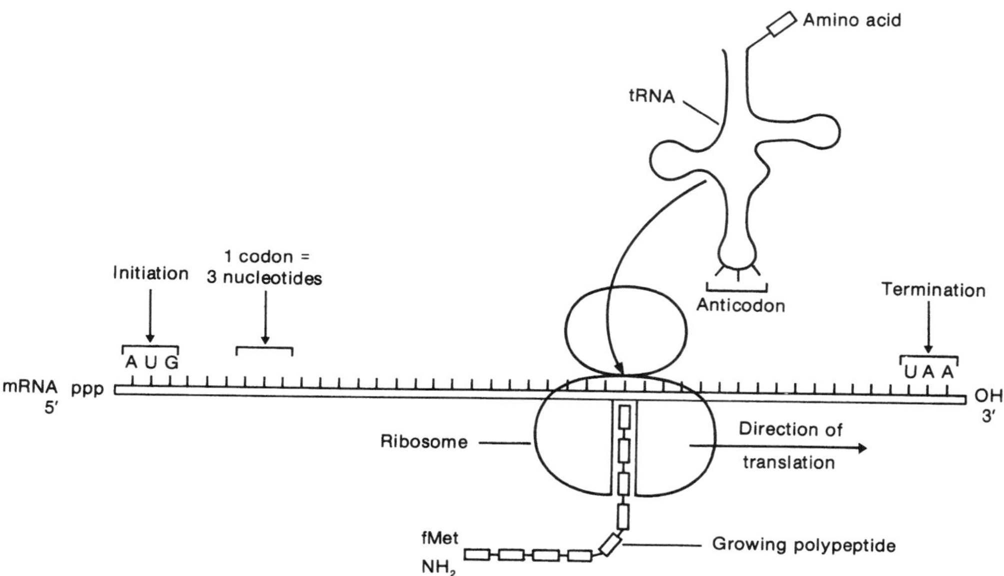

Figure 1.19. The machinery and raw materials essential for protein synthesis. Protein synthesis occurs in the cytoplasm, after exit of the spliced, capped, and poly A-tailed mRNA from the nucleus. The mRNA contains a short sequence of bases called the leader sequence, which forms hydrogen bonds with a short segment of the ribosome (rRNA). The invariable codon sequence AUG attracts an initiator transfer RNA (tRNA) with an anticodon (complementary) sequence that carries formylated methionine (fMet). When fMet is present at the site, the group of molecules is called the initiation complex. Actual synthesis begins when this complex is bound to a large ribosomal subunit, followed by attraction of a specific tRNA carrying the amino acid specified by the second codon in the mRNA sequence. Enzymatic formation of a peptide bond between the two amino acids then occurs, followed by a third, etc. This process always starts from the 5′ end of the mRNA and continues until one of three "stop" codons (UAA, UGA, UAG) is reached. These sequences function as stop codons because there is no tRNA that carries a corresponding anticodon to any of the three. With release of the last tRNA, the ribosomal subunits separate, releasing the newly formed polypeptide into the cytosol. Reprinted with permission from De Robertis EDP, De Robertis EMF Jr. Cell and Molecular Biology. 8th ed. Philadelphia: Lea & Febiger, 1987.

forces stabilizing the DNA higher order structure, in this case the double helix. The importance of hydrogen bonds lies less in stabilizing the double helix and more in the realm of directing the specificity of base pairing between complementary purines and pyrimidines. For example, adenine-thymine (AT) base pairs are joined by two hydrogen bonds, whereas a guanine-cytosine (GC) base pair has three hydrogen bonds. Consequently, GC-rich regions are held together more tightly than are AT-rich regions.

Restriction Enzymes

The wide array of enzymes, the restriction endonucleases, that digest intruder bacteriophage DNA has been a boon to studies with genes. Obviously, the biologic role of these enzymes was to protect bacteria from external DNA that might disrupt or kill the cell. But because these enzymes recognize specific sequences of bases in DNA, cutting each strand at a precise site, they afford investigators the opportunity to break down the genome into manageable pieces. Hundreds of restriction enzymes have been isolated, with the recognition site varying depending on the bacterial species. This provides an enormous arsenal for the researcher. Because recognition sites typically involve four to six base pairs that are palindromes (Figure 1.20), they cut both strands of DNA. Some restriction enzymes cut right along the axis of symmetry producing *blunt* ends, whereas others cut away from that axis producing overlapping pieces that are called "*sticky* ends." The advantage of using enzymes that produce sticky ends is that they can

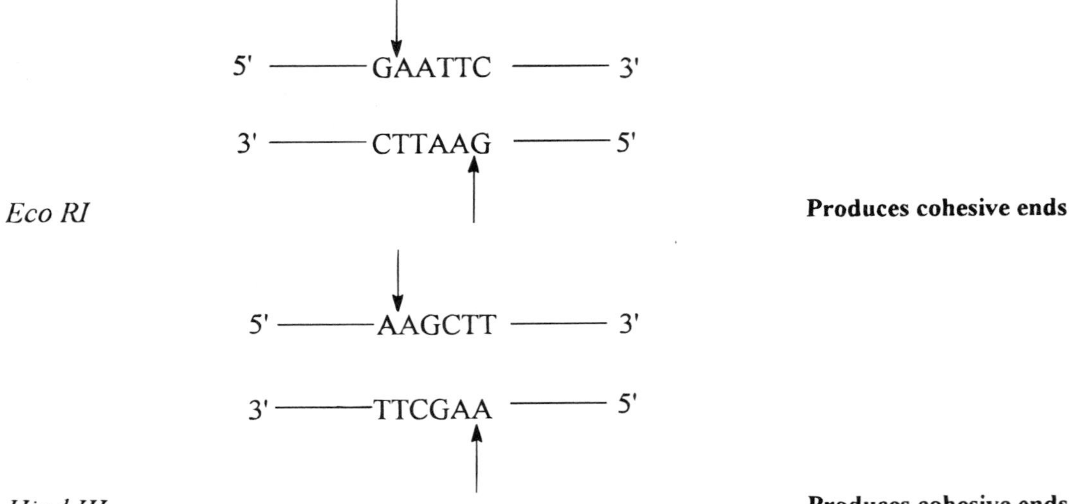

Figure 1.20. Restriction endonuclease recognition sites. Each double-stranded DNA fragment contains a base sequence that constitutes a recognition site for one of a pair of restriction endonucleases (Eco RI and Hind III, respectively). Note that each enzyme recognizes the site in both strands of a pair; consequently, the fragment produced also is a double strand. The products of both reactions illustrated have cohesive or "sticky" ends, which can be utilized in cloning experiments.

engage in base pairing. It is this ability of complementary sequences to base pair that underlies the ability to splice in a piece of foreign DNA into a segment of host DNA.

Gene Cloning

Cloning involves isolating precise DNA fragments from the total DNA of the organism and multiplying those fragments to generate amounts that can be manipulated in the laboratory (Figure 1.21). Cloning DNA exploits the ability of restriction endonucleases to cut nucleic acids at precise points in the sequence and of DNA ligase to splice that DNA fragment into a biologic vector. Using the same restriction enzyme, DNA from two different sources—the vector (host) and the target (foreign) DNA—can be cut to produce sticky ends. Such sticky ends will hybridize or anneal at low temperatures and can be linked covalently by DNA ligase. Once a vector has successfully incorporated the DNA sequence of interest into its genome, that sequence may be replicated to produce multiple copies. A practical vector must be maintained in the host cell and possess a site at which replication can begin.

Vectors for cloning include plasmids, bacteriophages, and yeast artificial chromosomes. Plasmids are circular pieces of DNA that exist separately from the bacterial chromosome in the cell cytosol. They are useful as vectors because they carry their own replication site and typically harbor genes that code for antibiotic resistance for the host bacterium. Thus, they can be selected by growing the bacteria on a medium with antibiotic. Bacteria in which plasmids contain the antibiotic resistance gene will survive such incubation. The drawback of plasmids is that they can clone only a sequence of 10 kb or less.

Bacteriophages are viruses that infect bacteria and can, therefore, serve as vectors. The eucaryotic genome is large because of intervening sequences and remote regulatory sequences, and, consequently, a plasmid cannot accommodate the large stretch of nucleotides. Yeast artificial chromosomes are new constructs made by humans that can accommodate 200 to 500 kb. Specifics concerning these various cloning vectors can be found by consulting the texts presented at the end of this chapter.

Cloning cDNA

Because human genes coding for proteins typically contain large stretches of noncoding introns

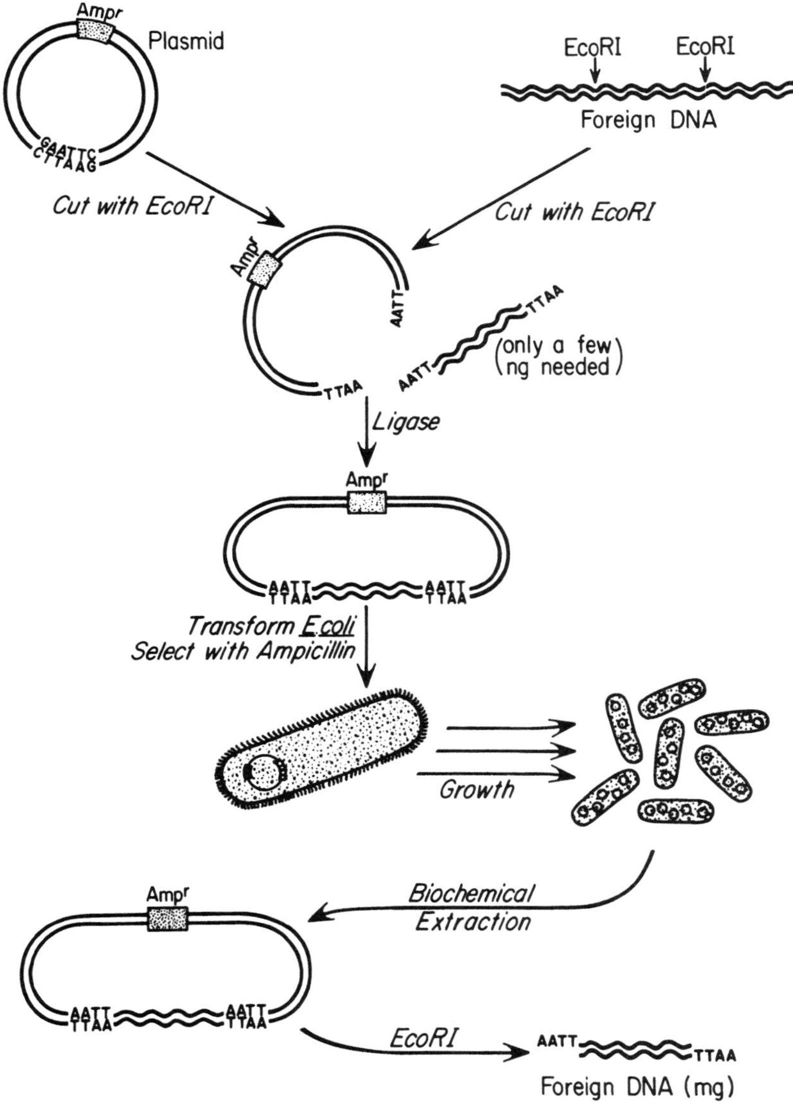

Figure 1.21. The fundamentals of gene cloning. The basic tool is a plasmid (a small circular section of double-stranded DNA that exists naturally in some bacteria and yeasts), which contains an antibiotic-resistance gene and a small amount of foreign DNA containing the gene to be cloned. Both the plasmid and the gene site of the foreign DNA must share the same restriction endonuclease recognition sites. Each is digested with the same restriction endonuclease, which results in double-stranded DNA with "sticky" single-stranded ends. The foreign DNA then can be covalently introduced into the plasmid using DNA ligase, resulting in a product called recombinant DNA. Bacterial cells that are antibiotic-sensitive then are permitted to take up the plasmid, and the recombinant cells are cultured through several replicative cycles after exposure to antibiotics to kill the cells that do not contain plasmid. Isolating the plasmid from the selectively-cultured bacterial cells again and subsequent digestion with the same restriction endonuclease will permit recovery of greater amounts of the cloned gene. Reprinted with permission from Holland JF, Frei E III, Bast RC Jr, et al. Cancer Medicine. 3rd ed. Baltimore: Williams & Wilkins, 1993.

that must be spliced out to create the final mRNA transcript, it often is preferable to start with mRNA itself. But, mRNA is more fragile than DNA, and it is not a suitable target to incorporate into a vector genome. The solution arises from another of nature's gifts to scientists—the reverse transcriptase, which is an RNA-dependent DNA polymerase that uses RNA to make complementary DNA (cDNA), thereby reversing the usual sequence DNA→RNA. These enzymes are found in RNA tumor viruses and account for the ability of these viruses to incorporate DNA sequences into the genome of eucaryotic cells (see the chapters on cancer and infection-viruses).

Because any given mammalian cell produces between 10,000 and 30,000 different proteins in its life cycle, a like number of different mRNA molecules also must be produced to encode those proteins. For most proteins, there are only about 1 to 10 copies of each mRNA per cell; therefore, cloning allows this mRNA to be amplified as cDNA.

Gene Libraries

A gene library is composed of fragments enclosed in multiple vectors; in aggregate, these fragments represent the entire genome of that individual. A gene library such as this is constructed using restriction enzymes so that the entire genome of the organism is subdivided into smaller sequences based on the frequency of appearance of the enzyme target sites. Generally, a restriction enzyme will be chosen if its target sites occur frequently within a particular genome. The vector for these fragments usually is bacteriophage lambda, which has been altered so that DNA segments not required for lytic growth are removed, providing ample room for target DNA. Once the genomic fragments are covalently linked to the phage DNA, the vector is encapsulated with lambda coat protein and permitted to infect host Escherichia coli.

Complementary DNA libraries are made by cloning all the mRNA expressed by a single cell type.

Blotting Methods

Using one or more various restriction enzymes on DNA from an organism produces many fragments of DNA that can be separated on agarose or polyacrylamide gels by electrophoresis. Once separated, the fragments can be visualized by staining with ethidium bromide, which fluoresces when it binds to DNA. But, the drawback is that the fragments are of unknown sequence (ie, they are anonymous).

Hybridization of fragments with nucleotide probes of known sequence is used for identification. This strategy capitalizes on the propensity of nucleic acid sequences to hybridize to their complementary strand. Blotting procedure begins by transferring the DNA fragments from the original gel to a piece of nitrocellulose paper (Figure 1.22). After denaturing the DNA on the nitrocellulose by heating, the paper is placed in a solution containing a radiolabeled probe complementary to the desired sequence in the DNA preparation. After washing off the excess probe, the blot can be used to expose a piece of film that reveals the location of the fragments that annealed to the radioactive probe. Instead, fluorescent markers could be attached to the probe.

Restriction Fragment Length Polymorphism

Restriction enzymes cut human DNA at randomly chosen locations because these enzymes exert no biologic action in humans. Alteration of the DNA sequence may result in either a gain or loss of a restriction-enzyme recognition site, which would create a polymorphism at that site. Because the number of base pairs between restriction sites is unlikely to be the same among various individuals whose DNA is treated with a restriction enzyme, this would lead to fragments of different sizes that could be resolved on electrophoresis and identified by Southern blotting. Because some restriction fragment length polymorphisms (RFLPs) (Figure 1.23) are tightly linked to certain genetic disorders, presence of the RFLP may be inherited, along with the inherited error. Another use is to identify and clone the actual gene for the inherited defect.

RFLPs are of limited use, however, because they involve a single base change. Because the chance of a base change altering a target site for a restriction enzyme is low, there is limited utility for searching for RFLPs. This limitation does not apply to the next category—*variable number of tandem repeats* (VNTRs). VNTRs are regions of noncoding repetitive DNA randomly scattered

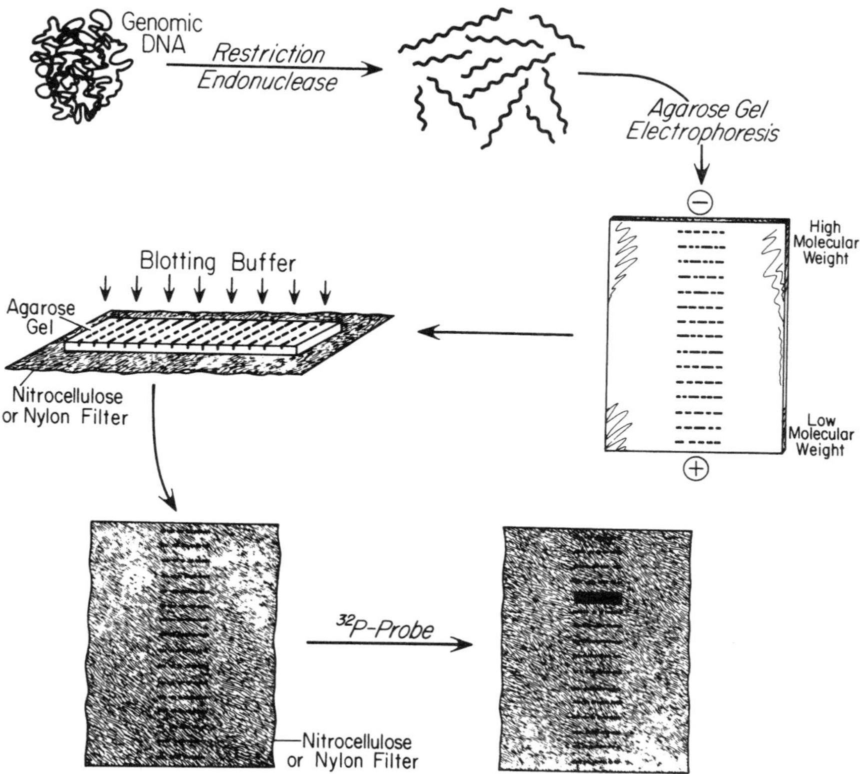

Figure 1.22. Southern blotting. The DNA containing the gene of interest is isolated and digested with a restriction endonuclease, resulting in multiple species of fragments from the original DNA sequence. These species vary widely in size (molecular weight) and are anonymous regarding their genetic content. They are separated according to molecular weight by agarose gel electrophoresis, resulting in the linear array of fragments, as shown. The gel then is placed over a nitrocellulose sheet or a nylon filter, and buffer is run through the gel, transferring the fragments to the underlying sheet or filter by capillary action. Using a P32-labelled probe in which the nucleotide sequence is complementary to a portion of the nucleotide sequence of the gene of interest, the fragments containing the gene will become radioactive. When the labelled sheet is exposed to radiograph film, the position of these fragments can be identified. Note that the more extensive the complementary sequence of the probe to the gene, the more selective and specific the identification. Thus, the technique requires that a portion of the gene sequence be known. Reprinted with permission from Holland JF, Frei E III, Bast RC JR, et al. Cancer Medicine. 3rd ed. Baltimore: Williams & Wilkins, 1993.

throughout the genome that are composed of a few tandem repeated sequences. Whether they have a function is unknown, but, because the frequency of their repetition varies widely among individuals, they are called *hypervariable regions*. Furthermore, because this variability is sufficiently unique for each individual, VNTRs can be used as a *DNA fingerprint*. In practice, by using probes for 10 to 12 distinct VNTR regions, it is possible to differentiate a particular individual from all others, unless there is an identical twin.

DNA Sequencing

Most studies with DNA ultimately rely on sequencing methods to determine the linear sequence of the gene (Figure 1.24). That sequence then will reveal the nature of the protein encoded by that gene. Not infrequently, the DNA sequence leads to insights about the anonymous protein.

The most widely used method for sequencing is that of Sanger, which relies on stopping DNA replication by a base-specific terminator. In this method, four separate sequencing reactions are

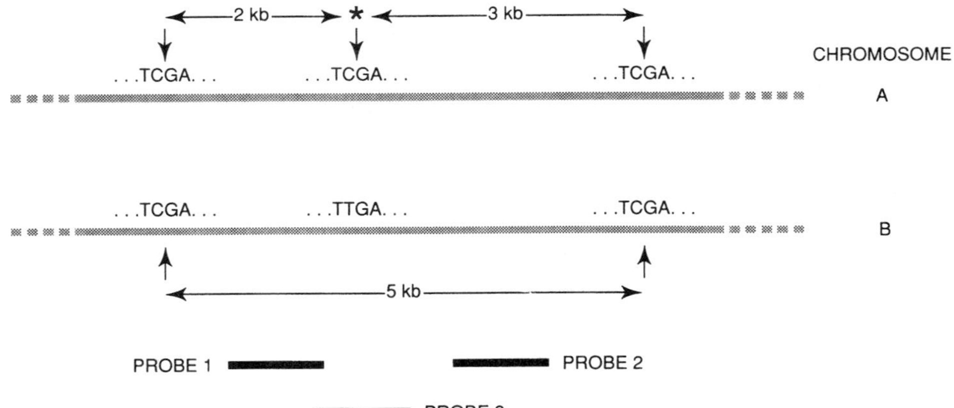

Figure 1.23. Concept of restriction fragment length polymorphism (RFLP). Base sequence variations in noncoding regions of DNA are common and do not affect the individual. Thus, because chromosomes A and B differ in sequence at the site marked by an asterisk, a restriction endonuclease that recognizes the sequence TCGA will cut chromosome A into two fragments identifiable by probes 1 and 2, but not by probe 3. Conversely, because the enzyme will not act on chromosome B, probe 3 will bind only to it, not to the two chromosome A fragments. This difference between two functionally identical chromosomes defines the meaning of DNA polymorphism. Reprinted with permission from Gelehrter TD, Collins FS. Principles of Medical Genetics. Baltimore: Williams & Wilkins, 1995.

run using a DNA polymerase, a short peptide primer, a mixture of all four deoxynucleotide bases (dNTP), and a dideoxynucleoside triphosphate (ddNTP) for one of the four bases. Because the ddNTPs do not have a 3′-OH group to link up with another dNTP, chain elongation ceases. The products of each reaction are separated by acrylamide gel electrophoresis and each reaction is run on a separate lane.

One of the most dramatic benefits resulting from the sequencing of DNA has been the ability to determine the *flanking regions* that regulate gene expression (Figure 1.25). When regulatory regions of multiple genes have been sequenced, *consensus sequences* have been revealed for promoters, enhancers, and binding sites for regulatory proteins (see below).

The *promoter* is located upstream from the start codons and represents the sequences that determine where a RNA polymerase binds to initiate transcription. *Enhancers* are regulatory sequences that augment the rate of transcription; like promoters, they are linked to the gene but, unlike promoters, they can be located either upstream or downstream from the transcription initiation site.

Gene Superfamilies

Sequencing data of a number of protein-coding genes reveals that many proteins are members of superfamilies of genes that bear a distinct kinship to each other. Examples of such superfamilies are the globins, the immunoglobulins, the serine proteases, and a group of cell surface receptors that share the seven-domain structure. Members of the seven-domain superfamily include the receptors for rhodopsin, β-adrenergic agents, and muscarinic acetylcholine agonists. Divergence of specific function from a primordial gene occurred because the copies of ancestral gene became altered over time through the effects of chance mutations. But, this is just the beginning of the divergence of derivative genes from an ancestor. In addition to repeated duplications and mutations, it is now clear that the discontinuous nature of the eucaryotic genome provides the additional ingredients necessary to create diversity by shuffling exons and inserting introns.

Polymerase Chain Reaction

The most recently added method to aid in the study of nucleic acids is the polymerase chain reaction (PCR), described in 1984. With this procedure, the DNA from one cell or one piece of hair can be amplified for sequencing or other studies. Two primers, complementary to the DNA of interest, are needed so that the polymerase will

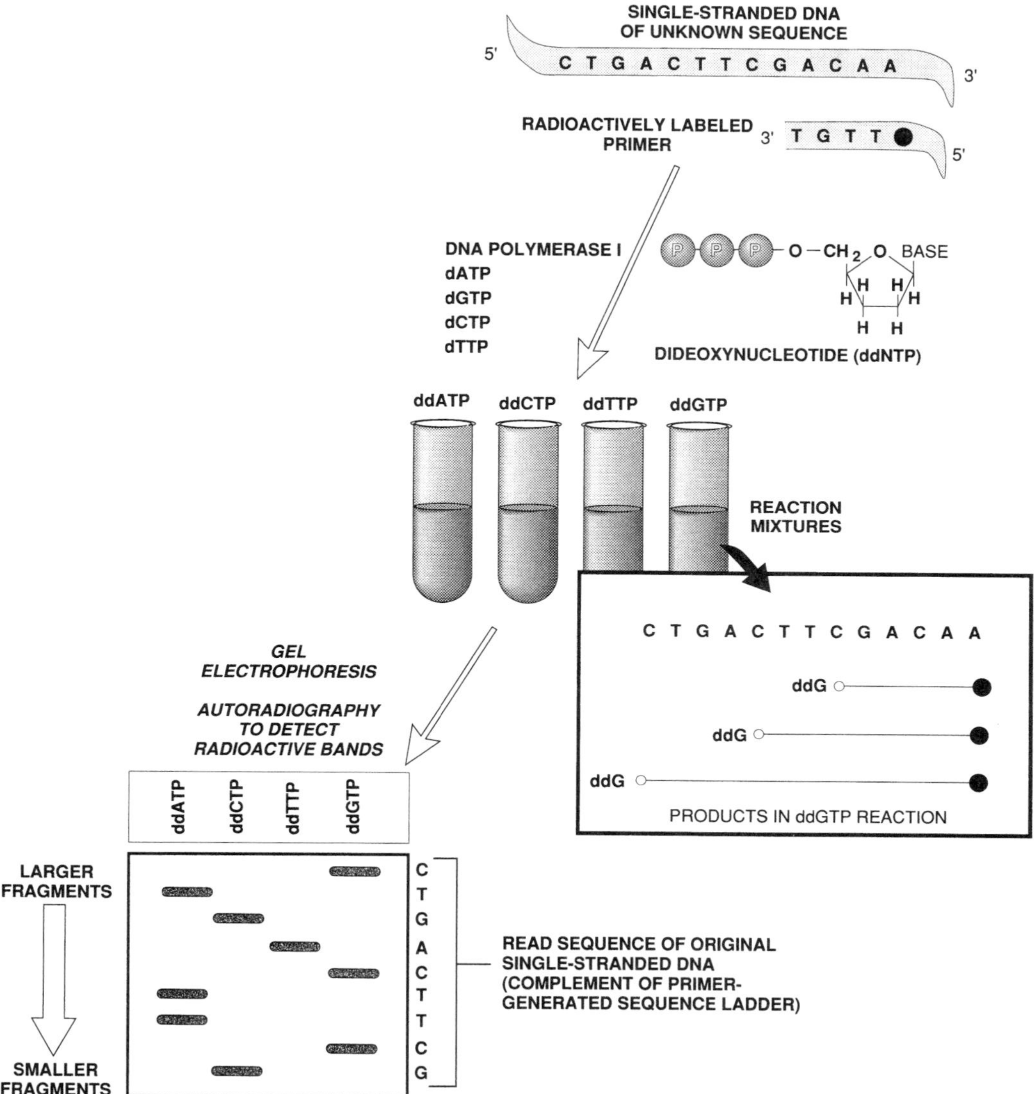

Figure 1.24. Determination of DNA base sequence by the "dideoxy" method. Native DNA is separated by heating or addition of acid orbase to ionize the bases into single strands. A short primer sequence is radioactively labelled to expedite synthesis and for subsequent identification. Using the separated strand, the complementary DNA strand is synthesized de novo in four individual vessels by DNA polymerase activity. A small amount of one of the four dideoxynucleotide compounds is added to each vessel; as the synthetic reaction proceeds in each case, incorporation of the dideoxy analogue causes elongation of the nucleotide chain to cease. Southern blotting of the synthetic products in each tube permits direct reading of the sequences as complementary to the primer sequence. Reprinted with permission from Gelehrter TD, Collins FS. Principles of Medical Genetics. Baltimore: Williams & Wilkins, 1995.

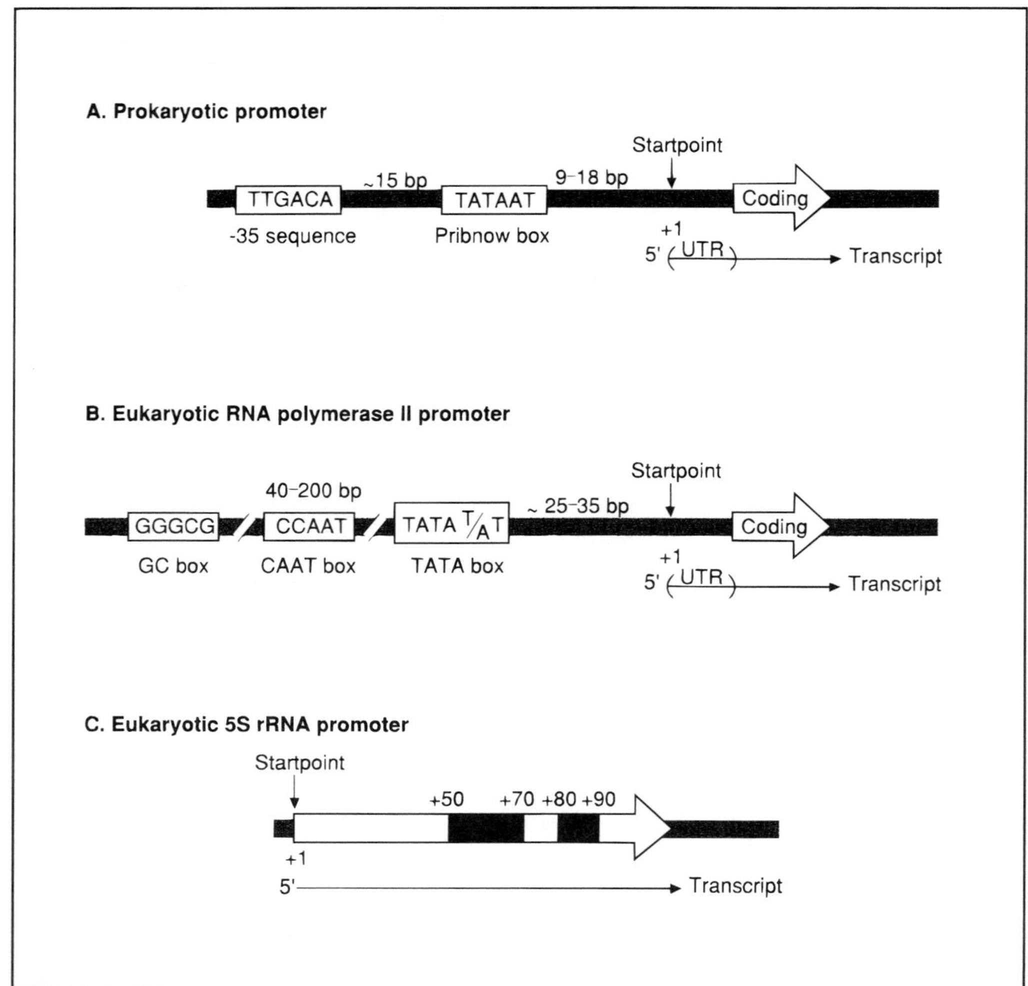

Figure 1.25. Gene flanking regions. Gene transcription, which requires at least four transcription factors to initiate, is under tight regulatory control. The first transcription factor to bind does so at a region called the TATA (T = thymine, A = adenine) box, which is a subunit of the 5′ flanking region called the promoter. The TATA box consists of the TATA sequence that is flanked at each end by about 25 bases that primarily are guanine and cytosine (G and C). Binding of the first transcription factor attracts others, and the resulting complex, called the promoter, provides the binding site for a RNA polymerase. Each RNA polymerase uses a different promoter, and a region upstream from the TATA box, called the CAAT box, controls the frequency of transcription. This action is regulated by a sequence called an enhancer through a mechanism that is undefined. Note that in both the procaryotic (A) and eucaryotic (B) gene, the startpoint for transcription begins upstream from the coding region, so that there is an untranslated region (UTR). A unique element of the RNA polymerase III promoter region is the downstream (3′) location, shown in (C). Pribnow box is a component of the procaryotic promoter and is named for the scientist who discovered it. Reprinted with permission from Davidson VL, Sittman DB. Biochemistry. Baltimore: Williams & Wilkins, 1993.

add bases onto the target DNA, filling in the gap between the primers (Figure 1.26).

Double-stranded DNA must separate into single strands for synthesis to continue. This is accomplished by heating the reaction mixture and by using a thermostable DNA polymerase from Thermus aquaticus, called Taq polymerase. These conditions allow successive rounds of heating and polymerization to continue without denaturing the enzyme. Now the procedure is automated, so that more than 1×10^9 copies of a particular DNA sequence can be synthesized within 1 to 2 hours.

PCR has been applied, with significant results, in the fields of diagnosing inherited disease and in forensic science.

Gene Mapping: Positional Cloning—Chromosome Walking and Jumping

For decades, a goal of geneticists has been to construct a map of each chromosome, detailing the location of each gene to understand the link between the individual's genetic endowment and susceptibility to disease. Single-gene defects represented the initial area of exploration, but now it is becoming possible to explore the genetic factors involved in polygenic disorders, such as diabetes mellitus and coronary artery disease.

With the creation of DNA libraries and the array of techniques developed for recombinant DNA studies, it is now possible to approach the development of a genetic map more directly than was feasible using the time-honored methods of classic genetics. Recall that DNA libraries are made by subjecting the genome of an individual to restriction enzyme digestion. In this way, thousands of fragments are produced. Because fragments are generated randomly, redundancy and overlap of sequences is unavoidable. But, this can be exploited.

In many instances (eg, Duchenne muscular dystrophy, cystic fibrosis, and Huntington's disease) the nature of the defective protein causing the disease could not be defined or identified. In that situation, without knowing what the gene specified, investigators had to resort to indirect methods referred to as *positional cloning*, previously called reverse genetics. These studies begin with the gene and work toward the protein, rather than identify the defective protein (as in most inborn errors) and work toward the gene.

A particularly fruitful approach has been *chromosome walking*. Using appropriate vectors, the cloned fragments will be composed of segments that overlap those of other cloned fragments. Once identified, these overlapping regions can be used to identify adjoining regions on the DNA. This is tedious work and requires multiple approaches including cloning and subcloning, restriction mapping, and sequencing. Details may be found by consulting the texts listed at the end of this chapter.

A variant of chromosome walking that greatly accelerates the march down the gene is *chromosome jumping*. In this procedure, clones that circularize a long stretch of bases are prepared, bringing the ends together (Figure 1.27). By deleting the intervening bases, it is possible to cover much greater distances on the gene than with chromosome walking. This method is described in the texts listed at the end of this chapter.

ORGANIZATION OF METABOLIC PROCESSES

Strategies of Metabolism

Krebs and Kornberg have divided metabolism into three phases (Figure 1.28). In the first phase, a nutrient of high molecular weight undergoes digestion or hydrolysis and is broken down into smaller units, which are then absorbed into the cell. Little, if any, energy is recovered during that step. In fact, a *priming reaction* requiring energy usually is necessary before further metabolism can occur. For example, in the case of the fatty acids, combining with coenzyme A to form the fatty acyl coenzyme A derivative is required. This reaction also requires the expenditure of ATP. In the case of glucose, the first step involved in its catabolism involves the formation of a phosphorylated derivative before entry into the glycolytic sequence. During the *second stage* of catabolism, substrates undergo *partial oxidation* with the formation of acetyl CoA, α-ketoglutaric acid, and oxaloacetic acid. During this phase, approximately one-third of the available energy in the chemical bonds is recovered. In the *final phase* of catabolism, *complete oxidation* of the metabolic end-products of the previous step occurs through the metabolic

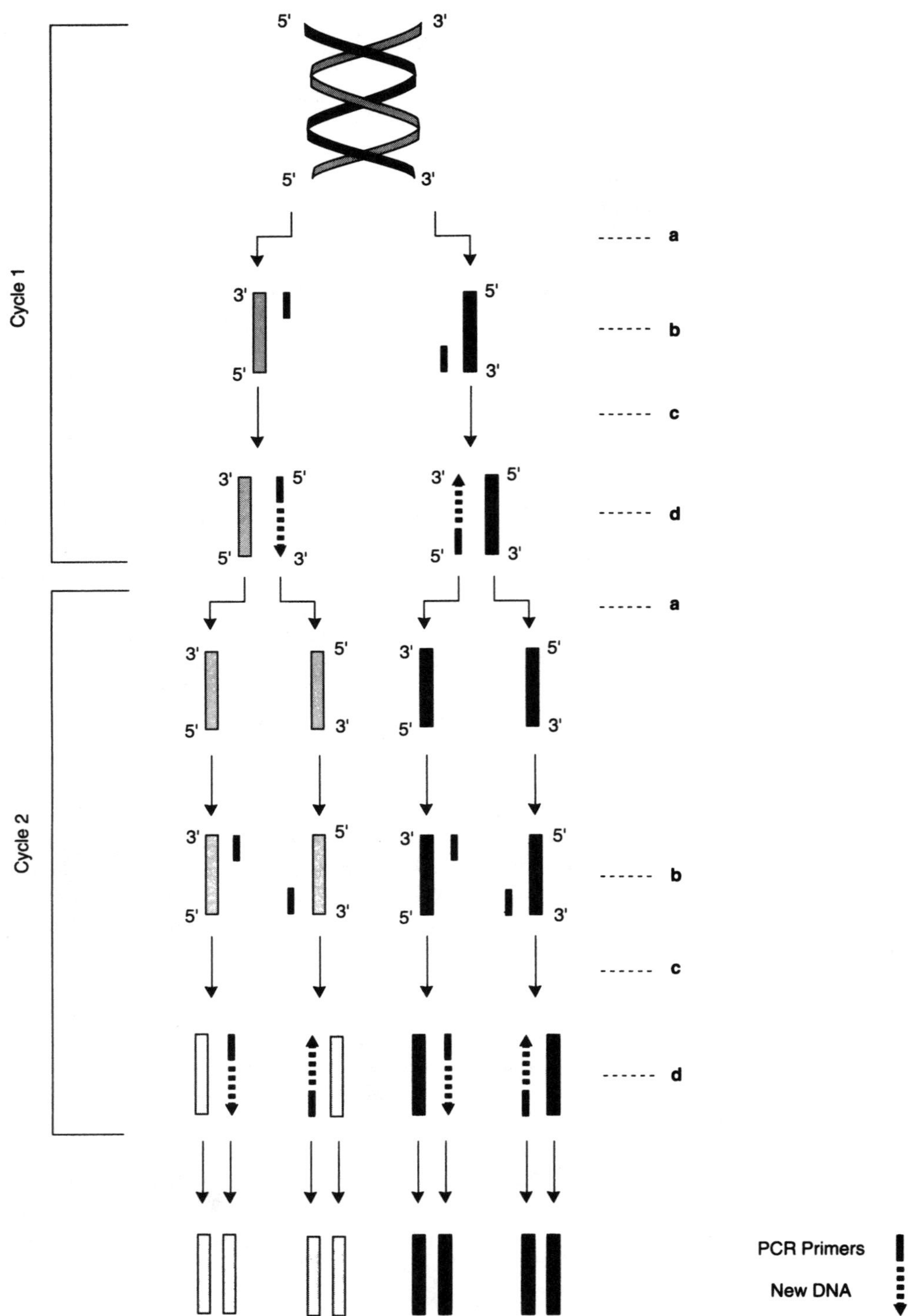

Cycle 1
Cycle 2
5'
3'
a
b
c
d
PCR Primers
New DNA

"mill" (ie, the citric acid cycle coupled with the energy released to form ATP). This latter process is termed *oxidative phosphorylation.*

Intermediary Metabolism

Intermediary metabolism involves the graded changes that biochemical compounds residing within the cell undergo as they are transformed into other molecules through chemical reactions. As discussed, these reactions are mediated by enzymes. Why are so many steps necessary to metabolize a particular compound (eg, glucose) into the final product of glycolysis (pyruvate)? First, the brisk conduct of the chemical reactions that constitute the process of life requires that the chemical conversions mediated by the enzymes occur quickly. Enzyme-substrate interaction involves binding of the substrate to the enzyme and, subsequently, the transformation of the substrate into its product. Having reviewed the nature of catalysis, it is clear that it is easier to cause a minor structural change in a compound in a short period rather than a major one. In addition, we must remember that enzymes have developed as a result of evolutionary pressure. Consequently, modest changes in the configuration of a particular compound are probably more easily achieved than major ones. Second, intermediary metabolism must accomplish two crucial functions responsible for the maintenance of the living process: (*a*) the storage of chemical energy in the form of ATP and (*b*) the provision of building blocks for the macromolecules comprising the highly organized structures of the cell.

A final consideration is that the highly organized nature of the life process demands tiers of control. Thus, multiple controls and redundancy of control may be possible after the metabolic sequence is divided into a multiplicity of steps.

Metabolic pathways have traditionally been divided into three types: *catabolic, anabolic, and amphibolic*. Degradative pathways in which substrates are broken down into products and liberated energy is stored as ATP are termed catabolic pathways. Synthetic pathways whereby small precursors are coalesced into larger molecules with energetic coupling being provided by ATP are termed anabolic pathways. Amphibolic pathways perform both of the above functions and are best exemplified in the tricarboxylic acid cycle.

HARVESTING ENERGY FROM FOODS

Because the foods we eat are largely composed of polymers, the first step in metabolism is digestion. The monomers liberated by digestion must be oxidized to produce ATP, which is the energetic coin of the realm for living organisms. Oxidation is the loss of electrons and requires the participation of an electron acceptor that takes up the liberated electrons. Although oxygen is the final electron acceptor for these oxidations for all multicellular organisms, many intervening steps usually are involved in the transfer of electrons (and hydrogen) to the coenzymes NAD^+ and FAD.

Glycolysis, the catabolism of glucose and other carbohydrates, is one of the oldest pathways and is found in all living things—anaerobic and aerobic. In organisms able to exploit the energy dividend that accrues from using oxygen as the final electron acceptor, glycolysis, which is anaerobic, is a prelude to the tricarboxylic acid (TCA) cycle and the electron transport chain (ETC), which are aerobic.

GLYCOLYSIS

Glucose is stored in many cells as glycogen, which is a polymer of considerable size (mass ca. 100

Figure 1.26. DNA amplification by polymerase chain reaction (PCR). This technique requires two short, laboratory-generated nucleotide primers in which the sequences are complementary to opposite strands of the DNA sequence of interest, which is thus bracketed by the primers. The need for the primers dictates that at least a part of the gene sequence is known. In cycle 1, double-stranded DNA is (a) heat denatured to separate the strands. The primers are added in excess (b) and spontaneously hybridize to their respective complementary sequences. At step (c), nucleotides and DNA polymerases permit extension from the primers (d), which actually represent the 5′ ends of the newly synthesized strands. Repetition (cycle 2) of the process results in geometric addition of newly synthesized material, so that after many cycles, nanogram quantities of DNA can be magnified by an order of magnitude or more. Reprinted with permission from Friedman JM, Dill FJ, Hayden MR. Genetics. Baltimore: Williams & Wilkins, 1992.

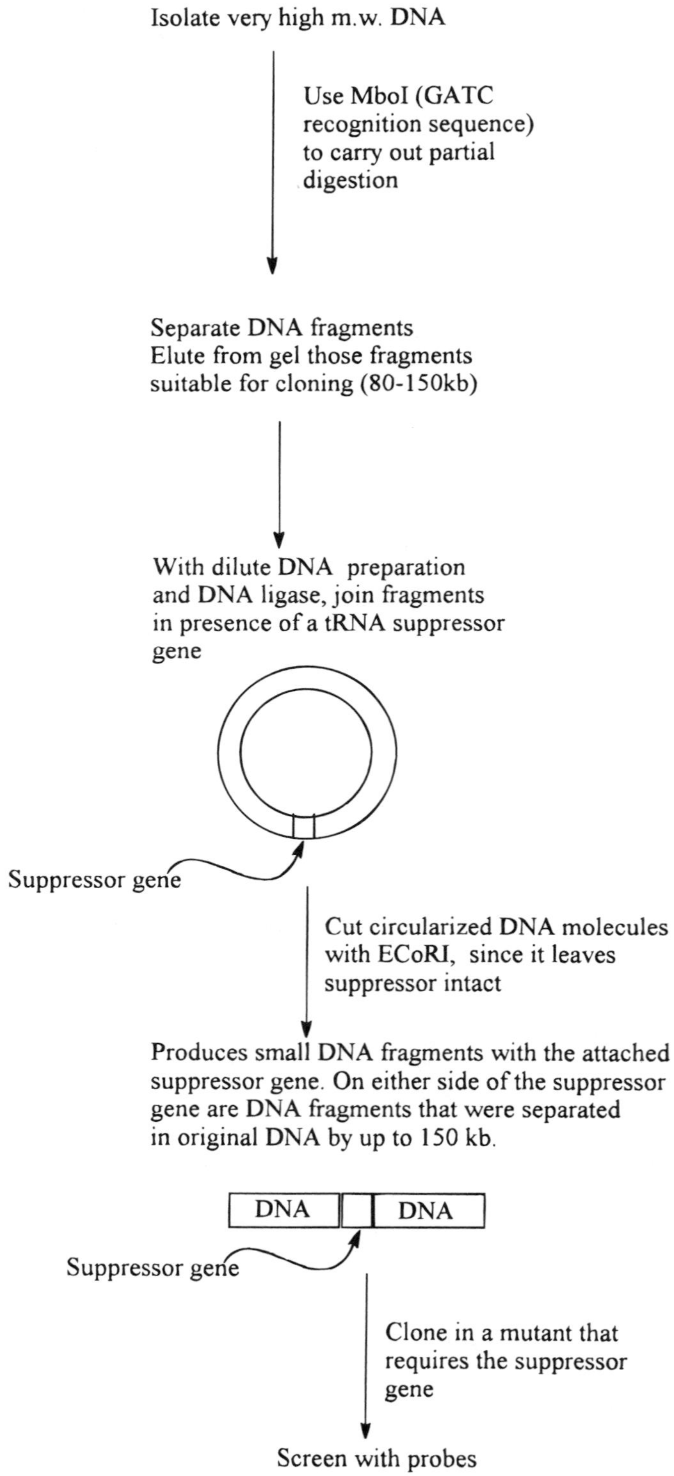

Isolate very high m.w. DNA

Use MboI (GATC recognition sequence) to carry out partial digestion

Separate DNA fragments
Elute from gel those fragments suitable for cloning (80-150kb)

With dilute DNA preparation and DNA ligase, join fragments in presence of a tRNA suppressor gene

Suppressor gene

Cut circularized DNA molecules with ECoRI, since it leaves suppressor intact

Produces small DNA fragments with the attached suppressor gene. On either side of the suppressor gene are DNA fragments that were separated in original DNA by up to 150 kb.

DNA | | DNA

Suppressor gene

Clone in a mutant that requires the suppressor gene

Screen with probes

Figure 1.27. Chromosome jumping is a strategy used in positional cloning that greatly accelerates the march down the chromosome.

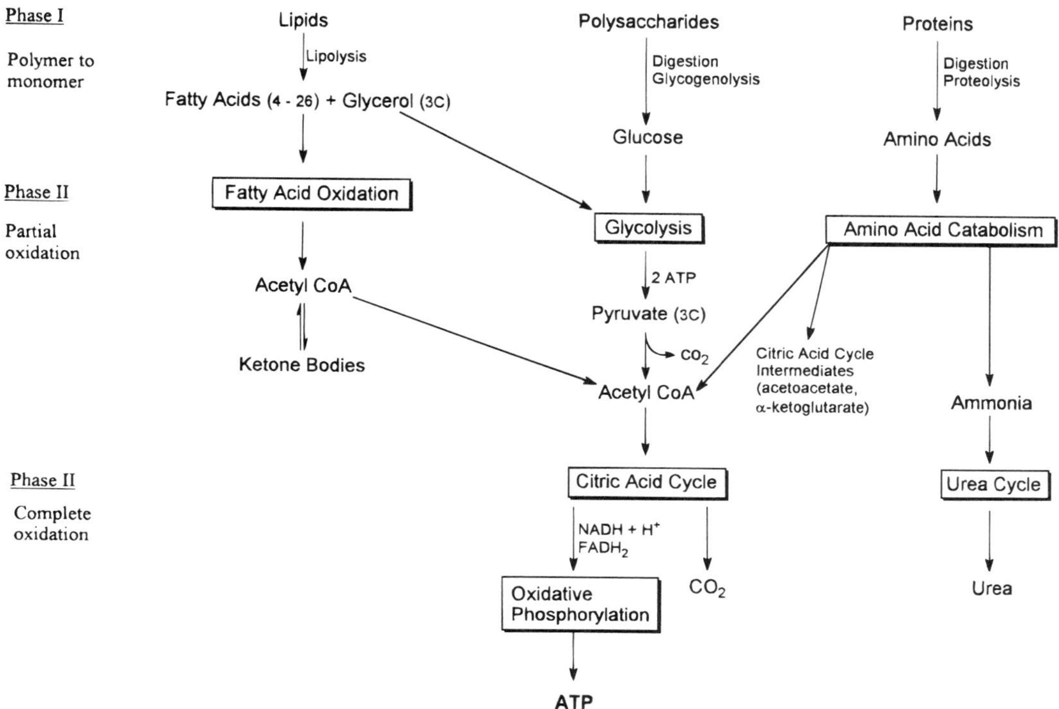

Figure 1.28. Stages of metabolism. Catabolic processes that generate ATP can be divided into three phases. The preparatory stages (phases I and II) harvest little energy, but phase III (complete oxidation) through the tricarboxylic acid cycle and the electron transport chain recovers a considerable amount of chemical energy as ATP.

million daltons) (this is further discussed in the chapter on carbohydrate disorders). Glucose plays a central role in cellular biochemistry for several reasons. First, as noted earlier, glycolysis (Figure 1.29) is a prelude to the energy-harvesting steps associated with the TCA cycle and ETC. Second, brain and red cells, and a few other cell types are obligatory consumers of glucose (see the chapter on hypoglycemia). Third, fat, which is the major storage form of energy and predominant source of energy for submaximal skeletal muscle activity, cannot be catabolized without oxaloacetic acid, an intermediate derived from glucose metabolism. Fourth, compounds other than glucose can enter the pathway during various steps.

The energy recovery from glycolysis is modest indeed—a net of two ATP after two are expended in early steps (hexokinase and phosphofructokinase) to activate the intermediates. A few steps later, glyceraldehyde-3-phosphate is oxidized in a step involving not oxygen but the coenzyme NAD^+ acting as an electron acceptor. Energy liberated during this step, when an aldehyde is converted to a mixed acid anhydride of a carboxylic acid and phosphoric acid, is used during the next step to generate ATP from ADP. Because the amount of NAD^+ in the cell is limited, it is essential that the NADH formed in step 6 of glycolysis be reoxidized to NAD^+. Otherwise, glycolysis will cease.

How is this NADH reoxidized in aerobic organisms? There are two shuttles that carry electrons from NADH into mitochondria because NADH itself cannot pass through the inner mitochondrial membrane. These two shuttles, the α-glycerophosphate shuttle and the malate-aspartate shuttle, are depicted in Figure 1.30. By these roundabout reactions, NADH is regenerated and electrons are passed to the ETC for generation of ATP.

But what happens if oxygen availability is limited, as found in sustained muscle exercise? In that case, the electrons and hydrogen held by NADH can be used in converting pyruvate to lactate. The ramifications of this reaction, catalyzed

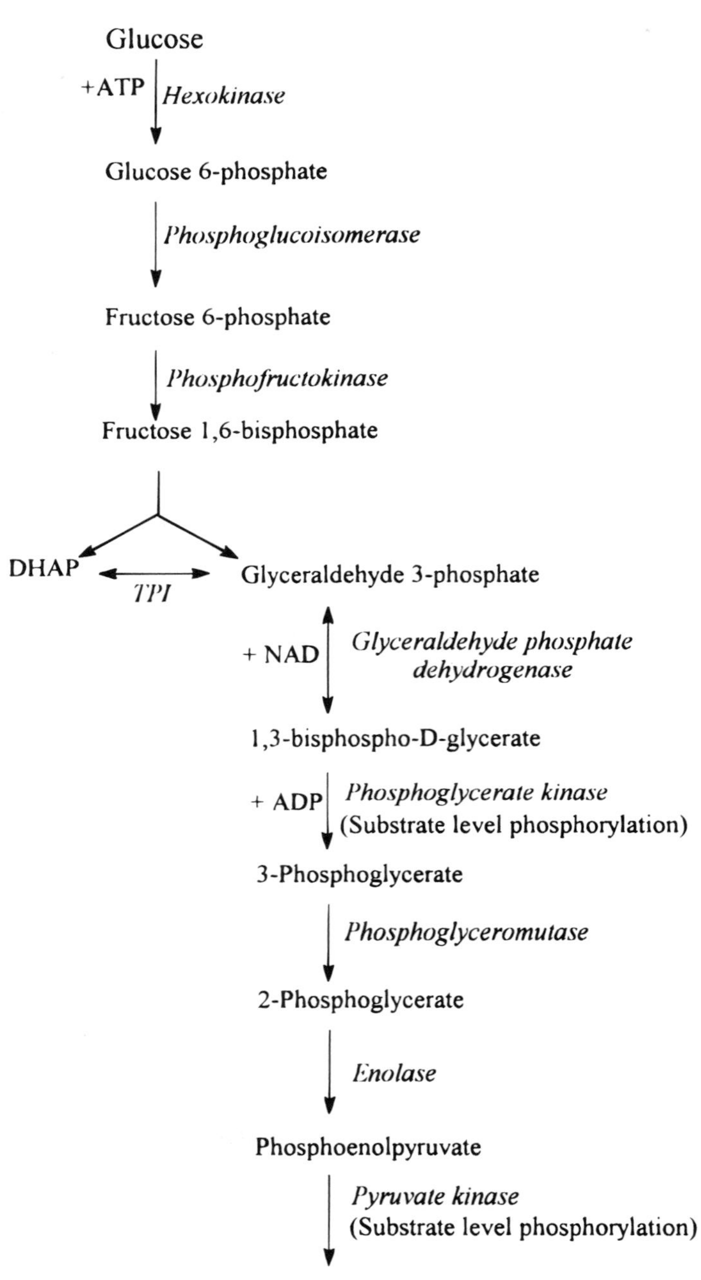

Figure 1.29. The glycolytic pathway. The overall function of glycolysis is to enzymatically convert a 6-carbon glucose molecule to a 3-carbon compound, pyruvate. Pyruvate is a common intermediate in (*a*) gluconeogenesis, (*b*) nonessential amino acid synthesis and, (*c*) fatty acid synthesis via conversion to acetyl CoA. Little net energy is recovered from the glycolytic process—the chief metabolic value of the process lies in the production of intermediate compounds essential to other anabolic pathways. For details of its operation, see the text.

by lactate dehydrogenase, in both physiologic and pathologic circumstances are explored further in the chapter on lactic acidosis.

FATTY ACID OXIDATION

In humans, at least one-half of the substrates used to generate ATP for liver, resting and submaximally exercising skeletal muscle, cardiac muscle, and kidney is derived from fat. This fat is predominantly in the form of triglyceride (see the chapter on lipids). Fatty acid catabolism (Figure 1.31), which occurs in mitochondria, requires oxygen. Despite the high caloric value, fat cannot be used for burst activity by muscle. This is because long chain fatty acids cannot readily pass through the inner mitochondrial membrane—they must be covalently linked to *carnitine*, which is a carrier molecule that hastens their passage. Once inside, the fatty acid-carnitine bond is severed, and the fatty acids then can enter the fatty acid oxidation pathway. This pathway is termed *β-oxidation* because the steps of the pathway produce a 2-carbon product, acetyl CoA, which is cleaved from the parent fatty acid at the β-carbon. Coenzyme A is the obligatory coenzyme for these reactions and also participates in the catabolism of several amino acids.

At two steps in the β-oxidation sequence, hydrogen and electrons are lost because they are captured by FAD in one instance and NAD^+ in the other. These reduced products, $FADH_2$ and NADH, undergo reoxidation when they give up their electrons to the ETC.

AMINO ACID METABOLISM

The first step in catabolism for most amino acids is removal of the amino group ($-NH_2$) in a transamination reaction (Figure 1.32) in which the acceptor is one of three α-keto acids: pyruvate, oxaloacetate, or α-ketoglutarate. The products of transamination are the cognate α-keto acid anions of the starting amino acid and alanine, aspartate, or glutamate from the three α-keto acid acceptors.

Further catabolism of the α-keto acid anion of the amino acid depends on the particular amino acid; but, the general strategy is similar to that experienced by fatty acids in β-oxidation. This is not too surprising because amino acids become short chain organic (fatty) acids when deprived of their amino group. What is noteworthy about the catabolism of the amino acid carbon skeleton is that the end-products are intermediates of either the TCA cycle or of glycolysis. By entering into these common metabolic routes, amino acids can be catabolized to make ATP or can be diverted for synthetic reactions.

Oxidative Metabolism

Acetyl CoA is produced not only by the oxidative decarboxylation of pyruvate (the final product of glycolysis), but also by fatty acid oxidation and oxidation of the α-keto acid anions of amino acids. Because there is still a considerable amount of energy locked up in AcCoA, it is the task of the TCA cycle and ETC (both mitochondrial processes) to harvest that chemical energy. During the TCA cycle (Figure 1.33), Acetyl CoA (two carbons) condenses with oxaloacetate (four carbons—derived from pyruvate) to form citric acid (six carbons). Citrate then undergoes a series of reactions in which it gives up hydrogen and electrons to NAD^+ and FAD.

The reduced coenzymes then enter the ETC and the transfer of electrons is associated with creation of a transmembrane potential difference across the inner mitochondrial membrane. This potential difference is called a *proton motive force* (Figure 1.34); it is this electrical and chemical force that is the proximate energy source for the generation of the majority of ATP that results from aerobic metabolism. The idea that a high energy state of the mitochondrial membrane, rather than a transient chemical intermediate, is the form in which energy is stored by mitochondria was so novel that it won Peter Mitchell the Nobel Prize in 1978 when it was confirmed. Further details of this far-ranging chemiosmotic theory and of the workings of the ETC can be found by consulting the texts listed at the end of the chapter.

Cellular Structure

To speak realistically about the life process, we must recognize that the physiologic chemical reactions, both enzymatic and nonenzymatic, and binding reactions associated with life must occur within a given bounded volume (ie, the cell). The cell is the basic unit of life; it is made up of subcellular organelles and cytoplasm that are maintained

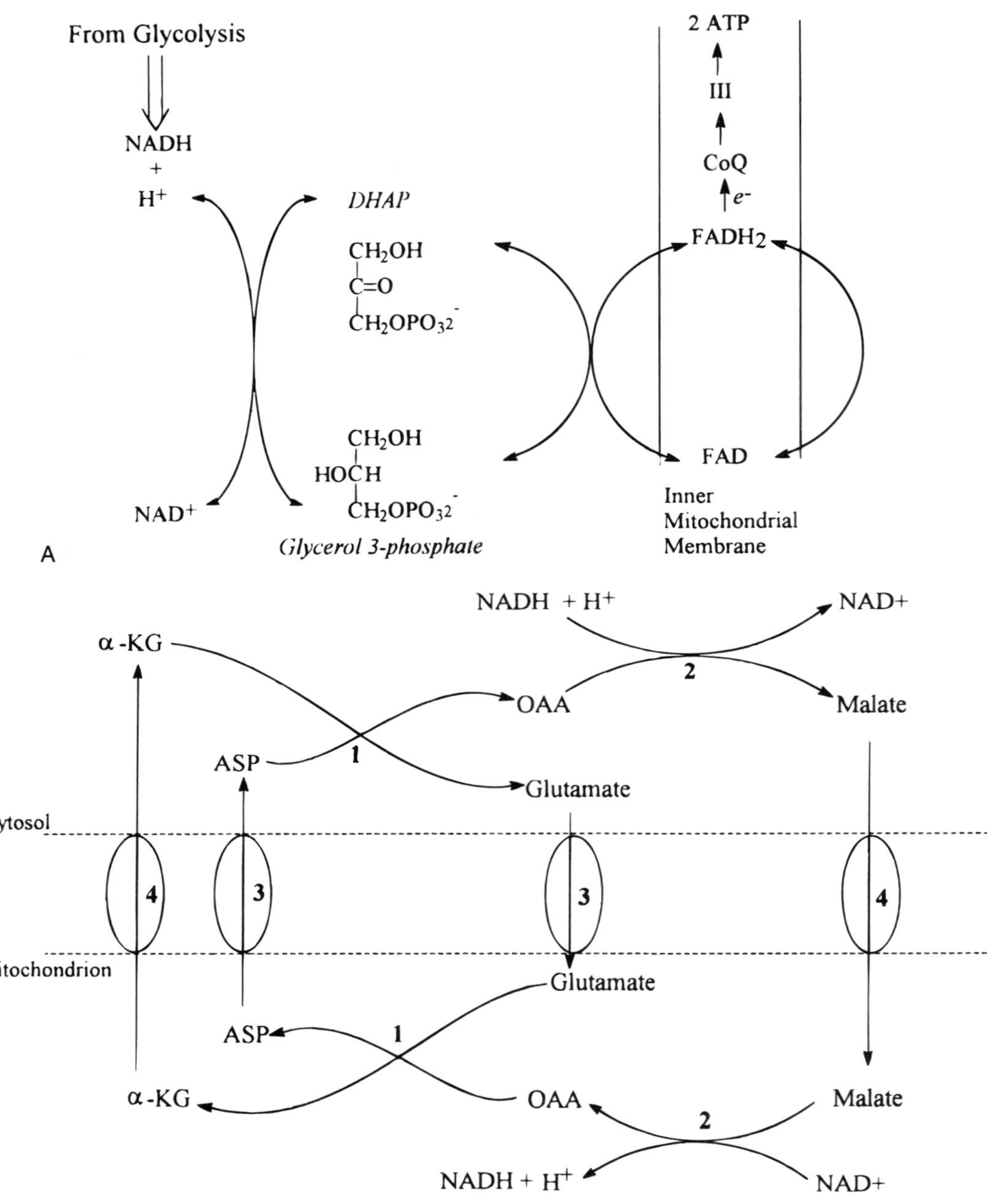

(1) Aspartate aminotransferase
(2) Malate dehydrogenase
(3) Glutamate-aspartate transporter
B (4) Malate α-ketoglutarate transporter

in a highly compartmentalized array (Figure 1.35). The cell is bounded by a plasma membrane and contains cytoplasm (cytosol) and many specialized structures (Table 1.4). Table 1.4 also lists the functions associated with these components and their relevance concerning metabolic disorders. The cell and its subcellular organelles are created as a result of the ability to form membranes; this depends on the physicochemical properties of hydrophobic phospholipids, which aggregate to form vesicles and on the insertion of hydrophobic proteins into the membrane, which then enable substrate transport into and out of the cell.

When a series of enzymatic reactions occurs in sequence, a *metabolic pathway* exists, and the product of each reaction serves as substrate for the next. The output of each pathway can become the input for the next, serving to link otherwise disparate metabolic routes. In many cases, the linking reactions must traverse organellar membrane barriers; thus, compartmentalization imposes spatial order and temporal control.

When the enzymes and resulting intermediates in a metabolic pathway coexist in fluid medium (eg, the cytosol), the number of times each enzyme and substrate can come into contact depends statistically upon their concentrations. For optimal flux through a pathway, each substrate must find its enzyme quickly and effectively. Organizing enzymes in a sequence through attachment to the matrix of the cytosol, which occurs with the glycolytic pathway enzymes, can account for the rapidity with which a metabolic sequence is traversed *in vivo*.

Metabolic Control Principles

The fact that a series of chemical reactions can form a metabolic pathway with an ordered sequence presupposes both organization and control. Metabolic pathways must proceed at a rate that is "just right." Operation at maximal rates would exhaust substrates or cause accumulation of toxic levels of one or more intermediates. Additionally, competition for sparse intermediates between various pathways might make one pathway nonfunctional. If metabolic pathways were to operate at minimal rates, the incessant production of ATP necessary to maintain energy-requiring processes would be insufficient and life would cease. Moreover, the ability to adjust to changing intracellular conditions no longer would be possible.

An inborn error of metabolism may result in accumulation of certain intermediates proximal to a metabolic block or lack of production of a key intermediate distal to that block. Changes such as these can have profound consequences on the conduct of that pathway and on other metabolic sequences that depend upon an intermediate from the genetically deranged pathway.

HORMONAL CONTROL OF METABOLIC PROCESSES

Similar to the coordinated activity of metabolic sequences within the cellular microcosm requiring the constant input of information to ensure the optimal activity of the component enzymes, the macrocosm of an organ needs an information system to integrate its activities with those of the var-

Figure 1.30. (A) The α-glycerophosphate shuttle. This process functions to convey electrons produced from the oxidation of glyceraldehyde-3-phosphate in glycolysis into the mitochondrion for ATP production. The carriage is NAD^+ in the cytosol, which cannot cross the mitochondrial membrane barrier. Thus, the electrons are transferred to dihydroxyacetone phosphate (DHAP) to form α-glycerophosphate, which, in turn, transfers the electrons to flavin adenine dinucleotide (FAD) and then down the electron transport chain, generating two ATP. (B) The malate-aspartate shuttle. Cytosolic accumulation of NADH leads to reduction (reaction #2) of oxaloacetate (2-keto-) to malate (2-alcohol) and regeneration of NAD for glycolysis. A specific, nonenergy-requiring transporter exchanges malate for α-ketoglutarate (reaction #4) across the mitochondrial membrane, thus introducing the electrons from the oxidation of NADH intramitochondrially. Within the mitochondrial matrix, reaction #4 regenerates oxaloacetate (OAA), once again forming NADH, which now can transfer the electrons to the transport chain and become reoxidized. The regenerated OAA is transaminated (reaction #1) to aspartate and α-ketoglutarate, using transported glutamate from the cytosol (reaction #3) as the source of the $-NH_2$ group. Reactions #3 and #4 remove the products of transamination (α-ketoglutarate and aspartate) from the mitochondrial matrix into the cytosol, where the reaction (#3, #1) takes place again to regenerate OAA and glutamate.

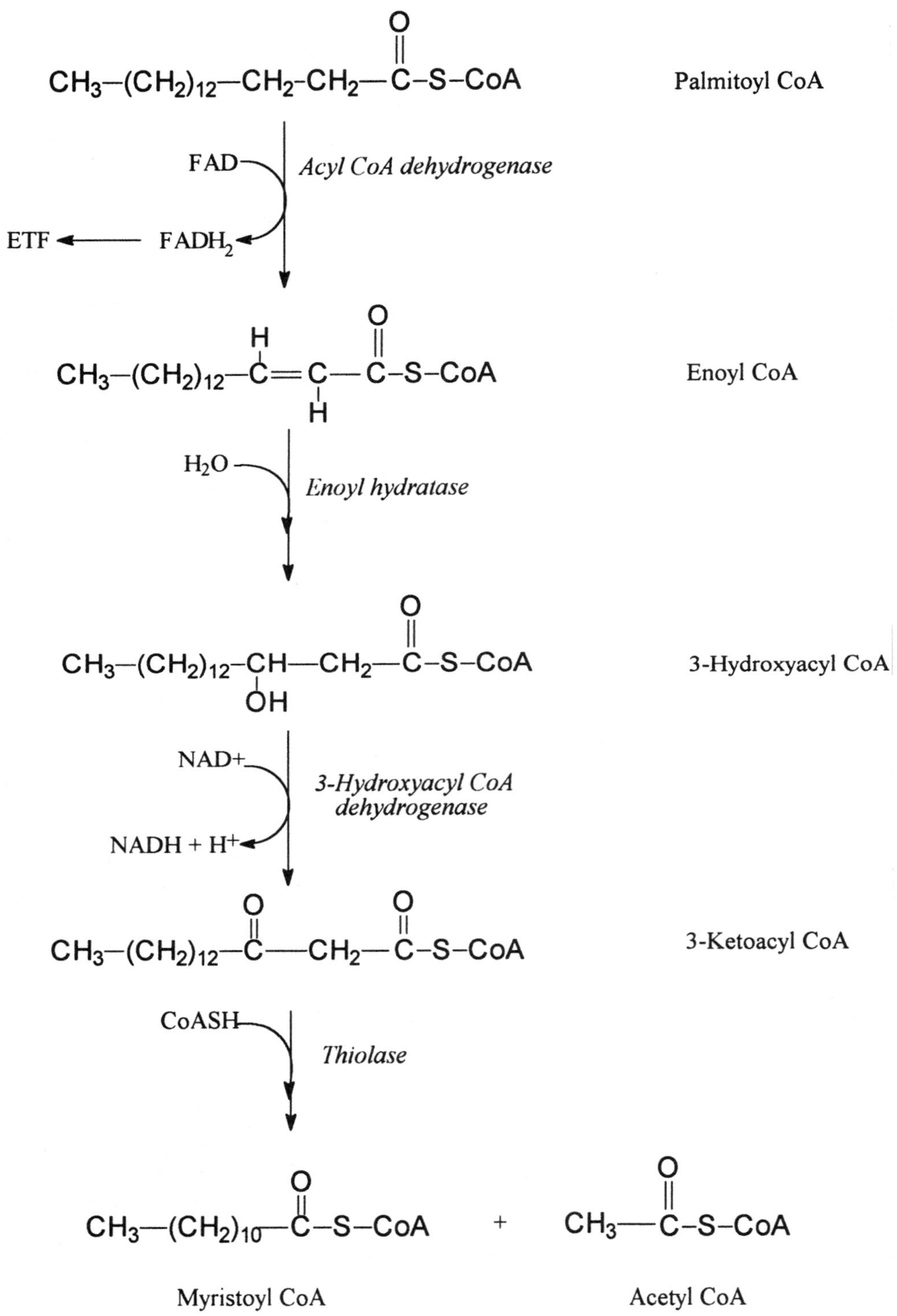

$$CH_3-(CH_2)_{12}-CH_2-CH_2-\overset{O}{\overset{\|}{C}}-S-CoA$$ Palmitoyl CoA

FAD → *Acyl CoA dehydrogenase*

ETF ← $FADH_2$

$$CH_3-(CH_2)_{12}-\overset{H}{\overset{|}{C}}=\underset{H}{\underset{|}{C}}-\overset{O}{\overset{\|}{C}}-S-CoA$$ Enoyl CoA

H_2O → *Enoyl hydratase*

$$CH_3-(CH_2)_{12}-\underset{OH}{\underset{|}{CH}}-CH_2-\overset{O}{\overset{\|}{C}}-S-CoA$$ 3-Hydroxyacyl CoA

NAD+ → *3-Hydroxyacyl CoA dehydrogenase*

NADH + H^+

$$CH_3-(CH_2)_{12}-\overset{O}{\overset{\|}{C}}-CH_2-\overset{O}{\overset{\|}{C}}-S-CoA$$ 3-Ketoacyl CoA

CoASH → *Thiolase*

$$CH_3-(CH_2)_{10}-\overset{O}{\overset{\|}{C}}-S-CoA \quad + \quad CH_3-\overset{O}{\overset{\|}{C}}-S-CoA$$

Myristoyl CoA Acetyl CoA

ious other organs. As expected, the level at which this control is felt initially is at the biochemical level (ie, at the *cell receptor*). The endocrine system is able to direct the conduct of metabolic processes by coordinating the activity of hundreds of millions of cells so that the biochemical response engendered is expressed at a physiologic level (Table 1.5). Today, it is clear that almost every tissue elaborates at least one hormone. A corollary of this synthetic capability is that almost all organs are acted upon by at least one hormone.

The coordinated activity of the components of the organism is attained by the correlation and interplay between two major systems: the endocrine system and the autonomic nervous system. Nerve endings release chemical transmitters, acetylcholine and norepinephrine, that often are found in the blood; consequently, they also may be thought of as hormones. The unique interrelationship between the endocrine and autonomic nervous systems is most significant at the level of the hypothalamus. The activities of both the autonomic and endocrine systems merge at this neural center, producing several hormones that act upon other endocrine glands and perform neurotransmission.

Feedback and feedforward controls, as discussed for control of enzyme activity, play important roles in the transfer of information to endocrine glands. To receive such information, cells that respond to a hormonal stimulus have specific hormonal receptors either upon or within particular cells. These receptors must possess discriminating ability based upon the principles of complementary interaction that are so important in enzyme action. Only proteins possess the capability for stereospecific binding and are coded for by the DNA. Hence, it can be expected that certain inherited endocrine conditions will depend upon abnormalities in receptor structure or function. Once the hormone interacts with its receptor, the information is transduced into *second* or *intracellular messengers* either through a series of events that leads to production of cyclic AMP or some other messenger, or through stimulation of DNA transcription into mRNA. As this ordered sequence of response continues, intracellular targets (usually enzymes) mediate the biochemical response that generates the action associated with the hormone. Feedback control, through servomechanism organization, ensures the capacity to modulate the response and correct for overshoot. In this way, control at the biochemical levels gains expression at the physiologic level.

G PROTEINS AND PLASMA MEMBRANE-MEDIATED SYSTEMS

Many of the polypeptide hormones and catecholamines initiate a series of events that begins by binding to the external surface of the plasma membrane at a specific hormone receptor. This results in activation of an effector and the subsequent increase in intracellular concentration of a signal molecule or second messenger. The second messenger then mediates intracellular effects that permit expression of specific tissue responses.

The importance of phosphorylation in regulating enzyme activity was first recognized for glycogen phosphorylase. Since then, the general approach of the cell in regulating enzyme activity by covalent modification of the protein, largely by phosphorylation, has led to the discovery of cyclic cAMP, a family of enzymes that phosphorylate other enzymes and G proteins that are intermediaries in the process (Figure 1.36). Each of these discoveries resulted in the awarding of a Nobel prize.

Fortunately for the cell, a pattern is followed as to which enzymes of intermediary metabolism are activated and which are inhibited by phosphorylation. Phosphorylation activates those enzymes that are involved in mobilizing energy that

Figure 1.31. The β-oxidation pathway. The intramitochondrial process begins with a C-16 fatty acid (palmitic) and results in cleavage of the carbon skeleton at the original β-carbon to form a C-14 fatty acyl CoA compound and acetyl CoA. Thus, CoA is an obligatory coenzyme in this process. Two protons and two electrons are salvaged by transfer to FAD at the first step, with a second pair of protons and electrons transferred to NAD^+ in the third step. In both cases, the electrons are passed down the transport chain and ATP is generated. It should be clear, then, why a single mole of C-16 fatty acid is a rich energy source for the body during fasting. ETF = electron transport flavoprotein.

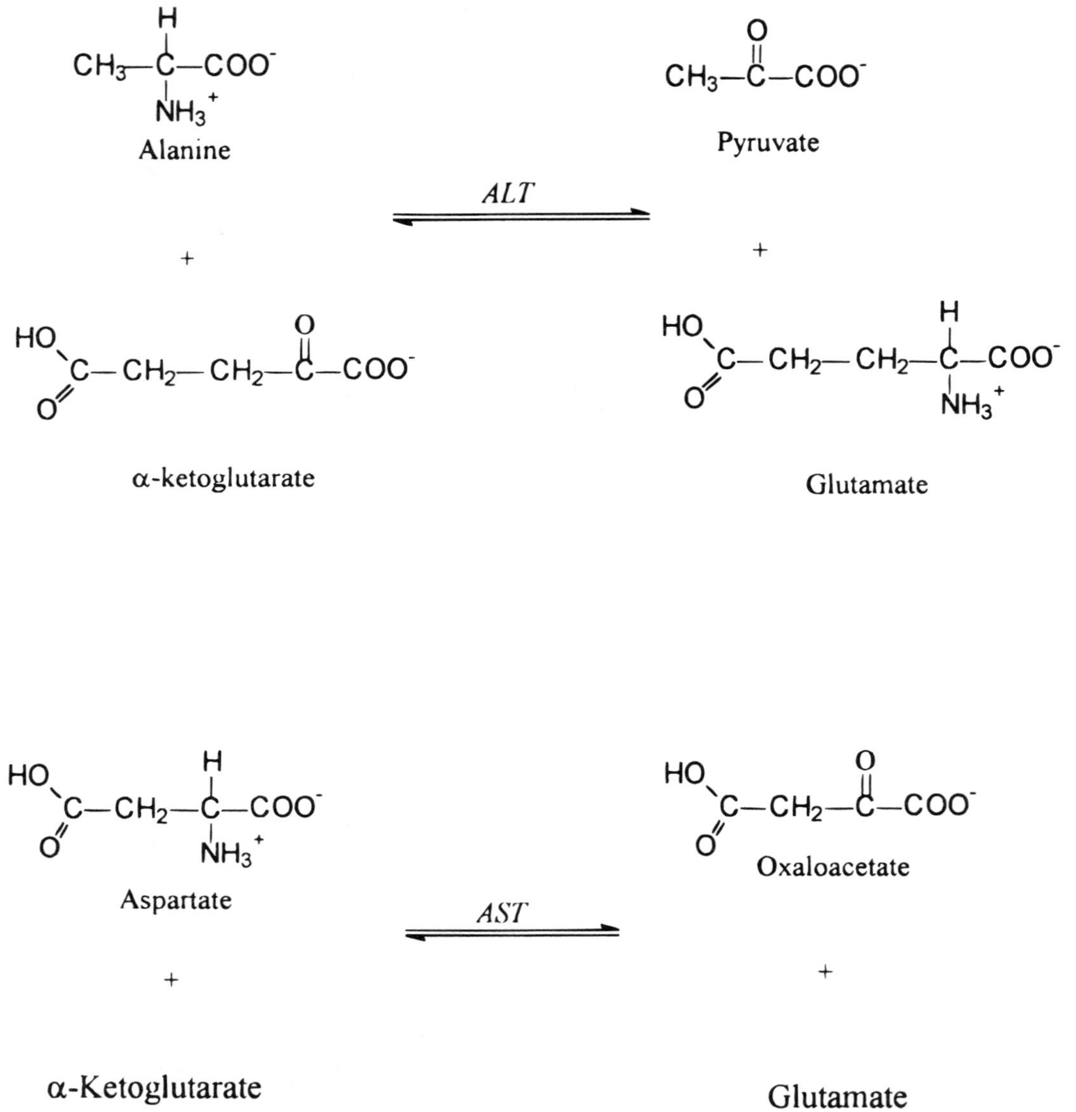

Figure 1.32. The transamination reaction. This process is a necessary step in the catabolism of amino acids and requires an acceptor for the $-NH_2$ group to be removed. The acceptor molecules are pyruvate, oxaloacetate, and α-ketoglutarate, all of which are α-keto acid intermediates in many metabolic processes and, therefore, are present in large quantities in most cells. ALT = alanine aminotransferase, AST = aspartate aminotransferase.

is stored in the form of glycogen and triglyceride, and simultaneously inactivates those enzymes involved in storing these sources of energy.

Many water soluble hormones, including glucagon, cannot pass through the lipophilic plasma membrane. Instead, they bind to a specific cell-surface receptor that activates the G protein that couples receptor occupancy to formation of cAMP. The best-known function of cyclic AMP is activation of specific intracellular protein kinases by binding to the regulatory portion of a specific protein kinase complex. Cyclic AMP binding leads to the regulatory subunit being dissociated from the catalytic portion, thereby activating it. Activated protein kinase phosphorylates other proteins (some of which also are protein kinases); the terminal phosphate of ATP is transferred to specific serine or threonine hydroxyl groups. Phosphorylation of various proteins can lead to either enzyme activation or inactivation. Other effects depend upon the protein phosphorylated, and include alterations in messenger RNA, alterations in enzyme synthesis, and changes in membrane permeability. By phosphorylating key proteins, protein kinases transform information received at the plasma membrane into a specific response of specific functional proteins.

The G protein exists in two states (Figure 1.36): active when guanosine triphosphate (GTP) is bound and inactive when guanosine diphosphate (GDP) is bound. When hormone binds to its receptor, that portion of the receptor on the inner aspect of the cell membrane experiences a conformational change that now provides a complementary binding site for the G protein. The ligand-receptor complex binds to the G protein and activates it by causing GDP to dissociate and GTP to bind instead. GTP binding then causes a subunit to dissociate from the G protein so that it can bind to adenylate cyclase prompting generation of cAMP. But under normal circumstances, the G protein has a "built-in timer" that expresses a GTPase activity after a brief period, causing GDP to be formed. With GDP bound, the G protein reverts to an inactive conformation. This control is of great importance because in both cholera and pertussis, G proteins are covalently modified, remaining permanently active and resulting in significant negative consequences for the host.

PHOSPHATIDYLINOSITOL EFFECT

Not all water-soluble hormones are linked via the cell membrane receptor-G protein interaction with adenylate cyclase. Another important signal transduction system involves membrane-bound phospholipids and culminates in an increase in intracellular Ca^{++} and activation of a Ca^{++}-sensitive protein kinase, called protein kinase C. This system also is linked to a G protein; but, in this case, the binding of hormone to the receptor leads to activation of membrane bound phospholipase C. This phospholipase acts on a minor membrane constituent, phosphatidylinositol 4,5-bisphosphate (PIP_2) to form two second messengers—diacylglycerol (DAG) and inositol 1,4,5-triphosphate (IP_3) (Figure 1.37). IP_3 diffuses into the cytosol and stimulates the release of Ca^{++} from the endoplasmic reticulum. DAG, on the other hand, remains in the membrane where it activates protein kinase C by increasing affinity of the latter for Ca^{++} and causing the calcium-protein kinase C complex to phosphorylate key proteins in the same manner as the cAMP links protein kinase A. Calcium released by IP_3 binds largely to calmodulin, a Ca^{++}-binding protein that interacts with intracellular proteins, altering their conformation and boosting their biologic activity.

HORMONES USING INTRACELLULAR BINDING PROTEINS

In contrast to polypeptide hormones and catecholamines, steroid and thyroid hormones do not act at the cell membrane; rather, they traverse the cell membrane and bind to an intracellular binding protein (Figure 1.38). This noncovalent complex then enters the nucleus and stimulates protein synthesis by acting on the chromatin or DNA itself, in a manner that is not well understood, which leads to synthesis of specific mRNAs. Intracellular binding proteins have been described for estrogens, progesterone, dihydrotestosterone, cortisol, aldosterone, 1,25-dihydroxycholecalciferol, and triiodothyronine. These hormone receptors are proteins that possess a high binding affinity for their specific hormones.

INBORN ERRORS OF METABOLISM

It is clear that the genetic endowment of the host is the crucial determinant of the individual's response to environmental stress. The complexity of the components of the genome that govern the responses of the host to an external stress (eg, acquired disease) is poorly understood. However, in the group of diseases known as inborn errors of metabolism, the relationship between a defect in the genetic endowment of the individual and the inability to cope with an environmental factor is, on the surface, more direct. For example, there are more than 100 electrophoretic variants of hemoglobin, but only a few of them are associated with clinical disease. Accordingly, there must be more variation in the structure of proteins within

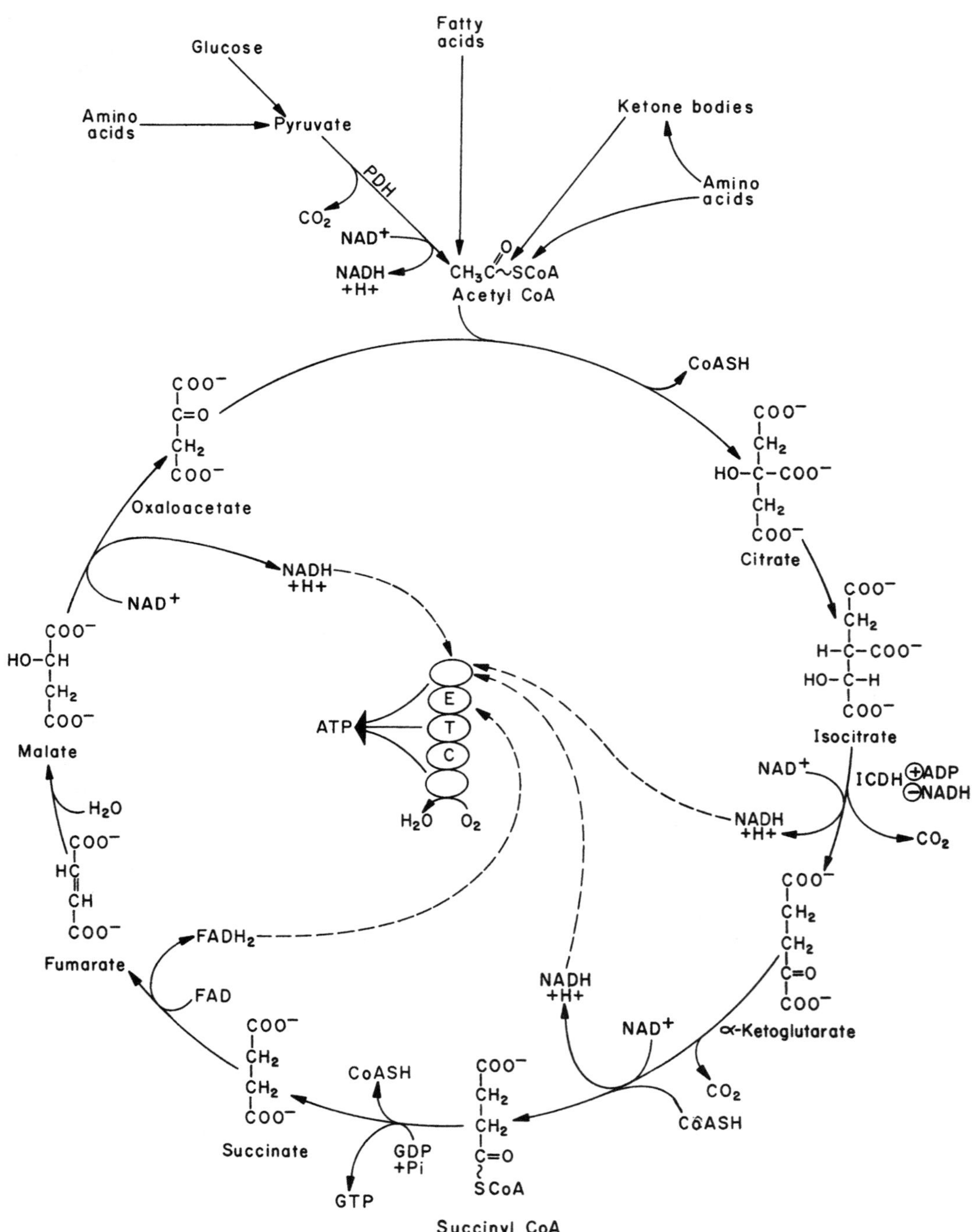

Glucose
Fatty acids
Ketone bodies
Amino acids
Pyruvate
PDH
CO_2
NAD^+
NADH +H+
Amino acids
$CH_3C\sim SCoA$
Acetyl CoA
CoASH
Oxaloacetate
Citrate
Isocitrate
NAD+
ICDH
⊕ADP
⊖NADH
NADH +H+
CO_2
α-Ketoglutarate
NAD+
NADH +H+
CO_2
CoASH
Succinyl CoA
CoASH
GDP +Pi
GTP
Succinate
FAD
$FADH_2$
Fumarate
H_2O
Malate
NAD+
NADH +H+
E
T
C
ATP
H_2O
O_2

the body than the number of clinical diseases. Stated differently, there are many variations in amino acid sequence that are compatible with retention of biologic functions because the configuration of the protein is altered minimally. As presently understood, inborn errors of metabolism result from the absence of or diminution in biologic activity of a protein whether the protein is actually missing or simply defective in its biologic function. Most of these defects involve enzymes. When an enzyme that usually is present in a particular metabolic pathway is functionally absent or deficient, either accumulation of the substrate involved in the abnormal enzyme step, or the absence or reduced formation of a product of that particular enzyme step may be expected. Indeed, each possibility often occurs. Concomitantly, metabolites that are rarely encountered in normal individuals often are found as the body attempts to rid itself of the substrate accumulating as a result of the defect. In fact, in many of the inborn errors of metabolism, the identification of some unusual metabolite may lead to diagnosis.

In addition to defects in enzyme activity, there are many genetic disorders that involve defects in the active transport of key substrates across cell membranes. This is not surprising because all available evidence supports the view that these carrier proteins act in a stereospecific fashion: being protein in nature, they also must be synthesized according to the information in the amino acid code.

The importance of Garrod's concept of inborn errors of metabolism cannot be overemphasized. Long before biochemistry became a science, Garrod proposed that inherited diseases were biochemical and that the response to all external disease-producing factors was biochemical as well. In fact, in 1908, he wrote, "The existence of chemical individuality follows of necessity from chemical specificity, but we should expect the differences between individuals to be still more subtle and difficult of detection." Today, we are reaping the intellectual and therapeutic harvest of his genius.

Etiology of Genetic Defects

Although mutations are the cause of genetic defects, we must remember that mutations also may act as the progenitors of variation within the genome, allowing for evolution of biochemical capability. Serving in both roles, mutations are both liabilities and assets. A point mutation affects a single nucleotide and may cause either a replacement of one of the bases, or an insertion or loss of a single amino acid. Such mutations are termed mis-sense or no-sense mutations. In the case of mis-sense mutations, a different amino acid is substituted at a given site in the protein (Hemoglobin S); with no-sense mutations, the change of the base sequence occurs when protein synthesis ceases when that altered nucleotide sequence is reached (eg, Thalassemia variants). A mutation may alter the properties of an enzyme so profoundly that the enzyme may no longer manifest any catalytic activity or it may become particularly susceptible to environmental denaturation or enzymatic destruction. Despite these dire possibilities, most mutations result in a substitution or replacement of a conservative nature and little or no functional or physical change is discerned in

Figure 1.33. Reactions included in the tricarboxylic acid (TCA) or Krebs cycle. The generation of the tricarboxylic acid citrate derives from acetyl CoA (AcCoA) and oxaloacetate (OA). The first carbon of OA becomes carbon 3 after a single rotation through the complete cycle; the reader must not make the mistake of believing that the OA is catalytic. AcCoA can be generated from many different substrates and sites within the cell; under normal conditions, the chief supply derives from glycolysis, with pyruvate dehydrogenase (PDH) acting as a major regulatory step. Note that generation of AcCoA from fatty acids is controlled partly by activation of AcCoA carboxylase, which commits malonylCoA to fatty acid synthesis, and feedback inhibition of PDH by AcCoA. Citrate is chemically converted through a series of reactions, many resulting in production of hydrogen ions and electrons that are converted to high-energy compounds and water through the heme-containing proteins of the electron transport chain (ETC). Note the unique production of GTP in conversion of succinyl CoA to succinate, the only high-energy producing step not requiring the ETC. Reprinted with permission from Marks DB. Biochemistry. 2nd ed. 1994; Baltimore: Williams & Wilkins, 1994.

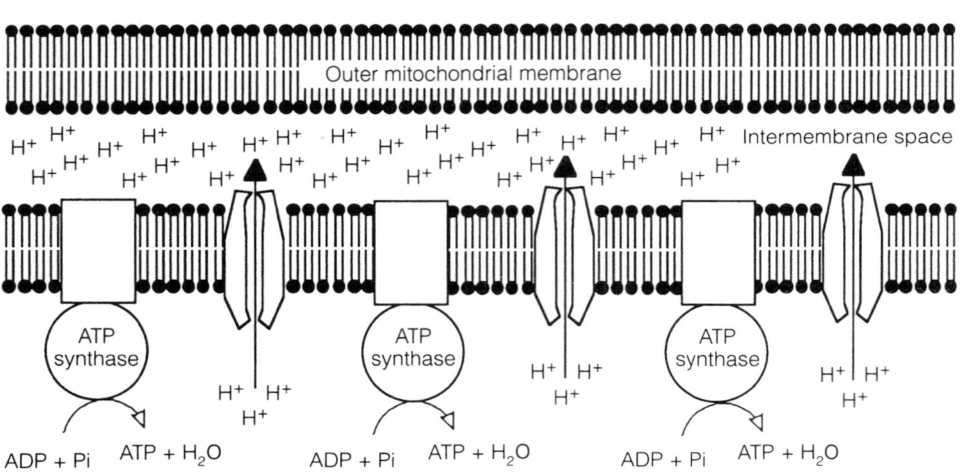

Figure 1.34. Electron transport and proton motive forces. This process is a result of chemiosmotic coupling, which relies on the pumping of hydrogen ions (protons) out of the inner matrix into the space between the inner and outer mitochondrial membranes. The electrochemical gradient thus created provides the energy to drive the ATP synthase reaction with formation of ATP from ADP and inorganic phosphate. ICDH = isocitrate dehydrogenase. Reprinted with permission from Gartner LP, Hiatt JL, Strum JM. Cell Biology and Histology. 2nd ed. Baltimore: Williams & Wilkins, 1993.

the final gene product. For example, the number of hemoglobin variants associated with disease is small compared with those that are distinguished from HbA only on the basis of electrophoretic or other laboratory analysis.

Mis-sense mutations are termed CRM-positive, while no-sense mutations are CRM-negative. CRM ("krim") means *cross reactive material* and indicates the presence of a protein that shows immunologic reactivity with antibodies developed against the normal enzyme. Of course, immunologic reactivity is not synonymous with catalytic activity: immunologic reactivity depends on immunologic determinants that can be distinguished from the unique three-dimensional ensemble that constitutes the active site of the enzyme.

More complex mutations and control errors are possible, but a complete discussion of these possibilities is beyond the scope of this book. (The general texts listed at the end of section I thoroughly discuss these possibilities.)

Inheritance Patterns of Genetic Defects

Genes are located either on the autosomal chromosomes or on the sex chromosomes. Sex-linked genes reside almost exclusively on the X chromosome because only one or two traits are known to be associated with the Y. Different templates of the same gene that occur at the same locus on homologous chromosomes are termed alleles. A homozygote possesses two identical *alleles* at a given gene locus, while a heterozygote has nonidentical alleles at the same locus. Hemizygotes have only one allele (eg, a male with an X-linked trait such as hemophilia).

When a trait is expressed in a heterozygote, it is presumed to be *dominant*; an expression requiring a double dose is called *recessive* and is expressed in the homozygote only. Depending on how a particular trait is identified, even a single dose of a recessive condition may have biochemical stigmata. For example, heterozygotes for cystinosis always are asymptomatic, but intracellular cystine levels are 8- to 10-fold greater than normal amounts of cystine (homozygotes have levels 100-fold greater than normal) so that the abnormal trait is partially expressed.

The underlying genetic complement is known as the genotype, and the overt expression of interaction of the genotype and the environment is the *phenotype*. Depending on the nature and the de-

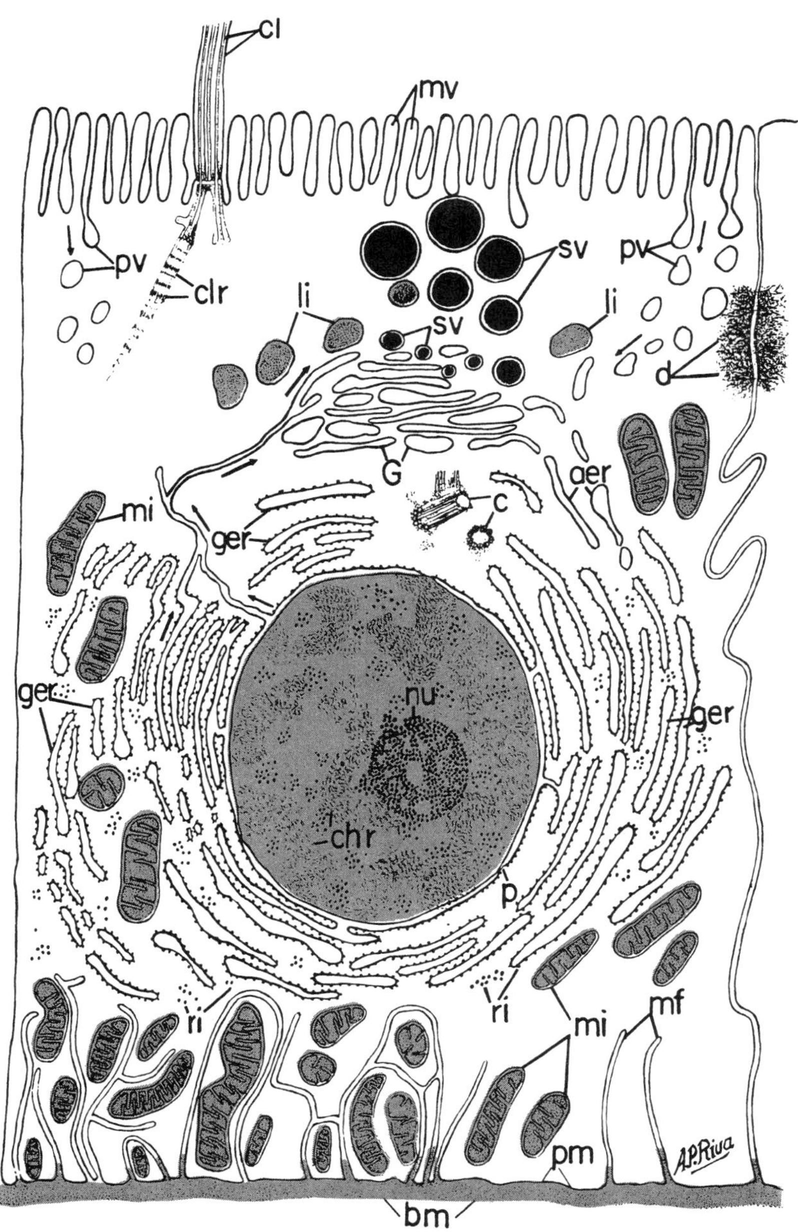

Figure 1.35. Composite diagram of an idealized animal cell. (Essential features of all types of cells are depicted; the intention was not to represent any single cell type.) aer = agranular endoplasmic reticulum, bm = basal membrane, c = centriole, chr = chromosome, cl = cilium, clr = cilium root, d = desmosome, G = Golgi complex, ger = granular endoplasmic reticulum, li = lysosome, mf = membrane fold, mi = mitochondria, mv = microvilli, nu = nucleolus, p = pore, pm = plasma membrane, pv = pinocytic vesicle, ri = ribosome, sv = secretion vesicle. Reprinted with permission from De Robertis EDP, De Robertis EMF Jr. Cell & Molecular Biology. 8th ed. Philadelphia: Lea & Febiger, 1987.

Table 1.4. Structures and Functions of the Cell

ORGANELLE	FUNCTIONS SERVED OR PERFORMED WITHIN OR BY THE ORGANELLE	IMPORTANCE IN METABOLIC DISEASES
Cell membrane (plasma membrane)	Selective permeability to ions, nutrients Acidification of urine by tubular membranes Absorption of digested products of hydrolysis of polymers in diet	Renal tubular disorders—primary (eg, RTA), secondary to toxins—Wilson's hereditary fructose intolerance, galactosemia Gastrointestinal absorptive disorders—primary congenital lactase deficiency, glucose-galactose absorptive defect Secondary—malabsorptive
Cytosol	Contains many metabolic sequences with enzymes highly ordered plus other organelles (see below) Glycolysis	Red cell metabolic defects
Mitochondria	Furnaces of the cell—carry out citric acid cycle, β-oxidation, and oxidative phosphorylation	
Lysosomes	Single-membrane vesicles that contain hydrolytic enzymes that break down complex lipids, membrane fragments, and mucopolysaccharides	Lysosomal storage diseases (eg, glycosphingolipidoses, mucopolysaccharidoses, mucolipidoses)
Endoplasmic reticulum and ribosomes	Protein synthesis at direction of mRNA made according to instructions in DNA	
Golgi apparatus	Stacked vesicles that are involved in secretion of polymers (often glycoproteins) made in cell to the exterior	Glycosylated proteins—many lysosomal enzymes and immunoglobulins are partially formed in the Golgi apparatus

gree of environmental stress, certain traits may be more or less expressible. The term *penetrance* denotes the percentage of individuals endowed with a given gene who express that gene under ordinary circumstances. Variability of expression of a given trait is the rule and is partially accounted for by the interaction of the genotype with the environment.

AUTOSOMAL DOMINANT INHERITANCE

Certain general rules characterize classic autosomal dominant inheritance, but they vary. According to statistical predictions, males and females should be equally affected, and an affected individual should have at least one parent who has the trait. Therefore, each sibling of an affected person has a 50% risk of manifesting the trait, and, similarly, each child of an affected person has a 50% chance.

There are several circumstances, however, under which these rules are broken:

1. The sex ratio of those affected may not be equal because of greater lethality of the mutation in one sex.
2. New mutations may account for affected children with normal parents. Achondroplasia exemplifies these situations; however, children with achondroplasia due to a new mutation will transmit the trait in a dominant fashion and their children will have a 50-50 chance of being affected.
3. Penetrance may be so low as to cause the defect to be subclinical in an affected individual (eg, acute intermittent porphryia).

Autosomal dominant traits generally are expressed in two ways: through abnormalities in embryogenesis, leading to structural defects, and late onset functional disorders without apparent early warning. Two embryogenetic defects are achondroplasia, and cleft lip and palate with pits of the lower lip. Huntington's chorea is a classic illustration of an autosomal dominant disorder with delayed onset and has received considerable public attention. Acute intermittent porphyria and hypercholesterolemia also have delayed onsets with dominant transmission.

In contrast to autosomal recessive disorders, few autosomal dominant diseases are understood in terms of the basic biochemical defects; possible defects may occur in structural proteins like colla-

Table 1.5. Major Hormonal Effects on Metabolism

	INSULIN	GLUCAGON	CORTICOSTEROIDS	HGH	THYROID	CATECHOLAMINES
Protein metabolism	Promotes cellular uptake of amino acids by muscle, liver, and other tissues→↓plasma amino acid concentration Stimulates protein synthesis (↑syn enz. of glycolysis, ↓syn enz. of gluconeogenesis) Inhibits protein degradation	In liver: Stimulates transport of amino acids Inhibits protein synthesis Accelerates protein degradation Stimulates gluconeogenesis (from amino acids) and ureogenesis	Stimulates catabolism in muscle and synthesis in liver (enzymes included: tryptophan pyrolase, tyrosine transaminase, gluconeogenic enzymes) Stimulates synthesis of all RNA species in liver	↑Nitrogen retention by muscle ↑Protein synthesis—stimulates synthesis of RNA polymerases ↑Cellular uptake amino acids	Acute: ↑liver protein Chronic: ↓peripheral and liver protein Stimulates activity of carbamyl phosphate synthetase	Epinephrine inhibits incorporation of amino acids into protein
Carbohydrate metabolism	Stimulates glucose transport into muscle, adipose tissue (uptake by liver not insulin dependent) where glucose can serve energy needs or be conserved ↑Glycolysis in muscle ↑Glucokinase activity in liver	Provides glucose as an energy source Stimulates glycogenolysis and gluconeogenesis Inhibits glycolysis: secreted when glucose availability↓—e.g., starvation, exercise, hypoglycemia	Stimulates gluconeogenesis Acts in concert with glucagon	↑Glycogenolysis ↑Glucose uptake by cells	Stimulates glycogenolysis and gluconeogenesis—acts in concert with catecholamines Stimulation of protein breakdown augments substrate supply to liver	Muscle—stimulates glycogenolysis Liver—stimulates glycogenolysis and gluconeogenesis
Fat metabolism	Acute: ↓lipolysis and ↑lipogenesis Chronic: ↑activities of lipogenic enzymes In fasting insulin↓, glucagon ↑→lipid mobilization Stimulates FA synthesis in liver; opposes ketogenic effect glucagon (mole for mole more potent than glucagon) FA's transported to adipose tissue (as CM + VLDL) are hydrolyzed by LPL (insulin dependent)—↑activity LPL→uptake FA into adipose tissue In adipose tissue, insulin stimulates re-esterification of FFA and inhibits depot fat lipase	Stimulates triglyceride hydrolysis in adipose tissue In liver, stimulates FA oxidation and ketogenesis (↑ cytoplasmic carnitine) Inhibits triglyceride release	Has a permissive effect on lipolysis; inhibits lipogenesis	Stimulates lipid mobilization from adipose tissue—acts synergistically with corticosteroids Stimulates ketogenesis	Stimulates mobilization of FFA from adipose tissue; ↑FA oxidation	Stimulates triglyceride hydrolysis; conversion of glucose to lipids; hepatic cholesterol synthesis

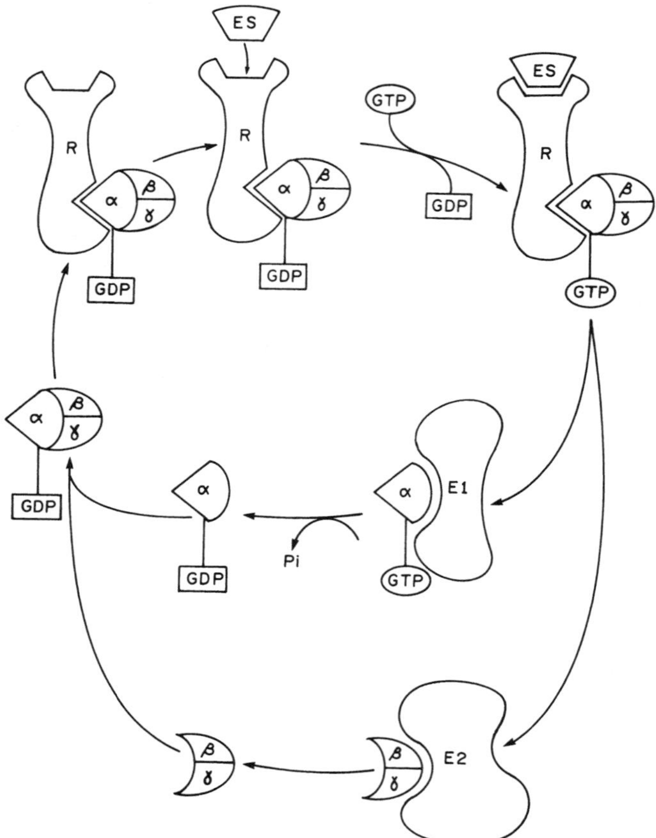

Figure 1.36. G protein activation. G proteins are trimers of α, β, and γ subunits that are bound to GDP on the α subunit and which interact with many types of membrane receptors. The purpose of these interactions is to couple cell surface receptors to intracellular responses. The complete G protein binds to a receptor as GDP is exchanged for GTP. The α-GTP subunit dissociates and directly or indirectly regulates effector molecules (eg, adenylate cyclase). The remaining $\beta\gamma$ subunit is freed to interact with other effector molecules (eg, ion channels and phospholipase A2). Because the α subunit possesses GTPase activity, it can hydrolyze GTP to GDP and reassociate with the $\beta\gamma$ subunit to repeat the process. Reprinted with permission from Holland JF, Frei E III, Bast RC, et al. Cancer Medicine. 3rd ed. Baltimore: Williams & Wilkins, 1993.

gen or in protein that regulates metabolic networks, or they may involve membrane receptors. Although parents heterozygous for early-onset hypercholesterolemia have a partial deficiency for the LDL receptor, their homozygous offspring do not possess cell surface receptors for low density lipoproteins. Autosomal dominant mutations manifest clinically when only 50% of the protein indicated is abnormal. Because 50% of residual enzyme activity almost is always enough in most metabolic settings, it is unlikely that enzymes are encoded by genes expressed in an autosomal dominant mode.

A structurally altered protein can account for some other autosomal dominant conditions. Certain hemoglobinopathies, such as hemoglobin C in which lysine is substituted for glutamine on the β-chain of the globin molecule, are examples.

Generally, autosomal recessive traits are more severe than autosomal dominant traits because a normal allele that modifies the phenotypic expression of the abnormal allele is present in dominant traits. This phenomenon is known as *co-dominance*; without this "safety valve," most autosomal dominant traits would be lethal *in utero*. On the other hand, autosomal recessive traits are pheno-

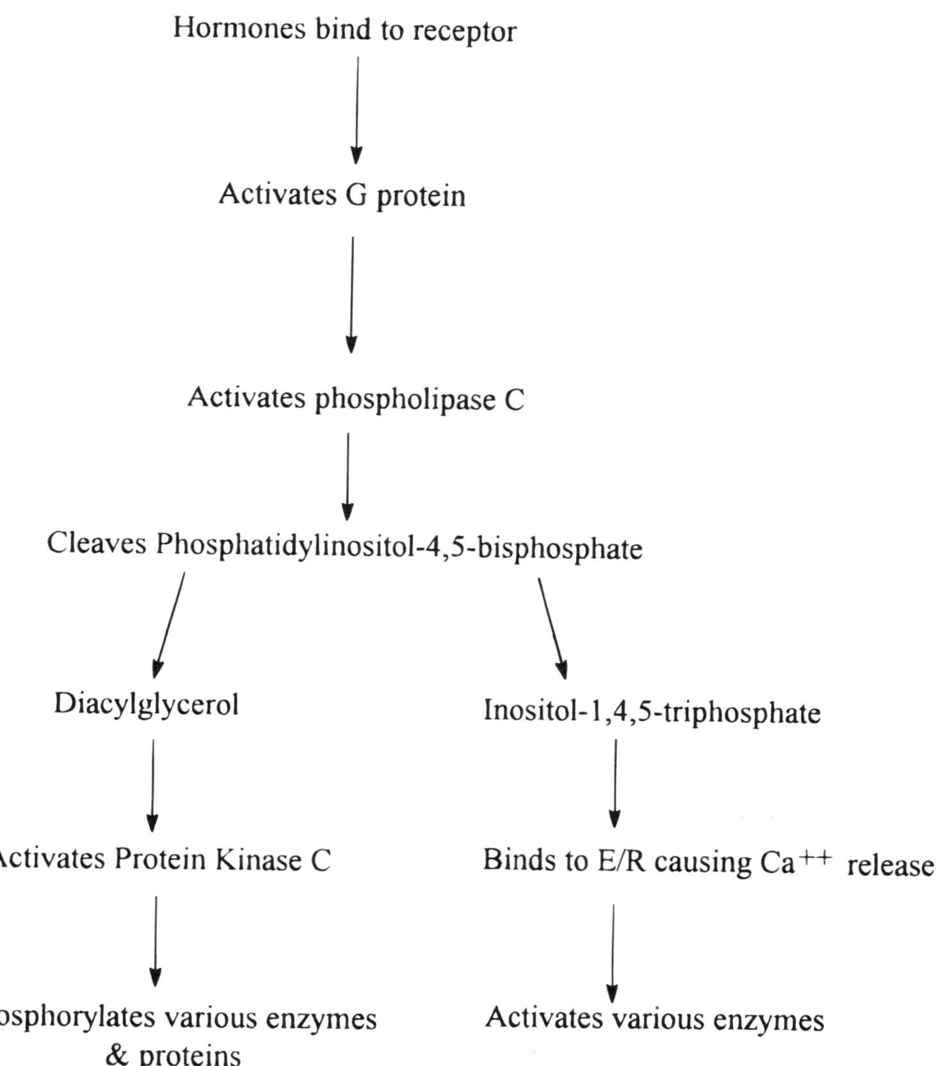

Figure 1.37. Nonadenyl cyclase cell signaling system. Binding of G protein to a membrane receptor proceeds as outlined in Figure 1.36, with activation of phospholipase C. In turn, activated phospholipase C elicits a multiplicity of intracellular responses, chiefly the release of calcium ion from the endoplasmic reticulum and the activation of protein kinase C, among several others.

typically expressed only in the absence of a normal allele, as will be discussed.

AUTOSOMAL RECESSIVE INHERITANCE

Autosomal recessive inheritance is characterized by equal representation between males and females with unaffected parents and a 25% chance at each pregnancy that offspring will be affected. Children who have a parent who is affected with an autosomal recessive disorder are heterozygous carriers of the abnormal gene.

As found with other rules of genetics, exceptions occur. Because heterozygotes possess approximately one-half of the normal complement of enzyme activity, they are asymptomatic; but, a loading test may show abnormal handling of a metabolite. However, routine screening tests are unlikely to identify an abnormality because reces-

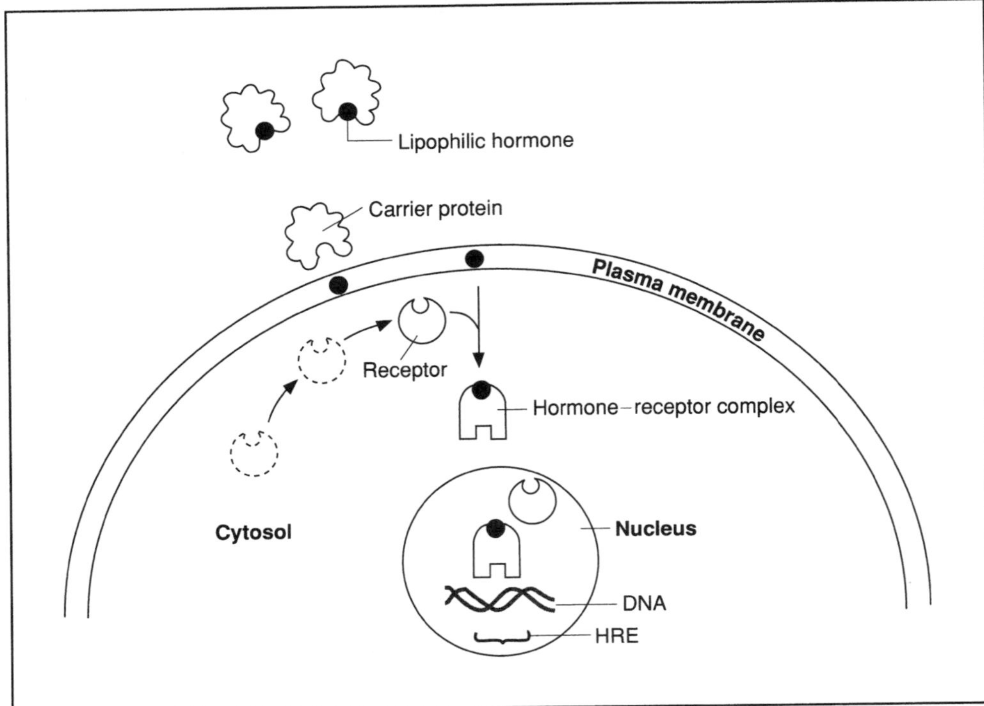

Figure 1.38. Lipophilic hormone is bound to a carrier protein. When the carrier protein-hormone ensemble binds to the plasma membrane, the hormone is released and enters the cell associating with an intracellular receptor. This hormone-receptor complex binds to a specific sequence of DNA, termed the hormone response element (HRE), initiating transcription of specific genes that are hormone responsive. Reprinted with permission from Davidson VL, Sittman DB. Biochemistry. Baltimore: Williams and Wilkins, 1993: 330.

sively inherited defects rarely affect rate-limiting enzymes. It is important to note that although the disease may be rare, the carrier state may not be uncommon. For example, phenylalanine hydroxylase deficiency (classic phenylketonuria) has a frequency of approximately 1 in 10,000 and a carrier frequency of about 1 in 50.

X-LINKED INHERITANCE

Males are affected in X-linked recessive inheritance; however, both their mother and carrier sisters usually are asymptomatic. A 50% chance exists that any male who is the offspring of a heterozygous female will be affected.

Concerning sex-linked inheritance, examination of a pedigree usually reveals an affected maternal uncle whose asymptomatic sister transmitted the disorder to her son. Male-to-male transmission does not occur because the father transmits the Y chromosome to his sons. As noted previously, although males with X-linked traits tend to be uniformly affected, female carriers usually are asymptomatic. Exceptions occur, however; for example, females with vitamin D-resistant rickets may be mildly affected. Females are genetic mosaics because of X inactivation (see the following text for details on the Lyon hypothesis); consequently, some carriers show mild manifestations. Examples are female carriers for Duchenne's muscular dystrophy who show an elevated creatine phosphokinase level in serum and also may have mild muscle dysfunction.

X-linked dominant inheritance occurs only in females because males receive only one X chromosome and will become symptomatic if it is defective. This form of inheritance resembles autosomal dominant inheritance. However, the two are distinguishable because although the mother will transmit the disorder to 50% of her sons or daughters, the father will transmit it to all of his daughters and none of his sons.

Several well-known X-linked recessive disorders exist, including glucose-6-phosphate dehydrogenase deficiency, hemophilia A, Duchenne muscular dystrophy, and Lesch-Nyhan syndrome. Color blindness also is inherited in an X-linked recessive fashion; but, because it is common in males, homozygous color-blind females will be encountered in clinical practice.

X-linked dominant inheritance is more common in females than in males, but clinical expression is attenuated in heterozygous-affected females, in contrast to hemizygous-affected males.

LYON HYPOTHESIS

For many years, mammalian geneticists had been puzzled by the fact that females who were homozygous for an X-linked disorder often presented with less significant symptoms clinically when compared with their hemizygous male counterparts. For example, contrary to expectation, a female hemophiliac patient who carries a double dose of the abnormal gene does not manifest a more severe coagulopathy than a male hemophiliac with the same specific gene disorder. Conversely, a heterozygous female occasionally may be as severely affected as a hemizygous male; however, this is less common. These extraordinary observations have been explained by the Lyon hypothesis, which simply states that only one X chromosome expresses its information in the mature cell. Hence, there always is one active X chromosome within a mature mammalian cell, regardless of the number of X chromosomes. Consequently, the number of Barr bodies in the cell is equal to the number of inactive X chromosomes.

According to the Lyon hypothesis, a functional X chromosome is randomly selected from the total available within each cell during embryologic development. Once inactivation of the remaining X chromosome(s) has occurred, all daughter cells will possess the same active X chromosome as their parent cells. Considering the principle of random selection, in a cell mass derived from an XX heterozygote embryo, 50% of the cells most likely will contain a normal active X and 50% most likely will have the abnormal X active. The clinical discrepancies mentioned earlier will occur because of variations of random distribution about the mean.

SUGGESTED READINGS

WEAK FORCES AND MACROMOLECULES

Cohn RM, Palmieri MJ, McNamara PD. Nonequilibrium thermodynamics, noncovalent forces, and water. In: Herman RH, Cohn RM, McNamara PD, eds. Principles of metabolic control in mammalian systems. New York: Plenum Press, 1980: 63.

Creighton TE. Proteins: structures and molecular properties. New York: W. H. Freeman, 1993.

Gierasch LM, King J. Protein folding: deciphering the second half of the genetic code. Washington, D.C.: American Association for the Advancement of Science, 1990.

Nall BT, Dill KA. Conformations and forces in protein folding. Washington, D.C.: American Association for the Advancement of Science, 1991.

Perutz M. Protein structure: new approaches to disease and therapy. New York: W. H. Freeman, 1992.

Rees DA. Polysaccharide shapes. New York: Halsted Press, 1977.

Richards FM. The protein folding problem. Sci Am 1991; 264(1):54.

Richards FM. An analysis of pacing in the protein folding problem. Q Rev Biophys 1994;26:423.

Saenger W. Principles of nucleic acid structure. New York: Springer-Verlag, 1984.

Saenger W. Structure and dynamics of water and surrounding biomolecules. Annual Review Biophysics Biophysical Chemistry 1987;16:93.

Tanford C. The hydrophobic effect: formation of micelles and biological membranes. 2nd ed. New York: Wiley-Interscience, 1980.

Wiggins PM. Role of water in some biological processes. Microbiol Rev 1990;54:432.

ENZYMES AND RIBOZYMES

Abeles RH, Frey PA, Jencks WP. Biochemistry. Boston: Jones and Barlett, 1992.

Adams RLP, Knowler JT, Leader DP. The biochemistry of the nucleic acids. London: Chapman and Hall, 1992.

Altman S, Baer M, Guerrier-Takada C, Vioque A. Enzymatic cleavage of RNA by RNA. Trends Biochem Sci 1986;11:515.

Altman S, Kirsebon L, Talbot S. Recent studies of ribonuclease P. FASEB J 1993;7:7.

Binkley RW. Modern carbohydrate chemistry. San Diego: Marcel Dekker, 1988.

Cech TR. The chemistry of self-splicing RNA and RNA enzymes. Science 1987;236:1532.

Dugas H. Bioorganic chemistry: a chemical approach to

enzyme action. 2nd ed. New York: Springer-Verlag, 1989.
Fersht A. Enzyme structure and mechanism. 2nd ed. New York: W. H. Freeman, 1985.
Jencks WP. Binding energy, specificity and enzymatic catalysis: the circe effect. Adv Enzyme Relat Areas Mol Biol 1975;43:219.
Knowles JR. Enzyme catalysis: not different, just better. Nature 1991;350:121.
Menger FM. Enzyme reactivity from an organic perspective. Accounts of Chemical Research 1993;26: 206.
Schramm VL, Horenstein BA, Kline PC. Transition state analysis and inhibitor design for enzymatic reactions. J Biol Chem. 1994;269:18259.
Symons RH. Ribozymes. Current Opinion Structural Biology 1994;4:322.
Walsh C. Enzymatic reaction mechanisms. San Francisco: W. H. Freeman, 1979.
Warshel A, Aqvist J. Electrostatic energy and macromolecular function. Annual Review Biophysics Biophysical Chemistry 1991;20:267.
Wittop Koning TH, Schumperli D. RNAs and ribonucleoproteins in recognition and catalysis. Eur J Biochem 1994;219:25.

REGULATION OF INTERMEDIARY METABOLISM AND CELL SIGNALING

Barford D, Johnson LN. The allosteric transition of glycogen phosphorylase. Nature 1989;340:609.
Berridge MJ. Inositol triphosphate and calcium signalling. Nature 1993;361:315.
Fischer EH. Protein phosphorylation and cellular regulation II (Nobel Lecture). Angewandte Chemie International Edition English 1993;105:1130.
Gilman AG. G proteins and regulation of adenylyl cyclase. JAMA 1989;262:1819.
Johnson LN, Barford D. Electrostatic effects in the control of glycogen phosphorylase by phosphorylation. Protein Sci 1994;3:1726.
Krebs EG. Protein phosphorylation and cellular regulation I (Nobel Lecture). Angewandte Chemie International Edition English 1993;32:1122.
Lefkowitz RJ. Clinical implications of basic research: G proteins in medicine. N Engl J Med 1995;332:186.
Offermans S, Schultz G. Complex information processing by the transmembrane signaling system involving G proteins. Naunyn-Schmiedebergs Arch Pharmacol 1994;350:329.
Perutz MF. Mechanisms of cooperativity and allosteric regulation in proteins. Q Rev Biophys 1989;22:139.
Rodbell M. The role of GTP-binding proteins in signal transduction: from the sublimely simple to the conceptually complex. Curr Top Cell Regul 1992;32:1.
Shenolikar S. Protein serine/threonine phosphatases—new avenues for cell regulation. Annu Rev Cell Biol 1994;10:55.

EUCARYOTIC GENOME AND PROTEIN SYNTHESIS

Brown TA. Genetics: a molecular approach. 2nd ed. London: Chapman and Hall, 1992.
Cousins RJ. Metal elements and gene expression. Annu Rev Nutr 1994;14:449.
Dorit RL, Schoenbach L, Gilbert W. How big is the universe of exons? Science 1990;250:1377.
Echols H, Goodman MF. Fidelity mechanisms in DNA replication. Annu Rev Biochem 1991;60:477.
Freemont PS, Lane AN, Sanderson MR. Structural aspects of protein-DNA recognition. Biochem J 1991;278:1.
Kozak M. Regulation of translation in eukaryotic systems. Annu Rev Cell Biol 1992;8:197.
Lewin B. Genes V. New York: Oxford University Press, 1994.
Martin KJ. The interactions of transcription factors and their adaptors, coactivators and accessory proteins. Bioessays 1991;13:499.
Merrick WC. Mechanism and regulation of eukaryotic protein synthesis. Microbiol Rev 1992;56:291.
Nilsen TW. RNA-RNA interactions in the spliceosome: unraveling the ties that bind. Cell 1994;78:1.
Noller HF. Ribosomal RNA and translation. Annu Rev Biochem 1991;60:191.
Pabo CO, Sauer RT. Transcription factors: structural families and principles of DNA recognition. Annu Rev Biochem 1992;61:105.
Roberts RJ. An amazing distortion in DNA induced by a methyltransferase (Nobel Lecture). Angewandte Chemie International Edition English 1994;33:1222.
Sharp PA. Split genes and RNA splicing (Nobel Lecture). Cell 1994;77:805.
Wang TS-F. Eukaryotic DNA polymerases. Annu Rev Biochem 1991;60:513.

RECOMBINANT DNA AND GENETIC ENGINEERING

Arnheim N, Erlich H. Polymerase chain reaction strategy. Annu Rev Biochem 1992;61:131.
Bickle TA, Kruger DH. Biology of DNA restriction. Microbiol Rev 1993;57:434.
Erlich HA, Arnheim N. Genetic analysis using the polymerase chain reaction. Annu Rev Genet 1992;26: 479.
Hardy KJ, Young HA, Lagoo AS. Molecular diagnostics. Immunology Allergy Clinics of North America 1994; 14:199.
Lucotte G, Baneyx F. Introduction to molecular cloning. New York: VCH Pub Inc, 1993.
McConkey EH. Human genetics: the molecular revolution. Boston: Jones and Barlett, 1993.
Rapley R, Walker MR. Molecular diagnostics. Oxford: Blackwell Scientific Publishers, 1993.
Riordan JR, Rommens JM, Kerem B-S, et al. Identification

of the cystic fibrosis gene: cloning and characterization of complementary DNA. Science 1989;245:1066.
Rommens JM, Iannuzzi MC, Kerem B-S, et al. Identification of the cystic fibrosis gene: chromosome walking and jumping. Science 1989;245:1059.
Ross DW. Introduction to molecular medicine. New York: Springer-Verlag, 1992.
Smith M. Synthetic DNA and biology (Nobel Lecture). Biosci Rep 1994;14:51.
Trent R. Molecular medicine. Edinburgh: Churchill Livingstone, 1993.
Watson J, Gilman M, Witkowski J, Zoller M. Recombinant DNA. 2nd ed. New York: Scientific American Books, 1992.

ORGANIZATION OF METABOLIC PROCESSES

Davidson VL, Sittman DB. Biochemistry. 3rd ed. Philadelphia: Harwal Publishing, 1994.
Krebs HA, Kornberg HL. Energy transformations in living matter. Berlin: Springer-Verlag, 1957.
Harold FM. The vital force: a study of bioenergetics. New York: W.H. Freeman, 1986.
Lehninger AL, Nelson DL, Cox MM. Principles of biochemistry. 2nd ed. New York: Worth Publishers, 1993.
Mathews CK, van Holde KE. Biochemistry. Redwood City, CA: Benjamin Cummings Publishing Co, 1990.
Nicholls DG, Ferguson SJ. Bioenergetics 2. London: Academic Press, 1992.
Zubay G. Biochemistry. 3rd ed. Dubuque, IA: William C. Brown, Publishers, 1993.

GENETIC DEFECTS

Friedman JM, Dill FJ, Hayden MR, McGillivray BC. Genetics. Malvern, PA: Harwal Publishing Co, 1992.
Holton JB, ed. The inherited metabolic diseases. New York: Churchill-Livingstone, 1994.
Scriver CR, Beaudet AL, Sly WS, Valle D, eds. The metabolic and molecular basis of inherited disease. 7th ed. New York: McGraw Hill, 1995.
Thompson MT, Mcinnes RR, Willard HF. Genetics in medicine. 5th ed. Philadelphia: W. B. Saunders, 1991.
Weatherall DJ. The new genetics and clinical practice. 3rd ed. Oxford: Oxford University Press, 1991.

chapter **2**

Growth and Neoplasia

GROWTH

The growth that a human infant experiences is a cause for wonder, even for the casual observer. The fetus and infant grow at stupendous rates, as does the youngster going through puberty; this demonstrates that cell division and growth proceed at a brisk pace during special periods throughout the early life of the individual. Indeed, the ability for cells to divide is an innate property of living things. We might ask why growth, as defined by increased number of cells and total mass, does not continue throughout life. From the approximately 5-μg fertilized ovum to the 3.25-kg term infant, weight increases 650 million times! If the growth rate over the first month of gestation persisted until the age of 20 years for an individual, body mass of that single individual would equal that of the known universe. This explains the need for inherent size limitations; however, it sheds no light on the mechanisms creating the limits. The change from the intra- to extrauterine environment cannot be the sole limiting factor because if the growth rate evidenced from birth to 1 year were to continue until the age of 20 years, the individual would be more than 1100 feet in height and weigh tens of millions of pounds. Such dimensions are "food" for fairy tales and science fiction but cannot apply to humans or any other life form as we know them. What, then, are the constraints that alter and moderate the growth of the rapidly enlarging infant to prevent the ultimate emergence of a colossus?

Fairy tales aside, the single fertilized egg eventually changes into an individual who comprises about 300 trillion cells—an awesome event in any case. Thus, although there are constraints on growth, the creation of an individual is nonetheless a wonder because growth must be integrated with differentiation as cells take on specialized functions. Thus, embryogenesis involves a multiplicity of processes including cell growth and division, hypertrophy, cellular migration, and biochemical and structural differentiation. During development, some cells are programmed to die as new structures are forged and new relationships established. Consequently, not only is growth a fundamental property of living things but so is the turnover of cells. Furthermore, to maintain the organism in good working order, wound healing also is a property of living creatures.

Returning to the issue of the constraints on growth, the predominant constraint appears to be the ratio of the surface area to the volume of the organism. The cell surface area varies as the square of the radius, while volume varies as the cube of the radius. Hence, the slightest increase in cell diameter affects the diffusion space out of proportion to the diffusion surface. The same considerations are true for a multicellular organism that grows while maintaining its form. Consequently, as an animal grows, its volume outstrips its surface area. This discrepancy "pushes to the limits" the food and oxygen that can be supplied to the organism. For multicellular organisms, this has meant development of an elaborate circulatory system to bring oxygen and substrates to the individual cells, with the exchange occurring at the capillary level. The expansion of the absorptive surfaces of the lungs and gastrointestinal tracts to optimize gas and food uptake has been coupled with the development of a circulatory system. Development of a circulatory system, lungs, and gastrointestinal tract raises another vital issue for the developing multicellular organism—differentiation of the body into specialized organs that perform these unique functions.

Differentiation Requires Repression of Genetic Information

Biochemical expression of the information contained in the genome requires both cell division and specialization. This means that various portions of the genotype are repressed in different cells so that various cell types express only some of the genes included in their entire genetic complement. This selective repression of some of the information in the genome permits the development of the various organs that, although genetically alike, are phenotypically distinct. These different organs collaborate to ensure the survival of the multicellular organism.

As a consequence of repression, cell types of a particular organ express certain characteristic biochemical and physiologic capabilities. Any two organs (for example, the brain and liver) that share certain biochemical capabilities (protein synthesis and glycolysis) have distinctly different biochemical phenotypes. In fact, of the estimated 100,000 genes in the human genome, it is speculated that almost half are devoted to proteins that are unique to the brain; these proteins are not expressed in any other organ. Obviously, a multicellular organism is not a simple composite of billions of cells. During the differentiation of the various organs, the biochemical capabilities are integrated with the structure of the organ to express the organ's full potential. Of course, the proliferation of cells and their subsequent specialization are determined by a plan that unfolds through the interplay of the genome and the environment. Not only will each organ develop a unique shape, but each will occupy a unique position in the organism. This overall developmental plan is not random, as congenital defects of organs powerfully testify. Needless to say, the subdivision of labor among the various organs means that the organs are dependent on each other for their optimal functioning and for the existence of the organism.

Because the genome contains the information for all of the proteins (both functional and structural) and because many external factors can alter growth, it is likely that growth depends upon the interaction between multiple genetic factors and the ever-changing environment. Such environmental factors include adequate supplies of water, oxygen, and substrates, and specific regulators and inhibitors. Consequently, it is becoming clear that growth involves complex simultaneous and sequential events that require the expression of multiple genes and the action of hormones and growth factors.

Like all life processes, the conduct of action begins at the level of the cell, which is the smallest entity evincing those properties characteristic of living things. Limitation of the raw materials for accretion of cellular protoplasm will restrict the organism's ability to perform certain specific functions and to grow, even in the presence of the appropriate stimulus. As noted, the abilities of cells to divide and the organism to grow appear to be inherent attributes of living things. And, as we will examine below, the ability of cells to divide bespeaks a close kinship between normal growth and neoplasia.

Homeobox Genes are Involved in Pattern Formation

Recent developments in molecular genetics have provided insight of how the patterns of various organs are developed. Originally stemming from work with Drosophilia melanogaster (the fruit fly), it is increasingly apparent that specific nucleotide sequences called homeoboxes exist; these sequences code for proteins that bind to sites on DNA and act as transcription factors that provide positional values or locators and, thus, specify the position of appendages and organs in the developing insect. Subsequent evidence has proved that these same genes function the same way in vertebrates and mammals to determine position. These homeobox nucleotide sequences show substantial conservation over the eons, with 70% to 90% being identical from species to species. The sequences are expressed during embryogenesis so that segmentation is defined by these control genes. In effect, these genes impose a pattern on a formless group of cells. The vertebrate counterparts of these genes are called Hox genes. Most notably, the homeotic genes are deployed along the chromosome in the same order as they are expressed in determining the position of appendages and organs along the anteroposterior axis of the embryo. This phenomenon is called colinearity.

Proteins encoded by these homeobox genes adopt a helix-turn-helix motif at their C-terminal end, a general structure that has been shown to express sequence-specific binding both to DNA and to proteins involved in transcription. Homeobox encoded-proteins are believed to set off a cascade, mediated by other gene products, that culminates in definition of a specific location for various appendages and organs along the anteroposterior axis. For instance, the gene encoding a cell-adhesion molecule (connectin) is influenced by homeotic genes.

The Cell Cycle

As might be expected, cell division is a highly regulated process that proceeds through a series of stages referred to as the cell cycle (Figure 2.1). A cell at rest, which is a time of intense biochemical activity but during which the cell is not preparing to divide, is said to be in stage G_o of the cell cycle. To prompt the cell to move on to the first phase of cell replication (G_1), various growth factors (see text below) must bind to appropriate receptors on the plasma cell membrane. These growth factors, like polypeptide hormones, act through well-described second messengers like cAMP, inositol triphosphate (IP_3), diacylglycerol, and Ca^{++}. Proteins synthesized at the directive of a special class of genes called proto-oncogenes that are normally involved in growth and differentiation (see section on neoplasia) augment the effect of growth factors. For example, the products of the proto-oncogenes fos and jun join together to form a dimer that acts as a transcription factor binding to DNA and advancing the sequence of steps that culminates in cell replication.

As noted above, there are two classes of signal molecules involved in cell growth and division: (*a*) those that confer the competence to synthesize DNA and (*b*) those that confer the ability to progress through G_1. Examples of competence fac-

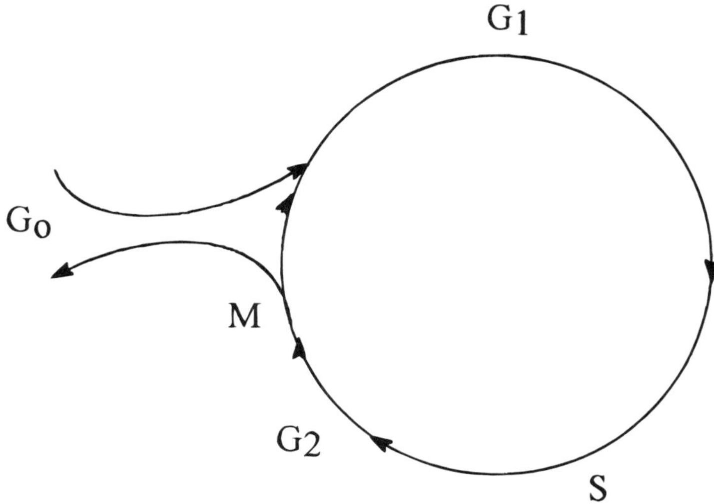

G1-period of biosynthesis

S- DNA synthesis ⟶ tetraploid DNA

G2 -gap between DNA replication and mitosis

M-mitosis

Go-a non-dividing state from which cell may again enter the cell cycle

Figure 2.1. The cell cycle.

tors for mesenchymal cells are platelet-derived growth factor (PDGF) and fibroblast growth factor; examples of progression factors are epidermal growth factor, insulin, insulin-like growth factor-I (IGF-I), and thyroid hormones.

Progress past that G_1 checkpoint requires additional cytoplasmic signals that will incite the cell to enter S (synthetic) phase, utilizing the cell's ability to undergo DNA replication. Under normal circumstances, the processes occurring in S phase take about 7 hours. This phase of synthesis of DNA and chromosomal proteins is followed by a gap called G_2, during which the cell doubles its cytoplasmic contents. Progress past the checkpoint in G_2 also requires participation of a group of protein kinases, which are called cyclin-dependent protein kinases (Cdk), and proteins that activate them, which are called cyclins. The cyclins bind to the Cdk molecules and regulate their protein kinase activity. At various points in the cell cycle, the cyclin-Cdk complexes are assembled, activated, and then dismantled. There are various classes of cyclins in eucaryotic cells, but, in general, appropriate members of the family bind to Cdk, forming maturation-promoting factor, to force the cell to enter mitosis; others bind to Cdk to trigger entry into S phase. Thus, different cyclins confer different catalytic activity on the kinases, and the fluctuating activity of protein kinase during various stages of the cell cycle is dependent on reversible phosphorylation-dephosphorylation.

It should be apparent that replication of DNA (S phase) and mitosis are the decisive events in the cell cycle. If the DNA is not completely replicated, then the daughter cells formed by mitosis will have incomplete sets of DNA, which will lead either to their death because they will not have a full complement of genes or to a high probability of malignant transformation because of the chromosomal damage.

Most notably, there is a checkpoint that exerts a "braking" effect on cells in G_1 if the DNA is damaged. This restraining effect of entry into S phase is imposed by products of a tumor suppressor gene that directs synthesis of a 53 kDa protein. This gene, p53, has achieved considerable notoriety because of its role in the causation of many cancers (see following text). It appears that the p53-encoded protein stimulates expression of another protein, p21, which is the proximate inhibitor of the cyclin-Cdk complex.

Growth Factors and Intrauterine Growth

A current definition of growth factors includes peptides that can either stimulate or inhibit cell division or those that induce differentiation of a specialized cell type. Actually, the response elicited by a particular growth factor (or hormone, for that matter) depends on cell type and state of development of the cell; therefore, in a cell that can no longer divide, the response is further differentiation. Because the hormones that enable cells to move through the cell cycle and divide are fundamental to life, we may assume them to be among the oldest of hormones and antedate those that regulate metabolic processes by eons.

Growth Hormone Directs the Synthesis of Insulin-Like Growth Factor

Growth hormone is secreted by the anterior pituitary in a pulsatile fashion that is spurred on by hypothalamic secretion of growth hormone-releasing hormone. Growth hormone, released into the bloodstream, stimulates liver to synthesize IGF-I, also known as somatomedin-C. IGF-I bears substantial structural similarity to insulin; the major difference is that the connecting (C) peptide is not cleaved from IGF-I as it is from insulin. IGF-I stimulates DNA synthesis and mitosis in many cell types including fibroblasts, muscle, and liver (Table 2.1). As a polypeptide signal molecule, IGF-I binds to its receptor on the external surface of the

Table 2.1. Properties of Insulin-like Growth Factor I

- Mass 7.6 kDa (70 amino acids)
- Significant sequence homology to insulin
- Single chain polypeptide with three disulfide bridges
- Unlike insulin, carried on a specific transport protein in plasma
- Stimulates DNA synthesis and cell division in fibroblasts, muscle, and liver
- Stimulates incorporation of sulfate into proteoglycans by chondrocytes
- Stimulates lipid and glycogen synthesis by adipose tissue
- In face of impoverished diet, IGF-I production ceases, which protects against using body protein for growth when individual is undernourished

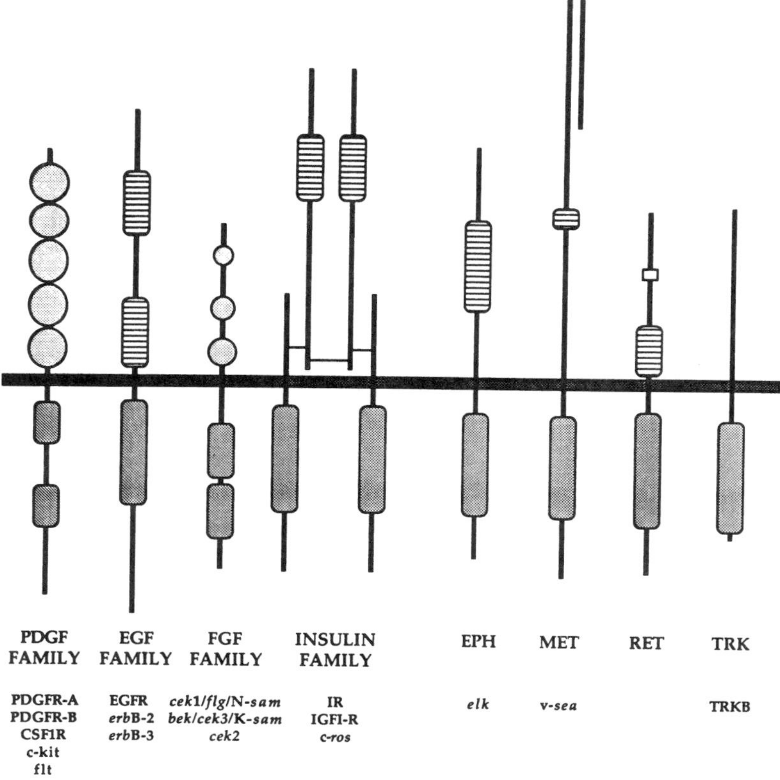

Figure 2.2. The protein kinase receptor family. A "family snapshot" of the class of protein kinase receptors is shown. The horizontal solid line represents the cell membrane; the upper area depicts the extracellular milieus and the lower portion depicts the intracellular milieus. The filled circles represent immunoglobulin domains; striped polygons represent cysteine-rich clusters; open box represent unique second domain of RET receptor; solid polygons represent tyrosine kinase domains. Reprinted with permission from Holland JF, Frei E III, Bast RC Jr, et al. Cancer Medicine. 3rd ed. Baltimore, MD: Williams & Wilkins, 1993.

plasma membrane of target cells. Just as insulin and IGF-I are structurally homologous, so are their receptors. Again, both receptors appear to act by triggering a tyrosine kinase-mediated signal on the internal face of the plasma membrane (Figure 2.2.)

Of note, secretion of IGF-I is not limited to the liver. In fact, multiple cell types can secrete IGF-I and synthesize receptors for IGF-I; this indicates that this growth factor can function in an autocrine fashion (ie, acting in an autostimulatory manner causing local amplification of growth signals). IGF-I and a related peptide, IGF-II, are important mediators of proliferation and differentiation of probably all eucaryotic cells. It also should be noted that IGF-I production by extrapancreatic cells is prima facie evidence of a genome common to all specialized cell types.

Other Growth Factors Participate in Growth and Development

Epidermal growth factor and transforming growth factor-α are mitogens that play an important role in fetal development. Binding of epidermal growth factor to its receptor initiates the phosphatidylinositol cascade (see Chapter 1) with production of IP_3 and diacylglycerol. As detailed in Chapter 1, Ca^{++} is recruited from intracellular compartments, and DAG activates a Ca^{++}-sensitive protein kinase. As a result, many growth-regulating genes are induced, including transcription factors that bind to DNA and the nuclear proteins produced by c-jun, c-fos, and c-myc, in which "c" stands for cellular.

Transforming growth factor-β is a very potent

inhibitor of the growth of epithelial cells, myeloid cells, and lymphoid cells. It appears to act through a checkpoint late in G_1 of the cell cycle. Nevertheless, it also stimulates synthesis of extracellular matrix and of bone.

PDGF, found in the α-granules of platelets, is a potent stimulator of fibroblast proliferation. It has been associated with the wound-healing process because it is released after tissue is damaged and it attracts macrophages to the site of injury. As discussed in Chapter 24, it may play an important role in the pathogenesis of arteriosclerosis and coronary artery disease.

Fibroblast growth factor stimulates new blood vessel formation (angiogenesis), aids in wound healing, and participates in utero by promoting differentiation of mesenchymal cell lines.

Nerve growth factor, the first to be isolated, is involved in stimulating differentiation and outgrowth of axons of sensory and sympathetic ganglia.

Table 2.2. Features of Hyperplasia and Hypertrophy

HYPERPLASIA	HYPERTROPHY
↑Cell number	↑Cell size and cytoplasm ↑Organelles ↑Functional capacity
EXAMPLES	EXAMPLES
Erythroid: hypoxia or hemolytic anemia	Cardiac: hypertension, valvular outflow disease
Lymph nodes: antigenic stimulation	Muscle: exercise
Breast: pregnancy and lactation	Kidney: removal of one kidney
Feet: pressure from tight shoe→corns or calluses	Sex organs: functional hypertrophy at puberty

Growth and Development

Although the stimuli for growth may be both general and tissue specific, we want to focus on what these signals accomplish and on the integrated or orchestrated quality of the growth process. Growth involves an increase in size of a part or all of the body. In utero, cell proliferation (ie, an increase in cell number) predominates over an increase in cell size and intercellular matrix in a process that involves the integration of DNA and RNA proliferation, protein synthesis, and cell division (Table 2.2). This phase of growth is characterized by hyperplasia, which indicates mitosis as the preponderant mode of growth. Although cell division continues after birth, increase in cell size begins to predominate as the mode of growth and eventually becomes the main component of growth. Nonetheless, cells are replaced in certain tissues, including blood, gastrointestinal epithelium, and epidermis, which are replenished continuously throughout the life of the individual. For example, about 2.5 million new erythrocytes are formed every second to replace senescent red cells (see Chapter 18).

Fundamentally, it is the interaction between enzymes and their environment that mediates growth; thus, it should be clear that adverse changes in hydrogen ion concentration, intracellular trace metals, and energy-yielding substrates, and limited availability of cofactors all can have profoundly negative effects on growth. An adequate supply of essential amino acids must be furnished to permit growth of tissue, which always is based on a protein matrix of structural and functional molecules.

And, of course, growth is closely related to an even more remarkable process—differentiation. Control of differentiation must occur during some complex interaction between the changing internal environment of the cell and the genome, and results in the formation of different tissues and organs of the multicellular organism over time. Unequivocal delineation of specific organs occurs early in the first trimester and, because differentiation has begun, growth in size and emergence of biochemical capabilities occur. Development may be designated as the process during which various organs acquire the biochemical apparatus to perform their physiologic functions. In the fully developed individual, the highly organized and specialized organ factories, described in Chapter 1, interact to orchestrate the functions of the organism.

Differences in Control of Fetal and Postnatal Growth

Distinctive differences exist between the fetus and the infant regarding the factors controlling growth. Most obviously, the fetus is a "captive audience" in utero, dependent upon the integrity of the placenta and uterus, and on maternal health and nutrition. The mother must supply the fetus with adequate glucose, lactate, and amino acids for energy needs while providing the raw material for accretion of new tissue. Less obviously, growth in utero is governed by the information contained in the genome. Among the hundreds of gene-directed influences on growth, the genome directs expression of various growth factors that are believed to exert determining influence on growth in utero. Maternal hormones, placental lactogen, and prolactin also appear to have growth-promoting properties. It has been suggested that part of the action of placental lactogen may be to shift the maternal energy supply to a fat economy, thereby diverting much needed glucose and amino acid away from the mother to the developing fetus. This situation contrasts with that of the infant, in whom thyroxine and growth hormone have important growth-stimulating roles.

Morphogenesis

The formation of the three layers of the embryo during gastrulation—ectoderm, endoderm, and mesoderm—are accompanied by changes in the expression of various proteins by the cells. Altering the expression of cell surface-adhesion molecules permits cells to depart from one site and take up permanent residence in a new site. Important groups of adhesion molecules are the Ca^{++}-dependent cadherins and the Ca^{++}-independent N-CAMs (neuronal cell adhesion molecules), which are expressed by different cell types and at different times during development (Figure 2.3). This temporal change in expression fosters new associations among cells. For example, cadherins have been associated with the development of epithelial sheets through joining cells by attaching to the cytoskeleton of adjacent cells. N-CAMs, as their name suggests, participate in the development of the central nervous system.

Other adhesion molecules, called integrins, mediate adhesion of cells to elements of the extracellular matrix, like fibronectin and laminin. A family of cell surface-binding proteins, the selectins, has been associated with the attachment and escape of phagocytic white cells from the blood to tissue spaces where an invading organism has set up a beachhead (see Chapter 19).

Among the enigmas surrounding differentiation

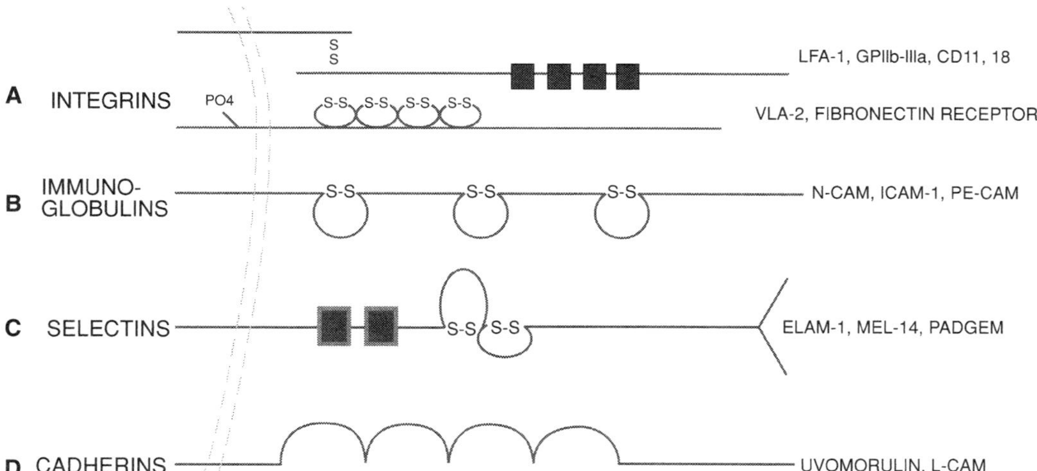

Figure 2.3. Cell adhesion receptor families. (A) Integrins are comprised of two subunits, α and β, each with cytoplasmic and transmembrane domains. Members of the integrin family are listed on the right. (B) Immunoglobulin family members include neural cell adhesion molecule (N-CAM), intracellular adhesion molecule-1 (ICAM-1), and platelet-endothelial cell adhesion molecule (PE-CAM). (C) Selectins include endothelial cell selectin (ELAM-1), lymphocyte selectin (MEL-14), and platelet selectin (PADGEM). (D) Cadherins mediate calcium-dependent adhesion phenomena and, thus, contain extracellular binding repeats (shown as the inverted U's). Reprinted with permission from McCarty DJ, Koopman WJ. Arthritis and Allied Conditions. 12th ed. Baltimore, MD: Williams & Wilkins, 1993:446.

and morphogenesis, perhaps none is more baffling than how the developing system integrates the timing and location of various cell types. Undoubtedly, there are signals that apprise various subunits of the state of development of other subunits, so that development is integrated in time and space. Such interactions probably include, but are not limited to, population density effects (critical mass phenomenon), inductive interactions, and inhibitory interactions. These signals may be transmitted through cell surface receptors, gap junctions, and local secretion of signal molecules—all of which influence neighboring cells to coordinate their response so target cells proceed through differentiation in unison.

Differentiation Involves Acquisition of New Properties and Loss of Former Properties

Cells that undergo differentiation acquire new biochemical abilities while they lose older capabilities that were expressed in less differentiated precursor cells. This has been most clearly shown for cells of the erythrocytic and granulocytic series, but is true of all cell lines. At the end of differentiation of a particular cell line, the aggregate biochemical and morphologic changes a cell has undergone renders it vastly different in form (organelle complement) and function (biochemical repertoire). The fact that differentiation is controlled regarding both time and place, meaning that there is a precise chronological order to the developmental changes a cell line undergoes, also must be considered. Furthermore, these changes occur in the company of other cells in that differentiating organ. When a designated change fails to occur, cell development is either arrested or profoundly distorted.

In Chapter 1, we emphasized the central role of control mechanisms in protecting the integrity of the organism against internal and external perturbations. This is most critical during growth because there are countless ways in which growth and development can be disturbed.

It should be clear that orchestration of life presupposes that no cell, tissue, or organ in the normal organism is ever permitted to "do its own thing." But, as we will see in the following text, that is precisely what happens when neoplasia develops. In the context of growth, a malfunctioning organ may be unable to do its part for the organism, resulting in the temporary or permanent impairment of certain higher order functions like growth and differentiation, depending upon the timing and nature of the abnormality. This may be illustrated by the effects of maternal phenylketonuria on a genotypically normal fetus. In such a case, maternal blood levels of phenylalanine greater than 12 mg/dl, extending throughout gestation, will result in disordered cerebral and cardiac development, even though the fetus was genetically heterozygous.

Postnatal Growth Can Be Affected by Illness

The fastest pace of growth in utero occurs during the early part of pregnancy, achieving a peak at about 5 months. Thereafter, the rate slows somewhat, and the relative decrease in growth rate persists until 3 years of age when a steady pace is achieved. This variable pattern of growth velocity, which begins in utero, is characteristic of growth throughout childhood. At the onset of puberty, growth rate accelerates until full adult stature is achieved.

Although growth in length proceeds most rapidly in early infancy, it begins to taper in the second year. This overall pattern must be linked to the concept of individual variations in growth. Consequently, major shifts in linear growth percentile rank are normal in early infancy; but by 2 years of age, a stable linear growth course, which the individual will follow until puberty, usually is firmly fixed. Linear growth up until puberty is a result of a predictable rate of bone growth, which is a result of endochondral bone formation.

Generally, between age 2 years and the onset of puberty, normal children maintain growth along a particular centile and tend not to stray from that growth curve. This has been termed channelization, and careful measurements reveal that healthy children often experience short-term fluctuations in height to remain on their predetermined centile for height. It is likely that minor intercurrent illnesses may cause growth velocity to be slowed down, which then begets a compensatory acceleration once the illness has passed. Chronic illnesses commonly cause greater delays in growth, but compensatory changes also can occur when successful therapy is achieved.

Because boys experience onset of adolescence later than girls, and because they usually achieve a greater adult height, it seems that the longer period of prepubertal growth in boys accounts for this discrepancy. In conditions that accelerate closure of the epiphyses, this pattern is reversed, furnishing further evidence for the importance of prepubertal growth.

Estimates of the caloric requirements for growth (ie, ATP used in protein synthesis) have been placed at between 2% and 13% of ingested calories. Thus, it is clear that any process that interferes with absorption of food or generation of ATP could adversely affect growth.

NEOPLASIA

Cancer Cells Violate the "Social Contract" of Tissues

Normal cells undergo differentiation to express the phenotype of the specific cell type; during differentiation, most cells lose the capacity to divide. Furthermore, differentiated cells respect intercellular and basement membrane boundaries, evincing what is called contact inhibition so that the cells do not intrude on each other's territory. In contrast, cells that have undergone malignant transformation proliferate without restraint, and, while becoming malignant, are stalled in an early stage of differentiation. Most notably, these aberrant cells can invade other tissues (secreting proteolytic enzymes to break down tissue barriers) and spread widely throughout the body (metastasis), and are disseminated by the blood and lymph. These additional tumors sap the strength of the host and eventually lead to its demise. One of the most striking features of malignant transformation in cells is the high rate of mutation and chromosomal damage that ensues.

Cancer-Causing Agents

Environmental hazards like ionizing radiation, ultraviolet radiation, and asbestos have been known to cause cancer. Smoking is associated with lung cancer and alcohol with oropharyngeal and esophageal cancer. Various chemicals, most notably aniline dyes and agents, that can crosslink DNA also have been implicated in carcinogenesis. It has been believed that many, if not all, of these agents cause cancer by damaging chromosomes and, by extension, specific genes. Intensive work with a class of viruses called retroviruses established unequivocal evidence of the role of aberrant genes in cancer causation. These viruses use a reverse transcriptase to fashion double-stranded DNA from RNA. That DNA then can be integrated into the host genome.

About 20 years ago, it was generally believed that RNA viruses could cause cancer in animals (Peyton Rous showed this in 1911), but it was not clear where the oncogenes—genes that participate in carcinogenesis—came from. It was widely assumed that they arose from the viruses themselves; therefore, scientists were surprised when hybridization studies showed that the oncogenes were acquired from the host and did not evolve from the viral genome. These first studies were performed with chickens, but now there is abundant evidence that sequences are contained in mammalian genomes, including humans, that bear a high degree of homology to those in the viral oncogenes. To distinguish the normal host gene from the viral oncogene, the term proto-oncogene was coined. Furthermore, the viral oncogene is referred to as v-onc, and its cellular precursor is called c-onc.

As noted previously, strong evidence exists that the cellular proto-oncogene plays a role in normal growth and development. It is only when the proto-oncogene is mutated or is controlled by inappropriate viral or other transforming signals that it can be compelled to participate in carcinogenesis. The findings that the viral sequences are devoid of introns and that the homologous human sequences bear the now-familiar intron-exon structure of eucaryotes contribute to the evidence that the cellular proto-oncogene is the precursor to the viral oncogene (see Chapter 1). Thus, the retrovirus pirates the host genome into its own DNA by virtue of its mode of replication mediated by the reverse transcriptase.

Multiple Steps Are Involved in the Development of Cancer

Cancer cells replicate continuously, all generations harboring the same genome. Thus, starting with a single abnormal cell, the relentless divisions produce a clone of tumor cells.

As more has been learned about the factors that cause malignant transformation, it has become clear that development of cancer does not depend upon a single event, but contains many steps and requires a series of alterations to the biochemical apparatus of the cell before a malignant cell is created. The need for a multistep process explains why most cancers occur later in life because it is the buildup of multiple insults to the cell, involving various genes, that eventually causes cancer to develop.

Role of Growth Factors and Oncogenes in Carcinogenesis

As we have seen, normal growth and development are tightly regulated processes that require social responsibility by the proliferating cells. In stark contrast is the chaotic picture of cancer cells dividing repeatedly without restraint, breaching tissue boundaries, and causing local invasion and distant metastases. Could it be that cancer represents a wicked imitation of normal growth, devoid of the normal constraints and checkpoints that are parts of normal growth and repair? There now is a great amount of evidence that strongly suggests that unrestrained growth that is characteristic of cancer arises out of the "escape" of normal growth processes from their genetically regulated boundaries. Some of the aberrant genes are mutated forms of dominantly expressed normal genes that participate in growth and development. These normal genes are called proto-oncogenes, and, as we will see, they can contribute to the development of malignancy. Other genes that behave in a recessive fashion are called tumor suppressor genes. These suppressor genes normally control passage through checkpoints in the cell cycle. When these suppressor genes are mutated, the checkpoints are easily breached.

It seems, therefore, that growth and development of a cell, either along normal or neoplastic lines, begin with growth factors and their receptors triggering a biochemical response within the cell that culminates in the nucleus where DNA replication takes place.

ONCOGENES AND PROTO-ONCOGENES FUNCTION IN CELL REPLICATION

Proteins encoded by cellular proto-oncogenes and their viral counterparts function in various signal transduction roles at the cell membrane, within the cytoplasm and in the nucleus. One group of oncoproteins are tyrosine kinases, which phosphorylate intracellular proteins involved in cell replication. A member of this group is encoded by the avian erythroblastosis virus erb-B gene and directs synthesis of a protein identical to the β-subunit of the epidermal growth factor receptor. That receptor possesses intrinsic tyrosine kinase activity. Another oncogene-encoded protein is similar to the PDGF receptor, and another bears homology with the IGF-I receptor. It could be conceived that if any of these receptors are altered by mutation so that they are expressed all the time, then controlled growth is replaced by relentless proliferation.

Another family of oncoproteins that reside in the cytoplasm are encoded by the ras family of oncogenes. Like G-proteins (Chapter 1), these oncoproteins bind GTP and, because they possess GTPase activity, also can hydrolyze it. They are linked to various second messengers. Unlike G-proteins, the ras oncoproteins are not composed of three different subunits; instead, they are monomeric. One of the ras oncoproteins, the result of a single nucleotide change in the normal ras gene, has little GTPase activity, which causes the protein to remain in the activated state for longer than usual and, thus, transmit a prolonged signal.

Finally, a nuclear oncogene family includes jun, fos (which we already have encountered), myc, myb, and erbA. The oncoproteins synthesized by these genes bind to specific sequences in DNA and function as transcription factors. For example, jun and fos form a dimer that binds to DNA, and erbA is an altered form of the thyroid hormone receptor that also binds to specific sequences in DNA. The amino acid sequence of the v-jun encoded oncoprotein is about 80% homologous with a nuclear transcription factor—AP-1. When the jun oncoprotein joins with the fos oncoprotein, they form a leucine zipper structure (Figure 2.4), which is one of the well-defined conformations that bind to DNA. Leucine residues are deployed in every seventh position of the α-helix that makes up the zipper. Two helices interact side

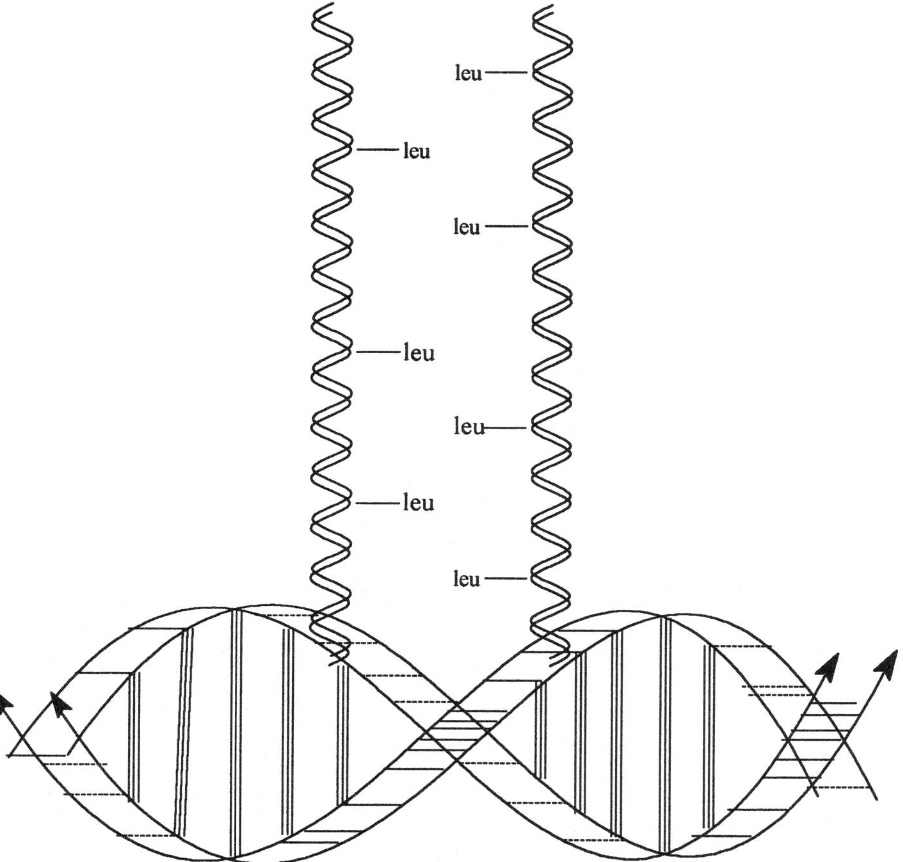

Figure 2.4. Leucine zipper. The leucine zipper is one of the structural motifs used by proteins that bind to DNA and, therefore, influence transcription. Proteins forming leucine zipper structures, like those produced by the proto-oncogenes jun and fos, are extended α-helices in which leucine occupies every seventh position. The in register orientation of the leucine residues is reminiscent of a zipper (hence the name) and stabilizes the intermolecular coil.

by side to form an intramolecular coil that bears similarity to the in register interactions of a zipper, hence the name.

VARIOUS GENETIC ALTERATIONS CAN CAUSE CANCER

Retroviral and many other studies have revealed that certain generic changes to genes or chromosomes can culminate in cancer (Figure 2.5). First, as we have seen, mutations in proto-oncogenes can direct synthesis of a product that is expressed continuously or inappropriately so that proliferation is out of control. Second, mutations may ablate regulatory sequences within the genome and cause a gene to be expressed constitutively, rather than conditionally (under the influence of hormones or growth factors).

Third, among the most striking abnormalities that cause cancer are chromosomal breaks followed by rearrangements between the two chromosomes. As a consequence, an oncogene then is controlled by regulatory elements that normally would not have any influence on the expression of that gene. There are several examples of this phenomenon; the two most intensive studies involve Burkitt's lymphoma and chronic myelogenous leukemia. In Burkitt's lymphoma, the proto-oncogene c-myc is translocated from its normal position on chromosome 8 to chromosome 14 (Figure 2.6) where it takes up residence next to some

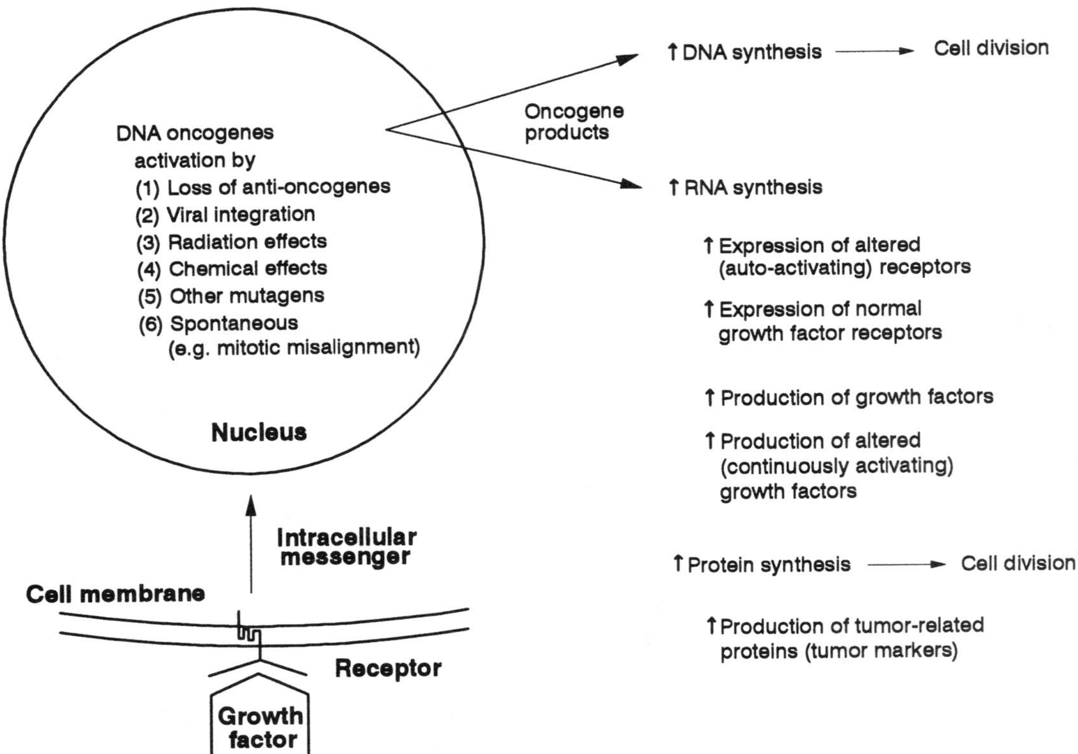

Figure 2.5. Factors leading to malignant transformation of cells. Insults initiating genetic alterations are shown within the boundary of the nucleus. Secondary consequences are listed to the right of the nucleus, all of which occur as a result of one or more of the initiating insults. Reprinted with permission from Noe DA, Rock RC. Laboratory Medicine: The Selection and Interpretation of Clinical Laboratory Studies. Baltimore, MD: Williams & Wilkins, 1994:152.

genes involved in the synthesis of immunoglobulins. In this new location, increased amounts of the c-myc encoded oncoprotein, which is a transcription factor, is made because expression of c-myc now is controlled by regulatory elements that control immunoglobulin production. In chronic myelogenous leukemia, reciprocal translocation occurs between chromosomes 9 and 22 in what is referred to as the Philadelphia chromosome. As a result of this translocation, a proto-oncogene called abl (Abelson virus of lymphoid tumors) is translocated from chromosome 9 to 22, directing the formation of an altered fusion protein with increased tyrosine kinase activity. It is this tyrosine kinase that then triggers a series of events that provides the impetus for malignant transformation in hematopoietic cells.

Fourth, overexpression of an oncogene by gene amplification can lead to cellular proliferation. This is a component of the action of c-myc that causes cancer; for example, that action involved in genesis of neuroblastomas. Finally, insertional mutagenesis is the term used to describe the carcinogenic effect of incorporating a piece of a viral genome into the host DNA. As a consequence, transcriptional control of a normal proto-oncogene now may be controlled by the errant viral sequences.

MUTATIONS IN TUMOR SUPRESSOR GENES ALSO CONTRIBUTE TO CANCER CAUSATION

When normal cells are fused with neoplastic cells, the hybrid produced often is nontumorigenic. This implies that the normal cells supplied some gene product that blocked tumorigenicity, and the genes were called tumor suppressor genes. A heritable form of retinoblastoma eye tumor is associated with a deletion on chromosome 13, called the

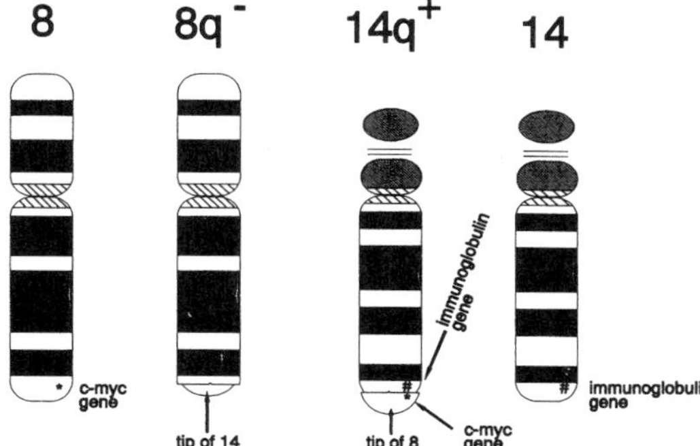

Figure 2.6. Translocation in Burkitt's lymphoma. Exchange of chromosomal material between the long arms of chromosomes 8 and 14 results in formation of abnormal chromosomes 8q and 14q. The proto-oncogene c-myc, normally contained on chromosome 8, is spliced into a region on chromosome 14 where it is controlled by a regulatory sequence involved in synthesis of immunoglobulins. Because c-myc codes for a transcription factor, the abnormal regulation of its production sets off a chain of cellular events resulting in the malignancy. Reprinted with permission from Nora JJ, Fraser FC. Medical Genetics: Principles and Practice. 4th ed. Baltimore, MD: Williams & Wilkins, 1994;356.

Rb 1 locus. Based on epidemiologic studies and statistical analysis, Knudson et al proposed that retinoblastoma would manifest when both alleles of a recessively inherited tumor suppressor gene were mutated. Although the first mutation would be inherited by the zygote, the second mutation would require a mutagenic event in somatic cells. Notably, loss of the Rb gene subsequently has been shown to contribute to the development of other tumors, including small cell lung carcinoma.

What does the product of the Rb gene do? There now is evidence that it codes for the synthesis of a nuclear protein that functions at the G_1 checkpoint of the cell cycle and modulates entry into S phase by binding to other regulatory proteins. Like Cdk, Rb undergoes phases of phosphorylation-dephosphorylation during the cell cycle.

The gene p53 also has been shown to be a tumor suppressor gene. As noted previously, p53 encodes a phosphoprotein that regulates entry into the S phase of the cell cycle. Loss of both copies of p53 could, therefore, abolish a vital restraint on cell proliferation. It is believed that the physiologic role of the p53 encoded protein is to hold cells that have suffered DNA damage in G_1 until that damage is repaired; if the DNA damage is not remediable, the cells die probably by apoptosis (programmed cell death). Absence of normal functioning p53 then may provide an opportunity for cells with damaged DNA to continue to proliferate without the restraining influence of p53 and thus become malignant.

V-SRC ENCODES A NONRECEPTOR TYROSINE KINASE THAT CONTRIBUTES TO MALIGNANT TRANSFORMATION

Oncogenes and growth factors first were linked together in 1983 when it was shown that the sis (simian sarcoma virus) oncogene encoded PDGF. If a normal growth factor were produced at an inappropriate level or for a prolonged period, it could lead to cell proliferation. Further studies showed that the sis gene product encoded the B chain of PDGF, which is a dimer of A and B units. If PDGF production is increased by an oncogene, it can augment the expression of subsequent steps in the cascade it triggers. Apparently, the next step is to activate a nonreceptor tyrosine kinase. This brings us back to the Rous sarcoma virus to see how PDGF production and nonreceptor tyrosine kinase were shown to be parts of a mitogenic signal system.

The proto-oncogene c-src corresponds to the oncogene v-src carried by the Rous sarcoma virus. Its oncoprotein, a tyrosine kinase with a mass of 60 kD designated $p60^{src}$, is anchored to the inner face of the plasma membrane through a fatty acid residue. How does $p60^{src}$ influence cell replication and how might abnormal activation lead to prolonged replication? The viral encoded oncoprotein phosphorylates a tyrosine residue on the internal face of fibronectin receptors. When phosphorylated, the receptor has decreased affinity for talin (one of the integrin cell adhesion proteins) and for fibronectin (a glycoprotein linking cells to the extracellular matrix). Furthermore, cells transformed by v-src secrete plasminogen activator, which is an enzyme that activates plasminogen to plasmin through limited proteolytic cleavage. Plasmin is an important fibrinolytic agent that maintains the fluidity of blood. In the context of cells in tissues, it appears that plasmin may lyse fibronectin and prevent covalent attachment of cells to each other. Of course, phosphorylation cascades are almost never limited to one protein, so it is likely that there are other protein targets, including vinculin, which is another attachment protein that binds to talin.

PDGF, a normal growth factor for fibroblasts, exerts a transitory effect decreasing cell adhesion when administered to quiescent fibroblasts. This effect is similar in kind but not in duration to that engendered by the c-src encoded oncoprotein. Thus, one purpose of growth factors is to weaken the attachments between cells to allow them to enter a DNA replicative phase and divide. It should be clear that when cells divide they cannot be tethered to other cells; therefore, the activation of plasminogen is useful when it occurs over a brief defined time. But, when prolonged, as with an oncogene, it could contribute to local tissue invasion and metastasis.

SUGGESTED READINGS

GROWTH AND DIFFERENTIATION

Alberts B, Bray D, Lewis J, et al. Molecular biology of the cell. 3rd ed. New York: Garland Publishing, 1994.

Baldwin HS, Buck CA. Integrins and other cell adhesion molecules in cardiac development. Trends in Cardiovascular Medicine 1994;4:178.

Cohick WS, Clemmons DR. The insulin-like growth factors. Annu Rev Physiol 1993;55:131.

Edelman GM, Crossin KL. Cell adhesion molecules: implications for a molecular histology. Annu Rev Biochem 1991;60:155.

Geiger B, Ayalon O. Cadherins. Annu Rev Cell Biol 1992; 8:307.

Gilbert SF. Developmental biology. 4th ed. Sunderland, MA: Sinauer, 1994.

Lehtonen E, Saxen L. Control of differentiation. In: Falkner F, Tanner JM, eds. Human growth. New York: Plenum Press, 1986:27.

Paro R. Mechanisms of heritable gene repression during development of drosophila. Curr Opin Cell Biol 1993; 5:999.

Roberts DJ, Tabin C. The genetics of human limb development. Am J Hum Genet 1994;55:1.

Rosenfield R, Cara JF. Somatic growth and maturation. In: DeGroot LJ, ed. Endocrinology. 3rd ed. Philadelphia: WB Saunders, 1995: 2549.

Ruderman N, Moses AC, Moller DE. Insulin, insulin-like growth factors, and their receptors. In: Arias IM, Boyer JL, Fausto N, et al. The liver: biology and pathobiology. 3rd ed. New York: Raven Press, 1994: 969.

Russell WE, Van Wyk JJ. Peptide growth factors. In: DeGroot LJ, ed. Endocrinology. 3rd ed. Philadelphia: WB Saunders, 1995:2590.

Sachs L. Regulators of normal development and tumor suppression. Int J Dev Biol 1993;37:51.

Tickle C. Patterning and morphogenesis and the development of organized tissues. In: Hodges GM, Rowlatt C, eds. Developmental biology and cancer. Boca Raton: CRC Press, 1994:129.

Underwood LE, VanWyk JJ. Normal and aberrant growth. In: Wilson JD, Foster DW, eds. Williams textbook of endocrinology. 8th ed. Philadelphia: WB Saunders, 1992:1079.

Walsh FS, Doherty P. Factors regulating the expression and function of calcium-independent cell adhesion molecules. Curr Opin Cell Biol 1993;5:791.

HOMEOBOX GENES

Dorn A, Affolter M, Gehring WJ, Leupin W. Homeodomain proteins in development and therapy. Pharmacol Ther. 1994;61:155.

Kenyon C. If birds can fly, why can't we? Homeotic genes and evolution. Cell 1994;78:175.

Gehring WJ, Affolter M, Burglin T. Homeodomain proteins. Annu Rev Biochem 1994;63:487.

Gehring WJ, Qian YQ, Billeter M, et al. Homeodomain-DNA recognition. Cell 1994;78:211.

Krumlauf R. Hox genes in vertebrate development. Cell 1994;78:191.

Lawrence P, Morata G. Homeobox genes: their function in drosphilia segmentation and pattern formation. Cell 1994;78:181.

Papavassiliou AG. Transcription factors. N Engl J Med 1995;332:45.

Rubenstein JL, Puelles L. Homeobox gene expression during development of the vertebrate brain. Curr Top Dev Biol 1994;29:1.

Ruddle FH, Bartels JL, Bentley KL, et al. Evolution of hox genes. Annu Rev Genet 1994;28:423.

CELL CYCLE

Diffley JF. Eukaryotic DNA replication. Curr Opin Cell Biol 1994;6:368.

Edgar BA. Cell cycle: cell-cycle control in a developmental context. Curr Biol 1994;4:522.

Hartwell LH, Kastan MB. Cell cycle control and cancer. Science 1994;266:1821.

Heichman KA, Roberts JM. Rules to replicate by. Cell 1994;79:557.

Hunter T, Pines J. Cyclins and cancer II: cyclin D and CDK inhibitors come of age. Cell 1994;79:573.

Jacobs T. Control of the cell cycle. Develop Biol 1992; 153:1.

King RW, Jackson PK, Kirschner MW. Mitosis in transition. Cell 1994;79:563.

Nurse P. Ordering S phase and M phase in the cell cycle. Cell 1994;79:547.

Sherr CJ. G1 phase progression: cycling on cue. Cell 1994;79:551.

Tassan JP, Schultz SJ, Bartek J, Nigg EA. Cell cycle analysis of the activity, subcellular localization, and subunit composition of human CAK (CDK-activating kinase). J Cell Biol 1994;127:467.

ONCOGENES AND TUMOR SUPPRESSOR GENES

Bishop JM. Retroviruses and oncogenes II (Nobel Lecture). Angewandte Chemie International Edition English 1990;29:716.

Bishop JM. Molecular themes in oncogenesis. Cell 1991; 64:235.

Bishop JM. Misguided cells: the genesis of human cancer. Biol Bull 1994;186:1.

Cantley LC, Auger KR, Carpenter C, et al. Oncogenes and signal transduction. Cell 1991;64:281.

Cooper GM. Oncogenes. Boston: Jones and Bartlett, 1990.

Cross M, Dexter TM. Growth factors in development, transformation, and tumorigenesis. Cell 1991;64:271.

DeClue JE, Lowy DR. Molecular aspects of organogenesis. In: Stamatoyannopoulos G, Nienhuis AW, Majerus PW, Varmus H, eds. Molecular basis of blood diseases. 2nd ed. Philadelphia: WB Saunders, 1994: 789.

Deuel TF. Polypeptide growth factors: roles in normal and abnormal cell growth. Annu Rev Cell Biol 1987;3: 443.

Donovan M, Demczuk S, Franklin G, Ohlsson R. Physiopathological roles of oncogenes in development and neoplasia. In: Hodges GM, Rowlatt E, eds. Developmental biology and cancer. Boca Raton: CRC Press, 1994:313.

Fantl WJ, Johnson DE, Williams LT. Signalling by receptor tyrosine kinases. Annu Rev Biochem 1993;62:453.

Harris CC, Hollstein M. Clinical implications of the p53 tumor-suppressor gene. N Engl J Med 1993;329:1318.

Heldin C-H, Westermark B. Platelet-derived growth factor: mechanism of action and possible in vivo function. Cell Regulation 1990;1:555.

Hunter T. Cooperation between oncogenes. Cell 1991; 64:249.

Jove R, Hanafusa H. Cell transformation by the viral src oncogene. Annual Review Cell Biology 1987;3:31.

Knudson AJ, Hethcote HW, Brown BW. Mutation and childhood cancer: a probabilistic model for the incidence of retinoblastoma. Proc Natl Acad Sci U S A 1975;72:5116.

Lanfrancone L, Pelicci G, Pelicci PG. Cancer genetics. Curr Opin Genet Dev. 1994;4:109.

LeRoith D, Baserga R, Helman L, Roberts CT, Jr. Insulin-like growth factors and cancer. Ann Intern Med 1995; 122:54.

Marcu KB, Bossone SA, Patel AJ. myc function and regulation. Annu Rev Biochem 1992;61:809.

Milner J. Forms and functions of p53. Semin Cancer Biol 1994;5:211.

Nowell PC. Chromosomes and cancer: the evolution of an idea. Adv Cancer Res 1993;62:1.

Nowell PC. Cytogenetic approaches to human cancer genes. FASEB J 1994;8:408.

Selter H, Montenarh M. The emerging picture of p53. Int J Biochem 1994;26:145.

Smith MR, Matthews NT, Jones KA, Kung HF. Biological actions of oncogenes. Pharmacol Ther 1993;58:211.

Ueda N, Shah SV. Apoptosis. J Lab Clin Med 1994;124: 169.

Xiong Y, Hannon GJ, Zhang H, et al. p21 is a universal inhibitor of cyclin kinases. Nature 1993;366:701.

Yarnold J, Stratton M, McMillan T, eds. Molecular biology for oncologists. Amsterdam: Elsevier, 1993.

Yuspa SH, Dlugosz AA, Cheng CK, et al. Role of oncogenes and tumor suppressor genes in multistage carcinogenesis. J Invest Dermatol 1994;103:90S.

chapter **3**

Kidney—Function and Malfunction

In the introductory chapter, we underscored the axial role proteins play in the life process and emphasized the importance of their three-dimensional structure to their functions. We discussed how the interactions between protein molecules and the aqueous environment determine this structure. Therefore, it is reasonable to assume that because living systems must be able to synthesize protein, the need for an aqueous environment is a prerequisite for life. Although aqueous-protein interactions are crucial, the functions of water in living systems extend beyond these interactions. Because of its high dielectric constant, water serves as an efficient solvent for small ionic molecules and as an efficient transfer mechanism for the heat produced during metabolism. In complex, multicellular organisms, extracellular water serves as a medium (in blood) by which cells within the organism communicate with each other.

Most hypotheses regarding the origin of life concur that life first emerged in a marine environment. Although such origins depended upon the creation of biologic molecules like amino acids and nucleotides, the major delimiting feature of the organism from its environment is the cell membrane, with its high lipid content stabilized by hydrophobic interactions. Thus, it is possible that the first living organism may have consisted simply of a cell membrane that surrounded an internal milieu, the chemical nature of which was only slightly different from that of the sea water that surrounded it. But delineation of the organism by virtue of its membrane led to a fundamental separation of two compartments: the extracellular fluid compartment (ECF) and the intracellular fluid compartment (ICF). No doubt, with the changes in the composition of the sea, the organism had to cope with the altered environment, in which sodium preponderated over potassium. To survive, the organism had to evolve means to select among the ions and compounds that traversed the delineating cell membrane. At the point where such selectivity evolved, a dynamically maintained difference was established between the ECF and the ICF. This, in turn, was the initial evolutionary step toward the escape of life from its marine environment. Phylogenetic studies have demonstrated the concomitant, progressive evolutionary changes in composition differences between ECF and ICF, and a trend toward terrestrial existence. The mammalian species, as we know it today, is composed of organisms that are able to sustain an independent existence by maintaining fluid and electrolyte homeostasis in the absence of a marine environment. It is, therefore, worthwhile to examine more closely the nature of the biologic order imposed by virtue of a cell membrane.

THE CELL MEMBRANE

The cell membrane is a bilipid layer structure with impregnated protein molecules throughout (Figure 3.1); hence, it is stabilized predominantly by hydrophobic interactions. Such a membranous barrier must limit the flow of materials traversing the structure in either direction, if only to confine the intracellular contents. For example, if the structure was merely porous and lacking more discriminative selectivity, the major limitation for traversing the barrier would be the molecular radii of the solutes present on either side of the membrane. This, of course, neglects the hydrophobic nature of the cell membrane. Such hydrophobicity further implies that unless pores are present in the overall structure, water will cross very slowly. Even if such pores are present, the speed at which small ions such as Na^+ will penetrate the membrane will depend upon the charge radius of the ion and the rate at which water penetrates the membrane.

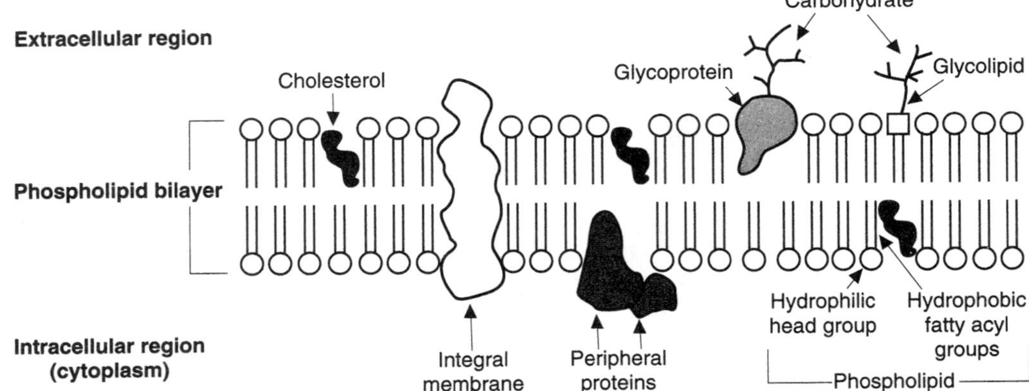

Figure 3.1. The cell membrane. The fundamental structure is that of a phospholipid bilayer, arranged in such a way that the most hydrophobic portions of the lipid components are oriented inward and toward each other. The resultant hydrophobic interactions are the chief stabilizing forces in maintenance of membrane integrity. A rough proportion exists between the amount and degree of unsaturation of the hydrophilic chains and the cholesterol content. This is because an unsaturated chain tends to bend, leaving a physical gap between itself and an adjacent, straight (unsaturated) chain that is filled with a cholesterol molecule. These factors, in the aggregate, are the chief determinants of the fluidity of the membrane. Note the need for greater area of the extracellular surface compared to the intracellular surface; this is chiefly a result of phospholipids and smaller polar groups (phosphatidylethanolamine and phosphatidylserine) being located on the inner surface, which permits a tighter radius to be created. Communications between the membrane and its external milieu are mediated by the glycoprotein and glycolipid components, each of which has polar carbohydrate side chains extending beyond the surface. Integral proteins extend through the membrane, and peripheral proteins generally are present only at one surface—the functions of each species remain unknown. Reprinted with permission from Marks DB. Biochemistry. 2nd ed. Baltimore: Williams & Wilkins, 1994.

Also, we must not fail to consider gases such as oxygen that are necessary to metabolic processes. Both oxygen and carbon dioxide are highly lipophilic and are known to traverse biologic membranes very rapidly.

By interposition of a cell membrane, the cell creates ECF and ICF compartments, which raises two additional matters. Because of the content of small ions such as sodium, potassium, and chloride in physiologic fluids, we must consider the relative concentrations of such small ions on both sides of the membrane. This transmembrane distribution must maintain electrochemical neutrality. Thus, although the internal aqueous environment enclosed by the membrane may contain higher concentrations of potassium than are found in the ECF, the total number of cations must be equivalent on both sides. This implies that another cation such as sodium will have to be higher in concentration in the ECF than in the ICF and is, indeed, the case.

Another issue introduced by existence of cell membranes concerns the principle of *osmotic pressure*. For our purposes, osmotic pressure will be thought of as a measure of the resistance that a membrane exerts on unidirectional flow of a given solute molecule; as a result, solvent molecules move in the direction of the solute. Thus, a large molecule such as a protein in the ECF cannot easily pass across the cell membrane barrier. Because of the necessity to maintain this protein molecule in solution, the water tends to flow outward from the cell toward the protein molecule. This tendency is measured in units known as milliosmoles (mOsm) and is related to the molecular weight of the substance and its concentration in the bathing medium. It is, however, important to understand that in situations where small ions pass with relative ease through membranes, the simple relationship that holds for proteins does not exist. Because the number of particles (colligative properties) determines osmotic pressure, substances that ionize affect osmotic pressure according to the degree of dissociation. For example, sodium chloride dissociates into sodium and chloride in such a fashion that at 0.154 molar concentration (that of body fluid), there are about 1.85 particles for each original molecule; these particles exert a pressure of 286 mOsm rather than the theoretical 308 mOsm.

Because all cell membranes with a few limited exceptions (such as the distal nephron of the kidney) are freely permeable to water, osmolality must be nearly, if not exactly, equal within cells and their surrounding extracellular fluids. This almost certainly is the case despite substantial differences in individual ion content and protein concentration between cells and ECF. To permit such ionic discrepancies to exist, other forces must be at work and energy must be expended. The Gibbs-Donnan equilibrium rule states that under equilibrium conditions, the product of concentrations of any pair of diffusible cations and anions on one side of the membrane will equal the product of the cations and anions on the other side of the membrane. For instance, when a nondiffusible ion is present on one side of a membrane, the situation is altered so that although the products of the concentration of the pairs of diffusible ions are equal, the concentrations on the two sides are and remain unequal. Within cells, organic phosphates and protein are nondiffusible and hold an excess of the cations potassium and magnesium. These forces are balanced by the remarkable ability of living cells to keep sodium out of the cell by continuous pumping. The Na^+ K^+ ATPase pumps sodium out of the cell in exchange for potassium at a ratio of 3:2. As a consequence of this pump mechanism, passive entry of sodium and associated water are prevented from proceeding unchecked. If water were to enter, cells would swell and eventually burst.

THE KIDNEYS

The kidneys maintain the composition of the extracellular fluid of the body and thus regulate the environment in which all cells reside—an environment that reflects the origin of life in the primeval oceans. Obviously, the fluid medium of the human body, in which widely diversified cells perform their functions, must provide a wide range of substances basic to these metabolic processes. It is the kidney that maintains the composition of this complex nutritional medium (termed the milieu interieur by Claude Bernard, the renowned 19th century physiologist) when confronted with a variable range of ingestion of solutes and water. Because there is continuous flux of water and solutes across all cell membranes, the kidney indirectly regulates the volume and toxicity of intracellular fluid as well.

In the normally functioning kidney, maintenance of fluid homeostasis depends upon the integration of four processes: (*a*) filtration of the plasma at the glomerulus; (*b*) selective reabsorption by the tubule of materials required to maintain the internal environment; (*c*) secretion by the tubule of certain substances from the blood into the tubular lumen for excretion in the urine; and (*d*) secretion of hydrogen ion and production of ammonia. Because there is secretion of a variety of waste substances and hydrogen ions in defense of blood pH from the blood into the kidney lumen, a net fluid loss occurs to maintain solubility of excreted solutes. Hence, it should be clear that cessation of this net fluid loss through the urinary tract is a serious disruption of function, irrespective of the underlying cause. Energy requirements for these secretory and reabsorptive processes amount to approximately 10% of renal basal oxygen consumption (Table 3.1).

At the end of a full-term gestation, each kidney contains between 850,000 and 1,000,000 nephrons. Because this constitutes the full complement of nephron units present in the mature kidney, by 36 weeks gestation further development of the organ consists of differentiation of the cell types into mature forms rather than formation of new units. It is significant that renal function in the normal neonate is not equivalent to that of the older child because of immaturity of nephron units. In the newborn, prenatal influences that impaired normal differentiation of the kidney will be reflected in clinical states that are relatively permanent because no mechanism exists for later differentiation of nephron units. It also is apparent that the complexity of organogenesis and the clear delineation of development of cell types before 36 weeks gestation can result in a multiplicity of renal abnormalities attributable to congenital influences.

Table 3.1. Renal Metabolism

STRUCTURE	CONSTITUENTS	METABOLIC CHARACTERISTICS
Cortex and outer medulla	70% of total kidney weight Straight limb proximal tubule Thick ascending limp loop of Henle Distal tubules	Aerobic environment Many mitochondria Citric acid cycle Fatty acids major fuel; others are glutamine and citrate
	Collecting tubules	Gluconeogenesis (linked to acid-base status, ie, ↓intracellular pH→↑gluconeogenesis)
Inner medulla and papilla	Thin limb loops of Henle Collecting ducts	Relatively oxygen poor Few mitochondria
	Early regions of thick ascending limb	Glycolysis (high levels of hexokinase and pyruvate kinase) Glucose major fuel

Glomerular Filtration

For descriptive purposes, glomerular filtration has been thought of as the forcing of water and small molecules through a sieve, with the driving force supplied by the arterial blood pressure in the efferent capillary. Actually, this is an oversimplification of a complex process. Nonetheless, the result of these contributing factors makes glomerular filtration a passive process that is dependent upon hydrostatic pressure. About one-fifth of the plasma (600 ml) coursing through the kidneys is filtered per minute at the glomerulus. One hundred twenty milliliters of this filtrate must pass through three layers: the capillary endothelium, the basement membrane, and the single-celled layer of epithelium of the Bowman's capsule. Glomerular capillaries are remarkable because they are approximately 100 times more permeable to water and ions than are capillaries elsewhere in the body. But these three layers working together form a barrier to macromolecules, an exclusion that seems to be based on molecular diameter and charge. This selectivity for macromolecules appears to reside in the basement membrane. This layer is acellular and comprises glycoproteins and glycosaminoglycans. Together these fixed glycoproteins and glycosaminoglycans (of which heparan sulfate proteoglycans constitute a major portion) bear negative charges that account for the repulsion of most proteins, which also are negatively charged in an aqueous milieu.

The epithelial cells of Bowman's capsule make up the third layer, which includes the filtration barrier. While thinking about these cells, let us imagine the primitive nephron unit as a cylinder with one blind end. As development of the nephron proceeds, the efferent and afferent arteriolar complex pushes progressively further into the blind end of the nephron. As a result, the capillary tuft eventually is surrounded by a double-walled structure with a space enclosed between the double walls that is continuous with the lumen of the tubule. The inner layer of the epithelial surface of this indentation is applied directly to the glomerular tuft and is separated only by its basal membrane; it is known as the visceral glomerular epithelium. The outer layer caused by the indentation, which is continuous with the inner layer, is known as the parietal or capsular epithelium. With continued development of the glomerulus, the outer or capsular epithelium remains a typical squamous layer of flat polygonal cells, but the layer of visceral epithelium becomes more extensively modified so that it is barely recognizable as epithelium in the typical sense. The mature epithelial cell of the visceral layer is known as a *podocyte*.

The podocytes are fitted with processes that radiate in a stellate manner; from these radiations, many secondary processes called *pedicels* or *foot processes* arise. Interdigitation of foot processes from adjacent podocytes generates a complex system of intracellular openings known as *slit pores*. In the electron micrograph, the relationship of the foot processes to the subjacent glomerular capillary reveals that the foot processes are arranged along the outer surface of a continuous basal lamina, which is their only separation from the endothelium of the underlying glomerular capillary

(Figure 3.2). Adjacent processes are separated by very narrow slits. These intracellular gaps are bridged by a thin dense line, which is a slit membrane. The slit membrane extends between the outer portions of the plasma membranes of adjacent foot processes of the visceral surface of the basal lamina. The opposite surface of the basal lamina, the endothelial lining of the glomerular capillary, also is thin and is thought to be penetrated by circular pores that are 700 to 900 A in diameter.

As yet, there is no comprehensive view of the structural-functional interrelationships that account for the remarkable permeability of the glomerulus. Two viewpoints, which are not necessarily mutually exclusive, are the pore theory and the basement membrane gel theory. The pore theory states that the diameter of membrane pores limits the nature of proteins that will be able to traverse the glomerulus; the basement membrane gel theory views the charge of the basement membrane to be the crucial factor in determining permeability characteristics. This latter view is supported by the presence of trace amounts of large proteins in the urine. Additionally, the evidence for pores is inferential. Thus, we see that, in addition to physiologic influences accounting for the filtration of blood by the capillary, morphologic features of the capillary contribute as well.

Once again, because of the presence of glycoproteins and heparan sulfate proteoglycans in various layers of the glomerular capillary wall, it is anticipated that electrostatic forces also would play a role in the selectivity of the glomerulus to passage of plasma proteins. Indeed, these anionic glycoproteins and proteoglycans retard the passage of albumin, which also behaves as an anion. Damage to the glycoprotein structural constituents, then, is one effect of albuminuria.

The process of filtration implies that a driving force enables the filtrate to traverse the capsular barrier. In the case of the glomerulus, the force driving filtration is the hydrostatic pressure of the blood. However, this driving force for filtration is counter-balanced by the following factors: (*a*) osmotic pressure of nonfilterable plasma components; (*b*) renal interstitial pressure, and (*c*) renal intertubular pressure. Thus, the net filtration pressure driving the formation of the actual glomerular filtrate generally has been accepted as 25 mm Hg.

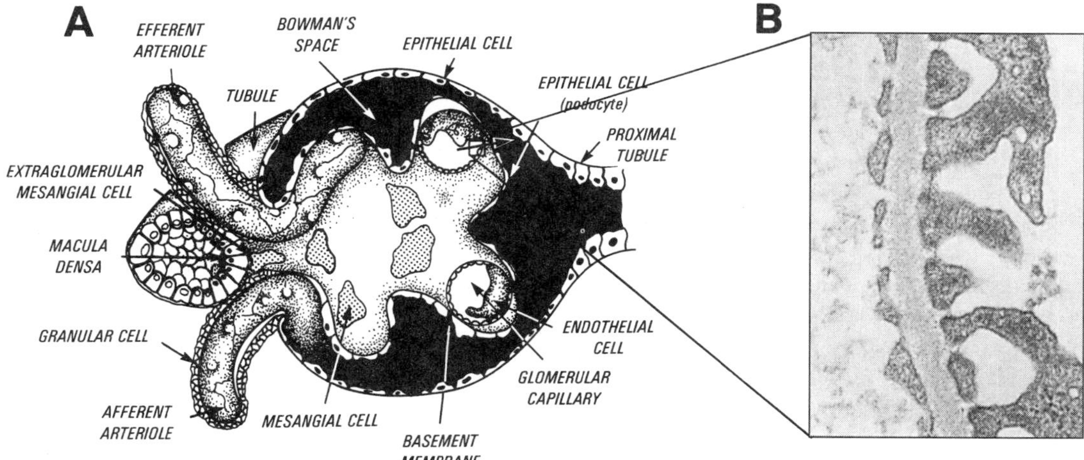

Figure 3.2. The glomerulus and glomerular epithelium. (A) Cross-section of the glomerulus. The pathway that water and small solutes follow as they are filtered from the glomerular capillaries into Bowman's space is indicated by an arrow. The filtered molecules must cross the fenestrated capillary endothelium, the basement membrane, and the epithelial cell layer of Bowman's capsule. Also illustrated are the components of the specialized structure where the tubule contacts its originating glomerulus, called the juxtaglomerular apparatus (JG apparatus). (B) Enlargement of the filtration barrier, showing (from left to right) the fenestrated capillary endothelium, the basement membrane, and the epithelial cell layer of Bowman's capsule. Reprinted with permission (Courtesy of Curtis B. Wilson) from West JB. Best & Taylor's Physiological Basis of Medical Practice. 12th ed. Baltimore: Williams & Wilkins, 1990:422.

More recent measurements, however, indicate that the net pressure may be closer to 15 mm Hg, at which approximately 120 ml of glomerular filtrate are formed in Bowman's capsule per minute in the normal adult.

Clearly, many factors can affect this glomerular filtration rate: (*a*) A significant drop in systemic blood pressure will result in a drop in the driving force of filtration so that the result in net filtration pressure may be equal to the opposing forces. (*b*) This same net effect could be created by partial obstruction of the arterial supply to the kidney or to the glomerulus. (*c*) Inflammatory processes may increase the interstitial renal pressure. (*d*) Increased resistance to flow in the tubular portion of the nephron due to obstruction distally also may affect the net filtration pressure. (*e*) Significant decreases in osmotically active components of plasma may increase the amount of filtration occurring at the glomerulus. (f) The various permeability barriers in the glomerulus may be adversely affected by disease so that the glomerulus does not function as a filter for the blood. In such cases, blood cells and plasma protein may leak through the damaged glomerular capillary complex and find their way into the urine.

Table 3.2. Constituents of Glomerular Filtrate and Urine

	GLOMERULAR FILTRATE (24 HR)	URINE (24 HR)
Metabolites		
Glucose	200 g	<50 mg
Amino acids	10 g	50–150 mg
Ions		
Sodium	24,000 mEq	50–200 mEq
Potassium	680 mEq	30–100 mEq
Chloride	20,000 mEq	50–200 mEq
Calcium	7–10 g	200 mg—restricted intake
Phosphorus	9000 mg	600–800 mg or 10 mEq
Magnesium	200 mEq	300 mg
Waste		
Urea	40–60 g	25–30 g
Creatinine	1.8–2 g	1–1.5 g
Urate	>95% reabsorbed	250–750 mg
Acidification Products		
H^+	pH 7.35	pH 5–6.5
Titratable acid	0	20–75 mEq
Bicarbonate	5000 mEq	2–5 mEq
Ammonium	<1 mEq	40–75 mEq
Water	180 l	1.5 l

The Proximal Tubule

Table 3.2 compares the normal constituents of glomerular filtrate and urine highlighting the marked changes that occur in the luminal fluid from one end of the nephron to the other. Having just examined the filtration properties of the glomerulus, it can be inferred that the ultrafiltrate entering the proximal tubule is composed of water and small molecules, such as glucose and electrolytes, in approximately the same concentration as in the plasma. Because the total volume of glomerular filtrate formed in 24 hours is about 180 L, it is clear that the individual could not survive for a long period without drastic alterations to this ultrafiltrate. Many of these changes occur in the proximal tubule, which is a segment of the nephron approximately 14 mm long and makes up the bulk of the renal cortex. The proximal tubule is composed of a convoluted portion (pars convoluta) and a straight portion (pars recta) (Figure 3.3).

The proximal portion of the proximal tubule is contiguous with the parietal epithelial layer of the glomerular capsule. Those proximal tubule cells are cuboidal or columnar epithelium with brushborder microvilli, which increase their absorptive capability. Indeed, the lumen of the proximal tubule normally appears narrow because of the huge numbers of brushborder microvilli that extend into the lumen. Numerous tubular invaginations exist between the microvilli and extend downward into the apical cytoplasm. These are the *apical canaliculi*, which probably are involved in the reabsorption of protein by the proximal tubule.

In addition to the reabsorption of filtered protein, the proximal tubule accomplishes the bulk of the reabsorption of glucose and amino acids, electrolytes (sodium, bicarbonate, phosphate, and potassium), and water (Table 3.3). Furthermore, the proximal tubule also has the capacity to actively secrete certain substances into the luminal fluid. Because all these processes occur simultaneously and bidirectionally, one cannot help but be impressed with the tasks accomplished by this simple epithelial tube. Indeed, the fact that miniscule amounts of any essential substance found in

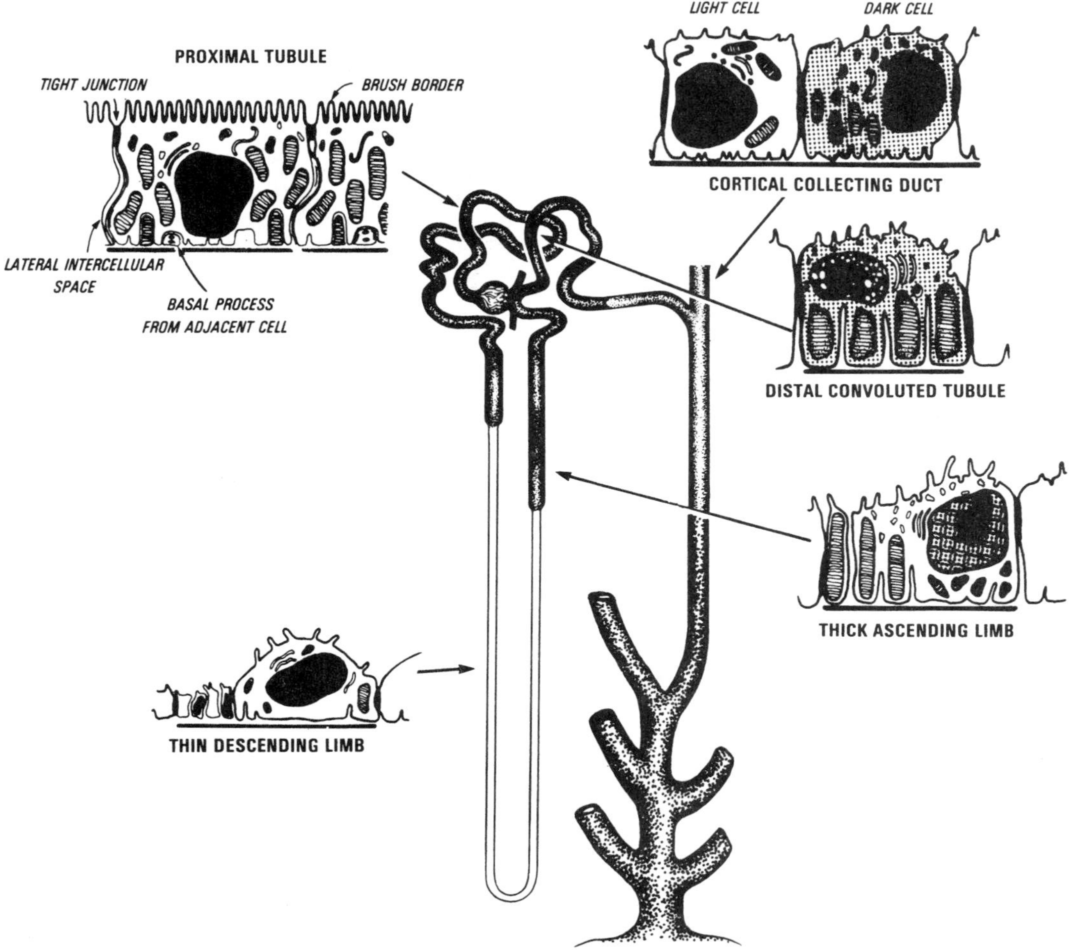

Figure 3.3. The nephron unit and the major features of the lining epithelium of each major portion. Note the relative paucity of brushborder microvilli in all areas except for the proximal nephron. For the specific functions of each segment, see the text and Table 3.3. Reprinted with permission from West JB. Best & Taylor's Physiological Basis of Medical Practice. 12th ed. Baltimore: Williams & Wilkins, 1990.

the blood, such as glucose or amino acids, ultimately appears in the urine is nothing short of awesome.

Also, 180 L of fluid passes through the relatively minute spaces of the nephrons at a rapid rate; therefore, the reabsorptive processes must be extremely efficient to remove a maximum amount of material from a large volume of fluid in a relatively short time. It is not possible for these functions to be carried out by the simple process of diffusion. In fact, solutes are removed from the glomerular filtrate, for the most part, by active (energy-requiring) reabsorptive processes. In addition, the selectivity of the reabsorptive processes necessitates the ability to recognize certain substances and to reject others. This function generally is ascribed to the presence of a membrane carrier for individual substances. Because some humans can reabsorb certain amino acids but cannot reabsorb others, it can be inferred that specific carrier molecules probably exist. For that matter, other disorders have been described in which glucose, bicarbonate, or phosphate may be wasted in the urine. These are considered in the last section of this chapter.

The localization of reabsorptive processes to

Table 3.3. Functions of Nephron Segments

	GLOMERULUS	PROXIMAL TUBULE (CONVOLUTED)	LOOP OF HENLE
Histology	Capillary endothelium more permeable than elsewhere in body	Brush border, many mitochondria E/M—lysosomes, Golgi, peroxisomes, lipid droplets	Thin descending and ascending—microvilli rare and short; few mitochondria
Permeability Characteristics	Permeable to spherical particles with M.W. <40,000; ready passage of substances with M.W. ~5000	Permeable to water, NaCl	Descending: permeable to water; impermeable to NaCl; urea Ascending: reverse of descending
Functions	Ultrafiltration of blood, 50–65 ml/min/nephron	Reabsorbs metabolites and ions essential to cell functions Isotonic, isoelectric reabsorption of 70% water, 70% Na^+ reabsorbed, 90% HCO_3 reabsorbed; H^+ secretion in distal PT. Secretion of drugs that are weak acids and bases Active reabsorption—glucose, amino acids, P_i, lactate (Na^+ linked)	Creates osmotic gradient to adjust osmolality of urine Water absorbed into hyperosmotic interstitial fluid that bathes descending limb In ascending limb passive NaCl reabsorption occurs with urea secretion. Net result is loss of solute with dilution of tubular fluid. In so doing salt without water is added to the medullary interstitium
Special Characteristics	GFR is dependent on renal plasma flow	Glomerulotubular balance (% Na^+ and water reabsorbed unchanged with change in GFR). Reabsorbtion inhibited by volume expansion, carbonic anhydrase inhibitors	Urea exerts osmotic effect on thin DLH

*PD = potential difference.

specific membrane carrier molecules implies a limit to the capacity of the molecule to bind its complementary solute. Thus, when the concentration of a given transported substance in the glomerular filtrate exceeds the capacity of the carrier system to remove it from the glomerular fluid, we speak of exceeding the "*threshold*" for that substance. A substance such as glucose is known as a high threshold substance. This implies that the blood glucose may vary widely in concentration, up to approximately 200 mg/dl before significant glucose is detectable in the urine. The maximum rate at which a substrate can be reabsorbed is known as the *tubular maximum* (T_m). In the case of glucose, this has been determined to be approximately 350 mg of glucose per minute. Assuming an arterial plasma level of 100 mg of glucose/dl and a glomerular filtration rate of 120 ml per minute, 120 mg of glucose are delivered into the glomerular filtrate each minute. However, not more than 1 g of sugar normally is excreted in the urine per day; this amounts to a total loss of 0.6% of the 173 g of glucose normally filtered through the glomerulus. Amino acids, which are handled in a fashion similar to that of glucose, show the same order of efficient reabsorption from the glomerular filtrate.

Of the 180 L of glomerular filtrate formed each day, approximately 150 L are reabsorbed in the proximal tubules. Although the volume of water in the luminal fluid is drastically decreased during its passage through the proximal tubule, the concentration of sodium does not change, nor does the osmotic pressure of the luminal fluid. There now is little doubt that active reabsorption of sodium ion occurs and is primary with respect to that of water, which follows passively. Under normal conditions, approximately 65% of the filtered sodium is actively reabsorbed at the proximal tubule site, and, to maintain electrochemical neutrality, chloride ion is reabsorbed simultaneously (Figure 3.4). Predictably, this reabsorptive process is carried out by the Na^+ K^+ ATPase.

In addition, there is persuasive evidence that

LOOP OF HENLE (THICK ASCENDING)	DISTAL DILUTING	DISTAL CONVOLUTED	COLLECTING SEGMENT
Cuboidal, basement membrane thinner than in proximal tubule	Macula densa—first part of distal tubule	Second part of DT	Extensive basal surface labyrinth
Impermeable to water	Impermeable to water, permeable to NaCl	Impermeable to water and NaCl	Permeable to water and NaCl in presence of ADH
Part of diluting segment. NaCl removed without water—key to countercurrent mechanism. Cl^- actively transported (Na^+ and K^+ passively) creates osmotic gradient in interstitium. Tubule fluid becomes more dilute	Makes final adjustments in excretion of Na^+, K^+, and H^+. Shows transition from Cl^- transport to Na^+ transport	Na^+ actively transported; negative transmembrane potential, ADH affects water permeability. Aldosterone ↑Na^+ reabsorption. Acid-base balance controlled	Active reabsorption Na^+; secretion of K^+ and H^+, impermeable to urea. In conjunction with distal tubule modulates final osmolality of urine to be excreted
Positive PD*	PD at beginning +8 mV gradually changes to −30 mV at end	Negative potential creates an electrochemical gradient for K^+ and H^+	Both Na^+ transport and voltage show mineralocorticoid dependency

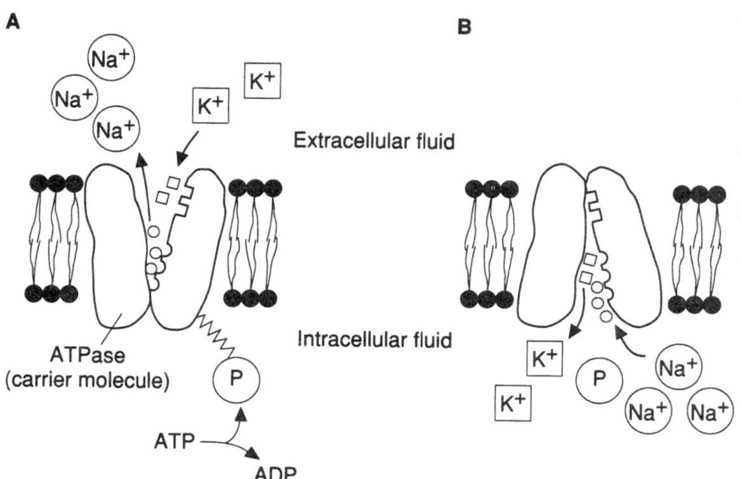

Figure 3.4. Na^+-K^+ATPase. (A) The energy contained in the high-energy phosphate bond induces a conformational change in the carrier, during which three Na^+ ions are transported out of the cell. A second conformational change occurs after two K^+ ions bind to the carrier on the outside of the cell, (B) transporting K^+ into the cell and causing the phosphate (designated P in figure) to dissociate from the carrier. Reprinted with permission from Bullock J, Boyle J III, Wang MB. Physiology. 3rd ed. Baltimore: Williams & Wilkins, 1995:7.

sodium reabsorption is the driving force for the active transport of glucose and amino acids. Such evidence includes, but is not limited to, demonstration of the dependence upon the presence of sodium ion for in vitro renal tubular transport of a variety of physiologic substrates. This process is referred to as *secondary active transport*.

Despite the enormous changes in volume and composition of the luminal fluid, the pH of the proximal tubular fluid remains almost the same as that of the glomerular filtrate. This is due mostly to the reabsorption of filtered bicarbonate. Bicarbonate reabsorption, (see Fig. 4.1) depends on the chemical reaction of water with carbon dioxide to form carbonic acid. The carbonic acid hydrolyses to form hydrogen ion and bicarbonate ion. The hydrogen ion produced diffuses into the luminal fluid down an electrical gradient to combine with the filtered bicarbonate. Carbonic acid formed in this manner is converted to CO_2 and water by hydrolysis. The sodium ion that had been filtered by the glomerulus and the filtered bicarbonate are actively reabsorbed by the tubular cell and ultimately enter the glomerular afferent capillary as sodium bicarbonate. In summary, the net result of this process is the reabsorption of one sodium ion and one bicarbonate ion in exchange for the loss of one CO_2 molecule, one water molecule, one chloride, and one hydrogen ion.

Both phosphate and potassium reabsorption primarily occur in the proximal tubule. Reabsorption of the filtered phosphate is restricted to the proximal tubule but is incomplete; therefore, some urinary loss occurs under normal circumstances. The filtered load of potassium, however, is completely reabsorbed in the proximal segment. Nevertheless, because the urine does contain some potassium, potassium must be derived by secretion in some other segment of the nephron.

Thus, we know that the composition of the fluid that is reabsorbed from the lumen of the proximal tubule strongly resembles that of the original glomerular filtrate. Having absorbed 65% to 70% of the water from the glomerular filtrate, the proximal tubule nevertheless ensures that pH, and concentration of glucose, amino acid, sodium, bicarbonate, phosphate, and potassium essentially are equivalent to that of the glomerular filtrate. There is much less urea and sulfate and no creatinine. Hence, the proximal tubule constitutes the main defense against excess loss of fluid and solute.

The Loop of Henle

As the urine passes through the nephron, it abruptly encounters a narrowing of the lumen from a width of about 60 μm in the true proximal tubule to a space about 15 μm in diameter. A concomitant change occurs in the epithelial lining of the lumen from the cuboidal epithelium of the proximal tubule to squamous epithelium. Also, the brushborder disappears abruptly and is replaced on the luminal surface by very sparse, irregularly oriented microvilli. These squamous cells rest upon a moderately thick basal lamina, and the cytoplasm contains relatively few organelles. Cytoplasmic extensions of neighboring cells interdigitate with each other somewhat in the same way as two meshing gears. If the course of the descending loop is traced, fewer and fewer cytoplasmic organelles in the cells are seen, until the inner zone of the medulla is reached and the actual loop is encountered.

The decreased amount of cytoplasmic organelles in this area of the nephron appears to be correlated with the lack of specialized function of this segment (Table 3.3). It is thought that the descending limb of the loop of Henle is freely permeable to sodium and to water, and the ascending limb is believed to be impermeable to water. In contrast to the other segments of the nephron, the voltage orientation across the thick ascending limb is positive (ca. + 7mV). NaCl transport in the loop of Henle differs from that in the proximal tubule. In the loop, Na^+, K^+, and Cl^- enter the tubule lumen via a Na^+-K^+-$2Cl^-$ carrier situated in the luminal membrane. The $Na \pm K^+$-ATPase pump, located in the basolateral membrane, returns sodium to the bloodstream; chloride does so via a specific Cl^- channel.

The cells of the ascending limb of the loop of Henle are the site of a sodium pump that moves Na^+ from the urine into the interstitial spaces of the medulla, increasing the osmotic concentrations in the medulla. Consequently, water leaves the descending limb of the loop of Henle by passive diffusion, and the urine becomes increasingly concentrated as it passes deeper into the medulla toward the bottom of the loop. Sodium is pumped out the lumen of the ascending limb into the interstitium, from which it escapes passively either into adjacent blood vessels or into the descending limb of the loop of Henle following a concentration gradient. Therefore, the descending limb of the loop contains fluid that is hypertonic with respect to plasma. As the fluid rounds the bend of the loop, the descending limb and the ascending limb contain fluids that are momentarily isosmotic. The osmotic pressure difference between the loops is abolished and the subsequent active secretion of sodium from the ascending limb creates a new osmotic difference; therefore, the tubular fluid descending to the tip becomes more hypertonic. In the meantime, the capillary blood vessels in the medulla, which are arranged in parallel rows, exhibit a simple countercurrent exchange because sodium is neither secreted nor reabsorbed actively by either limb of the capillary loop and simply follows the concentration gradient.

The net result of the action of the countercurrent system is that both the tubular fluid and the capillary blood become progressively more concentrated as they reach the tip of the loop, but subsequently more dilute as they ascend toward the cortex again. This process results in the delivery of a hypotonic urine to the distal convoluted tubule. In summary, the loop of Henle causes net reabsorption of sodium and production of a hypotonic urine.

The Distal Tubule

The cells of the distal convoluted tubule generally are cuboidal and have very small, sparse microvilli projecting into the lumen. As this portion of the nephron approaches the vascular pole of the glomerulus, it becomes attached at the angle between afferent and efferent arterioles. This junction is known as the *macula densa*, which is believed to play a role in two important processes: tubuloglomerular feedback and secretion of renin. Tubuloglomerular feedback is a complex process that regulates glomerular filtration rate (GFR). The specialized cells of the macula densa can sense either changes in flow or changes in sodium and chloride concentration in the fluid passing through them. When flow increases, the macula densa signals the juxtaglomerular apparatus to secrete a vasoconstrictor (possibly adenosine and prostaglandins) that constricts the afferent arteriole entering the glomerulus. The result is decreased GFR. In acute renal failure (see following text) tubuloglomerular feedback may prevent the loss of enormous volumes of fluid that would pose an immediate threat to the individual.

The other important role of the macula densa is controlling renin secretion. Renin is a proteolytic enzyme that, after being secreted into the blood by the kidney, catalyzes the removal of angiotensin from a circulating protein, angiotensinogen. A second enzyme, which is angiotensin-converting, catalyzes removal of a dipeptide from angiotensinogen and generates the potent vasoconstricting agent *angiotensin II*. During the creation of hemorrhage or other hypovolemic states, NaCl delivery to the macula densa decreases, eliciting a signal to increase secretion of renin and initiating the sequence of events listed previously in the text. Thus, by increasing arterial blood pressure, angiotensin II helps maintain perfusion of vital organs when the organism is confronted with fluid loss.

With the passage of urine thus far into the nephron, the major defense of the integrity of the extracellular fluid compartment already has been accomplished: the bulk of volume and solute excreted into the glomerular filtrate has been reabsorbed, the tonicity of the urine with respect to plasma has been adjusted in the loop of Henle, and the buffer base (bicarbonate) excreted into the glomerular filtrate has been reclaimed. Only one major task remains—the secretion of hydrogen ion for the maintenance of extracellular fluid pH (Table 3.3). This is a principal function of the distal tubule, which is the main site of acidification of the urine (see Chapter 4).

A distinction should be made with respect to the hydrogen ion secretion that occurs in the proximal tubule in exchange for one sodium and one bicarbonate ion: in the proximal tubule, there is little change in the pH of the urine. Although the mechanism for reabsorption of sodium and secretion of hydrogen ion by the distal tubule is similar to that by the proximal tubule, it is more straightforward (see Fig. 4.3). Carbon dioxide, derived from cell metabolism and from the blood combines with water in the cytosol of the distal tubular cell in the presence of carbonic anhydrase to form H_2CO_3. As in the proximal tubule cell, carbonic acid ionizes to hydrogen ion and bicarbonate ion. In the tubular lumen, however, sodium now is predominantly present as disodium hydrogen phosphate, which ionizes to form one sodium and the anion sodium hydrogen phosphate. At the luminal surface of the distal tubular cell, the ionized sodium is exchanged for the hydrogen ion produced intracellularly. The sodium ion thus reabsorbed is secreted into the blood with the bicarbonate ion derived from the carbonic anhydrase reaction. Thus, net reabsorption is one sodium and one bicarbonate, and one molecule of sodium dihydrogen phosphate is excreted in the luminal fluid.

The distal tubular cell has additional means to secrete hydrogen ions in the production of ammonia. These cells have a high concentration of the enzyme glutaminase, which converts glutamine to glutamate, liberating NH_3. Glutaminase appears to be activated and regulated by the intracellular pH of the distal tubular cell; its activity increases with decreased pH. The net effect of ammonia formation is in combination with hydrogen ion, either within the cell or in the tubular lumen, producing the ammonium cation. But in actual practice, the process is more indirect (see section on renal ammoniagenesis in Chapter 4). To preserve electrochemical neutrality, one sodium ion is reabsorbed in exchange for this ammonium cation. This sodium ion also can be combined with the bicarbonate ion produced intracellularly by the action of carbonic anhydrase, thus resulting in net secretion of one hydrogen ion for one ion of sodium reabsorbed with bicarbonate.

Also, another role of the distal tubular cell in regulation of pH is that it links the hydrogen ion secretory mechanisms with potassium ion. These two ions appear to compete for secretion into the tubular lumen because when hydrogen ion concentration inside the cell is high, potassium secretion is reduced; conversely, when intracellular potassium is increased, the secretory mechanism favors potassium and, therefore, more potassium will be secreted. This exchange always is made for sodium ions. The ion exchange mechanism, which proceeds independently, also is partially regulated by the adrenal mineralocorticoid aldosterone.

The solute exchange that occurs in the distal tubule is the last opportunity for the nephron to alter the solute composition of the urine. Beyond this point in the urinary tract, the only alterations that occur in urine composition are in volume and tonicity.

MECHANISM OF URINARY CONCENTRATION

Because water tends to follow solute in simple diffusion, cell membranes that are specialized for the conservation of body water, such as those lining the distal and collecting tubules of the kidney, must regulate the passive diffusion of water by selective permeability to solutes. The membranes of these cells appear to be selective in their ability to transfer sodium and urea, and water follows passively (Table 3.3). Under normal circumstances, the membranes of these cells are virtually impermeable to water and solute. But, in states of dehydration, the membranes appear to alter their permeability (presumably through conformational changes) to allow solutes (salt and urea) to cross the barrier and bring a corresponding quantity of water into the blood.

Concentration of the luminal contents is governed by both baro- and osmoreceptors. Baroreceptive control over fluid reabsorption occurs via the juxtaglomerular apparatus with activation of the renin-angiotensin system; osmoreceptive control emanates from the anterior hypothalamus.

Therefore, in a sense, the kidney exhibits autoregulation in fluid reabsorption because the angiotensin II produced by the system is initiated by the baroreceptor, which causes increased release of aldosterone from the adrenal gland. The effect of aldosterone primarily occurs on the distal tubule; the subcellular location is not yet precisely defined, although it acts at the nuclear level. Experimentally, aldosterone causes a rapid increase in RNA synthesis and thus indirectly increases the synthesis of protein and enzyme. However the biochemical effect is mediated, the effect of aldosterone on transport increases the retention of sodium, thus accentuating the exchange for potassium at the distal tubular level. Water moves in accordance with the shift toward increased concentration of sodium, therefore increasing the amount of water reabsorbed in the distal tubule. In addition, the level of serum potassium may have a direct effect upon the adrenal cortex in alteration of the secretion by that tissue of aldosterone. It should be recalled that although water will follow sodium, it also must be present as a solvent for the nontransported waste materials that are in the luminal tubule. This leads to a limitation in water reabsorption that is governed by the amount of water necessary to maintain the urinary solutes in solution.

Osmoreceptive control over the urinary concentration mechanisms primarily is located in the anterior hypothalamus. Contact of these osmoreceptors with hypoosmotic blood results in transmission of neural impulses to the posterior pituitary gland, which inhibits pituitary secretion of the antidiuretic hormone (ADH). In the absence of ADH secretion, the permeability of the wall of the distal and collecting tubules is meager, and diuresis results. On the other hand, with deprivation of water, the osmoreceptors stimulate secretion from the posterior pituitary, mediating an effect on permeability of the wall of the distal and collecting tubule with increased water reabsorption as a consequence. It is clear that the effect of ADH on the distal and collecting tubular cells is mediated through cyclic AMP; however, it is not understood how increased cyclic AMP accomplishes this. Whatever the mechanisms at the cellular level, the net effect on urinary concentration is impressive. Although the luminal fluid entering the distal tubule from the ascending limb of the loop of Henle is approximately one third isosmolar, the urine entering the terminal portion of the papilla may be up to five times isosmolar.

The daily requirement for electrolyte and urea excretion in the urine is 600 mOsm, which can be excreted in maximally concentrated urine (1200 mOsm/500 ml) or maximally diluted urine (60 mOsm/1 L). The actual osmolarity and volume usually will fall between these two physiologic extremes. Obviously, an individual with compromised renal function who cannot concentrate beyond 350 mOsm/L must excrete 1700 ml of urine to remove the 600 mOsm per day required.

PATHOLOGIC STATES OF THE NEPHRON

This section will focus on certain metabolic derangements of kidney function that accompany progressive renal insufficiency and will consider nephrolithiasis and disorders of tubular function. We begin, however, with a discussion of acute renal failure.

Acute Renal Failure

Acute renal failure (ARF) is the sudden and often reversible, rapid decline in renal function. It is marked by the inability to rid the body of nitrogenous wastes such as urea and creatinine. This profound renal dysfunction is reflected by worsening azotemia with serum creatinine rising by 0.5 to 1 mg/dl/day and serum urea increasing by about 10 mg/dl/day. Other common, but also varied, findings are the inability to excrete water and the inability to control electrolyte homeostasis. In cases when present, dramatic decrease in urine output to less than 400 ml/day, known as oliguria, can be impressive. But increasingly, it is becoming clear that oliguria is not the hallmark of ARF because nonoliguric forms frequently are recognized. Mounting evidence suggests that when nonoliguric forms occur, the renal insult is less severe than when oliguria occurs. Other features often associated with ARF are hyperkalemia, hyponatremia, hypocalcemia, hyperphosphatemia, and hyperuricemia.

By convention, causes of ARF are divided into three broad classes: prerenal, postrenal, and intrarenal (Table 3.4). Of the three, prerenal and intrarenal events account for the majority of disorders that result in ARF. But, as we will see, prerenal compromise of kidney function can progress to established renal failure once a threshold of damage has been exceeded. Established renal failure also is referred to as acute intrinsic renal disease and more often as *acute tubular necrosis* (ATN).

Prerenal causes stem from decreased perfusion of the renal parenchyma, which results from significant fluid losses; these losses can result from hemorrhage, loss of gastrointestinal secretions, loss into a third space, or exceptional losses via the urine (diuretics and diabetes insipidus). Prerenal ARF also may occur as a consequence of congestive heart failure, sepsis, anaphylactic shock, and liver failure. In these conditions, although blood volume is normal, the kidneys are not effectively perfused.

Postrenal causes stem from obstruction of either the ureter or urethra. *Intrarenal* generation of ARF results from vascular insufficiency or glomerular, interstitial, or tubular injury. The number of nephrotoxic compounds is growing, including commonly used antibiotics, particularly aminoglycosides, cephalosporins, and amphotericin B. Unfortunately, these agents are most likely to be used in treating seriously ill, hospitalized patients—individuals whose renal function already may be compromised.

Table 3.4. Etiology of Acute Renal Failure

PRERENAL	INTRARENAL	POSTRENAL
1. Perfusion:	1. Vascular:	1. Vascular:
severe vomiting	hypertension	renal vein thrombosis
diarrhea	eclampsia	neoplasm
poor fluid intake	vasculitides	2. Ureteral:
blood loss	2. Glomerulus:	lithiasis
hypotensive shock	acute glomerulonephritis	neoplasm
sepsis	3. Tubules:	clot
congestive heart failure	ischemia	urethral valves
anaphylaxis	bladder	neurogenic surgery
burns	myoglobinuria	
hemoglobinuria	hyperuricemia	
2. Anatomic:	oxalosis	
bilateral thromboembolism	interstitial	
thromboembolism of single kidney	nephritis	
aneurysm of aorta	4. Toxins:	
aneurysm of renal artery	many antibiotics	
	ethylene glycol	
	CC14	
	cisplatin	

PATHOPHYSIOLOGY

Intrarenal ARF is most frequently triggered by frank renal ischemia or by exposure to a nephrotoxin. But, prolonged prerenal failure (shock, hypovolemia, sepsis, and decreased cardiac output) also can eventuate in ARF (acute tubular necrosis). If the underlying cause of ARF does not lead to the patient's death, the kidney has a remarkable ability to recover from the insult, resulting in significant return of function. It is not an exaggeration to say that the kidney's ability to fully recover after ischemic injury is not matched by any other organ that has sustained injury of equal magnitude.

Conditions that limit renal perfusion, including hypotension and hypovolemia, lead to the development of acute renal failure in hospitalized patients (eg, those who are undergoing major surgery or who have suffered from hemorrhage as a result of major trauma). Systemic responses to counteract this decrease in effective circulating volume result in systemic vasoconstriction and increased thirst. The kidneys respond first by increasing absorption of sodium and water, but the decreased urine output results in increased blood urea. If the hypovolemia and diminished renal perfusion persist, GFR will decline further and result in worsening azotemia and diminished urine output. As we will see, tubules in the medullary region of the kidney are damaged during this latter stage of established ARF. And, if renal hypoperfusion persists for a prolonged period, as occurs in profound shock, disseminated intravascular coagulation and obstetric complications of frank acute tubular necrosis will occur.

Hospitalized patients who later develop renal failure frequently suffer from renal hypoperfusion and are exposed to various drugs that exhibit significant nephrotoxic potential. Nephrotoxins contribute to the development of renal failure because these drugs are concentrated within the kidney tubules, thereby accentuating their adverse effects on the kidney. Common nephrotoxins include the aminoglycosides, cephalosporins, and radiographic contrast material.

Four factors have long been implicated in the genesis of ARF: (*a*) renal vasoconstriction, (*b*) tubular obstruction, (*c*) backleak of glomerular filtrate, and (*d*) decreased glomerular permeability with decreased filtration. The clinical conditions that adversely affect renal perfusion cause glomerular permeability to decrease, which limits the amount of fluid delivered to the tubules. Worse yet, the initial vasoconstriction becomes persistent, depriving the tubules of oxygen and substrate. Tubular dysfunction supervenes, with sloughing of tubular cell basement membranes into the lumen, which causes a further decline in the already compromised tubular function.

Finally, backleak of some of the tubular filtrate into the peritubular capillaries negates much of the normal excretory work of the renal tubules.

WHY IS THE KIDNEY VULNERABLE TO HYPOXIA?

The kidneys receive about 20% to 25% of the total cardiac output; therefore, it would appear that they are lavishly supplied with oxygen. However, it is misleading to consider oxygenation of the kidneys from this perspective. In fact, regarding oxygenation, the kidney must be divided between the well oxygenated cortex (84 ml/min/100 g) and the relatively poorly oxygenated medulla (7.6 ml/min/100 g). Of the oxygen supplied, the cortex extracts only about 8%, although the medulla extracts almost 80%. This means that the low oxygen delivery coupled with high oxygen consumption leaves the medulla with little reserve when dealing with renal hypoperfusion and its attendant hypoxia. Thus, it could be stated that the medulla always is poised on the brink of hypoxia.

Is there a reason for keeping the medulla in this relatively hypoxic state, even under normal circumstances? The anatomy of the vascular system (vasa recta) of the countercurrent exchange system requires that the medullary hypertonic environment is not dissipated. Moreover, the amount of osmotic work occurring in the cells of that region (the medullary thick ascending limb cells) involves active reabsorption of sodium and chloride and imposes a high metabolic rate. It is this relatively hypoxic environment that is uniquely equipped to concentrate the urine and, thus, guard against fluid loss—an essential adaptation for terrestrial existence.

In a recent review of acute ischemic renal injury, Brezis and Epstein proposed that when the kidneys are injured, there is local release of various vasodilating agents including prostaglandins, adenosine, and nitric oxide. These agents act to increase blood flow to the medulla. In addition, another intrarenal mechanism decreases the transport work accomplished by these damaged medullary tubules. Increased delivery of sodium to the sensing apparatus in the macula densa is believed to be the agent that activates tubuloglomerular feedback. Adenosine may, in addition to improving medullary blood flow, intensify tubuloglomerular feedback. Recall that tubuloglomerular feedback is a mechanism that coordinates the GFR with solute delivery; therefore, when solute load increases, GFR decreases. This adaptation prevents excessive loss of fluid, but causes azotemia; it apparently is a price the organism is willing to pay while the kidney buys time to repair itself.

WHAT BIOCHEMICAL DERANGEMENTS UNDERLIE THE LESION IN ISCHEMIC RENAL FAILURE?

In most cells, the immediate consequences of hypoxia are decreased ATP and accumulation of breakdown products of high energy phosphates. In this aspect, the kidney is no exception. Deprived of adequate ATP to power the Na^+, K^+-ATPase and other transporters, sodium and calcium accumulate within the cell and cause swelling. Accumulation of intracellular calcium may activate various proteases including calpains and phospholipases. In addition, calcium can interfere with oxidative phosphorylation, further endangering the energy state of the cell.

A remarkable finding in renal ischemia is dissociation of the Na^+, K^+-ATPase from its normal mooring to the cell cytoskeleton on the basolateral surface of the proximal tubule cells (Figure 3.5). This loss of cell polarity further cripples the ability of the proximal tubule cells to generate a transcellular electrolyte gradient. This structural lesion can be repaired when ATP levels are normalized within the cell. There also is evidence that suggests generation of oxygen-free radicals during reperfusion, which also may contribute to membrane damage by extensive peroxidation of membrane phospholipids.

Chronic Renal Failure

Unlike acute renal failure, which often is reversible, chronic renal failure (CRF), unfortunately, is progressive and causes inexorable destruction of kidney structure and function. This is still more disturbing today because the leading causes of chronic renal failure are diabetes mellitus and hypertension—two diseases in which significant strides have been made to halt their progressive destruction of various organs.

Despite the fact that chronic renal failure is not reversible, the kidney and body evoke a host of adaptive mechanisms that dramatically increase

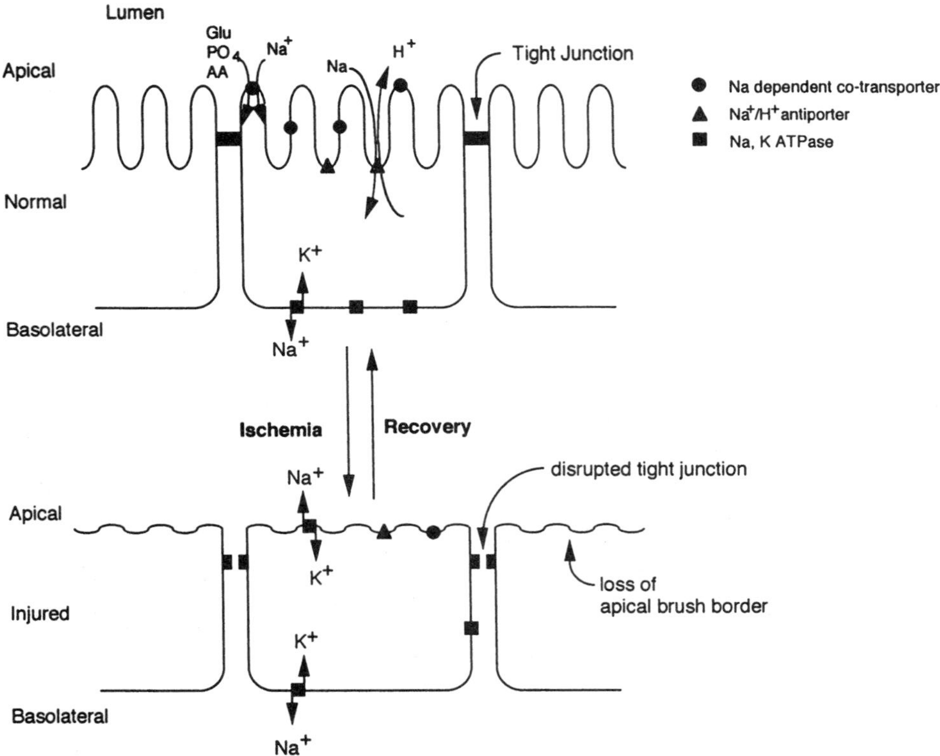

Figure 3.5. Effect of ischemia on polarity of proximal tubular membrane. In concert with the recurrent biologic theme of structure-function interrelationships, ischemia causes dissociation of Na+, K+-ATPase from its normal basolateral membrane site, affecting the ability of the cell to generate an electrochemical membrane gradient. There also is a disruption of the tight junctions, leading to abnormalities in fluid reabsorption. Note that luminal uptake of important substrates (amino acids, glucose, and Pi) is Na+-dependent; hence, decreased Na^+, K^+-ATPase activity increases loss of these important molecules. Restoration of oxidative metabolism and ATP levels results in repair and restoration of function. Reprinted with permission from Holliday MA, Barratt TM, Avner ED, et al. Pediatric Nephrology. 3rd ed. Baltimore: Williams & Wilkins, 1994:1181.

the capacity of each surviving nephron to handle the augmented solute and fluid load that occurs because of the wholesale loss of many nephrons. These adaptations entail increase in reabsorption and secretion by the surviving nephrons to maintain fluid and electrolyte homeostasis. But, there is considerable evidence that suggests that some of these adaptations will provide for the ultimate destruction of the hyperfunctioning nephrons: in the end, generalized glomerular sclerosis supervenes and kidney function deteriorates altogether. At that stage, *uremia* occurs and dialysis or transplantation is required to sustain the patient. As we will see, the term uremia is an abbreviated expression for all of the pathophysiologic derangements that lead to the clinical manifestations associated with end-stage renal failure. A progressive and irreversible loss of nephron function is common to all causes of chronic renal failure. It is possible to distinguish four separate stages in the evolution of renal failure: (*a*) diminished reserve, (*b*) insufficiency, (*c*) failure, and (*d*) the uremic syndrome. The biochemical and clinical characteristics of each are compared in Table 3.5.

The normal kidney is controlled by various hormones and other signal molecules that, under normal circumstances, act to control the economy of various solutes regulated by the kidney. When the

Table 3.5. Stages of Renal Failure

	DIMINISHED RESERVE	INSUFFICIENCY (INSTABILITY INTRODUCED)	FRANK RENAL FAILURE	UREMIA
Clinical	Asymptomatic or hypertension	Nocturia Patient tenuously balanced—perturbations of fluid and electrolytes, infection—may lead to azotemia and acidosis	Polyuria	GI, CNS, cardiorespiratory symptoms as result of renal decompensation, oliguria, bone disease, purpura, pruritus
Pathophysiology	Decreased creatinine clearance, but as a whole excretory and regulatory functions are intact	$Cr_{Cl} < 50$ ml/min (adult)	$Cr_{Cl} < 10–15$ ml/min	Uremic toxins—middle molecules, endocrinopathy (trade-off)
Laboratory Values	Hyperuricemia Proteinuria	Mild ↑BUN, creatinine Hyposthenuria Mild anemia	Serum Cr 5.5–11 mg/dl, ↓Ca, ↑P_i, Metabolic acidosis ↓Cl, ↓Na, ↑K^+—occasionally	Pronounced azotemia Hyperkalemia

kidney is damaged, these same signal molecules are elaborated to an increased degree, and can still direct the activity of the individual nephrons and maintain the normal concentrations of key solutes (ie, sodium, potassium, hydrogen ion, calcium, and phosphorus) in the extracellular fluid. At least one signal molecule is necessary to control the homeostasis of each solute. This adaptation seemed best understood in the case of phosphate and led Bricker et al in 1978 to formulate the *intact nephron hypothesis* which emphasizes the role hormones play in maintaining normal function. Of course, augmented function per nephron, when accompanied by diminishing numbers of functioning units, exacts its price—a "trade-off" in Bricker's terminology.

According to the intact nephron hypothesis, as the number of functioning nephrons decreases with progression of renal failure, the metabolic and transport activity of each nephron increases to defend the internal milieu. The nephrons accomplish this by sensing the level of the particular solute to be regulated and then operating in an oscillating manner, seeking to return the individual solute to its normal range, called the null point.

As we consider the ways in which the failing kidney adapts to maintain fluid and electrolyte homeostasis, we will find that the basic elements of the intact nephron hypothesis have been preserved, but that new data have forced modification of specific details.

SECONDARY HYPERPARATHYROIDISM AND THE TRADE-OFF HYPOTHESIS

Development of hyperparathyroidism during the course of renal failure forms the basis for the trade-off hypothesis, which postulates that hormones for which the main target is a region of the nephron provide the stimulus to augment tubular function. Because of excessive hormone secretion, this compensation is the price that other organs must pay to maintain calcium and phosphorus homeostasis. As the number of functioning nephrons diminishes, phosphate clearance decreases, generating an increase in serum phosphate that promotes calcification and consequently lowers the serum calcium concentration. To correct this imbalance, parathyroid hormone (PTH) secretion increases, augmenting phosphate excretion and defining a new set- point that persists until further nephron death forces repetition of the chains of events. Of course, a point is reached when compensating hyperparathyroidism can no longer affect tubular function: thereafter, serum calcium and phosphate persistently are abnormal and bone manifests the destruction of PTH stimulation.

More recent explanations for the secondary hyperparathyroidism of CRF define a role for calcitriol deficiency as well. Recall that formation of the active metabolite of vitamin D is accomplished by the kidney. It is clear that progressive renal failure is associated with diminished formation of $1,25(OH)_2D_3$, not only because of damaged renal tissue but also because the elevated intracellular inorganic phosphate inhibits the renal 1-α hydroxylase. With diminished levels of $1,25(OH)_2D_3$, calcium absorption from the gut is severely hampered; this acts as another stimulus to compensatory hyperparathyroidism. Skeletal lesions in chronic renal failure are not limited to the osteitis fibrosa of hyperparathyroidism. Rickets (decreased mineralization of osteoid as a consequence of lack of $1,25(OH)_2D_3$), osteoporosis (decreased bone volume), osteosclerosis, and metastatic calcification complete this varied and clinically distressing picture. In the treatment of secondary hyperparathyroidism, it is important to prevent hyperphosphatemia and replace deficient calcitriol.

SODIUM HOMEOSTASIS IN CHRONIC RENAL FAILURE

Patients in CRF can continue to excrete an amount of sodium chloride equal to that ingested until GFR has decreased to 10% of normal. In practical terms, this means that each nephron excretes considerably more sodium than in normal circumstances. Similar adaptations of function are evident when sodium chloride intake is drastically curtailed. In that circumstance, continued loss of sodium chloride occurs initially, but loss of salt diminishes dramatically in time, just as would occur with a normal kidney. This adaptive response by the failing kidney has spurred a search for the possible role of various hormones including aldosterone, atrial natriuretic peptides, a putative natriuretic hormone thought to inhibit the Na^+, K^+-ATPase, prostanoids, and perhaps others.

There is evidence that suggests that the activity of the Na^+, K^+-ATPase is decreased in uremia, perhaps because of a compound or compounds that accumulate in uremia and directly inhibit the activity of this vital membrane pump. Given the ubiquitous distribution of this pump, suppression of its activity by a circulating toxin could have wide ranging effects on the function of all cells.

GLUCOSE INTOLERANCE

Most patients with uremia show a delay in rate of fall of blood glucose to an oral or intravenous glucose tolerance test. Insulin resistance, thought to reside at the level of the glucose transport system in the cell or in the intracellular metabolism of glucose, accounts for this diabetic-like picture. This form of glucose intolerance may be distinguished from diabetes mellitus by the absence of fasting hyperglycemia or ketosis. Plasma insulin levels are elevated in uremia, probably as a result of both impaired sensitivity to insulin by peripheral tissues and diminished degradation by the kidney.

Studies of gluconeogenesis have demonstrated that glucose production in uremic patients is greater than that of control subjects. Uremic patients produce more alanine, which is a major gluconeogenic precursor, than do normal individuals. It is well known that glucagon levels are increased in CRF because of decreased clearance by the damaged kidney. Because glucagon has a decisive role in initiating gluconeogenesis, this is yet another factor in the carbohydrate intolerance of CRF.

TRIGLYCERIDE METABOLISM

Metabolism of fat also is affected in the uremic syndrome; patients usually exhibit hypertriglyceridemia but normal serum cholesterol concentrations. Peripheral insulin resistance is thought to contribute to hypertriglyceridemia, which underlies the propensity of premature atherosclerosis to occur with uremia. Furthermore, patients with uremic hyperlipemia also demonstrate elevations of the very low density lipoproteins (VLDL) (prebeta or alpha 2); considered together, these increases are the findings of type 4 hyperlipemia (see Chapter 15). The liver is the major site of synthesis of triglyceride, which is prepared for the circulation as a component of the VLDL. Peripheral adipose tissue is the major site of removal. Both increased rate of synthesis and decreased rate of removal are believed to contribute to hyperlipemia. Insulin resistance may augment the synthesis of triglyceride by liver, as lipolysis in adipose tissue augments plasma free fatty acids. In addition, evidence suggests that plasma triglycerides are removed more slowly in uremic patients than in normal individuals. Adipose tissue *lipoprotein lipase* activity, an insulin responsive enzyme, is decreased in uremia. Located in adipose tissue capillaries, adipose tissue lipoprotein lipase activity is responsible for removal of fatty acids from triglyceride; therefore, diminished activity is another consequence of insulin resistance. Further evidence that suggests abnormalities in the lipoprotein economy in uremia derives from the finding that both low density lipoprotein (LDL) (cholesterol rich) and high density lipoprotein (HDL) are decreased in patients with chronic uremia and in patients with inherited lipoprotein lipase deficiency.

PROTEIN METABOLISM

Because the gastrointestinal tract can efficiently absorb nitrogenous food-stuffs, the kidney must excrete waste products of nitrogen metabolism. This is reflected by the fact that elevated blood urea nitrogen (BUN) and serum creatinine characterize both acute and chronic renal failure. Although the kidney eliminates most urea, approximately a quarter of the urea produced by the liver re-enters the gastrointestinal tract, where it is hydrolyzed to ammonia by bacterial ureases. The ammonia thus produced diffuses passively into the portal blood during a process that appears to be related to HCO_3^- secretion into the gut. In patients with chronic uremia, a decrease in the extrarenal clearance of urea is attributable to the action of bacterial ureases, probably as a result of changes in the nature of the colonic mucosa. One of these changes may be decreased HCO_3^- secretion into the gut lumen. Thus, uremia is compounded by the occurrence of decreased extrarenal clearance of urea, which is added to the failing capacity of the nephron to excrete urea.

Several features of the uremia syndrome augment the difficulties with the protein economy. Among these is occult gastrointestinal bleeding, which can be responsible for a significant loss of protein. Digestion of the blood with reabsorption of nitrogen-containing constituents causes augmented urea production. The blood loss also leads to depletion of hemoglobin and albumin. Gastrointestinal loss of albumin is compounded by albuminuria. Furthermore, both potassium deficiency and hypercalcemia promote degradation of nitrogen-containing body constituents. The relative carbohydrate intolerance discussed previously in the text underlies these influences. Impairment of carbohydrate utilization processes will increase the rate of protein degradation to provide calories normally supplied by glucose.

UREMIA AND THE IDENTITY OF POSSIBLE TOXINS

Uremia is associated with a host of gastrointestinal, neuromuscular, hematologic, cardiorespiratory, and dermatologic manifestations that are ameliorated by dialysis, even though protein continues to be ingested. Moreover, in experimental studies, plasma from uremic patients interferes with many cell functions, but after dialysis fails to interfere with these functions. Such findings are tantalizing to many investigators and suggest that toxic metabolites are responsible for the uremic syndrome and abnormalities of cell function.

Uremic toxins include metabolites of nitrogen metabolism, such as the following: urea, creatinine, methylguanidine, guanidinosuccinic acid, phenols, indoles, and certain larger molecules—"the middle molecules" (MW 400–5000). As yet, a cause and effect relationship between the manifestations of the uremic syndrome and any of these molecules remains to be demonstrated. The evidence is characterized as suggestive at best.

As the logical extension of the trade-off hypothesis, considering the negative effects on certain organs, it has been proposed that the abnormalities in uremia are manifestations of endocrine-induced dysfunction or the presence of an inhibitor that affects the function of the Na^+, K^+-ATPase. According to this view, maintaining sodium balance in CRF requires increased production of the putative natriuretic hormone to elicit the increased Na excretion per surviving nephron. The trade off is postulated to be derangement in transmembrane Na^+ transport in other organs with the global consequences noted previously in the text. By interfering with the function of the ubiquitous Na^+-K^+-ATPase, sodium that would normally be extruded from the cell can accumulate, causing the transmembrane potential difference to decrease and resulting in some potassium exiting from the cell. This view of the uremic syndrome is both provocative and heuristic. Indeed, the intracellular sodium content of muscle, red cells, and nervous tissue are increased in individuals with uremia. Nonetheless, the cause of the uremic syndrome still must be viewed as an enigma.

Proteinuria

Urinary excretion of protein normally does not exceed 150 mg per day. About two thirds of this urinary protein originates from plasma of which approximately 10% is albumin. Many other plasma protein components have been identified in the urine; although some are intact, others are fragments. The majority of nonplasma protein excreted in urine is Tamm-Horsfall mucoprotein, which is secreted by the renal tubular epithelial cell.

It generally is accepted that urinary protein normally results from filtration across the glomerular barrier. Thereafter, as with other substances that gain entrance to the urine at the glomerulus, the ultimate amount excreted will depend upon the amount filtered and the amount reabsorbed in the tubule. The filtration process occurring at the glomerular level results from complex interactions involving protein size and shape, driving force for filtration, and pore size and functional integrity of the glomerular barrier. Functional integrity is largely determined by the polyanionic components of the endothelium, which represents an electrostatic barrier. Tubular protein reabsorption results from energy-dependent selective endocytosis.

There are four well-defined varieties of proteinuria: (*a*) Overflow proteinuria resembles the spillage type of renal tubular aminoaciduria we examined briefly earlier in this chapter. In this case, an abnormal quantity of low molecular weight proteins (eg, Bence-Jones protein) exists in plasma, which are filtered through the glomerular barrier relatively easily and saturate tubular reabsorptive processes. (*b*) Proteinuria of tubular origin, characterized by an absence of high molecular weight plasma proteins in the urine, occurs in the presence of normal quantities and types of proteins in the plasma and the glomerular ultrafiltrate. High molecular weight proteins are absent because they are not filtered through the glomerulus, which remains intact in this condition. (*c*) Specific inflammatory disease may result in a secretion of protein into the urinary tract. This is known as secretory proteinuria and is relatively uncommon. (*d*) Finally, the most frequent cause of proteinuria is glomerular proteinuria. This is the result of excessive filtration of plasma protein at the glomerular level and is almost always associated with large molecular weight proteinuria, the bulk of which is albumin.

Nephrolithiasis

Despite the fact that renal stone disease has been identified for many centuries, the propensity of certain individuals to form stones is poorly understood. Although about 70% of renal stones are composed of calcium oxalate or calcium phosphate, other stones also may cause clinical problems. These include uric acid, cystine, or struvite (triple phosphate—magnesium aluminum phosphate) stones. Urine is an exceedingly complex fluid, so it can be expected that stone formation is a complex matter. And although the presence of inorganic ions and organic waste products sets the stage for incorporation into stones, there are inhibitors of stone formation that curtail this tendency. They include pyrophosphate, citrate, and glycosaminoglycans. Thus, it is clear that many factors are involved in defining an approximation of solubility in this complex fluid. Such considerations are complicated further by fluctuations in osmolality, solvent capacity, pH, and ionic strength. These multiple factors and their complex inter-relationships are responsible for the lack of one-to-one correspondences between the chemical composition of renal stones and an excess of constituents in the urine. Regardless of how the crystal nidus forms, it acts as a matrix upon which further crystal growth and aggregation may occur, resulting in the formation of a clinically significant stone.

Nevertheless, when urine is supersaturated with certain ions and small molecules (calcium, urate, oxalate, cystine, and xanthine), the conditions are present for possible stone formation. But changes in pH, ionic strength, and composition of the urine, especially with respect to inhibitors of stone formation (pyrophosphate, magnesium, citrate, GAGs, urea, and peptides) may modify these propensities. Of course, anatomical defects that predispose to stasis greatly foster stone formation.

FLUID BALANCE

It is not our intent to restate what already has been covered in detail elsewhere (see texts listed in the suggested reading section at the end of the chapter). Rather, we prefer to discuss some general concepts that underlie what commonly is termed fluid balance. Maintaining adequate tissue perfusion to provide O_2 and substrates, and remove CO_2 and other metabolic wastes is vital to the normal function of an organ and to the health of the total organism. Perfusion is a function of the effective circulating volume, which is sensed in the arterial tree. As we have noted, the effective circulating volume is a function of total body stores of Na^+ and its associated anions because it is Na^+ that holds water in the extracellular compartment. By altering total body Na^+ through control of the Na^+ lost in urine, it is possible to control the effective circulating volume. When changes occur in the effective circulating volume, various sensors acting as stretch receptors activate a number of effectors. Some of these effectors (eg, the renin-angiotensin-aldosterone system and atrial natriuretic peptide) influence tubular reabsorption of, and therefore excretion of, Na^+ in the urine. Still others (eg, the sympathetic nervous system) modulate the state of venous constriction, consequently altering blood flow to the heart.

The other important property of extracellular fluids is osmolality. Although ensuring that perfusion of the body's organs takes precedence over maintaining an isoosmotic environment, undeniably drastic changes to the hypo- or hyperosmolar extremes have significant medical consequences. To understand this, consider that hypoosmolal states cause water to enter the brain, hence producing cerebral edema and central nervous system signs and symptoms. These include somnolence, altered consciousness, vomiting, headache, which may progress to seizures, coma, and even death. No less important is the fact that hyperosmolal states can cause cellular dehydration and shrinkage of the brain with tearing of cerebral vessels.

Humans and other mammals could not maintain the osmolality of body fluids within the required narrow range (280–295 mOsm) if the kidneys could not elaborate either a dilute or concentrated urine, depending on circumstances. As we have noted, this ability to form either a dilute or concentrated urine is a function of the countercurrent exchange mechanism, which can be modulated by the presence or absence of ADH. Ultimately, of course, the thirst mechanism exercises the most decisive control on osmolality by regulating fluid intake.

In a normal individual, thirst is the mechanism that induces ingestion of additional water to maintain fluid balance. In an adult, a loss of 350 to 700 ml in total body water is sufficient to stimulate the thirst centers of the central nervous system. The centers for control of thirst are located in the ventromedial and anterior hypothalamus and are close to or overlap the centers of the neurohypophysis, which regulate ADH. Because thirst is the regulator of the intake of water in man, ADH has a fundamental role in the regulation of water balance and in the control of water excretion. By altering the permeability to water of the cells of distal renal tubules and collecting ducts, ADH controls the amount of water reabsorbed and the volume of water excreted. Hence, the elements that interact to maintain the osmolality of the ECF are thirst, ADH, and the renal concentrating and diluting mechanisms.

In this control, water also serves as a solvent for biologically essential molecules. As we have stated, the concentrations of ions, proteins, and other organic molecules affect the osmolality of body fluids. Hence, these concentrations are important in determining the response of the body to fluid gains or losses. Obviously, ingestion of a large volume of deionized, distilled water would dilute all solubilized molecules, thus reducing their osmolar effect. As a result, two primary offsetting responses would occur: ADH secretion would be inhibited to maximize renal free water excretion, and adrenal mineralocorticoid (aldosterone) secretion would be increased to prompt sodium conservation by the distal tubule in an effort to increase the Na^+ concentration. Reversal of these responses would occur with ingestion of hypertonic saline, for example. Once again, we find that the kidney is the major factor in defense and regulation of both fluid and electrolyte balance.

Osmosis, Diffusion, and Reabsorption in Tissue Nutrition

The major exchanges of water, electrolytes, nutrient substances, oxygen, carbon dioxide, and other end products of metabolism occur by diffusion. Water and plasma electrolytes, which are very small ions, diffuse rapidly back and forth across capillary membranes. Capillary water exchanges with interstitial water several times a second. Sodium, chloride, glucose, and urea diffuse at different speeds, exchanging at rates of two times a second to 40 times a minute. Net transfer by diffusion depends on exchange down a concentration gradient with glucose and oxygen moving toward cells and with carbon dioxide, organic acids, and solvent water moving toward the capillary. Because of their lipid solubility, oxygen and carbon dioxide are free to diffuse across the entire capillary membrane, though water and electrolytes are believed to pass through minute pores in the endothelial membrane.

A balance of hydrostatic forces controls the distribution of fluid volume between plasma and the interstitial fluid compartments. Capillary hydrostatic pressure, including both blood pressure and gravity, and high capillary flow rates result in net flow from capillaries to the interstitial fluid. Colloid osmotic pressure of plasma protein, tissue elasticity, and slow capillary flow rates result in a net return flow into capillary. Anything that alters capillary permeability, such as injury due to heat, toxins, or prolonged hypoxia with acidosis, results in varying degrees of loss of plasma protein into the interstitial fluid. Loss of colloid osmotic pressure reduces return flow to the capillary and results in local expansion of the intracellular fluid space. Edema becomes clinically evident when the interstitial fluid volume increases by 5%.

One of the effects of differing concentrations of potassium and of other ions on opposite sides of the cell membrane is the development of an electrical potential across the membrane. A potential of −90 mv exists within muscle cells when compared to the ECF surrounding them. This negative potential may help to explain the rejection of chloride ion by most cells not involved in chloride transport; it also is the proximate cause of neuromuscular excitability (see Chapter 25).

As much as one third of the total resting energy of skeletal muscle cells may be directed to powering the sodium pump. When hypoxia or another metabolic insult interferes with their metabolism, cells swell because of dysfunction of the sodium-potassium ATPase pump. The mechanism for this swelling appears to be the entrance of sodium and chloride ions into the cell, producing increased intracellular osmolality, which results in increased intracellular water content as water follows solute. Simultaneously, potassium is lost from the cell, but not in amounts equivalent to that of the entering sodium; thus, a net gain in water results.

ELECTROLYTE HOMEOSTASIS

The importance of electrolyte homeostasis in clinical medicine cannot be overstated. Electrolytes share with water the phenomenon of dissociating into positively and negatively charged ions and, additionally, can variably affect the concentration of hydrogen ion in a solution, contingent both on the individual ion characteristics and on interaction with other completely and partially ionized substances in the solution. Major differences in specific ion characteristics exist between cell fluid (K^+ rich) and extracellular fluid (Na^+ rich). As we have noted, these differences are maintained by a substantial amount of energy, which is expended by cells that drive the sodium-potassium ATPase; these differences are critical to cell metabolism and survival.

The hydrogen ion concentrations of intracellular and extracellular fluid differ slightly. Both stay within narrow ranges because of a complex series of reactions within the organism and the selective ability of the kidney to excrete acid or base loads (see the section on acid-base balance in Chapter 4). Diets vary in the effective amount of acid and base they contain. As a rule, metabolic processes create an additional acid load, which must be excreted to maintain optimum pH. It should be apparent, therefore, that any discussion of electrolyte homeostasis must take these complex relationships into account. Without undue complexity, we will discuss the normal homeostatic mechanism for maintaining balance of water and the dominant electrolytes, sodium and potassium.

Water Balance and Osmoregulation

As we noted in the introduction to this section, changes in volume of cells in the central nervous system usually are associated with significant morbidity. For this reason, it is vital to be able to minimize any differences in the osmolality of the intracellular and extracellular compartments. If plasma osmolality and intracellular osmolality are identical, there will not be an osmotic force driving water either into (hypoosmolality) or out of (hyperosmolality) cells. Sensors located in the hypothalamus can detect increases in plasma osmolality of at least 2%, provoking both release of ADH and the sensation of thirst. A loss of 10% of circulating volume (a typical blood donation removes 5%) also provokes ADH release and markedly intensifies thirst.

Sodium Balance

With an adequate intake of sodium, regulation of sodium concentration of body fluids and of sodium balance primarily is renal. However, sodium balance is not merely a matter of glomerular filtration and of the secretion of sufficient aldosterone to control distal renal tubular reabsorption of sodium. Sodium salts are the primary determinant of the volume and composition of extracellular fluid and indirectly determine the osmolality and composition of cells as well. Extrarenal factors also are important in renal regulation of sodium balance.

In a normal adult of average size, approximately 120 ml of plasma are filtered through glomerular membranes each minute. This filtrate contains not only the electrolytes of plasma in their normal concentration in plasma water but also glucose, urea, uric acid, amino acids, and creatinine. From the daily total of 180 L of glomerular filtrate, more than eight times the total body sodium content and 250 times the average daily intake are reabsorbed. To maintain balance, about 99.5% of the filtered sodium and chloride, virtually all of the bicarbonate, and 92% of the potassium must be reabsorbed with all of the glucose, most of the amino acids, and a substantial portion of urea and uric acid.

INTRARENAL FACTORS CONTROLLING SODIUM BALANCE

Glomerular Filtration Rate

Because 99.5% of filtered sodium normally is reabsorbed, a small change in filtration rate represents a substantial reduction in the filtered load of sodium. With a rise in GFR, there is relatively little increase in sodium excreted, but a fall in GFR results in a disproportionate decrease in sodium excretion. These observations cannot be explained on the basis of what is known about the functions of the glomerulus in forming a plasma ultrafiltrate. Rather, the function of the tubule in sodium reclamation, combined with the observations mentioned previously in the text, led to the concept of *glomerulotubular balance*. Glomerulotubular balance provides a buffering device that enables the kidney to defend against large solute losses or gains that occur when GFR fluctuates. For instance, if GFR increased by as little as 2 ml/minute over a 24-hour period, without the adjustments due to glomerulotubular balance, the sodium excretion would increase by more than 20 g in the same period, which is almost double the average daily sodium intake. However, this protective mechanism does not play a major role in the relatively fine adjustments needed to maintain sodium homeostasis in the absence of prolonged changes in GFR. For further discussion of this fundamental concept of modern nephrology, refer to the sources listed at the end of this chapter.

Tubular Reabsorption

The proximal renal tubule probably is responsible for many of the changes in tubular sodium reabsorption that immediately occur after changes in GFR. The nature of the control of this system presently is unclear. Various mechanisms have been proposed, including linkage of sodium to bicarbonate reabsorption and increased ATP consumption with concomitant increases in Na^+-K^+-ATPase activity and sodium pumping. Aldosterone controls distal tubular sodium reabsorption and potassium secretion. Changes in dietary sodium intake induce reciprocal levels of aldosterone secretion by the adrenals; balance is maintained under normal conditions by this mechanism. Hence, aldosterone secretion results in Na^+ retention. Renin is the stimulus for aldosterone secretion; renin secretion is controlled by the effective arterial blood volume. In essence, arterial blood volume is the major factor regulating Na^+ retention.

EXTRARENAL FACTORS CONTROLLING SODIUM BALANCE

Volume Receptors

Increased renal sodium retention results from either a decrease in left atrial pressure or a decrease in blood volume. Conversely, increased sodium output results from either an increase in left atrial pressure or isotonic volume loading, unless cardiac output is decreased. Most investigators think that these responses result from stretch receptors that are present in the left atrial wall, which influence secretion of vasopressin and renal free water clearance. The precise relationship between the stretch receptors and the neurohumoral response is unclear.

Thirst

Increased osmolality of the ECF, whether due to decreased fluid volume or excessive sodium intake, will result in a sensation of thirst, which originates in the hypothalamus. Consumption of free water will reduce ECF osmolarity and curtail hypothalamic stimulation.

Hormonal Factors

Concomitant with the arousal of a thirst sensation, increased ECF osmolality stimulates hypothalamic osmoreceptors that elicit release of ADH from specialized nerve endings into the posterior pituitary and then into the blood stream. ADH induces increased permeability to water of the distal tubule and collecting duct. In addition, many factors such as sodium depletion and hyperkalemia elicit secretion of the adrenal mineralocorticoid, aldosterone. Aldosterone acts upon the distal tubule to enhance potassium secretion in exchange for sodium reabsorption.

Cardiac muscle cells located in the atria release a hormone that is capable of causing diuresis and natriuresis when the atria are distended. This hormone is called *atrial natriuretic peptide* and appears to act by both increasing GFR and inhibiting secretion of aldosterone. Although these effects of atrial natriuretic peptide are striking in normal subjects, the definitive role that ANF has in ensuring that the circulatory system does not become overfilled is unclear.

Disorders of Sodium Homeostasis

HYPERNATREMIA

As a rule, excessive levels of Na^+ in the body fluids, predominantly the ECF, are secondary to loss of hypoosmotic fluids. A primary hypernatremia (Figure 3.6) rarely is encountered, perhaps in part because of the vomiting induced by hypertonic saline ingestion. The conditions leading to fluid loss may be attributable to one of two basic states: inadequate replacement of obligatory losses or pathologic degrees of loss. As seen in Figure 3.6, water can be lost either alone or in combination with electrolyte; but, in the latter case, the water deficit exceeds that of sodium. In both of these situations, the loss is either via the kidneys or through extrarenal avenues. Addition of sodium to the body, although it can occur, is a less frequent cause of hypernatremia.

As noted, hypernatremia causes neurologic symptoms because brain cells become dehydrated when they lose water to the hypertonic environment that surrounds them. Because water loss by the brain, in a hyperosmolar setting, exceeds loss of electrolyte, the brain shrinks. To counteract these osmotic effects, Na^+ and Cl^- are imported from the ECF, CSF, and plasma, increasing the number of osmotically active particles.

When hypernatremia takes longer than 3 days to develop, it usually is considered to be chronic. In this situation, brain shrinkage is relieved by the accumulation of organic osmolytes, called *idiogenic osmoles*, within neurons and glial cells. Predominant among these idiogenic osmoles are glutamate, glutamine, taurine, and myo-inositol. Glutamate and glutamine are produced within the brain cells, and myo-inositol and taurine appear to be transported into the brain. Once these compounds have accumulated in brain, they depart slowly, accounting for the recommendation that repair of chronic hypernatremia be accomplished over 48 hours.

Critical to understanding clinical states involving hypernatremia is the awareness that such a state usually does not imply increased amounts of total body sodium, but rather increased concentration. Hence, increases in plasma sodium concentration may be found in spite of sodium depletion—recognizing this is vital to a rational therapeutic approach. In keeping with this principle, management of a hypernatremic state should be based upon provision of free water in excess, but not to the exclusion of sodium. An appropriate solution might consist of, for example, 5% dextrose in 0.45% saline; removal of the glucose by the organs will leave free water in amounts ade-

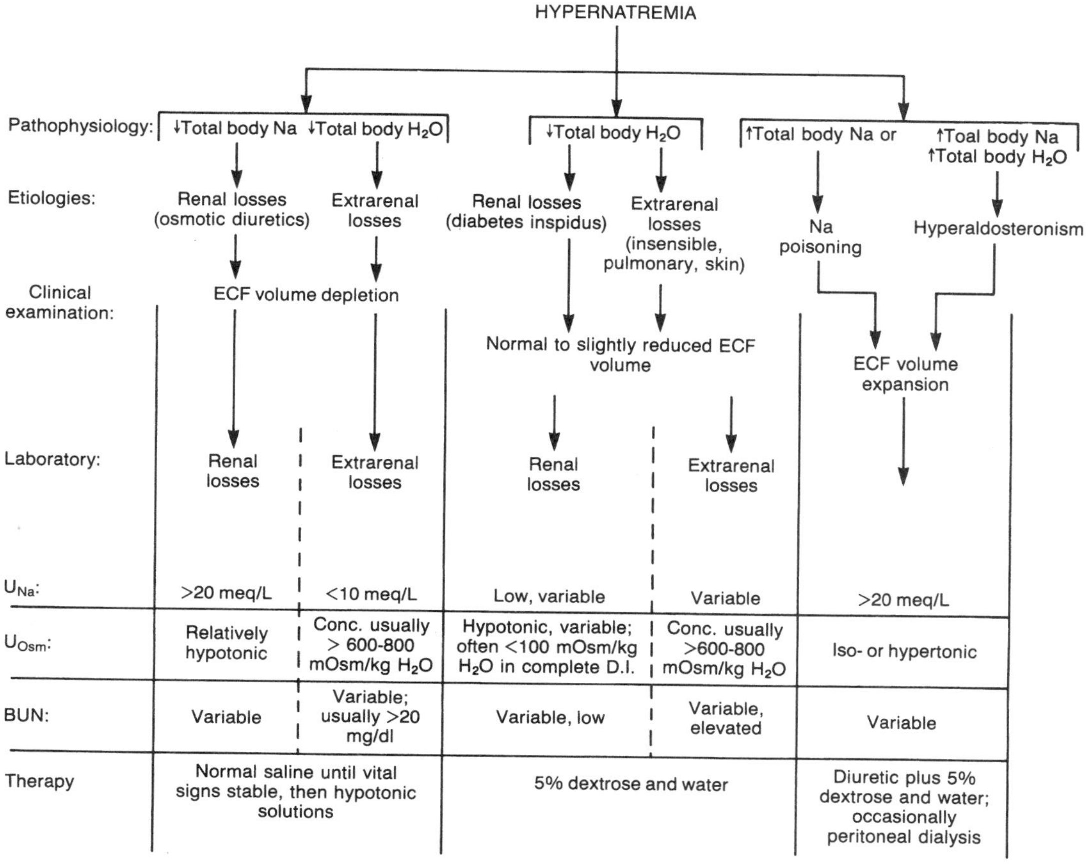

Figure 3.6. The clinical diagnosis and treatment of hypernatremia. Note that the most frequent causes of hypernatremia result in excess fluid loss or decreased fluid intake. Urine osmolality (U_{Osm}) in relation to urine sodium (U_{Na}) is of great value in assessing the state of the extracellular fluid (ECF). Conc. = concentration. Reprinted with permission from Fleisher GR, Ludwig S. Textbook of Pediatric Emergency Medicine. 3rd ed. Baltimore: Williams & Wilkins, 1993:677.

quate to reduce ECF osmolality, and the saline will permit repletion of total body sodium. More details of therapy can be found by referring to the texts listed in the suggested reading section at the end of this chapter.

HYPONATREMIA

Clinically, hyponatremic states are much more common than hypernatremic states. The most common variety of hyponatremia (Figure 3.7) is associated with hypovolemia that is treated inappropriately. In this situation, a decreased effective arterial volume occurs because of renal or extrarenal losses or accumulation of fluid within a "third space" (eg, pancreatitis, trauma, and burn). Regardless of the initial event, hyponatremia cannot develop unless the individual ingests or receives only water to replace the losses, rather than a balanced electrolyte solution. This especially is true during infancy when hyponatremia occurs as a consequence of vomiting and dehydration (eg, gastroenteritis); the hypotonic fluids given to the baby orally do not replace sufficient solute because large losses of both fluid and solute had occurred. Hyponatremia also occurs commonly in the elderly. Still, this may not be enough to maintain a hyponatremic state unless the individual cannot elaborate a dilute urine. Inappropriate secretion of ADH is one of the major derangements that maintain the hyponatremia. In some patients, ineffective water diuresis results from decreased delivery of adequate sodium to the loop of Henle and

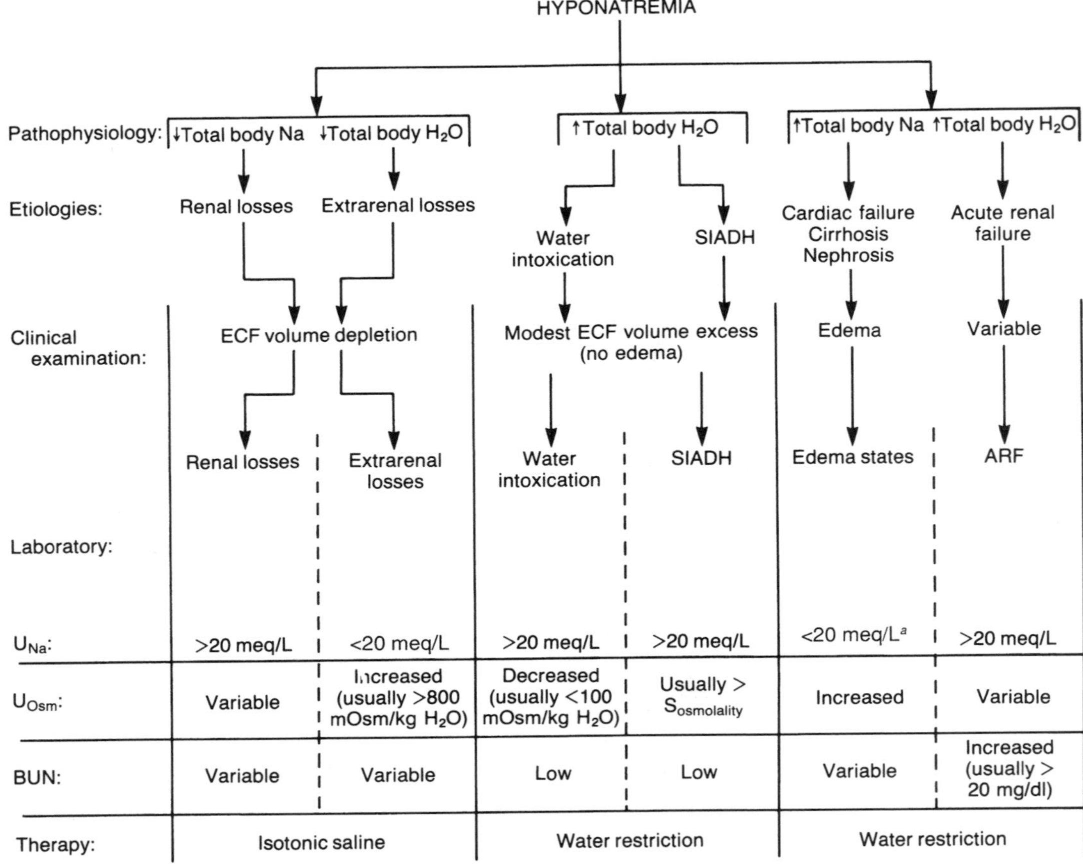

Figure 3.7. The clinical diagnosis and treatment of hyponatremia. It is imperative to distinguish sodium depletion from volume expansion because the erroneous treatment of one is likely to harm the other. Once again, U_{Osm} and U_{Na} aid in this distinction; note that U_{Na} should be measured in the absence of diuretic therapy. The syndrome of inappropriate antidiuretic hormone (SIADH) is a prominent complication of many other pathologic states—SIADH can be rapidly diagnosed by simultaneous measurement of plasma and urine osmolalities. Reprinted with permission from Fleisher GR, Ludwig S. Textbook of Pediatric Emergency Medicine. 3rd ed. Baltimore: Williams & Wilkins, 1993:674.

the distal tubule—the two nephron sites responsible for diluting the urine.

The relatively complete exclusion of sodium from the internal milieu of the cell and its role as the predominant extracellular cation makes sodium particularly vulnerable to depletion in states when extrarenal fluid loss (vomiting, diarrhea, and hemorrhage) is occurring. Low serum sodium concentration also may result from an abnormally high free water intake; in such circumstances, the hyponatremia is not a reflection of decreased total body sodium. When hyponatremia takes a longer time to develop, brain cells are able to extrude KCl, which decreases the tendency of the brain to swell, which regularly occurs in hypoosmolar states.

As noted, hyponatremia is a cardinal feature of a condition known as the syndrome of inappropriate ADH secretion (SIADH). This disorder, usually attributable to central nervous system disease of diverse etiologies, is caused by water retention by the kidneys in response to ADH that is inappropriately secreted, despite a serum osmolality that is markedly diminished. Excretion of a urine higher in osmolality than plasma, when the plasma is slightly lower than normal, is a major diagnostic feature of SIADH. Typically, SIADH is not associated with edema, but the reason may not be obvious. When water conservation in SIADH expands the total body water by 10% or more, a natriuresis ensues. This natriuresis is the result of atrial natriuretic peptide release and decreased proximal tubular reabsorption of sodium; the latter is appropriate to the volume expanded state.

Predictably, in hypoosmolar states, water moves into the brain causing cerebral edema. To counteract this effect, brain gives up solute from both extracellular (EC) and intracellular (IC) compartments, mitigating the initial accumulation of fluid. If the hyponatremia develops over a long enough period (generally longer than 48 hours), this response of the brain may mitigate neurologic symptoms. The chronic adaptation includes loss of organic osmolytes (mainly amino acids) and IC electrolytes.

Choice of a suitable therapeutic regimen for the patient with hyponatremia requires taking a painstaking medical history. Only in this fashion can the total body sodium be estimated on the basis of a probable etiology. More details of treatment can be found by referring to the texts that are listed in the suggested reading section at the end of this chapter.

Disorders of Potassium Homeostasis

Because potassium is the predominant intracellular cation of the body, it is predictable that fluctuations of serum potassium outside the normal range usually will represent large shifts in total body potassium. From a clinical perspective, the most important consequences of abnormalities in plasma potassium concentration stem from potassium's role in creating the resting membrane potential across all cells, particularly nervous and muscle cells. Because, to a first approximation, the resting membrane potential is determined by the difference in the distribution of IC and EC K^+ and accompanying anions, changes in plasma K^+ can have dramatic effects on the membrane potential. With *hypokalemia*, there is an excess of negative charge on the inside of the cell membrane, which causes the membrane to become *hyperpolarized*. In the hyperpolarized state, the cell becomes less sensitive to any signal that would normally trigger an action potential. On the other hand, when *hyperkalemia* prevails, the internal negative charge on the membrane diminishes, falling toward the threshold for *depolarization*. As a consequence, cells in a hyperkalemic milieu become more excitable. The most profound effects of changes in EC K^+ involve cardiac muscle and can cause serious and sometimes life-threatening arrhythmias (eg, ventricular fibrillation).

Thus, fluctuations in K^+ balance usually are accompanied by more drastic clinical findings than those found in disruptions of sodium homeostasis (Table 3.6).

HYPERKALEMIA

Potassium is filtered by the glomerulus and probably is completely reabsorbed in the proximal tubule. Urinary potassium excretion results from K^+ secretion at the distal tubular level, occurring by an Na^+-K^+ exchange mechanism. This mechanism is regulated by aldosterone, which promotes conservation of sodium and excretion of potassium.

In general, any factor impeding the ability of the cell to maintain membrane or metabolic integrity will cause a loss of intracellular K^+ and a corresponding increase in serum potassium. Such entities include crush injury, which is accompanied by alteration or destruction of cell membrane integrity, intravascular hemolysis, and acidosis. Clinically, any one of these disorders may be accompanied by acute renal failure, in which loss of the body's compensatory ability to excrete potassium may have an additive effect on serum potassium levels.

Acute renal failure itself is a common cause of hyperkalemia: The anuric phase totally deprives the body of the major excretory route for potassium and causes hyperkalemia, and the oliguric phase may perpetuate this condition. Proximal tubular damage subsequently may result in excessive losses leading to hypokalemia. Chronic renal failure, however, generally does not cause hyperkalemia, except in the end stage when GFR decreases and tissue catabolism increases.

The differential diagnoses of hyperkalemia including elevation of potassium due to improper handling of specimen or laboratory errors are listed in Table 3.7. Hyperkalemia may be defined as a serum potassium greater than 5.5 mEq/l. Note that glycogen breakdown may cause elevation of serum potassium. This can be rapidly reversed by the administration of insulin; when overlooked,

Table 3.6. Consequences of Disturbances in Potassium Homeostasis

ORGAN SYSTEM	HYPERKALEMIA	HYPOKALEMIA
Neuromuscular and Psychiatric	Ascending paralysis Flaccid paralysis Dysarthria Weakness	Weakness Myalgia Flaccid paralysis Depressive reaction Disorientation, confusion
Cardiovascular	Hypotension Arrhythmias Cardiac arrest	Arrhythmias Hypotension Potentiation of digitalis effect
Renal	Oliguria Uremic syndrome	Polyuria Sodium retention Paradoxical aciduria Edema
Gastrointestinal	Paralytic ileus Nausea, vomiting Abdominal pain	Paralytic ileus Decreased gastric acidity Growth retardation

this results in the development of hypokalemia during treatment of diabetic ketoacidosis. Physical findings of hyperkalemia result from abnormal neuromuscular function (see Chapter 25). By reducing the ratio between EC K^+ and IC K^+, hyperkalemia depolarizes excitable cells and makes them more excitable. Still, hyperkalemia is not consistently associated with EKG abnormalities; however, any laboratory value suggesting hyperkalemia requires an EKG tracing on the patient. If hyponatremia, hypocalcemia, or acidosis, alone or in combination, also is present, cardiac toxicity may be manifested at lower levels of serum potassium. The evolution of changes in the EKG are as follows: tall, peaked T wave; decreased T-T interval and increasing P-R interval; heart block; and cardiac standstill. Therapy to treat this disorder should be judiciously administered; details can be found by referring to the texts that are listed in the suggested reading section at the end of this chapter.

Table 3.7. Causes of Hyperkalemia

Decreased Potassium Excretion by Kidney
- Oliguric acute and chronic renal failure
- Use of potassium-sparing diuretics
- Mineralocorticoid deficiency (Addison's disease, congenital adrenal hyperplasia)

Excessive Potassium Intake
- Salt substitutes; oral KCl supplementation
- Intravenous potassium administration
  - Rapid infusion during fluid replacement therapy
  - Outdated blood

Shift of Intracellular Potassium to Extracellular Space
- Metabolic acidosis or acute respiratory acidosis
- Massive trauma or infection with widespread tissue damage
- Cytotoxic agents (eg, antimetabolites)
- Fresh water drowning
- Hyperkalemic periodic paralysis

Artifactual Elevation
- Specimen improperly obtained or mishandled in laboratory resulting in hemolysis

HYPOKALEMIA

Hypokalemia, represented by a serum potassium of less than 3.5 mEq/l, is most commonly associated with excessive urinary or gastrointestinal loss of potassium (Table 3.8). A low serum value may reflect depletion of total body potassium; but, in acute situations, hypokalemia may indicate only a shift into the cells. For example, this shift may occur in alkalosis and in insulin therapy.

Vomiting and diarrhea probably are the most common causes of hypokalemia because they result in excessive loss through the gastrointestinal tract. In general, secretions of the gastrointestinal tract contain large quantities of potassium and other electrolytes (see the chapter that discusses the gastrointestinal tract), which normally are reabsorbed. If the reabsorptive process fails, rapid depletion of total body potassium will occur. In addition, the volume depletion that occurs with these losses will elicit aldosterone secretion, and an acceleration of renal potassium secretion will result instead of sodium reabsorption.

Table 3.8. Causes of Hypokalemia

Increased Potassium Excretion by Kidney
Renal disease
Diuretic phase of acute renal failure, relief of urinary tract obstruction
Distal renal tubular acidosis
Fanconi syndrome (proximal RTA)
Bartter's syndrome
Interstitial nephritis
Pyelonephritis
Extrinsic renal causes
Diabetes mellitus
Diuretics (non-K sparing)
Hyperosmolar solutions (eg, mannitol, hypertonic glucose, urea)
Loading with hypertonic saline
Abnormalities of endocrine regulation
Cushing's disease
Primary aldosteronism
Secondary aldosteronism (hypertension, nephritis, etc.)
Drug-induced
Diuretics
Nonreabsorbable anion loads (penicillin)
Aspirin
Hypomagnesemia or hypercalcemia
Gastrointestinal Losses
Vomiting and diarrhea (severe)
Fistula or prolonged G.I. suctioning
Chronic laxative abuse
Frequent use of ion exchange resins
Malnutrition (<30 mEq/K$^+$/m^2/day)
Protein-caloric malnutrition
Prolonged I.V. alimentation with K$^+$-free fluids
Extracellular K$^+$ Shifts into Cells
Total parenteral nutrition
Alkalosis
Drugs
Familial Hypokalemia

The renal causes of hypokalemia are legion and include a variety of renal tubular syndromes, pyelonephritis, and the diuretic phase of acute renal failure (Table 3.8). The general attribute associated with each cause is the failure of normal tubular K$^+$ reabsorption. In addition, the osmotic diuresis of diabetic or iatrogenic glucosuria will accelerate tubular urine flow and diminish potassium reabsorption. In hypokalemic states, predictably the cell becomes hyperpolarized, which should make it less excitable. But, the cells soon become depolarized because hypokalemia reduces the usual permeability of neuromuscular cells. As a result, the duration of the relative refractory period is increased, as well as the risk of development of an arrhythmia.

Details of diagnosis and therapy of these disorders are beyond the scope of this discussion and may be found by referring to the texts listed in the suggested reading section at the end of this chapter.

Chloride, Bicarbonate, and the Anion Gap

The details of anion gap metabolic acidosis have been covered elsewhere in this text (see Chapter 4). The purpose of this section is to briefly summarize the relationship to acid-base homeostasis.

In any normal individual, there is a difference between serum Na^+ (the major extracellular cation) and the sum of serum Cl^- and HCO_3^- (the major extracellular anions). This difference is partially due to the presence of organic acids, the end products of metabolism, that contribute hydrogen ions and organic anions to the serum. Another portion of this difference (gap) is attributable to phosphate salts; but, we will not focus on this contribution for purposes of our present discussion. Because HCO_3^- is a major source of buffering anions in blood, addition of organic acids results in a decrease in HCO_3^-, and, ultimately, replacement of HCO_3^- by the unmeasured organic anion. Thus, the sum of the measured anions diminishes, and the gap between this sum and the serum sodium concentration increases.

Hyperchloremic acidosis, in which there is addition of strong acid (HCl) to the serum also results in a drop in serum HCO_3^-; this clearly is in contrast to the situation described previously in the text. This change, however, is offset by the increase in Cl^-, with no net change in the sum of serum anions. Thus, there is no increase in the anion gap. Hyperchloremic acidosis is characteristic of *renal tubular acidosis*.

DISORDERS OF AMINO ACID TRANSPORT

All plasma cell membranes can transport solutes from the extracellular to the intracellular environment. In fact, the transport of solutes across the cell membrane initiates the metabolism of many compounds, and most cells derive their nutrient material from the extracellular environment. Besides the ubiquity of such transport systems in all cells, a microvillus brush border uniquely equips cell membranes in the intestine and in the renal proximal tubule for transport because it greatly enhances the absorptive surface of the cells. It is at this brush border site where the various transporters for amino acids and other solutes are localized. These specialized cells are responsible for reabsorption or absorption of compounds from the lumen of the renal tubule or of the intestine and move these solutes across the cell into the blood stream. Thus, normal function of these cells is essential for the homeostatic maintenance of the entire organism.

Many inherited disorders have been described in which the function of one of the transporters in microvillus membranes of the proximal renal tubule cells and of the intestinal mucosa is abnormal. Many of these disorders, therefore, affect both the intestinal absorptive and the renal reabsorptive capabilities in the same patient. These genetic disorders of amino acid transport are among the most common inherited abnormalities. They include cystinuria (in its classic and variant forms), Hartnup's disease, iminoglycinuria, methionine, and tryptophan malabsorption syndromes. In addition, many diseases with diverse etiologies result in combined aminoaciduria, glycosuria, and phosphaturia, which is a constellation known as the renal Fanconi syndrome.

Disorders of Cystine and Dibasic Amino Acid Transport

CYSTINURIA

The most common inherited disorder of amino acid transport is classic cystinuria, which has been recognized since the early nineteenth century. It also has the highest morbidity because urinary tract cystine stones are formed and complications of pain, hematuria, and occasionally obstruction of the urinary tract are anticipated. Classic cystinuria is characterized by elevated urinary excretion of cystine, lysine, ornithine, arginine, and a cysteine-homocysteine disulfide. Diagnosis depends on demonstration of the typical pattern of amino acid excretion, not on the presence of urinary calculi or any of the concomitant clinical findings. Nevertheless, in most instances, patients will be suspected of having cystinuria because of symptoms associated with calculus formation. Abundant evidence has established that the excessive excretion of cystine and dibasic amino acids in these patients is due to an autosomal recessive genetic defect in the transport of these amino acids.

The tendency to form stones stems from excessive amounts of cystine in the urine, which is the least soluble of all naturally occurring amino acids. Cystine solubility is about 300 mg/L of urine at pH <7.5. Patients who form stones excrete over 250 mg per gram of creatinine, with total, 24-hour excretion of cystine ranging from 0.5 g to more than 1.5 g. Crystalluria and a tendency to stone formation are more likely to occur during hours of sleep when little water is ingested and urine volumes are small. Renal dysfunction in these patients is due to cystine calculus formation; no abnormality results from hyperexcretion of lysine, arginine, and ornithine.

Screening studies of newborns for cystinuria establish the incidence of homozygous disease at about 1 in 7000 births. Affected individuals usually present in the second, third, and fourth decades of life with signs and symptoms of urinary tract stones. Cystine calculi, however, have been found in patients as early as the first year of life and as late as in the ninth decade. The stones formed usually are composed of only cystine, but many contain other substances as well. Urate or oxalate stones occasionally are observed with cystinuria. In these cases, the nidus of the stone usually is cystine. Examination of the urine for typical hexagonal crystals of cystine can be very helpful in making the diagnosis.

The cyanide nitroprusside test is the most reliable screening procedure for detecting excessive cystine in the urine; a burgundy color reaction is produced when cystine concentrations are greater than 75 mg/l. Ideally, this test should be performed on a portion of urine that had been collected over a 24-hour period, which, if positive, can be quantitated for cystine and the dibasic amino acids.

Because the kidney damage that occurs with cystinuria is directly related to the excessive amounts of relatively insoluble cystine in the urine, any treatment regimen must focus either on decreasing cystine excretion or increasing its solubility. The simplest way to increase solubility is to increase the amount of solvent in which the cystine is dissolved. Practically, this means increasing the fluid intake to as much as 4 L per day to maintain urinary cystine below 300 mg/l. This regimen requires that patients imbibe water at least once a night and has been successful in up to 70% of patients in some series. Of course, its success depends on the patient's ability to maintain a regimen of generous fluid intake.

Alkalinization of the urine has been used as an adjunct for increasing cystine solubility. Success of this method depends on increasing the urine pH above 7.5, at which point cystine solubility increases appreciably. Typically, 40 to 60 ml qid of Shohl's solution is administered orally, but it is not easy to maintain an alkaline urine with a pH above 7.5 for long periods, which detracts from the efficacy of this method.

An effective therapeutic approach that decreases the actual excretion of cystine by forming more soluble mixed disulfide compounds uses D-penicillamine (β,β-dimethylcysteine). Oral administration of penicillamine to cystinuric patients results in the excretion of a product of a disulfide exchange (cysteine-penicillamine disulfide) in urine. Penicillamine administration also decreases plasma cysteine levels and leads to the salutary effect of decreasing urinary excretion of cystine because the filtered load presented to the kidney is diminished. As a consequence of both of these effects, the amount of urinary cystine is markedly decreased. The goal to maintain urinary cystine levels below 200 mg/g of creatinine usually can be accomplished by administration of 1 to 2 g of D-penicillamine per day in three or four equally divided doses. Although effective in preventing stone formation, D-penicillamine use does result in significant side effects including fever; rash; arthralgias; and rare, severe, hypersensitivity reactions.

HYPERDIBASIC AMINOACIDURIA (LYSINURIC PROTEIN INTOLERANCE)

Lysinuric protein intolerance is a defect of diamino acid transport expressed in both kidney and intestine and is characterized by failure to thrive, anorexia, vomiting, hepatosplenomegaly, abnormal liver function, and postprandial hyperammonemia. Inheritance is autosomal recessive. In contrast to cystinuria, cystine excretion is characteristically normal with low to normal plasma levels of lysine, ornithine, and arginine, but enormously elevated urinary levels of these three amino acids. Hyperammonemia is thought to be due to decreased intestinal absorption of lysine, ornithine, and arginine, creating a depletion of body stores. This results in a slowing of the urea cycle because of the ornithine deficiency, with consequent build-up of ammonia. Under normal circumstances, ornithine acts as the initial ammonia acceptor in the urea cycle, and arginine cleavage yields urea while regenerating ornithine. In patients with lysinuric protein intolerance, supplementation of the diet with either argininine or ornithine should normalize urea production when a normal diet is ingested. This is successful because of the remarkable increase in growth in affected children treated in this way.

Disorders of Neutral Amino Acid Transport

HARTNUP DISEASE

Hartnup disease is characterized by a pellagra-like skin rash, a reversible cerebellar ataxia that usually is most severe when skin lesions are florid, frequent and persistent headache, psychiatric symptoms ranging from emotional lability to frank delirium and hallucinations, and constant neutral aminoaciduria of renal origin.

A variety of physiologic stresses, including intercurrent febrile illness and inadequate nutrition, can cause aggravation of the clinical features with repeat episodes in childhood. The pivotal role of nutrition in these exacerbations, coupled with diminution in both frequency and severity of attacks as affected children get older, suggests relative deficiency of some dietary component during the rapid growth phases of childhood. Indoleacetic acid, a degradation product of tryptophan metabolism, generally is present in the urine of these patients, especially during periods of clinical relapse. Large amounts of the parent compound tryptophan also are present. Because the major fate of tryptophan is conversion to nicotinic acid and NAD, the conclusion that either tryptophan or niacin is relatively deficient in Hartnup disease is supported. Renal clearances of the neutral amino acids, including alanine, serine, threonine, valine, leucine, isoleucine, phenylalanine, tyrosine, tryptophan, histidine, glutamine, and asparagine, ranging from 8- to 20-fold normal levels in the presence of normal plasma amino acid levels, is characteristic of this disorder. These data indicate a defect of reabsorption of neutral amino acids in renal tubule cells. Subsequently, it was demonstrated that patients with Hartnup disease have a defect in intestinal absorption of tryptophan. It also has been shown that oligopeptides containing tryptophan, in combination with other amino acids, are absorbed normally in the intestines in these patients, accounting for the relative rather than absolute deficiency of tryptophan in affected patients.

Definitive diagnosis of Hartnup disease depends on urinary amino acid chromatography. Quantification of amino acid excretion is not necessary because the pattern of amino acids excreted in excess is pathognomonic of the disease.

Because the clinical findings appear to derive from inefficient intestinal absorption and increased urinary losses of amino acids, the most rational and innocuous treatment is to start the patient on a high protein regimen. Supplementation of the high protein diet with 40 to 200 mg of oral nicotinamide per day is appropriate because the treatment usually produces marked improvement in both skin and central nervous system involvement.

Fanconi Syndrome

The renal Fanconi syndrome is a generalized tubular dysfunction consisting of mellituria, generalized aminoaciduria, hyposthenuria, phosphaturia, hypercalciuria, hypernatriuria, proximal renal tubular acidosis with bicarbonaturia, proteinuria, and vitamin D-resistant rickets. Although Fanconi syndrome usually is thought of as secondary in a variety of diseases, both inherited and acquired, the underlying etiology eludes the physician in a significant number of cases. These cases of idiopathic Fanconi syndrome, although they do not have a well-established genetic basis, have been reported to be both autosomal recessive and autosomal dominant traits. It behooves the physician to undertake an extensive search for the cause in each case before labeling the patient with the diagnosis of "idiopathic" Fanconi syndrome. In childhood, the most commonly seen type is the secondary form; cystinosis occurs more frequently with this form than with the other potential causes that are listed in Table 3.9.

The hallmark of the Fanconi syndrome is a generalized aminoaciduria, which is unlike the specific genetic amino acid transport disorders that we previously have described. In Fanconi syndrome, there is no apparent selectivity, and amino acids of the acidic, basic, neutral, and iminoglycine groups are excreted in excess. Because of the global nature of the transport defect (amino acids, ions, hexoses, etc), the various transport systems must be affected in a way that destroys their ability to harness energy required for the transport process.

Recent evidence, which was obtained by using a rat kidney model produced by treatment with succinylacetone, suggests that changes occur at both the membrane and mitochondrial levels and, when combined, contribute to the clinical dysfunction. Succinylacetone, which is produced endogenously from tyrosine in individuals with hereditary tyrosinemia with the Fanconi syndrome, causes inhibition of membrane transport of sugars, amino acids, and sodium. Changes also occur in membrane fluidity, and there is

Table 3.9. Etiologies of the Fanconi Syndrome

GENETIC/METABOLIC	ACQUIRED/TOXIC
Idiopathic	Acute tubular necrosis
Cystinosis	Chemical ingestion
Busby's syndrome	Lysol
Galactosemia	Maleic acid (in rats)
Hereditary fructose intolerance	Nitrobenzene
Glycogen storage disease, type I	Chemical ingestion
Lowe's syndrome	Salicylates
Luder-Sheldon syndrome	Tetracycline (outdated)
Nephrotic syndrome (congenital)	Methyl-3-chromosome
Osteogenesis imperfecta	Streptozotocin
Renal tubular acidosis	Severe burns
Sickle cell disease	Heavy metal poisoning
Spherocytosis	Bismuth
Thalassemia	Cadmium
Tyrosinemia	Lead
Wilson's disease	Mercury
	Uranium
	Severe hypokalemia
	Protein malnutrition
	Hyperparathyroidism
	Vitamin deficiency (B_{12}, C, D)
	Multiple myeloma
	Transplant rejection

decreased mitochondrial oxygen consumption. These data are important because they demonstrate that treatment of normal renal tissue by an endogenous substrate can reproduce the tubular dysfunction. Hence, the only known true physiologic model is represented.

SUGGESTED READINGS

GENERAL

Brenner BM, Rector FC, eds. The kidney. 4th ed. Philadelphia: WB Saunders, 1991.

Massry SG, Glassock RJ, eds. Textbook of nephrology. 3rd ed. Baltimore: Williams & Wilkins, 1995.

Schrier RW, Gottschalk CW, eds. Diseases of the kidney. 5th ed. Boston: Little, Brown & Co., 1993.

Seldin DW, Giebisch G, eds. The kidney: physiology and pathophysiology. 2nd ed. New York: Raven Press, 1992.

STRUCTURE AND FUNCTION

Briere N, Magny P. Scanning electron microscopic observations of human fetal kidney maturing in vivo and in serum-free organ culture. Anat Rec 1993;235: 461.

Couchman JR, Abrahamson DR, McCarthy KJ. Basement membrane proteoglycans and development. Kidney Int 1993;43:79.

Kilberg MS, Stevens BR, Novak DA. Recent advances in mammalian amino acid transport. Annu Rev Nutr 1993;13:137.

Lee SJ, Sparke J, Howie AJ. The mammalian glomerulotubular junction studied by scanning and transmission electron microscopy. J Anat 1993;182: 177.

Myers BD, Guasch A. Selectivity of the glomerular filtration barrier in healthy and nephrotic humans. Am J Nephrol 1993;13:311.

Preuss HG. Basics of renal anatomy and physiology. Clin Lab Med 1993;13:1.

Rosenblum ND. The mesangial matrix in the normal and sclerotic glomerulus. Kidney Int Suppl 1994;45:S73.

Weber M. Basement Membrane Proteins. Kidney Int 1992;41:620.

PROXIMAL TUBULE

Beck JS, Laprade R, Lapointe JY. Coupling between transepithelial Na transport and basolateral K conductance in renal proximal tubule (editorial). Am J Physiol 1994;266:F517.

Biber J, Murer H. Towards a molecular view of renal proximal tubular reabsorption of phosphate. Renal Physiol Biochem 1993;16:37.

Custer M, Meier F, Schlatter E, et al. Localization of NaPi-1, a Na-Pi cotransporter, in rabbit kidney proximal tubules. I. mRNA localization by reverse transcription/polymerase chain reaction. Pflügers Archiv 1993;424:203.

LOOP OF HENLE

DuBose TD Jr, Good DW. Role of the thick ascending limb and inner medullary collecting duct in the regulation of urinary acidification. Semin Nephrol 1991;11:120.

Greger R, Bleich M, Schlatter E. Ion channel regulation in the thick ascending limb of the loop of Henle. Kidney Int Suppl 1991;33:S119.

Igarashi P, Reilly RF, Hildebrandt F, et al. Molecular biology of renal $Na(^+)$-H^+ exchangers. Kidney Int Suppl 1991;33:S84.

Imai M, Yoshitomi K. Heterogeneity of the descending thin limb of Henle's loop. Kidney Int 1990;38:687.

Kon V, Badr KF. Biological actions and pathophysiologic significance of endothelin in the kidney (editorial). Kidney Int 1991;40:1.

Kondo Y, Kudo K, Igarashi Y, et al. Functions of ascending thin limb of Henle's loop with special emphasis on mechanism of NaCl transport. Tohoku J Exp Med 1992;166:75.

Lang F, Rehwald W. Potassium channels in renal epithelial transport regulation. Physiol Rev 1992;72:1-32.

Sizeland PC, Chambers ST, Lever M, et al. Organic osmolytes in human and other mammalian kidneys. Kidney Int 1993;43:448.

MECHANISM OF URINARY CONCENTRATION

Chernoff R. Thirst and fluid requirements. Nutr Rev 1994;52:S3.

Joles JA, Rabelink TJ, Braam B, et al. Plasma volume regulation: defenses against edema formation (with special emphasis on hypoproteinemia). Am J Nephrol 1993;13:399.

Schafer JA. Salt and water homeostasis—Is it just a matter of good bookkeeping? 1993 Homer W. Smith Award. J Am Soc Nephrol 1994;4:1929.

Schrier RW, Niederberger M. Paradoxes of body fluid volume regulation in health and disease. A unifying hypothesis. West J Med 1994;161:393.

Wade JB. Role of membrane traffic in the water and Na^+ responses to vasopressin. Semin Nephrol 1994;14:322.

PATHOLOGIC STATES OF THE NEPHRON

Bohle A, Strutz F, Muller GA. On the pathogenesis of chronic renal failure in primary glomerulopathies: a view from the interstitium (editorial). Exp Nephrol 1994;2:205.

Brezis M, Epstein FH. Cellular mechanisms of acute ischemic injury in the kidney. Annu Rev Med. 1993; 44:27.

Brezis M, Rosen S. Hypoxia and the renal medulla—its implications for disease. N Engl J Med. 1995;332:647.

Bricker NS, Fine LG, Kaplan M, et al. "Magnification phenomenon" in chronic renal disease. N Engl J Med 1978;299:1287.

Buckalew VM, Jr. Pathophysiology of progressive renal failure. South Med J 1994;87:1028.

Cumming AD. Acute renal failure and sepsis: therapeutic approaches. Nephrol Dial Transplant 1994;9(suppl 4): 159.

Fish EM, Molitoris BM. Alterations in epithelial polarity and the pathogenesis of disease states. N Engl J Med 1994;330:1580.

Groeneveld AB. Pathogenesis of acute renal failure during sepsis. Nephrol Dial Transplant 1994;9(suppl 4):47.

Iaiana A, Schwartz D. Renal tubular cellular and molecular events in acute renal failure. Nephron 1994;68:413.

Jelkmann W. Biology of erythropoietin. Clinical Investigation 1994;72(suppl 6):S3.

Keane WF. Lipids and the kidney. Kidney Int 1994;46:910.

Laffi G, La Villa G, Gentilini P. Pathogenesis of the hepatorenal syndrome. Semin Liver Dis 1994;14:71.

Molitoris BA, Geerdes A, McIntosh JR. Dissociation and redistribution of the Na^+, K^+-ATPase from its surface membrane actin cytoskeletal complex during cellular ATP depletion. J Clin Invest 1991;88:462.

Nissenson AR. Erythropoietin overview—1993. Blood Purif 1994;12:6.

Ridley DM, Dawkins F, Perlin E. Erythropoietin: a review. J Natl Med Assoc 1994;86:129.

Schrier RW, Burke TJ. New aspects in pathogenesis of acute renal failure. Nephrol Dial Transplant 1994; 9(suppl 4):9.

Spivak JL. The clinical physiology of erythropoietin. Semin Hematol 1994;30(suppl 6):2.

Teschan PE. Uremia: an overview. Semin Nephrol 1994; 14:199.

Textor SC. Pathophysiology of renal failure in renovascular disease. Am J Kidney Dis 1994;24:642.

Wardle EN. Acute renal failure and multiorgan failure. Nephrol Dial Transplant 1994;9(suppl 4):104.

PROTEINURIA

Beetham R, Cattell WR. Proteinuria: pathophysiology, significance and recommendations for measurement in clinical practice. Ann Clin Biochem 1993;30:425.

Garella S. Pathophysiology and clinical implications of proteinuria. Nephrol Dial Transplant 1990;5(suppl 1): 10.

Vehaskari VM. Mechanism of orthostatic proteinuria. Pediatr Nephrol 1990;4:328.

UROLITHIASIS

Berland Y, Dussol B. New insights into renal stone formation. Curr Opin Nephrol Hypertens 1994;3:417.

Cao LC, Boeve ER, de Bruijn WC, et al. A review of new concepts in renal stone research. Scanning Microsc 1993;7:1049.

FLUID AND ELECTROLYTE HOMEOSTASIS

Arieff AI, Ayus JC. Treatment of symptomatic hyponatremia: neither haste nor waste (editorial). Crit Care Med 1991;19:748.

Berry PL, Belsha CW. Hyponatremia. Pediatr Clin North Am 1990;37:351.

Brem AS. Disorders of potassium homeostasis. Pediatr Clin North Am 1990;37:419-427.

Clapham DE. Potassium and tissue excitability. In: Seldin DW, Gerhard G, eds. The regulation of potassium balance. New York: Raven Press, 1989:57.

Cluitmans FHM, Meinders AE. Management of severe hyponatremia: rapid or slow correction? Am J Med 1990;88:161.

Conley SB. Hypernatremia. Pediatr Clin North Am 1990; 37:365.

Cserr HF, DePasquale M, Nicholson C. Extracellular volume decreases while cell volume is maintained by ion uptake in rat brain during acute hypernatremia. J Physiol 1991;442:277.

DeVita MV, Michelis MF. Perturbations in sodium balance. Hyponatremia and hypernatremia. Clin Lab Med 1993; 13:135.

Eiam-Ong S, Lonis B, Kurtzman NA, Sabatini S. The biochemical basis of hypokalemic metabolic alkalosis. Trans Assoc Am Physicians 1992;105:157.

Gruskin AB, Sarnaik A. Hyponatremia: pathophysiology and treatment, a pediatric perspective. Pediatr Nephrol 1992;6:280.

Gullans SR, Verbalis JG. Control of brain volume during hyperosmolar and hypoosmolar conditions. Annu Rev Med 1993;44:289.

Hill LL. Body composition, normal electrolyte concentrations, and the maintenance of normal volume, tonicity, and acid-base metabolism. Pediatr Clin North Am 1990;37:241.

Kamel KS, Bear RA. Treatment of hyponatremia: a quantitative analysis. Am J Kidney Dis 1993;21:439.

Kamel KS, Quaggin S, Scheich A, Halperin ML. Disorders of potassium homeostasis: an approach based on pathophysiology. Am J Kidney Dis 1994;24:597.

Kupin WL, Narins RG. The hyperkalemia of renal failure: pathophysiology, diagnosis and therapy. Contrib Nephrol 1993;102:1.

Mulloy AL, Caruana RJ. Hyponatremic emergencies. Endocrine Emergencies 1995;79:155.

Schrier RW. Body fluid volume regulation in health and disease: a unifying hypothesis. Ann Intern Med 1990; 113:155.

Soleimani M, Hattabaugh YJ, Bizal GL. Acute regulation of Na^+/H^+ exchange, $Na+:HCO_3^-$ cotransport, and Cl-/ base exchange in acid base disorders. J Lab Clin Med 1994;124:69.

Sterns RH. Treating hyponatremia: why haste makes waste (editorial). South Med J 1994;87:1283.

DISORDERS OF AMINO ACID TRANSPORT

Candito M, Vianey-Saban C, Ferraci JP, et al. Lysinuric protein intolerance. Urinary amino acid excretion at 2 and 9 days of age. J Inherit Metab Dis 1994;17:252.

Furlong TJ, Stiel D. Decreased uptake of L-cystine by duodenal brush border membrane vesicles from patients with cystinuria. Aust N Z J Med 1993;23:258.

Milliner DS. Cystinuria. Endocrinol Metab Clin North Am 1990;19:889.

chapter **4**

Acid-Base Physiology and Its Abnormalities

Hydrogen bonding (see Chapter 1) is a key force that maintains the structural integrity of biologic molecules. The structure of all proteins, including enzymes, is a critical determinant of function and is extremely sensitive to local hydrogen ion concentration. Thus, hydrogen ion concentration must be maintained within tight limits to not disrupt enzyme and membrane carrier function. Failure to do this will cripple enzyme-mediated reactions within the cell, leading to cell death. Limits of pH compatible with life generally are in the range of 7.0 to 7.8, which represents a change in hydrogen ion concentration of merely 86 nEq/liter. In terms of compatibility with life, the body is 100,000 and 1,000,000 times more sensitive to changes in extracellular $[H^+]$ concentration than to changes in potassium concentration and in sodium concentration, respectively. After discussing the remarkable efficiency of the kidney in regulating sodium and potassium reabsorption from the glomerular filtrate (Chapter 3), it is easy to imagine the multiple ways the kidney regulates hydrogen ion homeostasis.

It should be self-evident to the reader that defenses must be available against processes both internal and external to the cell that would incur dramatic changes in pH. Countermeasures must be prepared to act rapidly (buffering and respiratory compensation), and slowly and chronically (renal compensation). All of these factors have contributed to the evolution of a system well-adapted to deal with most situations. Yet, the multiplicity of needs has contributed to the complexity of the system, as well.

ENDOGENOUS ACIDS AND THE BICARBONATE BUFFER SYSTEM

Considering that the pH represents a convenient scale of expressing hydrogen ion concentration ($pH = -\log [H^+]$), we begin by highlighting the metabolic processes that tend to alter hydrogen ion concentration. The most significant contribution to H^+ balance comes from the cellular oxidation of substrates that produce carbon dioxide. Given a total daily CO_2 production in the range of 13,000 to 15,000 millimoles (mmol), it is obvious that normal metabolic processes are hazardous to life because of the vast amount of potential acid (carbonic acid) produced. As a standard for comparison, a 1 L bottle of Pepsi Cola contains 773 mmol/L of dissolved CO_2. It also is important to recognize that the solubility of gases varies with temperature and pressure; as temperature decreases, solubility of the gas increases. A striking example of this is the bubbling of an uncapped bottle of Pepsi Cola that occurs at temperatures much lower than normal body temperature. Accordingly, if CO_2 dissolved in the blood behaved like that in soda, very little gas could be dissolved, and the gas that was dissolved would form bubbles in microscopic vessels and, hence, would be dangerous. Indeed, this is the basic pathophysiologic event that occurs with the "bends," which all underwater divers fear, although it is dissolved nitrogen, rather than CO_2, that forms the bubbles in this situation.

Lungs Make a Physiologic Bicarbonate Buffer System Possible

Like all gases, CO_2 is soluble in water; under given conditions, the amount of CO_2 dissolved in a given volume of water is predictable. It is remarkable, however, that CO_2 spontaneously combines with water to form the weak acid, carbonic acid:

$$CO_2 + H_2O \leftarrow H_2CO_3 \leftarrow H^+ + HCO_3^-$$

Given the presence of the enzyme carbonic anhydrase (in at least small amounts) in most tissues, including the placenta, it is clear how useful this reversible series of reactions can be in hydrogen ion and CO_2 regulation.

We see yet again a superb illustration of the ingeniousness of evolution: because CO_2 always is created from energy-producing processes (particularly the tricarboxylic acid [TCA] cycle) evolution has found a way to utilize CO_2 as a buffer (asset) rather than allow it to become a burden on other homeostatic mechanisms. Because CO_2 quickly diffuses through biologic membranes on the basis of its partial pressure differential, it rapidly leaves the actively oxidizing cell and enters the interstitial fluid. While diffusing into the blood, it encounters the red cell that possesses considerable carbonic anhydrase activity and is, therefore, well-equipped to produce large quantities of bicarbonate. Moreover, because the reaction is freely reversible, any excess bicarbonate can be reconverted to CO_2 to be excreted by the lungs. Loss of CO_2 via the lungs accounts for the term "open system," which describes the bicarbonate buffer system and signifies that the lungs can dispose of CO_2 to compensate for the constant contribution by metabolic processes. It is this potential for constant equilibration that prevents the blood from behaving like an uncapped bottle of Pepsi Cola because undissolved CO_2 is either rapidly expired or converted to bicarbonate. If the tremendous capacity of the renal tubule to produce bicarbonate is considered, again expedited by carbonic anhydrase, it becomes obvious that the system can be adjusted another way.

Thus, a buffer solution mitigates change in pH, transforming strong acids or bases to weak ones and their salts. The bicarbonate solution described previously within the text meets the requirement to be a buffer. For example, addition of dilute HCl, which is completely ionized, would drive the reaction to the left, in the direction of $H_2CO_3^-$, leading to final production of CO_2 for pulmonary excretion and Cl^-, which then is combined with Na^+ and K^+ to form salts. In other words, the system has transformed a potentially devastating increase in hydrogen ion into CO_2 (which can be eliminated by the lungs), water, and salts. By these measures, the body increases its ability to tolerate potential changes in H^+ by more than 100,000 times. Although a buffer solution is most effective at mitigating pH shifts when its initial pH (7.35–7.45 in blood) is the same as its pKa, this limitation for the $HCO_3^-/H_2CO_3^-$ system, with a pKa of 6.1, is overridden by the body's ability to eliminate CO_2 via the lungs. Although achievement of such efficiency is not equal to the discovery of the mythological Philosopher's Stone, it certainly comes close!

By examining the physical laws that govern the behavior of gases in solution, we can make useful assumptions about the behavior of CO_2 in the body. Under environmental conditions that are compatible with human life, the pO_2/pCO_2 relationship of inspired air will be relatively constant, as will the atmospheric pressure of the air itself. The volume of solvent into which the gas can be dissolved also will remain more or less constant, and the temperature of the system will not vary more than about 5°F above or below normal body temperature of 98.6°F. The pressure, volume, and temperature factors are related to CO_2 solubility, according to Boyle's Law:

$$\text{solubility of gas} = K\,(\text{pressure}) \times (\text{volume}) / \text{temperature}$$

If the three variables (pressure, volume, and temperature) determining CO_2 solubility remain constant, then, given the inevitable production of CO_2 by metabolism, there has to be an exhaust. Thus, if it were not for the lungs, our blood would literally begin to boil shortly after birth. But it must be recognized that conversion of CO_2 to H_2CO_3 via erythrocyte carbonic anhydrase can serve only as a temporizing measure. An alternative exhaust system—the renal tubule—that governs bicarbonate balance must exist.

HCO_3^- and H_2CO_3 can be conveniently expressed in a useful form as the familiar Henderson-Hasselbalch equation:

$$\text{pH} = \text{pKa} + \log(\text{kidney/lungs}), \text{ where kidney} = [HCO_3^-] \text{ and lungs} = [H_2CO_3]$$

Given that it is more cumbersome to clinically measure H_2CO_3 in blood than pCO_2, with which H_2CO_3 is in equilibrium, insertion of the factor $0.03 \times pCO_2$ provides the actual value of $[H_2CO_3]$. Perhaps the most useful aspect of the Henderson-Hasselbalch equation is that it provides an instant means of determining the physiologic basis for a low or a high serum pH by substitution of the laboratory values. This is the basis for the terminology "metabolic" and "respiratory," which describes the causes of such changes. If there is proportional increase or decrease in both pCO_2 and [HCO_3^-], and little or no change in the normal ratio of 10 or in pH, we speak of "compensation," as in "compensated respiratory alkalosis." In the case of compensation, it is not possible to determine which organ is compensating for the other without more information. On the other hand, it is not difficult to clinically distinguish pulmonary from renal disease. Moreover, considering their respective functions, it is obvious that the lungs can make very rapid, minute-to-minute adjustments in maintaining a normal 10/1 ratio of plasma bicarbonate to pCO_2. On the other hand, the kidney effects more adjustments, which are complex and require a longer period to be accomplished.

The Lungs Adjust pCO_2 While the Kidneys Modulate HCO_3^- and Excrete H^+

The bicarbonate buffer system functions so well precisely because it results in a product that is volatile. We may, therefore, define CO_2 as a volatile acid and imply the existence of nonvolatile acids. Just as CO_2 produced by metabolism must promptly be buffered, so must nonvolatile acids be buffered before more definitive disposition can occur. Cellular proteins, bone, and the bicarbonate system perform this function.

In the adult, approximately one third of these nonvolatile acids is derived from the catabolism of proteins and the sulfur-containing amino acids (methionine and cysteine), which generates sulfuric acid. The partial oxidation of fatty acids and of glucose results in formation of β-hydroxybutyric, acetoacetic and lactic acids, accounting for another one third of the acid load. The final third is generated from ingestion of potential nonvolatile acid in the form of phosphoproteins and phospholipids, and nutrients that contain more inorganic anions than inorganic cations (eg, arginine-HCl, which liberates H^+ with catabolism). A normal adult generates 50 to 70 mEq/day of this nonvolatile acid load (Table 4.1). From the previous text, it is obvious that diets high in protein will result in a greater net nonvolatile acid burden than those that are vegetarian.

In the infant, especially the actively growing premature infant, the nonvolatile fraction of the total acid load is negligible. Because of the rapid growth rate, net protein catabolism is low and the contribution of sulfuric acid is correspondingly low. In addition, formula and breast milk, which are the exclusive nutritional sources for this age group, supply net alkali, in contrast to the mixed diet of older individuals, which is the source of nonvolatile acid. Organic acids from incomplete oxidation of fatty acids and glucose create a large proportion of the total nonvolatile acids. The other major source is the formation of bone because the synthesis of the hydroxyapatite of bone is associated with the release of nonvolatile acid. Together, these result in a total of 1 to 2 mEq/kg/day of nonvolatile acid in the infant and young child. From infancy to adolescence, the proportion of this load due to bone formation diminishes and that due to dietary intake and sulfur amino acid catabolism increases.

Although the daily nonvolatile acid load is small by comparison to the volatile acid generated, there is an obvious need for excretion that the lung cannot meet. The excretory organ that typically deals in the currency of solubilized, but nonvolatile substances, is the kidney. First, the kidney must reclaim the continuously filtered bicarbonate before any net acid can be excreted, as defined by our version of the Henderson-Hasselbalch equation. Thus, a total of about 4000 mEq/day of HCO_3^- must be reabsorbed and returned to the plasma to prevent severe depletion of body bicarbonate stores. The majority of this reabsorption occurs in the proximal tubule through a process that requires H^+ secretion (Figure 4.1). Knowing that there is a greater concentration of Na^+ than Cl^- in blood, it is apparent that additional sodium must be balanced electrochemically—a role largely played by bicarbonate. Thus, sodium bicarbonate is filtered at the glomerulus, from which it enters the lumen of the proximal tubule.

Renal Bicarbonate Reabsorption

There are two faces to the tubular cells of the nephron (Figure 4.1). One, the luminal surface, delivers material into the tubular lumen, while

Table 4.1. The Sources of Acid and Alkali Production

SOURCES	ADDED H^+ OR HCO_3^- AND MECHANISM
Cellular metabolism of dietary and tissue constituents	
Carbohydrates	Glucose $\xrightarrow{O_2}$ 2 lactate$^-$ + 2 H
Fats	Triglycerides $\xrightarrow{O_2}$ acetoacetate$^-$ + H^+
Nucleoproteins	Nucleic acids $\xrightarrow{O_2}$ urate$^-$ + H^+
Sulfur-containing amino acids Hydroxyapatite formation	Methionine $\xrightarrow{O_2}$ urea + CO_2 + H_2O + $SO_4^=$ + $2H^+$ $10Ca^{++}$ + $4.8HPO_4^=$ + $1.2H_2PO_4^-$ + $H_2O \rightarrow (Ca_3(PO_4)_2)_3 \cdot Ca(OH)_2$ + $9.2H^+$
Dietary intake of preformed or potential acid or alkali	
Phosphoproteins	Phosphoserine $\xrightarrow[\text{at pH 7.4}]{H_2O}$ ROH + $\xrightarrow[0.2\ H_2PO_4^-]{0.8\ HPO_4^=}$ + $1.8H^+$
Phospholipids	Lecithin $\xrightarrow[\text{at pH 7.4}]{H_2O}$ ROH + $\xrightarrow[0.2\ H_2PO_4^-]{0.8\ HPO_4^=}$ + $1.8H_2$
Metabolizable cations (NH_4Cl, arginine—HCl, etc.)	$R—NH_2^+Cl^-$ $\xrightarrow{O_2}$ urea + CO_2 + Cl^- + H^+
Metabolizable anions (K^+ citrate, Na^+ lactate, etc.)	$R—COO^-K^+$ $\xrightarrow{O_2}$ urea + CO_2 + K^+ + HCO_3^-
Fecal loss of actual or potential alkali	Fecal loss of $K^+HCO_3^-$ or of K^+ acetate$^-$, propionate$^-$, butyrate$^-$, etc.

* Modified from Harrington JT, Lemann J Jr. The metabolic production and disposal of acid and alkali. Med Clin North Am 1970;54:1543.

the other, the basolateral (antiluminal) surface, delivers solute into the bloodstream or the interstitium of the kidney. Polarity of the different membrane surfaces is a universal characteristic of transporting epithelia, and the tubule cells of the kidney are no exception. Deployment of the Na^+-K^+ -ATPase in the antiluminal membrane enables Na^+ to be continually extruded from the cell. This transcellular gradient can be coupled with the movement of solutes, through additional channels, so that the Na^+ gradient becomes the driving force for coupled movement of solute. Keeping this in mind, it is obvious that Na^+ will enter the cell at the luminal surface, following a favorable electrochemical gradient, in exchange for H^+. This intraluminal H^+ combines with the filtered HCO_3^- to form H_2CO_3, which is acted upon by carbonic anhydrase situated on the luminal membrane of the proximal tubule cell. Decomposition of this luminal carbonic acid liberates water for excretion and CO_2, which freely diffuses back into the cell. Cytosolic carbonic anhydrase acts upon the CO_2 within the proximal tubule, reconstituting H_2CO_3 within the cell. The dissociation of this H_2CO_3 regenerates a hydrogen ion for secretion into the lumen and HCO_3^-, which follows the actively reabsorbed Na^+ into the blood at the antiluminal surface. Because of the stoichiometry of the Na-HCO_3 co-transporter, three HCO_3^- exit with one Na^+. Of particular note is that there is no net acid loss because the H^+ secreted in exchange for Na^+ combines with HCO_3^- to form H_2CO_3, which is decomposed to CO_2 and H_2O. Also note that about 90% of the filtered $NaHCO_3$ is reabsorbed at the proximal tubular level of the nephron. Recent evidence suggests that the proximal tubule also may have a limited capacity for direct $NaHCO_3$ reabsorption: thus, only about 5% or less of filtered sodium bicarbonate reaches the distal tubule.

Bicarbonate reabsorption in the proximal tu-

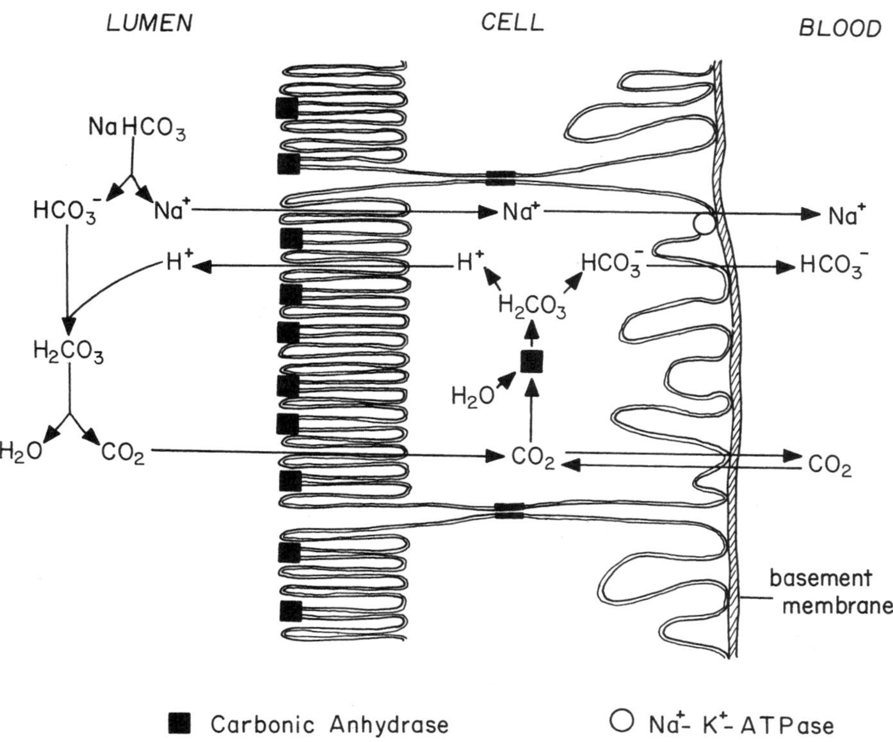

Figure 4.1. Bicarbonate reclamation in the proximal tubule. The essential element is the lack of net acid loss; indeed, the system simply reclaims 90% to 95% of the total bicarbonate filtered. Other details of the process are explained in the text.

bule is affected by many physiologic factors. The process is altered by the plasma pCO_2: a rise in pCO_2 results in enhanced proximal HCO_3^- reabsorption and an increase in plasma HCO_3^-; a fall in pCO_2 produces the opposite result. This response results from changes in plasma pCO_2 directly, not from changes in extracellular pH. Thus, infusion of HCO_3^- to normalize serum pH when pCO_2 is increased will not obliterate the enhanced renal HCO_3^- reabsorptive response by the proximal tubule. It is believed that the enhanced bicarbonate reabsorption in this situation is mediated at the cellular level by changes in intracellular pH, which is a direct function of both pCO_2 and HCO_3^-. Potassium and phosphate also may affect proximal tubule bicarbonate reabsorption through alterations in intracellular pH. Potassium deficiency causes an increase in intracellular $[H^+]$, lowering pH and enhancing HCO_3^- reabsorption. Distinct from deficiency, phosphate depletion will cause depressed proximal tubule bicarbonate reabsorption and increased intracellular pH. Phosphate excess leads to enhanced HCO_3^- reabsorption and metabolic alkalosis (see the following text), which is thought to result from decreased intracellular pH.

Parathyroid hormone also influences proximal tubular treatment of HCO_3^-. Hyperparathyroidism sometimes is associated with a metabolic acidosis (see the following text). Infusion of parathyroid hormone can depress bicarbonate reabsorption. The putative mechanism for this effect is as follows: parathyroid hormone acts directly upon adenyl cyclase to increase the concentration of adenosine 3′,5′-cyclic monophosphate (cAMP) inside the proximal tubule cell; this cAMP increase leads to enhanced HCO_3^- reabsorption. Parathyroid hormone also increases serum calcium and reduces serum phosphate; the latter leads to enhanced HCO_3^- reabsorption as previously discussed.

Does Systemic Fluid Balance Affect HCO_3^- Reabsorption?

Extracellular fluid volume, or effective arterial blood volume to be more precise, also can exert effects on proximal HCO_3^- reabsorption. Mediated by active transport processes, a multitude of small-molecular solutes, such as amino acids, glucose, phosphate, and, in particular sodium salts, is conveyed from the proximal tubular lumen into the lateral intercellular spaces (Figure 4.2). In this fashion, an osmotic gradient that leads to water reabsorption from the lumen through the "tight" junctions is created. The solution thus formed in the intercellular spaces can either enter the peritubular capillaries representing net reabsorption or it can leak retrograde into the proximal tubule lumen. The direction of this process is dependent on the balance of the Starling forces, which are largely determined by the volume and pressure of the arterial circulation.

One effect of systemic volume contraction is that hemoconcentration is produced, and corresponding absolute increases in the concentrations of all blood components occur. As a result, the kidney is affected through a greater decrease in the filtration fraction than in the glomerular filtration rate. This leads to an increase in the filtration fraction, which is that fraction of the plasma delivered to the kidney that enters the proximal tubule. This increase will cause enhanced fluid filtration of the already concentrated plasma, further increasing the concentration of the materials remaining in the postglomerular circulation. Because the plasma proteins are the major nonfiltered plasma components, peritubular capillary oncotic pressure increases, which leads to enhanced fluid uptake from the intercellular space. Extracellular volume expansion causes the reverse effects: with diminished peritubular capillary oncotic pressure, less fluid is taken up from the intercellular spaces, and the interstitial hydrostatic pressure will increase, leading to the backleak of fluid and solute through the tight junctions and into the proximal tubular lumen. The net effect is diminished fluid and solute (eg, $NaHCO_3$) reabsorption from the proximal tubule.

Net H^+ Excretion Occurs in the Distal Tubule and Collecting Tubule

In the distal and collecting tubules, luminal fluid with a pH of approximately 7.0 is converted to urine that has a pH as low as 4.5. The major feature of the luminal fluid that permits this rapid drop is the reabsorption of 95% of the filtered

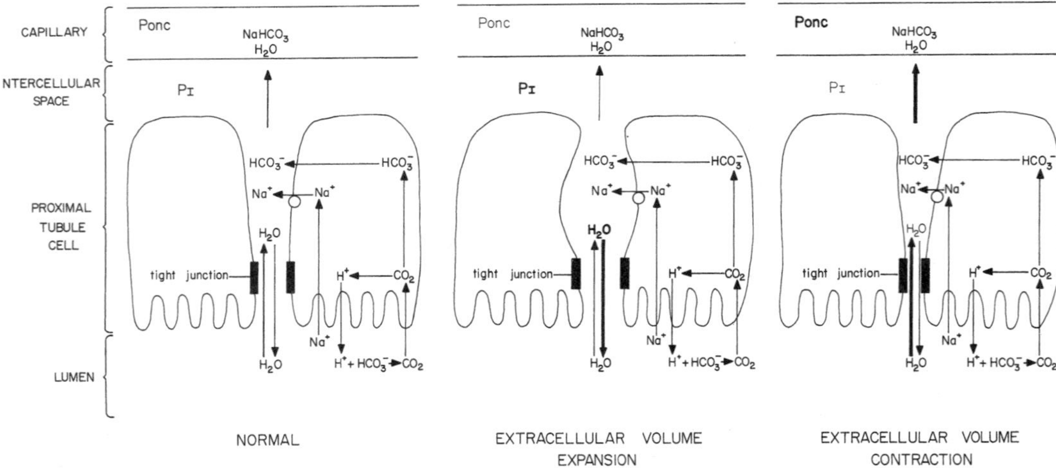

Figure 4.2. Influence of the extracellular volume state on sodium bicarbonate and water reabsorption in the proximal tubule. Extracellular volume expansion leads to increased intracellular hydrostatic pressure (P_I) and decreased peritubular oncotic pressure (Ponc); thus, a backleak of water and $NaHCO_3$ occurs into the proximal tubular lumen. Conversely, contracted extracellular volume leads to increased Ponc and decreased P_I; therefore, any backleak is minimized, and $NaHCO_3$ and water reabsorption is increased.

bicarbonate in the proximal tubule. At the same time, this loss of bicarbonate dramatically reduces the effectiveness of the emerging fluid as a bicarbonate-based buffer. Further reabsorption of the remaining 5% or less of the soluble bicarbonate in the distal and collecting tubules forces a shift to a pH of about 5.5 and reliance on an intraluminal buffer system consisting of HPO_4^{-2} and NH_3. Titration of these two major urinary buffers permits nonvolatile acid to be excreted. Before examining the mechanism that causes this, we stress that: (*a*) there is no net $[H^+]$ excretion in the proximal tubule, and (*b*) reabsorption of the bulk of $NaHCO_3$ in the proximal tubule allows the distal tubule and collecting tubule to focus their energies on net excretion of H^+ rather than on reclamation of bicarbonate.

The distal tubular secretory mechanism for $[H^+]$ is shown in Figure 4.3. Note that, unlike the proximal tubule, HCO_3^- reabsorption is not linked to Na^+/H^+ exchange. Instead, H^+ generated from cytosolic carbonic anhydrase activity is actively transported into the lumen by a H^+-translocating ATPase, which is capable of hydrogen ion secretion against $[H^+]$ gradients as large as 1000:1 or 3 pH units. The HCO_3^- remaining within the cell exits at the antiluminal surface through an exchange with Cl^-, thus accounting for the requisite delivery of Na^+ to the distal site for H^+ secretion. The distal and collecting tubules have "nonleaky" tight junctions, which permit maintenance of the large gradients generated between blood and tubular lumen, thus leading to excretion of the secreted H^+.

This, however, is not the whole story because normal urinary volume is not large enough to excrete the entire acid load necessary for maintenance of homeostasis, even with large $[H^+]$ gradients. At a urine pH of 4.5, only 0.00006 mEq of H^+ is excreted in 1500 ml of urine without buffer. Recall that increasing urinary volume decreases effective plasma volume; this diminished plasma volume in turn alters bicarbonate reabsorption in the proximal tubule.

Fortunately, the urine contains several buffers that permit the excretion of large amounts of H^+ without requiring the urine pH to fall lower than 4.5. Hydrogen ion excretion by these buffers results in what is termed titratable acidity. A major member of this buffer group is HPO_4^{-2} with a pKa of 6.8, which rapidly becomes converted to $H_2PO_4^-$ as urine pH falls below 6.0. By contrast to the tiny amount of H^+ that can be excreted in 1.5 L of urine at pH 4.5 without buffer, P_i excretion, all of which is available for buffering, amounts to about 10 mEq/24 hours. Additional urinary buffers include creatinine, uric acid, and β-hydroxybutyrate, none of which are as important as P_i. Citrate also has been implicated as a urinary buffer; because unexcreted citrate is metabolized by liver to form bicarbonate, urinary loss of citrate is equivalent to excretion of bicarbonate. The quantity of alkali required to increase the urine pH to 7.4 defines the titratable acidity of the urine.

Renal Ammoniagenesis is a Vital Link in Net Acid Excretion

The discerning reader will have noticed that the processes described previously within the text can account for only less than half of the daily load of nonvolatile acid. In fact, the major vehicle for acid excretion is ammonia (NH_3), the same compound that the liver fixes in urea (see Chapter 5), because it is a potent neurotoxin. In contrast to the long-held view that ammonia functions as a urinary buffer, which is expressed in the following:

$$H^+ + NH_3 \longleftarrow NH_4^+$$

ammonia, in fact, is more than 99% protonated (NH_4^+) at physiologic pH. Thus, hypothetically, if the kidney was capable of producing NH_3, which is freely diffusible across the cell membrane, entry of the NH_3 into the lumen and protonation to NH_4^+ (not diffusible) would account for at least one excreted H^+. Although this appears simple in theory, the process by which NH_4^+ excretion accomplishes net H^+ elimination is more complex.

The source of renal ammoniagenesis is glutamine, the same compound that functions at a systemic level as a metabolic "sink" for free ammonia produced by amino acid catabolism. This, however, does not suggest that the kidney can function as an alternative means for free ammonia excretion. In fact, some ammonia generated by the kidney from glutamine metabolism is returned to the systemic circulation for conversion to urea by the liver, thus adding to the net urea cycle load. Glutamine is a glucogenic amino acid and, in the pro-

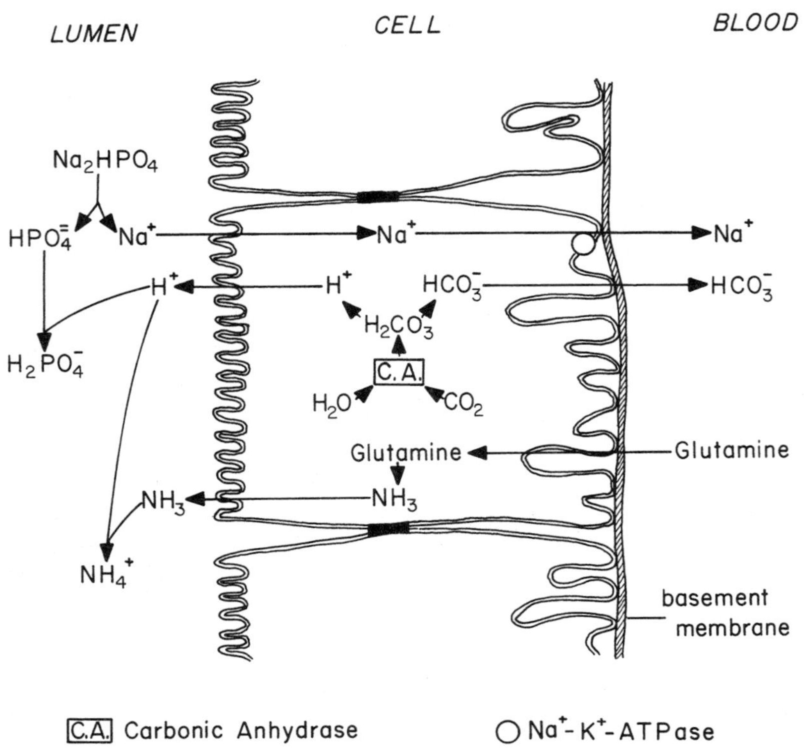

Figure 4.3. Distal tubular mechanism of net H^+ excretion. Renal pH regulation occurs in the distal tubule, where active transport of H^+ derived from cytosolic generation of H_2CO_3 and net reabsorption of HCO_3^- occur. This mechanism is distinct from that of the proximal tubule because the H^+ transport does not need Na^+/H^+ exchange. Another important feature of this region is the presence of "nonleaky" tight junctions, which facilitate maintenance of the large gradients thus established. Finally, the gradient is largely dissipated through combination of the eliminated H^+ with the urinary buffers, chiefly NH_3 and disodium phosphate. Reabsorption of a HCO_3^- molecule results in elimination of a Cl^- and a K^+ that offsets the sodium simultaneously reabsorbed.

cess of its catabolism, yields 2 NH_4^+ and 2 HCO_3^- per molecule:

$$\text{glutamine} \longrightarrow \text{pyruvate} + 2(NH_4^+) + 2(HCO_3^-)$$

By returning the bicarbonate thus generated to the systemic circulation, with concomitant excretion of the ammonium ions into the urine, the net effect is increased plasma bicarbonate. But, if the liver uses some portion of the bicarbonate to convert any systemically released ammonium to urea (including that from the kidney), the amount of "new" bicarbonate formed is diminished. Thus, to generate "new" bicarbonate, the α-ketoglutarate (from glutamine) must be metabolized to a neutral end product and the NH_4^+ must be excreted in the urine. If NH_4^+ is excreted in the urine, it will not have to be fixed in urea, which would consume HCO_3^-. The current view of the role of NH_4^+ in acid-base balance is presented in Figure 4.4.

The regulation of renal ammoniagenesis has been investigated for many years. As a result of this interest, it is clear that more is involved than simple membrane diffusion based on ionic charge. For example, NH_4^+ can be transported in the proximal tubule by both the Na^+/H^+ exchanger and the Na^+-K^+ATPase. In addition, NH_4^+ also can substitute for K^+ in the action of a Na^+, K^+, $2Cl^-$ transporter molecule found in the loop of Henle. In addition to these factors, many others

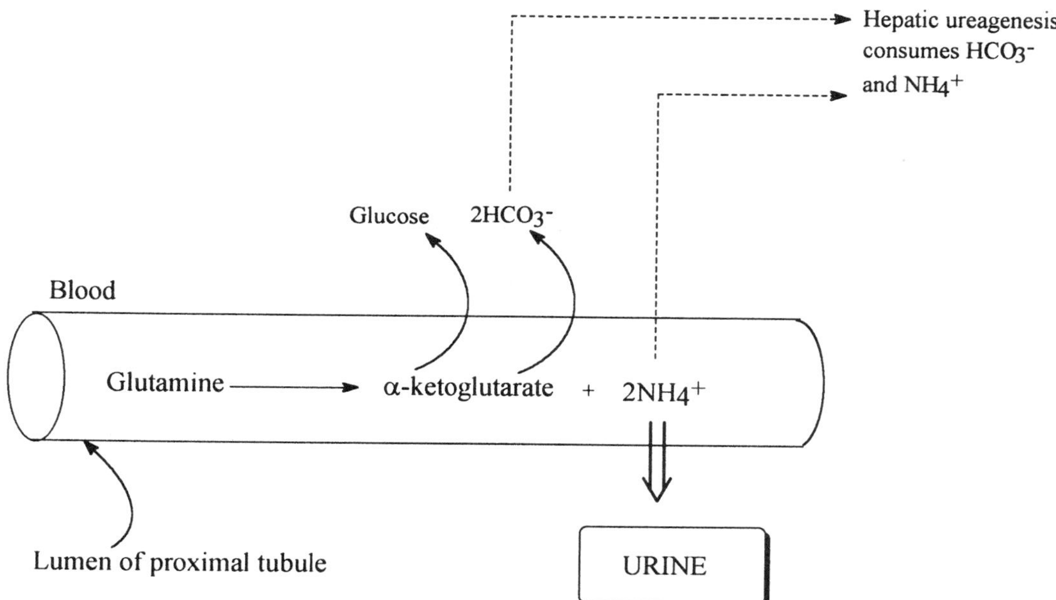

Figure 4.4. Renal ammoniagenesis. Catabolism of glutamine by the kidney results in formation of α-ketoglutarate and $2NH_4^+$; further catabolism of the α-ketoglutarate leads to net recovery of a molecule of glucose and production of $2HCO_3^-$. Regardless of the extent that urea is synthesized by the liver, "new" bicarbonate generated in glutamine catabolism is consumed. Conversely, the process generates additional urinary buffer to the extent that NH_4^+ thus produced is excreted in urine.

have been implicated: changes in circulating volume affect NH_4^+ excretion, K^+ depletion and hypocalcemia enhance, and hyperkalemia and hypercalcemia decrease renal ammonia production. The clinical relevance of these observations remains to be determined, but sufficient evidence exists to state unequivocally that renal ammoniagenesis and its role in H^+ excretion are more complex than previously believed. Despite this complexity, however, the potential for ammoniagenesis by the kidney, coupled with the equilibrium shift toward formation of NH_4^+ at physiologic pH, provides the basis for net acid excretion by the kidney.

Putting It All Together

In summary, the kidney maintains acid-base balance by first reclaiming filtered bicarbonate in the proximal tubule through H^+ secretion. The magnitude of this process is modulated by the state of the extracellular fluid volume, serum potassium, and pCO_2. Hydrogen ion secretion at this level of the nephron does not result in net H^+ excretion because all of the H^+ is used to reclaim HCO_3^-. Net hydrogen ion excretion does, however, take place in the distal tubule, where it is used to titrate luminal NH_3 and HPO_4^{-2}, increasing the urine hydrogen ion concentration 1000-fold.

In the distal tubule, the secreted H^+ emanates from dissociation of water. The other product of dissociation, OH^-, combines with CO_2 in the cell to form HCO_3^-, which is catalyzed by carbonic anhydrase. Bicarbonate then can enter the blood through the antiluminal membrane. New HCO_3^- forms, however, when secreted H^+ combines with HPO_4^{-2} or when NH_4^+ excretion is coupled with the metabolism of the carbon skeleton of glutamine. In those cases, the bicarbonate passes back into the blood. This new bicarbonate replaces bicarbonate previously titrated by H^+, thus replenishing that buffer system. Distal H^+ excretion is influenced by sodium delivery, potassium concentration, and aldosterone secretion from the adrenal cortex. The major means of net H^+ excretion is renal ammoniagenesis, which is influenced by urine pH, potassium and calcium concentrations of plasma, and plasma pH. Present knowledge of the regulation of renal ammoniagenesis is limited.

CLINICAL DISORDERS OF ACID-BASE BALANCE

At the beginning of this chapter, we noted the critical importance of the H^+ ion in governing the conformation of biologic molecules and, thus, their function. It is fair to say that the hydrogen ion could be considered the most influential chemical ion in living organisms. As such, it is clear that any abnormality in regulation of $[H^+]$ in body fluids will have far-reaching implications for all cells, irrespective of the etiology of the dysfunction. Thus, discussion of those disturbances that impact on the organism warrants placement in the first section of this book.

Centered in a normal arterial pH range of 7.35 to 7.45, fluctuations in pathologic states can occur from pH 6.8 to 7.8, which are the limits compatible with life. Thus, we can define acidosis as a pH less than 7.35 and alkalosis as a pH greater than 7.45; note that excess or deficit of $[H^+]$ can exist without change in pH, described as acidemia and alkalemia, respectively. The changes in $[H^+]$ without pH changes account for the use of the word "compensated" to describe either acidosis or alkalosis that has not resulted in an abnormal pH shift. The final issue involving terminology relates to primary source of the alteration. Thus, if a change in pCO_2 occurs, the disturbance is classified as respiratory; if the fundamental abnormality is in $[HCO_3^-]$, it is called metabolic.

With any primary disturbance in pCO_2, the compensatory mechanism is a secondary change in the renal handling of HCO_3^- and the excretion of acid and ammonia that will tend to normalize the blood pH. With any primary alteration in $[HCO_3^-]$, a secondary change in the pulmonary excretion of CO_2 will occur, again tending to normalize the blood pH. Thus, compensation for metabolic disturbances occur through the lungs, whereas the kidneys compensate for pulmonary disturbances. Again, each of the two organs adjusts by a different mechanism and at a different rate, which was addressed earlier in this chapter. In general, the compensatory response of the lungs is more rapid than that of the kidney. On the other hand, the kidney can mount a more sustained response to acid-base disequilibration.

Metabolic Abnormalities

METABOLIC ACIDOSIS

In clinical practice, physicians are likely to see more metabolic acidosis than any other acid-base disturbance. Therefore, a sound understanding of the nature of this entity is absolutely essential. Given what we already have written about the importance of H^+ homeostasis to normal enzyme function, it already should be apparent that disruptions in this system will have multiple and far-reaching clinical implications. Not considering the manifestations of any primary disorder that causes acidosis (eg, diabetic ketoacidosis), acidosis itself produces clinical signs and symptoms. These include depression of left ventricular function and decreased peripheral vascular resistance, the combination of which leads to severe hypotension. Further decrease in pH, contributed to by the ensuing hypoxia and accumulated lactic acid, can result in pulmonary edema and ventricular arrhythmias. The pulmonary response to acidosis will be clinically perceived as hyperpnea and tachypnea, the body's means of "blowing off" CO_2 in attempts to buffer the accumulating hydrogen ion. Also noteworthy is the effect of increased hydrogen ion that causes enhanced binding of oxygen by hemoglobin, which diminishes oxygen delivery. Central nervous system dysfunction may occur, including depression of mentation and occasionally seizures. Chronic acidosis will lead to bony changes of osteopenia and osteoporosis, ultimately causing growth failure in children and pathologic fractures.

Based on the anion gap or "delta," metabolic acidosis can be divided into two major categories. The anion gap is the difference between the sum of the plasma $[Na^+] + [K^+]$ and the sum of the plasma $[Cl^-] + [HCO_3^-]$. Because K^+ varies little compared with the other three factors, the calculation generally is expressed as:

$$\text{Anion Gap} = [Na^+] - \{[Cl^-] + [HCO_3^-]\}$$

which normally is equal to 12 ± 4 mEq/L. Of course, because the laws of electroneutrality must be satisfied, there is not a true gap between plasma cations and anions, but an apparent one. The apparent gap results from the usual practice of routinely omitting measurement of anions such as plasma proteins, phosphate, sulfate, and organic acid radicals.

An increased anion gap represents an increase in strong acids and may, in certain clinical settings, be an important clue for diagnosis of an organic acidemia (see Chapter 13). Moreover, bicarbonate administration will only temporarily remedy the accumulation of these strong acids. These acids titrate body buffers, leading to a drop in plasma bicarbonate and its replacement by the "invisible" acid anion. A classic example of this is diabetic ketoacidosis, in which the ketoacids acetoacetic and β-hydroxybutyric rapidly dissociate within the pH range of 6.8 to 7.8. The H^+ thus liberated titrates $NaHCO_3$ in plasma to H_2CO_3 and then to CO_2 for elimination by the lungs. The sodium salts (buffered ketoacids) remain behind in the circulation, raising the anion gap, because both sodium and chloride concentrations are unchanged.

Table 4.2 lists the major diseases associated

Table 4.2. Causes of Increased Anion Gap

NONGENETIC

1. Shock
2. Ketosis (starvation, alcoholism, diabetes mellitus)
3. Renal failure
4. Diarrhea of infancy
5. Ingestions (salicylate, methanol, ethylene glycol, ethanol)

GENETIC

1. Disorders of carbohydrate metabolism (includes pyruvate)
   Glycogen storage disease, pyruvate carboxylase deficiency, pyruvate dehydrogenase deficiency, fructose-1,6-diphosphatase deficiency, phosphoenolpyruvate carboxykinase deficiency, mitochondrial complex I, III and IV deficiencies
2. Disorders of fatty acid metabolism (often also ↑NH3)
   Short chain acyl-CoA dehydrogenase (SCAD) deficiency, medium chain acyl-CoA dehydrogenase (MCAD) deficiency, long chain acyl-CoA dehydrogenase (LCAD) deficiency, glycerol kinase deficiency
3. Disorders of amino acid metabolism (often also ↑NH3)
   Maple syrup urine disease, isovaleric acidemia, -methyl crotonyl-CoA carboxylase deficiency, β-hydroxy-β-methylglutaric aciduria, α-methylacetoacetyl-CoA thiolase deficiency, acetoacetyl-CoA thiolase deficiency, propionic acidemia, methylmalonic acidemia, glutaric acidemia (types I and 2), 5-oxoprolinuria, α-ketoglutarate dehydrogenase deficiency, fumarase deficiency

with an anion gap metabolic acidosis. The clinical severity of metabolic acidosis, in terms of survival, deserves healthy respect, as does the resistance of an anion gap to correction with bicarbonate therapy. Many of these illnesses are caused by inborn errors of metabolism and lead to generation of strong organic acids, which, because of the metabolic block, become dead-end metabolites. Any acute cause of cellular hypoxia will lead to generation of lactic acid, which probably is the most common cause of an increased anion gap. Diarrhea that occurs during infancy, which typically leads to anion gap acidosis from the starvation ketosis. Strong organic acids are formed by bacteria in the gut acting on undigested food and these acids are absorbed and accumulate in plasma. Because of dehydration, there is decreased renal excretion of all these organic anions. Renal failure leads to accumulation of phosphate and sulfate anions, and the inability to excrete the daily nonvolatile acid load. With the shift away from the use of aspirin in the pediatric age group, salicylate toxicity is diminishing in frequency as a cause of anion gap acidosis. On the other hand, the frequency of ethanol intoxication is increasing in all age groups, and is a common cause of ketone body and lactic acid increases, which result in an increased anion gap.

More common clinically, hyperchloremic (normal anion gap) metabolic acidosis is associated with many acute disorders, particularly those of the gastrointestinal tract. It is important to note that in this form of acidosis, although the bicarbonate is depressed, the serum chloride is proportionately increased. Therefore, the sum of the anions does not vary substantially from that found in a normal situation. Maintenance of a normal delta distinguishes the two types of metabolic acidosis; failure to recognize this may lead to a significant delay in diagnosis. In fact, the most likely cause of hyperchloremic metabolic acidosis is the loss of bicarbonate, such as in acute diarrhea in which increased Cl^- occurs because of renal compensation. Mechanistically, the continuing loss of bicarbonate through the intestine leads to enhanced renal tubular attempts to reclaim bicarbonate and secrete H^+, the latter through Na^+/H^+ exchange. The relatively low bicarbonate in glomerular filtrate causes an excess of Na^+ over HCO_3^- reabsorption, which leads to enhanced passive Cl^- reclamation. Thus, although bicarbonate in plasma remains low, electroneutrality is maintained through passive Cl^- reabsorption after active Na^+/H^+ exchange.

Rare but important causes of hyperchloremic metabolic acidosis are the renal tubular acidosis (RTA) disorders that involve proximal or distal tubular HCO_3^- or H^+ handling, respectively. The pathogenesis of proximal (Type II) RTA at a physiologic level is straightforward and easy to understand. Because bicarbonate reabsorption almost is 95% complete at the level of the proximal tubule, any decrease in this capacity will be quickly reflected in disturbance in acid-base homeostasis. Thus, in Type II RTA there is a reduced capacity for HCO_3^- reabsorption, increased bicarbonate loss in urine, and a hyperchloremic metabolic acidosis of varying severity, depending upon the degree of bicarbonate-wasting. The reduced HCO_3^- tubular maximum is easily demonstrated by measuring bicarbonate loss during a bicarbonate infusion in a patient with a depressed plasma bicarbonate. However, the biochemical mechanisms at fault in this disorder are not clear, although many possibilities have been proposed. Among these, one that is likely to be true is a defect in the Na^+-K^+-ATPase on the antiluminal membrane surface, which normally is responsible for generation of an intracellular sodium deficit in relation to the proximal tubular lumen. This deficit drives Na^+ transport across the cell and helps to drive bicarbonate reabsorption from proximal cell to blood; therefore, a defect in this system clearly would lead to deficient bicarbonate reclamation.

Unlike Type II RTA, which rarely appears as an isolated finding, distal (Type I) RTA is common. Etiologies include autosomal dominant inheritance; certain drugs; and renal, systemic, and autoimmune disorders (Table 4.3). Also, in contrast to Type II, Type I frequently is associated with nephrocalcinosis and significant nephrolithiasis. Recall that net H^+ excretion occurs only at the level of the distal tubule, whereas the proximal tubule engages in net bicarbonate reabsorption. Thus, it is predictable that deficits in secretion of H^+ or other impairments in net H^+ excretion will be reflected in a more severe degree of systemic acidosis than that seen in Type II RTA. Consequently, bone will be used as a backup buffer, resulting in loss of calcium, magnesium, and phosphate in urine. The resulting hypercalciuria pre-

Table 4.3. Causes of Normal Anion Gap Acidosis

NONGENETIC

1. Diarrhea
2. Small bowel fluid loss (ostomy)
3. Ureterosigmoidostomy
4. Primary hyperparathyroidism
5. Drugs: Total parental nutrition, cholestyramine, carbonic anhydrase inhibitors, acidfying agents (eg, CaCl2, NH4Cl)

GENETIC

1. Proximal renal tubular acidosis (type 2)
   Primary, secondary (see Chapter 3)
2. Distal renal tubular acidosis (type 1): Primary, secondary (SS disease, Ehlers-Danlos syndrome, Sjögren's syndrome, hereditary fructose intolerance, Wilson's disease, Fabry's disease)

disposes to renal stone formation. However, as in Type II, there is no clear understanding of the biochemical abnormalities, although several have been postulated. These include diminished H^+ secretion as a consequence of deficient H^+-translocating ATPase or increased back-diffusion (leakage) of this translocated H^+ ion.

Given that both Types I and II RTA cause a hyperchloremic metabolic acidosis, their presence may be easily overlooked. An important diagnostic clue is a urine pH that is inappropriately high in relation to a simultaneous blood pH. In fact, this clue defines the clinical presence of RTA, in general. Distinction between the two types may not be possible using this criterion alone, although it is legitimate to state that Type II patients are likely to have a lower urine pH than Type I patients because net H^+ excretion mechanisms are intact in the former. This, however, is true only when plasma bicarbonate has reached the level of the lowered tubular maximum (ie, when the patient is acidotic). As a result, a Type II patient infused therapeutically with bicarbonate may excrete an alkaline urine similar to that produced by a Type I patient. Measurement of urinary citrate excretion can help to make the distinction because hypocitraturia typically is associated only with Type I disease.

METABOLIC ALKALOSIS

This clinical entity may be defined as the result of a net gain in alkali or a loss of acid, which leads to a rise in serum [HCO_3^-] and pH. As initially discussed, some degree of respiratory compensation exists, through hypoventilation, in response to the change in pH. However, because of the overriding need to maintain an adequate pO_2, this response is limited to an increase of up to 50–55 Torr, regardless of the severity of the alkalosis.

Metabolic alkalosis can be divided into two major categories based on urinary chloride concentration and response to saline infusion. In the first category, the urine Cl^- is less than 10 mEq/L, and the alkalosis is saline-responsive. An excellent example of this is pyloric stenosis, in which persistent vomiting leads to loss of HCl and fluid and generates an increase in plasma $[HCO_3^-]$ and extracellular volume contraction. The volume depletion stimulates proximal tubular bicarbonate reabsorption, maintaining the raised plasma $[HCO_3^-]$ when an increased filtered load is present. Furthermore, the volume contraction stimulates aldosterone secretion, enhancing Na^+/K^+ exchange in the distal nephron and causing hypokalemia. Hypokalemia exacerbates the alkalosis by inducing exchanges of intracellular K^+ for extracellular H^+ and increased H^+ for Na^+ in the distal nephron. Because of these phenomena, an acid urine exists with a systemic alkalosis. Treatment of this type of metabolic alkalosis should include correction of the volume depletion with saline infusion, which would facilitate excess bicarbonate excretion and normalization of the pH. Other causes of saline-responsive metabolic alkalosis are listed in Table 4.4.

The second type of metabolic alkalosis is unresponsive to saline and is associated with a high urine chloride and hypertension. Most causes of this form of metabolic alkalosis are etiologically related to mineralocorticoid excess. Primary hyperaldosteronism is a classic example, in which persistently elevated secretion leads to increased NaCl reabsorption and consequent volume expansion. Obviously, this would rapidly lead to overhydration and death, if left unchecked. However, other mechanisms, such as atrial natriuretic factor, moderate the aldosterone-driven proximal tubular sodium reabsorption with the resulting volume expansion. The ensuing increase in distal tubular sodium delivery, in response to the hyperaldosteronism, causes accelerated exchange of K^+ and H^+ for Na^+. The latter mechanism directly causes the alkalosis, which is magnified in degree as potassium loss continues because hypokalemia enhances proximal tubular $NaHCO_3$ uptake. Other causes of this type of metabolic alkalosis are listed in Table 4.5.

Table 4.4. Causes of Saline-Responsive Metabolic Alkalosis

Pyloric stenosis
Vomiting
Upper GI suction
Congenital chloride diarrhea
Laxative abuse
Diuretic abuse
Cystic fibrosis
Chloride-deficient formulas in infants
Posthypercapnea syndrome
Poorly reabsorbable anion administration
Post-treatment of organic acidemias

Table 4.5. Causes of Saline-Resistant Metabolic Alkalosis

Primary hyperaldosteronism
Cushing's syndrome
Hyper-reninemic hypertension
Renal artery stenosis
Heritable block in steroid hormone synthesis
17α-OH deficiency
11β-OH deficiency
Licorice
Liddle's syndrome
Bartter's syndrome
Severe potassium deficiency

RESPIRATORY ACIDOSIS AND ALKALOSIS

All causes of respiratory acidosis relate to a diminished capacity for elimination of CO_2 through the lungs. The specific etiologies are legion and may be temporary (eg, foreign body aspiration) or chronic (eg, emphysema). Anything that interferes with gas exchange, whether it is diminished expansion and contraction of the lungs or accumulation of fluid or other material in the alveoli, will lead to rapid increase in pCO_2 and a decrease in blood pH. Decline in pH results from a shift in the bicarbonate buffer system toward formation of H_2CO_3 from increased pCO_2 and subsequent dissociation of the carbonic acid and release of H^+. Immediate means of offsetting this $[H^+]$ increase include buffering by intracellular proteins and a shift of HCO_3^- from the erythrocytes in exchange for extracellular chloride. These responses, however, are restricted in their magnitude and clearly cannot compensate for any significant disturbance, especially of prolonged duration. The major compensatory mechanisms, of course, reside in the kidney where H^+ can be excreted and bicarbonate reabsorbed. As we already have discussed, however, this process requires several days to become maximally effective. This is the chief reason for the danger of acute hypercapnea in disorders such as asthma, in which CO_2 accumulation may occur more rapidly than compensation, resulting in severe acidosis and CO_2 narcosis, and loss of respiratory effort. Obviously, therapeutic efforts must be directed at immediately improving the effectiveness of gas exchange; in many cases, this should be done even before treating the cause of the event.

Respiratory alkalosis obviously represents the opposite end of the spectrum and occurs when CO_2 excretion is increased through the lungs. The decrease in pCO_2 shifts the bicarbonate buffer equilibrium away from $H^+ + HCO_3^-$ toward $CO_2 + H_2O$. Immediate ionic shifts occur, as in respiratory acidosis, between the extracellular and intracellular compartments to acutely buffer the resulting pH change. These include H^+ release from proteins in exchange for Na^+ and K^+, and a shift in extracellular HCO_3^- into the erythrocyte in exchange for Cl^-. In this situation, erythrocytic lactic acid, the chief product of red cell metabolism, also is used as a source of H^+. Once again, the kidney is key to sustained compensation for decreases in pCO_2, where decreased bicarbonate reabsorption occurs in response. Table 4.6 lists major causes of respiratory alkalosis.

Table 4.6. Causes of Respiratory Alkalosis

Causes
CNS lesions
trauma
cerebral hemorrhage
infection
anxiety
Pulmonary disorders
pneumonia
pulmonary embolus
asthma
mild pulmonary edema
restrictive lung disease
Systemic disorders
hyperthyroidism
endotoxemia
anemia (severe)
fever
pregnancy
Hyperammonemia
hepatic failure
reye's syndrome
lysinuric protein intolerance
urea cycle disorders
carbamylphosphate synthetase deficiency
ornithine transcarbamylase deficiency
citrullinemia
argininosuccinic aciduria
arginase deficiency
Pharmacologic agents
salicylate intoxication
paraldehyde intoxication
epinephrine
progestational agents
amphetamines
Mechanical overventilation

Mixed Disturbances

In the real world of clinical medicine, life is not a simple encounter with one disease process in each patient. Indeed, some patients present with multiple problems, each of which may have a different impact on the acid-base status, and the measured pH may reflect the overall effect. Having stated this, it should be clear that it is possible for substantial offsetting effects on body buffers to result in a normal pH. Notwithstanding this possibility, there is still an obvious need to identify and treat each of the abnormal factors. In view of the complexity of the homeostatic mechanisms for maintenance of acid-base balance, partial treatment of the overall disruption easily could result in disastrous consequences.

Identification of each process involved first depends upon carefully taking a history and performing a physical examination, as well as several pieces of laboratory data. As in all of clinical medicine, the best guide to diagnosis is a history that was carefully taken, which can supply relevant information such as vomiting without diarrhea or vice versa, diuretic use, possible drug ingestion, etc. Without this information, laboratory data may not be properly interpreted. By the same token, physical assessment of hydration, nature of respiratory effort, odors, etc can be critical determinants of contributing factors to acid-base imbalance. There are many simple systems that have been devised to quickly assess whether a mixed disturbance is present, some of which are covered in the works listed in the suggested reading section at the end of this chapter. Practically speaking, most patients with mixed acid-base problems will have at least a minimal shift in pH; a careful assessment of electrolytes and blood gas results will reveal incomplete compensation. Thus, diagnostically, directing attention toward the cause of the incomplete compensation, particularly when a history has been carefully taken and a physical examination has been performed, usually will reveal other factors that affect the body buffers.

SUGGESTED READINGS

GENERAL CONCEPTS

Bourke E, Hausinger D. pH homeostasis: the conceptual change. Contrib Nephrol 1992;100:58.

Jones DP, Chesney RW. Development of tubular function. Clin Perinatol 1992;19:33.

Saleh AM, Rombola G, Batile DC. Intracellular H^+ buffering power and its dependency on intracellular ph. Kidney Int 1991;39:282.

BICARBONATE REABSORPTION

DuBose TD. Reclamation of filtered bicarbonate. Kidney Int 1990;38:584.

RENAL ACIDIFICATION AND AMMONIAGENESIS

Gennari FJ, Maddox DA. Renal regulation of acid-base homeostasis. In: Seldin DW, Giebisch G, eds. The kidney: physiology and pathophysiology. 2nd ed. New York: Raven Press, 1992.

Halperin ML, Kamel KS, Ethier JH, et al. Biochemistry and physiology of ammonium excretion. In: Seldin DW, Giebisch G, eds. The kidney: physiology and pathophysiology. 2nd ed. New York: Raven Press, 1992.

Hamm LL. Renal handling of citrate. Kidney Int 1990;38: 728.

Hamm LL, Alpern RJ. Cellular mechanisms of renal tubular acidification. In: Seldin DW, Giebisch G, eds. The kidney: physiology and pathophysiology. 2nd ed. New York: Raven Press, 1992.

Hamm LL. Renal handling of citrate. Kidney Int 1990;38: 728.

Kurtz I, Dass PD, Cramer S. The importance of renal ammonia metabolism to whole body acid-base balance: a reanalysis of the pathophysiology of renal tubular acidosis. Miner Electrolyte Metab 1990;16:331.

Nissim I, Nissim I, Yudkoff M. Adaptation of renal tricarboxylic acid cycle metabolism to various acid-base states: study with ⟨3-13C,5-15N⟩glutamine. Miner Electrolyte Metab 1991;17:21.

Nissim I, Cattano C, Lin Z, Nissim I. Acid-base regulation of hepatic glutamine metabolism and ureagenesis: study with 15N. J Am Soc Nephrol 1993;3:1416.

Schoolwerth AC. Regulation of renal ammoniagenesis in metabolic acidosis. Kidney Int 1991;40:961.

CLINICAL DISORDERS OF ACID-BASE BALANCE

Boon L, Blommaart PJ, Meijer AJ, et al. Acute acidosis inhibits hepatic amino acid uptake: implications for regulation of acid-base balance. Contrib Nephrol 1994;110:133.

Carlisle EJ, Donnelly SM, Halperin ML. Renal tubular acidosis (RTA): recognize the ammonium defect and pH or get the urine pH. Pediatr Nephrol 1991;5:242.

Decaux G, Schlesser M, Coffernils M, et al. Uric acid, anion gap and urea concentration in the diagnostic approach to hypernatremia. Clin Nephrol 1994;42: 10.2.

Eiam-Ong S, Lonis B, Kurtzman NA, Sabatini S. The biochemical basis of hypokalemic metabolic alkalosis. Trans Assoc Am Physicians 1992;105:157.

Katsura K, Ekholm A, Siesjo BK. Coupling among changes in energy metabolism, acid-base homeostasis, and ion fluxes in ischemia. Can J Physiol Pharmacol 1992; 70(suppl):S170.

Osther PJ, Bollerslev J, Hansen AB, et al. Pathophysiology of incomplete renal tubular acidosis in recurrent renal stone formers: evidence of disturbed calcium, bone and citrate metabolism. Urol Res 1993;21:169.

Ozand PT, Gascon GG. Organic acidurias: a review. Part 1. J Child Neurol 1991;6:196.

Paulson WD, Gadallah MF. Diagnosis of mixed acid-base disorders in diabetic ketoacidosis. Am J Med Sci 1993; 306:295.

Preuss HG. Fundamentals of clinical acid-base evaluation. Clin Lab Med 1993;13:103.

Sabatini S, Kurtzman NA. Pathophysiology of the renal tubular acidoses. Semin Nephrol 1991;11:202.

Tizianello A, Garibotto G, Robaudo C, Deferrari G. Renal ammoniagenesis in humans with chronic potassium depletion. Kidney Int 1991;40:772–778.

Winter SD, Pearson JR, Gabow PA, et al. The fall of the serum anion gap. Arch Intern Med 1990;150:311.

chapter **5**

Liver

ANATOMY, STRUCTURE, AND FUNCTION

Anatomically, the liver is interposed between the portal and systemic circulations. Thus, all material absorbed from the intestine into the bloodstream must flow via the portal circulation to the liver, where it is processed or distributed, or both, through the systemic (caval) blood to the rest of the body. The exceptions are long-chain fatty acids that are incorporated into chylomicrons and enter the mesenteric lymphatics, traveling to the thoracic duct. These chylomicrons leave the thoracic duct and directly enter the systemic circulation.

The liver has a commanding role in carbohydrate, fat, and amino acid metabolism, and its biochemical versatility is expressed by the production of bile. Bile is a major factor in digestion of lipid (Chapter 15), thus involving the liver in determining the extent of fat entry into the lymphatics. The liver also guards against invading microorganisms: it is armed with a generous complement of macrophages.

It is currently thought that the *acinus* is the functional unit of the liver (Figure 5.1). The acinus embraces the liver parenchymal cells that are supplied by terminal branches of the portal vein and hepatic artery. Because liver cells are deployed in rows or plates that are one-cell thick, and the afferent blood supply nearest to cells is located in zone 1 and that furthest from the cells is located in zone 3, a gradient to the blood supply exists. Consequently, as the blood moves along a row of cells, it gives up O_2 and nutrients, and the cells furthest from the portal venule and hepatic arteriole receive the least O_2 and nutrients. Moreover, as listed in Table 5.1, there is also a zonation to the enzymatic pathways deployed along the liver plate. Cells closest to the afferent blood vessels are more richly endowed with enzymes to conduct gluconeogenesis and ureagenesis, whereas those closer to the hepatic venule participate in glycolysis and glycogen synthesis.

Hepatocytes, which represent 60% of the total cell population of the liver, are polyhedral shaped epithelial cells with three distinct surfaces. These are the *basal* or *sinusoidal* surfaces, which encounter the blood brought by the portal vein and hepatic artery; the *canalicular* surfaces, which make up the wall of the bile canaliculus and into which the hepatocyte secretes; and the *intercellular* surfaces, where contiguous hepatocytes abut. It should be apparent that transport activities at the sinusoidal surfaces proceed in two ways: (*a*) uptake from the blood and (*b*) secretion into the blood, both of which are facilitated by the Na^+-K^+ ATPase and various specific transport proteins.

As would be expected, the intercellular surface of the hepatocyte is adapted for communication among cells with gap junctions, and for adhesion by specialized molecules (integrins), tight junctions, and desmosomes.

Because the canalicular surface also is required to secrete various compounds (in this case, into the bile), it has specialized transport systems as well. Three separate carrier systems indigenous to the canalicular membrane transport are those for leukotrienes, bile salts, and drugs.

Functionally, in addition to the roles outlined previously in the text, the liver occupies a central position in the metabolic economy, serving not only as the major processing center for nutritional components, but also in drug and heme catabolism. The liver also is the central organ of gluconeogenesis, thus playing a major part in glucose homeostasis. Finally, the liver is the source of most of the coagulation factors and albumin, and the only organ that can produce urea from ammonia. This organ is capable of numerous metabolic reac-

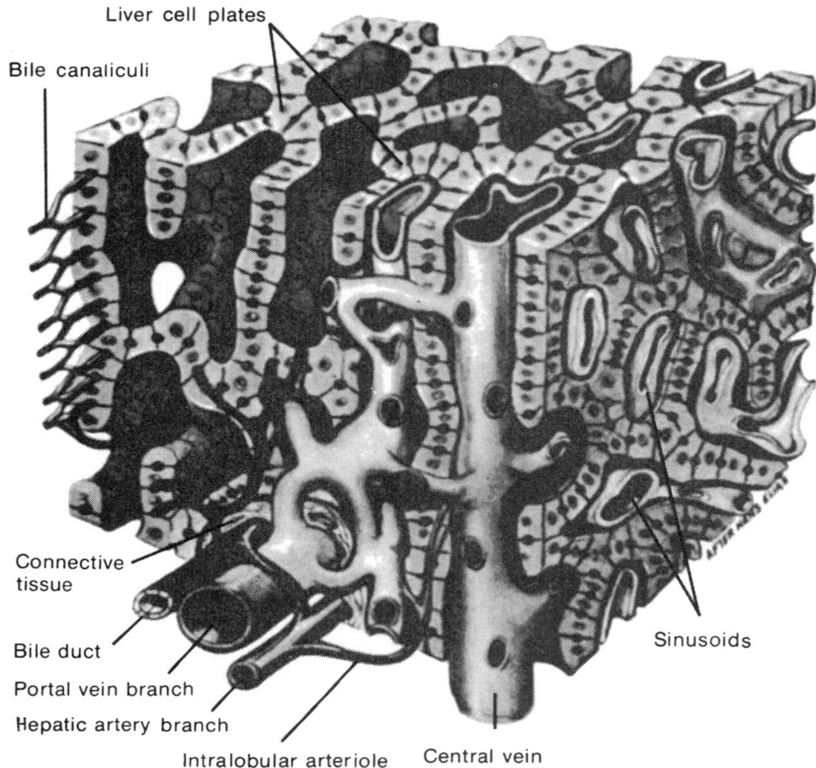

Figure 5.1. Hepatic lobular architecture. Arterial blood (for oxygenation) and intestinal venous blood (for metabolic processing) are carried to the liver by the hepatic arteries and the portal vein, respectively. After passing over the plates of hepatic parenchymal cells, this blood arrives at the central vein and flows into the caval vessels. Bile, produced by the hepatocytes, flows from the bile canaliculi to the cholangiole and then into the bile ducts of the portal canal. Thus, blood flows in a direction opposite to that of the bile. Reprinted with permission from Routh JI. Liver Function. In: Tietz NW, ed. Fundamentals of Clinical Chemistry. 2nd ed. Philadelphia: WB Saunders, 1976.

Table 5.1. Liver Zones Cirrhosis

Zone 1
Blood supply near
Metabolically most active cells—rich in oxidative enzymes, mitochondira
Most resistant to destruction by pathologic process
Zone 2
Intermediate in proximity to blood supply and level of metabolic activity and susceptibility to injury
Zone 3
Furthest from blood supply
Most vulnerable to injury
Least able to regenerate
Rich in anaerobic enzymes—lactate dehydrogenase and enzymes of drug metabolism

tions and interconversions, without which the organism would not survive. To expedite this vast diversity of functions, the liver is endowed with a multiplicity of enzymes strategically deployed in cytosol, endoplasmic reticulum, Golgi, mitochondria, lysosomes, and peroxisomes. Indeed, the list of metabolic capabilities of the liver reads like a textbook of biochemistry.

Uptake of nutrients, hormones, and xenobiotics from the blood occurs at the sinusoids; also, substances are modified by the liver and are re-introduced into the blood stream at the sinusoids. These transport functions are mostly the task of the endothelial cells equipped with numerous fenestrations. Other cells localized to the sinusoids include macrophages (Kupffer cells), natural killer cells (pit cells), and lipocytes. *Macrophages* in the liver, as elsewhere, defend against invading microbes and probably play a role in removal of endotoxin and antigens. *Pit cells* participate in destruction of tumor cells and cells that have been invaded by viruses.

Lipocytes (Ito cells) store vitamin A and other retinoids. When hepatocytes are damaged, they release a protein that causes lipocytes to transform into *myofibroblast-like* cells. These cells, once activated, are believed to be the site where much of the synthesis of connective tissue and extracellular matrix protein occurs. The liver heals after minimal injury; but when the injury is repetitive (see the following section on cirrhosis), repair is chaotic and culminates in hepatic fibrosis. This distinction between a single episode of liver injury and repeated episodes is all the more striking because the liver retains a near-embryonic potential for regeneration, enabling it to survive loss of much of the organ and regain normal capacity for function. However, when the injury is repetitive, something triggers an overresponse that causes scarring instead of healing.

Carbohydrate Metabolism

Intestinal absorption of dietary sugars requires that the complex carbohydrates be hydrolyzed to monosaccharides, resulting in production of glucose, galactose, and fructose. The large quantities of carbohydrate typically ingested would suggest a high intraluminal carbohydrate concentration, driving absorption at the epithelial cell surface. At the same time, a percentage, perhaps as high as 50%, of the glucose passing through the intestinal mucosa is converted to lactate. Thus, the portal blood carries both monosaccharides and lactate to the liver for processing. The lactate is salvaged by gluconeogenesis, resulting in additional glucose for hepatocyte metabolism, glycogen synthesis, or release into the circulation. It remains unclear whether the lactate is derived from glycolytic metabolism of the intestinal epithelium in support of its own needs, or whether this conversion subserves some other purpose in the context of glucose absorption.

As the major organ sustaining the blood glucose, it should be obvious that the liver extracts minimal amounts of dietary glucose for support of its own metabolic needs. Its metabolic requirements are ordinarily satisfied through amino acid and fatty acid catabolism. Common sense reasoning has long suggested that glucose emerging from the portal vein would be promptly utilized by the liver for metabolism. Nevertheless, when this notion is experimentally tested, it is found to be not entirely true. When an animal is re-fed carbohydrate after fasting, little glucose is taken up directly, but the liver accumulates glycogen. This discrepancy between minimal glucose uptake and brisk glycogen synthesis has been called the *glucose paradox* and has been explained as follows: glucose absorbed from the gut bypasses the liver, being taken up instead by muscle that carries the glucose through glycolysis, liberating lactate, alanine, and pyruvate. These 3-carbon gluconeogenic precursors then return to the liver where they enter the gluconeogenic pathway and are incorporated into glycogen.

What is the rationale for this roundabout approach to the synthesis of glycogen? By letting other tissues have the first chance at the absorbed glucose, the liver adjusts its metabolism to the metabolic state of the entire organism, no matter what substrate emerges from the portal vein. In so doing, the liver exploits its enormous metabolic repertoire for the greater good of the organism.

It is important to recognize that, despite its potential for substantial glycolytic capacity, only under extremely adverse circumstances does the liver produce much lactate. Again, common sense would tell us that if the major body sources of lactate are muscle and red cell, with the liver assigned the task of energy conservation through gluconeogenesis, then net hepatic lactate production would defeat the purpose of this cycle and result in severe systemic lactic acidemia. This situation occurs clinically, however, when severe hypoxia forces the hepatocyte to rely upon glycolysis for survival; muscle tissue simultaneously releases large amounts of lactate for the same reason. Thus, deprived of hepatic gluconeogenesis, the organism becomes both acidotic and hypoglycemic.

Hepatic disposition of the other two common dietary hexoses, galactose and fructose, occurs by differing pathways. Galactose is converted to glucose-6-phosphate (see Chapter 11), and then enters the total glucose pool in the hepatocyte. Galactose-1-phosphate uridyl transferase is an important enzyme in this conversion pathway, the genetic deficiency of which results in the disorder *galactosemia*. However, fructose is phosphorylated to fructose-1-phosphate and ultimately is converted to triose phosphates, which can either proceed to form pyruvate or be utilized for gluconeogenesis. Interruption of this pathway by genetic deficiency of fructose-bisphosphate aldolase, the enzyme responsible for cleavage of the hexose to two triose units, results in the disorder *hereditary fructose intolerance* (see Chapter 11).

It is important to recognize that, despite the ability of the body to convert these hexoses to glucose, normal synthetic reactions require galactose to produce complex structural materials like glycoprotein and glycolipid. Both of these classes of complex molecules are galactose-rich. Thus, the human organism comes equipped to convert dietary glucose to galactose to protect against galactose deficiency; the physician can safely eliminate all sources of dietary galactose in treatment of galactosemia because of this synthetic capacity.

Lipid Metabolism

Central to its role in lipid metabolism is the liver's capacity to synthesize cholesterol de novo from acetyl CoA; a major portion of this cholesterol then is converted to bile acids. This synthetic ability is important because of the critical function that bile acids have in digestion of dietary lipid in the intestine, contributing significantly to their solubilization, absorption, and transport. It should be clear that the insolubility of lipid in the fundamentally aqueous human organism is incompatible with the great demands for fat as a source of energy for muscle, heart, liver, and cell membrane synthesis. Thus, without the presence of bile acids, much dietary lipid would pass through the intestine, creating both an energy deficit and steatorrhea (stools with high fat content); these circumstances are illustrated by biliary atresia, in which clinical malnutrition and steatorrhea develop.

Bile acids act on intestinal lipid to create an emulsification of tiny particles, consisting predominantly of triglycerides. This enables the pancreatic lipase to cleave fatty acids from the glycerol skeleton (Figure 5.2), even though the protein itself is surrounded by water. The increase in polarity resulting from liberation of the free carboxyl group leads to a corresponding increase in aqueous solubility and improved absorption. This absorption occurs through formation of micelles; bile salts also are critically important for this process. (This is more extensively discussed in Chapter 15.) Medium chain triglycerides contain fatty acids that are shorter than 12 carbons. When these are hydrolyzed by pancreatic lipase, the medium chain fatty acids enter the portal circulation and are carried directly to the liver for metabolism.

For many years it has been assumed that most synthesis of new fat derives from excess dietary carbohydrate and that de novo lipogenesis occurs in the liver. Remarkably, there is now evidence to suggest that little de novo synthesis occurs in the adult human liver. But, it is clear that individuals ingesting an excess of carbohydrate gain weight over time. How are these observations reconciled? Studies have revealed that when a modest, but not marked, excess of carbohydrate is consumed for several weeks the main effect is a dramatic suppression of fatty acid oxidation with carbohydrate supplanting lipid as an energy source. Consequently, fat stores are spared while carbohydrate is burned. Nevertheless, because human liver possesses the enzymatic machinery to carry out de novo lipogenesis, the question "What

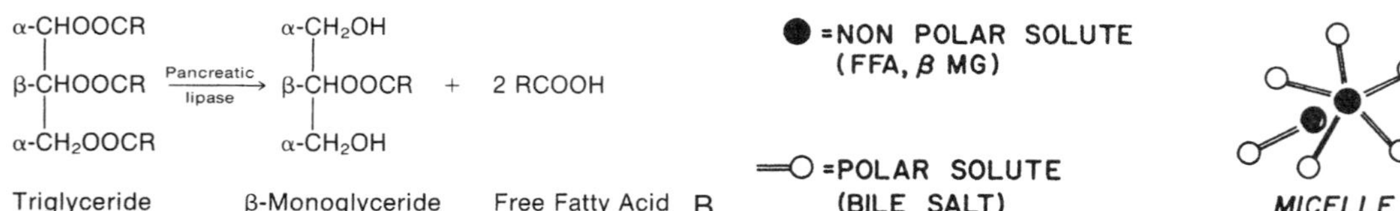

Figure 5.2. (A) Action of pancreatic lipase on intestinal triglycerides. The enzyme releases two free fatty acid moles from each triglyceride molecule, leaving a *β*-monoglyceride product as well. (B) Structure of a micelle. In an aqueous medium, the nonpolar free fatty acids (FFA) and *β*-monoglycerides (MG) are solubilized by association with polar bile acids. Reprinted with permission from Achkar E, Farmer RC, Fleshler B. Clinical gastroenterology. 2nd ed. Baltimore: Williams & Wilkins, 1992:302.

function does this pathway serve?" needs to be asked. Surely, de novo lipogenesis is likely to be important in utero when the pace of myelination increases during the third trimester. An additional function may be to produce malonyl CoA, which, as a precursor to fat, functions as the major metabolic signal curtailing β-oxidation and ketogenesis (Chapter 9). Other products of de novo lipogenesis (eg, palmitate) also may exert a regulatory influence. As we will see elsewhere, the lipogenic pathway can be activated in pathologic states such as diabetes mellitus, glucose-6-phosphatase deficiency, and various other hypertriglyceridemic states.

Quantitatively, the major aspect of lipid metabolism that occurs in the liver is conversion to ketone bodies. Despite the attention that these compounds attract under conditions that upset homeostasis, they are normally present at low concentrations (β-OH-butyrate + acetoacetate < 0.5 mM). Because the ketogenic amino acid leucine is completely metabolized in muscle (see following text), it should be apparent that muscle uses a considerable amount of ketone bodies that are produced in the liver from lipid. What distinguishes the muscle as a ketolytic tissue from liver as a ketogenic one is the presence of the enzyme, 3-keto acid CoA transferase in muscle (also brain), permitting transfer of a CoA moiety from succinyl CoA to acetoacetate to form acetoacetyl CoA (Figure 5.3). The formation of the compound 3-hydroxy-3-methyl-glutaryl (HMG) CoA is key to the entire process; 3-hydroxy-3-methyl-glutaryl CoA can be produced through direct catabolism of leucine in muscle or by condensation in liver of acetoacetyl CoA (from beta-oxidation) with acetyl CoA (from any source). In muscle, this compound is cleaved to acetyl CoA and acetoacetate, the latter to be converted to its CoA derivative. Conversely, in liver, HMG CoA is cleaved to acetyl CoA and acetoacetate with release of the latter into the blood for transport to peripheral tissues. Hence, the liver produces, while muscle utilizes acetoacetate.

Synthesis and catabolism of lipoproteins are functions of the liver that are qualitatively as important as ketogenesis, but occur at a smaller quantitative level. Lipoproteins are distinguished by their relative densities, due to variable proportions of protein and lipid, and subserve the need to transport lipid intact from tissue to tissue. Details of the metabolism of these molecules are extensively discussed elsewhere in this text (Chapter 15).

Amino Acid Metabolism

In health, the body utilizes dietary amino acids for three purposes: endogenous protein synthesis, production of specialized molecules (eg, hormones), and to generate chemical energy. Although energy can be derived from catabolism of one or all dietary amino acids, synthesis of normal body protein requires a high degree of selectivity and an adequate supply of the requisite individual amino acids. Thus, humans are equipped to convert one amino acid to another by transamination to off-set fluctuations in dietary intake from meal to meal. This is a primary function of the liver, and the amino acids that can be interconverted are called *nonessential.* Others, for which human enzyme systems are not able to fashion the carbon skeleton, are known as *essential*. In the case of deficiency of one or more of the essential amino acids, endogenous protein synthesis will be severely hampered, and the bulk of the remainder will be utilized for energy production or glycogenesis via gluconeogenesis. Hence, the liver has a decisive role in homeostatic maintenance of amino acid supply, and functions as the main site of coordination between amino acid and carbohydrate metabolism as well. Although such functions clearly require tight regulation of the pathways involved, little is known of how the liver communicates with peripheral tissues in determining overall body needs.

Metabolism of the branched chain amino acids (BCAAs) valine, leucine, and isoleucine occurs mostly in muscle, thus constituting a major exception to the general rule that the liver is central to amino acid metabolism. Although the liver is the major ketogenic organ, catabolizing fatty acids and releasing ketone bodies for peripheral breakdown, muscle tissue is the primary location for production of ketone bodies from leucine and isoleucine; valine results in production of succinyl CoA, as does part of the isoleucine molecule. Hence, muscle can completely catabolize the branched chain amino acids, independent of the liver. Despite

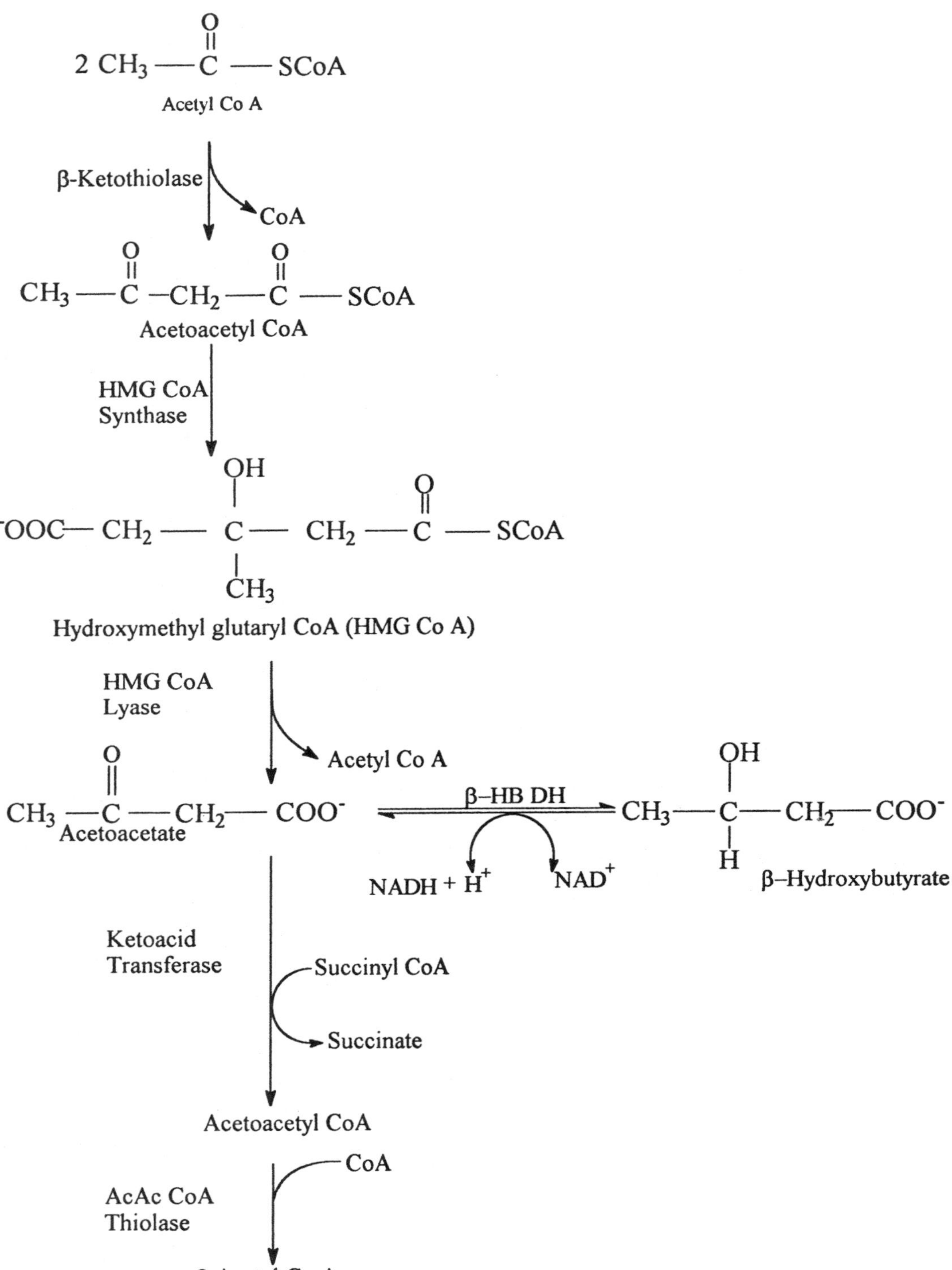

Figure 5.3. The pathway of hepatic ketogenesis. In liver, production of the key compound 3-hydroxy-3-methyl-glutaryl CoA (HMG CoA) depends upon the action of β-ketothiolase for formation of acetoacetyl CoA. Note that CoA is an obligatory cofactor in the process of formation of free acetoacetate, at which point the freed acetyl CoA can be reused. Acetoacetate is in equilibrium with β-hydroxybutyrate, as mediated by the enzyme β-hydroxybutyrate dehydrogenase (β-HB DH), an NADH-dependent reaction.

this, liver also can metabolize the branched chain carbon skeletons.

After dietary protein meets needs for new protein synthesis and for synthesis of specialized molecules, any excess is metabolized in liver, except for the BCAAs, as noted previously in the text. Because other nutrients usually are available in a mixed meal, the carbon skeleton of ingested amino acids are not completely metabolized by the tricarboxylic acid (TCA) cycle. Rather, these carbon skeletons are used to make new glucose. Despite the fact that amino acid oxidation is not complete in liver, amino acids, nonetheless, provide liver with one half of its energy requirement. It has been suggested that by delegating the task of metabolizing most amino acids to liver, the liver can export glucose to be used by extrahepatic organs. Thus, extrahepatic sites no longer need to synthesize a wide array of amino acid catabolizing enzymes and, instead, metabolize glucose. A considerable savings in energy results from not having to synthesize these enzymes. It should be clear, then, that gluconeogenesis is a major means to dispose of dietary protein.

Why are the BCAAs catabolized in muscle and not in liver? Again, it has been speculated that if BCAA oxidation occurred in liver, the liver would have to divert O_2 from other processes (eg, detoxification) to consume the BCAAs. Seen in another light, if amino acids were catabolized completely in liver, the process would generate an excess of adenosine triphosphate (ATP)—a situation that will not occur because of at least two reasons: first, it is wasteful, and second, ATP as a polyanion would disrupt cellular function. Inhibition of pyruvate dehydrogenase by ATP and acetyl CoA formed from amino acid catabolism, and of pyruvate kinase by high alanine and decreased fructose-1,6-diphosphate prevent the liver from completely oxidizing the amino acids. However, the almost constant demand for ATP by muscle, a tissue richly supplied with oxygen, makes muscle an excellent site for BCAA oxidation. Given that 1 mole each of leucine, isoleucine, and valine provides a maximal yield of 101 moles of ATP, the BCAAs also are an excellent source for this ATP. Thus, assigning BCAA metabolism to muscle permits liver to maintain its extraordinary capability to perform numerous biochemical processes—a capability it exercises while defending the nutritional integrity of all cells. Note that during fasting, the three branched chain amino acids combined represent only about 9% of the total amino acids released from skeletal muscle, as compared to alanine, glutamine, and glycine, which represent 50%. Because glutamine and alanine represent only about 10% of muscle protein, but constitute half of the amino acids exported by muscle, it is evident that the branched chain amino acids furnish the amino groups to transaminate α-ketoglutarate to glutamate and pyruvate to alanine. Therefore, muscle plays a major role in both gluconeogenesis and ureagenesis while conserving for itself the carbon skeletons of the branched chain amino acids. These carbon skeletons provide muscle a high-energy yield in the form of ATP per amino acid molecule that is completely catabolized.

Hepatic protein synthesis is impressive and should not be overlooked; it amounts to about 48 g of protein per day. Albumin is the major protein synthesized (ca. 12 g), but other vital proteins made by liver include coagulation factors, various transport proteins, and inhibitors of serine proteases, like α_1-antitrypsin.

THE NITROGEN ECONOMY AND HYPERAMMONEMIA

Hyperammonemia represents a failure by the liver to dispose of excess ammonia, which is a *neurotoxic agent* that is derived from catabolism of nitrogen-containing compounds. Ammonia normally is converted to urea in the liver and is excreted as such in the urine. Hyperammonemia is, therefore, a disorder representing abnormal nitrogen retention. To understand the pathogenesis of hyperammonemia, a basic comprehension of body nitrogen economy is necessary.

Most body nitrogen is contained in protein, which constitutes 20% of adult dry body weight. This protein, both structural and enzymatic, must be constantly replenished if nitrogen balance is to be maintained. Table 5.2 lists the amount of nitrogen lost in the stool, sweat, and urine, as well as the nitrogen needed for normal growth and replacement. The requirement for protein is, for all practical purposes, a constant one because no appreciable amount of protein is stored. In Chapter 1, we discussed that protein molecules are relatively labile, being stabilized by weak forces; thus,

Table 5.2B. Normal Nitrogen Balance

1. Must replace: Nitrogen lost + nitrogen needed for growth
2. 1st year: Losses = 60 to 150mg/kg/day (urine, stool, sweat)
   Growth = 100 mg/kg
   Total = 160 to 250 mg/kg/day
3. In terms of protein this amounts to:
   1st year requirement: 1.5 g protein/kg/day
   2nd year requirement: 1.0 g protein/kg/day
   or
   6 to 7 per cent total calories

they must undergo constant degradation and resynthesis.

As we noted in Chapter 3, an important function of the nephron is to reabsorb physiologically important molecules, such as amino acids. Because certain amino acids cannot be synthesized de novo by the human organism (essential amino acids), this renal mechanism generally functions to the body's advantage. However, it must be remembered that dietary protein intake of the average human usually is indiscriminate with respect to both quantity and quality. Hence, the potential for accumulation of amino acids would exist if intake and renal conservation exceeded the body's requirements, were it not for the capacity to utilize such excess for nonsynthetic purposes. Thus, the inability to store excess dietary protein as body protein accounts for the presence of ammonia in body fluids because the primary result of excess dietary nitrogen is the oxidation of the constituent amino acids. The basis for the release of ammonia during this process is that catabolism of all amino acids is absolutely dependent upon removal of all amino groups because no aminated intermediate can enter the Krebs cycle.

Remember that transamination translocates amino groups from amino acids to α-keto acids (eg, as between alanine and α-ketoglutarate, producing pyruvate and glutamine). When α-ketoglutarate is converted to glutamate, a gluconeogenic substrate is temporarily lost. If the amino group can be removed from glutamate, then the carbon skeleton (α-ketoglutarate) can participate in gluconeogenesis. Two routes are available to deaminate amino acids and feed substrate into gluconeogenesis: (*a*) the glutamate dehydrogenase reaction

$$\text{Glutamate} + \text{NADP}^+ + H_2O \rightarrow \alpha\text{-KG} + NH_3 + \text{NADPH} + H^+$$

and (*b*) participation of aspartate in the urea cycle. When aspartate donates its amino group it becomes oxaloacetate, which has several possible outcomes, one of which is participation in gluconeogenesis (see the text below that discusses the urea cycle).

As described previously in the text, ammonia is produced by the glutamate dehydrogenase reaction. The amino acids in excess of basal requirements are catabolized. In all but a few cases, such as lysine, the first step in this oxidation pathway is the removal of the amino group via a transamination reaction, forming the keto analogue of the amino acid. Subsequent transamination to form glutamate and metabolism of glutamate via the glutamate dehydrogenase reaction generates ammonia. Further catabolism of various organic acid derivatives of the amino acids allows the end-product to enter the Krebs cycle, where it is catabolized to carbon dioxide and water and results in formation of ATP. Of course, as we have noted, a major fraction of these organic acids will be used in gluconeogenesis.

Free Ammonia Toxicity

Note that the total plasma amino acid concentration is equal to approximately 50 mg/dl, although the blood ammonia concentration is dramatically lower—roughly three orders of magnitude less—and is measured in μg/dl. The difference results from the organism's need to protect itself from the devastating toxicity of free ammonia. The biochemical basis for this toxicity remains incompletely defined and is discussed in the section on hepatic encephalopathy. Despite the controversy regarding mechanisms, the toxic properties of this simple molecule are apparent because of the clinical response of the brain to elevation of blood ammonia. Accordingly, the survival of the organism depends upon maintenance of ammonia at very low concentrations in all body tissues, especially the brain. Because protein intake in excess of need results in amino acid oxidation with simultaneous liberation of amino nitrogen, a land-based existence demands a means of ammonia detoxification. This means is the urea cycle (Krebs-Henseleit cycle), which is depicted in Figure 5.4. Because it is unlikely that excessive protein intake can overload the cycle, increases in blood ammo-

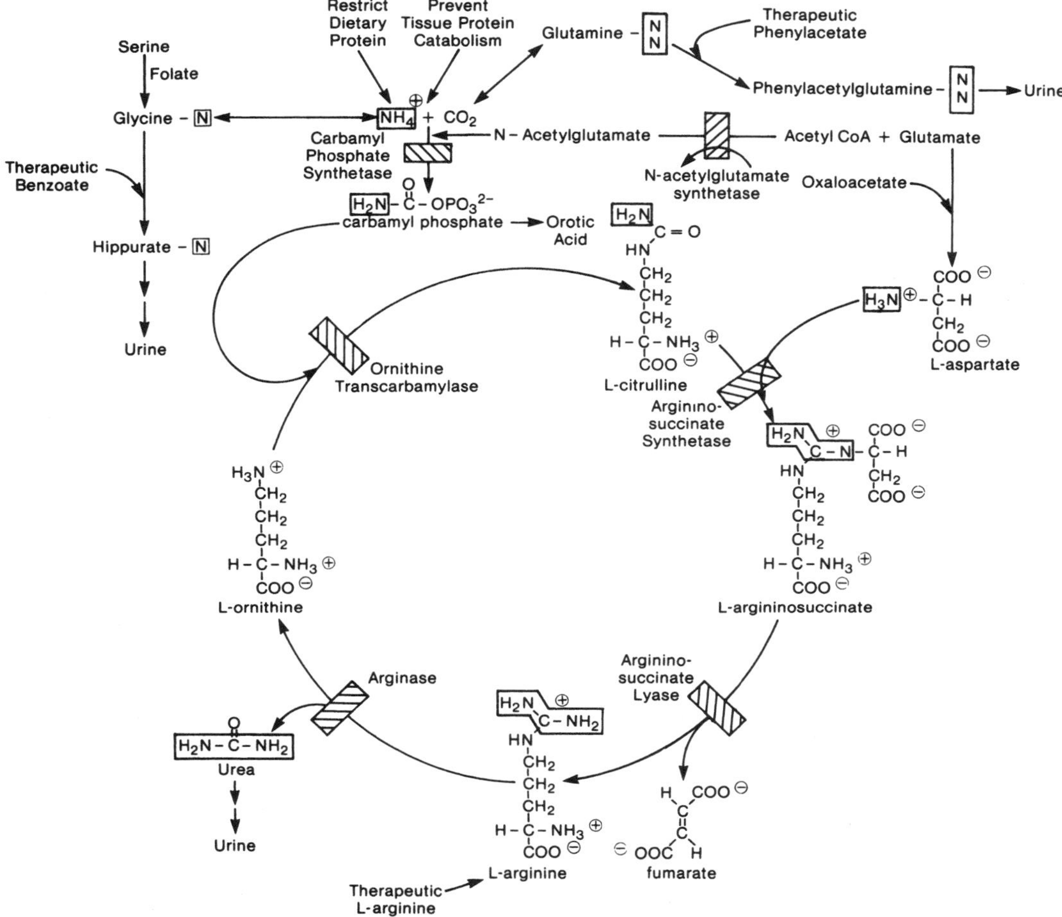

Figure 5.4. The Krebs-Henseleit (urea) cycle. The origins and disposition of waste nitrogen are enclosed in boxes; overall, the cycle operates to fix waste nitrogen into urea for detoxification and excretion. Genetic defects in the pathway are shown as hatched bars; all are inherited as autosomal recessive traits except the ornithine transcarbamylase deficiency, which is an X-linked disorder. A defect in the enzyme N-acetylglutamate synthetase will interfere with activation of carbamyl phosphate synthetase, the normal process by which urea cycle activity is regulated. Generation of L-aspartate from oxaloacetate occurs by means of the enzyme aspartate aminotransferase, which results in production of a keto acid metabolic substrate (eg, pyruvate from alanine). Therapeutic modalities also are shown when each is maximally effective in removing waste nitrogen. Reprinted with permission from Shils ME, Olson JA, Shike M, et al. Modern Nutrition in Health and Disease. 8th ed. Baltimore: Williams & Wilkins, 1994: 12.

nia represent decreases in disposition. This can occur either by fewer functioning hepatocytes (eg, alcoholic cirrhosis) or impairment of the urea cycle at one or more steps.

The Urea Cycle

We have noted previously that glutamate-derived ammonia provides substrate directly for the carbamyl phosphate synthetase (CPS) reaction (Figure 5.4). In addition, there are numerous reports of partial urea cycle activity present in a variety of tissues other than liver, the only organ in which the cycle is known to be complete. Subsequent, careful investigations have demonstrated that the generation of urea cycle intermediates through partial cycle activity is important to both local detoxification, in nonhepatic sites, and the main-

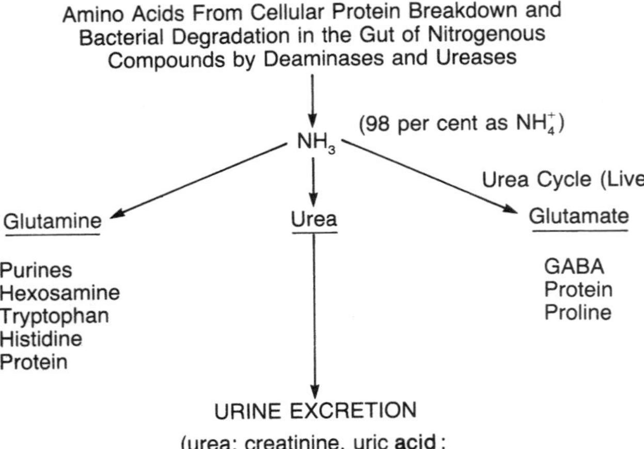

Figure 5.5. Alternative means of waste nitrogen disposal. The chief alternative routes are the synthesis of glutamate and glutamine, each of which can be incorporated further into other synthetic pathways. However, the latter pathways are strictly regulated genetically, making it impossible to produce more under conditions of increased substrate. Thus, glutamate and glutamine are the metabolic "sinks" for excess ammonia.

tenance of low free ammonia in blood, while simultaneously contributing precursors for the complete urea cycle in liver. These interorgan relationships are complex (Figure 5.5); for example, glutamine produced in muscle by glutamine synthetase serves as a metabolic fuel to intestine. The intestine releases free ammonia, alanine (formed from transamination of pyruvate), and citrulline. Although the free ammonia and alanine reach the liver, the citrulline is taken up by kidney, which converts it to arginine, thereafter releasing it to the liver for conversion to urea and ornithine. Thus, waste-nitrogen disposal is not a task only for the liver. In fact, muscle and kidney are major sources of glutamine for liver, feeding into the CPS reaction.

At the same time, free ammonia is processed by the liver, being introduced into the urea cycle by an interesting de novo synthetic process. The initial entry of NH_3 into the cycle is dependent upon the enzymatic (CPS)-mediated formation of carbamyl phosphate from CO_2 and ammonia. As discussed in Chapter 1, the catalytic function of an enzyme is directly related to molecular conformational changes occurring as a consequence of substrate binding. Binding of CPS to its substrates appears to be dependent upon a rapid shift from the dimeric to the monomeric form induced by binding of the ligand N-acetylglutamate (NAG) to the enzyme. Thus, NAG is an activator of CPS and its availability is, therefore, essential to the normal operation of the urea cycle.

Synthesis of NAG is exclusively mitochondrial and proceeds by the following reaction:

$$\text{AcetylCoA} + \text{glutamate} \rightarrow \text{N-acetylglutamate} + \text{CoA}$$

mediated by N-acetylglutamate synthetase. Consideration of the role of NAG in activation of CPS, the portal into the urea cycle, should reveal that metabolic fluxes of carbohydrate and fat make the predominant contributions to availability of acetyl CoA. Likewise, α-ketoglutarate produced by the Krebs cycle, which is the transamination partner for formation of glutamate, is equally important. Thus, by indirectly affecting availability of substrates for synthesis of NAG, metabolism of sugars, fats, and amino acids impacts upon regulation of the urea cycle.

Following formation of carbamyl phosphate, this one-carbon compound is combined with the C5-amino group of ornithine to form citrulline. The combination of the C5-amino group and carbamyl phosphate is the nidus of the urea molecule ultimately generated, a process that essentially is complete with the next step. In this next step, aspartic acid is linked through its amino group to the carbonyl group of the carbamyl phosphate moiety, forming argininosuccinic acid. With formation of argininosuccinic acid, the two waste-nitrogen atoms destined for excretion as urea are now covalently linked, having been derived from free ammonia and aspartic acid. Alternatively, the first nitrogen may arrive in the liver by way of peripherally-formed citrulline (see previous text). In neither case, however, does hepatic ornithine supply nitrogen for urea synthesis.

Cleavage of argininosuccinic acid with production of the four-carbon dicarboxylic acid, fumaric acid, permits generation of one NADH. When fumarate is converted to malic acid in the Krebs cycle, NADH is generated. And when the electrons carried by NADH are transferred through the electron transport chain, 3 moles of ATP are generated. Consequently, energy needed to fix ammonia and energy produced essentially are in balance. The product of this reaction is arginine, a molecule that may be viewed as a guanidino-substituted ornithine. Cleavage of the guanidinium group generates urea and ornithine. Urea formation thus results in excretion of two waste nitrogen atoms whereas regenerating the original ornithine renews the catalytic compound that will bear the next NH_2 groups to be excreted.

Aspartate, which supplies the second of the two NH_2 groups excreted as urea, is easily generated by the addition of an amino group to oxaloacetate during a transamination reaction mediated by *aspartate transaminase;* glutamate is a major donor of the amino group during this process. Aspartate transaminase, a cellular enzyme liberated into the circulation with tissue damage, is identical with the familiar *glutamate-oxaloacetate transaminase (SGOT)* commonly used for laboratory diagnosis of cardiac and liver disease. This enzyme is important to the urea cycle because of how α-ketoglutarate can be reversibly transaminated from virtually any other amino acid to form glutamate. Thus, using glutamate as a metabolic "go-between," the amino-nitrogen from any amino acid can enter the urea cycle.

Ammonia Disposal Independent of the Urea Cycle

Free ammonia is so toxic to the central nervous system that means of protection have been developed through evolutionary pressures (Figure 5.5), in addition to the urea cycle. Note that the theoretical capacity of the urea cycle in a normal subject to handle waste nitrogen exceeds any normal dietary protein intake. Thus, the presence of additional safeguards against elevation of free ammonia in body fluids provides convincing evidence for the absolute need to maintain low levels of ammonia.

The glutamate dehydrogenase reaction can be used to form glutamate from α-ketoglutarate and free ammonia. In an additional step mediated by glutamine synthetase, glutamine can be generated from glutamate and free ammonia:

$$\text{glutamate} + NH_2 + ATP \xrightarrow{Mg^{++}} \text{glutamine} + ADP + Pi$$

Or:

$$\alpha\text{-ketoglutarate} + 2NH_2 + ATP \xrightarrow{Mg^{++}} \text{glutamine} + ADP + Pi$$

These two reactions create what often is called a *metabolic "sink"* for excess ammonia, in addition to forming the synthetic pathway for an important precursor in purine synthesis (see Chapter 16). Because the urea cycle is complete only in liver, the presence of glutamine synthetase in brain, skeletal muscle, heart, lung, and kidney maintains ammonia within safe limits in these organs. Glutamine also is a nontoxic way to transport ammonia in the blood; it carries its "cargo" to the liver for ureagenesis.

Apart from these reactions, an additional means exists—transamination—the importance of which cannot be overstated. As we have noted, during transamination, the amino group of glutamate can be passed along to the carbon skeletons of other amino acids that are derived from glucose. A prime example of this is the transamination from glutamate to pyruvate to form α-ketoglutarate and alanine, mediated by alanine-pyruvate transaminase (ALT). This enzyme also is used in a laboratory test to assess cardiac and liver damage. Note that not only does the transamination process link ammonia metabolism to nonessential amino acid synthesis, but it also provides a major link between the nitrogen economy and gluconeogenesis. Once again, we see the beauty and are forced to marvel at a system that, over eons, has learned to do more with less, so to speak!

Hepatic Encephalopathy

Hepatic encephalopathy, primarily seen in adults, gets its name from the neuropsychiatric syndrome associated with advanced liver failure. Debate continues over whether ammonia is the direct or the only cause of the encephalopathy and has led to a constructive view of the pathogenesis of the encephalopathy. A prevailing belief exists that hepatic encephalopathy results from multiple complex biochemical changes within the brain, both regional and general. Thus, there is no necessary conflict between the notion that impairment of normal ammonia metabolism in the liver is the cause and the belief that there is a complex metabolic basis for hepatic encephalopathy.

Hepatic encephalopathy usually is associated with advanced liver failure, which may be precipitated by ingestion of protein, bleeding into the gastrointestinal tract, or acid-base imbalances. It also may represent the effects of worsening liver function without a specific precipitating event occurring. Hepatic encephalopathy is one of many metabolic encephalopathies (see Chapter 26) in which no permanent structural changes in neurons occur. As the encephalopathy worsens, symptoms evolve from mild confusion to lethargy and personality changes to disorientation and confusion that culminates in coma. This progression may be encountered in any metabolic encephalopathy and, therefore, is not specific for hepatic encephalopathy. But evidence of advanced liver disease as manifested by jaundice, decreased serum albumin, ascites, abnormal coagulation tests unresponsive to vitamin K administration, increased blood ammonia, and evidence of portal hypertension (dilated abdominal veins) suggest hepatic failure as the basic cause of the encephalopathy.

Because the progression of hepatic encephalopathy leads to greater depression of neural function, it is believed that the compounds that accumulate because of liver failure act to increase inhibitory influences on nervous transmission. Because the brain is not equipped with the urea cycle, immediate removal of ammonia depends on glutamine synthetase. This enzyme is principally localized to astrocytic cells. Cerebrospinal fluid (CSF) glutamine is elevated in hepatic encephalopathy and may be used as an index of brain ammonia accumulation. Also, increased ammonia in the brain interferes with neurotransmission, particularly at glutaminergic synapses, and contributes to astrocytic dysfunction and development of cerebral edema.

In addition to ammonia, mercaptans and short and long chain fatty acids accumulate in cirrhosis. The production of *mercaptans* results from impaired metabolism of methionine, whereas the fatty acids collect because hepatic fatty acid oxidation likewise is impaired. All of these compounds can behave as neurotoxins and may contribute to the clinical manifestations of hepatic encephalopathy.

Gamma amino butyric acid (GABA), the main inhibitory neurotransmitter in brain, acts by increasing neuronal permeability to Cl^-, which causes the membrane to become hyperpolarized and makes it more refractory to transmit an action potential (see Chapter 26). In hepatic encephalopathy, there appears to be a benzodiazepine-like compound produced that augments the activation of the gamma amino butyric acid receptor, leading to central nervous system depression. Whether these benzodiazepine-like compounds are produced endogenously or ingested (xenobiotics) is unknown.

DERANGEMENTS OF AMINO ACID METABOLISM IN LIVER FAILURE MAY CONTRIBUTE TO HEPATIC ENCEPHALOPATHY

In addition to the rampant hyperammonemia that attends cirrhosis, there are instructive derangements in the plasma amino acid pattern of these patients. Most notably, the aromatic amino acids increase while the BCAAs decrease. When liver function progressively declines, the aromatic amino acids exit the liver without having been metabolized to any significant degree. Because peripheral tissues have little ability to metabolize the aromatic amino acids phenylalanine, tyrosine, and tryptophan, their levels increase.

With respect to the BCAAs, plasma insulin concentrations remain somewhat elevated in cirrhosis because of decreased clearance of the insulin by the diseased liver. Insulin increases glucose uptake in muscle; it also increases uptake of BCAAs. Because muscle is the predominant site of BCAA catabolism, the insulin effect on uptake accentuates the role of muscle in disposal of BCAAs.

In terms of hepatic encephalopathy, it has been suggested that if phenylalanine and tyrosine increase, they could inhibit tyrosine hydroxylase, thereby hampering synthesis of dopamine and norepinephrine. This might lead to synthesis of "*false neurotransmitters*" like octopamine and β-phenylethanolamine by decarboxylation in the large intestine, which could compete at catecholamine receptor sites, thereby blocking neural transmission.

The typical neurologic findings of hepatic encephalopathy—asterixis, myoclonus, grimacing, and others generally associated with any toxic encephalopathy—thus are believed to stem from several biochemical dysfunctions, as discussed previously in the text. Yet, although there are many hypotheses as to what causes the neuropsychiatric symptoms of hepatic encephalopathy, we still do not fully understand how hepatic dysfunction causes central nervous system dysfunction.

From the clinician's point of view, however, it is important to note that little difference exists between the constellation of findings in hepatic encephalopathy and hyperammonemia of any cause. Indeed, a recent report details the onset of an inborn error of the urea cycle in an older individual as a result of anticonvulsant therapy. Consequently, blood ammonia levels should be measured immediately, with other parameters of liver function, whenever this syndrome is suspected; disposal of ammonia is just as much a "liver function" as metabolism of bilirubin. (Review of the biochemistry that is addressed in the previous section of this chapter should convince the reader of this.)

Primary Disorders of the Urea Cycle

Interruptions of the urea cycle due to inherited genetic defects have been reported for each of the enzymatic steps. Because this pathway is vital to maintenance of nitrogen homeostasis and detoxification of ammonia, any defect in its operation predictably will result in hyperammonemia. However, as with virtually all inborn errors, clinical variations exist within each designated disorder, presumably deriving from the degree of residual enzyme activity and environmental stress imposed upon the individual. The literature is growing concerning the adult onset varieties of these disorders in previously asymptomatic adults. This underscores the importance of assessment of ammonia simultaneously with bilirubin and other accepted parameters of liver function in any encephalopathic individual at any age. These variations are summarized in Table 5.3, with inheritance patterns provided for each.

It is important to note that ornithine transcarbamylase (OTC) deficiency is unique among this group because it is inherited as an X-linked trait, which behaves, in some respects, as a dominant trait in the heterozygous female. Thus, at a functional level, presence of the abnormal ornithine transcarbamylase gene often is more visible than in other cases. Consequently, important clues can be elicited by taking a careful history that includes neonatal male deaths and maternal protein intolerance associated with migraine-like headaches. In fact, clinically affected female heterozygotes have become ill or died because of hyperammonemia that was not recognized until late in the course. However, the explosive neonatal hyperammonemia caused by the abnormal gene almost is exclusively seen in male infants.

The general principles regarding treatment of urea cycle defects follow the biochemical events in normal ammonia metabolism. For the male infant affected with fulminant-onset hyperammonemia, the two key treatments are discontinuation of protein intake and, whenever possible, hemodialysis. It is imperative to note that discontinuation of protein does not equal removal of all caloric sources because deprivation of calories is likely to exacerbate the hyperammonemia as a result of muscle catabolism. Chronic therapy involves supply of marginally adequate protein for normal growth with calories delivered as carbohydrate and fat, and chemical agents that assist in alternate means of ammonia disposal. These treatment modalities are extensively reviewed in the texts listed in the suggested reading section at the end of this chapter.

Secondary Hyperammonemia in Organic Acidemias

The general symptom complex of irritability, lethargy, and poor feeding associated with hyperammonemia is common to many other diverse disorders in the young infant. However, while searching for the cause of elevated blood ammonia, urine must be examined for ketones and organic acids because of the frequent association of an organic acidemia and secondary hyperammonemia. This secondary hyperammonemia occurs by an instructive mechanism, which shows how a single enzyme defect can disrupt other, apparently unrelated reactions.

Table 5.3. Urea Cycle Defects and Hyperammonemia Syndromes

CONDITION	GENETICS	CLINICAL FINDINGS	BLOOD AMMONIA*	AMINO ACID ELEVATIONS IN PLASMA	URINARY METABOLITES	ENZYME DEFECT (TISSUE TO ASSAY)	TREATMENT
Carbamyl phosphate synthetase deficiency	AR	Neonatal catastrophe	3+	Glutamine, alanine, lysine	Normal orotic acid	Carbamyl phosphate synthetase (liver, jejunum)	Hemodialysis or peritoneal dialysis ↓Protein intake Benzoate or phenylacetate Keto-analogues
Ornithine transcarbamylase deficiency	XD	1. Neonatal catastrophe 2. Hypotonia, lethargy secondary to protein intolerance 3. Variability in female	2+ to 3+	Glutamine, alanine, lysine	Orotic acid↑	Ornithine transcarbamylase (liver, jejunum)	Same as above
Citrullinemia	AR	Severe neonatal presentation Subacute Occasional normal adults	Usually 2+ to 3+ after protein	Citrulline	3+ Citrulline + Neutral acidic amino acids	Argininosuccinic acid synthetase (white blood cells, skin fibroblasts, liver)	Protein restriction, benzoate, arginine
Argininosuccinicaciduria	AR	Severe Subacute Ataxia, convulsions Friable hair	2+ after protein normal fasting	Argininosuccinic acid	Argininosuccinic acid, glutamine, alanine, lysine, ± orotic acid†	Argininosuccinase (red and white blood cells)	Protein restriction, benzoate Arginine
Hyperargininemia	AR	Neurologic, hepatomegaly	2+	Arginine	Arginine, cystine, lysine, ornithine	Arginase (red blood cells)	Protein restriction
Hyperornithinemia	AR	Protein intolerance Lethargy, ataxia, convulsions	2+	Ornithine	Homocitrulline, ornithine		
Ornithinemia with gyrate atrophy	AR	↓Visual acuity → blindness	normal	Ornithine	Ornithine	Ornithine amino transferase	Protein restriction, creatine
Lysinuric protein intolerance	AR	Protein intolerance, mental retardation	2+	Ornithine	Lysine, cystine, citrulline, arginine	Defective transport of dibasic amino acids	Citrulline

* Degree of elevation: + mildly elevated; 2+ moderately elevated; 3+ markedly elevated.
† ± occasional finding.

Recapitulation of the role of N-acetylglutamate (NAG) in activation of the CPS reaction will remind the reader that NAG facilitates a rapid shift of CPS from the inactive dimeric form of the protein to an active monomer. Because NAG is synthesized de novo from acetyl CoA and glutamate, any decrease in availability of one or both of these substrates will diminish NAG production, hence CPS activation. Availability of CoA becomes a limiting factor in cell metabolism in the organic acidemias because acyl CoA intermediates build up as a result of the metabolic block. In addition, these acyl CoA intermediates are thought to competitively inhibit NAG synthetase and to directly inhibit CPS. Furthermore, intramitochondrial conversion of acyl CoA to acylcarnitine, to conserve free CoA, leads to carnitine deficiency by urinary excretion of acylcarnitines. Thus, the nature of the urinary acylcarnitines excreted is a means to identify a specific metabolic defect resulting in an organic acidemia. Clinically, whether it is the hyperammonemia or the accumulated organic acid intermediates that cause the symptoms remains unknown.

Finding an elevated plasma glycine is a helpful clue in separating primary from secondary hyperammonemia. Although intrinsic urea cycle defects are not normally accompanied by an increase in plasma glycine, elevations of glycine commonly are seen in the organic acidemias. In such cases, the hyperglycinemia is secondary (as is the hyperammonemia) and is produced as a result of the inhibition of the mitochondrial glycine cleavage multienzyme complex. Because synthesis of glycine de novo is simultaneously accelerated, consuming ammonia in the process, such a mechanism actually may be protective and forms the basis for the use of benzoate in the treatment of hyperammonemia.

HEME CATABOLISM AND BILIRUBIN REMOVAL

Jaundice (icterus), a yellowish discoloration of skin, ocular conjunctiva, and hard palate, is such a striking clinical finding that virtually any observer, with or without medical training, can recognize it. While examining a jaundiced patient, a medically trained individual would reflexively palpate the liver because this organ is the major site of heme degradation, producing bilirubin and other pigmentary substances that cause icterus. It should be recognized, however, that initiation of the breakdown of hemoglobin, which is the major source of these pigments, occurs in the reticuloendothelial system, predominantly in the spleen. Many other tissues, notably the liver, can initiate heme catabolism, when the heme derives from cytochromes and other hemoproteins. Quantitatively, of course, the net contribution from these other hemoproteins is minor (about 20%) compared with that contributed by hemoglobin breakdown.

To initiate heme catabolism, the heme moiety first must be freed from its corresponding hemoprotein, liberating the heme. *Heme oxygenase* is a microsomal enzyme that uses molecular O_2 to open the heme ring, converting it to an open chain called *biliverdin* (Figure 5.6). The enzyme catalyzes the opening of an α-methene bridge, the carbon of which is converted to *carbon monoxide.* This reaction is the only source of CO in humans. Note that only heme-containing porphyrins are substrates for heme oxygenase, accounting for the observation that in the porphyrias (see Chapter 17), the free porphyrins are excreted intact. Because iron must remain in the porphyrin ring during the first stage of the heme oxygenase catalyzed reaction, it seems likely that iron is a participant in the reaction mechanism. Subsequently, the iron is released and biliverdin is generated. The biliverdin is promptly reduced (at its central methylene bridge) to *bilirubin,* a reaction that is catalyzed by biliverdin reductase.

One would think that bilirubin, with its polar propionic acid side-chains and keto groups, would be water soluble; this, however, is not true. The explanation for the lack of water solubility comes from x-ray crystallographic studies showing that polar groups on bilirubin that potentially could engage in hydrogen bonding to water are instead engaged in intramolecular hydrogen bond formation. Consequently, bilirubin adopts a rigid-tile structure that shuns water.

Transport, Conjugation, and Excretion of Bilirubin

Irrespective of the tissue origin of the bilirubin, it escapes from the cell into the blood, where it immediately is bound by plasma albumin, which

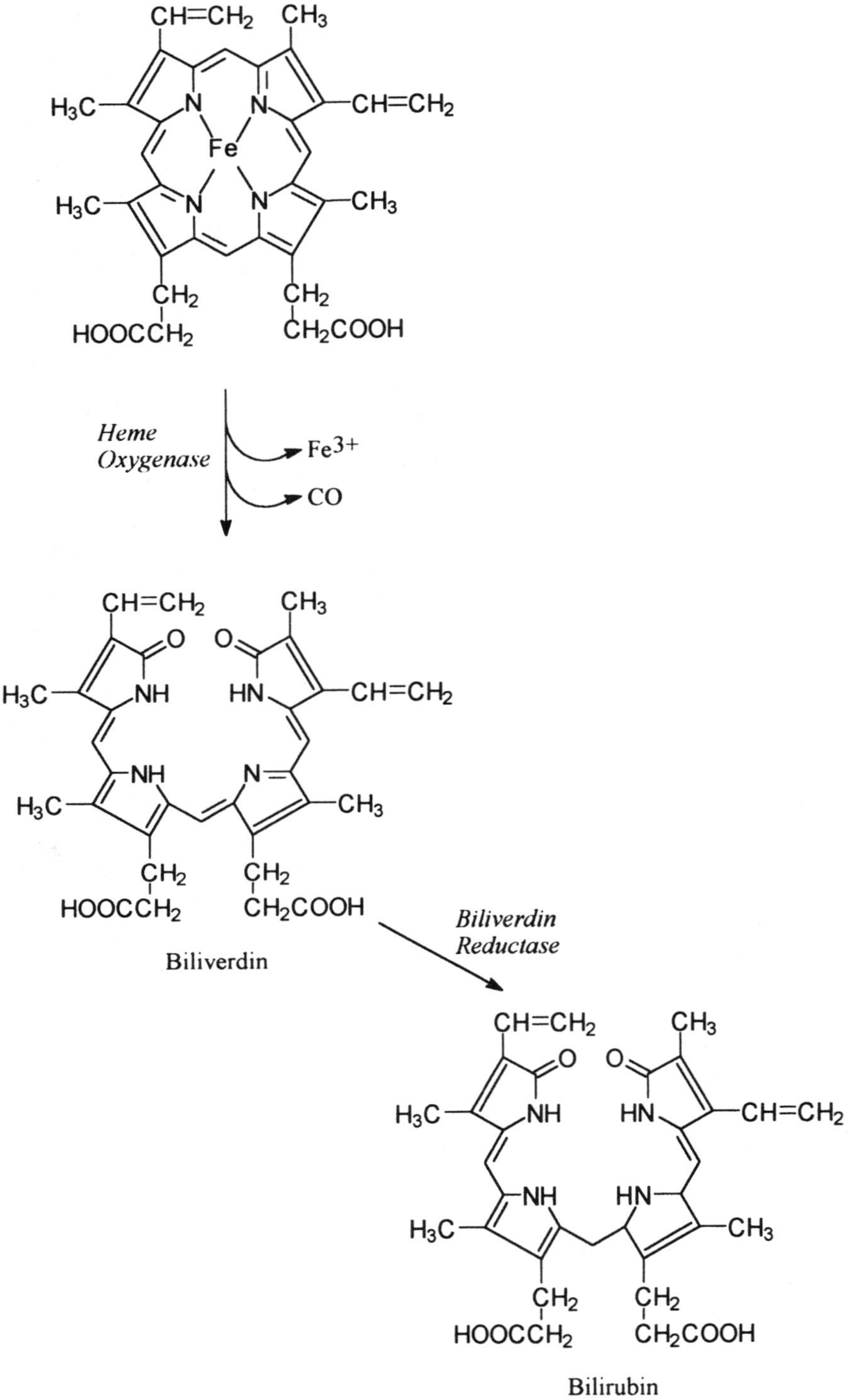

Heme Oxygenase

Fe^{3+}

CO

Biliverdin

Biliverdin Reductase

Bilirubin

Figure 5.6. Degradation of heme. Only iron-containing porphyrins (heme) are substrates for heme oxygenase. Using molecular oxygen, the enzyme mediates cleavage of an α-methene bridge in the porphyrin ring. The iron then is removed for recycling, and an open-chain compound called biliverdin is produced. The reaction also produces carbon monoxide and it is unique in this respect in human metabolism. In a subsequent step, the "hinge bond" of biliverdin is reduced by biliverdin reductase to produce bilirubin.

has a high affinity for bilirubin (Table 5.4, Figure 5.7). Free bilirubin must be bound in some form to prevent precipitation because of its limited aqueous solubility; consequently, the high concentration and the avid binding by albumin represent definite advantages. However, remember that albumin binds many other substances, especially drugs; therefore, drug administration may cause bound bilirubin to be displaced and become deposited in tissues. Albumin-bound bilirubin (measured as unconjugated) is transported in plasma to the liver sinusoid, where the bilirubin leaves the plasma compartment and enters the hepatocyte. The process by which this occurs is not completely understood, but it is certain that the albumin-bilirubin complex dissociates; while the albumin remains outside the hepatocyte, bilirubin enters the cell through a carrier-mediated process under physiologic conditions. To prevent intracellular precipitation in the aqueous cytosol, a protein called *ligandin* (or Y-protein) avidly binds the entering bilirubin.

At this stage, with bilirubin cleared from the circulation and safely within the hepatocyte, bilirubin must be removed from the cell because there is finite capacity for its storage. This is accomplished by enzymatic conversion of ligandin-bound bilirubin to glucuronylated (conjugated) bilirubin in the endoplasmic reticulum. Conjugation interferes with the intramolecular hydrogen bonds, thereby rendering bilirubin water soluble. The process by which bilirubin physically reaches the enzyme active site is not yet understood. The enzyme, *UDP-glucuronosyltransferase*, is an integral microsomal protein and needs membrane lipids for its activity. This activity is directed at various substrates, resulting in transfer of the glucuronyl moiety to form a *glucuronide*. In bilirubin, because of the presence of two propionic acid side chains, the reaction results in both mono and diglucuronide conjugates of bilirubin. The latter products are soluble in aqueous medium.

Bilirubin glucuronides are thought to be transported out of the hepatocyte against a concentra-

Table 5.4. Bilirubin metabolism

STEPS		DISORDERS
Production	↑	Hemolysis (isoimmunization, red cell enzyme and membrane defects, infections)
RBC breakdown (accounts for late peak)		"Physiologic" jaundice
Myoglobin, catalase, cytochromes		Drugs
Early labeled—hepatic heme turnover, ineffective erythropoiesis		Ineffective erythropoiesis
Transport		Competition for binding sites on serum albumin
Hepatic uptake		Competition for membrane-binding sites
	Unconjugated	
Membrane transit		Decreased ligandin in neonate
Intracellular carrier proteins		Gilbert's disease
Conjugation		
In endoplasmic reticulum		Neonatal immaturity (decreased UDP-glucuronyltransferase activity)
With UDP-sugar		Crigler-Najjar syndrome, Arias variant
		Gilbert's disease
		Inhibition by breast milk
		Inhibition by drugs
		Congenital hypothyroidism
Secretion into bile canaliculus	↓ ↑	Secretory mechanism not fully functional in neonate
		Dubin-Johnson syndrome; Rotor's syndrome
		Hepatitis; cholestasis (galactosemia, tyrosinemia, hereditary fructose intolerance, cystic fibrosis, α_1-antitrypsin deficiency)
		Cirrhosis
	Conjugated	
Elimination		Mechanical obstruction
Bacterial degradation		
± Enterohepatic circulation	↓	

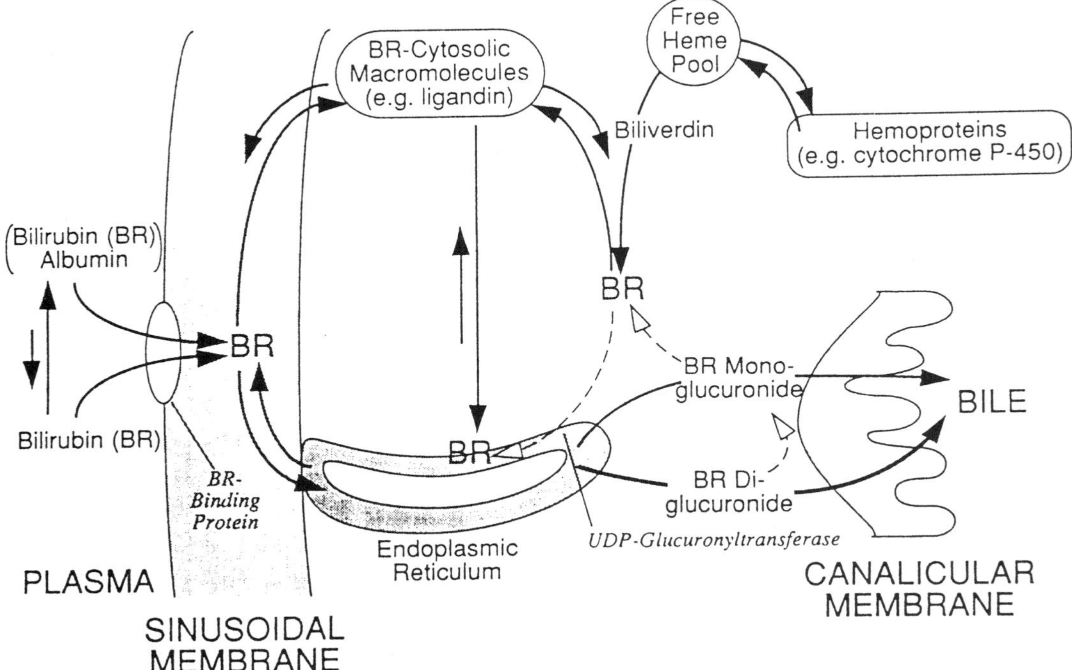

Figure 5.7. Transport, conjugation, and excretion of bilirubin. Unconjugated bilirubin, bound to circulating albumin, is presented to the sinusoidal surface of the hepatocyte, where the complex is cleaved and the free bilirubin is transported into the cytosol by a carrier-mediated process. To prevent precipitation of the highly insoluble free bilirubin, it is bound to an intracellular protein, ligandin or Y-protein, for transport into the endoplasmic reticulum. At this site, the bilirubin is enzymatically transferred (UDP-glucuronyltransferase) from ligandin to glucuronic acid to form soluble bilirubin mono- and diglucuronides (conjugated bilirubin). The UDP-glucuronate is formed from UDP-glucose in a separate reaction, mediated by UDP-glucose dehydrogenase. Conjugated bilirubin is believed to be actively transported out of the hepatocyte across the canalicular membrane surface and eventually reaches the gall bladder. Reprinted with permission from Achkar E, Farmer RG, Fleshler B, et al. Clinical Gastroenterology. 2nd ed. Baltimore: Williams & Wilkins, 1992:533.

tion gradient, which implies energy expenditure. Moreover, data indicate that transport, rather than conjugation, is the rate-limiting step in removal of bilirubin from the hepatocyte. It is clear that maximal bilirubin excretion rate is closely related to bile flow, and the relationship of bilirubin excretion to bile salts also may be important in this process. In any case, excretion of conjugated bilirubin into bile initiates the cycle called the enterohepatic circulation (Figure 5.8). Bile reaching the intestine from the gall bladder eventually is exposed to bacterial action, whereby conjugated bilirubin is converted to urobilin (which is colored) and reabsorbed. Urobilin is carried back to the liver and resecreted into the bile, and thence into the feces, which accounts for the color of stool. A small amount also passes into the systemic circulation and is excreted by the kidney as urobilinogen.

Hyperbilirubinemia Has Many Causes

It is important to recognize the clinical relevance of the individual steps involved in bilirubin metabolism because jaundice frequently is encountered in medical practice. With an understanding of the physiology and biochemistry of bilirubin, it is possible to isolate particular phases of the sequence based upon a relationship between conjugated and unconjugated bilirubin levels in serum. For instance, if one is aware that UDP-glucuronosyltransferase activity usually is low in the newborn, then an elevation in unconjugated (indirect-reacting) bilirubin should be antici-

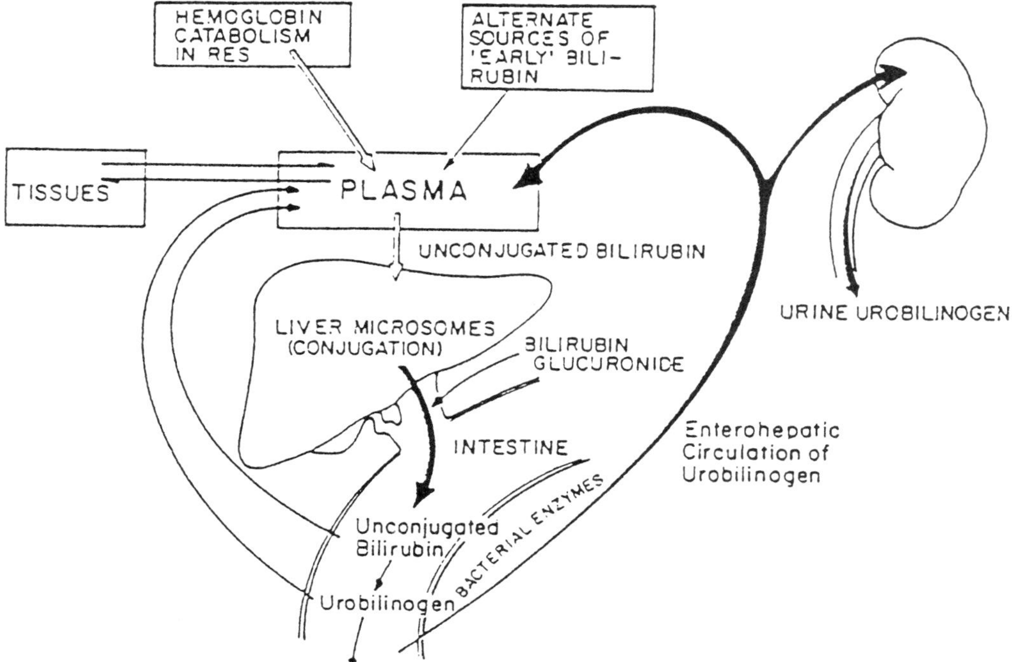

Figure 5.8. Major routes of bilirubin elimination. A major portion of the bile that reaches the bowel via the common duct is converted to urobilin by bacterial action. Urobilin is reabsorbed and returned to the liver, where it is resecreted into the intestine via the bile, thus describing a complete cycle called the enterohepatic circulation. A small portion of the reabsorbed urobilin enters the systemic circulation, where it is excreted as urinary urobilinogen. Note that conversion of conjugated bilirubin within the bowel is not equivalent to total production; the remainder is excreted unchanged. RES = reticuloendothelial system. Reprinted with permission from Kaplowitz N. Liver and Biliary Diseases. Baltimore: Williams & Wilkins, 1992; 534.

pated. This accounts for the physiologic jaundice of the newborn. If, however, an infant shows a substantially elevated conjugated bilirubin level, then it can be assumed that jaundice occurred because of an impairment in the removal of the end-product of an intact biochemical pathway. Inborn errors like galactosemia, tyrosinemia, and hereditary fructose intolerance cause hepatocellular damage and increases in both unconjugated and conjugated bilirubin in plasma. Acquired diseases, which include diffuse hepatocellular disease such as hepatitis and cirrhosis, also are attended by increases in both conjugated and unconjugated bilirubin in plasma.

Although a massive hemolytic crisis from transfusion of incompatible blood can increase the serum unconjugated bilirubin to more than 4 mg/dl, a hemolytic anemia with chronic low grade erythrocyte destruction is not likely to generate an amount of heme that would exceed the capacity of the normal liver to handle the bilirubin load.

Not unexpectedly, some inherited defects in UDP-glucuronosyltransferase activity (Crigler-Najjar syndromes and Gilbert's syndrome) are associated with unconjugated hyperbilirubinemia (Table 5.4). Moreover, some inherited defects in transport of bilirubin out of the hepatocyte (Dubin-Johnson and Rotor syndrome) are associated with increased conjugated bilirubin in plasma (Table 5.5). As listed in Table 5.4, complete absence of UDP-glucuronosyltransferase usually is fatal because of the damage to the central nervous system caused by deposition of bilirubin; this is called *kernicterus*. Fortunately, most of the inherited defects of bilirubin are treatable or are medical curiosities. Again, it is important to remember that in hepatitis and cirrhosis, bilirubin metabolism is likely to be severely impaired because of jaundice

Table 5.5. Hyperbilirubinemias

INHERITED UNCONJUGATED HYPERBILIRUBINEMIAS				
DISORDER	DEFECT	BILIRUBIN	TREATMENT	COMPLICATIONS
Crigler-Najjar type I	Absence of UDP-GT	>20 mg/dl	Liver transplant	Kernicterus
Crigler-Najjar type II	↓↓ UDP-GT	<20 mg/dl	Phenobarbital	Usually none with treatment
Gilbert's syndrome	Slightly ↓ UDP-GT	<3 mg/dl	None required	None
INHERITED CONJUGATED HYPERBILIRUBINEMIAS				
DISORDER	DEFECT	BILIRUBIN	TREATMENT	ASSOCIATED LAB FINDINGS
Dubin-Johnson syndrome	Impaired biliary secretion	2–5 mg/dl	None required	Urinary coproporphyrin shows ↑ type I (type III is normal)
Rotor's syndrome	↓ hepatic uptake and storage	2–5 mg/dl	None required	↑ both types I and II coproporphyrins

UDP-GT = UDP glucuronosyltransferase

and elevation of both unconjugated and conjugated bilirubin in plasma.

Laboratory Estimation of Bilirubin

For over 100 years, bilirubin has been measured by variations of the diazo method, which was introduced by Ehrlich. Conjugated bilirubin reacts in aqueous solution within 1 minute in what is called the *direct* method. In a separate reaction, involving alcohol or caffeine, which prevent formation of the intramolecular hydrogen bonds, total bilirubin can be measured. To obtain the unconjugated (indirect-reacting) bilirubin, the conjugated form is subtracted from the total.

About 30 years ago, using high performance liquid chromatography (HPLC), four separate bilirubin fractions were found in serum: (*1*) unconjugated, (*2*) bilirubin monoglucuronide, (*3*) bilirubin diglucuronide, and (*4*) covalently bound bilirubin. The last fraction, called delta (δ) bilirubin, represents bilirubin that is covalently bound to albumin. Because it gives a direct reaction in the diazo test, it is conjugated bilirubin. Patients with predominantly conjugated hyperbilirubinemia will manifest an increase in the δ fraction over time.

Puzzles About Heme Catabolism

As a final note to this section, it may have occurred to the reader to ask, "Why not conserve heme, which is a vital metabolic compound, after having invested so much in its production?" (see Chapter 6). Although there are no definitive answers to this question, several speculations can be proposed. The first and most obvious is that free heme may be more toxic than unconjugated bilirubin; both primarily are intracellular compounds. However, in the treatment of acute intermittent porphyria, infusion of heme does not seem to be associated with any significant toxicity. Another possibility is that the predominant source of heme catabolism derives from the hemoglobin of senescent red cells, which are captured and processed in the reticuloendothelial system; hence, the bulk of free heme initially is released within a cell type that is not equipped to recycle it. Experimental evidence suggests that in liver, which actively synthesizes many hemoproteins other than hemoglobin, only about 20% of labelled heme is broken down through heme oxygenase. The fate of the remainder is not known, but there is no a priori reason to believe that it may not be recycled. Finally, evidence suggests that bilirubin may serve as a natural antioxidant.

DRUG METABOLISM

Many drugs are lipophilic compounds that, once absorbed into the bloodstream, easily traverse cell membranes. In most instances, the safest therapeutic agents do not remain in unmodified form for prolonged periods; if they did, they might exert noxious effects. The liver, in particular, metabolizes these drugs and other foreign compounds, called xenobiotics, into derivatives that more easily are removed from the body. The strategy is to make the lipophilic compound more hydrophilic, thereby encouraging renal elimination.

Two general types of reactions accomplish this: (*a*) *oxidation* or unmasking of a polar functional group (called *phase 1 reactions*); and (*b*) *conjugation* with water soluble materials such as glucuronic acid, sulfuric acid, amino acids, or acetic acid (called *phase 2 reactions*). The phase 1 oxidative reactions are mediated by members of the *cytochrome* P_{450} class of enzymes, whereas the conjugation reactions are catalyzed by *transferases* and use activated compounds such as UDPglucuronic acid and phosphoadenosine phosphosulfate.

The anatomical position of the liver virtually guarantees its exposure to any orally administered agent. Practicing biologic economy, the hepatocyte frequently will manage a drug by using a pathway that has evolved for common metabolic substrates. For example, if a drug resembles an alcohol, the liver may partially metabolize it through the alcohol dehydrogenase step and thus decrease or eliminate the drug's biologic activity. Most xenobiotics will be transformed by phase 1 or phase 2 reactions acting alone or in combination.

DISEASES OF THE LIVER

Despite its huge metabolic reserve and many capacities, the central role of the liver in metabolizing nutritional components renders it susceptible to the effects of dysfunction in other organs. A prime example is hepatomegaly as a consequence of congestive heart failure, when the primary pathology is located within the cardiovascular system. Another example is extrahepatic cholestasis resulting in hepatocellular damage. However, some disorders primary to the liver, such as phenylketonuria, do not harm the liver but dramatically affect other organs, such as brain. Other disorders primary to the hepatocyte, such as alpha-1-antitrypsin deficiency and hereditary tyrosinemia, cause significant hepatocellular damage with consequent secondary effects on other tissues. Thus, the differential diagnosis of hepatic dysfunction can be complicated, unless it is approached in an orderly and thoughtful fashion.

Because hepatic dysfunction can present in various forms (eg, tenderness, enlargement, jaundice, etc), the initial task in diagnosis is to assess all other organ systems to determine whether there is primary or secondary involvement of the liver. Herein, we again emphasize the importance of carefully taking a history and performing a physical examination. Primary diseases of the liver may cause apparent "primary" pathology in distant organs; an excellent example of this is an inborn error of the urea cycle that causes hyperammonemia and accompanying central nervous system abnormalities. In such a case, unless hyperammonemia is considered, critical time will be wasted looking for other causes of vomiting and coma. Abnormal states that secondarily involve the liver are more common; blockage of the common bile duct causing jaundice is an example.

Enlargement (Hepatomegaly)

Simplistically, the liver is a tough, distensible bag that contains a certain number of cell types that are restricted in variety. Accordingly, an increase in the size of the "bag" must be due to fluid or solid substance accumulation inside or outside the cells, an increase in one or more cell types, or a combination of these. Intuitively, an increase in fluid will result in more rapid increase in liver size than solid substance accumulation because fluid shifts occur during a shorter period and fluid, unlike solid matter, is noncompressible. Hence, an obstruction to blood flow proximal to the liver causes a rapid increase in liver size, which is the usual consequence of right-sided heart failure. Even in cases when a tumor of specific cell type grows quickly, sudden increases in liver size are likely to be related to hemorrhage within the tumor or to erosion into a large vessel with bleeding into the liver parenchyma.

Hepatomegaly secondary to accumulation of

solid substances can reflect many conditions, either because the hepatocytes are storing excess material or because they cannot process this material for some intrinsic reason. In some disorders, the cells can produce what they cannot break down, as in the glycogen storage diseases. In most disorders such as these, hepatic enlargement may not be clinically detected for a long time because storage occurs in increments of micrograms of material per day. An exception to this is when the liver expands rapidly as seen in diabetic ketoacidosis that is treated with glucose and insulin, wherein large amounts of glycogen and triglyceride accumulate in liver. Regardless of this, the broad clinical entities, inflammation, and fatty infiltration cause hepatomegaly over days to months, not within hours. Although edema associated with a cellular inflammatory response can account for enlargement of the liver secondary to an infectious or toxic insult, the underlying events leading to hepatomegaly due to fatty infiltration are grounded in abnormal biochemistry.

Fatty Liver

Although the liver is the source of production of ketone bodies from fatty acids, histologic examination of normal liver reveals that large amounts of fat are not typically found in hepatic tissue. The chief reason for this is the liver's capacity to both oxidize fat and to package it as very low density lipoproteins (VLDL) to be shipped to adipose tissue for storage. Formation of VLDL involves the synthesis of apoproteins and assembly of lipoproteins, which involves an ability to make both lipid and protein. Although there are limits to how much fat can be carried through β-oxidation to generate ATP (based on energy needs), apparently no such limit exists for how much fat can be reesterified into triglyceride. Reesterification must occur before triglyceride is incorporated into VLDL. Because lipoprotein formation and secretion of VLDL are more complicated processes than reesterification, it is likely that many conditions will cause reesterified fat to remain in the liver and await transport out as VLDL. Thus, it is reasonable to state that any factors leading to impairment of lipid or of protein metabolism, or to their integration by the liver, will result in fat accumulation. Such factors are: impaired triglyceride clearance (VLDL secretion), increased hepatic lipogenesis, decreased fatty acid oxidation, and increased lipolysis in adipose tissue resulting in augmentation of the flow of lipid to the liver. Starvation, which limits the amino acid supply for synthesis of the protein portion (apolipoprotein) of the molecule, is a common cause of lipid accumulation in the liver; the enhancement of lipid release from adipose tissue adds to the rate of lipid storage during starvation.

In chapter 10, we will consider diabetes mellitus from the perspective of a cellular state of glucose starvation accompanied by unbridled release of lipid from adipose tissue; each derangement is a consequence of insulin deficiency. Thus, it is obvious that diabetes will result in a fatty liver. Moreover, because the liver is a major site of lipid synthesis, in cases where dietary carbohydrate greatly exceeds the needs, diversion of carbohydrate into lipogenesis will contribute to development of fatty liver.

Thus far, our emphasis has been on primary disruption of carbohydrate metabolism. However, impairment of lipid metabolism also can lead to rapid development of fatty liver. The best example of such a situation is a deficiency of medium chain acyl CoA dehydrogenase (MCAD), which is a key enzyme in beta-oxidation. The nature of the defect (see Chapter 13) is that fatty acids of six or more carbons chain length cannot be catabolized to acetyl CoA, resulting in accumulation behind the deficient step. Under fasting conditions, the normal response of lipid release from storage depots to meet energy demands initiates the impaired cellular efforts to meet these demands through beta-oxidation, which leads to lipid deposition and fatty liver.

Vitamin deficiencies, particularly those involving the B-complex, will result in fatty liver. The mechanisms for this are complicated and differ for each individual B vitamin. Thus, details are beyond the scope of this text, but can be found in the texts listed in the suggested reading section at the end of this chapter. Exogenous toxins (eg, ethyl alcohol) can cause fatty liver through their effects on mitochondrial oxidation, by a mechanism that also is common to sepsis and hypoxic shock. Therefore, as seen from the examples of disrupted carbohydrate, lipid, protein, and oxygen utilization discussed previously in the text, it appears that the common denominator in development of fatty liver is any adverse effect on the balance of energy utilization that is out of proportion to that seen under physiologic conditions.

Alcohol and the Liver

Excess alcohol does not affect only the liver. In fact, it injures all organs, including the central nervous system. But perhaps the most significant effect of alcoholism is its corrosive influence on personal and family life. Society is becoming attuned to these hazards, but reasons why people abuse ethanol are multifactorial and will not be simply resolved given the thousands of years alcohol has been ingested by humans.

One of the must baffling aspects of alcohol abuse is that only about 20% to 30% of heavy drinkers (defined as those who consume 150 to 200 g ethanol/d for 15 to 20 years) go on to develop serious liver disease. This area of ignorance may someday offer promise for therapeutic intervention.

Alcohol can produce reversible liver changes (fatty liver), severe but potentially reversible changes (alcoholic hepatitis), and virtually irreversible changes (alcoholic cirrhosis). Alcoholic hepatitis is characterized by liver cell necrosis and inflammatory changes and is a precursor to cirrhosis. Attention currently is focused on the potential roles of acetaldehyde, changes in redox potential, and toxic radicals in the pathogenesis of serious alcohol-related liver disease.

ALCOHOL METABOLISM

Under normal circumstances, 80% of the metabolism of ethanol (the only form of alcohol that we will consider in this text) occurs in the liver; the remainder is broken down by the gastrointestinal epithelium. In either tissue, the predominant pathway for catabolism is through the enzyme *alcohol dehydrogenase* (Figure 5.9), which is present in cytosol and mitochondria:

$$C_2H_5OH + NAD^+ \text{ v } CH_3CHO + NADH + H^+$$

The relationship between the usual concentrations of ethanol available to the enzyme and the affinity of the protein for its substrate are the factors that cause this system to predominate.

However, under conditions when circulating ethanol concentration exceeds the Km of alcohol dehydrogenase (1 mM), (ie, when intake exceeds one to two drinks), another enzyme bound to endoplasmic reticulum becomes active in ethanol metabolism, the microsomal ethanol oxidizing system. The *microsomal ethanol oxidizing system* is a member of the family of cytochrome P_{450} enzymes and has a Km for ethanol of about 10 mm:

$$C_2H_5OH + NADPH + H^+ + 1/2O_2 \leftrightharpoons CH_3CHO + NADP^+ + H_2O$$

There are several consequences to the increase in the $NADH/NAD^+$ ratio caused by brisk metabolism of ethanol through the ADH reaction. First, because the lactate dehydrogenase reaction proceeds at a faster pace than the malate-aspartate shuttle, lactate levels increase, which causes hyperlacticacidemia. Because lactate competes with urate for excretion by the kidney, urate levels increase as well. An additional factor in the hyperuricemia is increased rate of urate formation because of augmented ATP breakdown. Ethanol is converted to acetaldehyde, which is then converted to acetate. Formation of acetyl CoA from acetate consumes ATP and, with sufficient ethanol ingestion, can significantly decrease cell ATP, which leads to enhanced production of uric acid (see Chapter 16).

Second, gluconeogenesis is stymied because of paucity of pyruvate and oxaloacetate. Third, β-hydroxybutyrate accumulates, again as a sink for electrons and hydrogen from NADH. Fourth, fatty acid oxidation is inhibited by increased NADH levels. Fifth, NADH and acetyl CoA inhibit pyruvate dehydrogenase, causing fat to be esterified rather than oxidized. Together, these fourth and fifth consequences contribute to development of fatty liver. Sixth, increased export of low density lipoproteins occurs, generating hypertriglyceridemia.

With the catabolism of ethanol through either of the previous two reactions, acetaldehyde is further broken down by *aldehyde dehydrogenase*:

$$CH_3CHO + NAD^+ \leftrightharpoons CH_3COOH + NADH + H^+$$

Given the changes in cellular metabolism known to occur in the liver as a consequence of

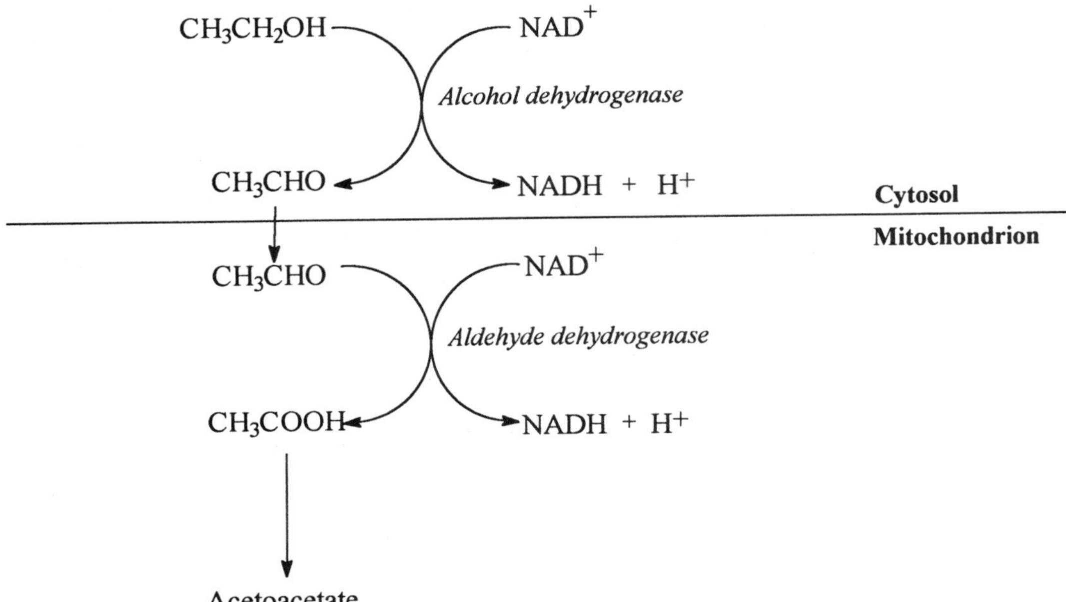

Figure 5.9. Major pathway for ethanol metabolism. One molecule of ethanol, metabolized to acetate, yields a total of four, reducing equivalents to the electron transport system and resulting in ATP formation. Consequences of substrate overload of the pathway are discussed in the text.

impaired nutrition, the interplay of alcohol intake and nutrition has been thought to be a basis for development of liver disease and cirrhosis. Dietary surveys of alcoholics generally show that ethanol intake ranges from 20% to 50% of total daily calories; the average daily calorie intake was not subnormal in any of these studies. Despite this, a consistent finding among alcoholics is malnutrition, often as a consequence of subnormal protein intake, which ranges from 6% to 11% of total calories in these same studies. However, studies with baboons that were conducted in the 1970s showed that it was possible to produce liver disease in animals who ingested ethanol, but who otherwise ate an adequate diet. Furthermore, the fact that cirrhosis is not found in individuals who have experienced prolonged starvation suggests that the ethanol, or one of its metabolites, causes the liver damage, not malnutrition. Nevertheless, evidence suggests that malnutrition potentiates the hepatotoxic effects of ethanol (see following text). In humans, enriched protein nutritional status has a significant beneficial effect on the outcome of liver function testing, but does not exert any substantial impact on the histopathologic findings. Thus, whereas improved nutrition is essential to successful clinical treatment of alcoholism, dietary alterations alone cannot be expected to reverse or prevent the physical changes leading to development of cirrhosis.

A more recent approach to the puzzle of what causes alcoholic liver disease has been an examination of the mechanisms involved in acetaldehyde-mediated liver cell injury. A major aspect to these studies is the alcohol-based induction of the microsomal ethanol oxidizing system, which becomes a significant source of acetaldehyde production under conditions of chronic, moderate to high levels of ethanol consumption. Although acetaldehyde is converted to acetate, and thence to acetyl CoA, which can undergo complete oxidation, the rate of formation of acetaldehyde exceeds the capacity for its oxidation in the presence of high ethanol concentrations.

An important consequence of hepatocyte acetaldehyde accumulation is the formation of *aldehyde-protein adducts*. Because acetaldehyde is a reactive electrophile, it binds covalently to various cellular proteins that contain lysine or sulfhydryl groups, including tubulin of the cytoskeleton. It has been proposed that these protein-containing adducts are recognized as foreign substances, rendering them antigenic with consequent antibody formation. The results include enzyme inactivation, alterations in microtubules, mitochondria, and plasma membranes due to the high affinity of acetaldehyde for sulfhydryl groups in the constituent amino acids of protein. In addition to these significant toxic effects, acetaldehyde also causes cellular glutathione depletion as a result of direct binding to both cysteine and glutathione itself. Depletion of a major intracellular-reducing factor exposes the cell to free radical damage, especially in the mitochondria where scarcity of glutathione is most severe.

Alcohol is the primary human toxic exposure because of its widespread consumption in the world's population. Although individual levels of ingestion vastly differ, it is important to understand the mechanisms involved in ethanol metabolism and their relationship to toxic liver damage. This especially is true because the liver is a major detoxification center for other potential toxins, the metabolism of which might further enhance ethanol toxicity or vice versa. Moreover, consider the nutritional environment in which ethanol is consumed because protein malnutrition is more likely to be a baseline state in Third World countries than in the developed countries. Thus, although the cellular pathology of ethanol toxicity may be common to all who consume alcohol, the extent and rapidity of development of liver disease will vary with social conditions. Given the historical record of the human race, in which every civilization has created alcoholic beverages, it is more practical to find means to prevent hepatocellular damage than to hope that self-induced abstention will become the rule.

Viral Hepatitis

Viral hepatitis is an inflammation of the liver that most commonly is the result of infection with one of the following five agents: hepatitis A virus (HAV), hepatitis B virus (HBV), hepatitis C virus (HCV), hepatitis D virus (HDV), and hepatitis E virus (HEV). In aggregate, these five viruses account for greater than 90% of cases of acute viral hepatitis. Nonetheless, other viruses, including members of the herpes family (Epstein-Barr virus, cytomegalovirus, herpes), yellow fever virus, and rubella, also cause hepatitis. Remarkably, in the acute stages, the clinical findings of common forms of hepatitis (HAV–HEV) are virtually indistinguishable. They differ, however, in mode of transmission and tendency to cause chronic liver disease, with chronic disease found in 10% to 20% of patients afflicted with HBV, HCV, and HDV. Sometimes, much emphasis is placed on their differing incubation periods, but unless the physician confronts an epidemic or an unequivocal exposure, incubation periods may not be helpful in determining etiology. In fact, once hepatitis is suspected based on flu-like prodrome, jaundice, aversion to smoking or coffee, anorexia, or pain on palpation of the liver, establishing the specific etiologic agent relies on laboratory testing.

It would be misleading, however, to suggest that most cases of acute viral hepatitis are accompanied by jaundice. Sometimes the only clues to liver involvement are elevation of serum transaminases (alanine aminotransferase [ALT] > aspartate aminotransferase [AST]), which may be found during an annual medical evaluation, or vague feelings of malaise.

Hepatitis A Virus

HAV is a 27 nm RNA enterovirus, belonging to the same family as polio virus and Coxsackie virus. HAV is transmitted by the fecal-oral route and is thus most prevalent among the very young, the retarded, and those subsisting under crowded unsanitary conditions. Certainly, in developing nations, where public sanitation is limited, HAV abounds. Furthermore, it can be transmitted by clams and oysters. HAV is an enterovirus that enters via the gastrointestinal tract and travels to the liver to set up a focus of infection. During the preicteric phases, the virus is shed into the bile and from there into the feces. Notably, once jaundice appears, the likelihood of the virus shedding further and, therefore, of infectivity diminishes drastically. Moreover, jaundice coincides with increased antibody titers to the virus.

Diagnosis depends on demonstrating an acute immune response reflected by IgM antibody against HAV (*anti-HAV IgM*). As will be discussed in Chapter 19, IgM is the first antibody made to a foreign agent (antigen) with IgG production following weeks later. IgM antibody for HAV establishes an acute infection, whereas the presence of IgG for HAV confirms a previous exposure. As with many viral infections, the presence of IgG antibody confers lifelong immunity.

As opposed to HBV and HCV, HAV has no propensity to generate a chronic carrier state or, worse yet, chronic hepatitis.

Hepatitis B

HBV poses a major worldwide medical problem because of the tendency for development of chronic liver infection in about 10% of patients initially infected. Although HBV can resolve without sequelae, if chronic infection develops, there is an almost 40% chance of progression to chronic active hepatitis or hepatocellular carcinoma. HBV is a DNA virus that uses a reverse transcriptase during replication.

Three forms of HBV are encountered: (*a*) coat or surface protein, (*b*) the complete virus, and (*c*) the inner core. The surface antigen (*HBsAg*) is a 22 nm particle that represents excess viral-capsid protein, the function of which is to surround the viral DNA. The *complete virus* is a 42 nm particle that contains the viral DNA, a DNA polymerase, and a protein kinase; it is referred to as the Dane particle and is the infectious agent. Finally, the *nucleocapsid* is a 27 nm particle that contains hepatitis core antigen (*HBcAg*) and hepatitis e antigen (*HBeAg*). It can be produced by treating the intact virion with a nonionic detergent, which causes the surface antigen (HBsAg) to dissociate. In serum, HBsAg envelopes outnumber, at least by 100:1, the intact Dane particle. Most cases of HBV are acquired by a parenteral route: exposure to blood (drug abusers, male homosexuals, chronic hemodialysis patients) and through intimate contact (saliva and semen). Those living in the same household should not share razors and toothbrushes.

It might be expected that the liver damage associated with HBV is caused by the cytopathic properties of the virus, but this evidently is not the case. Rather, T-cell mediated immune mechanisms (Chapter 19) cause the damage to the hepatocyte.

Table 5.6. Serologic Tests in a Patient Who Presents with Hepatitis

ACUTE HEPATITIS	POSITIVE TEST CONFIRMS
IgM anti-HAV	Acute Hep A
IgM anti-HBc	Acute Hep B
HBsAg	Chronic Hep B if IgM anti-HBc is negative
Anti-HCV	Acute Hep C
HCV-PCR	Acute Hep C (+ early in illness)
CHRONIC HEPATITIS	
HbsAg	Hep B− if (+) then test for HBeAg or HBV-DNA to find out if active viral replication is occurring
Anti-HCV	Hep C− confirm with RIBA

RIBA = recombinant immunoblot assay

Hepatitis C

Because serologic testing for HAV and HBV preceded that for HCV by many years, the commercial blood supply could be rendered free of HBV, and it became clear that HAV was not transmitted via blood. The majority of cases of hepatitis that occurred *after transfusion*, therefore, were assigned to the category of nonA-nonB, which remained an enigma until 1988 when HCV was shown to be at the root of most of these cases.

Distressingly, like HBV, HCV has a tendency to become chronic, with a 20% to 40% chance of progressing to cirrhosis. Both liver failure and hepatocellular carcinoma are sequelae of chronic HCV.

Laboratory tests for HCV include *anti HCV IgG antibody*, which does not become positive until after the acute infection and, therefore, cannot be used in diagnosis. Remarkably, this antibody does not confer immunity. The definitive test for HCV is HCV-PCR because it is positive early in the illness and it is sensitive.

Table 5.6 lists the major serologic tests in the diagnosis of a patient presenting with HAV through HCV.

Hepatitis D

HDV is an incomplete virus that cannot replicate and infect the hepatocyte unless HBV present. As expected, transmission of this agent is via the same routes that disseminate HBV—parenteral and intimate contact. HDV is cloaked in the HBsAg. Individuals sustaining combined HBV and HDV infections are at increased risk for fulminant hepatitis with rapid onset of hepatic failure. This virus, like HBV and HCV, tends to cause chronic active hepatitis.

Hepatitis E

HEV is an RNA virus and is transmitted like HAV by the fecal-oral route. It has thus far been responsible for epidemics in Southern Asia, North Africa, and Central America.

Cirrhosis

The astounding regenerative powers of the liver can be "a double-edged sword," impacting on the health as it does on the dysfunction of the organ itself. Key to the integrated function of the hepatic acinus, the basic functional unit of the liver, is the blood supply and its anatomical relationship to the biliary and lymphatic microcirculation. In relationship to distance from the portal venule and hepatic arteriole, hence nutrient and oxygen supply, the cells of the lobule can be divided into three zones (Table 5.1). Clearly, the ability of a cell to withstand any noxious influence is related to the nourishment and oxygen supply that it receives. Thus, cells in zone 3, furthest from the arterial supply, are likely to be most adversely affected. As these hepatocytes die and degenerate, they are replaced by cells from the inner zones and the new collagen synthesized at the cell surface. Collagen elaboration is responsible for maintenance of the normal cellular orientation and anatomical relationships within the hepatic lobule.

The extent to which collagen is elaborated is critical to the normal regeneration process. If synthesis is out of proportion to what is required for tissue repair and restoration of normal cellular architecture, *hepatic fibrosis* results. Hepatic fibrosis is, by definition, the increased synthesis of new connective tissue in an abnormal distribution. Because this material normally is responsible for maintenance of normal cell relationships, it is obvious that fibrosis results in abnormal cellular architecture. Although it is not clear what the critical events are in determining the extent of the collagen synthetic response to injury, the process unfortunately becomes self-perpetuating once it is initiated. Indeed, the resulting abnormal cellular orientations to each other and to the arterial supply lead to further cell death and a more exaggerated fibrotic process. As the process continues, fibrotic tissue increasingly replaces the cell mass of the liver, while the tremendous cellular reproductive abilities lead to self-annihilation.

Cirrhosis of the liver is a pathologic entity that has come to be synonymous with a relentless process ending in liver failure. It represents the liver's final common pathway of response to many entities (Table 5.7) and culminates in a progressive decay of liver function. All of these disorders cause necrosis of liver cells, and the liver responds by excessive elaboration of extracellular matrix that is haphazard in distribution and thus distorts normal hepatic architecture. Regenerative nodules also are characteristic of cirrhosis and represent hyperplasia of remaining liver cells that are arranged into irregular plates, further contributing to disruption of the structural patterns of the liver. These regenerative nodules impart a nodular structure to the cirrhotic liver.

Specific factors related to the development of hepatic cirrhosis are the nature, extent, and chronicity of the insult to the parenchyma. The immense regenerative power of the organ is illustrated by

Table 5.7. Causes of Cirrhosis of the Liver

GENETIC	NONGENETIC
Galactosemia	Toxins
Glycogen storage disease	alcohol
Tyrosinemia type I	isoniazid
Hereditary Fructose Intolerance	methotrexate
	methyldopa
α_1-Antitrypsin deficiency	Hepatitis
Budd-Chiari syndrome	tertiary syphilis
Wilson's disease	Cardiovascular
Hemochromatosis	chronic right ventricular failure
Cystic fibrosis	
Hereditary hemorrhagic telangiectasia	Biliary obstruction
Absence (agenesis) of ducts	Tumor (commonly pancreatic)
Abetalipoproteinemia	Lithiasis of common duct
Other:	Chronic pancreatitis
Thalassemia	Anatomic strictures
Sarcoidosis	Chronic active hepatitis
Lipid storage disease	Jejunoileal bypass
Mucopolysaccharidoses	

the fact that if two thirds of a rat liver is removed, the normal mass is quickly restored and the final result will be indistinguishable from the original. In this case, however, the insult is specific, albeit extensive, and extremely acute. Conversely, in alcoholism, the insult is more diffuse in distribution to most or all hepatocytes, at least as extensive as in the previous example, and chronic. Thus, it is not surprising that cirrhosis is more the rule than the exception in alcoholic individuals, whereas cirrhosis is uncommon under most other circumstances.

Cirrhosis results in profound changes in liver structure. With elaboration of connective tissue (collagen content doubles) and extracellular matrix, wound contraction eventually causes the liver to shrink. Besides distorting the liver architecture, the accumulating connective tissue imposes a barrier to transport between the hepatocytes and sinusoids. One of the most clinically apparent consequences of cirrhosis is increase in portal pressure caused by the synergy of disrupting factors: distortion of liver architecture, reduction in the number of fenestrations in sinusoidal epithelial cells, the transport barriers set up by collagen overgrowth, and increased production of agents that increase vascular tone.

Moreover, whereas liver regeneration is an orderly process orchestrated by various cytokines (especially transforming growth factor β_1), in cirrhosis, the repair process is disorderly and causes scar formation instead of regeneration. In regenerating liver, types V and III collagen predominate, whereas in cirrhosis, the collagen elaborated by transformed lipocytes is mostly type I. No less important, whereas in regeneration, the collagen is laid down to restore normal architecture, in cirrhosis, collagen is deployed in a chaotic fashion.

SUGGESTED READINGS

GENERAL

Arias IM, Boyer JL, Faust N, et al, eds. The liver: biology and pathobiology. 3rd ed. New York: Raven Press, 1994.

Boyer TD, Zakim D, eds. Hepatology. 2nd ed. Philadelphia: WB Saunders, 1990.

Gitnik G, Hollander D. Principles and practice of gastroenterology and hepatology. 2nd ed. Norwich, CT: Appleton and Lange, 1994.

ANATOMY, STRUCTURE, AND METABOLIC FUNCTION

Agius L, Peak M, Alberti KG. Regulation of glycogen synthesis from glucose and gluconeogenic precursors by insulin in periportal and perivenous rat hepatocytes. Biochem J 1990;266:91.

Desmet VJ. Organizational principles. In: Arias IM, JL Boyer, Fausto N, et al, eds. The liver: biology and pathobiology. 3rd ed. New York: Raven Press, 1994.

Ekataksin W, Wake K. Liver units in three dimensions: I. organization of argyrophilic connective tissue skeleton in porcine liver with particular reference to the "compound hepatic lobule." American Journal of Anatomy 1991;191:113.

Gazelle GS, Lee MJ, Mueller PR. Cholangiographic segmental anatomy of the liver. Radiographics 1994; 14:1005.

Gebhardt R. Metabolic zonation of the liver: regulation and implications for liver function. Pharmacol Ther 1992;53:275.

Gebhardt R, Jonitza D. Different proliferative responses of periportal and perivenous hepatocytes to EGF. Biochem Biophys Res Commun 1991;181:1201.

Gumucio JJ, Bilir BM, Moseley RH, Berkowitz CM. The biology of the liver cell plate. In: Arias IM, Boyer JL, Fausto N, et al, eds. The liver: biology and pathobiology. 3rd ed. New York: Raven Press, 1994.

Haussinger D. Nitrogen metabolism in liver: structural and functional organization and physiological relevance. Biochem J 1990;267:281.

Hellerstein MK, Christiansen M, Kaempfer S, et al. Measurement of de novo hepatic lipogenesis in humans using stable isotopes. J Clin Invest 1991;87: 1841.

Hubbard AL, Barr VA, Scott LJ. Hepatocyte surface polarity. In: Arias IM, Boyer JL, Fausto N, et al, eds. The liver: biology and pathobiology. 3rd ed. New York: Raven Press, 1994.

McCuskey RS. The hepatic microvascular system. In: Arias IM, Boyer JL, Fausto N, et al, eds. The liver: biology and pathobiology. 3rd ed. New York: Raven Press, 1994.

Miyai K. Structure-function relationship of the liver in health and disease. In: Gitnik G, Hollander D. Principles and practice of gastroenterology and hepatology. 2nd ed. Norwich, CT: Appleton and Lange, 1994.

Molino G. The functioning liver mass. Ricerca In Clinica E In Laboratory 1991;21:9.

Quistorff B, Katz N, Witters LA. Hepatocyte heterogeneity in the metabolism of fatty acids: discrepancies on zonation of acetyl-CoA carboxylase. Enzyme 1990;46:59.

Quistorff B. Metabolic heterogeneity of liver parenchymal cells. Essays Biochem 1990;25:83.

Sasse D, Spornitz UM, Maly IP. Liver architecture. Enzyme 1992;46:8.

Wehmeyer N, Gunderson H, Nauman J, et al.

Determination of the glycogen synthesis pathway by 13C nuclear magnetic resonance analysis. Metabolism 1994;43:38.

THE NITROGEN ECONOMY AND HYPERAMMONEMIA

Ferenci P, Puspok A, Steindl P. Current concepts in the pathophysiology of hepatic encephalopathy. Eur J Clin Invest 1992;22:573.

Hawkins RA, Mans AM. Brain metabolism in hepatic encephalopathy and hyperammonemia. Adv Exp Med Biol 1993;341:13.

Hellerstein MK, Munro HN. Interaction of liver, muscle and adipose tissue in the regulation of metabolism in response to nutritional and other factors. In: Arias IM, Boyer JL, Fausto N, et al, eds. The liver: biology and pathobiology. 3rd ed. New York: Raven Press, 1994.

Jungas RL, Halperin ML, Brosnan JT. Quantitative analysis of amino acid oxidation and related gluconeogenesis in humans. Physiol Rev 1992;72:419.

Minuk GY. Gamma-aminobutyric acid and the liver. Dig Dis 1993;11:45.

Mousseau DD, Butterworth RF. Current theories on the pathogenesis of hepatic encephalopathy. Proc Soc Exp Biol Med 1994;206:329.

Riegler JL, Lake JR. Fulminant hepatic failure. Med Clin North Am 1993;77:1057.

Smit JJ, Bosman DK, Jorning GG, et al. The relationship between plasma free fatty acids and experimentally induced hepatic encephalopathy in the rat. Clin Chim Acta 1991;197:95–104.

Swain M, Butterworth RF, Blei AT. Ammonia and related amino acids in the pathogenesis of brain edema in acute ischemic liver failure in rats. Hepatology 1992;15:449.

Treem WR. Inherited and acquired syndromes of hyperammonemia and encephalopathy in children. Semin Liver Dis 1994;14:236.

Weissenborn K. Recent developments in the pathophysiology and treatment of hepatic encephalopathy. Baillieres Clin Gastroenterol 1992;6:609.

Sherlock S. Fulminant hepatic failure. Adv Intern Med 1993;38:245.

DISEASES OF THE LIVER

Anderson P, Cremona A, Paton A, et al. The risk of alcohol. Addiction 1993;88:1493–1508.

Avogaro A, Beltramello P, Gnudi L, et al. Alcohol intake impairs glucose counterregulation during acute insulin-induced hypoglycemia in IDDM patients. Evidence for a critical role of free fatty acids. Diabetes 1993;42:1626.

Caballeria J. First-pass metabolism of ethanol: its role as a determinant of blood alcohol levels after drinking. Hepatogastroenterology 1992;39(suppl 1):62.

Chowdhury JR, Chowdjury NR, Wolkoff AW, Arias I. Heme and bile pigment in metabolism. In: Arias IM, Boyer JL, Fausto N, et al, eds. The liver: biology and pathobiology, 3rd ed. New York: Raven Press, 1994.

Crabb DW. Recent developments in alcoholism: the liver. Recent Dev Alcohol 1993;11:207.

Day CP, Yeaman SJ. The biochemistry of alcohol-induced fatty liver. Biochim Biophys Acta 1994;1215:33.

Foster GR, Carman WF, Thomas HC. Replication of hepatitis B and delta viruses: appearance of viral mutants. Semin Liv Dis 1991;11:121.

French SW. Nutrition in the pathogenesis of alcoholic liver disease. Alcohol Alcohol 1993;28:97.

Gorelick DA. Recent developments in alcoholism: pharmacological treatment. Recent Dev Alcohol 1993;11:413.

Goldin R. The pathogenesis of alcoholic liver disease. Int J Exp Pathol 1994;75:71.

Gregorio GV, Mieli-Vergani G, Mowat AP. Viral hepatitis. Arch Dis Child 1994;70:343.

Grisolia S, Minana M-D, Grau E, Felipo V. Control of urea synthesis and ammonia detoxification. In: Grisolia S, Felipo V. Cirrhosis, hyperammonemia and hepatic encephalopathy. New York: Plenum Press, 1994.

Kumar S, Pound DC. Serologic diagnosis of viral hepatitis. Postgrad Med 1992;92:55.

Lee WM. Acute liver failure. New Engl J Med 1993;329:1862.

Lieber CS. Hepatic and metabolic effects of ethanol: pathogenesis and prevention. Ann Med 1994;26:325.

Mammen EF. Coagulation abnormalities in liver disease. Hematol Oncol Clin North Am 1992;6:1247.

Rojkind M. Fibrogenesis in cirrhosis: potential for therapeutic intervention. Pharmacol Ther 1992;53:81.

Weiner FR, Esposti SD, Zern MA. Ethanol and the liver. In: Arias IM, Boyer JL, Fausto N, et al, eds. The liver: biology and pathobiology. 3rd ed. New York: Raven Press, 1994.

chapter **6**

Heme Biosynthesis

Considering the pivotal roles of photosynthesis, oxygen transport, and oxidative metabolism in the life process, the importance of chlorophyll and heme-containing proteins cannot be overestimated. Both chlorophyll and heme are porphyrins (ie, tetrapyrrole molecules that form chelates with many metal ions, most notably magnesium and iron). Magnesium is the chelated metal in chlorophyll, whereas ferrous (Fe^{++}) iron serves this function in heme.

Although heme generally is thought of as critical to the survival of the mammalian organism because of its role as the oxygen-binding component of hemoglobin, heme also has a key part to play as a component of hemoproteins, such as the cytochromes. Thus, despite the enormous gaps in our knowledge about intracellular heme homeostasis, it is important to gain some understanding of heme biosynthesis and its regulation in various tissues. Because the erythroid precursor (hemoglobin) and the liver (cytochrome P_{450}) are the major producers of heme, they have been studied extensively. But all cells that conduct oxidative phosphorylation also produce heme.

A general characteristic of evolutionary strategy involves a means of de novo synthesis of many compounds that are critical to survival. In this regard, heme is a prime example of such a strategy; it requires the ubiquitous succinyl-CoA and glycine molecules as starting substrates. Moreover, the process requires both cytosolic and mitochondrial enzymes and concludes with the enzymatic inclusion of iron into the porphyrin (tetrapyrrole) ring at the inner mitochondrial membrane. Hence, the overall synthesis depends upon numerous shuttle steps and three basic substrates; it is important to remember that iron is a substrate that is transported from outside the cell to the inner mitochondrial membrane. The process by which this is carried out is only partially characterized.

In addition to the above, another process occurs—homeostatic maintenance. It should be clear that either insufficient or unchecked heme synthesis will have disastrous consequences; some of the clinical entities associated with heme biosynthesis result from inherently abnormal regulatory processes. These consequences are discussed in the chapter on the porphyrias (Chapter 17).

We also call to the reader's attention a fundamental philosophical question that bears upon another area of our ignorance. Because biologic processes are inherently economical, being refined by evolution, we inquire, "Once heme is made, is it conserved and reused?" Presently, we know nothing about heme recycling and next to nothing about heme catabolism in relation to recycling. Indeed, some have defined a pathway for catabolism of heme that does not depend upon bilirubin formation (the presumed major fate of heme), but remains totally uncharacterized. It is possible that this pathway is coincident with what we are calling recycling. In sum, we have a great deal to learn about this critical area of metabolism, which has implications for oxygenation of tissues, electron transport, and ATP synthesis, as well as detoxification of many drugs and other exogenous toxic compounds.

BIOCHEMICAL OVERVIEW OF PORPHYRIN AND HEME SYNTHESIS

At the outset of this discussion, it should be recognized that a complete block in heme biosynthesis (regardless at which step in the eight-step process), which extends to all cells of the organism, most likely will be fatal and result in death of the embryo. Thus, certain features of this pathway can be accurately intuited: (*1*) erythroid and nonerythroid tissues have different regulatory characteristics; (*2*) these differences also extend from one nonerythroid tissue to another; (*3*) all known defects in the pathway are only partial; and (*4*) based upon the latter, autosomal dominance with variable expressivity might be the most probable inheritance.

The overall pathway is depicted in Figure 6.1, which illustrates eight enzymatically mediated steps. The first and final three of the eight reactions occur within the mitochondrion, whereas the intermediate four are located within the cytosolic compartment. Of the total, genetic defects have been described in all but the initial step (ALA synthase), which is considered to be a major site of pathway regulation in nonerythroidal cells. ALA synthase is encoded by a nuclear gene sequence; its regulatory properties primarily reside in its short half-life (about 70 minutes) and variations in its specific activity based upon absolute increases in protein from de novo synthesis. These properties permit relatively rapid responses to stimuli and inhibitors, thus controlling flux of substrate further down the pathway.

In nonerythroid tissues, particularly the liver, it generally is accepted that the major factor regulating ALA synthase is the intracellular heme concentration, representing a prime example of feedback control of a pathway. By contrast, in erythroid tissue, heme synthesis appears to be regulated at the last step (ferrochelatase) through heme-induced inhibition of iron uptake, whereas ALA synthase activity in erythroid cells is unaffected by heme concentration. In keeping with this difference in regulatory properties, recent evidence suggests differences in subunit molecular weights between the enzymes synthesized by chick erythroid and liver cells in vitro.

Heme regulation of ALA synthase in the liver is best understood, where it is known to exert at least three separate effects. Before discussing these, however, it is important to point out that regulation of heme biosynthesis has not been examined extensively in tissues, except liver, which is an unfortunate result of the clinical classification of porphyrias as "hepatic" disorders. Heme is known to have the following effects on hepatic ALA synthase: *1*) inhibition of purified enzyme at concentrations that do not impair activity in crude homogenate; *2*) inhibition of cleavage of a precursor sequence and translocation of the synthesized enzyme from cytosol to mitochondrion; and *3*) direct repression of enzyme synthesis de novo. It is currently believed that the latter mechanism is the most important under physiologic circumstances, because the heme concentration necessary for repression of ALA synthase synthesis is in the range of 0.1 micromolar, which is at least two orders of magnitude less than is required for the other two effects of heme. Precisely where the regulatory heme pool resides within the cell is another area of relative ignorance, although some evidence suggests that the exchangeable heme moiety of tryptophan pyrrolase may be the source of cellular regulatory heme. Overall, however, two significant pieces of information can be found in the literature: (*1*) in liver, ALA synthase is a major feedback regulatory step in heme biosynthesis, and (*2*) little is known of heme regulation of this enzyme in nonhepatic tissues.

The regulatory properties of the heme biosynthetic pathway are relevant to an understanding of the various acquired and inherited clinical abnormalities, termed porphyrias. Those porphyrias that cause induction of ALA synthase activity are associated with neurologic symptoms, believed to be caused by increased intracellular concentrations of *δ-amino-levulinate (ALA)*. But, there is reason to believe that regulation of heme biosynthesis in extrahepatic tissues will be important to understanding the pathogenesis of neuropathies and other complications of these disorders.

After generation of ALA, the pyrrole porphobilinogen is synthesized from two molecules of ALA through the action of ALA dehydratase, a process that occurs in the cytosolic compartment. ALA dehydratase isolated from liver is an octameric enzyme, in which all subunits seem to be identical. Zinc is a normal requisite for enzyme activity; for example, substitution of lead for zinc is the putative explanation for ALA dehydratase inhibition seen in lead toxicity. In nonerythroidal tissues, the specific activity of ALA dehydratase is two- to five-fold greater than that of ALA synthase, diminishing its role as a rate-limiting step in the biosynthetic sequence. Interestingly, however, there data suggest that ALA dehydratase is inhibited by heme in both liver and erythroid tissues; the physiologic relevance of these observations remains to be clarified.

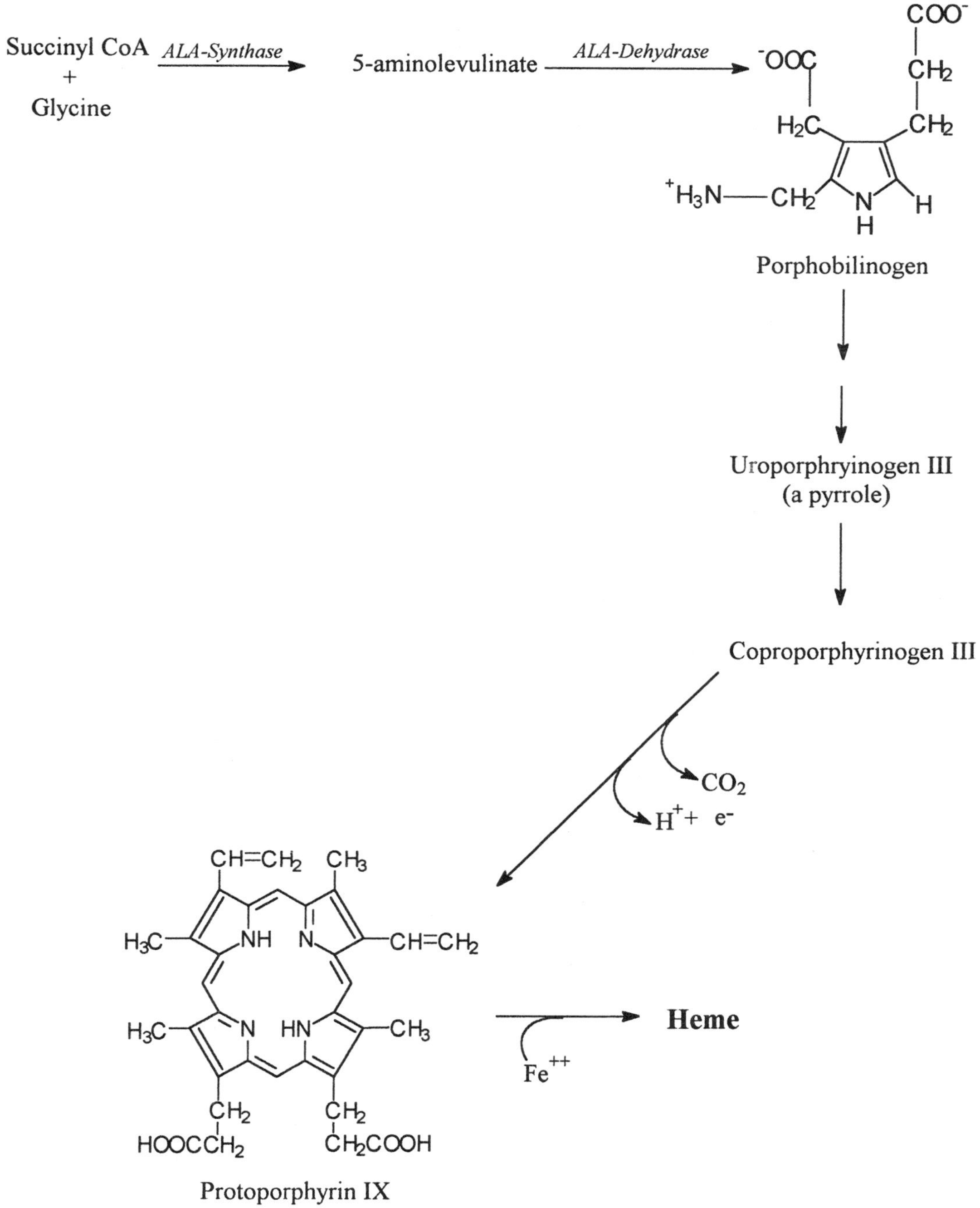

Succinyl CoA + Glycine → *ALA-Synthase* → 5-aminolevulinate → *ALA-Dehydrase* → Porphobilinogen

Uroporphryinogen III (a pyrrole)

Coproporphyrinogen III

CO_2

$H^+ + e^-$

Protoporphyrin IX

Fe^{++}

Heme

Figure 6.1. The general scheme of heme biosynthesis. The pathway is shown in overview. In nonerythroidal tissues, regula tion of the pathway occurs chiefly at ALA-synthase by increased or decreased rate of transcription, transfer of the enzyme from ribosome into mitochondria, or by direct inhibition of the enzyme within the matrix. In erythroidal tissue, regulation occurs at the last step, the insertion of iron by the action of ferrochelatase, through heme-induced inhibition of iron uptake. Porphobilinogen is the building block that is used to create the tetrapyrrole.

Porphobilinogen (PBG), formed as the monopyrrole product of the ALA dehydratase reaction, subsequently is linked to three other PBG molecules in a polymerization reaction mediated by PBG deaminase to form the straight chain tetrapyrrole called hydroxymethylbilane. Data support the existence of at least two separate isozymes in erythroid and nonerythroid tissues, the latter in rat liver being susceptible to inhibition by a wide variety of di- and trivalent metals. In relationship to the preceding two enzymatic steps, specific activity of PBG deaminase in nonerythroid tissue approximates that of ALA synthase; thus, under normal circumstances, flux through the pathway occurs at a rate that is below that where PBG deaminase activity would become rate-limiting.

Hydroxymethylbilane is rapidly converted to uroporphyrinogen III by the action of uroporphyrinogen (UROgen) cosynthase, a step that represents a critical branch point in heme biosynthesis because hydroxymethylbilane also undergoes a spontaneous cyclization to form UROgen I. The latter compound cannot be acted upon by the subsequent enzyme sequence, thus rendering it a by-product of heme biosynthesis and a marker for UROgen cosynthase deficiency. In relation to PBG deaminase, the specific activity of UROgen consynthase is considerably higher in all tissues examined thus far; the rate of formation of UROgen III enzymatically is fast enough to prevent spontaneous formation of UROgen I. It is important to note that each intermediate in successive steps is in the porphyrinogen, or reduced form of porphyrin, with the exception of protoporphyrin. With the exception of ferrochelatase, none of the mediating enzymes will act upon a porphyrin as a substrate, thus rendering porphyrins metabolic by-products. Interestingly, UROgen cosynthase is product-inhibited; however, the significance of such end-product inhibition has not been examined.

The next step in the enzymatic sequence is the conversion of UROgen III to COPROgen III, mediated by UROgen decarboxylase. This enzyme is located in the cytosolic compartment and also acts upon UROgen I to yield COPROgen I. The reaction consists of decarboxylation of the four acetic acid ring substitutions in UROgens I and III to methyl groups; the reaction rate is most rapid when UROgen III is the substrate. The enzyme is inhibited by heavy metals, such as lead and mercury, and is inactive with a porphyrin substrate. Reported specific activities of URDgen decarboxylase in various tissues are much lower than those of UROgen cosynthase, but orders of magnitude higher than those of PBG deaminase, with a half-life of several hours.

Further conversion of COPROgen III to PROTOgen IX requires return to the mitochondrion, a process that has two obvious implications: (*1*) COPROgen III must penetrate the mitochondrial membrane, and (*2*) COPRO oxidase, which acts upon COPROgen III, must be mitochondrial membrane-associated. Because COPRO oxidase is located within the space between inner and outer mitochondrial membranes, it can be inferred that the outer mitochondrial membrane surface is permeable to COPROgen III. The enzyme has an absolute requirement for oxygen, for which no other oxidant can substitute. Unlike other oxidases, COPRO oxidase does not contain any metal. Because the catalyzed reaction results in sequential decarboxylation and reduction of two of the four propionic acid substituents, an intermediate compound called harderoporphyrinogen is formed by conversion of the first propionic acid side chain.

As mentioned earlier, ferrochelatase requires protoporphyrin (distinct from protoporphyrinogen) as a substrate. Hence, PROTOgen IX must be converted to PROTO IX for production of heme. This step is mediated by the enzyme PROTO oxidase, which removes six hydrogen atoms from the PROTOgen IX, thus converting the porphyrinogen to porphyrin. Although this oxidation also can occur nonenzymatically, remember that the preceding enzyme steps have absolute requirements for the reduced porphyrinogens so that the milieu in which the reactions occur must be carefully maintained in a reduced state by the cell. Accordingly, spontaneous conversion of PROTOgen IX to PROTO IX in a reduced environment cannot reliably subserve the heme biosynthetic requirements, necessitating an enzyme to mediate a relatively unfavorable reaction. This is, after all, what enzymes are supposed to do! Indeed, reducing agents, such as glutathione, enhance the activity of this enzyme, "stacking the deck" in favor of this otherwise unfavorable reaction. It is not known precisely where the molecule is located in the mitochondrial membrane, but it is reasonable to suggest that it is in the intermembrane space or the inner membrane itself because the next step in the sequence occurs at the inner membrane surface.

The final step of heme biosynthesis, mediated by ferrochelatase, requires two substrates and results in a single product. Thus, whereas one substrate, PROTO IX, has been synthesized in immediate proximity to ferrochelatase, the other, ferrous iron, must get to the enzyme to be incorporated into heme. Unfortunately, our understanding of the mechanisms by which iron reaches the inner mitochondrial membrane is so rudimentary that this aspect of the ferrochelatase reaction too often is ignored. Nonetheless, it must get there in the proper oxidation state or heme biosynthesis will be adversely affected; with increased knowledge of how this occurs, individuals suffering from apparent ferrochelatase deficiency will be identified who, in fact, have cellular iron transport abnormalities and completely normal PROTO IX synthesis.

The history of biochemical genetics is replete with similar stories, once again illustrating the principle that different genotypes may result in similar phenotypes. Another interesting feature of ferrochelatase is its relative lack of specificity: other porphyrins, specifically deutero- and mesoporphyrin, can serve as substrates, whereas cobalt or zinc can serve as a substitute for iron and enhance the enzyme's specific activity. Thus, substrate availability exerts a powerful regulatory effect on heme biosynthesis, underscoring the importance of iron transport within the cell.

As a final addition to this overview, we note that examination of the pathway under experimental porphyric conditions, both in vivo and in vitro, has yielded many interesting observations. Many of these suggest that control of heme biosynthesis in tissues other than liver and erythroid cells may be vastly different, involving other steps in addition to, or instead of, the ALA synthase or ferrochelatase enzymes. As these mechanisms are clarified further, it may help to explain hitherto poorly understood associated findings, such as psychopathology and peripheral neuropathy, seen in patients with inherited defects of heme biosynthesis.

SUGGESTED READINGS

Bishop DF. Two different genes encode delta-aminolevulinate synthase in humans: nucleotide sequence for the housekeeping and erythroid genes. Nucleic Acids Res 1990;18:7187.

Bissell DM, Guzelian PS. Degradation of endogenous hepatic heme by pathways not yielding carbon monoxide: studies in normal rat liver and primary hepatocyte culture. J Clin Invest 1980;65:1135.

Chadwick DJ, Ackrill K, eds. Ciba Foundation Symposium 180. The biosynthesis of tetrapyrrole pigments. Chicester: Wiley, 1994.

Jordan PM. Highlights in haem biosynthesis. Current Opinion Structural Biology 1994;4:902.

May BK, Borthwick IA, Srivastava G. Control of 5-aminolevulinate synthase in animals. Curr Top Cell Regul 1986;28:233.

Nakahashi Y, Taketani S, Okuda M, et al. Molecular cloning and sequence analysis of cDNA encoding human ferrochelatase. Biochemical Biophysical Research Communications 1990;173:748.

Romeo PH, Raich N, Dubart A, et al. Molecular cloning and nucleotide sequence of a complete human uroporphyrinogen decarboxylase cDNA. J Biol Chem 1986;261:9825.

Shemin D. The biosynthesis of porphyrins. Harvey Lect 1954;50:258.

Traugh JA. Heme regulation of hemoglobin synthesis. Semin Hematol 1989;26:54.

Tsai SF, Bishop DF, Desnick RJ. Human uroporphyrinogen III synthase: molecular cloning, nucleotide sequence and expression of a full-length cDNA. Proc Natl Acad Sci U S A 1988;85:7049.

Wetmer JG, Bishop DF, Cantelmo C, Desnick RJ. Human 5-aminolevulinic acid dehydratase: nucleotide sequence of a full-length cDNA clone. Proc Natl Acad Sci U S A. 1986;83:7703.

Yamamoto M, Kure S, Engel JD, Hiraga K. Structure, turnover, and heme-mediated suppression of the level of mRNA encoding rat liver delta-aminolevulinate synthase. J Biol Chem 1988;263:15973.

part **II**

Disorders of Metabolism

chapter 7

Hypoglycemia

Because the brain unrelentingly requires glucose to fuel its activities, hypoglycemia of even brief duration can have dire consequences for cerebral function. In contrast, most tissues (except for brain, red cell, testis, renal medulla, and adrenal medulla) can use any one of a number of available substrates to supply their energy needs. Apart from when prolonged starvation occurs, during which ketone bodies supply much of the brain's fuel, the brain does not exhibit this flexibility. Decrease of blood glucose to below 40 mg/dl, or a precipitous decrease from elevated but momentarily insufficient (even if normal) levels, can trigger symptoms of cerebral dysfunction. In response, secretion of epinephrine occurs to counteract the decrease in glucose. The hyperepinephrinemia produces symptoms triggered by hypoglycemia, including sweating, trembling, hunger, and tachycardia. Central nervous system manifestations, called *neuroglycopenia*, include repeated yawning, headache, blurred vision, and confusion. Persistent hypoglycemia may precipitate coma and seizures. In the pediatric age group, because the brain is still developing, repeated or prolonged hypoglycemic episodes may alter brain function permanently, not only because of inadequate ATP to maintain ionic gradients but also because glucose is a precursor to myelin membrane lipids.

GLUCOSE HOMEOSTASIS AND HYPOGLYCEMIA IN THE FASTED STATE

Most people spend little time eating, stopping only for relatively short periods to replenish depleted reserves. Indeed, for many, meals are more a social event than a biochemical one. Needless to say, there must be ways for the body to store the fruits of the infrequent "feast" so that there will be undiminished access to fuels during the more common "fast." For example, if the individual fasts overnight for 10 to 12 hours, that individual is in a fasted state the next morning (Figure 7.1). He or she will depend on a series of metabolic adaptations to make the transition from feasting to fasting. The liver, with its remarkable capacity for glycogenolysis, gluconeogenesis, and ketogenesis, is at the center of these adaptations (Figure 7.2).

Let us begin our examination of the fasted state by defining it as the point at which fuel homeostasis depends on stored dietary fuels to meet the organism's metabolic needs. This point is referred to as the *postabsorptive state* and usually refers to the metabolic conditions that prevail after an overnight fast of 10 to 12 hours. Blood glucose levels are stable after such a fast and are maintained by hepatic glycogenolysis (75%) and hepatic gluconeogenesis (25%). The gluconeogenic precursors used by the liver are lactate, pyruvate, alanine, and glycerol. If fasting continues for 12 to 24 hours, gluconeogenesis assumes the commanding role in supporting the blood glucose because available liver glycogen stores are almost exhausted. By 24 hours of fasting, free fatty acids assume a greater role in providing for the metabolic needs of muscle, and, coincidentally, ketogenesis accelerates in liver. From 48 hours on, ketone bodies increasingly become a source of fuel for various organs, including the brain. If fasting gives way to starvation, by 40 days, ketones supply about 75% of the energy needs of the brain (Figure 7.3). Together, these metabolic adaptations stabilize the blood glucose; provide alternate fuels for muscle, heart and gut; and provide ketones as a vital fuel for the brain. By limiting the impetus for continued gluconeogenesis, these adaptations stave off the breakdown of the body protein. Continued destruction of muscle protein inevitably involves the diaphragm and intercostals, among oth-

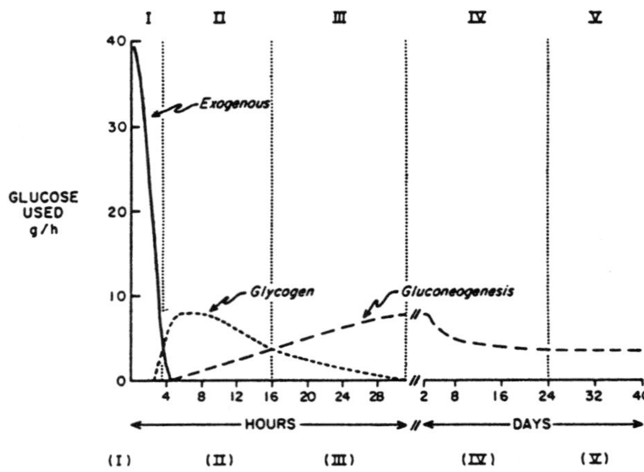

Figure 7.1. The five phases of fasting glucose homeostasis. The vertical axis represents glucose utilization in grams per hour, whereas the horizontal axis shows time, initially in hours and subsequently in days. Phase I lasts over 4 hours; all tissues utilize exogenous glucose and the rate of utilization is higher than at any subsequent time during a 40-day fast. Phase II is characterized by glycogen utilization with increasing gluconeogenesis over the next 12 hours to support a glucose utilization rate less than 50% of the average Phase I rate; note that liver ceases to use glucose in Phase II. By the end of Phase III, at about 32 hours, virtually all of the glucose utilized is supplied by hepatic and renal gluconeogenesis. From 32 hours until the 40th day of a fast, the sole origin of utilized glucose is gluconeogenesis; from the inception of Phase IV, all tissues except red blood cells and renal medulla have begun to utilize alternative metabolic fuels. The data shown are obtained from a 70-kg male who ingested 100 g of glucose and then fasted for 40 days. Reprinted with permission from Kahn CR, Weir GC. Joslin's diabetes mellitus. 13th ed. Baltimore: Williams & Wilkins, 1994:99.

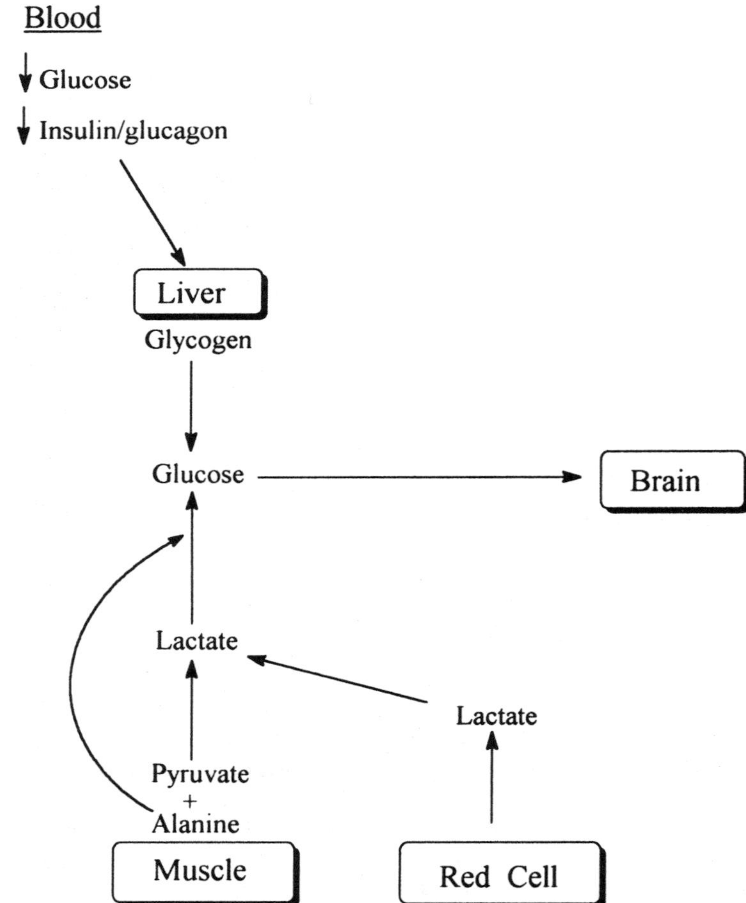

Figure 7.2. Changes in glucose metabolism by tissues in response to fasting. Initial events are a decrease in blood glucose concentration, which leads to a decrease in the insulin/glucagon ratio, chiefly as a result of a drop in insulin. Glucagon, which is both glycogenolytic and ketogenic, is freer to both promote its actions in the liver and support the blood glucose concentration. An important feature of the adaptation mechanisms is the supply of gluconeogenic substrate in the form of lactate. The latter is chiefly derived from the red cell mass, which is absolutely dependent on glycolysis. An important secondary source is the muscle mass, which can quickly convert to use of ketones for its own needs, thereby permitting alanine made from pyruvate to escape into the blood where it is carried as gluconeogenic substrate to the liver. These adaptations extend over the initial 24 to 36 hours of fasting.

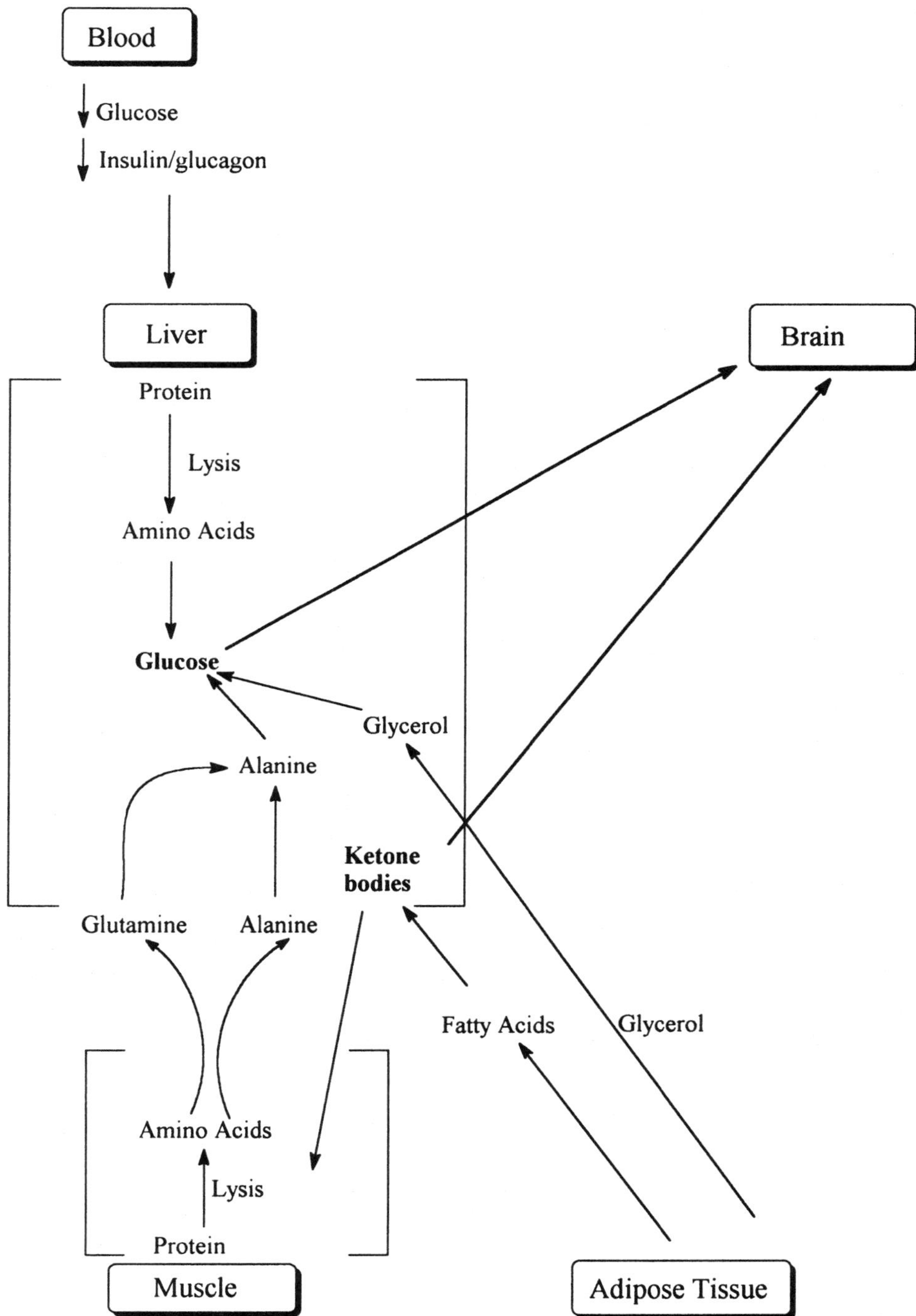

Figure 7.3. Metabolic adaptations to starvation. Key differences of starvation from those of simple fasting are the major contribution of fatty acids and glycerol, as well as amino acids derived from tissue protein to the pool of substrates. Fatty acids, released from adipose tissue, reaches the liver via the circulation, where they undergo β-oxidation. Ketone bodies thus produced are released to muscle, where they are oxidized to conserve gluconeogenic substrate, and to brain to spare glucose. Glycerol, produced from complete hydrolysis of triglyceride, is released to liver for gluconeogenesis. Direct degradation of liver protein produces a wealth of gluconeogenic amino acids, whereas in muscle, protein is hydrolyzed and the gluconeogenic amino acids are conveyed to liver in the circulation. Muscle proteolysis, prolonged over many weeks, leads to the impressive muscle wasting found in marasmic individuals.

ers, enfeebling respiration and leading to pneumonia and the individual's demise. Basic to understanding these metabolic adaptations are changes in the *insulin:glucagon ratio*. As blood glucose decreases to around 80 mg/dl, circulating insulin declines to insignificant levels. However, when the blood glucose hovers around 50 mg/dl, glucagon secretion is initiated. Insulin is regarded as an *anabolic* or *storage* hormone because it facilitates uptake, metabolism, and storage of glucose, fat, and protein. Moreover, it stimulates glycogen synthesis and curtails gluconeogenesis. No less important, it also stimulates fat synthesis in liver and adipose tissue and decreases proteolysis in liver while activating protein synthesis in muscle.

During fasting, insulin levels decrease so that insulin-dependent tissues (adipose and muscle) are not able to compete with brain for available blood glucose. In concert with reduced circulating insulin levels during fasting, a time will occur when there is no net synthesis of glycogen by liver and muscle, of glycerides by liver and adipose tissue, or of protein by muscle. This occurs earlier than might be expected, based on the decline in insulin levels alone due to the release of *glucagon*, the counter-regulatory hormone that directly antagonizes the action of insulin. Glucagon is released by pancreatic alpha-cells as a consequence of decline in blood glucose concentration. Glucagon enhances the metabolic effects of the decreasing insulin levels, triggering glycogenolysis and stimulating both gluconeogenesis (from lactate and pyruvate) and lipolysis. Increased β-oxidation of fatty acids provides fuel for many organs and furnishes the liver with the raw material to generate ketone bodies. Glycerol liberated during triglyceride breakdown also contributes to the pool of gluconeogenic precursors.

These actions of glucagon may be augmented by *epinephrine*, which further enhances glycogenolysis and lipolysis. Overall, progressive glycogenolysis helps to sustain the blood glucose. Lactate and pyruvate produced by muscle, skin, and red cells are used by liver to maintain gluconeogenesis. Ultimately, however, the decisive adaptation to long-term starvation is increasing availability of circulating ketones derived from the partnership in which adipose tissue provides fatty acids and the liver converts them to ketones. The augmented ketone body production in fasting and starvation provides a hint of the gross overproduction of ketones that attends diabetic ketoacidosis, in which glucagon (and the other counter-regulatory hormones) are unopposed by insulin.

Because neurons and red cells do not have insulin receptors, relative insulin deficiency does not suppress glucose uptake and utilization by these tissues. Conversely, liver, muscle, and adipose tissue will experience decreased glucose uptake when circulating insulin levels decline. Without insulin-stimulated glucose uptake and the ready availability of free fatty acids, liver, muscle, heart, and kidney progressively rely on oxidation of fatty acids. In all but the liver, oxidation is complete. But in liver, increased use of fatty acids not only provides for its own energy needs but, more importantly, augments output of ketone bodies (see Chapter 9).

OVERVIEW OF CAUSES OF HYPOGLYCEMIA

From the combined perspectives of pathophysiology and clinical history, it is valuable to divide causes of hypoglycemia into three categories: (*1*) drug or toxin induced; (*2*) fasting hypoglycemia and; (*3*) postprandial hypoglycemia.

Drug- or Toxin-Induced Hypoglycemia

Insulin increases glucose uptake by adipose tissue and muscle, and not only augments glucose uptake in liver, but concomitantly decreases gluconeogenesis. Thus, abnormally high levels of insulin not in accord with the blood glucose level can cause hypoglycemia. In fact, given the prevalence of diabetes mellitus, the most common cause of hypoglycemia worldwide is insulin-induced hypoglycemia in the insulin-dependent diabetic. It is estimated that patients with insulin-dependent diabetes mellitus taking one to two doses of insulin daily will experience approximately one mild episode of hypoglycemia per week. Patients on a more rigorous regimen that attempts to achieve normoglycemia (see Chapter 10) will experience on average two such episodes per week. Thus insulin-dependent diabetes and hypoglycemia "go hand-in-hand." Not surprisingly, the second most common cause of hypoglycemia in a diabetic is sulfonylurea-induced hypoglycemia. Thus, on a worldwide basis, hypoglycemia in the diabetic is the most common setting in which hypoglycemia occurs.

Ethanol ingestion, especially in the poorly nourished chronic alcoholic, also is a common cause of hypoglycemia. Ethanol metabolism produces a great deal of NADH. But for gluconeogenesis to proceed from lactate, NAD^+ is required. Thus, with an inappropriately high $NADH/NAD^+$ ratio, gluconeogenesis is severely hampered. Other effects of ethanol include interference with release of alanine from muscle and uptake of lactate, glycerol, and alanine by liver. In sum, ethanol not only blocks release and uptake of key gluconeogenic precursors but also inhibits the gluconeogenic pathway itself.

Fasting Hypoglycemia

In a nondiabetic, hyperinsulinemia most likely occurs because of a functioning pancreatic *islet cell adenoma* or insulinoma. Insulinomas, although relatively common in adults, with a peak incidence between 40 and 60 years, are rare in infants and children. Hypoglycemia occurs with these tumors because the insulin level is either inappropriately elevated when fasting or exercise occurs, or does not decrease as it would normally under those conditions.

Deficiency of one or more of the counter-regulatory hormones that cause hypoglycemia also occurs more frequently in adults than in children. Such entities include panhypopituitarism, or isolated growth hormone deficiency, and hypoadrenalism. Isolated glucagon deficiency, although exceedingly rare, has been reported.

Hypoglycemia can be a consequence of fulminant hepatitis caused by infectious agents or toxins such as chlorinated hydrocarbons. Passive venous congestion of the liver in congestive heart failure can interfere with hepatic glycogenolysis, thereby causing hypoglycemia. When cirrhosis and sepsis coincide, it is likely that that patient has hypoglycemia.

Precursors for gluconeogenesis can be limited during pregnancy, uremia, and severe malnutrition. Hypoglycemia in association with renal failure is second only to insulin-induced hypoglycemia in frequency. This should not be surprising because the most common cause of renal failure is diabetic nephropathy. But, other factors also contribute to hypoglycemia in uremia. For example, significant caloric deprivation results from anorexia and vomiting. This is compounded by deficiency of gluconeogenic precursors and impairment of hepatic glycogenolysis and gluconeogenesis.

Postprandial Hypoglycemia

Postprandial or reactive hypoglycemia occurs within 2 to 5 hours after eating. In the pediatric age group, hereditary fructose intolerance (see Chapter 11) can provoke hypoglycemia when sucrose or fructose is ingested. Reactive hypoglycemia also is found in patients who have dramatically shortened transit times into the duodenum because of gastric surgery. A hyperinsulin response to this "flood" of ingested nutrients is believed to cause this form of alimentary hypoglycemia.

In contrast to the above conditions, most patients clinically diagnosed by physicians, or more commonly self-diagnosed, as suffering from reactive hypoglycemia cannot be shown to have chemical (by lab test) hypoglycemia. Even when the blood glucose decreases after ingestion of a mixed meal, these subjects often do not experience any hypoglycemic symptoms. It is clear that the oral glucose tolerance test is not helpful in evaluating these patients. Many of these individuals consume diets with a surfeit of refined carbohydrates. Salutary effects in the majority of these subjects can be achieved by consuming a balanced diet with complex carbohydrates making up the carbohydrate component. The root cause of the symptoms in many of these patients remains an enigma.

Hypoglycemia in Infants and Children

Fasting hypoglycemia (even after a short fast) is more common in infants and children than in adults. At least two factors account for this susceptibility to hypoglycemia: First, an infant's brain is almost adult size and, therefore, consumes a larger percentage of available stored fuels in the infant than does the adult brain in its host. Second, evidence suggests that provision of precursors for gluconeogenesis, most notably alanine, cannot meet the infant's needs as it does in adults. While considering the diagnosis of hypoglycemia in the pediatric age group, it is useful to consider three different categories: (*1*) transient neonatal hypoglycemia; (*2*) persistent neonatal and infantile hypoglycemia; and (*3*) childhood hypoglycemia.

It is important to recognize that although the older child may manifest many of the hypoglycemic symptoms found in adults, findings in the infant are entirely nonspecific. They include poor feeding, cyanosis, apnea, hypothermia, hypotonia, poor ability to be aroused, and seizures. These same findings can occur in infants with any life-threatening inborn error of metabolism as well as sepsis or meningitis. Because all of these disorders pose considerable jeopardy to the baby, one must be alert to subtle signs of potentially serious disease.

Transient Neonatal Hypoglycemia

Transient neonatal hypoglycemia occurs most frequently in infants who are small for their gestational age and in premature infants. These infants do not have the adequate body fuel stores to sustain the blood glucose level. Because adequate nutrition will reverse this problem, although this form of hypoglycemia is not innocuous, it will be shortlived. Perhaps the most common form of transient neonatal hypoglycemia occurs in infants born to diabetic mothers. These babies suffer from transient hyperinsulinemia.

Persistent Neonatal and Infantile Hypoglycemia

In infants and young children, islet cell dysplasia is the most frequent cause of hyperinsulinism and usually presents within the first 3 months of life. Hypoglycemia in these patients usually is so severe that almost total pancreatectomy is required. The somatostatin analogue, octreotide, can sustain these infants while preparations are made for surgery. Octreotide inhibits insulin release by the dysfunctional pancreas.

As a group, the various *inborn errors* of gluconeogenesis and of amino acid and fatty acid metabolism are important, treatable causes of hypoglyce-

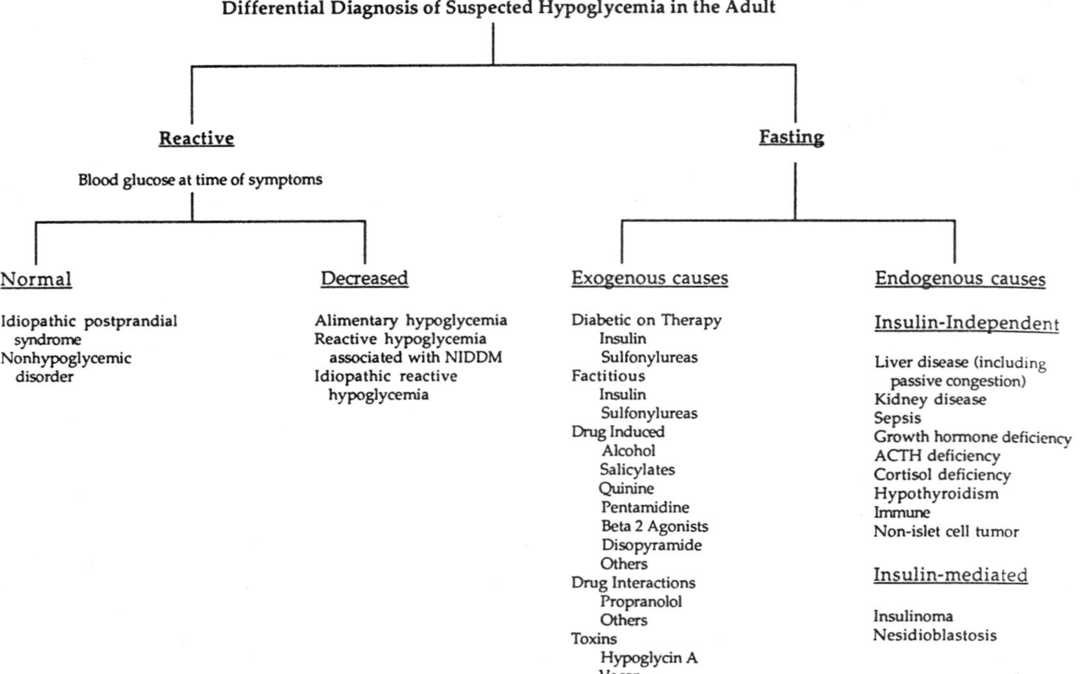

Figure 7.4. Differential diagnosis of suspected hypoglycemia in the adult. Reprinted with permission from Kahn CR, Weir GC. Joslin's diabetes mellitus. 13th ed. Baltimore, Williams & Wilkins, 1994, p 980.

Table 7.1. Differential Diagnosis of Hypoglycemia

NEONATAL
Stressed Infant
Asphyxia
Hypothermia
Sepsis, meningitis
Hyaline membrane disease
Adrenal hemorrhage
Intrauterine undernutrition (limited fuel stores)
Placental abnormalities
Prematurity
Multiple pregnancies
Intracranial injury
Hyperinsulinism (most common cause under 1 year of age)
Islet cell adenoma, hyperplasia
Maternal diabetes mellitus
Erythroblastosis fetalis
Beckwith-Wiedemann syndrome
Sudden discontinuance glucose infusion
Inborn Errors
Defects in gluconeogenesis
Defects in glycogenolysis
Branched-chain amino acid disorders
Congenital adrenal hyperplasia
INFANCY AND CHILDHOOD
Ketosis—? limitation of gluconeogenic precursors
Hyperinsulinism
Disorders of gluconeogenesis—gluconeogenic enzymes, organic acidemias
Disorders of glycogenolysis
Deficiency of insulin antagonistic hormone: thyroid, adrenal, pituitary
Other
Reye's syndrome (liver failure)
Severe malnutrition (kwashiorkor)
Salicylate toxicity

mia in the early pediatric age group. That doesn't mean, however, that milder forms may not present later in childhood. For fatty acids to provide an auxiliary energy source to glucose and to generate ATP to fuel gluconeogenesis, β-oxidation must be intact. If normal β-oxidation is not possible, as in medium chain acyl dehydrogenase deficiency, meeting the metabolic needs of tissues will depend on glycogenolysis and gluconeogenesis. Complete oxidation of lipid yields more than twice the amount of energy per mole compared to glucose. Thus, without the ability to use fats, hypoglycemia can be expected unless there is continuous food intake.

If either glycogen synthesis or the ability to release free glucose from glycogen were impaired, an important short-term fuel source would be unavailable to sustain the blood glucose. The same may be stated for defects of gluconeogenesis, which impair the ability to generate glucose from lactate, pyruvate, alanine, and glycerol. Predictably, such gluconeogenic defects result in hypoglycemia in the fasted state.

Hypoglycemia in the Older Child

In the age group between 18 months and 5 years, the most common cause of substrate unavailability is *ketotic hypoglycemia*, a condition that seems to depend on the inability to provide adequate alanine to support gluconeogenesis. Happily, this is a transient form of hypoglycemia because by ages 8 to 9 years, symptoms in most of these patients spontaneously remit. Whereas most children will become hypoglycemic with a 24- to 36-hour fast, subjects with ketotic hypoglycemia will do so within 12 to 24 hours. Avoidance of prolonged fasting usually maintains these children.

EVALUATION OF PATIENTS WITH HYPOGLYCEMIA

As depicted in Figure 7.4 and Table 7.1, causes of hypoglycemia can be broken down into: (*1*) those resulting from drugs and toxins of which insulin- and sulfonylurea-induced hypoglycemia are most common; (*2*) fasting hypoglycemia in which the disorders of the pediatric and adult age groups vary because of the importance of inborn errors in pediatrics and; (*3*) postprandial or reactive hypoglycemia. A critical component of the evaluation of any patient with hypoglycemia in whom the diagnosis is not obvious is the metabolic and clinical response to a prolonged fast. Table 7.2 lists the effects of a prolonged fast on various metabolic parameters in different disorders associated with hypoglycemia. In children, 12 to 24 hours may be required to develop hypoglycemia, whereas, in adults, 48 hours may be necessary. Prolonged fasting in a previously symptomatic individual should be conducted under careful monitoring with intravenous access in place.

Table 7.2. 24-Hour Fasting Studies in Various Causes of Hypoglycemia

	GLUCOSE	FFA	KETONES	LACTATE	PYRUVATE	ALANINE	INSULIN	OTHER
Normal	↓	↑	↑	Slightly ↓	Slightly ↓	Slightly ↓	↓	
Normal newborn (<12 hours)	↓	↑	↓	Slightly ↑	Slightly ↑	Slightly ↑	N	Maturational delay in both gluconeogenesis and ketogenesis
Hyperinsulinism	↓[1]	↓	↓	N	N	N	±↑	Large birth weight infant Glucagon will ↑ glucose—overcome inappropriate conservation of liver glycogen
Ketotic hypoglycemia	↓[2]	↑	↑[3]	Slightly ↓	Slightly ↓	Slightly ↓	↓	Exaggeration of normal response Perinatal problems; cataracts rarely; growth retarded; ↓ adipose tissue
Defect gluconeogenesis (G-6-Pase deficiency)	↓[1]	↑	±↑	↑	↑	↑	↓	Hepatomegaly
Defect glycogenolysis (debrancher)	↓[1]	↑	↑	N	N	N	↓	Hepatomegaly
Growth hormone deficiency	↓[2]	↑	↑(↓)?	N	N	N	N	
Panhypopituitarism	↓[1]	↑(↓)	↑	N	N	↓↓	N	(↓ lipolysis sometimes in early infancy)
Cortisol deficiency	↓[2]	↑	↑	N	N	↓	N	Glucocorticoids ↓
SGA infant (pattern suggests delay in onset gluconeogenesis)	↓	↓	↓	↑	↑	↑	N	Defect in hepatic fatty acid oxidation to form ketones
Defect in hepatic fatty acid oxidation	↓[2]	↑	↓	N-sl↑	?	N	N	Examples: Systemic carnitine deficiency; glutaric aciduria type II; HMG CoA lyase deficiency; carnitine palmityl transferase deficiency

N = Normal
1 = Hypoglycemia develops several hours (3–12) after beginning of fast.
2 = Hypoglycemia develops 12 or more hours after beginning of fast.
3 = Ketonuria precedes ↓ in glucose.

SUGGESTED READINGS

Bonham JR. The investigation of hypoglycemia during childhood. Ann Clin Biochem 1993;30:238.

Comi RJ. Approach to acute hypoglycemia. Endocrinol Metab Clin North Am 1993;22:247.

Cryer PE. Glucose counterregulation: prevention and correction of hypoglycemia in humans. Am J Physiol 1993;264:E149.

Frier B, Fisher M, eds. Hypoglycemia and diabetes: clinical and physiological aspects. London: Edward Arnold, 1993.

Gerich JE, Mokan M, Veneman T, et al. Hypoglycemia unawareness. Endocr Rev 1991;12:356.

Mitrakous A, Fanelli C, Veneman T, et al. Reversibility of unawareness of hypoglycemia in patients with insulinomas. N Engl J Med 1993;329:834.

Service FJ. Hypoglycemia. Med Clin North Am 1995;79:1.

Zeller J, Bougneres P. Hypoglycemia in infants. Trends in Endocrinology and Metabolism 1992;3:366.

chapter **8**

Lactic Acidosis

Most commonly, lactic acidosis occurs as a secondary phenomenon under conditions in which cellular respiration is impaired because of inadequate oxygen delivery. At a physiologic level, transient lactic acidosis occurs when the person exercises so vigorously that an oxygen debt is incurred. But the metabolic capacity of the liver and kidney to dispose of that lactate renders such accumulation innocuous. From a pathologic perspective, however, lactic acidosis occurs in shock, septicemia, and hypoxemia. In vasogenic shock, the arterial vascular tone deteriorates causing a drastic decrease in oxygen delivery to the tissues. Clinical conditions in which vasogenic shock occurs include sepsis, trauma, anaphylaxis, and adrenal crisis. Hypovolemic shock, from hemorrhage or severe dehydration, and cardiogenic shock, from acute myocardial infarction or pulmonary embolus, also are attended by lactic acidosis. The common denominator of these conditions is a lack of oxygen as the final electron acceptor of the electron transport chain, which is the dominant ATP-generating mechanism in all cells with mitochondria.

There also are primary causes of lactic acidosis associated with various inborn errors of metabolism effecting gluconeogenesis, the pyruvate dehydrogenase complex, and the cytochromes of the electron transport chain. These primary causes may pose a particular diagnostic challenge because the infant or young child affected with one of these disorders also may suffer from a secondary cause of lactic acidosis such as sepsis.

When lack of oxygen compromises ATP generation, the remaining option for the cell is to revert to an anaerobic mode of glucose metabolism. Recall that because fatty acids also must be metabolized under oxidative conditions, they do not represent an auxiliary fuel when oxygen availability is limiting. Because glycolysis produces only 1/19 as much ATP as the combined actions of the tricarboxylic acid cycle and the electron transport chain produce, it is clear that glycolysis will have to create a surplus of pyruvate to generate an equivalent amount of ATP. For glycolysis to proceed unabated, NADH formed in the glyceraldehyde-3-phosphate dehydrogenase reaction must be recycled to NAD^+ because only a meager amount of NAD^+ exists in the cell. Normally, two shuttles (Figure 8.1) transfer reducing equivalents into the mitochondrion, thus regenerating NAD^+. But when mitochondrial function is hindered because of inadequate oxygen availability, the reduction of pyruvate to lactate, catalyzed by lactate dehydrogenase (LDH), becomes a major safety valve that permits regeneration of NAD^+. This temporary expedient provides more NAD^+ to generate ATP, without which the cell could not survive. But it also produces lactate, which, under these hypoxic conditions, builds up to cause lactic acidosis. Glycolysis per se does not cause the accumulation of H^+; rather, when ATP is converted to ADP and P_i, one H^+ is produced. Normally, both the tricarboxylic acid cycle and gluconeogenesis consume H^+; therefore, lactic acidosis results when these pathways are blocked. As we have noted, this occurs most commonly when there is an inadequate supply of oxygen; but, an inherited block in gluconeogenesis, the tricarboxylic acid cycle, or the electron transport chain can have the same effect.

Although no unambiguous definition of lactic acidosis exists, there seems to be general agreement that lactic acidosis occurs when the serum lactate level is persistently elevated above the 4 to 5 mM range, which is associated with a decrease in the arterial blood pH. For many years, the prevalent view was that over-production of lactate was the predominant cause of lactic acidosis. However, as discussed below, in many instances, under-utilization by the liver and kidney, particularly due to defects in gluconeogenesis, can have a greater effect than over-production.

LACTATE AND PYRUVATE METABOLISM

Lactate, the final product of anaerobic metabolism of glucose, exists in equilibrium with pyruvate through the reaction catalyzed by the enzyme lactate dehydrogenase:

$$\text{Pyruvate} + H^+ + \text{NADH} \underset{\longrightarrow}{\overset{\text{LDH}}{\longleftarrow}} \text{Lactate} + \text{NAD}^+ \quad (1)$$

Or:

$$L/P = k \times ([\text{NADH}] \times [H^+])/[\text{NAD}^+] \quad (2)$$

There is much interest in the lactate/pyruvate ratio, which, as shown in equation (2), is dependent upon three cytosolic variables: pyruvate concentration, the $NADH/NAD^+$ ratio (in turn, reflecting the redox state of the cytosol), and the hydrogen ion concentration in the cytosol. Of course, the $NADH/NAD^+$ couple is a major source of reducing potential within the cell, thus occupying a position of great importance in the regulation of metabolism. Abundant experimental data suggest that the mitochondria normally are 50- to 100-fold more reduced than the cytosol. This discrepancy between the state of reduction of the cytosol and that of the mitochondria limits the value of the serum lactate/pyruvate ratio as an indicator of the *tissue* lactate/pyruvate ratio. Nor can this ratio be used as an accurate determinant of tissue redox states, according to equation (2). With this caveat in mind, measurement of lactate and pyruvate nonetheless may be useful in defining certain acquired and inherited disorders of lactate and pyruvate metabolism, although the serum values of those metabolites should not be considered as representing a one-to-one correspondence with the likely tissue levels.

LACTIC ACID METABOLISM

According to equation (1), the sole pathway for production of lactate is from pyruvate. Because lactate cannot be metabolized further and its only metabolic fate is conversion back to pyruvate, it is a metabolic dead-end product (Figure 8.2). Furthermore, the enzymatically mediated reaction depicted in equation (1) maintains an equilibrium state in favor of lactate, with a ratio of lactate to pyruvate of approximately 10:1, at rest, in plasma.

With respect to clinical measurements of lactate, it should be recognized that any methodology based upon color development cannot be expected to discriminate between optical isomers of the same molecule. Because L(+)-lactate is the ste-

Figure 8.1. (A) The α-glycerophosphate shuttle. This process functions to convey electrons produced from the oxidation of glyceraldehyde-3-phosphate in glycolysis into the mitochondrion for ATP production. The carriage is NAD^+ in the cytosol, which cannot cross the mitochondrial membrane barrier. Thus, the electrons are transferred to dihydroxyacetone phosphate (DHAP) to form α-glycerophosphate, which, in turn, transfers the electrons to flavin adenine dinucleotide (FAD) and then down the electron transport chain generating two ATP. (B) The malate-aspartate shuttle. Cytosolic accumulation of NADH leads to reduction (reaction #2) of oxaloacetate (2-keto-) to malate (2-alcohol) and regeneration of NAD for glycolysis. A specific, nonenergy-requiring transporter exchanges malate for α-ketoglutarate (reaction #4) across the mitochondrial membrane, thus introducing the electrons from the oxidation of NADH intramitochondrially. Within the mitochondrial matrix, reaction #4 regenerates oxaloacetate (OAA), once again forming NADH, which now can transfer the electrons to the transport chain and become reoxidized. The regenerated OAA is transaminated (reaction #1) to aspartate and α-ketoglutarate, using transported glutamate from the cytosol (reaction #3) as the source of the $-NH_2$ group. Reactions #3 and #4 remove the products of transamination (α-ketoglutarate and aspartate) from the mitochondrial matrix into the cytosol, where the reaction (#3 and #1) occurs again to regenerate OAA and glutamate.

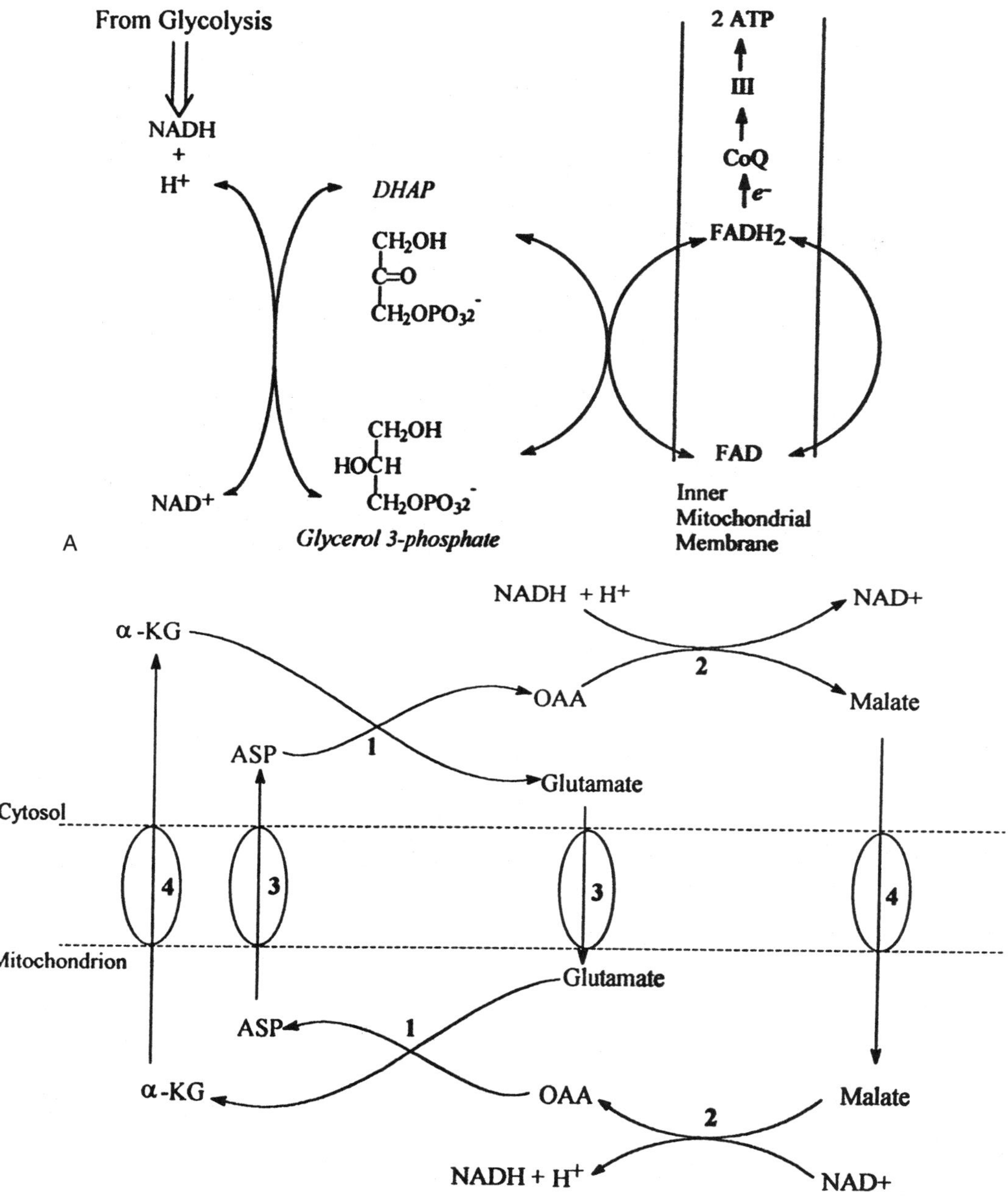

(1) Aspartate aminotransferase
(2) Malate dehydrogenase
(3) Glutamate-aspartate transporter
B (4) Malate α-ketoglutarate transporter

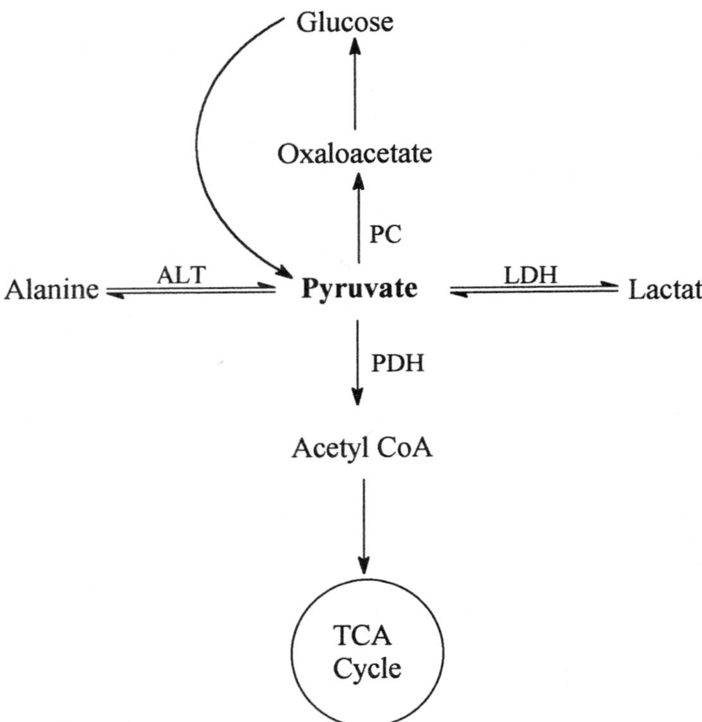

Figure 8.2. Overview of the metabolic fates of pyruvate. Of the four alternative fates depicted, the only irreversible direction is conversion to acetyl CoA by pyruvate dehydrogenase (PDH) action, followed by complete oxidation. The conversion to lactate by lactate dehydrogenase (LDH) represents a metabolic "dead-end," although the reaction favors lactate in a ratio of 10:1. Pyruvate carboxylase (PC) is the initial enzyme step in gluconeogenesis, whereas the action of alanine aminotransferase (ALT) explains the nonessential amino acid status of alanine.

reoisomer produced in mammalian metabolism, whereas D(−)-lactate generally is the form produced by bacteria, colorimetric tests may be inaccurate under some clinical conditions. Hence, regarding diagnosis, it is important to distinguish the type of test being used by the clinical laboratory; tests based upon the use of L(+)-lactate dehydrogenase will provide information about L-lactate, exclusively. For these reasons, it is sometimes appropriate to determine serum lactate by both enzymatic and colorimetric methodologies.

PYRUVATE METABOLISM

Pyruvate is a metabolite that is so important in intermediary metabolism that it (like glucose-6-phosphate and acetyl-CoA) is a "crossroads metabolite," with its pivotal role emphasized in a multiplicity of metabolic processes. Pyruvate is produced from three primary sources (Figure 8.2): *a*) glucose through glycolysis, *b*) certain amino acids (predominantly alanine), and *c*) lactate via the lactate dehydrogenase reaction. Four major processes provide for the disposition of pyruvate: *a*) direct transamination to yield alanine, *b*) carboxylation to oxaloacetate to permit entry into the gluconeogenic sequence of reactions or into the tricarboxylic acid cycle, *c*) enzymatic reduction to form lactate, and *d*) oxidative decarboxylation to acetyl-CoA. Just as pyruvate contributes to regeneration of glucose through gluconeogenesis, it also can contribute to regeneration of amino acids from which it is derived. This becomes apparent by tracing the fate of the carbon atoms introduced into the Krebs cycle by formation of acetyl CoA from pyruvate: one of the two carbons from each molecule of acetyl CoA that condenses with oxaloacetate to form citrate reappears as part of the molecule of oxaloacetate regenerated after one turn of the cycle. Because several of the Krebs cycle intermediates can undergo transamination (eg, alpha-ketoglutarate to form glutamate), various amino acids that include a part of the original acetyl CoA molecule can be formed. Another potent determinant of the status of the pyruvate-lactate dyad is hydrogen ion concentration. From equation (2), a decrease in pH, representing an increase in $[H^+]$, could increase lactate. But, when pH decreases, flux through glycolysis slows. How, then, can this happen? Once again, regulation of metabolism accounts for this apparent paradox: a decrease in intracellular pH is responsible for inhibiting phosphofructokinase, the rate-limiting enzyme of the glycolytic pathway. As a consequence of this inhibition, pyruvate production from glucose is slowed, resulting in diminished lactate production.

LACTATE FORMATION AND THE CORI CYCLE

Although all tissues are capable of conducting glycolysis, the predominant lactate producers of the human body are skin, erythrocytes, muscle, renal medulla, intestinal mucosa, retina, and when present, tumor tissue. In a healthy person at rest, about 1400 mmol or 115 g of lactate are produced over a period of 24 hours. Estimates of lactate production at rest by these organs are as follows: 29 g by red cells, 29 g by skin, 17 g by brain, 16 g by white skeletal muscle, 15 g by renal medulla, and 8 g by the gut. With the exception of the red cell, relatively poor vascularization in proportion to their requirements for oxygen is common to all of these lactate producers, which leads to the conclusion that tissue hypoxia can be expected to result in lactate production. In the case of the erythrocytes, which are cells without mitochondria, it is clear that oxidative metabolism of pyruvate cannot be carried out, resulting in conversion of pyruvate to lactate.

The task of disposing this considerable lactate load (115 g) is left to the liver (75 g) and kidney and red muscle (40 g). Vesting the liver and kidney with the capacity both for gluconeogenesis and oxidation of lactate creates an impressively economical system. The red muscle contributes to lactate disposal via oxidative metabolism because muscle is unable to carry out gluconeogenesis. The small net acid excretion by the kidney (approximately 1 mEq/kg/day) amply illustrates how efficient and important to homeostasis are the combined roles of these three organs in lactate removal. Although lactate is freely filtered by the glomerulus, the renal threshold for lactate is five to six times the normal serum lactate level, resulting in a fractional excretion under normal circumstances of 1% to 2%. Thus, tubular reabsorption of filtered lactate leads to replenishment of renal glycogen stores through gluconeogenesis, return of filtered lactate to the circulation, and/or consumption of lactate by renal tissue through oxidation of pyruvate for energy.

Liver metabolizes lactate primarily through gluconeogenesis, simultaneously maintaining intracellular glycogen stores and releasing free glucose into the circulation to be used by the glucose-dependent tissues of the body. Subject to the control mechanisms discussed earlier, a calibrated amount of the total is consumed through oxidative metabolism to subserve the liver's energy needs. In addition to these routes, resting red skeletal muscle can participate in lactate removal through oxidative metabolism. However, considerable debate remains as to the extent of this contribution during clinical lactic acidosis (in contradistinction to the state after exercise).

Clinical conditions contributing to the development of lactic acidosis are numerous and varied (Table 8.1). Considering the contribution of the liver to lactate removal, it should be apparent that hypoxia resulting in compromise of the liver's ability to oxidize lactate would convert this organ from a lactate user to a lactate producer. Because the liver is the primary means of removal of circulating lactate, such a reversal in metabolic stance could result in a rapid increase in plasma lactate levels. In adults, biguanide therapy frequently has been reported as a cause of fulminant lactic acidosis.

INBORN ERRORS ASSOCIATED WITH LACTIC ACIDOSIS

In children, sepsis is foremost among the common causes of lactic acidosis; the frequency of association between sepsis and inborn errors of metabolism, which may themselves contribute to elevated lactate, is a common cause of confusion during diagnosis. It should be assumed that any child with lactic acidosis and sepsis has an inborn error of metabolism until proven otherwise.

Patients with inborn errors in which lactic acidosis is a prominent feature (Table 8.1) frequently manifest neurologic symptoms including ataxia,

Table 8.1. Conditions Associated With Lactic Acidosis

DEFECT/CONDITION	CLINICAL FEATURES AND LAB FINDINGS	BIOCHEMICAL DEFECT
Disorders of Gluconeogenesis		
Glucose-6-phosphatase deficiency	Hypoglycemia, hyperlipemia, hyperuricemia, hepatomegaly, xanthomas, failure to thrive	
Fructose-1,6-diphosphatase	Hypoglycemia, failure to thrive, seizures, hepatomegaly	
Pyruvate carboxylase	Variable hypoglycemia, failure to thrive, mental retardation, acidosis, variable hepatomegaly, seizures	
PEPCK	Hypoglycemia, hypotonicity, hepatomegaly, developmental delay, failure to thrive	
Disorders of Pyruvate Catabolism		
Pyruvate dehydrogenase multienzyme complex	Neurologic manifestations—spectrum from intermittent ataxia, chorea to coma and death, mental retardation, hepatomegaly, acidosis, hypoglycemia, variable optic atrophy	Different components of multienzyme complex involved in various patients
E_3-Dihydrolipoyl dehydrogenase	Elevation lactate, α-ketoglutarate and branched-chain amino acids, optic atrophy, lethargy, hypertonia, stridor	E_3 component of pyruvate, α-ketoglutarate and branched-chain keto acids dehydrogenase is same enzyme
Leigh's subacute necrotizing encephalopathy	Seizures, vomiting, mental retardation, weakness, blindness, peculiar sobbing respirations	One patient had pyruvate carboxylase defect Others—defective activation of PDH complex
Pyruvate dehydrogenase phosphatase	Tachypnea, hypotonia, lethargy, seizures, coma, death No hypoglycemia, ketoacidosis	

irritability, and motor and mental retardation. In some of these patients, plasma lactate levels will be only modestly elevated, but cerebrospinal fluid (CSF) lactate will be more strikingly so. The blood lactate should be determined in any patient with a metabolic acidosis and elevated anion gap for which an explanation is not readily available. Evaluation of such patients must be painstaking and is best approached with a detailed protocol. Two such protocols are those of Robinson, and Haas and Nyhan, which can be found by consulting the texts that are listed in the Suggested Readings section at the end of this chapter.

TREATMENT

Ideal management of any disease process must be directed at the underlying cause(s); in this respect, lactic acidosis is no exception. However, it is especially important to recognize that lactate accumulation results from and contributes to wide-ranging disruptions in cellular metabolic function, unlike hyperchloremic metabolic acidosis (see Chapter 4), which can be compensated by transmembrane electrolyte pool shifts. These disruptions may result in both increased production of lactate and a concomitant decrease in both excretion and utilization. Hence, standard forms of therapy for acidosis, including the administration of bicarbonate and glucose, ameliorate the situation only to the degree that the alkali replenishes the depleted bicarbonate buffer pool. This can be only temporary because continued production of lactate will rapidly consume this increment. In some cases, if a metabolic error is present, a glucose infusion will fortuitously treat the underlying error, and the patient's acidosis will remit and return only when a full diet is reinstituted. In cases such as this, the clinician should consider the possibility of an inborn error of metabolism.

Theoretically, a promising therapeutic tool for treatment of lactic acidosis is the compound dichloroacetate. This agent, which activates pyruvate dehydrogenase and enhances production of acetyl CoA, has been used successfully in treatment of biguanide-induced lactic acidosis, and experimentally in treatment of hypoxia-induced lactic acidosis in dogs. Regrettably, it has achieved only minimal success in treating adults with a variety of disorders that result in accumulation of lactate. Thus far, therapeutic trials in infants and children with inborn errors of metabolism are sparsely reported and inconclusive.

A new buffering agent, carbicarb, may offer some promise in treating lactic acidosis and other metabolic acidoses. This agent is an equimolar mixture of sodium bicarbonate and sodium carbonate, and has the theoretical advantage that it does not produce CO_2.

SUGGESTED READINGS

Buchalter SE, Crain MR, Kreisberg R. Regulation of lactate metabolism in vivo. Diabetes Metab Rev 1989;5:379.

Haas RH, Nyhan WL. Disorders of organic acids. In: Berg BO, ed. Neurologic aspects of pediatrics. Boston: Butterworth Heinemann, 1992:64.

Halperin ML, Kamel KS, Cheema-Dhadli S. Lactic acidosis, ketoacidosis, and energy turnover. Mt Sinai J Med 1992;59:1.

Kerr DS. Lactic acidosis and mitochondrial disorders. Clin Biochem 1991;24:331.

Kruse JA, Carlson RW. Lactate metabolism. Crit Care Clin 1987;5:725.

Madias NE. Lactic acidosis. Kidney Int 1986;29:752.

Mizock BA. Lactic acidosis. Dis Mon 1989;35;236.

Robinson BH. Lactic acidemia (disorders of pyruvate carboxylase, pyruvate dehydrogenase). In: Scriver CR, Beaudet AL, Sly WS, Valle D, eds. Metabolic and molecular basis of inherited disease. 7th ed. New York: McGraw Hill, 1995:1479.

Stacpoole PW. Lactic acidosis. Endocrinol Metab Clin North Am 1993;22:221.

chapter **9**

Ketogenesis

KETONE BODY PRODUCTION

Placing a major lipid storage depot in the intestinal mesentery, with venous drainage directly into the hepatic portal vein, creates an ideal anatomical situation for the liver as the major site of ketone body production. Conversely, such an anatomical arrangement also guarantees that a major share of ingested dietary lipid will pass directly to the liver for immediate metabolism or processing to very low density lipoproteins (VLDL) for export and storage in adipose tissue.

Within the hepatocyte (Figure 9.1), fatty acids are activated to their fatty acyl CoA analogues by the enzyme fatty acid thiokinase, which is located in microsomes and the outer mitochondrial membrane. After this step, the fatty acyl CoA compounds can proceed in one of two directions: (*1*) they can react with glycerol to form mono-, di- and triglycerides in what is termed an esterification or (*2*) they can undergo β-oxidation. Because long chain fatty acids cannot penetrate the inner mitochondrial membrane to undergo β-oxidation, transfer of these fatty acids across that barrier requires formation of the acyl carnitine derivative. This reaction is mediated by the enzyme carnitine acyltransferase I (CAT I), which is located on the outer face of the inner mitochondrial membrane.

Ketone bodies represent a vital alternative to glucose; they are used to fuel the activities of the brain and various other organs after fasting has continued for 24 to 48 hours. Ketones are generated in a metabolic partnership in which adipose tissue provides the free fatty acids and liver metabolizes these fatty acids to the ketones, acetoacetate and β-hydroxybutyrate. Because triglycerides stored in adipose tissue represent the body's largest energy reserve (ca. 150,000 kcal), it is appropriate that adipose tissue sustain the individual, especially when fasting gives way to starvation. The role of triglycerides in sustaining the individual during prolonged starvation is important because there is only enough glucose in the blood stream and glycogen in the liver to meet the brain's glucose requirement for 10 to 12 hours. If muscle breakdown were forced to support gluconeogenesis without the vital contribution of fatty acids mitigating the need for glucose, then the individual would survive only 1 to 2 weeks of starvation. Part of the life-sustaining adaptation to prolonged starvation is the production of ketones by the liver; ketones are a water-soluble form of fat that dramatically decreases consumption of glucose. Ketones help maintain brain function while providing an auxiliary fuel for other organs. In functioning in this way, fatty acids and ketones prolong life by preserving protein stores.

Two biochemical adaptations are required to maximize ketogenesis—one already noted is the increase in lipolysis with release of fatty acids from adipose tissue. The other is to increase the liver's capacity for β-oxidation and ketogenesis; if this does not occur, most of the fatty acids arriving at the liver will only be reesterified to triglyceride. Some of this triglyceride will be stored in liver whereas most will be incorporated into low density lipoproteins for export to peripheral tissues (see Chapter 15). To ensure that ketogenesis is brisk, a change must occur in the hormonal milieu of the fasted individual; this change is characterized by a decline in insulin and an increase in glucagon levels. With high glucagon and low insulin levels, the hormonal set characteristic of fasting and starvation, not only is ketogenesis stimulated but gluconeogenesis and lipolysis as well.

A major goal of those who examine the biochemical adaptation to starvation has been to determine how the high-glucagon and low-insulin condition stimulates ketone body formation. The chain of events begins with glucagon decreasing

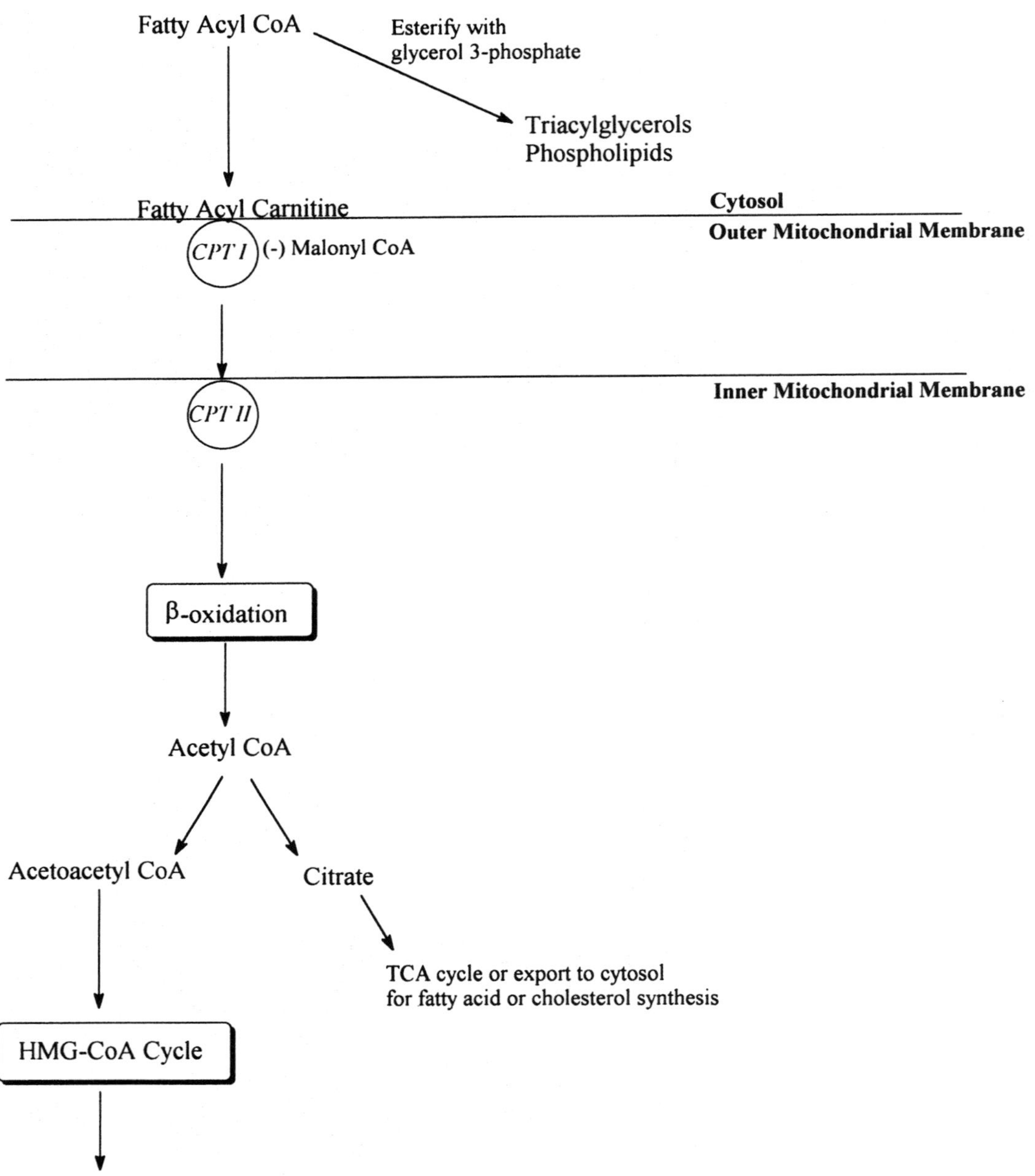

Figure 9.1. Overview of fatty acid transport and metabolism in the hepatocyte. After initial "activation" through thiokinase activity and conversion to acyl CoA analogues, two major directions are open: either cytosolic synthesis of more complex lipids or reaction with carnitine via carnitine acyltransferase I (CAT I) to form an acyl carnitine compound. CAT I activity is regulated by cytosolic concentrations of malonyl CoA, the initiating compound in fatty acid synthesis. Because one of the anabolic effects of insulin is to promote fatty acid synthesis, insulin causes inhibition of CAT I and therefore β-oxidation, as well; glucagon has the opposite effects on the system. An acylcarnitine translocase protein conveys the molecule across the mitochondrial membrane barrier, where CAT II recycles the carnitine outward toward the cytosol and reforms the acyl CoA within the mitochondrial matrix. The latter compound then undergoes β-oxidation with formation of ketone bodies.

Table 9.1. Metabolic States of the Liver

CARBOHYDRATE REPLETE	STARVATION (KETOSIS)
Low glucagon : insulin ratio	High glucagon : insulin ratio
Malonyl CoA ↑	Malonyl CoA ↓
Fatty acid synthesis is brisk	Fatty acid synthesis is inhibited
Fatty acid oxidation is inhibited	Fatty acid oxidation is activated
Malonyl CoA inhibitory effect on CAT ensures formation of triglycerides and VLDL	Glucagon acutely stimulates ketogenesis by limiting formation of malonyl CoA

glycolytic flux and dramatically increasing gluconeogenesis. Glucagon acts in a cAMP dependent manner, causing phosphorylation of the bifunctional enzyme PFK-2/FBPase-2. This enzyme both produces and dismantles F-2,6-P_2, which is the most potent activator of glycolysis in liver. This allosteric effector activates PFK-1, which is the major regulatory enzyme of glycolysis. In the presence of glucagon, the FBPase-2 activity is enhanced and consequently F-2,6-P_2 levels decrease, in turn increasing flux through gluconeogenesis. But with decreased flux through glycolysis, less pyruvate forms, which causes decreased formation of mitochondrial citrate, the precursor to cytosolic acetyl CoA. Acetyl CoA is used by acetyl CoA carboxylase, which is the initial enzyme in the fatty acid biosynthetic pathway, to produce malonyl CoA. In addition to its role in fatty acid synthesis, malonyl CoA is a potent inhibitor of CAT I. Inhibition of CAT I diverts fatty acids from β-oxidation to fatty acid synthesis and esterification. However, in fasting and starvation, when glucagon levels increase and insulin levels decrease, malonyl CoA levels also decrease. Under these conditions, β-oxidation is enhanced, leading to a glut of acetyl CoA that is converted to ketones.

As expected, hepatic levels of malonyl CoA fluctuate in conjunction with rates of fatty acid synthesis (Table 9.1). Thus, under conditions in which there is excess glucose, large amounts of malonyl CoA will be present in large amounts and net lipid synthesis will occur. Obviously, for net synthesis of fatty acids to occur, β-oxidation must be inhibited—a demand met by interaction of malonyl CoA with CAT I, thus inhibiting entry of fatty acyl CoA into the mitochondria.

Thus, intracellular regulation of fatty acid metabolism occurs at the level of the mitochondrial membrane. In the "fed state," with a large carbon flux through glycolysis, intracellular levels of acetyl CoA increase, creating more than is required for TCA cycle operation. As a result, malonyl CoA accumulates in the cytosol, in turn inhibiting fatty acyl CoA entry into the mitochondrion. Therefore, metabolic disposition of fatty acyl CoA compounds must occur via conversion to glycerides, which is the only remaining pathway open to them. Conversely, in fasting and starvation, less acetyl CoA is formed from glycolysis, which results in decreased CoA levels. In the absence of its inhibitor, malonyl CoA, the CAT I system transfers fatty acyl CoAs into mitochondria, where they undergo β-oxidation to acetyl CoA.

Biochemical and Physiologic Correlates of the Regulatory Mechanisms

As we have noted, the liver occupies a central position in the economy of ketone bodies and is the major site of ketone body production. As might be expected from its role in production, the liver is unable to consume ketones for its own energy needs. Although this makes sense, the biochemical reason for this is that further metabolism of ketone bodies requires acylation to the corresponding thioester. Succinyl CoA: 3-oxoacid transferase (Figure 9.2), the enzyme responsible for this conversion, is absent in liver but present in peripheral tissues.

In ketogenesis, cleavage of the thioester bond to generate the free ketones occurs via a complex pathway (Figure 9.2). Direct deacylation by *deacylase* occurs, but this is considered to be a minor path. In the quantitatively more important route, acetoacetyl CoA and acetyl CoA are combined (HMG CoA synthase), and subsequently the HMG CoA is cleaved (HMG CoA lyase) to yield acetyl CoA and free acetoacetate. In the HMG CoA lyase step, in its characteristically economical fashion,

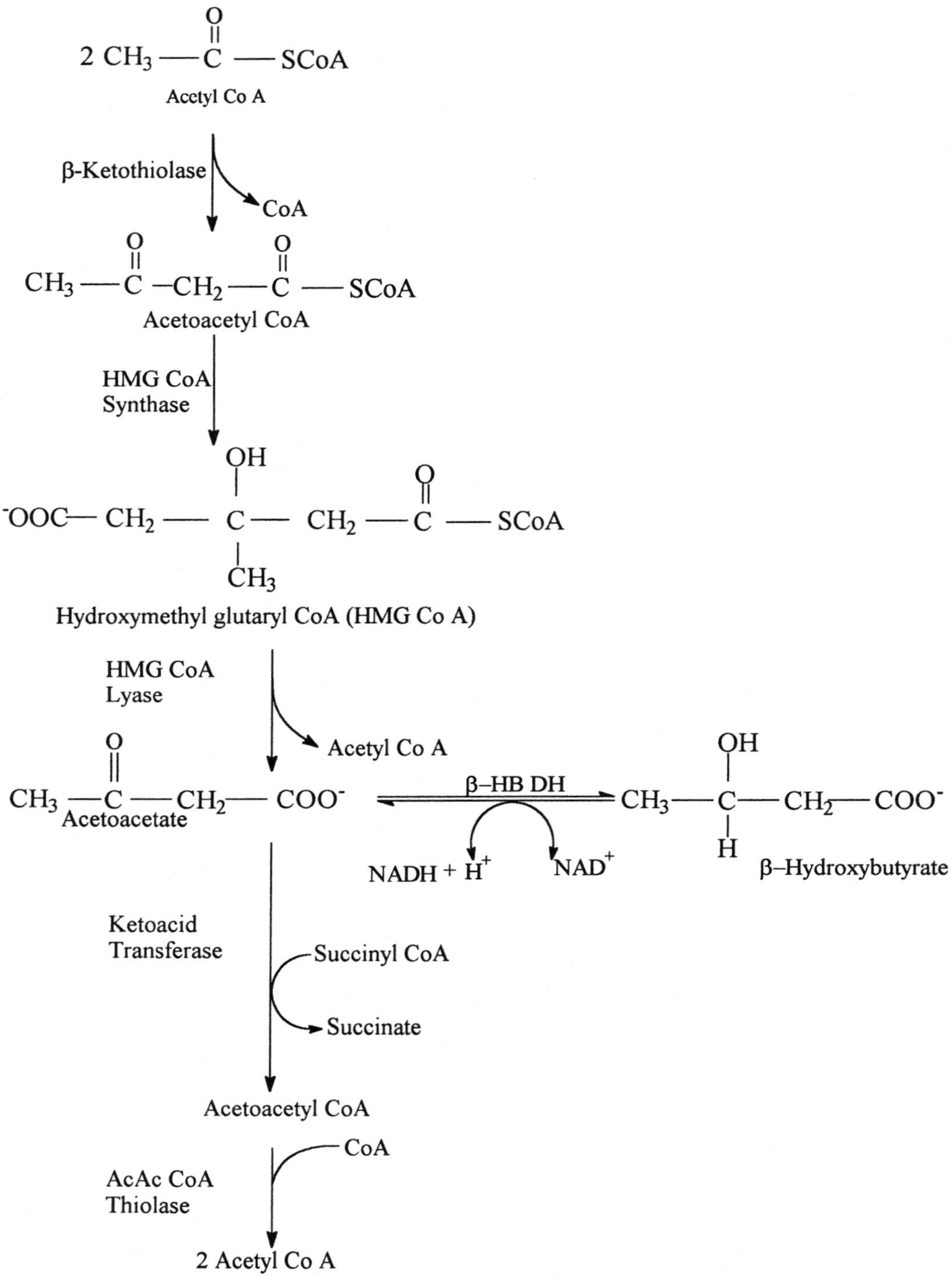

$$2\ CH_3-\overset{O}{\overset{\|}{C}}-SCoA$$

Acetyl Co A

β-Ketothiolase → CoA

$$CH_3-\overset{O}{\overset{\|}{C}}-CH_2-\overset{O}{\overset{\|}{C}}-SCoA$$

Acetoacetyl CoA

HMG CoA Synthase

$$^{-}OOC-CH_2-\underset{CH_3}{\underset{|}{\overset{OH}{\overset{|}{C}}}}-CH_2-\overset{O}{\overset{\|}{C}}-SCoA$$

Hydroxymethyl glutaryl CoA (HMG Co A)

HMG CoA Lyase → Acetyl Co A

$$CH_3-\overset{O}{\overset{\|}{C}}-CH_2-COO^{-} \rightleftharpoons CH_3-\underset{H}{\underset{|}{\overset{OH}{\overset{|}{C}}}}-CH_2-COO^{-}$$

Acetoacetate ⇌ (β–HB DH; NADH + H^+ → NAD^+) β–Hydroxybutyrate

Ketoacid Transferase (Succinyl CoA → Succinate)

Acetoacetyl CoA

AcAc CoA Thiolase (CoA)

2 Acetyl Co A

Figure 9.2. The reactions of ketogenesis. Net production of ketone bodies from fatty acids occurs in liver because liver lacks the enzyme ketoacid transferase. Thus, the depicted pathway ends in liver at the level of acetoacetate formation from the HMG CoA lyase step. The acetoacetate then is exported into blood, where it exists in equilibrium with β-hydroxybutyrate in a fashion directly analogous with the pyruvate-lactate system. β-HBDH = β-hydroxybutyrate DH, HMG = hydroxymethylglutaryl.

the cell conserves part of the energy required to cleave a C-C bond of HMG by converting a hydroxyl to a keto-group on the β-carbon of acetoacetate.

Acetoacetate and β-hydroxybutyrate are readily interconvertible in liver and enter the blood from the liver to meet needs of other tissues. Note that the ketone bodies are not intermediates of fatty acid β-oxidation. In contrast to intermediates of fatty acid degradation, which are the "activated" coenzyme A derivatives, the ketone bodies exist free both intra- and extracellularly. Moreover, β-hydroxybutyrate generated from fatty acid synthesis has the D-configuration as opposed to the L-configuration of the intermediate form from long-chain fatty acid oxidation. Once again, evidence of the basic parsimony inherent in metabolic regulatory systems exists: separation of the fatty acid synthetic (endoplasmic reticulum) process from β-oxidation (mitochondria) plus generation of the same chemical compound in different stereoisomers provide the advantages both of topography and enzyme stereospecificity in handling metabolic substrates.

Role of Peroxisomes in Ketogenesis

Peroxisomes, which are subcellular organelles bounded by a single bilamellar membrane, are ubiquitous in mammalian cells and possess a wide range of biochemical functions among which is a unique type of β-oxidation. In contradistinction to the mitochondrion, peroxisomes (*1*) do not require carnitine for fatty acid entry, (*2*) raise the fatty acyl CoA to a higher degree of unsaturation (enoyl CoA) by an oxidase-mediated step resulting in direct reduction of H_2O_2, and (*3*) may require carnitine for removal of end products. An important consequence of the relatively high fatty acid permeability of the peroxisomal membrane is the organelle's capacity to metabolize the very long chain fatty acids, lignocerate (C24:0) and hexacosanoate (C26:0), which are poorly handled by mitochondria. Other functions include catalysis of cholesterol side-chain shortening, chain shortening of unsaturated acyl-CoAs (C16:1-C22:1), breakdown of dicarboxylic acyl-CoAs, and plasmalogen biosynthesis.

Although peroxisomes can contribute to diet-induced ketogenesis, the extent to which this occurs has been estimated at one-third or less of the total ketone production. Regulation of peroxisomal β-oxidation is directly related to intracellular ATP concentration, suggesting that a major function of this oxidative process is generation of acetyl-CoA under anabolic conditions, when fatty acid catabolism is not required for energy generation. The reverse is, of course, true for mitochondrial β-oxidation, when increases in the ATP/ADP ratio are inversely related to fatty acid catabolism and result in slowing of ketogenesis. Predictably, the nature of the regulatory mechanisms in each β-oxidative process would decrease the peroxisomal contribution to ketogenesis when mitochondrial ketogenesis is maximal.

With continued research, the pivotal metabolic role of the ketone bodies in the energy economy of the body has become obvious. In particular, the integrated use of glucose and lipid in meeting energetic needs of tissues is such that when plasma glucose is low, as with carbohydrate restriction (starvation) or in diabetes mellitus (when it cannot be utilized), plasma free fatty acids increase. Concomitantly, plasma ketone bodies also increase, providing yet another fuel when glucose is unavailable for body needs. This adaptation has been termed physiologic ketosis and should be viewed as a normal switching mechanism. Indeed, because the increased ketone body production is met by increased utilization, only a negligible increase in plasma levels occurs.

It seems curious that the body should provide fat as a fuel in two different forms. First, free fatty acids are less soluble in aqueous media than are ketone bodies, and second, fatty acids uncouple oxidative phosphorylation; and, of course, they can be used by the brain after prolonged fasting, extending the time the individual can survive famine.

PATHOLOGIC KETOSIS

As we have noted, for ketosis to develop, adipose tissue must augment output of free fatty acids and the liver must divert these lipids from triglyceride synthesis (esterification) to β-oxidation and ketogenesis. The signals that cause mobilization of lipid from adipose tissue stores include glucagon, epinephrine, and the adrenal steroids. These hormones cause (*1*) hydrolysis of triglycerides within the adipocyte; (*2*) transport of free fatty acids out of the adipocyte, facilitated greatly by albumin in plasma; and (*3*) distribution in the circulation to various organs of the body. Recall that as plasma glucagon levels increase, insulin levels decrease; the net effect is that fatty acid mobilization increases while glucose utilization decreases.

As we already have noted, increase in the glucagon:insulin ratio also facilitates fatty acid oxidation in the hepatocyte by depressing glycolysis and inhibiting acetyl CoA carboxylase (through a phosphorylation-dephosphorylation mechanism), causing a drop in malonyl CoA levels and increasing transport of fatty acyl CoA into the mitochondria for β-oxidation. The manner in which the increased rate of acetoacetyl CoA production consequent to this process is integrated with the HMG CoA pathway to release increased amounts of free acetoacetate into the blood is not well defined. In any case, when the above adaptations result in accelerated ketone body production and release beyond what peripheral tissues are capable of utilizing, total ketone body (acetoacetate and β-hydroxybutyrate) levels in blood begin to rise above the usual 0.1 mM.

A working definition of ketosis has been proposed to be a total blood ketone body level above 0.2 mM. With this level, it is important to distinguish between physiologic ketosis, pathologic ketosis, and ketoacidosis. Elevations in total ketone bodies above the 0.2 mM level may be the result of a stimulus and response that are normal. For example, in fasting, late pregnancy, and vigorous exercise (all normal states), blood ketones may reach 2 mM. Such states are considered to represent *physiologic ketosis*. The most common form of *pathologic ketosis* is found in insulin-dependent diabetes mellitus, a state in which almost no insulin exists to counteract the gluconeogenic, lipolytic, and ketogenic actions of glucagon and the other hormones that antagonize the actions of insulin. Because ketone bodies are strong acids, they may accumulate in the blood so that blood buffers can no longer maintain a normal pH; this state is known as *ketoacidosis*.

Starvation Ketosis

The discussion of carbohydrate metabolism (see Chapter 11) emphasizes that total body glycogen stores cannot meet energy demands for a period longer than about 10 hours. Depletion of hepatic glycogen during fasting "sets the stage" for ketone body production from lipids by reducing the supply of acetyl CoA from glycolysis, hence reducing the malonyl CoA levels that have been depressing the transfer of lipid into mitochondria. In addition, the ketogenic liver is characterized by an elevated carnitine content. The means by which hepatic carnitine is increased remains obscure, but glucagon is believed to play a role. Within the first 12 to 24 hours of fasting, this increase in β-oxidation is reflected in an increase of total blood ketone body concentration from less than 0.2 mM to about 0.3 mM. Although this change appears to be minimal, it must be appreciated that this increase occurs when peripheral tissues are increasingly utilizing ketones. Fasting, prolonged for 48 to 72 hours, results in blood ketones rising up to 3 mM. This 10-fold increase in an alternate energy substrate, despite accelerated peripheral consumption of ketones, illustrates the tremendous ketogenic capacity of the liver. In the normal adult, these changes occur in a normoglycemic state, with insulin levels depressed but not virtually absent as in insulin-dependent diabetes mellitus.

Important differences exist between the newborn and adult regarding the above responses to fasting. In the immediate neonatal period, the human infant is capable of increasing serum free fatty acids to levels that are adequate for ketogenesis, yet serum ketone bodies remain below 0.4 mM for up to 12 hours of fasting. In contrast to the adult, this low level does not represent increased utilization because blood glucose levels continue to decrease despite appropriately low insulin and increased glucagon levels. Even in clinically hypoglycemic infants, ketogenesis cannot elevate serum ketone body concentration above 0.4 mM. The reasons for these findings remain speculative; at least two factors, fewer mitochondria and lower carnitine acyltransferase in the cells of newborn tissues, appear to be involved. Whatever the reasons, the relative defect in ketogenesis in the neonate has important implications: ketone body utilization by the brain must be severely restricted because ketone body extraction from blood is linearly proportional to blood levels. Accordingly, when a sick neonate has large amounts of ketones in its urine, this must be regarded as unusual, indicating a possible inborn error resulting in production of various organic acids other than the typical ketone bodies associated with β-oxidation and ketogenesis.

Clearly, ketogenesis in starvation requires some regulation because ketone body production in excess of consumption would result in ketoacidosis and total metabolic disarray. In fact, starvation for longer than 72 hours does not result in a further increase in blood ketones, and in prolonged fasting, blood ketones tend to decrease. The primary control mechanism accounting for these observations appears to be the direct ability of ketone bodies to elicit a release of insulin from the pancreatic islets, causing suppression of lipolysis. Evidence suggests that ketone bodies exert a direct antilipolytic effect on adipose tissue. Thus, despite the enormous potential of the liver to produce ketone bodies during starvation, this ability is "kept in check" by indirect feedback mechanisms. The system is, in fact, self-limited by product inhibition; this process is examined in more abstract terms in Chapter 1.

Diabetic Ketoacidosis

As noted above, a basic regulatory factor that controls the massive ketogenic ability of the liver is restriction of lipolysis by stimulating pancreatic insulin release. This release is prompted by fatty acids and ketone bodies. Thus, even when prolonged starvation is experienced, some insulin continues to be secreted, keeping ketone body formation "in check." Failure of this feedback loop in insulin-dependent diabetes mellitus results in unfettered ketone body production by the liver because of unrestricted availability of free fatty acids. Because the free fatty acids are increased to extremely high values (2.5 to 3.5 mM), the liver (in this insulinopenic state) is driven to produce ketone bodies in great excess of the ability of extrahepatic tissues to utilize them. Consequently, blood ketone body concentration approaches 20 mM, generating a life-threatening metabolic acidosis. Hepatic fatty acid oxidation capacity and ketogenesis are maximal, owing to the increased glucagon:insulin ratio and consequent massive adipose tissue breakdown.

Acetoacetate and β-hydroxybutyrate, both strong organic acids, are completely dissociated at body pH (pK = 3.8), each producing (per millimole) 1 mEq of hydrogen ion and keto acid anion. However, uncontrolled ketone body production soon leads to acidosis, which ensues when body buffer base is consumed and respiratory compensation is no longer able to maintain a normal pH. Under normal circumstances, when ketones are oxidized by brain and skeletal muscle, bicarbonate (consumed by acid buffering) is replenished by metabolism of ketones.

Evidence exists that the hyperketonemia of starvation and diabetic ketoacidosis is partially attributable to a concomitant impairment of utilization in the periphery as well as to overproduction. Insulin-deficient dogs utilize ketones at a slower rate than do normal dogs; the rate increases with insulin administration. The mechanism of this reversal remains obscure, but in diabetic ketoacidosis, impairment of ketone body utilization can be a major contributing factor to the severity of the disease.

SUGGESTED READINGS

Halperin ML, Cheema-Dhadli S. Renal and hepatic aspects of ketoacidosis: a quantitative analysis based on energy turnover. Diabetes Metab Rev 1989;5:321.

Hood VL, Tannen RL. Regulation of acid production in ketoacidosis and lactic acidosis. Diabetes Metab Rev 1989;5:393.

McGarry JD, Woeltje KF, Kuwajima M, Foster DW. Regulation of ketogenesis and the renaissance of carnitine palmitoyltransferase. Diabetes Metab Rev 1989;5:271.

Quant PA. The role of mitochondrial HMG-CoA synthase in regulation of ketogenesis. Essays Biochem 1994;28:13.

chapter **10**

Diabetes Mellitus

Each of the preceding three chapters has dealt with aspects of the pathophysiology of diabetes mellitus. Hence, the reader should be well-equipped to follow the discussion about this common and important disease. Despite our incomplete understanding of the biochemical basis for the multiplicity of late complications of diabetes mellitus, the dominant role of hyperglycemia and nonenzymatic glycosylation of many proteins in the pathogenesis of diabetes are becoming clearer. In the chapter on ketogenesis, we noted how the insulin-deficient diabetic state can be likened to starvation in the midst of plenty of metabolic fuel due to the absence of insulin. Diabetes is the prototypical endocrine disorder that involves derangements of hormonal interaction and their consequent effects on metabolic pathways. Because of this reason, we have preceded our discussion about diabetes mellitus with considerations of acid-base balance, hypoglycemia and ketogenesis, building a foundation for a thorough examination of a disease that includes all these and more.

Diabetes mellitus is a common disease, which affects 2% to 4% of the population of most industrialized nations where incidence has been determined. Its manifestations arise from relative or absolute deficiency of insulin or resistance to insulin action on target tissues. Insulin has many effects (Table 10.1) that lead to the storage of glycogen, fat, and protein. In muscle and adipose tissue, it recruits glucose transporters to the plasma membrane, thereby increasing uptake of glucose and utilization by those tissues. By stimulating glycolysis in adipose tissue and liver, it enhances acetyl CoA formation, ultimately stimulating lipogenesis. As the main storage hormone, it inhibits breakdown of glycogen, fat, and protein—effects that are opposed by the counter-regulatory hormones glucagon, cortisol, epinephrine, and growth hormone.

In the relative or absolute absence of insulin, undiminished secretion of counter-regulatory hormones results in hyperglycemia. Persistent hyperglycemia causes microvascular disease throughout the body, resulting in retinopathy, nephropathy, and neuropathy. Hyperglycemia and other less well-defined factors contribute to the macrovascular complications as well, which include coronary artery, cerebrovascular, and peripheral vascular disease.

DIABETES MELLITUS SYNDROMES

One of the earliest recorded clinical descriptions of diabetes mellitus included the statement, "being melted down of the flesh and limbs into urine," written by an observer in the second century A.D. Although this quote sheds no light on how the dissolution occurs, the statement represents a marvelously accurate mental picture of the untreated insulin-dependent diabetic. Indeed, before the discovery of insulin in 1921, all insulin-dependent diabetic patients were consigned to this fate. Aside from the discovery of penicillin, nothing has so abruptly and significantly altered medical therapy as has the work of Banting and Best. But, we must lay to rest the popular misconception that insulin therapy has rendered the disease fully treatable, as is the case with penicillin and streptococcal pharyngitis. Unfortunately, nothing could be further from the truth; indeed, the experience with insulin since 1921 has been as much a tragic disappointment as it has been a major triumph of modern medicine.

Diabetes mellitus is a generic term for many disorders of differing etiology that cause persistent hyperglycemia and a variety of long-term complications grouped under the rubric of microvascular and macrovascular derangements. The two domi-

Table 10.1. Known Effects of Insulin

A. Direct

1. ↑ glucose transport into liver, skeletal muscle, and adipose tissue cells; also may similarly affect most other cell types to a lesser degree.
2. ↑ amino acid transport chiefly into skeletal muscle, but as with glucose, many other cell types as well.
3. ↓ hormone-sensitive lipase in adipocytes, thus inhibiting fatty acid mobilization.
4. ↑ synthesis in most tissues of protein, fat, and glycogen in varying proportions, depending on the cell type by influencing gene transcription.

B. Indirect

1. Antagonism of glucagon-induced effects on glucose metabolism in liver through inhibition of cAMP-dependent protein kinase.
2. ↓ cAMP levels in the hepatocyte by (?) inhibiting phosphodiesterase activity.
3. ↓ circulating glucagon by suppression of gene expression.

nant diabetic syndromes are termed insulin-dependent diabetes mellitus (IDDM or type I) and noninsulin-dependent diabetes mellitus (NIDDM or type II). Distinguishing features of these two categories are listed in Table 10.2. Patients with NIDDM are further subdivided between the obese (85%) and those who are not obese (15%). There are many secondary causes of diabetes mellitus, most of which arise from increased secretion of one of the counter-regulatory hormones. These forms are rare compared to IDDM and NIDDM, but will, at times, be encountered by a practitioner.

Insulin-Dependent Diabetes Mellitus

Type I or IDDM accounts for 10% to 20% of patients with diabetes mellitus. Because of the virtual absence of insulin secretion, it is the form associated with ketoacidosis (see Chapter 9). Although a genetic component to IDDM is unmistakable—40% of monozygotic twins of an individual with IDDM will develop overt diabetes—it also is clear that genetics alone is not sufficient to explain the phenomenon. This nominal genetic contribution must be contrasted with the situation in NIDDM, in which a monozygotic twin of a patient with NIDDM has almost a 100% chance of developing NIDDM, usually within a year's time. In case of IDDM, recent evidence has implicated a viral infection and autoimmune response as major contributory factors. The current view is of a multiallelic inheritance nature, conferring upon an individual the predisposition to develop the disease, combined with provocative influences, such as specific viral infections or endogenously created autoimmune disorders. Thus, the development of IDDM results from a coincidence of multiple factors, even when the individual harbors the genetic predisposition.

DEFINITION AND PATHOPHYSIOLOGY

Because knowledge about the causes of diabetes is imprecise, devising a rigorous definition is difficult. Most authorities agree that only a clinical definition can accommodate our present state of ignorance. Thus, diabetes mellitus may be defined

Table 10.2. Features of Types I and II Diabetes Mellitus

CHARACTERISTIC	TYPE I	TYPE II
Age of onset	Generally in pre- or adolescent; may appear at any age	Typically older than 35 years; may appear at any age
Nature of onset	Often sudden	Slow, insidious
Genetic predisposition	Related to specific HLA factors	Strongly familial; unrelated to HLA
Secondary environmental factors	Viruses, toxins	Obesity
B-cell autoimmunity	Present at initial episode	Not present
Insulin secretion	Generally absent or delayed	Reduced in amount
Body habitus	Thin, can appear cachectic	Usually normal or obese
Symptoms at onset	Polyuria, polydipsia, weight loss, hunger; ketoacidosis common	Often none, or mild Type I; no ketoacidosis
Long-term secondary	Retinopathy, nephropathy, neuropathy; onset after 5 years	Similar to Type I complications, but usually late in disease
Insulin dependency	Absolute	Occasionally

as a state of diminished glucose tolerance, usually due to insulin deficiency or resistance, with all of the accompanying biochemical and microvascular consequences attendant upon such a state of sustained hyperglycemia.

An individual's inability to respond to a standard glucose load by maintenance of the blood glucose within the range defined by a normal population is called diminished glucose tolerance. A normal individual maintains the blood glucose within these limits by conversion of glucose to glycogen, by oxidation of glucose for energy, or as a building block for conversion to other biologically important molecules. Therefore, a diminished glucose tolerance implies an impairment in one or more of these processes. Indeed, a derangement of all of these reactions are found in the diabetic individual. Hence, in the diabetic, the body wastes glucose, spilling all glucose in excess of the minimal amount that it can utilize without insulin into the urine (Figure 10.1). Such profligacy clearly violates the usual frugality of metabolic processes.

If we accept the notion that the body is wasting glucose, then it is simple to see how closely, conceptually speaking, the ancient definition cited above reflects the actual pathophysiologic mechanisms underlying diabetes mellitus. The "melting" phenomenon is related to the body's cells starving for usable glucose (because of insulin deficiency), while excess blood glucose is lost in the urine. In a sense, the body is "blind" to the calories supplied, blithely wasting these calories while starving. Such a paradox has very far-reaching implications, including weight loss due to fat consumption and life-threatening ketosis as a consequence of ketone body production (see the section on ketogenesis in Chapter 9). Part of this weight loss is also attributable to breakdown of muscle protein and loss of muscle mass because gluconeogenesis is fed by amino acid precursors. Both of these phenomena are direct consequences of loss of the antilipolytic and protein anabolic actions of insulin, respectively.

An important secondary consequence of elevated blood glucose levels is the appearance of glucosuria, which occurs when circulating glucose exceeds the renal tubular capacity for reabsorption from the lumen. Because all materials excreted in urine must be solubilized, any increment in the amount of such material will necessitate an increase in the volume of water lost in the urine as well. Hence, we note another aspect of the "melting" phenomenon referred to by the ancients and can account for another portion of the dramatic weight loss experienced by a diabetic patient. However, it is the clinically unobservable consequences of this increased water loss on electrolyte and acid-base balance that wreak the greatest havoc and constitute the most acute and potentially dangerous problems encountered by these individuals.

Because membrane permeability to glucose in muscle and adipose tissue largely depends on the presence of insulin, an increase in glucose concentration of the extracellular compartment represents an increase in effective osmotic pressure in this fluid space. Hence, cellular water is lost to the interstitium, resulting in intracellular dehydration. Such a shift in fluid also will result in dilution of extracellular electrolytes with a corresponding increase of intracellular electrolytes. Thus, electrolytes also will flow out of the cell down the existing concentration gradient. Keep in mind that, in the absence of insulin, the initiating process (ie, hyperglycemia) continues to worsen, in turn forcing the above process to continue. At least two factors contribute to the hyperglycemia: sustained gluconeogenesis and inability of muscle and adipose tissue to use glucose in the absence of insulin. Therefore, intracellular dehydration and electrolyte depletion may be massive in an acutely ill patient. Compounding the effect of osmotic shifts at the cellular level is the steadily increasing urinary volume due to increasing glucosuria; this "*osmotic diuresis*" is the major cause of fluid, sodium, and chloride losses from the body.

Another concern is the loss of intracellular potassium and total body potassium depletion that occurs in diabetic ketoacidosis. Several factors contribute to this loss: (*1*) the breakdown of muscle protein results in liberation of about 3 mEq of potassium per gram nitrogen; (*2*) glycogenolysis, which liberates 1 mEq of potassium per 3 g of glycogen; and, (*3*) increased aldosterone secretion resulting from the hyponatremia, which enhances distal tubular potassium secretion. Consequently, the vascular potassium compartment, which always is minuscule compared to the intracellular pool, remains relatively normal when massive body losses occur through renal excretion.

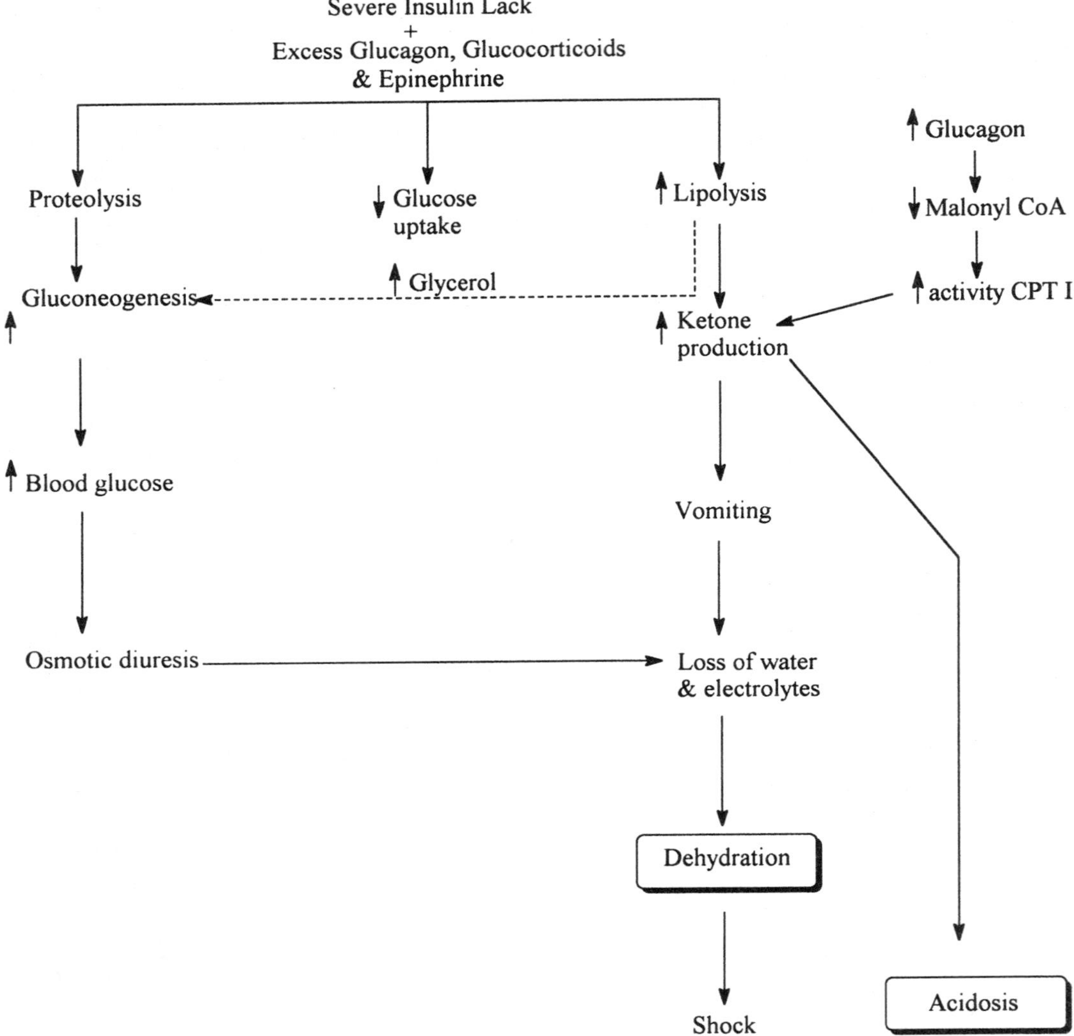

Figure 10.1. The pathogenesis of diabetic ketoacidosis. The initiating insult is a relative or absolute deficiency of insulin. Thus, viewed from within the cell, there is a lack of glucose for fuel, which causes triggering of humoral responses appropriate for a state of hypoglycemia (↑ glucagon, ↑ adrenal glucocorticoids, ↑ epinephrine). These cause accelerated lipolysis, increased gluconeogenesis, and enhanced proteolysis, all of which occur normally as a response to starvation, the state of the diabetic organism as seen by the cell. However, in the absence of insulin, the cell cannot use the massive amounts of glucose presented to it; thus, glucose becomes a waste product, whereas fat provides the basic metabolic fuel. Because regulation of CPT I and, secondarily, β-oxidation depend upon negative feedback by malonyl CoA on CPT I, the inhibition of acetyl CoA carboxylase for malonyl CoA production by ↑ glucagon results in unrestricted ketogenesis. Finally, osmotic diuresis and electrolyte loss lead to dehydration and shock, combined with severe acidosis deriving from the enormous excess of circulating ketone bodies.

On the basis of the above, we can explain most of the clinical findings of diabetic ketoacidosis. *Weight loss* is due to loss of both fat and muscle tissue, as well as to water loss manifested as polyuria. *Ketoacidosis* is secondary to the drastically increased lipolysis with ketone body production. *Weakness* arises from electrolyte losses (especially of potassium) due to osmotic and dilutional shifts. Thirst mechanisms, induced by all of the water and electrolyte alterations, cause the observed polydipsia. If ingested fluids are low in electrolyte content, dilutional effects will be enhanced. Finally, keep in mind that the inciting event (ie, hyperglycemia due to insulin deficiency) will continue to worsen and accelerate these pathophysiologic and clinical consequences unless insulin is administered.

Noninsulin-Dependent Diabetes Mellitus

A "worst-case scenario" has been considered in the preceding paragraphs, including an examination of the consequences of a complete insulin deficiency, as seen in Type I diabetes mellitus. However, keep in mind that diabetes is a syndrome; hence, the clinical picture of the Type I diabetic patient represents the relatively uncommon individual at one end of the spectrum of severity. Indeed, most diabetic patients (80%–90%) may be closer to the opposite end of this spectrum and are categorized as noninsulin-dependent, or Type II, patients. These individuals frequently present for reasons other than hyperglycemia, manifesting instead nephropathy, retinopathy, coronary artery disease, or peripheral circulatory problems. Nevertheless, some patients with NIDDM first present with polyuria, polydipsia, fatigue, and worsening stamina.

Although many Type II diabetic individuals are obese, there is no necessary relationship between obesity and diabetes mellitus. The sine qua non of Type II diabetes is a relative resistance to the development of ketosis, based upon a relative, rather than absolute, deficiency of insulin. Under baseline conditions, circulating insulin levels may be low, normal, or above normal (in association with insulin resistance). The resistance to ketosis underscores the extraordinary sensitivity of lipolysis to insulin, as compared to glucose metabolism, which requires higher levels of insulin for normal operation. Hence, patients with NIDDM may manifest either fasting or stress hyperglycemia unaccompanied by a corresponding degree of ketosis. Ketosis, however, may appear in Type II patients under circumstances of severe metabolic stress such as sepsis. The microvascular complications associated with hyperglycemia in diabetes mellitus, Type I patients also are found in Type II patients, although these complications frequently require a longer period to develop, probably because blood glucose levels do not reach the same heights in Type II.

Diabetic Ketoacidosis and Nonketotic Hyperglycemia

Over time, a view has emerged that regards diabetic ketoacidosis and nonketotic hyperglycemia not as distinct disorders but, rather, as the opposite ends of a continuum of hypoinsulin states (Table 10.3). This continuum occurs because less insulin is required to suppress lipolysis than that required to increase glucose uptake by insulin-sensitive cells. It follows that in NIDDM, in which some insulin still is secreted, lipolysis and ketogenesis are suppressed, but gluconeogenesis continues unabated. However, in IDDM, with the virtual absence of insulin, lipolysis and ketogenesis occur at a high rate and can result in diabetic ketoacidosis.

Plasma glucose above the renal threshold for reabsorption prompts a brisk osmotic diuresis, which causes the body to lose water and electrolytes. Compounding this tendency to hypovolemia are osmotic shifts of fluid in which intracellular water enters the extracellular space to cover the added glucose, only to have this fluid exit the body because of the unremitting osmotic diuresis. Most importantly, hyperglycemia, like hypernatremia, most profoundly affects the brain. With increase in the plasma osmolality, water moves out of brain cells, causing cellular dehydration. When the plasma osmolality reaches the dangerous thresh-

Table 10.3. Features of Diabetic Ketoacidosis and Nonketotic Hyperosmolar Coma

DKA	NKH
Urine- glucose ↑↑ ketones ↑↑ Plasma- glucose ↑↑ ketones ↑↑ bicarbonate ↓↓ anion gap ↑↑	Urine- glucose ↑↑ ketones (−) Plasma- glucose ↑↑ >600 mg/dl ketones − to ± bicarbonate- >20 meq/l anion gap- normal
Almost complete lack of insulin	Some insulin present that prevents ketogenesis
Precipitated by omission of insulin, infection, or intercurrent illness	Precipitated by acute infection, vomiting, uremia. More frequent in the elderly

old of 340 to 350 mosmol/kg, *coma* is a likely consequence. In nonketotic hyperglycemia, the glucose concentration usually is greater than 800 mg/dl, with a plasma osmolality elevated beyond the danger threshold. A key factor in the genesis of nonketotic hyperglycemia is the inability of the patient to gain access to water because of physical disability, insensitivity of the thirst mechanism, or neurologic impairment. If the patient imbibes water, he or she can regain the loss from the osmotic diuresis. But when water ingestion abates (eg, in diabetic hyperglycemia), kidney function deteriorates. With decreased glomerular filtration rate, less circulating glucose in excess of the renal threshold for reabsorption is excreted, remaining instead in the blood stream where it continues to collect, reaching levels of 800 to 1000 mg/dl.

Many experts believe that the propensity to coma stems from the hyperglycemia and its effects on brain cell volume and function, and not from the ketoacidosis. Consequently, if coma occurs either in diabetic ketoacidosis or nonketotic hyperglycemia, it is the result of the hyperglycemia.

Diagnosis

The diagnosis of Type I diabetes mellitus in the acute-onset stage is straightforward. All that is required is to demonstrate that the clinical complaints of weight loss, polyuria, and polydipsia ("melting of the flesh") are related to the laboratory findings of hyperglycemia, relative ketoacidosis, and glucosuria. It is imperative that the physician demonstrate that the origin of detectable glucosuria is related to a prerenal hyperglycemia because renal tubular dysfunction alone also may result in glucosuria. For the same reasons, it is important to be certain that ketosis is present when hyperglycemia occurs because there are many disorders that present with hypoglycemia and ketosis. For demonstration of hyperglycemia in a patient presenting with glucosuria and ketonuria, a random blood sugar level should be sufficient for diagnosis, without recourse to special maneuvers, such as glucose tolerance tests. By definition, if the patient is "diabetic enough" to be producing excessive ketones, then glucose tolerance already is impaired sufficiently to result in hyperglycemia.

Diagnosis of pre-Type I or pre-Type II diabetes usually will require definitive demonstration of impaired glucose tolerance by provocative testing. Pre-Type I should be considered in closely related individuals when one or more persons already have developed clinical symptoms; in such situations, the two criteria of a normal fasting blood glucose and an elevation of greater than 140 mg/dl 2 hours after glucose challenge must be satisfied. Type II diabetes may be diagnosed if the following are satisfied: (*1*) fasting plasma glucose level greater than 140 mg/dl (no further criteria need be met), or (*2*) normal fasting glucose but a 2-hour and an additional, earlier timed sample in excess of 200 mg/dl after a standard, 75-g oral glucose load. Early in the course, the Type II patient may be distinguishable by demonstration of a normal fasting blood glucose level, combined with a 30-, 60-, or 90-minute sample, after a 75-g oral glucose load, in excess of 200 mg/dl and a 2-hour level between 140 and 200 mg/dl. The latter group of patients is considered to have "chemical diabetes."

Treatment

Treatment regimens usually will break down into two general categories, dictated by the diagnosis of Type I or II diabetes. A patient with Type I disease is, or will become, entirely dependent upon insulin and will remain so for life. Hence, any individual presenting with the acute stage of diabetic ketoacidosis should be considered to be insulin-dependent and treated with insulin without delay. However, a rational approach to the fluid and electrolyte disturbances addressed above is equally important in therapy. Failure to do so in a patient treated with an appropriate insulin dosage may result in death because of the intercompartmental fluid and electrolyte shifts that proceed rapidly in response to enhanced glucose metabolism. Thus, provision of adequate quantities of sodium, potassium, and free water is vital to a successful outcome in treatment of diabetic ketoacidosis. The physician also should realize that normalizing plasma electrolyte levels by intravenous administration does not necessarily indicate that intracellular pools have been adequately replenished.

Regimens for treatment of Type II diabetes are less well-standardized. In an individual with Type II diabetes, when diminished glucose tolerance may be accompanied by obesity, weight reduction alone may significantly impact upon the body's glucose regulatory capacity. Oral hypoglycemic agents may help both obese patients and those who are not obese to achieve tight glycemic control; these agents generally enhance insulin secretion by the pancreatic beta cells. Development of insulin resistance in both Type I and Type II patients can be minimized by the use of human, rather than porcine or bovine, insulin. It is common knowledge that nutrition plays an important role in the appropriate management of diabetes mellitus, and this aspect of treatment should not be overlooked in both groups of patients: the distribution of calories and the nutrient nature of caloric intake must be addressed.

A final statement concerning the management of Type I diabetics needs to be added. In the early stages of onset, such patients frequently exhibit a partial remission, termed the "honeymoon" phase of their disease. The reasons for this are unclear, but it is thought that any remaining beta cells are restored to normal function after appropriate treatment, thus increasing circulating insulin levels. During this phase of disease, insulin requirements decrease dramatically, occasionally to the point when the patient may not require any exogenous insulin at all. This period tends to end abruptly when an intercurrent infection occurs, after which the patient becomes permanently insulin-dependent. Most experts urge continuing insulin (even if the dose is only one unit) during this honeymoon, so that the patient does not unrealistically expect that he or she will not continue to require insulin.

Late Complications in Diabetes Mellitus

As stated earlier, the discovery of insulin has resulted in simultaneous triumph and tragedy. Although the triumphs are well-recognized, the tragic consequences of microvascular and macrovascular complications of diabetes mellitus in long-term survivors frequently are overlooked. The ultrastructural feature common to each such complication is the presence of vascular deposits of carbohydrate-containing plasma proteins. In capillaries this leads to thickening of the basement membrane, whereas in larger vessels, smooth muscle proliferation and increased collagen formation narrows their lumina. Worse yet, all vessels damaged in diabetes mellitus ultimately exhibit cellular hypertrophy and hyperplasia, further compromising the patency of the vascular lumen. Several mechanisms have been proposed to account for how this thickening develops:

1. Increased activity of the biosynthetic pathway for synthesis of glycoproteins, which are major membrane constituents. Several studies have demonstrated that such an increase occurs as a result of insulin deficiency and hyperglycemia or both.
2. Nonenzymatic covalent attachment of glucose (glycosylation) to the amine groups of peptides, especially the epsilon amino groups of lysine residues, resulting in altered three-dimensional conformations and slower rates of breakdown of glycosylated proteins, owing to reduced efficiency of proteases in dismantling these cross-linked proteins. Evidence suggests that glycosylation or glycation of various proteins proceeds through several phases, the earliest of which are reversible. But at a certain point, these changes become irreversible, with the formation of advanced glycosylation endproducts. The importance of an irreversible stage in the pathogenesis of vascular disease is that even though good glycemic control may have been achieved, at that point the process is not responsive to lowering of the blood glucose level.
3. Conversion of glucose to sorbitol and fructose in tissues not sensitive to insulin, such as Schwann cells and the lens, which cannot metabolize these compounds. The increased osmotic pressure causes swelling and disruption of normal cellular metabolism.
4. A relationship between the degree of hyperglycemia and the rate of platelet aggregation and agglutination effected by increased production of platelet-derived growth factor. Such a mechanism, which is known to occur, leads to formation of microemboli. Sustained hyperglycemia also stimulates macrophages to localize in certain arteries, "setting up" incipient atheromatous lesions.

Although we have thus far emphasized the role of hyperglycemia per se in the development of the long-term complications of diabetes, this is not "the whole story." Macrovascular coronary artery disease and cerebrovascular disease, the major causes of mortality among diabetics, develop through the interplay of hyperglycemic effects (as described above) and at least two other factors. First, even before the onset of overt diabetes manifested by fasting hyperglycemia, the insulin-resistant state engenders hyperinsulinemia. Among its myriad functions, insulin acts as a growth factor causing fibroblast proliferation in arterial endothelium. Second, even in the prediabetic insulin-resistant state, many patients exhibit a dyslipidemia characterized by increased very low density lipoproteins (VLDL) and decreased high density lipoproteins (HDL).

In addition to the results of laboratory studies, there is clinical evidence that proves that persistent hyperglycemia plays a major causative role in microvascular pathology. In a long-term multicenter study (Diabetes Control and Complications Trial), patients whose blood glucose was maintained in a tight range (average = 155 mg/dl) suffered from fewer diabetic complications. But tight control demands careful monitoring and multiple injections of insulin, which are associated with a greater tendency to hypoglycemia. With NIDDM, diet and exercise are the most physiologic means to achieve better glycemic control. But for now, the retinopathy, neuropathy, nephropathy, and hypertensive complications of diabetes mellitus evidence the tragic delay in establishing the relationship between hyperglycemia and microvascular complications and the scarcity of simple strategies to achieve euglycemia in this too common disease.

DIABETIC RETINOPATHY

With the completion of the multicenter study discussed above, there is now convincing clinical evidence that the incidence of long-term complications in diabetes mellitus can be diminished by adherence to a regimen of tight control of the blood glucose concentration. It has long been evident that complications of diabetes mellitus are dependent on the duration of diabetes mellitus and on how tightly the blood glucose is controlled.

Retinopathy is among the most common complications of diabetes mellitus and is the major cause of all newly reported cases of blindness. The earliest eye lesions are microaneurysms of the terminal retinal capillaries. Damaged retinal capillaries become more permeable to lipids and proteins that leak into the interstitial space, forming "hard exudates."

Over time, the abnormal retinal vessels become occluded, causing ischemia and infarctions that appear as *"cotton-wool" exudates*. The retina responds to the ischemia by new vessel formation; but, these vessels are deployed in a haphazard fashion, often extending into the vitreous. Hemorrhage and traction by glial and vascular elements can lead to retinal detachment. Nevertheless, the risk of blindness in any patient is probably less than 10%.

DIABETIC NEPHROPATHY

The most common form of end-stage renal disease (ESRD) is caused by long-standing diabetes mellitus. But, although retinopathy is almost universal in diabetic patients, not all patients develop nephropathy. As might be anticipated, a greater percentage of patients with IDDM (35%–45%) develop nephropathy than do patients with NIDDM (<20%). Nephropathy begins with microalbuminuria and overt proteinuria supervenes over the ensuing 5 to 10 years, but only in those patients who will develop ESRD. It takes more than 20 years for ESRD to develop in susceptible patients with IDDM. Note that even in patients with ESRD, death is caused by concomitant cardiovascular disease, as is the case for all patients with diabetes mellitus.

Diabetic nephropathy first affects the glomerular vessels, but later glomerular basement membrane wall thickening also occurs. Progression to ESRD entails contraction of kidney size with development of diffuse glomerulosclerosis. Diabetic patients with ESRD are candidates for hemodialysis and renal transplantation.

DIABETIC NEUROPATHY

Disease of the peripheral nerves is common in diabetes mellitus, and symptoms will depend on which nerves are affected. Not only are peripheral nerves vulnerable, but so are cranial nerves and autonomic nerves. Symmetrical neuropathy, the most common form, causes loss of sensation in the lower extremities, rendering diabetic patients particularly prone to leg and foot lesions, with a greatly increased incidence of gangrene and consequent amputation. Autonomic dysfunction can affect the gastrointestinal tract, bladder, heart, vascular tone, and ability to achieve an erection.

CARDIOVASCULAR DISEASE IN DIABETES MELLITUS

Diabetes mellitus greatly disrupts the lipoprotein economy, causing increased triacylglycerol and decreased HDL concentrations. For these and reasons that are yet to be discovered, a premature development of cardiovascular disease occurs in diabetes of both sexes. Hence, the protective effect of estrogens in premenopausal women is not evidenced in patients with diabetes mellitus. When glycemic control is erratic, sustained hyperglycemia is likely to cause glycosylation of lipoproteins, which is an effect that may promote atherosclerosis because these modified lipoproteins bind to vascular endothelium.

As noted above, foot problems are common in diabetic patients. Peripheral vascular disease and peripheral neuropathy collude to cause the greatly increased incidence of foot gangrene. With anticipatory foot care including meticulous hygiene, comfortable shoes or sneakers, and prompt medical attention when problems arise, diabetic foot problems usually can be avoided.

Again, it is vital to recognize that blood glucose testing by the patient provides valuable information on which to base the insulin doses. This engages the patient as an active participant in his or her care, makes tight control possible, and should help forestall the disturbing late complications of diabetes mellitus.

SUGGESTED READINGS

GENERAL

Kahn CR, Weir GC, eds. Joslin's diabetes mellitus. 13th ed. Baltimore: Williams & Wilkins, 1994.

Rifkin H, Porte D Jr, eds. Diabetes mellitus. 4th ed. New York: Elsevier, 1990.

Taylor SI. Diabetes mellitus. In: Scriver CR, Beaudet AL, Sly WS, Valle D, eds. Metabolic and molecular bases of inherited disease. 7th ed. New York: McGraw-Hill, 1995: 843.

Unger RH, Foster DW. Diabetes mellitus. In: Wilson JD, Foster DW, eds. Williams textbook of endocrinology. 8th ed. Philadelphia: WB Saunders, 1992:1255.

PATHOPHYSIOLOGY

Atkinson MA, Maclaren NK. The pathogenesis of insulin-dependent diabetes mellitus. N Engl J Med. 1994;331: 1428.

Fleckman AM. Diabetic ketoacidosis. Endocrinol Metab Clin North Am 1993;22:181.

Gerich JE. Control of glycemia. Baillieres Clin Endocrinol Metab 1993;7:551.

Kitabchi AE, Wall BM. Diabetic ketoacidosis. Med Clin North Am 1995;79:9.

Lorber D. Nonketotic hypertonicity in diabetes mellitus. Med Clin North Am 1995;79:39.

Siperstein MD. Diabetic ketoacidosis and hyperosmolar coma. Endocrinol Metab Clin North Am 1992;21:415.

Yki-Jarvinen H. Action of insulin on glucose metabolism in vivo. Bailleres Clin Endocrinol Metab 1993;7:903.

METABOLIC INTERRELATIONSHIPS

Dunn FL. Hyperlipidemia in diabetes mellitus. Diabetes Metab Rev 1990;6:47.

Ginsberg HN. Lipoprotein physiology in nondiabetic and diabetic states. Relationship to atherogenesis. Diabetes Care 1991;14:839.

Hollenbeck CB, Coulston AM. Effects of dietary carbohydrate and fat intake on glucose and lipoprotein metabolism in individuals with diabetes mellitus. Diabetes Care 1991;14:774.

Howard BV. Lipoprotein metabolism in diabetes. Curr Opin Lipidol 1994;5:216.

Seymour CA, Byrne CD. Triglycerides and disease. Postgrad Med J 1993;69:679.

Sonksen PH, Russell-Jones D, Jones RH. Growth hormone and diabetes mellitus. A review of sixty-three years of medical research and a glimpse into the future? Horm Res 1993;40:68.

LONG-TERM COMPLICATIONS

Clarke CM Jr, Lee DA. Prevention and treatment of complications of diabetes mellitus. N Engl J Med 1995; 332:1210.

Nathan DM. Long-term complications of diabetes mellitus. N Engl J Med 1993;328:1676.

The Diabetes Control and Complications Trial Research Group. The effect of intensive treatment of diabetes on the development and progression of long-term complications in insulin-dependent diabetes mellitus. N Engl J Med 1993;329:977.

chapter **11**

Disorders of Carbohydrate Metabolism

Abnormalities in the disposition of ingested carbohydrates can be primary, because of genetic mutations, or secondary to a vast array of causes. Because of space constraints, we have restricted discussion to primary disorders involving disposition of galactose, fructose, and glycogen. Additional information on carbohydrate metabolism can be found in the chapters on hypoglycemia (Chapter 7), diabetes mellitus (Chapter 9), and the endocrine disorders (Chapter 20). Discussion of carbohydrate malabsorption can be found in the chapter on gastrointestinal disorders (Chapter 22).

GALACTOSE

In relation to normal blood glucose concentration, blood galactose levels may be high, normally ranging from 10 to 20 mg/dl. Lactose, which is a glucose-galactose disaccharide, is the major carbohydrate in milk; thus, virtually all human infants are exposed to dietary galactose in the earliest stages of life. Consequently, the clinically significant defects in galactose metabolism are most likely to first appear during early infancy, although symptoms may be absent in babies who are on a diet that consists of soy-based formula. Because lactose is present in most commercially prepared food products, any defect eventually will be unmasked by the appearance of symptoms.

Although galactose contributes to glycogen synthesis by generation of glucose-1-phosphate via the Leloir pathway (Figure 11.1), its chief function is to serve as a vital component of glycolipids and glycoproteins. These glycoprotein and glycolipid structural molecules are major constituents of cell membranes; these molecules play a crucial role in the structure and function of each cell. Hence, the capacity to interconvert glucose and galactose through an epimerization reaction at C-4 (the asymmetric carbon atom at which glucose and galactose differ) is imperative to synthesis of cell membranes and myelin. Enzyme mediated epimerization explains how galactose can be eliminated from the diet without attendant consequences.

Galactokinase Deficiency

Galactokinase catalyzes the initial step in galactose metabolism, with deficiency of the enzyme clinically characterized by bilateral cataracts developing in early infancy. When the enzyme is absent, galactose accumulates and is converted, deficiency of the enzyme being characterized by bilateral cataracts developing in early infancy. When the enzyme is absent, galactose accumulates and is converted to galactitol, via aldose reductase, an enzyme (in the lens) with a Km for galactose in the range of 12 mM. Thus, increases slightly above the usual blood galactose levels result in significant flux through the aldose reductase catalyzed reaction. Galactitol formed within the lens is not freely diffusible; it accumulates in the lens and generates an increase of osmotic pressure with diffusion of water into the lens. Not surprisingly, a close relationship exists between the rates of galactitol formation and water accumulation and the pace of cataract development.

Despite the only finding being cataracts in this disorder, all patients described have manifested galactosuria and deficient red cell galactokinase, thus ruling out a tissue-specific defect in lens only. Isoelectric studies confirm this, showing a single isozyme in all tissues examined. Most significantly, absence of damage to other organs when blood galactose concentrations are as high as 100 mg/dl strongly suggests that galactose is not toxic at high levels, except in the lens. This especially is noteworthy considering the multior-

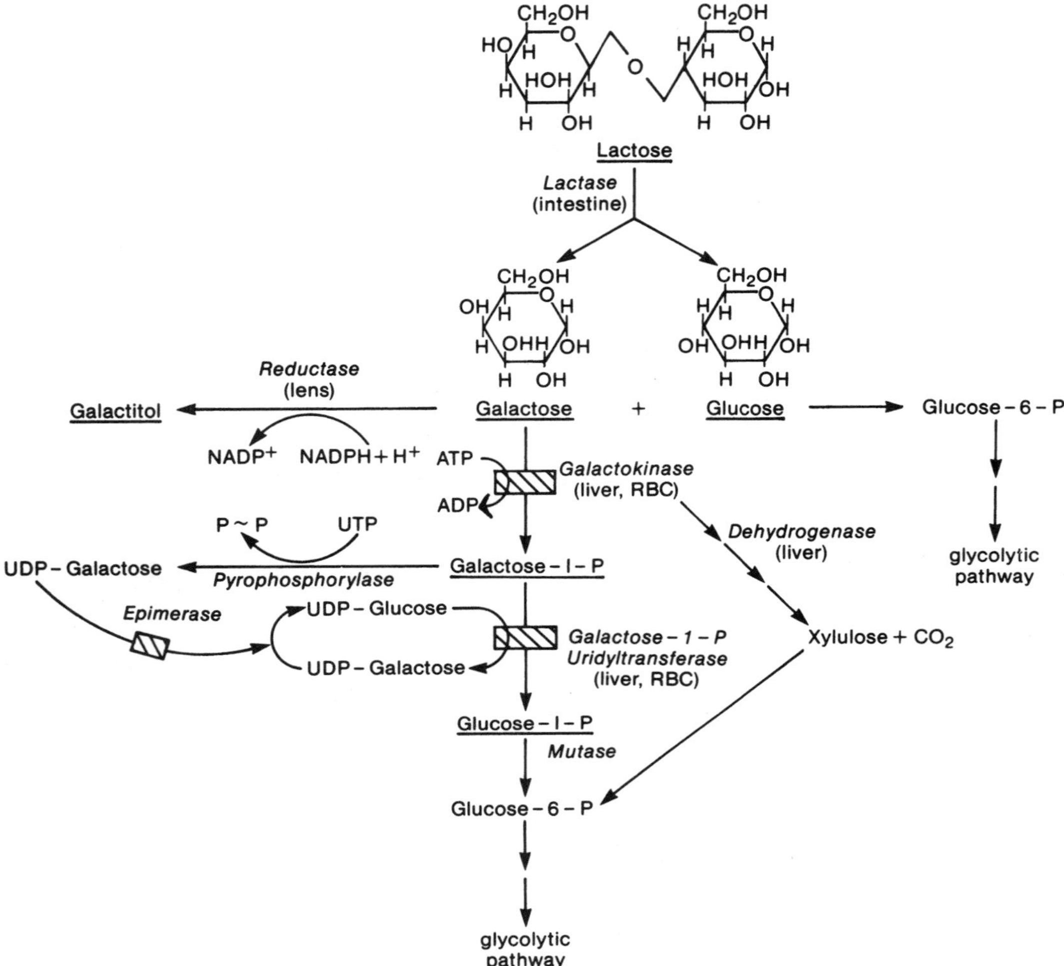

Figure 11.1. Metabolism of galactose by the Leloir pathway. The chief source of galactose in the human diet is the lactose contained in dairy products. Intestinal cleavage of lactose leads to absorption of galactose and glucose as monomers. The galactose reaches the liver via portal blood, where it is initially phosphorylated by a specific galactokinase. Transfer of the galactose moiety to UDP in exchange for glucose in a step mediated by galactose-1-P uridyltransferase produces UDP-galactose. The latter then is acted upon by an epimerase with production of UDP-glucose in a reversible reaction, which provides the basis for galactose production from glucose, as well. The other product of the transferase reaction, glucose-1-P, can be directly converted to glucose-6-P by the action of a mutase, thus allowing entry into glycolysis. Known genetic defects in galactose metabolism are shown by hatched boxes. Reprinted by permission from Shils ME, Olson JA, Shike M, et al. Modern nutrition in health and disease. 8th ed. Baltimore: Williams & Wilkins, 1994.

gan involvement in classic galactosemia at equivalent blood levels (see following text). Treatment relies on complete elimination of dietary sources of galactose, which requires careful reading of package labels to avoid products containing lactose. On such a regimen, results have been encouraging and have included elimination of cataracts and absence of other sequelae.

Galactose-1-Phosphate Uridyl Transferase Deficiency

Galactose-1-phosphate uridyl transferase (gal-1-P UT) links gal-1-P and uridine nucleotide by "exchanging" the glucose moiety of UDPglucose and galactose to form UDPgalactose and glc-1-P. The uridyl transferase is subject to potent inhibition by glc-1-P, and other uridine nucleotides are strong inhibitors, competing with UDPglc.

Deficiency of transferase leads to accumulation of both gal-1-P and galactose because galactokinase is inhibited by gal-1-P. In contrast to the paucity of findings in galactokinase deficiency, the clinical picture of transferase deficiency involves multiple systems, including liver, kidney, and brain, as well as the lens. It is this difference in accumulated intermediates between galactokinase deficiency and transferase deficiency that has led to the hypothesis that gal-1-P is the toxic agent in transferase-deficient galactosemia; however, definitive proof is not yet available.

Clinically, an affected infant will appear normal until the first few milk feedings. Thereafter, there will be a rapid progression of vomiting; hyperbilirubinemia; poor weight gain; hepatomegaly; cataracts, which may be present at birth; developmental failure; and renal Fanconi syndrome (see Chapter 3). A high incidence of associated gram negative sepsis occurs in these babies; some authors believe that proven E. coli sepsis is a specific indication for a search for galactosemia. Death can occur early from sepsis or later from liver failure. Both causes usually are preventible if recognized and vigorous measures are taken to reverse the course of galactose associated toxicity. If the infant does not die because of sepsis, mental retardation and hepatic cirrhosis can be expected if galactose ingestion continues.

A newly recognized consequence of transferase deficiency that occurs later in life is primary ovarian failure with absence of menarche in pubertal age females. It is believed that this results from destruction of oocytes during the fetal or neonatal period.

Laboratory diagnosis has been simplified by the availability of neonatal screening programs in many areas. But, given realistic time constraints in operation of these programs, it is likely that a positive result from a screening test will coincide with acute onset of symptoms; the clinician will need to confirm the results immediately. This most simply is done by examining the infant's urine for the presence of reducing sugars before empirically changing the infant's nutritional base. Testing for reducing sugars always should be performed in association with a specific test for urine glucose because both glucose and galactose are reducing sugars.

Several allelic variants of the classic transferase abnormality exist, resulting in differing mutant protein products. The most common is the Duarte variant, estimated to be carried in combination with the normal gene in 8% to 13% of the US population. Other less common variants include Los Angeles, Rennes, Indiana, and Chicago. Thus, whereas heterozygotes for the classic mutation show about 50% of normal transferase activity, Duarte homozygotes cannot be distinguished on the basis of enzyme activity. Furthermore, the other allelic variants provide the basis for mixed heterozygosity, which, on enzyme assay, will show activity ranging from 0% to 50% of normal. Therefore, the prudent physician will examine the genotype of the parents and the infant, and will not be guided by enzyme activity alone.

Treatment of the classic disorder includes meticulous elimination of galactose from the diet; the need for treatment of variants is less defined. We believe that any infant with evidence of transferase activity less than 50% of normal and blood galactose above the normal range while on a lactose-based formula should be treated, at least for the first several years of life, to permit normal development of the brain.

Uridine Diphosphate-Galactose-4-Epimerase Deficiency

Originally recognized as a distinct entity in 1972, deficiency of the epimerase initially was categorized as a "condition" because all affected individuals appeared to be well. The first reported subject was identified because of an elevated galactose level on screening of newborns. Subsequent study revealed normal blood galactose and activities of galactokinase and uridyl transferase, but no epimerase activity in red blood cells. Two years later, the child was thriving while on a diet that included normal galactose intake. In this patient, circulating red and white blood cells were epimerase-deficient, yet skin and liver cells showed normal activity. Although measurement of red cell epimerase activity is a convenient means to make a diagnosis, the role of the liver and other organs in galactose homeostasis should not be ignored. This particularly is important because epimerase deficiency in these other sites might result in different clinical findings than does the innocuous genetic condition heretofore described.

Indeed, patients deficient in liver and red cell epimerase have been reported. As expected, in such affected individuals, dietary galactose results in a clinical "picture" identical to that of transferase-deficiency galactosemia, with patients manifesting failure to thrive, hepatomegaly, jaundice, and galactosuria. Cataracts have been reported in one patient with epimerase deficiency.

Another important issue is the fact that the epimerase is a bifunctional enzyme; it is necessary for the conversion of N-acetylglucosamine to N-acetylgalactosamine. Because the latter compound is incorporated into glycoproteins and glycolipids, complete epimerase deficiency would be expected to have a detrimental effect on central nervous system development. But, in the cases thus far described, about 10% of normal activity for the N-acetylglucosamine to N-acetylgalactosamine reaction remains. The implication of this residual activity is that total deprivation of dietary galactose would render the epimerase-deficient patient completely unable to form N-acetylgalactosamine. Hence, in this disorder, as in many of the aminoacidopathies, there must be judicious restriction, rather than complete elimination, of the offending agent—in this case, galactose.

FRUCTOSE

Fructose is present in most fruits and vegetables. Thus, fructose is an important dietary constituent for the majority of the world's population who obtain the bulk of their nutrition from these food sources. Statistically, there is much greater opportunity for exposure to dietary fructose than to galactose because much of the population forgoes milk as a nutritional staple after early infancy.

Another important feature of fructose is that it is not an insulin secretagogue. This implies that regulation of fructose metabolism is independent of glucose metabolism, a fact proven by studies of patients with aberrant fructose metabolism. Fructose also is important to synthesis of glycoproteins because it is the precursor for endogenous production of mannose, which is an important constituent of glycoproteins. There are three genetic defects known in fructose metabolism, two of which are in the fructose catabolic pathway and the third positioned in a central location in the gluconeogenic pathway. It is important to recognize that, because insulin does not affect fructose metabolism, fructose given in high doses to normal subjects has toxic metabolic and clinical effects similar to those found in individuals with genetic defects in fructose metabolism.

Fructokinase Deficiency (Essential Fructosuria)

Clinically benign, fructokinase deficiency is more appropriately termed a condition than a disease. Hepatic fructokinase is the enzyme responsible for initial phosphorylation of fructose to fructose-1-P (Figure 11.2). Deficiency of fructokinase prevents fructose from entering the glycolytic pathway, except to the extent fructose-6-P can be formed by hexokinase. Consequently, fructose levels in blood increase rapidly after an oral load, resulting in levels far in excess of those found in normal controls, and decrease slowly over a period of 6 hours or more.

Most importantly, the fact that lactate, urate, and phosphate change little, if at all, in affected individuals challenged with oral fructose helps to clarify the pathophysiology of fructose toxicity. Because these compounds are dramatically affected in patients with hereditary fructose intolerance (see following text) and in normal controls who receive high intravenous doses, it appears that toxicity depends on the ability to form and accumulate fructose-1-P. Moreover, evidence of abnormal results from liver function tests in both individuals with hereditary fructose intolerance and controls given high fructose bolsters the concept that the liver usually is the center of fructose metabolism.

Fructose-1,6-Bisphosphate Aldolase Deficiency (Hereditary Fructose Intolerance)

Typically, an infant with hereditary fructose intolerance (HFI) will grow normally when fructose is absent from the diet. However, with the introduction of fruits and juices, fructose, sucrose, and sorbitol are ingested and symptoms are likely to appear.

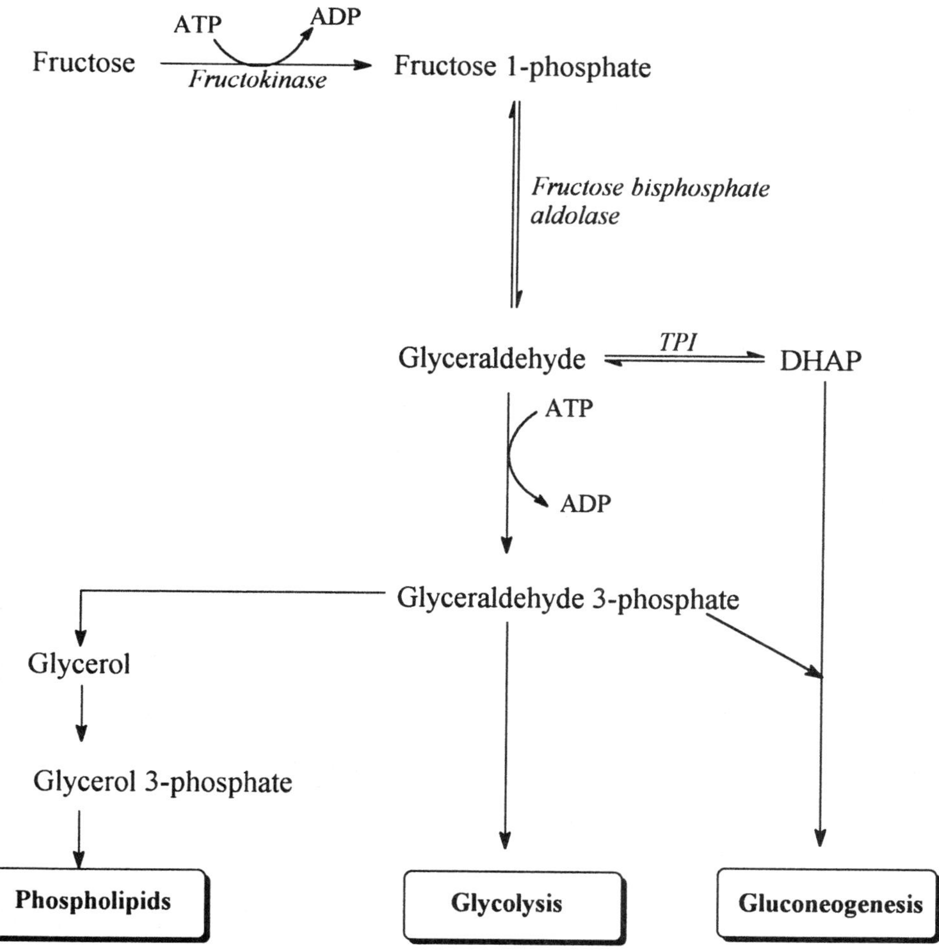

Figure 11.2. Fructose metabolism. The initial step in fructose metabolism is formation of fructose 1-phosphate through the action of fructokinase. Cleavage of this compound by the enzyme fructose bisphosphate aldolase (aldolase B) results in formation of glyceraldehyde, which can be acted upon further by triose phosphoisomerase (TPI) to produce the gluconeogenic precursor compound dihydroxyacetone phosphate (DHAP). Glyceraldehyde can be phosphorylated, providing it access to three pathways: 1) phospholipid synthesis, 2) glycolysis, 3) gluconeogenesis. A defect in fructokinase leads to essential fructosuria, which is an insignificant condition. But, hereditary fructose intolerance, caused by a defect in aldolase B, has a multiplicity of associated biochemical and clinical consequences.

Clinical manifestations range in severity from profound failure to thrive with progressive liver dysfunction to the adolescent or adult enjoying apparently good health except for occasional vomiting, abdominal pain, and hypoglycemia after ingesting offending foods. Nonetheless, fructose intolerance may have serious and even fatal consequences because of hepatic dysfunction.

A major source of confusion in understanding HFI lies in the fact that the liver contains one of three distinct isozymes, each possessing various degrees of activity with fructose-1,6-DiP and fructose-1-P as substrates. The deficient enzyme in liver, aldolase B, retains about 25% of control activity with the diphosphate while showing less than 5% of normal activity with the monophosphate. Biochemically, the significance of this becomes clear when it is realized that fructose-1,6-diP is a key intermediate in the glycolytic pathway. If complete failure to cleave this compound into the trioses dihydroxyacetone phosphate and glyceraldehyde-3-P occurred, the individual would be unable to use dietary hexoses and a fatal defect probably would occur in utero. However, inability to handle fructose-1-P, although not innocuous, only "disconnects" the entry of fructose as a substrate into glycolysis.

Because of the relative residual activities of the defective aldolase, glycolysis proceeds unimpeded under baseline conditions. Consequently, if fructose is avoided, the inability to cleave fructose-1-P to triose fragments causes no problem. An understanding of the metabolic disposition and effects of fructose under normal circumstances can help clarify events in aldolase B-deficient patients.

NORMAL FRUCTOSE METABOLISM

As discussed earlier, ingested fructose enters metabolism via formation of fructose-1-P, mediated by fructokinase. The cleavage of this substrate by aldolase B in liver, kidney, and intestine results in the formation of triose fragments, dihydroxyacetone phosphate and glyceraldehyde. If, instead, glucose is the initial substrate, hexokinase will produce glucose-6-P, which, in turn, is converted to fructose-6-P by phosphohexose isomerase. Fructose-6-P is next phosphorylated by phosphofructokinase to fructose-1,6-diP. Fructose-1,6-diP is the mainstream glycolytic intermediate for aldolase B, the action of which will produce the two phosphorylated triose fragments. This series of conversions constitutes the first three steps of glycolysis, which is the chief portal of entry for glucose into the tricarboxylic acid cycle. Of course, reversal of the fructose-phosphate cleavage, using the trioses as substrate, is an important mode of entry into gluconeogenesis.

CONSEQUENCES OF ALDOLASE B DEFICIENCY: DECREASE IN INTRACELLULAR ATP CONCENTRATION

Aldolase B deficiency results in a multiplicity of metabolic and physiologic consequences. First, and most obvious, fructose ingestion leads to accumulation of large amounts of fructose-1-P, with intracellular levels approaching 10 mM. This accumulation has important consequences, most notably sequestration of inorganic phosphate and depletion of ATP. At the same time, failure to produce ATP enhances catabolism of the adenine nucleotides to uric acid (see following text), elevating uric acid in both blood and urine. Because uric acid competes at the renal tubule for secretion of lactate, hyperlactic acidemia ensues. Lactate continues to be produced by the body because the isozymes aldolase A and C are unaffected in this disorder; each contributes to cleavage of the fructose-1,6-diP, with subsequent production of pyruvate (lactate).

Hypoglycemia and Other Abnormalities

As noted previously, hypoglycemia is a regular feature of HFI when fructose is ingested. Data support the view that glucose homeostasis in HFI is upset because gluconeogenesis is insufficient and glycogenolysis is inhibited in the liver. The primary defect in gluconeogenesis, inability to reverse fructose-phosphate cleavage, already has been explained. This defect is exaggerated by a secondary inhibition of glucose phosphate isomerase by fructose-1-P, impairing the alternate pathway of conversion of fructose to fructose-6-P via hexokinase, with ultimate production of glucose-6-P. Compounding the obvious impact of these effects on glucose homeostasis are the combined inhibitory effects of high fructose-1-P and low inorganic phosphate on glycogen phosphorylase a. Phosphorylase a is the chief regulatory step in glycogenolysis and source of most of the glucose released from glycogen. Hence, an important mechanism for maintenance of the blood glucose concentration is undermined by fructose ingestion.

The liver is not the only organ involved in aldolase B deficiency; the defect is expressed in kidney and intestine as well. The relationship of the defect to the epigastric pain and vomiting that occurs after the ingestion of fructose, even in normal individuals, remains unexplained. A patient with HFI exposed to fructose develops a severe, Type II, renal tubular acidosis (see Chapter 4) and generalized proximal tubule dysfunction, the combination of which represents the renal Fanconi syndrome (see Chapter 3).

Lactic acidosis can be partly accounted for by competition at the renal tubule with uric acid. An additional component may be conversion of fructose-1-P directly to fructose-1,6-diP by phosphofructokinase. This reaction would create an avenue for generation of three-carbon units that could contribute significantly to the lactate pool.

TREATMENT

It should be clear that the key to treatment of HFI is elimination of dietary fructose. Because fructose intake typically is limited or absent in neonates by virtue of breast-feeding or ingestion of lactose-based formulas, the medical history can be revealing if a delay in onset of symptoms occurs until fructose is introduced into the diet. Thus, a typical history would include 3 to 6 months of normal growth and general good health with a sudden onset of anorexia, vomiting, lethargy, and failure to thrive that is coincident with beginning ingestion of fruits or certain vegetables. Also noteworthy in the history is the voluntary avoidance of such foods by older children in the absence of symptoms.

Fructose-1,6-Bisphosphatase Deficiency

Fructose bisphosphatase deficiency adversely affects gluconeogenesis. In contrast to the function of aldolase, which is to cleave the diphosphate into triose fragments, fructose bisphosphatase removes the 1-phosphate group, producing fructose-6-P. Formation of fructose-6-P is a key step in gluconeogenesis that circumvents the irreversible phosphofructokinase step in glycolysis. Deficiency of fructose bisphosphatase causes lactic acidosis, hyperventilation, hypoglycemia, and ketosis.

It is important to realize that generation of fructose-1,6-diP, the further metabolism of which is impaired in this disease, is only peripherally related to an overall defect in dietary fructose metabolism. The diphosphate is synthesized through the usual gluconeogenic pathway, by action of aldolase, from condensation of two triose phosphate fragments, which are glycolytic intermediates and need not derive from fructose. The lesson to be learned is that removal of dietary fructose will have little impact on the pathogenesis of the disease, which is fundamentally a gluconeogenic defect, irrespective of the sources of substrate for this process.

As in other disorders of gluconeogenesis, fasting or other metabolic stresses such as fever or infection will provoke onset of clinical symptoms. As in HFI, glycogenolysis is impaired by inhibition of phosphorylase through accumulation of phosphorylated intermediates, chiefly fructose-1,6-diP and glycerol-3-P, combined with a decrease in inorganic phosphate. The profound hypoglycemia that results leads to accelerated fatty acid catabolism, producing ketosis. Release of alanine from muscle further enhances the pool of three-carbon gluconeogenic precursors. Again, as in HFI, increased catabolism of adenine nucleotides leads to hyperuricemia, whereas competition with lactate in the renal tubule contributes to lactic acidosis. Of course, because of the defect in the gluconeogenic pathway, lactate rapidly accumulates.

Key to any treatment are avoidance of fasting and provision of adequate amounts of exogenous glucose. Acute episodes are readily treated with intravenous bicarbonate and glucose, but survival relies on appropriate diagnosis and therapy to prevent hypoglycemia.

GLYCOGEN

As the body's warehouse for glucose storage, glycogen constitutes an extremely important pool of metabolic substrate. This pool is so vital to our survival that failure to accumulate normal stores of glycogen in the final trimester of gestation could lead to eradication of the human race. Because the body can extract from this glucose reservoir, each of us survives the earliest moments of postnatal life. Moreover, the tight regulation and integration of glycogen metabolism in glucose homeostasis also confirm the importance of this process. Whereas tissues other than liver synthesize and store glycogen, the body extracts only from hepatic glycogen stores when needed. As a rule, nonhepatic tissue glycogen stores are used at their site and contribute little, if at all, to maintaining the blood glucose level. Thus, although various tissues may be affected by abnormalities of glycogen synthesis or breakdown, any manifestations related to hypoglycemia generally result from the same abnormalities expressed in liver. Finally, in addition to defects in integral enzymes of the glycogen pathways, these abnormalities may include defects in regulatory enzymes. All of these abnormalities are categorized as the glycogenoses or glycogen storage disorders.

At a molecular level, glycogen is an excellent example of the ingenuity of nature. Storage of glucose as monosaccharide units within the cell would lead to an increase in osmotic pressure, which would severely disrupt the integrity of the cell. But, by polymerizing the monosaccharide units into a large, highly branched molecule, solubility is reduced and, simultaneously, each unit remains accessible for generation of glucose. Considering that the glycogen molecular mass is in the range of 180 million daltons, compared to glucose molecular mass of 180 daltons, the extent and efficiency of this storage system is evident.

Structurally, glycogen is a polymer of D-glucose units joined in α-1,4-ether linkages into straight chains, which branch at α-1,6-linkages. Without such branch points, the polymer would be far less accessible to degradative enzyme action because it would assume a molecular structure that would preclude the requisite enzyme-substrate intimacy. A disorder in which branch points are not fashioned has been described and results in cellular injury, as will be discussed below.

Synthesis of glycogen begins by condensation of two D-glucose units (in the form of UDPglc), mediated by the enzyme glycogen synthase. Clearly, deficiency of this enzyme would lead to failure of glycogen synthesis; such a disorder has been described. As the 1,4-linked polymer grows, branching occurs at approximately every 12 glucose units by transfer of at least six of the 1,4-linked residues to a separate branch joined to the original chain through a 1,6-link (Figure 11.3). As this branching process continues, mediated by amylo-1,4-1,6-transglucosidase, the molecule grows steadily in size and complexity. Unabated, the synthesis of glycogen would result in enormous storage granules, cellular damage, and organ failure. Such a disorder has been described and will be reviewed later.

Offsetting the synthesis of glycogen is, of course, its degradation with release of free glucose from liver, or metabolism of glucose-6-P within the cell. The initial step in glycogenolysis is catalyzed by phosphorylase which mediates cleavage of 1,4-glycosidic bonds to the point at least four glucose residues removed from a 1,6-glycosidic branch (Figure 11.4). The product of each phosphorolytic cleavage is glucose-1-P. Although its action appears to be limited, phosphorylase is the rate-controlling enzyme of glycogenolysis; as such, its activity is regulated by many factors. Genetic deficiency of phosphorylase has been reported. To continue its action on glycogen, phosphorylase requires that the residual glucose branch be elongated once more. To accomplish this by addition of new glucose units would be less efficient than to enzymatically remove the four glucose units by cleaving the 1,6-link and reattaching it to a new 1,4 sequence, a reaction mediated by the debranching enzyme. In fact, only three 1,4-linked units are transferred, with release of the fourth at the point of the 1,6-linkage as free glucose. Deficiency of the debrancher is described in the following text.

It should be recognized that glucose-1-P released by phosphorylase action is converted to glucose-6-P by phosphoglucomutase, the only enzyme shared in common by glycogenesis and glycogenolysis. The glucose-6-P thus produced is (*1*) available to the cell for metabolism via glycolysis, (*2*) may be converted back to glucose-1-P by the mutase, or (*3*) may be cleaved to free glucose by glucose-6-phosphatase and released from the cell. Deficiency of glucose-6-phosphatase prevents release of glucose derived from glycogenolysis, except for the single monomer derived from the cleavage at the 1,6-branchpoint, and is the basis for a well-known disorder (Von Gierke's disease) of glycogen metabolism.

Several hormones, with glucagon being the principal one, influence glycogenolysis, causing release of free glucose. This action of glucagon is mediated through a series of sequential steps involving cAMP and protein kinase activation of phosphorylase to the active "a" form. An important diagnostic implication of this stimulation of glycogenolysis by glucagon is that failure of glucagon to elevate blood glucose in a hypoglycemic state suggests a defect either in glycogenolysis or in glycogen synthesis. Another important regulator of glycogen metabolism is epinephrine, the action of which also is mediated through cAMP. A third cAMP-independent glycogenolytic effector is the phosphoinositide cascade, triggered by vasopressin, angiotensin, and β-adrenergic agonists. The actions of cAMP and of the products of the phosphoinositide cascade, inositol triphosphate, and diacylglycerol, are discussed in Chapter 1.

Thus far, we have mentioned only those effectors that stimulate glycogenolysis. There are

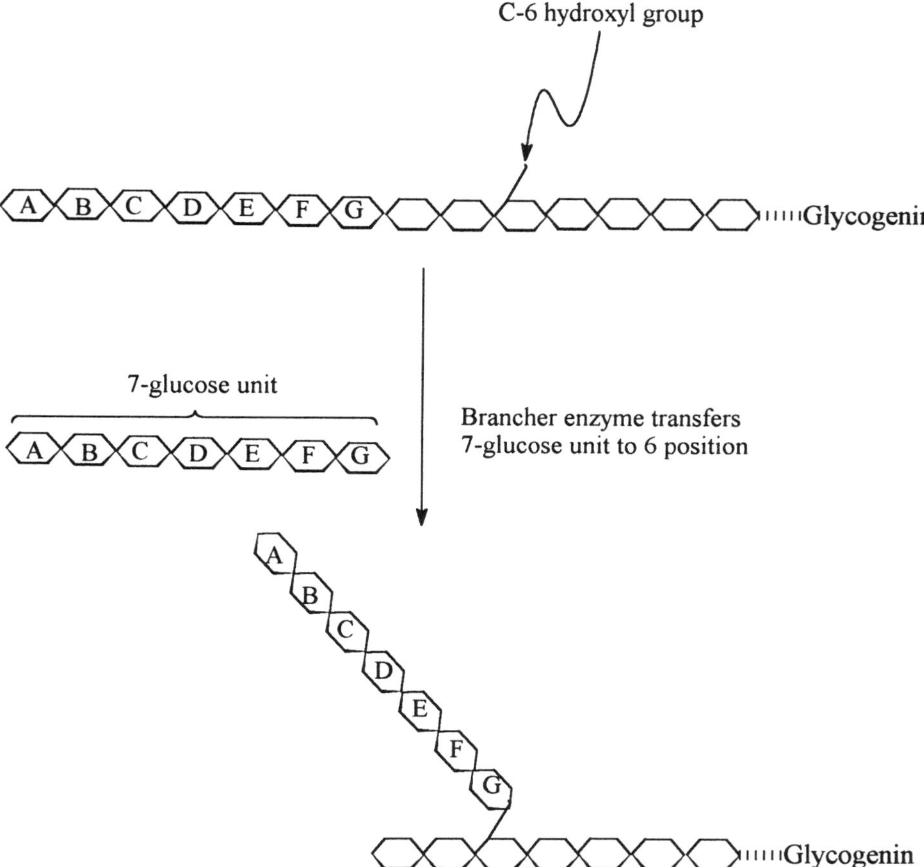

Figure 11.3. Formation of branches in glycogen synthesis. Straight chains of glucose units (A-G) are formed in 1,4-linkage by the action of glycogen synthase. Glycogenin is an autocatalytic, self-glucosylating primer protein for this process. As the straight chain elongates, at every 10 to 12 residues, amylo-1,4-1,6-transglucosidase transfers a minimum of six residues to a C-6 hydroxyl group, forming the branch through a 1,6 linkage. Creating multiple branches in glycogen increases its accessibility to enzymes that act on it both to increase its size or to degrade it to defend the blood glucose concentration.

equally potent effectors of net synthesis, the chief one being insulin. As the key hormone that stimulates glucose storage, it is to be expected that insulin antagonizes the action of glucagon. Insulin's overall effect is to activate glycogen synthase and inhibit phosphorylase. The potency and rapidity of insulin's action on glycogen metabolism is most clearly evident in the first 2 hours of insulin therapy in diabetic ketoacidosis (see Chapter 10), when the rapid hepatic enlargement is due to redeposition of glycogen. Another important feature of insulin action is that it hastens glucose uptake into the liver cell by stimulating glycogen synthesis.

Finally, glycogen granules, like solid material within the cytosol, are taken up by lysosomes for enzymatic degradation. To the extent that this occurs within the cell, the glucose freed by the process derives independently of the phosphorylase-regulated steps of glycogenolysis. Once glycogen is intralysosomal, it is attacked by α-glucosidase, which is capable of hydrolyzing both 1,4- and 1,6-linkages, releasing free glucose as the sole product of the reaction. We must emphasize, however, that this is not intended to provide glucose as a source of energy, but is a degradative pathway for glycogen within the lysosome that would otherwise be "choked" with stored material as in glycogenosis II (see following text).

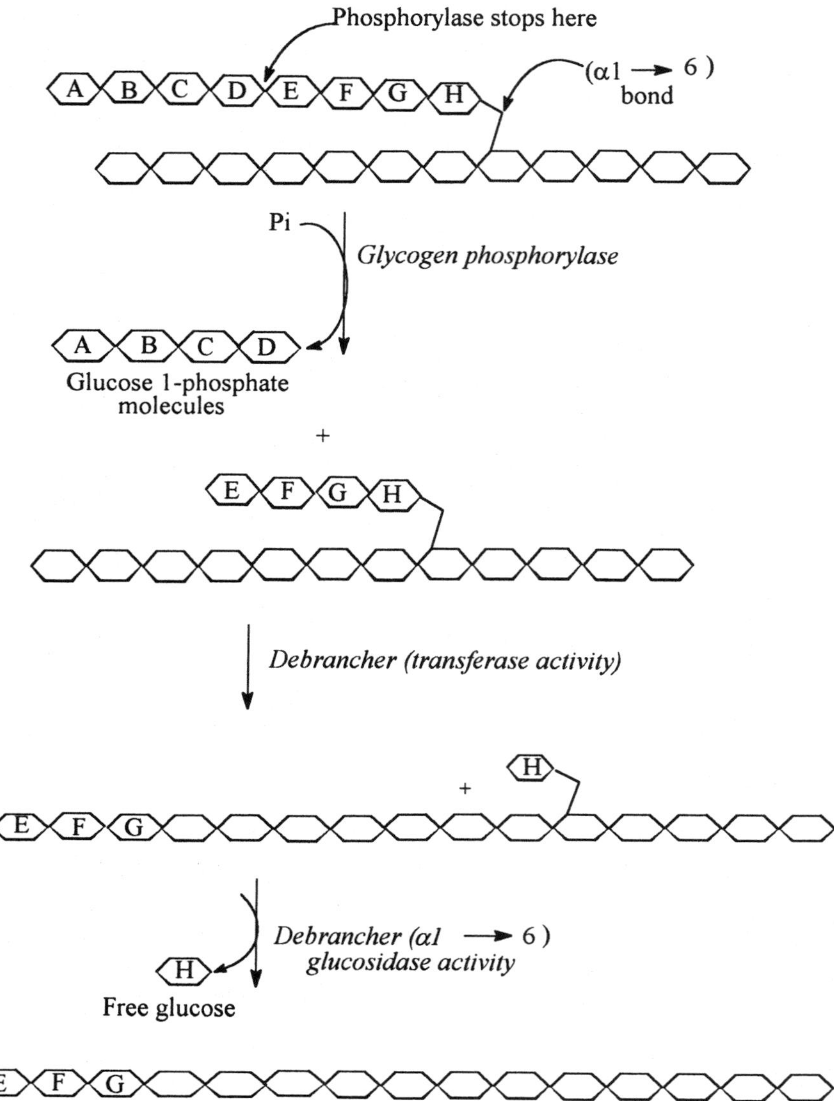

Figure 11.4. Degradation of glycogen. The initial step is 1,4-hydrolytic cleavage by phosphorylase action (A-D) at a point four residues removed from a 1,6 branch, with production of glucose 1-phosphate molecules from the tetramer removed. Through debrancher transferase activity, the first three (E-G) of the remaining four (E-H) branches are linked with the straight chain, where they can be acted upon by phosphorylase. The final residue (H) is removed by debrancher $\alpha 1 \rightarrow 6$ glucosidase activity and is released as free glucose.

We now are ready to consider the glycogenoses. In doing so, we must keep in mind that gene expression, enzyme activities, and enzyme regulatory mechanisms vary between the tissues. This caveat has important implications because some gene defects are expressed in specific tissues and not in others. A convenient classification of these disorders results in two broad groups: those affecting liver and those affecting muscle. Liver defects manifest hepatomegaly, variable degrees of hypoglycemia, and other metabolic abnormalities. Muscle defects present with exercise intolerance, cramps, pain, inability to elevate the blood lactate level, and occasionally myoglobinuria.

Considering the biochemical explication of glycogen metabolism presented above, we have chosen to organize the following discussion based on the order of the enzyme defect in the cycle, starting with synthetic defects and proceeding to degradative defects.

Glycogen Synthase Deficiency (Glycogenosis Type 0)

Glycogen synthase deficiency is a rare disease thought to be inherited in an autosomal recessive manner. Consistent with an inability to form glycogen at a normal rate, patients manifest fasting hypoglycemia and ketosis, unresponsive to glucagon. Presentation may be with seizures after an overnight fast. Equally consistent, in the fed state, patients experience hyperglycemia and lactic acidemia, under which conditions glucagon increases the hyperglycemia and decreases the circulating lactate by promoting hepatic gluconeogenesis. Glycogen synthase activity is deficient in liver, but not in red cells, muscle, or cultured skin fibroblasts. The single inconsistency in the findings has been the presence of decreased amounts of normally structured glycogen in the liver, which remains unexplained.

From a physiologic point of view, this enzyme defect renders the liver unable to structure a reserve of glycogen. Effectively, the organism can no longer rely on glycogenolysis to defend the blood glucose during early fasting and must turn to gluconeogenesis, which may not begin promptly enough to render the individual symptom-free.

Treatment is avoidance of fasting with ingestion of adequate protein to provide substrate for gluconeogenesis and complex carbohydrates so that hyperglycemia and hyperlactic acidemia are not produced.

Amylo-1,4 1,6-Transglucosidase (Branching Enzyme) Deficiency (Glycogenosis Type IV, Amylopectinosis, Andersen's Disease)

Because deficiency of the branching enzyme, as expected, would lead to abnormally long, relatively straight glucose polymers, the histopathologic observations of abnormal glycogen deposition and cellular are easily explained. Clinically, this rare autosomal recessive disease appears in the first year of life with progressive hepatosplenomegaly, eventually leading to cirrhosis. Neuromuscular findings include hypotonia, developmental retardation, and muscular atrophy. Progression is fairly rapid, with death usually occurring within the first 3 years.

There are some interesting and unexpected features of this disease. Chief among them is that the liver glycogen content is well within normal limits, which is consistent with the usual absence of hypoglycemia. This strongly suggests that the cellular damage is a consequence of the abnormal structure of the glycogen rather than its quantity. Furthermore, it emphasizes the ability of the glycogenolytic enzymes to degrade the abnormal molecule, at least to a certain extent. Another interesting finding is the presence of the 1,6-linkage at approximately 50% of the normal frequency per molecule. It is possible that this is due to the ability of the amylo-1,6-glucosidase reaction of glycogen degradation to proceed in the reverse direction, although the equilibrium lies far in the direction of cleavage.

Phosphorylase Complex: Liver Phosphorylase (Type VI) and Phosphorylase B Kinase (Type VIII)

Although the clinical aspects of this disorder are related to deficient phosphorylase activity, three distinct genetic lesions account for abnormalities of the phosphorylase complex. The simplest is a partial (mild to severe) deficiency of the hepatic phosphorylase protein that obviously results in impairment of glycogenolysis. The other two genotypic defects affect the phosphorylase kinase system, so that phosphorylase b cannot be converted into the active form, phosphorylase a. One form is inherited as an X-linked trait primarily affecting the liver, whereas the other is autosomal recessive and involves liver and muscle. Thus, liver is involved in all three forms and hepatomegaly is common to all. Muscle involvement in the autosomal recessive form of phosphorylase kinase deficiency generally is mild so that patients may suffer no functional impairment.

Perhaps the oddest feature of the disorder is that hypoglycemia is infrequent and mild. Based on the enzymatic defect, one would anticipate that such patients would suffer from relatively severe hypoglycemia, which would be unresponsive to glucagon. Attenuation of the hypoglycemia can be explained by the fact that there is no impediment to gluconeogenesis because the defect does not affect formation or cleavage of glucose-6-P. Lactate and urate levels are normal and ketosis appropriately develops during fasting.

Treatment is based on avoidance of fasting.

Muscle Phosphorylase Deficiency (Glycogenesis Type V, McArdle's Syndrome)

During strenuous exercise, patients with muscle phosphorylase deficiency experience cramps, which limit their exercise tolerance. Clinical onset occurs later in childhood or during adolescence. Because the defect is confined to skeletal muscle, the explanation for its late onset can be found in the relative changes in muscle bulk that occur throughout development. Between ages 10 and 18 years, the ratio of lean body mass to height increases in males by close to 185% and in females by almost 75%. Hence, when muscle is deficient in phosphorylase, there will be a greater bulk of muscle to move as a consequence of the increase in muscle mass. This added burden will tax the ability of the phosphorylase-deficient individual to generate sufficient energy for vigorous activity, thus precipitating clinical presentation.

The most common clinical presentation is exercise intolerance, which often is accompanied by cramping if exercise is vigorous. A less common finding is myoglobinuria, also associated with periods of intense exercise. Characteristically, plasma lactate does not increase with exercise and serum creatine kinase is elevated several-fold above normal levels at rest. Although muscle depends predominantly on fatty acids for energy under basal conditions, when burst activity is required, it can rapidly convert to metabolism of glucose derived from its own glycogen stores. Normally, anaerobic burst activity results in increased lactate output. A defect in muscle phosphorylase impairs this energy conversion, rendering the muscle less able to meet the demands of an increased work load and reducing lactate output, which might also affect lactate availability in liver for gluconeogenesis.

At a cellular level, deprivation of normal energy reserves leads to membrane damage, which results in release of creatine kinase, other muscle enzymes, and myoglobin. Because of its relative small size, myoglobin is excreted in the urine, usually constituting a benign but startling finding. Clinical diagnosis can be approached by examining the venous lactate response to ischemic exercise. Nuclear magnetic resonance (NMR) has been used to make the noninvasive diagnosis of muscle phosphorylase deficiency by estimating muscle pH, ATP, and phosphocreatine concentrations during aerobic and anaerobic exercise. Muscle biopsy is required for definitive enzymatic diagnosis.

Treatment is based on avoidance of heavy exercise because under basal conditions, muscle metabolism is relatively normal. Acute episodes can be treated with oral glucose because the hyperinsulinemic response increases cellular glucose uptake and metabolism to meet increased demand. Although long-term prognosis is good, renal failure, which rarely occurs secondary to myoglobinuria, is a major complication.

Amylo-1,6-Glucosidase (Debrancher) Deficiency (Glycogenosis Type III, Cori's Disease)

Most patients with debrancher deficiency show involvement of liver and muscle; but, in some patients, dysfunction of only one of these organs predominates. In the first patient reported, the underlying enzyme defect was suspected on the basis of the abnormal glycogen structure, with its very short outer branches.

Clinically, there is noteworthy hepatomegaly and mild hypoglycemia. These apparently contradictory observations can be easily reconciled when the biochemical function of the enzyme is appreciated. In the presence of normal phosphorylase activity, glycogen can be degraded at its 1,4-linkages to a limited extent, with the formation of glucose-1-P. If it cannot be further degraded in the absence of debrancher, a "limit dextrin" accumulates alongside newly synthesized, normally structured glycogen—hence, the marked hepatomegaly. However, formation of glucose-6-P permits release of free glucose from the liver through the action of glucose-6-phosphatase, albeit to a lesser extent than normal. This modest contribution in support of the blood glucose from liver helps to blunt the hypoglycemia which stems from inadequate access to liver glycogen.

The frequent observation of hypertriglyceridemia and hypercholesterolemia can be explained by mechanisms detailed below for glucose-6-phosphatase deficiency. In contrast to glucose-6-phosphatase deficiency, however, Type III patients rarely experience lactic acidosis or hyperuricemia because gluconeogenesis is patent and glycolysis is not being flooded with metabolites. The response to glucagon in patients with debrancher deficiency also is predictable: under fasting conditions, no response is elicited, whereas in the postprandial period, there is a hyperglycemic response. Treatment, therefore, entails avoidance of fasting and liberal access to protein to sustain gluconeogenesis. The long-range prognosis generally is good: most patients achieve normal adult stature and development, and the liver regresses in size to normal.

Glucose-6-Phosphatase Deficiency (Glycogenosis Type I, Von Gierke's Disease)

Positioned as the "gatekeeper" of free glucose release from the hepatocyte, glucose-6-phosphatase is critical to total body glucose homeostasis, as well as to regulation of the glycogen cycle within the liver cell. It is the terminal enzyme of both glycogenolysis and of gluconeogenesis. Consequently, in the absence of this enzyme, the phosphate group on glucose-6-phosphate cannot be removed and glucose cannot escape from the cell. As a result, a clinical hallmark of glucose-6-phosphatase deficiency is frequent and often profound hypoglycemia, recalcitrant to glucagon of either endogenous or exogenous origin. Remarkably, the chemical hypoglycemia often is not symptomatic, prompting the suggestion that lactic acid is an alternate substrate for the brain.

Accompanying the hypoglycemia is a severe lactic acidosis, which stems from an inability to produce free glucose from lactate. Because free glucose cannot be released from the liver cell, glucose-6-phosphate only can be reconverted to glycogen or proceed through glycolysis. Thus, the liver, which normally functions as a consumer of lactate, which is released from muscle and other organs (Chapter 8), instead becomes a producer of lactate, leaving the body with urinary excretion as its sole means of lactate disposal.

Access to the renal route of excretion also is restricted, as in HFI, because of great elevations in blood uric acid levels and the resultant competition between lactate and urate at the renal tubule for excretion. The hyperuricemia derives from increased catabolism of adenine nucleotides provoked by shortage of inorganic phosphate for regeneration of ATP. This deficit of inorganic phosphate is brought on by accumulation of phosphorylated glycolytic intermediates. Moreover, adenine deaminase, which limits the rate of breakdown of AMP to uric acid, normally is strongly inhibited by inorganic phosphate. Thus, reduction of intracellular Pi activates this enzyme and the subsequent catabolic pathway. Release of uric acid into the blood not only enhances plasma lactate accumulation as a result of renal tubular competition, but also creates a potential hazard for nephrolithiasis.

Another characteristic of von Gierke's disease is a constellation of serum lipid abnormalities, including increases in triglyceride, cholesterol, and phospholipid levels. If one considers that the metabolic state of the liver in comparison to the periphery in glucose-6-phosphatase deficiency is the same as that in diabetic ketoacidosis (ie, the liver is glucose-rich whereas the periphery is glucose-starved), these lipid abnormalities can be readily explained. To begin with, the increased flux of hepatic glucose-6-P through glycolysis results in an increase in glucose-derived acetyl CoA. Elevation of acetyl CoA leads to activation of the lipogenic regulatory enzyme, acetyl CoA carboxylase, with consequent formation of malonyl CoA. Formation of malonyl CoA is the first committed step in fatty acid synthesis and results in enhanced de novo synthesis of fatty acids. Increase in malonyl CoA has an additional consequence: inhibition of carnitine acyl (palmitoyl) transferase. This inhibition prohibits transfer of fatty acids across the mitochondrial membrane and drastically reduces the rate of β-oxidation and ketogenesis. Increased formation of triose fragments from glycolysis also enhances the formation of glycerol-3-P, the skeleton upon which triglycerides form. The net result of all this is increased release of triglycerides, in the form of very low density lipoproteins (VLDL), from liver.

Added to the above is the release of free fatty acids from adipose tissue as a result of the insulinopenia when blood glucose is low. Free fatty acids are esterified in the liver and either stored in vacuoles or released as VLDL (see Chapter 15).

Inasmuch as "stockpiling" glycogen in the fetal liver is a key feature of the final trimester, depending on the extent and degree of placental glucose transfer, liver enlargement may be present at delivery in an affected infant. Again, because both glycogenolysis and gluconeogenesis are stymied by this defect, hypoglycemia will occur within hours of birth if the infant is not furnished a source of glucose. Of course with early feeding becoming the norm, hypoglycemia will not become apparent until the interval between feedings becomes prolonged.

With time, xanthomata may appear on the extremities, prompted by the serum lipid abnormalities. As the abdomen becomes increasingly protuberant from hepatomegaly, the extremities become increasingly wasted in appearance. Tendency to bruise, frequent nose bleeds, and melena may be noted—findings related to abnormalities in platelet adhesiveness, either from the hypoglycemia per se or defects in platelet metabolism. As a consequence of those biochemical events detailed above, which restrict β-oxidation, ketonuria is uncommon despite the severe degree of hypoglycemia.

Definitive diagnosis of Type I disease can be made only by enzyme assay in liver specimens. The majority of liver biopsy samples from patients evidencing classic von Gierke's disease will have deficient glucose-6-phosphatase activity. About 10% will manifest substantially enhanced enzyme activity after freezing and thawing. This finding is consistent with the existence of a transport protein, glucose-6-P translocase, which transports the substrate across the microsomal membrane, bringing it in contact with glucose-6-phosphatase. Freeze-thawing breaks down the integrity of the microsomal membrane barrier. Thus, deficiency of either the enzyme or the transport protein will produce similar clinical pictures, termed Types Ia and Ib, respectively.

Treatment of this disease is demanding and complex, and must be directed at supplying ongoing glucose requirements while continuing to meet protein demands without supplying excessive lipid in the diet. In the infant, this usually requires continuous overnight nasogastric infusion. In the older child, the nasogastric infusion can frequently be replaced by raw cornstarch supplements, which are slowly hydrolyzed in the gastrointestinal tract, providing a continuous source of glucose monomers. With prompt diagnosis and treatment, survival has been extended into adulthood with good results. But with this improved survival, complications have emerged, particularly in Type Ib disease. Perirectal abscesses and superinfection, by pyogenic organisms, of insignificant skin trauma can produce severe illnesses in these patients. A significant number of Type Ib patients who are older also have developed renal failure, which most likely developed because of tubular involvement by glycogen storage as well. An additional long-term complication of Type Ib is pseudocolitis. The characteristic leukopenia leading to these events has been successfully treated with granulocyte-colony stimulating factor.

Acid α-Glucosidase Deficiency (Glycogenosis Type II, Pompe's Disease)

It needs to be stressed that deficiency of α-glucosidase constitutes a lysosomal defect, rather than a disorder of glycogen metabolism. Thus, although Pompe's disease truly is a disease of glycogen storage, the biochemical basis is different from those disorders already discussed. In essence, the enzyme deficiency will be manifested in any tissue synthesizing glycogen and in which lysosomes can be found. For this reason, Pompe's disease can be considered a generalized glycogenosis affecting most tissues.

There are two main forms of Pompe's disease: onset of symptoms occurs during early infancy in one form, whereas the other presents with milder findings during adolescence or adulthood. There is no correlation between the extent of α-glucosidase deficiency and clinical symptoms; therefore, the biochemical basis for the different clinical forms remains obscure. The onset of symptoms that occurs during early infancy, defined as the first year of life, chiefly involves the heart, skeletal muscle, and central nervous system. A varying combination of weakness, respiratory difficulties, and cardiac failure exists, with a marked discrepancy between the extent of symptoms and the mental alertness of the patient. Moreover, the muscular weakness is paradoxical given the accentuated size and firmness of the muscle itself. The heart frequently is enlarged and the ECG is definitely abnormal, displaying an enormous QRS wave complex on electrocardiogram. Although the liver becomes enlarged, there is no evidence of dysfunction. Cardiac involvement or respiratory failure usually leads to death within the first 2 years of life.

In view of the conspicuously abnormal clinical picture, there is a notable absence of pathophysiologic events related to glycogen metabolism. Hypoglycemia, ketosis, or lactic acidosis do not occur and responses to glucagon and epinephrine are entirely normal. However, none of this is difficult to comprehend once we understand the basic defect. Because α-glucosidase is an intralysosomal enzyme, its function is limited to disposing of glycogen that makes it way into the lysosome. Inasmuch as support of glucose homeostasis derives from the glycogen cycle itself, whatever percentage of glycogen is lost to the lysosome readily can be replaced. But when α-glucosidase is deficient, lysosomal glycogen cannot be degraded, leaving it to accumulate.

Definitive diagnosis can be made by enzyme assay on a muscle biopsy specimen. At present, there is no treatment for this disease, as is true for most lysosomal storage diseases.

Phosphofructokinase Deficiency (Glycogenosis Type VII)

This disorder has been considered in the chapter on muscle diseases (Chapter 25). Its clinical presentation is similar to that of muscle phosphorylase deficiency (McArdle's disease) with two distinguishing features. First, glucose fails to relieve symptoms in phosphofructokinase deficiency. Second, the defect is expressed in red blood cells, prompting hemolysis and hyperbilirubinemia.

In both muscle phosphorylase deficiency and phosphofructokinase deficiency, the nature of the defect precludes production and release of lactate. Nevertheless, myoglobinuria is seen in both.

Phosphofructokinase deficiency can be diagnosed by red cell enzyme assay, which will show approximately 50% of normal activity. There is residual activity because the enzyme is a tetramer, and the red cells contain a form with two subunits that are shared by muscle. Symptoms can be avoided by abstaining from strenuous exercise.

SUGGESTED READINGS

Arion WJ, Canfield WK. Glucose-6-phosphatase and type I glycogen storage disease: some critical considerations. Eur J Pediatr 1993;152:S7.

Burchell A. The molecular basis of type I glycogen storage disease. Bioessays 1992;14:395.

Burchell A, Waddell ID. The molecular basis of the genetic deficiencies of five of the components of the glucose-6-phosphatase system: improved diagnosis. Eur J Pediatr 1993;152:S18.

Chen Y-T, Burchell A. Glycogen storage diseases. In: Scriver CR, Beaudet AL, Sly WS, Valle D. The metabolic and molecular bases of inherited disease. 7th ed. New York: McGraw-Hill, 1995:935.

Cox TM. Aldolase B and fructose intolerance. FASEB J 1994;8:62.

DeBarsy T, Hers H-G. Normal metabolism and disorders of carbohydrate metabolism. Bailleres Clin Endocrinol Metab 1990;4:499.

Dunger DB, Holton JB. Disorders of carbohydrate metabolism. In: Holton JB, ed. The inherited metabolic diseases. New York: Churchill-Livingstone, 1994:21.

Gitzelmann R, Steinmann B, Van den Berghe. Disorders of fructose metabolism. In: Scriver CR, Beaudet AL, Sly WS, Valle D. The metabolic and molecular bases of inherited disease. 7th ed. New York: McGraw-Hill, 1995:905.

Parker PH, Ballew M, Greene HL. Nutritional management of glycogen storage disease. Annu Rev Nutr 1993;13:83.

Segal S. The challenge of galactosemia. International Pediatrics 1993;8:125.

Segal S, Berry GT. Disorders of galactose metabolism. In: Scriver CR, Beaudet AL, Sly WS, Valle D, eds. The metabolic and molecular bases of inherited disease. 7th ed. New York: McGraw-Hill, 1995:967.

Talente GM, Coleman RA, Alter C, et al. Glycogen storage disease in adults. Ann Intern Med 1994;120:218.

Van den Berghe G. Inborn errors of fructose metabolism. Annu Rev Nutr 1994;14:41.

chapter **12**

Disorders of Amino Acid Metabolism

It is useful to categorize the aminoacidopathies as a separate group of inborn errors of metabolism because they involve one or another step in the intermediary metabolism of one or more amino acids, distinct from carbohydrate or lipid pathways. All the same, any metabolic chart at a brief glance will show the multiple interfaces between these three major pathways; hence, such a classification is, at best, an artificial one. This is further underscored by a fourth class of disorders known as the organic acidemias (see Chapter 13), which are distinct from aminoacidopathies only because their primary biochemical markers are the keto- and/or hydroxy-acid metabolic intermediaries of amino acid breakdown. To simplify the discussion as much as possible, we have confined the following discussion to those disorders in which the primary biochemical marker of a metabolic disease is a ninhydrin-positive compound.

Even this straightforward "yardstick," however, will have its critics because a disease such as argininemia, presently classified as a urea cycle disorder, is diagnosed because of plasma elevations of the ninhydrin-positive, bona fide amino acid, arginine. By the same token, we then must include alkaptonuria, the classic Garrodian "inborn error of metabolism" in some other category, because homogentisic acid is not ninhydrin positive, although it is produced directly from tyrosine. In any case, we will stick firmly with the criterion stated above in the interests of simplicity.

As a practical matter, those amino acids that are avidly reabsorbed by the kidneys—phenylalanine, tyrosine, methionine, the branched-chain amino acids, and proline—are more likely to be elevated in plasma than in urine of patients with mild or intermittent variants of metabolic defects. Perhaps the most important time for measuring plasma amino acids is after a diagnosis is established and the physician needs to monitor the effects of the dietary regimen.

PHENYLKETONURIA (PKU)—PHENYLALANINE HYDROXYLASE DEFICIENCY

Phenylalanine is an aromatic amino acid containing a benzenoid ring which cannot be fashioned by human cells; therefore, it is an essential amino acid. As with all amino acids, its principal fate is incorporation into new protein. Of course, if protein is ingested in amounts that exceed synthetic needs or production of specialized signal molecules, like dopamine and norepinephrine, then the excess will be catabolized to generate ATP.

This disorder, inherited as an autosomal recessive trait, is the prototype aminoacidopathy, as defined above. Affected infants generally are clinically indistinguishable from normal newborns. Nonspecific, commonly associated features of the affected neonate include vomiting, fretfulness, and occasional jitteriness. The single clinical finding in the young, untreated infant that is commonly overlooked by parents is a peculiar musty odor, due to phenylacetic acid excretion. Precisely because PKU presents in such a nonspecific manner and leads to such devastating mental retardation if untreated, every state in the United States and most countries in the Western Hemisphere have population screening programs for this disease. These programs, besides resulting in the obvious benefits of early diagnosis and therapy, have provided excellent information about the frequency of the mutant gene in humans, thereby establishing a sound basis for genetic counseling and development of prenatal diagnostic techniques.

The biochemical defect in classic PKU lies in a deficiency of phenylalanine hydroxylase, which normally facilitates the conversion of phenylalanine to tyrosine (Figure 12.1). Thus, the plasma amino acid profile of an affected infant should (and does) show a marked elevation in phenylala-

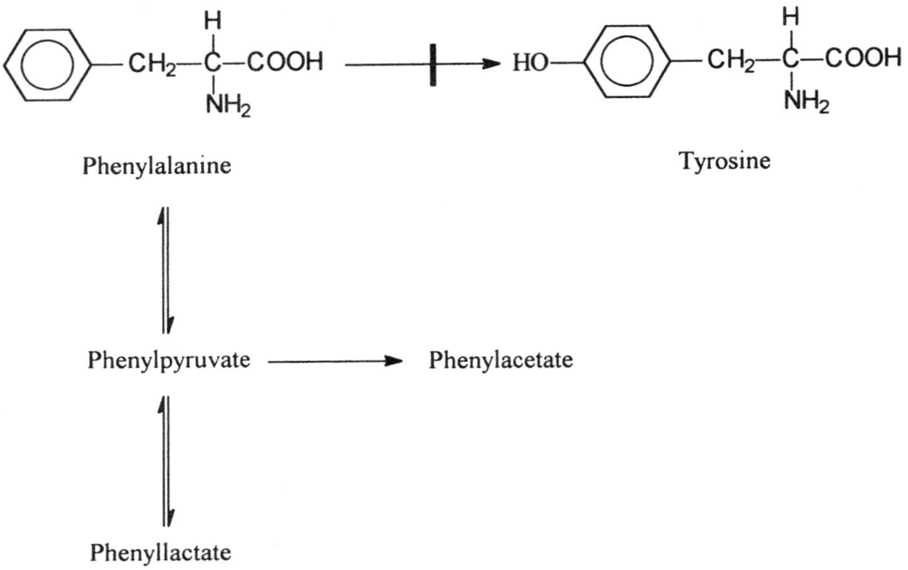

Phenylalanine —|→ Tyrosine

Phenylpyruvate → Phenylacetate

Phenyllactate

Figure 12.1. Pathways of phenylalanine catabolism. The conversion of phenylalanine to tyrosine is the usual route of catabolism and clearly explains why phenylalanine is an essential and tyrosine is a nonessential amino acid. The enzyme mediating the reaction, phenylalanine hydroxylase, has an absolute cofactor requirement for tetrahydrobiopterin. In an enzymatic cycle, tetrahydrobiopterin gives up its hydrogens to the hydroxylase reaction and, in the process, becomes converted to dihydrobiopterin; the latter compound then is enzymatically reconverted to the tetrahydro- form. Defects in the biopterin cycle also produce a clinical picture consistent with phenylketonuria. These phenylketones are produced as shown, by activation of an alternative pathway resulting in formation of the α-keto analogue of phenylalanine, phenylpyruvic acid. The enzyme mediating the removal of the amino group has a considerably higher K_m than that of the hydroxylase; phenylalanine must accumulate before the alternative pathway is activated.

nine concentration and a low to deficient level of tyrosine. In this sense, because the substrate acted upon by the deficient enzyme is an essential amino acid, taken in by diet, PKU fits our definition of an aminoacidopathy perfectly. However, a biochemical consequence of increasing phenylalanine within cells is provision of the substrate to alternate minor pathways at concentrations at which these minor pathways become operative. In other words, under normal circumstances, the control mechanism for phenylalanine conversion to tyrosine is almost exclusively the affinity of phenylalanine hydroxylase for the substrate, relative to the affinity of the transaminase which converts phenylalanine to phenylpyruvate. In an individual with PKU, transamination of phenylalanine becomes the predominant metabolic pathway, with production and excretion of the organic acid intermediate (Figure 12.1). Historically, this point is important because the presence of phenylpyruvate in urine led to biochemical characterization of the disease by means of the ferric chloride test. Clinically, it is equally important because it is phenylacetate, a derivative of phenylpyruvate, that is responsible for the characteristic, musty odor.

Treatment of PKU consists of phenylalanine restriction and tyrosine supplementation. It cannot be emphasized strongly enough, however, that this management requires great skill and effort. Because essential amino acids are required for normal growth, thereby precluding complete dietary deprivation, it is vital that plasma amino acids are monitored to assess the effects of changes in the dietary regimen. Moreover, the resultant growth, which is included in the "therapeutic success," will inevitably lead to greater caloric and other nutritional demands. Meeting these demands as these individuals reach adolescence would challenge the wisdom of Solomon. A way to deal with the restrictive nature of the diet is to employ dietary "holidays." For instance, beginning at age 10 years, the patient is given 1 "unrestricted" day every 2 months. At age 12 years, the frequency may be increased to every month. On these special days, patients can eat anything they want and need not ingest the phenylalanine-restricted formula.

A final problem regarding PKU that demands urgent attention is that of so-called maternal PKU. Because we have successfully cleared the "hurdles" of treatment of PKU, with preservation of normal cerebration in an increasing number of affected adults, there is a significant number of bright and productive women with PKU who want to have families of their own. Within the past 10 years, it has become apparent that such women who become pregnant without prior control of their blood phenylalanine levels bear children who have a staggeringly high incidence of microcephaly, mental retardation, and major cardiac anomalies. Unlike their mothers, these infants are not genetically totally deficient in phenylalanine hydroxylase, leading to the obvious conclusion that intrauterine exposure of the developing fetus to high phenylalanine concentrations must be prevented. This has engendered a coordinated attempt to provide dietary therapy in conjunction with family planning and genetic counselling to women who have successfully negotiated the hazards of a childhood complicated by PKU. The nutritional and psychological impact of PKU control for a woman who previously led a normal life is enormous and requires skill and sensitivity. The problems of maternal PKU reiterate the lesson learned from the long-term management of diabetes mellitus: every therapeutic advance that provides longer life expectancy is likely to introduce the offsetting disadvantages inherent in previously unrecognized long-term effects of the disease.

TYROSINEMIA—(FUMARYL ACETOACETATE HYDROLASE DEFICIENCY)

From a clinical point of view, the hereditary, infantile form of tyrosinemia is the most devastating. In its most acute form, affected infants present with failure to thrive; hepatomegaly; jaundice; vomiting; ascites; coagulopathy; and a peculiar, cabbage-like odor within the first 6 months of life. Although specific clinical recognition is not always easy, the symptoms and signs clearly are indicative of significant disease, unlike PKU which is far more subtle. Hence, screening of newborns, although desirable, usually is not performed on a mass basis.

Diagnosis of hereditary tyrosinemia traditionally has relied on demonstration of elevated blood levels of tyrosine and methionine out of proportion to other amino acids. The methionine elevation appears to be a secondary consequence of the severe liver dysfunction and is unrelated to the primary enzyme defect. The primary defect actually is located at a point that is four metabolic steps (two of them irreversible) removed from tyrosine itself, a situation that makes it difficult to envision how elevated tyrosine is related to the enzyme deficiency (Figure 12.2). In fact, the actual enzyme defect is located at a point beyond cleavage of the ring compound derived from tyrosine (homogentisic acid) at the step where fumarylacetoacetate is split into fumarate and acetoacetate. The enzyme mediating this cleavage, fumarylacetoacetate hydrolase, has been shown to be deficient in liver, kidney, and cultured fibroblasts from affected infants. Its presence has been established in normal human brain, suggesting that it may be deficient in this organ as well in these babies. As in PKU, accumulation of fumarylacetoacetate behind the block results in activation of an alternate enzyme pathway, with conversion to succinylacetoacetate and spontaneous decarboxylation to succinylacetone. Indeed, succinylacetone is now considered to be a biochemical marker for the disease, which is much more specific for the defect than elevated blood tyrosine and methionine levels. Parenthetically, succinylacetone is a potent inhibitor of heme biosynthesis, accounting for associated porphyria-like findings. It should be noted that urinary excretion of a highly specific organic acid derivative might logically qualify tyrosinemia for membership among the organic acidemias. Furthermore, the distance in metabolism between the parent amino acid, tyrosine, and the excreted marker, separated by two irreversible metabolic steps, raises the real question as to whether blood tyrosine elevation represents a secondary rather than a primary result of the enzyme defect.

Treatment is extremely difficult and generally unrewarding because hepatic damage usually is so severe and progressive that clinical progression is not substantially altered. The principles of ther-

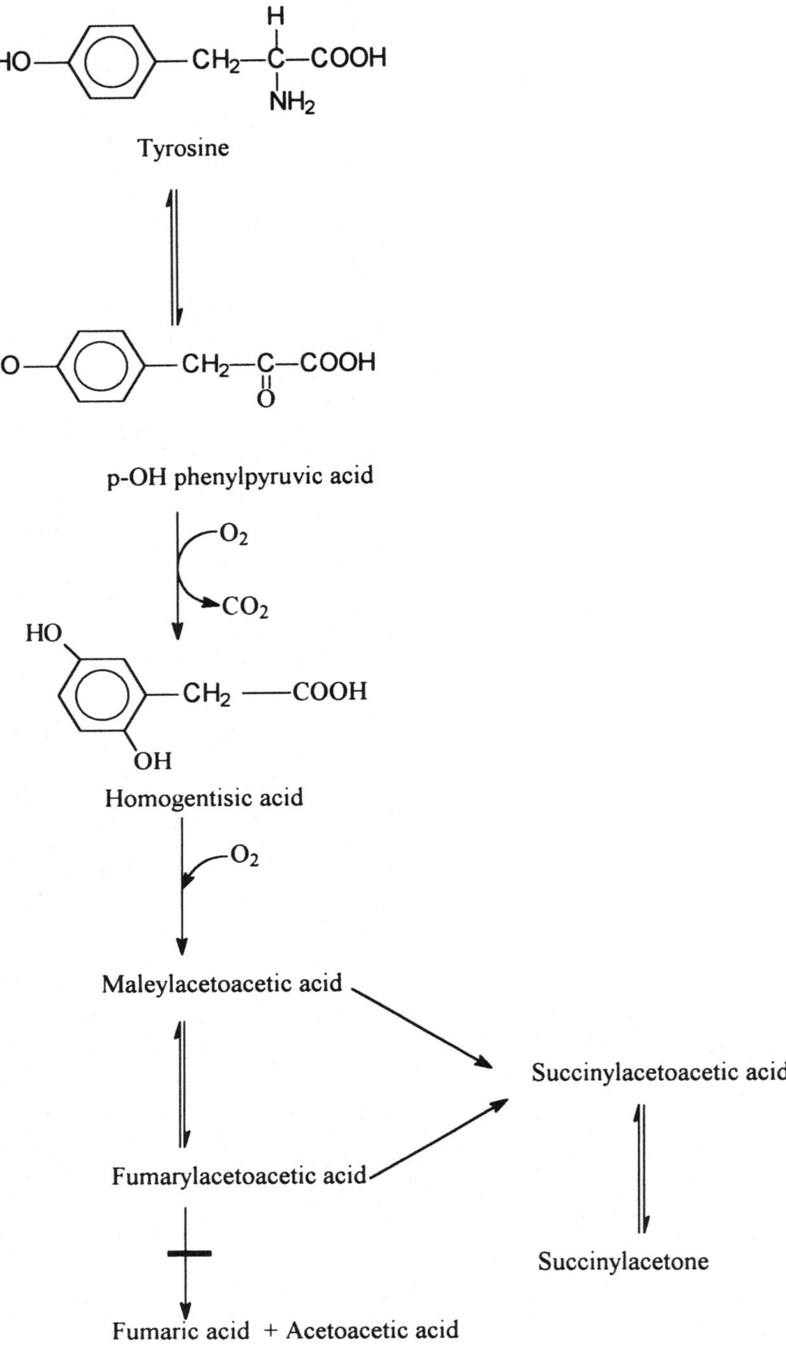

Figure 12.2. Pathway of tyrosine catabolism. Deficiency of tyrosine aminotransferase leads to an oculocutaneous disorder (tyrosinemia II, or Richner-Hanhart syndrome). Transient deficiency of p-OH-phenylpyruvic acid oxidase is assumed to be the cause of transient neonatal tyrosinemia, frequently responsive to vitamin C. Deficiency of homogentisic acid oxidase results in alcaptonuria, one of the disorders that led Garrod to propose the term "inborn errors of metabolism." Finally, deficiency of fumarylacetoacetate hydrolase (fumarylacetoacetase) causes hereditary tyrosinemia (tyrosinemia I). Production of the intermediate succinylacetoacetic acid results in formation of succinylacetone, presumably through spontaneous decarboxylation. The latter compound inhibits active transport across membranes and inhibits heme biosynthesis at the 5-aminolevulinic acid dehydratase step. The normal end-products of the pathway both are able to enter the Krebs cycle.

apy, as in PKU, rest upon reduced loads of phenylalanine, tyrosine, and methionine to decrease flux through the tyrosine catabolic pathway and normalize the measured biochemical pathways. Significantly, neither dietary therapy nor liver transplantation completely eliminates excretion of succinylacetone. This is not surprising when one realizes that inasmuch as blood tyrosine should never be permitted to fall below normal range, the kidney, which also expresses the enzyme defect, will continue to produce succinylacetone. There is evidence in rats that this compound is sequestered in the brain when exogenously administered, a finding that may help explain the high incidence of neurologic abnormalities in affected infants.

NONKETOTIC HYPERGLYCINEMIA (GLYCINE CLEAVAGE SYSTEM DEFICIENCY)

This autosomal recessively inherited disorder must be considered along with other causes of neonatal catastrophe, because the clinical presentation usually involves a phenotypically normal newborn who almost immediately exhibits listlessness, lack of spontaneous movement, opisthotonos, myoclonus and/or grand mal seizures, and hiccups. A critically important diagnostic feature is the remarkable absence of a significant acid-base disturbance in such a dramatically ill neonate. Progression to coma and respiratory arrest may occur as rapidly as a matter of hours after "burst suppression" patterns, with otherwise complete disorganization.

What is remarkable about this defect is that it affects metabolism of a nonessential, ubiquitous amino acid, yet it causes such terrible devastation in an otherwise normal infant. The probable underlying cause of the central nervous system dysfunction may reside in glycine's action as an inhibitory synaptic neurotransmitter. It is now clear that the distinctive laboratory finding in this disorder is a ten-fold elevation in the ratio of cerebrospinal fluid (CSF): plasma glycine concentrations, which is a reflection of the expression of the enzyme defect in brain as well as liver. This defect resides in the glycine cleavage enzyme complex (Figure 12.3), a tetrameric protein that normally functions in the conversion of glycine to serine, the major glycine catabolic pathway.

It is important to understand that identification of abnormal quantities of glycine in urine or plasma or both is not sufficient to make the diagnosis because glycine may be elevated in many other disorders. Moreover, because glycine is not normally identified by routine clinical laboratory procedures, quantitative glycine measurements in CSF and plasma are imperative in any suspected case.

Treatment modalities have been uniformly unsuccessful, most likely because glycine is a nonessential amino acid, which may be synthesized from a multiplicity of sources thus confounding efforts to reduce cellular pools. Medications that compete with glycine for central nervous system binding sites, used in attempts to reduce the neurologic consequences of high glycine levels in brain, have not substantially altered either the clinical picture or the ultimate course. The physician's primary mandate, therefore, must be to make the correct diagnosis to provide prenatal diagnosis in subsequent pregnancies and prevent a recurrence of such tragedy.

HOMOCYSTINURIA (CYSTATHIONINE β-SYNTHASE DEFICIENCY)

Homocystine is the sulfhydryl-linked, dimeric form of homocysteine, which is a normal intermediate in the synthesis of cysteine from methionine—a process known as the transsulfuration pathway. The presence of homocystine in urine, originally thought to be a specific biochemical marker for an autosomal recessive deficiency of cystathionine synthase activity, is now recognized as representative of a syndrome, albeit a distinctly abnormal finding. In the interests of brevity, we will consider here only the synthase-deficient patient; a comparison of this disorder with others that produce homocystinuria can be found in Table 12.1.

Because of the deleterious effects of homocystine on normal collagen cross-linking, many of the clinically manifestations of cystathionine synthase deficiency are collagen-related. A frequently seen consequence of abnormal collagen cross-linking

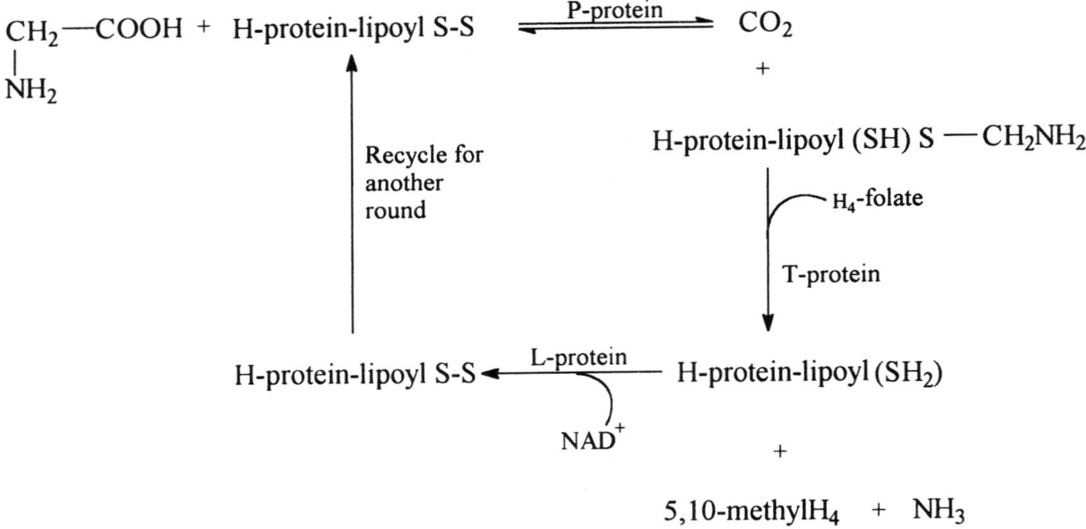

P-protein contains pyridoxal phosphate
H -protein contains lipoic acid
T-protein catalyzes THF dependent step
L-protein is a lipoamide dehydrogenase

Figure 12.3. The mechanism of glycine cleavage. Catabolism of glycine by this multicomponent enzyme system leads to production of CO_2 + NH_3 + NADH + a 1-Carbon fragment transferred to tetrahydrofolate (THF) to form 5,10-methylene-tetrahydrofolate. The reducing equivalent of NADH is conveyed to the electron transport chain. Transfer of the methylene-unit to another molecule of glycine results in synthesis of serine. After removal of the amino group, the serine can be metabolized as pyruvate.

Table 12.1. Comparison of Clinical and Biochemical Features in Three Forms of Homocystinuria*

FEATURE	CYSTATHIONINE β-SYNTHASE DEFICIENCY	DEFECTIVE COBALAMIN COENZYME SYNTHESIS	$N^{5,10}$-METHYLENE-TETRAHYDROFOLATE REDUCTASE DEFICIENCY
Mental retardation	common	common	common
Growth retardation	no	common	no
Dislocated optic lenses	almost always	no	no
Thromboembolic disease	common	no	rare
Megaloblastic anemia	no	rare	no
Homocystine in blood and urine	increased	increased	increased
Methionine in blood and urine	increased	normal or decreased	normal or decreased
Cystathionine in blood and urine	decreased	normal or increased	normal or increased
Methylmalonate in blood and urine	normal	increased	increased
Serum cobalamin	normal	normal	normal
Serum folate	normal or decreased	normal or increased	normal or decreased
Response to vitamin	pyridoxine	cobalamin (B_{12})	folate
Response to dietary methionine restriction	helpful	harmful	harmful

* From Bondy PK, Rosenberg LE Metabolic Control and Disease. Philadelphia: WB Saunders Co, 1980.

in this disease is osteoporosis; the poor ground substance for ossification leads to disrupted bone formation and increased turnover. Although osteoporosis is rare during childhood, homocystinuria is the most common cause when it appears. Pathologic fractures are a common consequence of osteoporosis in homocystinuria. Defective collagen formation also affects the eye, where lax suspensory ligaments permit dislocation of the lens.

Within the first 12 to 14 years of life, approximately 50% of homocystinuric individuals will suffer ectopia lentis, an event preceded clinically by extraordinarily rapid refractive error changes due to changes in shape and position of the lenses. The final major feature of this disease is the marked propensity for significant thromboembolic events, usually seen after the second decade of life, but which may occur even in infancy. The specific mechanism by which these occur is now well understood—abnormal intimal structure, caused by the abnormal collagen, has been documented and undoubtedly contributes. Moreover, these patients have increased platelet turnover, which likely is a reflection of a continual process of adhesion to the abnormal intima. An extremely portentous consequence of the propensity for major embolic events in these individuals is the marked increase in morbidity and mortality associated with general anesthesia and surgery. Hence, surgery and general anesthesia should be avoided at all costs, except in the most extreme cases. Indeed, deaths after routine eye surgery have been reported.

The biochemical defect is deficiency of cystathionine synthase activity, which mediates the conversion of homocysteine to cystathionine (Figure 12.4). Because homocysteine can be recycled to methionine via a B_{12}-dependent enzymatic pathway, both homocysteine and methionine accumulate as a result. Hence, screening techniques aimed at identification of hypermethioninemia in newborns have been used in some states. The major difficulty inherent in such programs lies in the absence of reliable, prospective data regarding the initial level of methionine in affected newborns and the rate of rise during the neonatal period. Hence, routine screening of newborns within the first 3 days of life cannot identify all potential cases and will lead to significant underestimates of the true incidence of the disease in the population. The major effect of this is to place the responsibility for diagnosis "squarely upon the shoulders" of the clinician. Laboratory screening for homocystinuria can be easily accomplished by paper chromatography of urine. Although the cyanide-nitroprusside spot is popular because it is easy to use, it is prone to false negative results and, therefore, is less desirable as a screening technique.

Once diagnosed, the initial therapeutic approach should be directed at determining whether the individual is pyridoxine (B_6)-responsive. Patients who are in the B_6-responsive group will achieve partial or complete normalization of plasma and urine methionine and homocystine levels. Although the mechanism for this effect is not clear, it is thought that binding of the mutant protein to its cofactor may increase its stability, thus decreasing turnover within the cell and achieving higher absolute quantities of partially active enzyme. Compelling evidence supports the use of up to 1000 mg per day of pyridoxine to ameliorate many of the clinical consequences of the enzyme defect. Because remethylation of homocysteine to methionine constitutes a vital part of a folic acid-mediated cycle, leading to thymidine (hence, DNA) synthesis, folate supplementation is equally important; deficiency of folate may impair any potential therapeutic response to pyridoxine. For the B_6 nonresponsive group of patients, dietary control of methionine intake remains the mainstay of therapy. Recently, controlled studies using betaine or choline to enhance remethylation of homocysteine to methionine have reduced homocystine levels in this group of patients.

Despite earlier evidence that there was no significant increase of coronary artery or atherosclerotic heart disease risk among obligate heterozygotes for cystathionine synthase deficiency, two recent studies have shown an association between increased plasma total homocystine levels and premature occlusive arterial disease. These data have important implications for preventive efforts against cardiovascular disease, because early identification and therapy of heterozygotes might significantly reduce morbidity and mortality in these individuals, as well as contribute to genetic counselling efforts in preventing occurrence of the homozygous state.

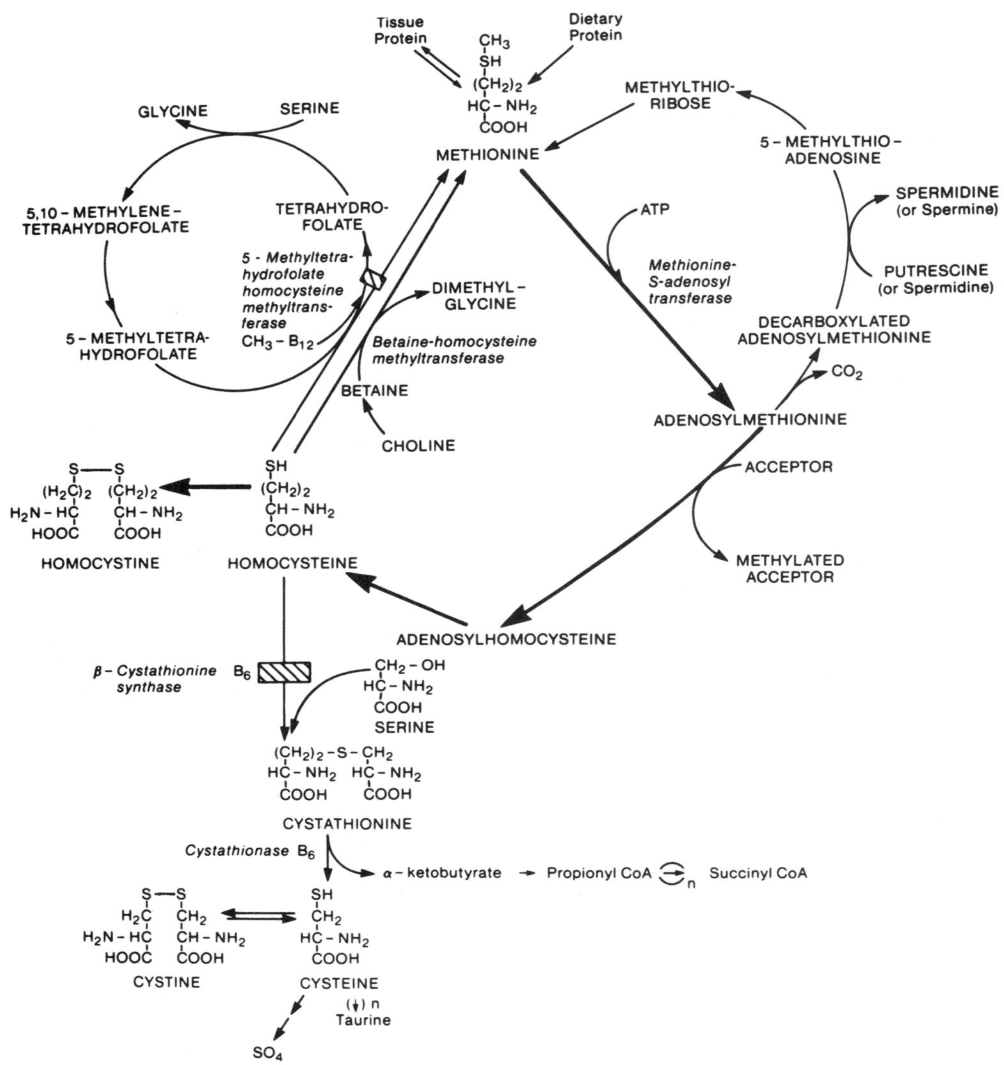

Figure 12.4. Sulfur-containing amino acid metabolism. This sequence also is known as the transsulfuration pathway, because the overall result is the transfer of a sulfur residue from methionine to serine to form cysteine, with the formation of α-ketobutyrate as a secondary product. The latter must be converted to propionyl CoA for further metabolism, explaining the need to restrict methionine in propionic acidemia. Note the multiple cofactor requirements of this pathway, including folic acid and methylcobalamin for conversion of homocysteine to methionine and pyridoxine for β-cystathionine synthase activity. An alternative pathway for conversion of homocysteine to methionine requires betaine as a methyl-donor. Classic homocystinuria is due to a deficiency of β-cystathionine synthase, which results in accumulation of homocysteine and reformed methionine via the cofactor-dependent pathways. Note that homocysteine is rapidly oxidized to homocystine and cleared by the kidney. Reprinted with permission from Shils ME, Olson JA, Shike M, et al. Modern Nutrition in Health and Disease. 8th ed. Baltimore: Williams & Wilkins, 1994.

CYSTINOSIS (LYSOSOMAL TRANSPORT DEFECT)

Among the chief causes of the renal Fanconi syndrome, which is a generalized tubular dysfunction, is cystinosis, which is an autosomal recessive disorder that tends to be insidious in its presentation. As the name cystinosis implies, the hallmark of the disease is cystine storage in most organs and cell types. Chief among these, in relation to the clinical presentation, are the cornea and the renal tubular epithelium. Accordingly, frequently presenting symptoms include tearing and photophobia, as well as symptoms relating to generalized renal tubular dysfunction, such as polyuria (hyposthenuria), weight loss (dehydration), unexplained fevers (dehydration), and muscle weakness (hypokalemia). Commonly, infants will present with failure to thrive and unexplained glucosuria. It is important to know that there is never a disturbance of systemic glucose homeostasis; the glucosuria is renal tubular in origin. A generalized aminoaciduria may accompany the glucosuria; the underlying mechanism is tubular dysfunction for all of these renal manifestations. Severe acidosis may occur in conjunction with dehydration because of a renal tubular defect in bicarbonate reabsorption (renal tubular acidosis [RTA], Type 2). Later in infancy, an affected child may refuse to bear weight and show physical signs of rachitic bone disease, which results from decreased conversion of 25-hydroxycholecalciferol to the 1,25-dihydroxy analogue by the affected kidney and compounded by the chronic acidosis.

Although it was recognized long ago that lysosomal storage of cystine crystals constituted the chief histopathologic feature of this disease, the molecular nature of the defect has been elucidated only within the last decade. The insolubility of the cystine molecule engendered the concept that defective intracellular metabolism of protein-derived cystine led to storage of the excess, precipitated material, in much the same fashion as is seen in lysosomal storage of any biologically nondegradable molecule. Moreover, the intracellular capacity for reduction of cystine to cysteine greatly exceeds the maximum solubility limit of cystine in the medium. Thus, investigators were unable to achieve cystine concentrations in the medium, which resulted in detectable intracellular cystine; therefore, they were unable to examine various aspects of intracellular cystine disposition. This problem was resolved by using the compound cystine dimethyl ester, which is more soluble than cystine and readily crosses biologic membranes. The compound then was hydrolyzed by lysosomal esterase, releasing free cystine within the cell. Thus, it became possible to demonstrate a markedly abnormal rate of egress of free cystine from cystinotic lysosomes compared to normals, leading to its accumulation and precipitation. Although many other lysosomal storage disorders have been previously described, none had been shown to be related to defective transport of the stored material; hence, cystinosis was the first demonstration of a lysosomal membrane transport defect.

Our heightened understanding of the nature of the disorder has contributed greatly to development of a rational therapeutic approach involving the compound cysteamine. This substance produces a rapid depletion of intralysosomal cystine by a novel mechanism. Cysteamine enters the lysosome, where it reacts with cystine to form a soluble cysteamine-cysteine disulfide, which is a structural analogue of lysine that is recognized and transported out of the lysosome by the lysine transport system. The clinical consequences of cysteamine therapy, continued for at least 1 year, include maintenance of glomerular function at normal levels (although no improvement is seen in tubular function) and marked improvement in linear growth. Hence, with symptomatic treatment of the acidosis and pharmacologic therapy for the rickets, children who previously would have been dwarfed and eventually would have died from end-stage renal disease can now be expected to live much more normal lives than those who suffered from this condition before them, although no cure exists at the present time.

Finally, it is noteworthy that cystinosis usually is categorized as an aminoacidopathy, despite the fact that cystine and other blood amino acid levels are normal. Urinary amino acids usually are increased dramatically, although cystine excretion is not seen in excess of the others. Hence, there is no specific biochemical marker that can be used, either in diagnosis or in classification; the designation aminoacidopathy, therefore, must be based on the abnormal metabolism of cystine.

UREA CYCLE DEFECTS

These disorders are characterized by impairment of ammonia metabolism due to deficiency of one of the enzymes involved in urea synthesis. Because the major metabolic source of ammonia is amino acid metabolism, this group of disorders can be considered to be aminoacidopathies. Although the neonatal presentation of each of these diseases is accompanied and typified by hyperammonemia, subacute presentations also have been described, characterized by delayed development. In the latter cases, hyperammonemia may be seen only at times of significant metabolic stress, or after protein loading. Moreover, many organic acidemias may present with moderate to severe hyperammonemia during metabolic decompensation, further confusing the diagnosis. With these caveats, a brief discussion of this group of disorders follows.

Clinical Presentations

Each of the urea cycle disorders most commonly presents during the neonatal period; the clinical picture is dominated by the signs and symptoms of hyperammonemic encephalopathy. These include early lethargy, poor feeding, vomiting, convulsions, and coma—hence, the term neonatal catastrophe is used to describe this picture (Table 12.2). A second mode of presentation, the subacute, is characterized by onset during early infancy, after the neonatal period, and manifested by vomiting, feeding difficulties, failure to thrive, and delayed development. Occasionally, a third type of presentation, termed the late-onset form, is seen and usually occurs after the age of 2 years. Aside from the obvious difference between a neonate dying while in a hyperammonemic coma and a 2-year-old child who is alive but developmentally delayed, the clinical distinction between these types of presentation is useful only if it reminds us that these disorders may present in various ways and, therefore, should be considered in differential diagnosis more frequently.

Biochemical Defects

Deficient activity of each of the enzymes in the urea cycle pathway (Figure 12.5) occurs through autosomal recessive inheritance, except for ornithine transcarbamylase deficiency, which occurs as an X-linked dominant trait. The liver commonly is viewed as the only organ that is entirely competent to produce urea from ammonia, whereas other cell types are partially competent to carry out this conversion. Hence, this portion of the individual's genetic endowment is fully expressed only in the liver. Because initial incorporation of free ammonia into the cycle occurs via carbamoyl phosphate synthetase activity, deficiency of this enzyme is the most likely to produce a fulminant neonatal catastrophe. Two forms of this enzyme exist: (*a*) CPS II, which is cytosolic and contributes primarily to pyrimidine formation and (*b*) CPS I, which is exclusively mitochondrial and the exclusive contributor of reaction product to the urea cycle. An extraordinary feature of CPS I is its complete inactivity in the absence of the compound N-acetylglutamine, synthesized mitochondrially from acetylCoA and glutamine by the enzyme N-acetylglutamine synthetase (NAGS). Accordingly, we must consider N-acetylglutamine synthetase as an intrinsic part of the urea cycle. Bereft of this enzyme, an affected individual has the phenotypic features of a CPS I deficient individual.

Carbamoyl phosphate is condensed intramitochondrially with ornithine; the reaction is mediated by ornithine transcarbamylase to form citrulline. Because deficiency of this enzyme prevents normal transfer of incorporated ammonia, two immediate consequences occur: (*a*) carbamoyl phosphate accumulates within the mitochondrion until some is transferred to the cytosol, resulting in increased rate of synthesis and catabolism of pyrimidines, and increased orotic acid production; and (*b*) a rapid increase in unincorporated free ammonia produces the clinical picture of a neonatal catastrophe, as in CPS I deficiency.

Once citrulline formation has occurred, this compound enters the cytosol where it is combined with aspartic acid by the enzyme argininosuccinic acid synthase (ASAS) to form the product argininosuccinic acid. If citrulline can be formed, its exit from the mitochondrion provides a possible excretory route for waste nitrogen; waste nitrogen can escape from the cell and undergo urinary excretion as citrulline. This occurs in citrullinemia, when the individual is deficient in ASAS activity.

Table 12.2. Urea Cycle Defects and Hyperammonemia Syndromes

CONDITION	GENETICS	CLINICAL FINDINGS	BLOOD AMMONIA*	AMINO ACID ELEVATIONS IN PLASMA	URINARY METABOLITES	ENZYME DEFECT (TISSUE TO ASSAY)	TREATMENT
Carbamyl phosphate synthetase deficiency	AR	Neonatal catastrophe	3+	Glutamine, alanine, lysine	Normal orotic acid	Carbamyl phosphate synthetase (liver, jejunum)	Hemodialysis or peritoneal dialysis ↓Protein intake Benzoate or phenylacetate Keto-analogues
Ornithine transcarbamylase deficiency	XD	1. Neonatal catastrophe 2. Hypotonia, lethargy secondary to protein intolerance 3. Variability in female	2+ to 3+	Glutamine, alanine, lysine	Orotic acid†	Ornithine transcarbamylase (liver, jejunum)	Same as above
Citrullinemia	AR	Severe neonatal presentation Subacute Occasional normal adults	Usually 2+ to 3+ after protein	Citrulline	3+ Citrulline + Neutral acidic amino acids	Argininosuccinic acid synthetase (white blood cells, skin fibroblasts, liver)	Protein restriction, benzoate, arginine
Argininosuccinicaciduria	AR	Severe Subacute Ataxia, convulsions Friable hair	2+ after protein normal fasting	Argininosuccinic acid	Argininosuccinic acid, glutamine, alanine, lysine, ± orotic acid†	Argininosuccinase (red and white blood cells)	Protein restriction, benzoate Arginine
Hyperargininemia	AR	Neurologic hepatomegaly	2+	Arginine	Arginine, cystine, lysine, ornithine	Arginase (red blood cells)	Protein restriction
Hyperornithinemia	AR	Protein intolerance Lethargy, ataxia, convulsions	2+	Ornithine	Homocitrulline, ornithine		
Ornithinemia with gyrate atrophy	AR	↓Visual acuity → blindness	normal	Ornithine	Ornithine	Ornithine amino transferase	Protein restriction, creatine
Lysinuric protein intolerance	AR	Protein intolerance, mental retardation	2+	Ornithine	Lysine, cystine, citrulline, arginine	Defective transport of dibasic amino acids	Citrulline

* Degree of elevation: + mildly elevated; 2+ moderately elevated; 3+ markedly elevated.
† ± occasional finding.

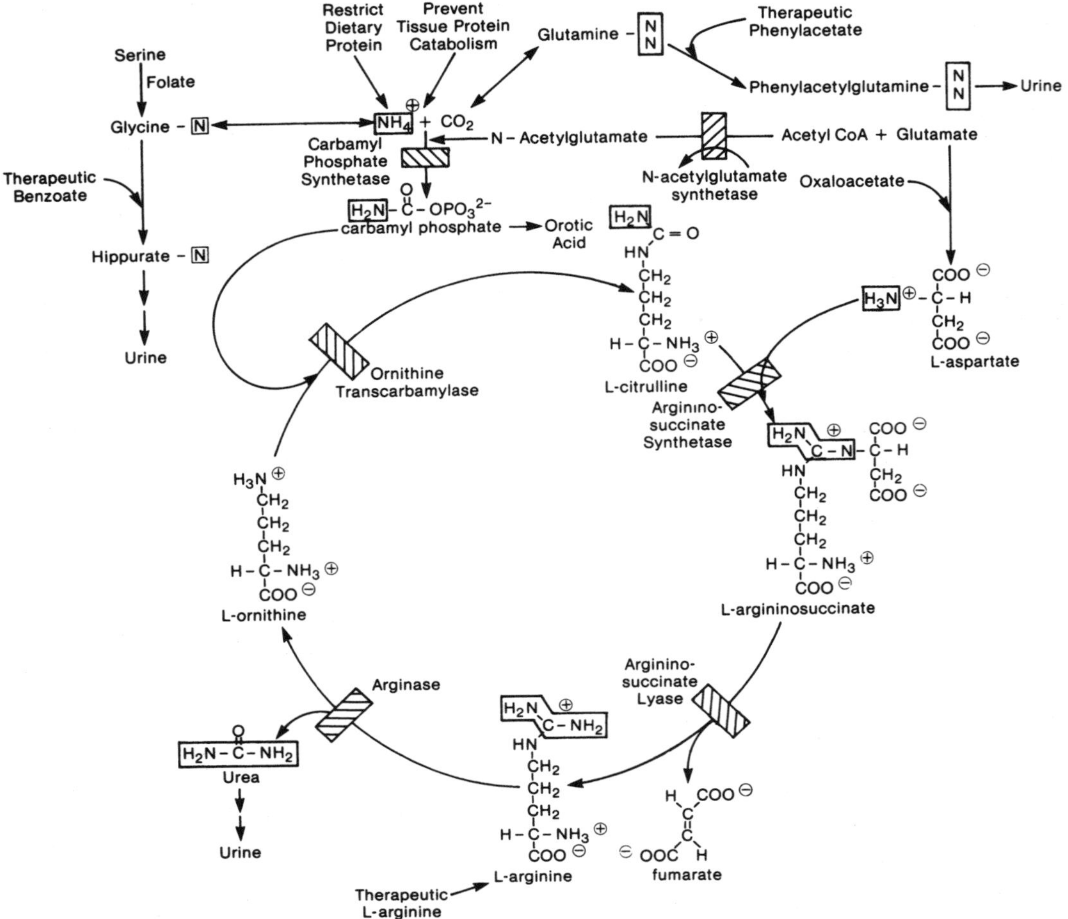

Figure 12.5. The detoxification of ammonia by the urea cycle. The cycle, as shown, is complete only in the liver. Thus, whereas other tissues, notably the kidney, can produce intermediates, the ultimate task of conversion of free ammonia to urea rests with the hepatocyte. In cases when a proximal block exists in the cycle, addition of more distal intermediates (eg, citrulline or arginine) can encourage activity of the remainder of the pathway. Use of benzoic acid as a therapeutic modality takes advantage of the liver's capacity to conjugate benzoate with glycine to form hippurate, with excretion of the latter and resynthesis of glycine from a subsequent nitrogen. Phenylacetate accepts two nitrogens by conversion to phenylacetylglutamine and is an important aspect of both acute and chronic treatment of urea cycle defects. Note that although restriction of protein helps to reduce free ammonia production, excessive restriction will encourage tissue protein catabolism, thereby offsetting the beneficial effect. It is this precarious balance that makes these disorders difficult to treat. Reprinted with permission from Shils ME, Olson JA, Shike M, et al. Modern Nutrition in Health and Disease. 8th ed. Baltimore: Williams & Wilkins, 1994.

The potential for waste nitrogen excretion, albeit less than normal, also can somewhat modify the fulminant clinical course seen in the previous two enzyme deficiencies. Hence, in citrullinemia, there generally is a wider spectrum of clinical presentation, although the majority of reported patients, even those who have experienced late onset, have suffered some degree of mental impairment.

Regarding the reaction mechanism of ASAS, it is important to understand that formation of argininosuccinate leads to incorporation of an additional ammonia molecule, because aspartic acid is synthesized endogenously by transamination of oxaloacetate produced by the Krebs cycle from glutamate (see Chapter 5), with consequent production of alpha-ketoglutarate which reenters the Krebs cycle.

Thus, deficiency of argininosuccinic acid lyase, the next enzyme in the cycle and the cause of argininosuccinic aciduria, also might lead to a wide spectrum of clinical presentation. Indeed, many more patients having argininosuccinic aciduria with long-term survival are described compared to those suffering from the previous three disorders. This situation likely is due to the fact that, although nitrogen excretion rate is slowed, individuals with this disorder still are competent to excrete two (rather than one) ammonia molecules via synthesis: first of carbamoyl phosphate and then of argininosuccinate. However, in these cases, arginine cannot be liberated, thus interrupting the cycle and diminishing regeneration of the catalytic compound, ornithine.

Cleavage of argininosuccinate normally results in the formation of arginine and fumarate. Again, it is important to note that arginine contains two ammonia molecules deriving from endogenous sources; fumarate, of course, enters the Krebs cycle. The arginine thus produced is cleaved to urea and ornithine, thus completing the cycle. Failure to carry out this step, because of deficient activity of arginase, is the biochemical basis for the disorder argininemia.

As with all metabolic pathways, the urea cycle must be subject to some form of regulation. However, whereas most pathways are internally regulated by various combinations of relative enzyme activities, end-point inhibition, and associated cofactor regenerative cycles, these factors play little, if any, role in regulation of the urea cycle. The activities of each of the enzymes in this pathway can handle more substrate than they usually are supplied under normal circumstances, obviating the first two factors, whereas none of the proteins are cofactor dependent. Thus, control of the pathway's activity is thought to reside in the synthesis of N-acetylglutamate; mitochondrial fluctuations in concentration of this compound result in rapid changes in CPS I activity, without which no free ammonia will enter the cycle. Keeping in mind that the substrates for formation of N-acetylglutamate, acetylCoA and glutamate, derive primarily from carbohydrate and lipid or from oxidative metabolism via the Krebs cycle, respectively, this mechanism provides a focus for regulation of urea production in relation to the minute-to-minute net metabolic fuel balance of the individual. Thus, the economy and beauty of this regulatory system is easy to appreciate.

Diagnosis

The key to timely diagnosis of this group of diseases is clinical suspicion. Although the same may be said of other entities in clinical medicine, few other disorders present with such catastrophic and nonspecific, or such chronic and subtle findings. The common notion that because a defect may exist in the urea cycle, the blood urea nitrogen value will be very low and assist in diagnosis is not true for patients with milder forms. Subjects with partial defects typically will have a normal blood urea nitrogen (BUN), because urea can be generated by urease-producing bacteria in the intestine. In fact, the primary diagnostic finding is hyperammonemia, although, for reasons briefly mentioned above, this may be difficult to demonstrate in some cases. In the less subtle, catastrophic situations, hyperammonemia is clear and unequivocal. However, in the more chronic presentations, blood ammonia levels may be elevated only after a protein load or during acute, intercurrent illness. Plasma glutamine, the amino acid charged with carrying amino groups to the liver in a nontoxic state, also is elevated. Glutamine thus acts as a buffer for plasma-free ammonia.

Once confirmed, hyperammonemia must be viewed as a clue, and its cause sought. Especially in older infants, a distinction between urea cycle defects, organic acidemias, and Reye's syndrome must be made, although Reye's syndrome always is viewed as a diagnosis of exclusion of the first two possibilities. A common point of differentiation is the absence of an anion gap metabolic acidosis, which is the rule in urea cycle defects, especially during acute episodes. In such cases, plasma amino acids should be measured, and the clinician should look for great elevations or depressions in urea cycle-related compounds, such as arginine, ornithine, glutamate, and glutamine. Also keep in mind that, during this search for a cause, if the patient is treated with intravenous glucose, a clinical improvement is likely because of the protein-sparing effect of carbohydrate with decreased amino acid catabolism and diminished ammonia production. Such an event should not be misinterpreted and the search for an etiology should not be aborted.

Treatment

Treatment of these diseases is far more complex than in aminoacidopathies such as PKU because normal rates of endogenous protein turnover can be relied upon to produce a constant minimum of waste-nitrogen load. The basic therapeutic principles aim to approach this minimum by dietary protein restriction and to utilize what remains of the urea cycle enzymes to accelerate ammonia excretion. Recent, additional measures take advantage of transamination and glycine acylation reactions to further enhance ammonia excretion in the form of other aminated compounds. Dietary restriction of protein is a therapeutic mainstay and should be calculated to provide the minimum essential for growth. More than this requirement will generate an additional ammonia load via catabolism; less will encourage net negative nitrogen balance with the same disastrous consequences. Moreover, this protein intake must be of sufficient quality to ensure adequate intake of all essential amino acids, or the ingested protein will be consumed for energy and increase the ammonia load proportionately.

Supplementation of the protein intake with urea cycle intermediate compounds will drive the remaining, intact steps in the pathway at a maximal rate. The need to achieve this is based upon the fact that excessive quantities of urea cycle intermediate compounds are less neurotoxic than free ammonia, although it is uncertain that they are, in themselves, harmless. Thus, in ornithine transcarbamylase deficiency, addition of large quantities of citrulline will drive the portion of the cycle beyond the block, accelerating incorporation of aspartate at the ASAS step and resulting in net excretion of one molecule of endogenous ammonia per molecule of citrulline.

Finally, addition of sodium benzoate and sodium phenylacetate to the therapeutic regimen addresses the problem of the second molecule of ammonia normally excreted via the urea cycle. Benzoic acid is rapidly detoxified in the liver by the enzyme glycine acylase to form benzoyl-glycine, or hippurate. In turn, hippurate is rapidly cleared by the kidney. The underlying principle is to "siphon off" glycine in this fashion, thus enhancing endogenous resynthesis of the cleared glycine from two sources: (*a*) from serine, produced by conversion of the glycolytic intermediate 3-phosphoglycerate to 3-phosphohydroxypyruvate and transamination from glutamate; and, (*b*) directly, from carbon dioxide, ammonia and methylenetetrahydrofolate, mediated by the enzyme glycine synthase. Each of these pathways incorporates an additional ammonia molecule into a new glycine molecule, which is then available for benzoate conjugation. Sodium phenylacetate is used to conjugate glutamine, synthesized in two steps from alpha-ketoglutarate; acetylation of glutamine results in production of the compound phenylacetylglutamine, which also is rapidly cleared by the kidney. It follows that plasma glutamine levels will be reduced as the ammonia load lessens and will increase as ammonia increases. Thus, together, plasma glutamine and ammonia are excellent guides to whether therapy is working.

In various combinations, these treatment modalities have had a significant impact on the long-term survival of urea cycle-deficient individuals who, in earlier years, would have died as neonates. Although many such children also seem to show fewer adverse effects on central nervous system integrity while undergoing treatment, it is still too early to be sure of the ultimate outcome. Finally, it cannot be emphasized strongly enough that there is need for the earliest possible diagnosis and therapy, to avoid, as much as possible, the neurotoxic effects of free ammonia.

SUGGESTED READINGS

Fernandes J, Saudubray J-M, Tada K, eds. Inborn metabolic diseases. Heidelberg: Springer-Verlag, 1990.

Jakobs C, Jaeken J, Gibson KM. Inherited disorders of GABA metabolism. J Inherit Metab Dis 1993;16:704.

Kaufman S. New tetrahydrobiopterin-dependent systems. Annu Rev Nutr 1993;13:261.

Pollitt RJ. Amino acid disorders. In: Holton JB, ed. The inherited metabolic diseases. 2nd ed. New York: Churchill Livingstone, 1994:67.

Scriver CS, Beaudet AL, Sly WS, Valle D, eds. The metabolic and molecular bases of inherited disease. 7th ed. New York: McGraw-Hill, 1995. (Also, see chapters 27, 28, 31–37, 39, and 40).

Treacy E, Childs B, Scriver CR. Response to treatment in hereditary metabolic disease: 1993 survey and 10-year comparison. Am J Hum Genet 1995;56:359.

chapter **13**

Disorders of Organic Acid Metabolism

In human biochemistry, organic acids are derived during the intermediary metabolism of basic nutritional components, especially amino acids and fatty acids. Strictly speaking, it could be argued that amino acids already are organic acids because they possess a carboxylic acid function. However, by convention, it is not until the amino group is removed from a parent amino acid that the resulting compound is termed an organic acid. In fatty acids, any defect in beta-oxidation can result in greater reliance on an alternative catabolic process for handling fatty acids, termed omega-oxidation, which causes compounds that cannot be metabolized, called dicarboxylic acids, to accumulate. Disorders of the Krebs cycle also have been described, in which the familiar di- or tricarboxylic acid accumulates behind the block. Because carbohydrates feed into the TCA cycle they also result in production of organic acids. The reader should understand that categorizing disorders of organic acid metabolism separate from those associated with parent compounds (eg, phenylketonuria) is more a matter of convenience than biochemical reality. Accordingly, we have chosen to include maple syrup urine disease (MSUD) in the group of organic acid disorders. MSUD illustrates the artificiality of the distinction between aminoacidopathies and organic acid disorders, perhaps better than any other such disease.

Many disorders of organic acid metabolism share a fulminant or catastrophic presentation during the neonatal period with their prototype, MSUD. Therefore, they always should be included in the workup of neonatal sepsis, because the etiology of metabolic acidosis and central nervous system dysfunction cannot be determined on clinical grounds alone. As in MSUD, diagnostic use of the nose can provide evidence of a specific organic acidemia, although such evidence depends upon the volatility of the accumulated compounds, which frequently is too low to allow for detection by this means. It also is essential to keep in mind that the bone marrow suppression associated with the accumulation of many of the organic acid intermediates makes the infant more susceptible to supervening infection; therefore, leukopenia in a septic baby may be a secondary manifestation of a more basic metabolic abnormality.

The organic acidemias, like many autosomal recessive diseases, exhibit multiallelic inheritance, explaining the heterogeneous clinical presentations exhibited in diseases known to be inherited in a classic Mendelian fashion. This multiallelism, initially demonstrated as "complementation groups" in cell culture, now is being traced to different DNA base-substitutions at the same gene locus.

Accordingly, in a so-called mixed heterozygote, one abnormal gene may dictate synthesis of an abnormal protein that exhibits different enzymatic activity from that dictated by the complementary abnormal gene. Thus, various patients with the same biochemical phenotype of a specific disease nevertheless may manifest different degrees of enzymatic deficiency, and exhibit different clinical presentations and outcomes. As a result, initial presentation of an organic acid disorder may occur after the immediate neonatal period, during the first year of life, or beyond. Indeed, it is unlikely that no manifestations would be exhibited during the first year of life (Table 13.1). Typically, in patients who present after the neonatal period, there is deterioration after an intercurrent illness, dehydration, or a minor surgical procedure done under general anesthesia. In each instance, the common denominator is the increased metabolic stress superimposed upon an individual with an enzymatic defect and diminished reserve capacity to meet this stress. The tissue catabolism is orchestrated by adrenal steroids and cytokines. Note

Table 13.1. Mode of Presentation of Organic Acidemias

Neonatal Catastrophe
- Acidosis (anion gap)
- Ketosis and ketonuria
- Tachypnea
- Neurologic findings
- Neutropenia, anemia, and thrombocytopenia

Failure to Thrive and Vomiting During the First Year of Life
- Deterioration with infection or diarrhea
- Vomiting
- Progressive delay in psychomotor development
- Acidosis—usually seen with exacerbations but is occasionally persistent
- May be history of protein intolerance leading to symptoms
- Neurologic symptoms with exacerbations

Onset After the First Year of Life
- Episodes of ketoacidosis after a minor infection
- May be lethargy, seizures, or coma with such attacks

that seizures are a prominent component in the later infantile presentations.

Initial biochemical suspicion of the presence of an organic acid disorder should be based upon calculation of the anion gap (see Chapter 4). An increase in the anion gap or delta suggests the presence of unmeasured, negatively charged anions—lactate is a prominent example. Such a finding obligates the physician to search for such compounds and appropriate therapies must be considered until a firm diagnosis is made. Keep in mind that the absence of ketones when hypoglycemia is present is very unusual and suggests the possibility of a defect in beta-oxidation of fatty acids. As indicated earlier, evidence of bone-marrow suppression (leukopenia, thrombocytopenia, and anemia) should raise suspicion of a secondary hematopoietic toxicity due to unmeasured organic anions. Elevations of blood glycine and ammonia levels are commonly seen in these disorders; glycine is elevated as a consequence of toxic inhibition of a subunit of the glycine cleavage enzyme. Elevations of ammonia occur because of toxic inhibition of N-acetylglutamate synthetase, the ensuing decrease in N-acetylglutamate concentration, and diminished activation of carbamoylphosphate synthetase, which is the first enzyme in the urea cycle (see Chapter 5).

In general, the major clinical manifestations of these disorders stem from the toxic effects of the organic anions produced as a result of the specific enzymatic deficiency. Hence, the clinical picture will tend to be nonspecific because many of the organic acidemias present in similar ways. As with most forms of toxicity, failure to consider the possibility can result in serious morbidity or death or both without a diagnosis. A final, exceedingly important note is that, as with other toxicities, the time to suspect the diagnosis and take action is during the acute stages when levels of the toxic materials are high and easily detectable. Thus, blood and urine samples should be obtained at the outset, coincident with cultures, etc, ensuring the presence of metabolites that may give important clues to the diagnosis.

DEFECTS IN BRANCHED CHAIN AMINO ACID CATABOLISM

Maple Syrup Urine Disease

The characteristic presentation of an infant with classic MSUD is nonspecific. There may be difficulty in feeding, accompanied by listlessness and occasional vomiting developing within the first 3 to 5 days of life. Irrespective of whether the infant is fed or starved, there will be a progressive metabolic acidosis due to accumulation of branched chain keto acids proximate to the enzymatic block. Hence, any time branched chain amino acids present themselves for catabolism to the body's cells, whether they are dietary or endogenous (from muscle protein breakdown), acidosis will ensue. The most likely clinical scenario is the infant who is listless and difficult to feed who, therefore, is fed less and becomes increasingly catabolic. This vicious cycle will lead to further decreased intake, a severe metabolic acidosis, coma, and death. A high-pitched, unpleasant cry is indicative of central nervous system toxicity, demonstrated in animals to result directly from excess of branched chain keto acids. Other signs of central nervous system toxicity can be seen, such as hypotonia and seizures. Of course, no physician could possibly base a clinical diagnosis of MSUD solely on the above findings, because they are all common to sepsis of the newborn and neurologic disorders in the neonate.

What is distinctive about MSUD is the odor for which it is named and which appears coincident with the earliest onset of neurologic symptoms. The specific nature of the compound that causes the odor is unknown, but the odor is detectable even to a casual observer in urine, saliva, stool, cerumen, and sweat. In the words of a physician who has referred such a patient to us, "the stool smells like my Sunday morning pancakes!"

An understanding of the biochemical defect is basic to a rational therapeutic approach. This especially is true because identification of the odor is justification for initiating treatment after obtaining proper samples for definitive diagnosis. Initial catabolism of the branched chain amino acids depends upon transamination, thus yielding the corresponding keto acid analogues (Figure 13.1). Further breakdown of these keto acids occurs within mitochondria and involves a branched-chain keto acid dehydrogenase multienzyme complex that acts on all three keto acids, resulting in release of CO_2 from each and formation of coenzyme A-linked derivatives. This step is defective in MSUD, thus resulting in accumulation of the keto acids and forcing reverse transamination to result in accumulation of the parent amino acids, as well.

Clinically, the accumulation of the keto acids results in the enormous anion gap that typically is seen in these infants at presentation. This emphasizes the fact that although providing intravenous bicarbonate to such an infant will help in buffering the organic acids, it will do nothing to permanently restore body buffers unless the rate of generation of the keto acids is simultaneously slowed. Accordingly, the levels of free branched chain amino acids must be reduced; hemodialysis, when it is available, is an effective means by which

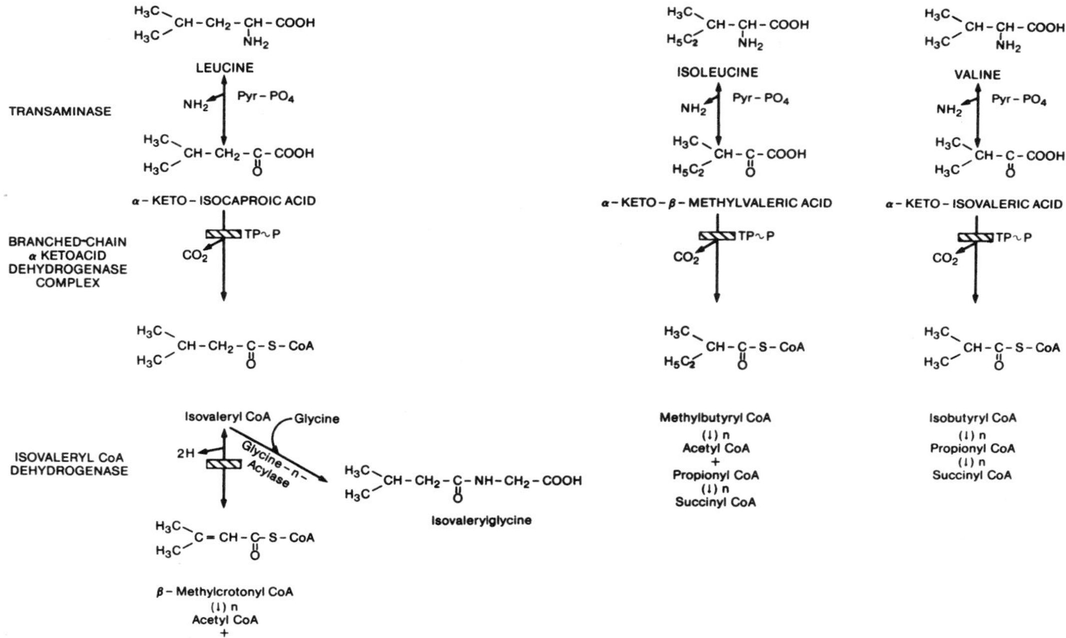

Figure 13.1. Catabolic pathways of branched chain amino acids. In a step common to all three, transamination produces α-ketoacid analogues; the reversibility of the transamination process permits reformation of the parent amino acids when a block exists distally. This, however, is true only if the block is at the dehydrogenase step because there is no way to reverse the decarboxylation occurring at that point. Note that the branched-chain α-ketoacid dehydrogenase complex can utilize all three branched chain amino acids as substrate; a defect in this enzyme results in maple syrup urine disease. A subsequent defect in the leucine catabolic pathway (isovaleryl CoA dehydrogenase deficiency) that prevents conversion of isovaleryl CoA to β-methylcrotonyl CoA is the cause of isovaleric acidemia. TP ~ P = thiamin pyrophosphate, (n) = multiple additional enzyme steps. Reprinted with permission from Shils ME, Olson JA, Shike M, et al. Modern Nutrition in Health and Disease. 8th ed. Baltimore: Williams & Wilkins, 1993.

to achieve this if the infant is critically ill—otherwise, peritoneal dialysis may be used. Moreover, keep in mind that the origin of the free amino acids in a fasting infant is the release of amino acids from muscle protein as an energy source. Hence, it is vital to provide a caloric source sufficient to slow down this process; a combination of glucose and lipid intravenously may be effective in this regard. It also is important to remember that the serum ammonia may be moderately elevated, which can add to the obtundation that these infants experience. Because this is a secondary feature, caused by inhibition of the urea cycle, reduction of the keto acids as suggested above should facilitate production of urea with rapid reduction in blood ammonia level.

Long-term treatment modalities depend upon supplying adequate nutrition for growth and development, but not so much that any excess materials (particularly protein) must be catabolized for energy. Predictably, this same principle applies to all inborn errors that must be treated with dietary restrictions. Therefore, it is imperative to understand a few basics of human nutrition: "essential" amino acids cannot be synthesized and, therefore, must be available from the diet for normal protein synthesis to occur. Lack of one or more of these essential compounds will cause protein synthesis to cease, no matter how many total calories are supplied; and, adequate nonprotein calories must be available in the diet to prevent utilization of dietary protein for energy. Based upon these principles, treatment of MSUD consists of a combination of a formula that is totally free of the branched chain amino acids (but otherwise complete) plus a source of these three amino acids that will deliver the appropriate amounts for growth. Of course, use of the formula alone eventually will result in a repetition of the acute onset phase because of muscle protein breakdown. Hence, treatment of MSUD and related disorders is akin to walking a tightrope between providing too little or too much. The only way to stay on the rope is to engage in close followup with periodic monitoring and tight dietary control. All of this implies the need for a specialized program, usually available at an academic medical center, where biochemical monitoring and nutritional counseling are readily available.

Isovaleric Acidemia ("Sweaty Feet" Syndrome)

We include isovaleric acidemia at this particular point to expand on principles already mentioned in the section above on MSUD, and to contrast certain aspects of the two diseases to show how different, yet similar organic acidemias can be clinically. To start with, it should be obvious to the reader that the eponym with which this disease is blessed will make it relatively simple to distinguish it with one's nose, not only from MSUD but from virtually all other clinical entities. The odor is so potent, for example, that it would be possible to determine from the nursing station that there is a patient with isovaleric acidemia somewhere on the ward. Thus, the disease cannot be overlooked if one has alert senses, no matter how much baby powder the nurses may use to attempt to make the infant presentable.

In relation to MSUD, the enzymatic defect in this disease is one step further along the catabolic pathway for leucine, at isovaleryl CoA dehydrogenase, which also is a mitochondrial enzyme (Figure 13.1). The accumulation of isovaleryl CoA leads to cleavage of this compound to release free coenzyme A for other metabolic sequences involving organic acids; this, of course, also leads to release of free isovaleric acid. Within the mitochondrion, this excess of free acid can be conjugated with carnitine (see Chapter 9) to form a nontoxic isovaleryl-carnitine, which leaves the mitochondrion and eventually is excreted in the urine. If a balance is maintained between the rate of isovaleric acid production and carnitine supply, this system works well in preventing problems. An additional backup detoxification system for isovalerate exists in liver, where conjugation to glycine is carried out to form isovaleryl-glycine, which is also excreted in urine. However, when these two systems are overwhelmed, free isovaleric acid begins to escape from the cell and is excreted into urine, giving the infant the unmistakably foul odor so characteristic of the disease.

Thus, it should be apparent that if an infant is emitting the odor of isovaleric acid, it is extremely likely that there are clinical signs also present that result from the toxicity of the free acid. A knowledge of the detoxification pathways, however, provides immediate access to at least two therapeutic modalities: administration of large amounts of glycine to accelerate formation of isovalerylglycine; and, oral carnitine supplementation for enhancement of acylcarnitine formation and excretion. Protein must never be totally withheld, because endogenous protein breakdown will result; however, protein intake should be restricted to no more than 1.5 g/Kg/day. Moreover, provision of nonprotein calories as glucose is imperative, to "spare" the leucine from being sent through the catabolic pathway for energy production.

Other Branched Chain Amino Acid Disorders

LEUCINE

Defects in each one of the enzymatic steps mediating leucine catabolism have been described. Further metabolism of isovaleryl CoA by removal of two hydrogens (isovaleryl CoA dehydrogenase) results in formation of beta-methylcrotonyl CoA. Deficiency of beta-methylcrotonyl CoA carboxylase results in accumulation of free beta-methylcrotonic acid, although beta-methylcrotonylglycine may be present without the free acid (Figure 13.1). It is important to recognize that excretion of this compound also occurs in disorders of biotin metabolism that affect all biotin-dependent carboxylases. But, in this disorder of leucine catabolism, an isolated deficiency of beta-methylcrotonyl CoA carboxylase is present, which leads to metabolic acidosis, coma, and death without treatment. Unfortunately, there is no reliable evidence that this defect responds to large doses of biotin; thus, treatment depends upon protein restriction to reduce total leucine intake to that required for anabolic processes.

Normal carboxylation of beta-methylcrotonyl CoA produces beta-methylglutaconyl CoA. A defect in hydration (beta-methylglutaconyl CoA hydratase) of this compound causes it to accumulate in the disorder 3-methylglutaconic aciduria. However, most peculiarly, the majority of patients who have been reported to have this urinary finding did not have a demonstrable enzyme deficiency. In fact, the majority of affected individuals had more clinically severe disease than the few patients with the documented deficiency of the hydratase. It is likely that the patients showing normal in vitro hydratase activity are excreting 3-methylglutaconic acid as a consequence of an undetermined metabolic error that secondarily affects the leucine pathway.

In the direct catabolic pathway of leucine, the final step is to cleave the product of the hydratase reaction, beta-hydroxy-beta-methylglutaryl CoA, to acetoacetic acid and acetyl CoA (3-hydroxy-3-methylglutaryl CoA lyase). A defect at this step leads to the disorder known as 3-hydroxy-3-methylglutaric aciduria. As with 3-methylglutaconic aciduria, urinary findings have been described in patients who did not have a measurable enzyme deficiency. Patients with or without the enzyme defect appear to be equally severely affected, although a distinguishing clinical feature of the enzymatically deficient infants is a severe metabolic acidosis, which frequently presents during the first week of life. A few patients with normal enzyme activity have been found to have partial or complete urea cycle defects, illustrating the importance of proper and prompt diagnosis to appropriate therapy. A true enzyme deficiency at this step would mandate reduction of both dietary leucine and fat because synthesis of ketone bodies from each substrate will be deficient.

Recall that beta-hydroxy-beta-methylglutaric acid also serves as a substrate for biosynthesis of cholesterol and related compounds, through formation from ketone bodies, a reaction mediated by cytoplasmic 3-hydroxy-3-methylglutaryl CoA synthetase. The subsequent step, decarboxylation by 3-hydroxy-3-methylglutaryl CoA reductase, results in formation of mevalonic acid, which then is phosphorylated to mevalonic acid-5-phosphate, mediated by mevalonate kinase. Deficiency of mevalonate kinase has been described, resulting in mevalonic aciduria. The few patients who have been determined to have this defect present such a heterogeneous clinical picture that it is unwise to generalize about clinical presentation in this disorder. Interestingly, metabolic acidosis is not a feature of this disorder because mevalonic acid is rapidly cleared by the kidney. Accordingly, tremendous quantities of mevalonate have been found in the urine of affected patients. Appropriate therapy has not yet been determined.

ISOLEUCINE

Defects in the isoleucine catabolic pathway generally occur as parts of a more global disorder, as

Table 13.2. Organic Acidemias

CONDITION	GENETICS	SCREENING TESTS	AMINO ACID AND ORGANIC ACID ELEVATIONS IN PLASMA	URINARY METABOLITES	ENZYME DEFECT	TREATMENT
Maple syrup urine disease*	AR	Odor $FeCl_3$—grey-blue 2,4-DNP—yellow ppt.	3+ Leucine 2+ Isoleucine 2+ Valine	Ketoacids Alloisoleucine	α-Keto acid decarboxylases multienzyme complex	Severe form—peritoneal dialysis; special formula Thiamine 100 mg/day
Isovaleric* acidemia	AR	Odor 2,4-DNP+	3+ Isovaleric acid 2+ Glycine BCAA—normal	+ Isovaleryl glycine—latent 3+ Isovaleryl glycine—overt β-Hydroisovaleric acid	Isovaleryl-CoA dehydrogenase	Glycine for form conjugate (250 mg/kg/day) Low protein diet
β-Methylcrotonyl glycinuria*	AR	Odor	β-Methylcrotonyl glycine β-OH Isovalerate	β-Methylcrotonic acid β-Methylcrotonyl glycine β-Hydroxyisovaleric acid	β-Methylcrotonyl CoA carboxylase (putative)	Biotin
3-Hydroxy-3-methylglutaric aciduria*	AR	Severe hypoglycemia and acidosis 2+ NH_3, odor 2,4-DNP—negative	Glutamine Alanine Lysine BCAA	3+ 3-Methylcrotonic acid 3-Methylglutaconic acid 3-OH-3-Methylglutaric acid + to 2+ 3-OH-3-Methylbutyric acid 3-Methylglutaric acid	3-Hydroxy-3-methylglutaryl-CoA lyase	High carbohydrate, protein-restricted diet
α-Methylacetoacetic aciduria	AR	+ to 2+ NH_3 2,4-DNP+	Isoleucine and propionate levels normal	3+ α-Methyl-β-OH butyric acid α-Methylacetoacetic acid Tiglyglycine n-Butanone	β-Ketothiolase	Protein restriction

Methylmalonic aciduria*	AR	Anion gap p-Nitroaniline + to 2+ NH_3	3+ Methylmalonic acid 2+ Glycine	3+ Methylmalonic acid Long-chain ketones Propionic acid β-OH propionic acid Methylcitrate β-OH-n-valeric acid	Methylmalonyl racemase or mutase Abnormal adenosylcobalamin synthesis	Prenatal vitamin B_{12} to mother
Holocarboxylase synthase (mixed carboxylase) deficiency*	AR (probable)	Anion gap Odor 2,4-DNP+	Variable, often BCAA	β-methylcrotonic, β-methylcrotonyl-glycine, β-OH isovalerate, propionic, OH-propionic, methyl citrate	Holocarboxylase synthetase	Biotin
Propionic acidemia* (ketotic hyperglycinemia)	AR	+ to 2+ NH_3, ketones + FeCl, keto-stix 2,4-DNP+	Propionic acid Glycine	3-OH propionate, methylcitrate, propionate, propionylglycine, butanone, pentanone and hexanone	Propionyl-CoA carboxylase	Biotin, protein restriction
Multiple acyl CoA dehydrogenase defect* (glutaric aciduria-II)	AR (probable)	Hypoglycemia, abnormal liver function tests, 3+ FFA		Glutaric, ethylmalonic, adipic, suberic, sebacic, isobutyric, isovaleric and butyric acids	Multiple Acyl CoA dehydrogenase	
Formiminoglutamic aciduria	AR (probable)	± Anemia, abnormal EEG, ventricular dilatation	Formiminoglutamic acid (FIGLU)	Formiminoglutamic acid (FIGLU), hydantoin-5-propionic acid	Glutamate formimino-transferase	Folate

(continued)

Table 13.2. *(continued)*

CONDITION	GENETICS	SCREENING TESTS	AMINO ACID AND ORGANIC ACID ELEVATIONS IN PLASMA	URINARY METABOLITES	ENZYME DEFECT	TREATMENT
D-Glyceric acidemia* c̄ hyperglycinemia	Unknown	No ketoacidosis	Glycine Glyceric acid	Glycine, glyceric acid	d-Glyceric dehydrogenase	
s̄ hyperglycinemia	Unknown	3+ Acidosis − Ketones	Glyceric acid	Glyceric acid, lysine, cysteine	Unknown	Bicarbonate
α-Ketoadipic aciduria	AR (probable)	Self-abusive	Phenylalanine α-Aminoadipic acid	α-Aminoadipic acid, αhydroxyadipate	?α-Ketoadipate dehydrogenase	None
Pyroglutamic aciduria* (5-oxoprolinuria)	AR	+ Hemolytic anemia 2+ to 3+ acidosis	5-Oxoproline Proline Tyrosine	5-Oxoproline	Glutathione synthetase	Cystamine (?)
Hyperglycinemia c̄ ketosis due to defect in isoleucine metabolism	Unknown	Ketonuria, thrombo-cytopenia, neutropenia, hyperammonemia	Glycine Threonine	Hyperglycinuria, butanone, hexanone	Unknown	Protein restriction
Glutaric Aciduria (Type I)	AR	Choreoathetosis + acidosis	Glutaric Glycine	Glutaric, glycine, β-OH-glutaric, glutaconic	Glutaryl-CoA-dehydrogenase	Protein restriction Riboflavin, 4-amino-3 (4-chlorophenyl)-butyric acid

* May present as a neonatal catastrophe.
\+ minimal elevation; 2+ moderate elevation; 3+ marked elevation; BCAA = branched-chain amino acids.

in propionic or methylmalonic acidemias (see following text). The major defect in isoleucine catabolism is deficiency of beta-ketothiolase (alpha-methylacetoacetyl CoA thiolase), which is the enzyme that catalyzes cleavage of alpha-methylacetoacetyl CoA to acetyl CoA and propionyl CoA. As a consequence of this deficiency, cleavage occurs instead of the CoA moiety, with formation of alpha-methylacetoacetic acid and alpha-butanone, which is the decarboxylation product of the acid. The clinical presentation widely varies, although most patients experience a significant metabolic ketoacidosis as the initial insult. This rapidly regresses with ordinary intravenous glucose and fluid therapy. Recurrence is minimized by dietary protein restriction and, if subsequent acidotic episodes are not severe and are promptly treated, the prognosis is good.

VALINE

Isolated defects in the valine catabolic pathway are reported as or more infrequently than those in the isoleucine pathway. Therefore, the known enzyme deficiencies will not be discussed, but they are summarized in Table 13.2.

Defects Involving More Than One Branched Chain Amino Acid

Within this category, it is appropriate to note once more that maple syrup urine disease represents the prototype defect. For extensive discussion of MSUD, refer to section 1 (Defects in Branched Chain Amino Acid Catabolism) of this chapter. The remaining disorders in this category are propionic acidemia and a specific form of methylmalonic acidemia; both involve valine and isoleucine (Figure 13.2). Neither of these are responsive to cofactor, either in vivo or in cell culture; thus, they are considered in this text separately from the vitamin-responsive disorders (see below).

Propionic acidemia results from a deficiency of the mitochondrial enzyme propionyl CoA carboxylase, which mediates conversion of propionyl CoA to methylmalonyl CoA during catabolism of valine, isoleucine, methionine, threonine, odd-chain length fatty acids, and cholesterol. Although this enzyme has a cofactor requirement for biotin, no cases that have responded to biotin administration have been reported thus far. This should lead the reader to correctly conclude that the clinical disorder results from an abnormal apoprotein, the activity of which cannot be boosted by increased cofactor availability. This apoprotein is composed of alpha and beta subunits, each one of which is coded for by a separate gene locus; each also is located on a separate chromosome. Thus, an abnormal apoprotein may result from an independent mutation at either locus, which creates the potential for mixed or compound heterozygotes.

Deficiency of the carboxylase activity results in accumulation of propionyl CoA behind the block. Because so many substrates normally contribute to the flux through this step, cellular coenzyme A deficiency might occur if cleavage of propionyl CoA to free propionic acid did not occur. However, because free propionate is toxic, this compound normally is conjugated within the mitochondrion to carnitine to form propionylcarnitine. This molecule then is transported into the cytosol and from there into the plasma for rapid clearance by the kidney. Thus, in the presence of normal carnitine stores, free propionic acid can be "buffered" by the cell, so that the major urinary excretion product that can be identified is propionylcarnitine. It may be worth mentioning that the enzyme in liver that is responsible for formation of acylglycine compounds and that contributes importantly to detoxification of isovaleric acid has such a low affinity for propionate that it makes no contribution to its disposal. Thus, whereas in isovaleric acidemia, the patient has the capacity to either conjugate with glycine or with carnitine, in propionic acidemia, only one of these options is available to the cell—carnitine.

As with most other organic acidemias, there are no unique features associated with the clinical presentation of propionic acidemia. The most common biochemical features include ketoacidosis, hyperglycinemia, and hyperammonemia. Although the basis for the acidosis is clear from the nature of the defect, the etiology of the ketosis remains unclear. Elevation of the glycine likely is a secondary phenomenon due to inhibition of the glycine cleavage enzyme by the free propionate. Increased ammonia derives from a secondary inhibition of the urea cycle, probably at the site of N-acetylglutamate synthetase. A feature of propionic acidemia that can have major clinical import is the development of bone marrow suppression, due

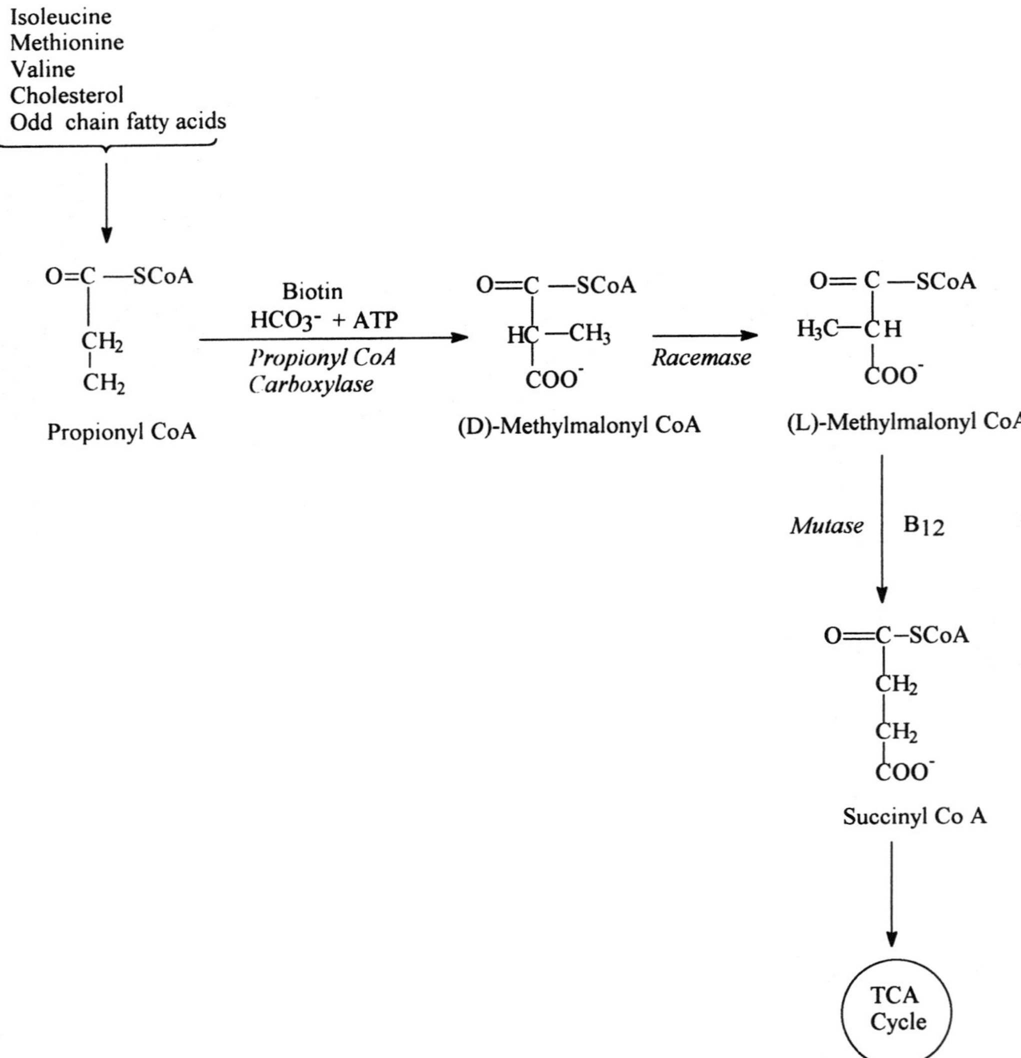

Figure 13.2. Catabolism of compounds resulting in propionic or methylmalonic acids. Formation of propionyl CoA is critical in utilization of many compounds for energy production. Further metabolism requires biotin-dependent carboxylation to form methylmalonyl CoA; inability to carry out this step results in the disorder propionic acidemia. In a B_{12}-dependent subsequent step, methylmalonyl CoA is converted to succinyl CoA; a defect at this point results in methylmalonic acidemia. Note that accumulation of CoA compounds results in cleavage of CoA and release of the corresponding free acid, accounting for many of the symptoms and signs.

to a direct toxic action of propionate on the marrow. The result is thrombocytopenia, leukopenia, and decreased red cell mass; the most devastating aspect of this complication is that marrow suppression renders the patient all the more susceptible to infection, in turn creating even more severe ketoacidosis.

The effective, acute management of propionic acidemia relies upon provision of large amounts of intravenous glucose to spare endogenous protein breakdown, thus addressing generation of propionate at the source. Bicarbonate administration will temporarily ameliorate the systemic acidosis. As soon as the patient is able to tolerate oral medication, it is advisable to provide L-carnitine to assist in conjugation of the propionate for renal excretion. Chronic management consists of close monitoring of dietary intake of methionine, valine, isoleucine, and threonine, administered as a supplement to a special formula totally deficient in these four essential amino acids. Provision of L-carnitine ensures a buffer mechanism for the cells, thus increasing the patient's tolerance for metabolic stress.

In view of the very wide clinical spectrum of this disorder, it is difficult to provide a definitive prognosis for any specific individual. It is, however, clear that in any affected child who had once developed severe ketoacidosis, the potential for significant morbidity and even death exists with any subsequent metabolic stress. Early attention to all clinical illness is imperative and requires close followup.

The disease known as methylmalonic acidemia represents a group of different molecular disorders, two of which are due to absent or extremely deficient methylmalonyl CoA mutase activity as a result of either extremely unstable apoprotein or drastically reduced affinity of apoprotein for cofactor (adenosylcobalamin). The biochemical lesion resulting from this enzymatic defect is at the point where propionyl CoA is converted to L-methylmalonyl CoA (Figure 13.2), with a racemization to D-methylmalonyl CoA as an intermediate; thus, the same nutritional substrates are involved in both diseases. As with other disorders in this category, clinical signs and symptoms are nonspecific. Diagnosis is readily approached by assessment of urinary methylmalonate, using a simple color test followed by gas-chromatographic study. Because the process of racemization is reversible, small amounts of beta-hydroxypropionate may be present, but the quantitative relationship will heavily favor methylmalonate. It is necessary to restrict dietary intake of the same substances interdicted in the case of propionic acidemia, and acute management also should follow the same general outline. One final comment is germane: Because it is not possible to clinically define which patient with methylmalonic aciduria will fail to respond to cofactor administration, all such patients should be treated with pharmacologic doses (1–2 mg) of cyanocobalamin on initial presentation and until such distinction conveniently can be made.

Vitamin-Dependent Diseases

Because catabolism of the branched chain amino acids involves complex enzyme proteins, several of which have cofactor dependence, there are many disorders described that represent abnormalities of conversion of vitamin to cofactor or faulty interaction of cofactor with apoprotein. Based upon present understanding of apoprotein conversion to holoenzyme by association with cofactor, it is clear that defects at this level can be a result of a multiplicity of possible abnormalities. Among these are normal apoprotein associated with abnormal conversion of vitamin to cofactor or the converse, abnormal enzyme-mediated linkage of apoprotein to cofactor, normal linkage with an abnormal active site on the apoprotein, etc. It is vital to understand that any given abnormal enzyme-cofactor combination, no matter in what molecular fashion the abnormality exists, will create a phenotypic picture that will not betray any clues as to the molecular cause. Stated in a different way, one phenotype may represent several different abnormalities at the same enzymatic locus. Consequently, treatment always should be directed at the entire spectrum of possible abnormalities, at least until further studies can be performed to clarify the underlying biochemical abnormality.

A cardinal example of the above situation is methylmalonic acidemia, which we already have discussed briefly under the previous category of disorders. Therein, we noted the need for acute treatment with cobalamin in the newly diagnosed patient, from which it can be inferred that methylmalonyl CoA mutase is dependent upon cobalamin for its normal activity. In fact, this enzyme is one of only two that have been conclusively demonstrated in mammals to have such a requirement. Thus, at the simplest level, it can be surmised that vitamin B_{12} deficiency deriving either from diet alone or from failure of normal intestinal absorption (as in pernicious anemia) can be a cause of methylmalonic aciduria. In such cases, the enzymatic block is created by a deficiency of B_{12} alone, with all of the other processes entirely intact and functional. Moreover, due to the nature of the problem, development of clinical symptoms would be expected to be slow, as indeed they are in pernicious anemia (see Chapter 18). It is correct to reason that in the case of all enzymatic reactions involving dietary vitamin sources of cofactor, deficiency of one or more of these sources will affect enzyme activity over time. Such nutritionally based disorders as beri-beri perfectly illustrate this principle.

Holocarboxylase synthetase (multiple carboxylase) deficiency is another member of this group of disorders. Clinical biochemical examination of an affected patient reveals evidence of impairment in at least three of the four known carboxylases, located in the pathways of leucine, propionate, and pyruvate metabolism (Figure 13.3). However, because it is extremely unlikely that three indepen-

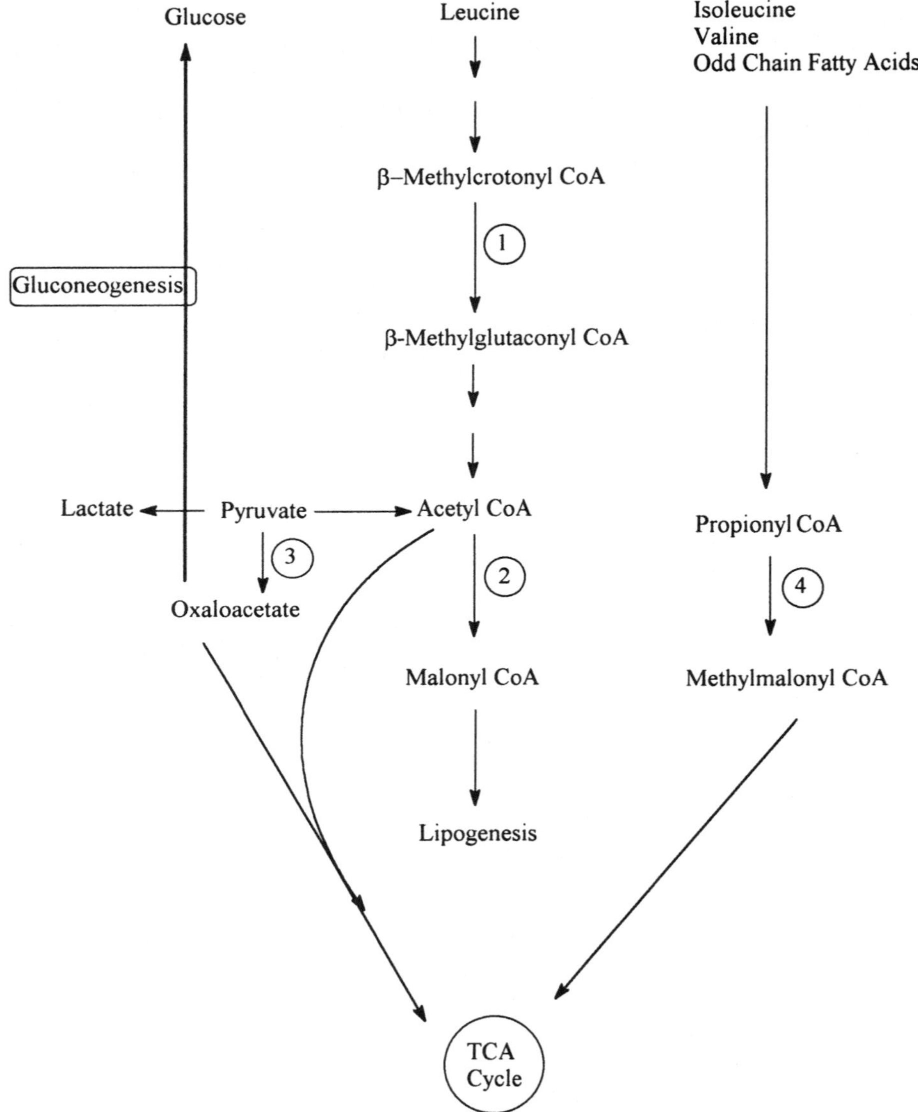

Figure 13.3. Pathways requiring biotin-dependent enzyme activity. Four enzymes are biotin-dependent. In each case, the biotin is attached covalently to the apoprotein through a lysine residue, which is a bond that requires a separate enzyme (holocarboxylase synthase) to establish. Thus, holocarboxylase synthase deficiency also is known as multiple carboxylase deficiency. 1 = β-methylcrotonyl carboxylase, 2 = acetyl CoA carboxylase, 3 = pyruvate carboxylase, 4 = propionyl CoA carboxylase. Enzymes 2 and 3 are critical regulatory points in fatty acid synthesis and gluconeogenesis, respectively.

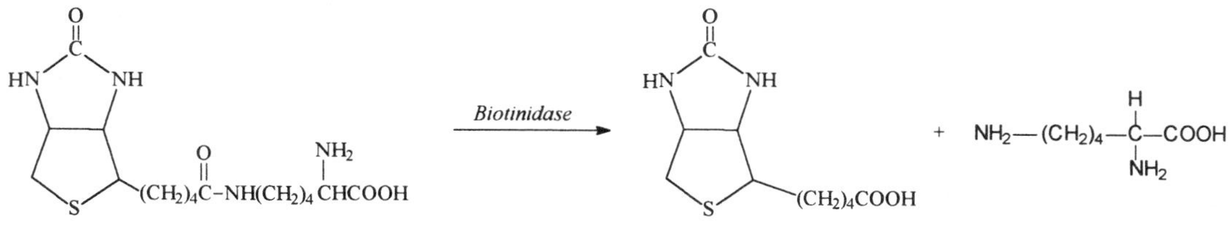

Figure 13.4. The biotin salvage reaction. As a holocarboxylase protein is degraded intracellularly, the biotin is released still bound to lysine in a compound known as biocytin. The latter form the substrate for the enzyme biotinidase, which cleaves this covalent bond, releasing free biotin. Deficiency of biotinidase is the basis for the juvenile-onset multiple carboxylase deficiency. The generally less abrupt onset of symptoms in biotinidase deficiency easily is explained as a consequence of a slowly evolving biotin deficiency due to inability to recycle. Thus, the affected individual has a higher dietary requirement than normal to maintain equilibrium.

dent genetic mutations would occur in an individual, it is more realistic to consider the possibility of a unifying factor common to all three enzymes. This unifying factor is the absolute requirement for the vitamin biotin to form a holoenzyme. Linkage between biotin and the respective apoenzyme is covalent, and formation of the covalent bond is mediated by the enzyme holocarboxylase synthetase. In the event of a deficiency of this synthase, such linkage cannot be established normally, rendering the apoenzymes inactive and resulting in a clinical picture consistent with deficiency of the carboxylase apoproteins. Long-term studies have demonstrated the efficacy of pharmacologic biotin therapy in affected individuals. In fact, prenatal therapy can be safely administered to pregnant women who are carrying an affected fetus.

As with other metabolic errors, holocarboxylase synthetase deficiency was initially thought to present as either an early infantile or a later juvenile disorder, depending upon the extent of enzyme deficiency and the environmental stresses. It is now recognized, however, that the two entities are distinct; the juvenile form is due to a deficiency of biotinidase (Figure 13.4). This enzyme is important in recycling endogenous biotin released from degraded holocarboxylases, so that when absent, biotin cannot be reclaimed and the affected individual develops an increasing degree of biotin deficiency. Eventually, the amounts of biotin present are insufficient to form holoenzymes from the newly synthesized apoproteins, so that the patient develops a biochemical picture entirely consistent with multiple carboxylase deficiency at an older age. Clearly, in this instance, supplemental biotin will entirely reverse this situation. Presently, newborn populations are conveniently screened for biotinidase deficiency in several states and many other countries.

DISORDERS OF FATTY ACID METABOLISM

Clinical and biochemical descriptions of disorders of fatty acid metabolism are relatively recent, although the process of beta-oxidation, by which fatty acids are catabolized, has been understood for many years (Figure 13.5). Although it has been suggested that the reason for this is that this pathway does not play a major role in energy generation in nonfasting states, it is at least as likely that the oversight was due to the unusual, late infantile presentation of most of these disorders. An additional difficulty is due to the absence of any abnormal organic acid intermediates during a state of health, thus making retrospective diagnosis impossible. As we have seen, this is not the case in other entities, such as isovaleric acidemia. In any case, interest in this group of disorders has burgeoned since 1972, when the first case of carnitine palmitoyl transferase deficiency was reported. A major stimulus for this awakening interest has been recognition of the clinical similarities between many of these disorders and Reye's syndrome.

Systemic Carnitine Deficiency

This disorder is elusive, inasmuch as many of the earlier reports were based on measurement of low serum carnitine levels in symptomatic patients and family members, with a somewhat hastily

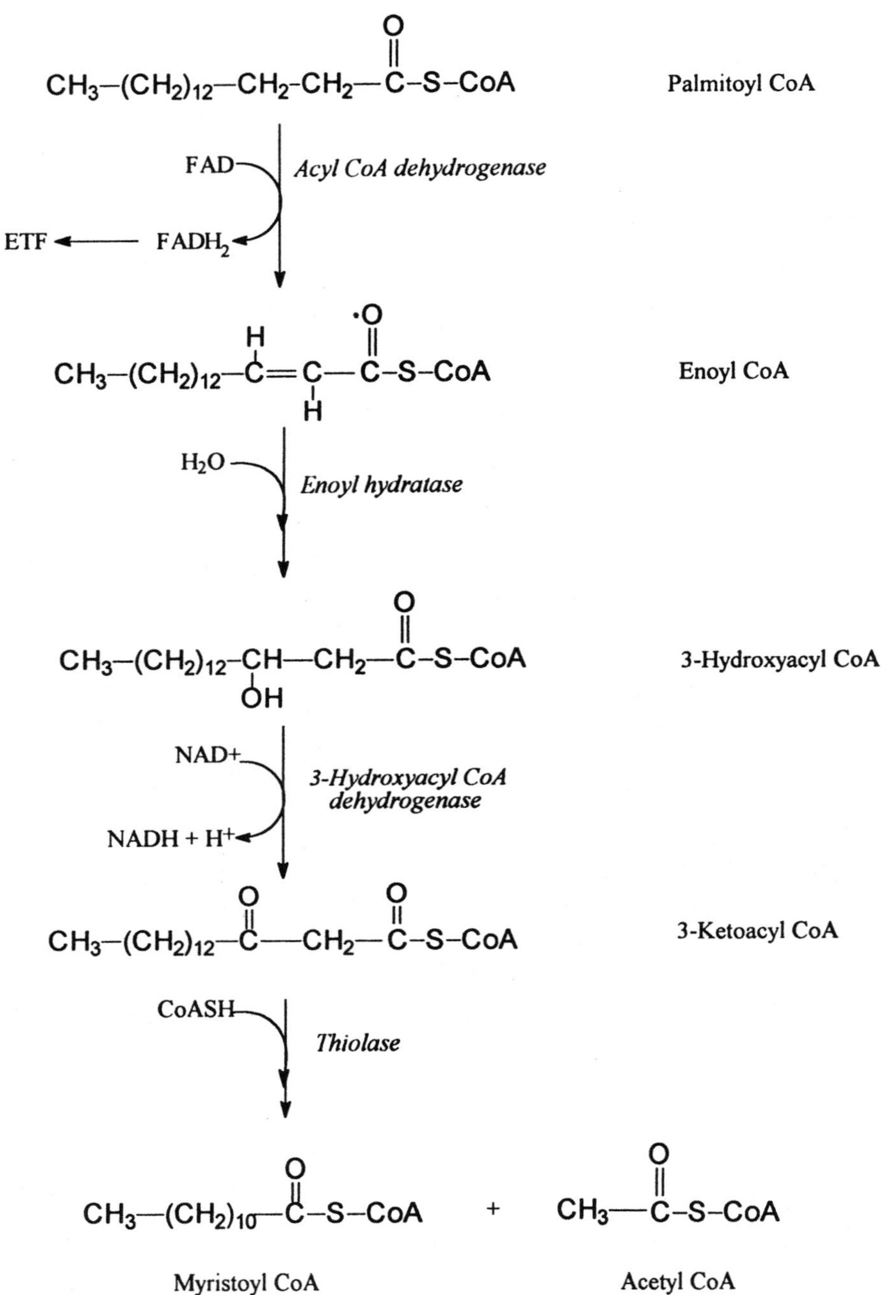

Figure 13.5. Fatty acid (β-) oxidation. Activation of the fatty acid to an acyl CoA compound is the entry step to the pathway, and consumes 1 mole of ATP per mole of fatty acid. Following activation, the acyl CoA compound is acted upon by one of three separate acyl CoA dehydrogenases (short-, medium-, or long-chain), depending upon the length of the carbon chain. Deficiency of medium-chain acyl CoA dehydrogenase is considered to be among the most common of inborn errors of metabolism. The 3-carbon then is hydroxylated (enoyl CoA hydratase) in preparation for the α-β bond cleavage. In the next step, the oxidation state of the 3-carbon is raised by action of 3-hydroxyacyl CoA dehydrogenase to render the α-β bond less stable and easier to cleave. In the final reaction, a second CoA moiety is introduced, and the α-β bond cleaved to form a two carbon acetyl CoA and a second acyl CoA two carbons shorter than the original in the thiolase mediated step. A single multienzyme complex carries out the last three steps, and specific defects in each function have been described or proposed.

drawn conclusion that there must be a genetically mediated reduced carnitine synthesis among these individuals. Subsequent studies have pointed to increased renal clearance of carnitine in such individuals, with no evidence for diminished synthesis found. Nonetheless, the combination of muscle weakness, hypotonia, poor fasting ketone response, and low serum carnitine still frequently is referred to as a "primary systemic carnitine deficiency." Because carnitine is endogenously synthesized by a relatively complex pathway, however, little doubt remains that a true case of impaired synthesis eventually will be uncovered.

Acyl CoA Dehydrogenase Deficiency

A defect in fatty acid catabolism at this locus (Figure 13.5) is the most commonly described disorder of beta-oxidation. Indeed, it is thought that it occurs as commonly as phenylketonuria (PKU) in the newborn population. Following entry of a fatty acyl-carnitine molecule into the mitochondrion, the fatty acyl moiety is reconjugated to coenzyme A and further metabolized, according to carbon chain length, by one of three dehydrogenases. The latter operate, with some degree of overlap, on C_4-C_6 (short chain), C_6-C_{12} (medium chain), and C_{12}-C_{18} (long chain) fatty acids. The general reaction carried out by these dehydrogenases is the removal of two hydrogens, creating a double bond between the alpha and beta carbons, and transfer of the electrons thus generated to electron transfer flavoprotein. These are eventually channeled into the electron transport chain, with the ultimate generation of ATP and water. Thus, an impairment in this process will result in an accumulation of fatty acylCoA intermediates of carbon chain lengths that correspond to the specificity of the defective dehydrogenase.

Of the three potential defects, deficiency of the medium chain acyl CoA dehydrogenase (MCAD) is the most common. As with many of the inborn errors of metabolism, there is a wide variation in clinical spectrum. During episodes of illness, however, prominent findings are hypoglycemia and hyperammonemia. In this regard, the disorder commonly is mistaken for Reye's syndrome; indeed, the majority of such cases may be MCAD deficiency. These clinical findings frequently are presaged by an episode of vomiting and lethargy. Although intercurrent illnesses of childhood are common causes of metabolic decompensation in a previously asymptomatic child with an inborn error, it is difficult to state with assurance that the initial precipitant is a viral gastroenteritis. This is because vomiting and lethargy may be caused by the encephalopathic action of the acyl compounds derived from the enzymatic deficiency, the acidosis that ensues, or the hyperammonemia that is a secondary consequence of deranged liver function, as well as by a viral illness. Major distinguishing features of this disorder, in contrast to the urea cycle disorders, are the hypoglycemia, the acidosis, and the relatively moderate level of hyperammonemia. Another peculiar feature of MCAD deficiency is that onset frequently occurs during late infancy; it often is misdiagnosed and does not reoccur until childhood. In the interim, the child has grown and developed normally.

This, of course, stresses the difficulty with diagnosis, which entirely relies upon laboratory detection of dicarboxylic acids and their glycine conjugates in the urine. One complication in this regard is that these can be extremely difficult to find in a convalescent patient; therefore, it is imperative that this disorder be considered as part of the differential at the initial presentation. Theoretically, treatment with carnitine would be logical to enhance mitochondrial formation of acyl-carnitine conjugates, as in other organic acid disorders. Reduction of the proportion of dietary fat and a compensatory increase in carbohydrate is equally logical, combined with a decreased overnight fasting interval. Early intervention with intravenous glucose is imperative to abort development of the full-blown clinical consequences.

The incidence of long- and short-chain acyl CoA dehydrogenase (LCAD and SCAD, respectively) deficiencies seem to be much lower than the MCAD defect. In both, the clinical spectrum varies widely and the diagnosis is difficult to make without a high degree of clinical suspicion. Interestingly, with SCAD deficiency, there appears to be a variant in which the defect is expressed only in muscle; such individuals may be less severely affected in infancy.

Multiple Acyl CoA Dehydrogenase Deficiency (Glutaric Aciduria II)

As discussed earlier, with multiple carboxylase deficiency, evidence of several enzymatic deficiencies in a single patient indicates the likelihood of a defect common to all affected enzymes. This is the case in this disorder, when deficiency of electron transfer factor adversely affects the function of all three acyl CoA dehydrogenases involved in β-oxidation. It also impairs function of other cellular dehydrogenases, including several in branched chain amino acid catabolism, glutaryl dehydrogenase, sarcosine dehydrogenase, dimethylglycine dehydrogenase, and 2-hydroxyglutarate dehydrogenase. Distinct from MCAD deficiency, for example, affected infants usually present early with a fulminant metabolic acidosis and subsequently die, although a later-onset variety is reported, albeit less frequently. No treatment is available, although use of methylene blue therapy has been reported, but with limited success. A major diagnostic feature of this disease is the presence of a "sweaty foot" odor, attributable to the excretion of free isovaleric acid. Hence, urinary organic acid profiling is imperative for the diagnosis to be accurate, even when an infant appears to be clinically affected with a well-delineated disorder. Although the newborn population is not screened for this disorder, it frequently has been reported and is thought to be one of the more common inborn errors.

The complexity of beta-oxidation itself, together with the multiple enzyme systems with specificity for various carbon chain lengths, virtually ensures that defects in many, if not all, of the other enzymes of the pathway eventually will be reported. Hence, although the study of the fatty acid catabolic pathway has been neglected in the past, it has gained the focus of intense interest and activity over the last 20 years. The difficulty for the clinician encountering affected patients lies in the nonspecificity of symptoms and the absence of effective screening modalities. This becomes an even more serious issue when one realizes that the estimated incidence approximates that of PKU. We hope that such methodologies become rapidly available.

SUGGESTED READINGS

Brass EP. Overview of coenzyme A metabolism and its role in cellular toxicity. Chem Biol Interact 1994;90: 203.

Chalmers RA. Disorders of organic acid metabolism. In: Holton JB, ed. The inherited metabolic diseases. 2nd ed. New York: Churchill Livingstone, 1994:115.

Fernandes J, Saudubray J-M, Tada K, eds. Inborn metabolic diseases. Heidelberg: Springer-Verlag, 1990.

Ozand PT, Gascon GG. Organic acidurias: a review. Parts 1 and 2. J Child Neurol 1991;6:196,288.

Rhead WJ. Inborn errors of fatty acid oxidation in man. Clin Biochem 1991;24L:319.

Scriver CR, Beaudet AL, Sly WS, Valle D, eds. The metabolic and molecular bases of inherited disease, 7th ed. New York: McGraw Hill, 1995. (See chapters 34, 40, 41, and 45).

Shih VE. Detection of hereditary metabolic disorders involving amino acids and organic acids. Clin Biochem 1991;24:301.

Shimizu N, Yamaguchi S, Orii T. A study of urinary metabolites in patients with dicarboxylic aciduria for differential diagnosis. Acta Paediatr Jpn 1994;36:139.

chapter **14**

Nutritional Disorders

The science of human nutrition traditionally has been ignored by the medical profession; basic scientists have increased our understanding of this area, but application of this knowledge has been designated to hospital dieticians and nutritionists. Although the practicality of this traditional arrangement is not an issue here, it must be remembered that a physician is obligated to attend to all aspects of a patient's medical care. Because the quality and quantity of an individual's dietary intake have an immense impact on overall health, especially in those who are ill, it is imperative for a physician to be acquainted with some general principles of human nutrition.

Perhaps the most straightforward way to illustrate the role of nutrition is to use an analogy: life, which is based on an almost unimaginable degree of order, implies constant resistance to disorder, embodied by the thermodynamic term entropy. Just as a stone can be rolled up a slope, be held in the same position on that slope, or roll down, the infant normally exists in a state of negative entropy, the healthy adult in zero entropy, and the dying person in positive entropy. Because entropy is measurable in calories, we may state that an infant takes in more calories than are given off as entropy (heat energy), whereas at the other end of the spectrum, the dying person consumes fewer calories than are released to maintain cellular organization. Thus, the caloric content of foods and how they are used by the organism are directly related to the fundamental thermodynamic principles that underlie life itself.

The equally important, qualitative aspects of nutrition are more subtle, and they are largely ignored in the clinical practice of medicine. Although everyone is familiar with the fact that the human body is composed of protein, fat, and carbohydrate, the nuances of the appropriate proportions of these dietary constituents in the diet receives little attention in clinical practice. Moreover, the role of trace elements in reaching and maintaining normal body composition frequently is neglected, except under circumstances when pathophysiologic states exist, such as hypomagnesemia. To add to the problem, although most physicians decry the popular folklore advocating the need for supplemental vitamins, few clinicians could detail for their patients the reasons why their resistance to self-treatment might be valid.

For the above reasons, it is our purpose to provide the basis for an understanding of the qualitative relationships involving various human nutritional components, and how these are related to human disease. We hope to give the reader enough insight to be able to apply nutritional biochemistry to the clinical practice of medicine.

QUANTITATIVE PRINCIPLES OF HUMAN NUTRITION

Let us return first to the analogy of a stone on a slope to best illustrate the role of quantitative nutritional concepts. According to simple laws of physics, if a stone is to ascend a slope, it must gain "potential" energy—the other aspect to this gain, of course, is the implication that some source must invest the energy, paying for this otherwise improbable event. If, conversely, the stone descends the slope, it loses potential energy in proportion to how far toward the base it rolls, in the process transforming the potential to "kinetic" energy. Some of this kinetic energy can be harnessed to perform work, or be given up as entropy, until the stone rests at a lower state of potential energy. In any event, perfect efficiency in harnessing the energy is not possible. The alternative to ascent or descent is maintenance of the stone's position at a constant point between top and bottom of the slope, which is clearly a situation that would require a constant input of energy to resist the tendency of the stone to roll to the bottom. Most healthy, young adult human beings generally exist in this state while asleep—to stay alive, they must use energy.

Thus, with the analogy between a stone poised in one location on a slope and a healthy adult human during sleep, we may use the concept of the basal metabolic rate, which is the rate at which energy must be consumed to satisfy those most fundamental cellular activities noted above to preserve a status quo existence at complete rest (ie, to keep the stone from rolling the remainder of the distance down the slope). Although no external work is being performed, energy nonetheless must be expended to support muscular movements of breathing, myocardial contractions, and maintenance of muscle tone and overall metabolic homeostasis. The last expenditure predominantly involves the maintenance of transmembrane ionic potentials. More than 90% of the oxygen consumed by cells involved in these processes is reduced to water via the mitochondrial electron transport system. Practically, this energy expenditure is expressed as milliliters of O_2 (equivalent to kilocalories) per minute consumed per square meter surface area (or per kilogram lean body mass). It also should be apparent that illness will increase the slope, thus imposing additional energy demands on the individual to maintain the status quo. Because of this reason, superimposed illness causes acute decompensation in patients with chronic nutritional deprivation or inborn errors of metabolism. Such patients, whose metabolic needs have increased, cannot meet this increased metabolic demand, either because of lack of fuel or because of inherent or acquired impairment in the response mechanisms. Thus, the interplay between maintenance of internal homeostasis and environmental stress has immediate relevance to overall nutritional status. Clearly, inadequate energy supply will impact adversely on this balance.

Several factors, including infection, fever, pregnancy, lactation, exposure to cold, and hyperthyroidism, increase basal energy expenditure. A frequently overlooked issue is that growth of the organism is analogous to pushing the stone further up the slope, making greater energy expenditure an essential feature of accretion of tissue. Recall that amino acids used in protein synthesis must be converted to an active intermediate (AA-AMP), a process that requires ATP. To the extent that carbohydrate and lipid can be used to supply this ATP, protein is spared from subserving an energy-generating role. For example, if the basic caloric needs of an infant sleeping approximately 16 of every 24 hours, but undergoing an awesome rate of growth, are calculated, it is not surprising to find that these requirements are about 150% greater (in Kcal/kilogram body weight/day) than those of a normally active young adult. Thus, caloric (energy) value of the infant's diet is critical; this point sometimes is obscured by the small volume of intake relative to the adult.

QUALITATIVE PRINCIPLES OF HUMAN NUTRITION

Although considerably more complex than the quantitative aspects of nutrition, how the human organism interconverts and utilizes various nutritional components is a more challenging and interesting area of study. A moment's thought will convince the reader that, depending upon the nature of the diet, an individual can be quite strong and either lean or obese, or very weak and either lean or obese. What are the reasons for these variations? Naturally, exercise has a role to play, but it cannot be overemphasized that no amount of exercise will increase muscle mass in the absence of adequate raw material for muscle protein synthesis. In the same manner, an individual consuming more than sufficient protein to meet caloric needs will not build muscle tissue but will, instead, become obese. Thus, more is involved in achieving the stature of a Greek god than adequate protein and calories. All too often, excess calories eventually will become fat because of the capacity of the human body to interconvert carbohydrate, lipid, and amino acids in keeping with metabolic needs.

Role of Essential Nutrients

Because dietary protein cannot be utilized completely and because protein sources vary in the availability of the amino acids they provide, it is important to consume high-quality proteins or a mixture of food sources to provide a balance of amino acids. Moreover, how much protein one needs to ingest is modified by caloric intake because the more calories ingested, the less diversion of amino acids will occur to generate energy.

Recall that of the 21 naturally occurring amino acids, 10 are considered essential, meaning that they cannot be produced from endogenous substrates and, therefore, must be supplied by dietary sources. The immediate implication of this is the need for adequate dietary protein intake to provide these 10 essential amino acids. There also is a more subtle implication: each of the 10 must be supplied in adequate amounts because a deficiency of even one essential amino acid will render the other nine inadequate as far as the organism is concerned. Therefore, the quality of dietary protein is exceedingly important. The reader may ask, "Why does a deficiency of one have so much impact?" Consider that the average body protein is composed of 21 amino acids in specific proportions, synthesized by orderly and sequential linkage each to the next. If one of these members of the chain is absent, the linkage process is interrupted and the complete protein can not be synthesized. Consequently, incomplete protein is instead consumed to make ATP, rendering the organism protein deficient.

A glance at a photograph of a concentration camp survivor is sufficient to convince anyone that both fat and body protein can be consumed for energy to sustain essential life processes. What, if any, process determines which is consumed and how rapidly? The answer lies in the ratio of protein/nonprotein calories consumed in the diet. If the diet contains sufficient amounts of nonprotein (carbohydrate, fat) calories to supply the energy needs of the body, the protein component of the diet will be left free for protein synthetic requirements. If, conversely, the diet consists exclusively of protein, energy needs will be met by consumption of all or a part of the protein-based calories. Placed within the context of current weight-reduction diet fads, it should be apparent that the ideal diet maintains adequate protein intake while reducing nonprotein calories to the amount required for basic needs. In such a situation, additional energy requirements will be met by catabolism of fat stores, with resulting weight loss. Any other approach either will have little effect or will compromise body protein synthesis.

Essential Fatty Acids

Apart from essential protein intake, there are other mandatory requirements, which include essential fatty acids, minerals, trace elements, and, of course, certain vitamins. Nature has endowed various foodstuffs with adequate amounts of these components; therefore, if the diet is varied and well balanced, there is no need for additional supplementation. Although we will discuss each of these components in turn, the subject of essential fatty acids deserves special mention. It is a common oversight to think that fat has no other role than to serve as an energy source in metabolism. At the same time, it is self-evident that body fat can be synthesized, leading to the implicit assumption that fat is a sign of overeating and thus inherently "bad." In fact, lipid has a major role in the structure of all cell membranes, thus subserving a critical function in the life of the cell. However, as discussed earlier with regard to amino acids, the human organism lacks mechanisms to accomplish certain specific synthetic processes, despite the fact that many endogenous lipid molecules are synthesized de novo from acetylCoA. A specific limitation is related to introduction of double bonds into the growing fatty acid chain; the general rule is that any fatty acid with fewer than seven carbon atoms beyond the last double bond must be acquired from dietary plant sources, because animals lack an enzyme system by which to desaturate this area of the molecule. Thus, such fatty acids are considered essential components of the diet; inadequate intake has some significant clinical consequences, including seborrheic rashes, alopecia, and failure to thrive. Because the unsaturated fatty acids have vitally important structural roles in membrane lipid composition, it is likely that cell membrane functions, particularly those of neural cells, might be adversely affected by deficiency. Another important role for polyunsaturated fatty acids is as precursors to the eicosanoid class of signal molecules, which includes the leukotrienes, prostaglandins, and thromboxanes.

With this brief discussion of the general qualitative principles of human nutrition, we are ready to consider specific disorders. Various aspects of this subject, including vitamin and trace metal intake, will be addressed in relation to deficiency states; however, remember that general quantitative nutritional deficiencies, as in protein calorie malnutrition, or aberrant dietary habits also may involve vitamins and trace elements.

STARVATION AND PROTEIN CALORIE MALNUTRITION

We define starvation as a state in which intake is of normal composition but in amounts insufficient to sustain the processes that maintain homeostasis. This state can be translated into suboptimal caloric intake with consequent weight loss, which is a common technique dieting Americans use. Although most people see the beneficial aspects of weight loss as a justification for adhering to such a regimen, it is vital to remember that if the total diet is simply decreased by 50% in calories, all components including vitamins and minerals are proportionately diminished. Thus, with caloric deficiency, there is an increasing degree of vitamin and trace element deficiency. This is vividly illustrated by the well-known association of rickets with starvation in young children.

An interesting example of the effect of starvation on protein metabolism is afforded by the inherited disorder phenylketonuria (PKU) (see Chapter 12). In this disorder, elevated phenylalanine levels in blood are reduced by restriction of dietary phenylalanine intake, whereas all other nutritional components are permitted to vary according to the child's appetite. Thus, except for restriction of phenylalanine, protein intake is otherwise comparable to that of any child of the same age. If, however, protein intake is restricted in the child with PKU, even with the same daily quantity of phenylalanine as before, blood phenylalanine will increase. Of course, this is due to the body's inability to continue endogenous protein synthesis at a normal rate when exogenous protein sources of essential amino acids become rate-limiting. The increased blood phenylalanine that results is the biochemical marker for this state because, in PKU, this amino acid cannot be further metabolized to tyrosine. Naturally, in the genetically normal child, the blood phenylalanine level would not increase under the same circumstances because any excess would be converted into tyrosine and further metabolized for energy. Nonetheless, the example of PKU illustrates how the human body seeks to exploit every available energy source under adverse circumstances.

The natural consequence of inadequate intake of all dietary components to meet ongoing needs is the eventual development of a deficiency state. It should be clear that, although the human body achieves a degree of efficiency in fuel usage vastly higher than that of the best man-made machine, no system is perfectly efficient, thus making losses inevitable. For example, the renal tubule is approximately 95% efficient in reabsorption of amino acids from the glomerular filtrate; thus, under any conditions, there is an inevitable 5% loss in urine. Moreover, all molecules of the human body turn over, albeit at a relatively slow rate, with less than 100% efficient reutilization of their basic components in replacement synthesis. To meet such needs, the organism begins to dismantle endogenous, less critical molecules and to divert the component parts into reconstructing vital materials that have broken down. This results in a process of "autodigestion," which, coupled with the combined losses through the kidney and combustion for basic energy needs, leads to the clinically perceived weight loss and eventual cachexia.

Hormonal Response to Prolonged Fasting and Starvation

Underlying the clinical findings in starvation are the humoral regulatory effects of the hypothalamic-pituitary axis, coupled with the glucose counter-regulatory hormones, insulin and glucagon. Because certain tissues, predominantly the red cell mass and brain, have an absolute dependency on glucose for metabolic fuel, a steady supply of glucose is required for survival, even during complete fasting. Thus, humoral responses are directed at preserving body protein and (within that one constraint) providing glucose for dependent tissues, whereas other tissues are converted to alternate fuel consumption.

At the initiation of fasting, glucose supplies are maintained by glycogenolysis and gluconeogenesis, prompted by a gradual decline in circulating insulin levels. As this process continues, the decrease in insulin and increase in glucagon simultaneously slow glucose catabolism by nondependent tissues and enhance release of fatty acids from adipose tissue stores. Production of ketone bodies from these fatty acids in the liver leads to the state of "fasting ketosis," and enhances use of these ketones as metabolic fuel by those tissues equipped to do so. Primary examples of organs that efficiently utilize ketones are cardiac muscle and brain, thus ensuring maintenance of critical functions. An additional effect of decreasing insulin levels is that amino acid uptake by peripheral tissues is slowed, thus making the carbon skeletons available for gluconeogenesis. This, however, is a double-edged sword because a simultaneous decrease in muscle protein synthesis results from limited supply, and amino acids are released from preexisting muscle protein as the latter undergoes normal turnover. The net result of all of this is that the weight loss that occurs secondary to starvation over a prolonged period is a consequence not only of fat catabolism but of muscle protein loss as well.

It should not be construed, however, that the losses of critical protein stores proceeds in an entirely haphazard or unrestricted fashion. As in all forms of stress undergone by the human organism, additional protective mechanisms come into play. Through central nervous system control via the hypothalamus, starvation elicits hypersecretion of growth hormone that exerts an anabolic effect on cellular protein metabolism, thus tending to counteract the catabolic demands of starvation. Because conservation of proteolytically released amino acids for synthesis of critical enzymes is at least as imperative as conversion to glucose, there must be a way that urea cycle activity is controlled. However, although the actions of glucagon and epinephrine on proteolysis have been established, the mechanisms controlling urea production in starvation are poorly understood. In this regard, keep in mind that amino acids can be interconverted by transfer of the amino group to an alpha-keto acid analogue with no net change in total ammonia. However, generation of urea from the same amino group implies a net loss of an amino acid from the body pool. Thus, the 10-fold decrease in urea excretion during prolonged fasting is impressive evidence of increased amino acid conservation, rather than consumption. Moreover, such a dramatic decrease in urea production implies very tight regulatory control of nitrogen metabolism, which is consistent with the ability of the adult human to survive a 2-month starvation period.

Thus, when confronted with severe nutritional deficits, the human body responds in an orderly fashion to protect itself from essential nutrient losses. The apathy and lack of physical activity associated with prolonged starvation also may be viewed as part of this protection because this diminishes the need for caloric expenditure for nonessential purposes. Undoubtedly, the efficiency of these responses to starvation has evolved to protect survival of the human species living under vastly different conditions from what most readers living in industrialized nations have experienced. Nonetheless, unfortunately, there are tens of millions of people in the world today who continue to experience chronic nutritional deprivation, if not outright starvation.

Kwashiorkor

Kwashiorkor is a state of chronic semistarvation in which there is a relatively normal caloric intake with inadequate protein to meet ongoing needs. Because satisfaction of hunger depends upon a combination of food volume and caloric value, in regions of the world where readily available foods are carbohydrate-rich and protein poor, kwashiorkor is relatively common.

Because insulin is a chief regulatory mechanism in initiating the body's response to starvation, it should be apparent that a proportionally high carbohydrate intake will enhance insulin secretion. In a real sense, this "confuses" the normal response mechanisms, leading to enhanced fatty acid synthesis and diminished amino acid release from muscle, despite the deficits of both in the diet. The reduction in circulating amino acids causes decreased hepatic albumin synthesis and consequent edema, which may be severe in such patients. The combination of retention of body fat and edema gives the false impression of a relatively good state of nutrition in contrast to the starved or marasmic individual (Table 14.1). The increased fatty acid synthesis by the liver results in fatty infiltration and hepatomegaly. In addition, because of the reduced amino acid release, there

Table 14.1. Comparison of Marasmus and Kwashiorkor

	MARASMUS	KWASHIORKOR
Dietary etiology	Partial nutritional deprivation of all components in normal proportion	Diminished protein intake with relatively normal caloric increment
Duration prior to clinical presentation	Months to years, dependent on degree of deprivation	Weeks to months, dependent upon relative protein intake and superimposed stress (infection)
Clinical features	↓ Growth rate (both weight and height), ↓ physical activity, apathy, weight/height for age <80% of normal, sunken cheeks, monkey-like facies, hair sparse and brittle, nails slow in growth, hypoglycemia, hypothermia	Appear fairly well-nourished, irritable, anorectic, hepatomegaly with fatty infiltration, mild-severe edema, hyperkeratotic skin lesions with superficial ulceration, petechiae, ecchymosis, hair loss, rapid decompensation in face of infection
Laboratory findings	Hb 8-10 g/dl, serum IgD 4.0 ± 1.1 mg/dl, serum albumin >2.8 g/dl, total WBC normal to mildly elevated	Hb <8 g/dl, serum IgD 13.5 ± 4.3 mg/dl, serum albumin <2.8 g/dl, absolute lymphocytopenia, anergic response
Clinical course	Ravenous appetite, frequent constipation, relatively resistant to intercurrent infection, rickets, terminal signs are depression of vital signs, hypoglycemia, hypothermia	Anorectic, diarrhea common, diminished ability to resist infection, rapid decompensation and death due to secondary infection
Therapy and mortality	Small, frequent feedings, initially meeting only maintenance requirements and gradually in concentration and volume; mortality generally low	Reintroduction of protein must be cautious, overload may result in cardiac failure; mortality generally is high

is impairment of immunoprotein synthesis and a resulting decreased resistance to infection. The latter often causes these patients to suddenly succumb to overwhelming bacterial infection, in contrast to the marasmic patient who maintains a relatively normal level of resistance.

Complications of Refeeding

Although it may seem obvious that refeeding patients who are chronically starved is good, one must proceed with caution. With refeeding, catabolism gives way to anabolism with uptake of K^+, Mg^{++}, and phosphorus into the cell. If the pace of refeeding proceeds too rapidly, hypokalemia may ensue with the risk of severe arrhythmias. Diarrhea may be another complication because the gastrointestinal tract mucosa has been attenuated with loss of disaccharidase activity. Finally, ingestion of water and production of metabolic water can tax the contractility of the heart of such patients, precipitating congestive heart failure.

OBESITY

Obesity is widespread in the industrialized world, carrying with it an increased risk for noninsulin-dependent diabetes mellitus, hypertension, cardiovascular disease, gallbladder disease, and sex steroid responsive cancers. Due to the progression of insight in this area of nutritional biochemistry, it has become increasingly evident that obesity cannot be attributed to a lack of will on the part of the overweight subject. This is not to suggest that caloric intake does not exceed caloric expenditure, but it is now clear that there are multigenic, psychologic, and metabolic factors that also influence the tendency to gain weight and the ease with which pounds can be shed.

One of the most interesting psychologic factors in obesity is the persistent underestimate of how much food obese subjects claim they eat versus how much they actually eat. If one adds to this the preference many in the Western Hemisphere have for a high fat diet, it is easy to see how someone can ingest a significant number of calories as fat. It has been speculated that this preference for fatty foods may be genetic. After all, from the perspective of survival during famine, obesity has considerable adaptive value.

Weigle has reviewed evidence in support of the view that an as yet unidentified hormone responds to the total body fat to maintain adipose tissue stores fairly constant. According to this view, increased total body fat prompts secretion of this hormone, which contributes to a feeling of satiety. If this is true, then effective and safe pharmacologic therapy for some forms of obesity may be feasible.

Childhood obesity is more likely to be associated with an increase in the number of fat cells (hyperplasia). Obesity beginning later in life generally results in an increase in size of fat cells (hypertrophy). Clinically, obesity on a hyperplastic basis is much more resistant to treatment. The reason for this is not clear; but, once these cells are formed, their number remains constant, even if their size diminishes. Metabolic differences among individuals may arise because, in some individuals, it takes fewer calories to maintain body temperature and carry out intermediary metabolism in general. Recent evidence bolsters the view that the body adjusts metabolic rates downward to maintain the body weight near its usual level when the individual attempts to shed calories.

This does not mean that the laws of thermodynamics are suspended in such individuals. From a practical point of view, if calories are restricted and energy expenditure is augmented, especially through a regular exercise program, anyone should be able to lose weight. But because obese individuals have very low exercise tolerance, increased physical activity usually is not prominent in their attempts at losing weight. At any rate, the problem is consolidating the loss of weight, rather than losing it in the first place. To begin, many individuals go on "crash" diets of limited palatability and do lose weight. At that point, they consider themselves "home free" and revert to their earlier dietary habits with predictable results. Perhaps the most important concept clinically in the management of obesity is that the overweight individual has to change eating habits for the rest of his or her life.

As noted above, if the individual adopts a diet of fewer than 1100 calories to achieve weight loss, it will be necessary to supplement the diet with vitamins and minerals because it will be deficient in those constituents. Exercise can benefit overall health, but it can be disheartening for overweight people to learn that 1 lb = 3500 kcal and that only high intensity exercise burns calories rapidly. Certainly, more modest exercise does contribute to weight loss, but the individual must be prepared to maintain a regular exercise program for months, if not for life, to make those burned calories count.

ROLE OF VITAMINS IN NUTRITION

Vitamins are organic compounds that are found in the diet. Some (vitamin A, niacin) can be endogenously synthesized, but such synthesis will not meet the body's requirement; therefore, supplementation in the diet is necessary. Unlike dietary carbohydrates, fats, and proteins, which subserve energy and structural needs, vitamins do not serve as energy sources or cellular building blocks. Rather, they function largely as cofactors for enzymes, some serving as cosubstrates whereas others are actually structural elements combining with enzyme protein molecules to form "holoenzymes." This implies that until the holoenzyme forms, the enzyme protein alone either would be totally inactive or substantially deficient in activity, as is indeed the case. It is important, however, to understand that not all enzyme proteins require formation of a holoenzyme to perform their functions. Moreover, it is equally important to remember that native vitamins do not participate in formation of holoenzymes, but must first be metabolized to an "active" form. With some vitamins, such as thiamine, this implies chemical modification of the molecule (eg, thiamine pyrophosphate); with others, such as biotin, covalent bonding occurs by a separate enzyme between the inactive enzyme protein and the vitamin. Activated vitamins usually are termed "cofactors" to distinguish them from the native dietary forms. Hence, enzymes that require vitamins to form holoenzymes are known as "cofactor-dependent."

Another important factor in adequate vitamin supply is appropriate transport from the gut lumen to the interior of the cell. An instructive clinical example of an interruption in this process is the disease called pernicious anemia. Pernicious anemia results from dysfunction of all vitamin B_{12}-requiring metabolic pathways due to lack of B_{12} supply when there is normal dietary B_{12} intake. Large oral doses of supplementary B_{12} do little to ameliorate the disease, whereas small intramuscular B_{12} doses restore the individual to normal health. The basic defect lies in failure to transport dietary B_{12} across the gut mucosa, which is a vital first step in appropriate nutritional balance of any component. Vitamins also must be transported by the blood from the gut to cells, across cell membranes, transported within the cell, and enzymatically activated or bound or both to the appropriate enzyme protein. Hence, the mechanism of formation of a cofactor in its final form is a complex process, with the potential for interruption at many steps. Failure to form normal amounts of activated cofactor, if prolonged for any reason, will cause a clinical picture of deficiency specific to the vitamin in question. Elaboration of the actual biochemical defect, however, requires painstaking investigation. At the same time, knowledge of the defect often is essential to the design of effective therapy, as in various forms of methylmalonic acidemia and cofactor-deficiency PKU. With humans, vitamins, for the most part, are not endogenously synthesized; therefore, dietary intake is the sole source of supply. Because the middle-class in America generally is over-nourished, it is probably fair to state that the vitamin supplements used "willy-nilly" by this group of people are an example of conspicuous consumption and likely doing more harm than good.

However, vitamin deficiencies often are discussed in books as if each one occurred in isolation; in reality, a diet deficient in one vitamin (especially the B vitamins) is likely to be impoverished of several. Hence, it is inappropriate to attribute clinical manifestations to one vitamin without considering whether the diet is sufficiently poor to implicate several vitamin deficiencies. Vitamin deficiencies are a concern especially in the elderly, in whom intake of food may be less than optimal.

Patients suffering from malabsorption, alcoholism, or food fadism and patients undergoing total parenteral nutrition (TPN), hemodialysis, or treatment with drugs that interfere with vitamin absorption or action are most likely to experience deficiency of multiple vitamins. Physicians must be aware of the possibility of deficiencies of micronutrients in such individuals.

ROLE OF TRACE ELEMENTS IN NUTRITION

The role of trace elements in human nutrition has assumed an increasingly important position as ecological awareness has grown in the world. This provides the best example of how the biologic integrity of the human race depends upon sound environmental policies. Because the first biologic forms evolved in the oceans, it is not surprising that these organisms found ways to use many of the elements contained in the soil that constantly eroded into the oceans. Accordingly, as life forms evolved onto land and began to establish a food-chain, these elements continued to play vital roles in biologic systems. At a biochemical level, the trace elements chromium, copper, cobalt, manganese, molybdenum, selenium, and zinc interact with enzyme proteins (Table 14.2). The multivalent properties of these trace metals serve to add stability to the polyanionic protein molecule, which thus enhances reactivity and increases biologic half-life. The metal may participate in formation of the active site or may help to stabilize the higher order structure necessary for enzymatic activity (see Chapter 1). Because humans are omnivorous, intake of these metals from both plants, which remove them from soil, and animals, which gain them from plants, is enhanced. Hence, depletion or chemical modification of these trace elements by soil pollutants pose serious threats to both plant and animal life at the most fundamental level of life—the enzyme.

The average dietary intake of the trace metals is small, in a range comparable to that of the vitamins, implying that deficiencies can occur with equal rapidity in both cases. However, vitamin deficiencies are better characterized and, therefore, are more likely to be recognized clinically. Nonetheless, we are steadily becoming more aware of the fact that a trace metal deficit may underlie a recognizable dietary vitamin deficiency. Further work in this area may better define the clinical ramifications of deficiencies of the trace elements. Table 14.3 lists the major clinical abnormalities associated with various trace elements.

The similarity between vitamins and trace metals in requiring direct interaction with protein to exert biologic effects extends beyond this to an overall similarity in metabolism. At least two trace metals have specific intestinal transport carriers, as the disease acrodermatitis enteropathica illustrates for zinc and primary hypomagnesemia illustrates for magnesium. Thus far, no specific defects in intestinal uptake of the other trace metals have

Table 14.2. Biologic Roles of Trace Metals

TRACE ELEMENT	ASSOCIATED MOLECULE OR ENZYME	FUNCTIONS
Copper	Ceruloplasmin	(a) Oxidation of $Fe^{2+} \rightarrow Fe^{3+}$ (ferroxidase) (b) Copper transport in blood (c) Oxidation of phenols (phenoloxidase)
	Tyrosinase	(a) Hydroxylation of tyrosine → DOPA (b) Oxidation of DOPA → quinone (ending in melanin)
	Lysyl oxidase	Production of allysine in collagen formation: $HC{-}(CH_2)_3{-}C{-}NH_2 + O_2 + H_2O \rightarrow$ $HC{-}(CH_2)_3{-}C{=}O + NH_3 + H_2O_2$
	Amine oxidase	Oxidation of lysine $\epsilon{-}NH_2$ groups: $R{-}CH_2{-}NH_2 + O_2 \rightarrow R{-}C{=}O + H_2O_2 + NH_3$
	Dopamine β-hydroxylase	Conversion of dopamine → norepinephrine
	Uricase	Oxidation of uric acid → allantoin
	Mitochondrocuprein	Found in liver lysosomes, may be sequestered storage form of cuprothionein
	Diamine oxidase Spermine oxidase Benzylamine oxidase	Involved in establishment of cross-links in elastic and collagenous tissue
	Cytochrome c oxidase (also contains heme)	Catalyzes transfer of electrons: reduced cytochrome c + $O_2 \rightarrow$ oxidized cytochrome c + $H_2O + O^-$
	Superoxide dismutase (also contains zinc)	Catalyzes conversion of free radical: $O_2^- + O_2^- + 2H^+ \rightarrow O_2 + H_2O_2$
Zinc	Carbonic anhydrase	Catalyzes formation of bicarbonate: $CO_2 + H_2O \rightleftharpoons H_2CO_3 \rightleftharpoons H^+ + HCO_3^-$
	Lactate dehydrogenase	Conversion of pyruvate↔ lactate
	Alkaline phosphatase	Nonspecific hydrolysis of phosphate esters: $R{-}O{-}\overset{O}{\overset{\|}{\underset{OH}{\underset{\vert}{P}}}}{-}OH + H_2O \rightleftharpoons ROH + HO{-}\overset{O}{\overset{\|}{\underset{OH}{\underset{\vert}{P}}}}{-}OH$
	Carboxypeptidase A and B	Cleavage of C-terminal peptide bond
	Alcohol dehydrogenase	NAD-dependent oxidation of alcohol: $R\overset{H}{\overset{\vert}{\underset{H}{\underset{\vert}{C}}}}{-}OH + NAD^+ + O_2 \rightarrow R\overset{O}{\overset{\|}{C}}{-}OH + NADH + H^+$
	Leucine aminopeptidase	Cleavage of N-terminal leucine from peptides
	L-Aminolevulinate dehydrogenase	Condensation of 2-aminolevulinates to form porphobilinogen
	Glutamate dehydrogenase	Ammonia detoxification
	Retinene reductase	Conversion of retinol → retinaldehyde
	Aldolase	Cleavage of fructose-1-phosphate → glyceraldehyde and dihydroxyacetone phosphate
	Malate dehydrogenase	Oxidation of malate → oxaloacetate in Krebs cycle
	Pyridoxal phosphokinase	Phosphorylation of dietary pyridoxine
	RNA polymerase DNA polymerase Reverse transcriptase Thymidine kinase	Replication and transcription of genetic code
	Superoxide dismutase (see Copper)	

(continued)

Table 14.2. *(continued)*

TRACE ELEMENT	ASSOCIATED MOLECULE OR ENZYME	FUNCTIONS
Manganese	Pyruvate carboxylase	Conversion of pyruvate → oxaloacetate
	Pyruvate kinase	Removal of phosphate from PEP and transfer to ADP
	PEP carboxykinase	Conversion of oxaloacetate → PEP
	Creatine kinase	Transfer of phosphate from ATP → creatine
	Adenylate kinase	Conversion of 2ADP → ATP + AMP
	Enolase	Conversion of 2-phosphoglycerate → PEP
	Histidase	Conversion of histidine → urocanate
	Acetyl CoA carboxylase	Conversion of acetyl CoA → malonyl CoA
	Palmitate-synthesizing system	Synthesis of palmitate from acetyl CoA
	N-Acetylgalactosamine transferase	Transfer of *N*-acetylgalactosamine from UDP to glycolipid
	Galactose transferase	Transfer of galactose from UDP to glycolipid
	Serine hydroxymethyl transferase	Conversion of serine → glycine
	Glycylglycine dipeptidase	Cleavage of Gly-Gly peptide bond → 2 Gly
	NADP-specific isocitrate dehydrogenase	Production of reducing equivalents: Isocitrate + NADP ⇌ NADPH + H^+ + oxalosuccinate ⇌ αKG
	Phosphatidylinositol kinase	Synthesis of phosphatidylinositol: CDP-diacylglycerol + inositol → phosphatidy l-inositol + CMP
	6-Phosphogluconate dehydrogenase	Decarboxylation of 6-phosphogluconate to form CO_2 + D-ribulose-5-phosphate
Magnesium	Acyl CoA synthetase	Conversion of fatty acid → fatty acid CoA
	Argininosuccinate synthetase	Conversion of citrulline and aspartate to form ASA (urea cycle)
	Kinases (in glycolysis)	Phosphate group transfer reactions
	Mevalonate kinase	
	Phosphomevalonate kinase	
	Pyrophosphomevalonate kinase	De novo cholesterol synthesis from acetyl CoA
	Sialyl transferase	Transfer of *N*-acetylneuraminic acid from CMP to lactosylceramide
	Glutamine synthetase	Conversion of glutamate + NH_3 + ATP → glutamine + ADP + P_i
	γ-Glutamylcysteine synthetase	First step in glutathione synthesis
	Actomyosin ATPase	Muscle contraction
	5-Oxoprolinase	Conversion 5-oxoproline → glutamate in γ-glutamyl cycle
	Propionyl-CoA carboxylase	Carboxylation of propionyl-CoA → methylmalonyl CoA
	Transketolase	Conversion of D=xylulose-5-phosphate + ribose-5-phosphate ⇌ D-sedoheptulose-7-phosphate + D-glyceraldehyde-3-phosphate
Molybdenum	Xanthine oxidase (also contains iron)	Conversion of hypoxanthine → xanthine → uric acid
	Aldehyde oxidase	Oxidation of acetaldehyde → acetic acid
	Sulfite oxidase (also contains heme)	Oxidation of –SH → SO_3^{-2} → SO_4^{-2}
Chromium	Glucose tolerance factor	? Enhances binding of insulin to cell surface receptor
Cobalt (as vitamin B_{12})	Methylmalonyl CoA mutase	Isomerization of methylomalonyl CoA to succinyl CoA
	S-Adenosylmethionine methyl-transferase	Regeneration of methionine from homocysteine by methyl group transfer
Selenium	Glutathione Peroxidase	Protection of tissues from oxidative damage by converting H_2O_2 → H_2O

Table 14.3. Clinical Abnormalities of Trace Metal Disturbances

	COPPER	ZINC	MAGNESIUM	CHROMIUM	SELENIUM	CADMIUM
Deficiency	Neutropenia Hypochromic, microcytic anemia Osteoporosis Periosteal changes Pathological fractures Tortuosity of arterial vessels Hypotonia	Growth retardation Anorexia Hypogeusia Skin lesions Diarrhea Lethargy Irritability Alopecia Delayed puberty	Muscle wasting Apathy Diaphoresis Tachycardia Numbness Convulsions Delirium PVC, ventricular fibrillation Trachycardia, ventricular fibrillation Coma Death	Impaired glucose tolerance Relative insulin resistance		
Toxicity	Nausea Vomiting Diarrhea Headache Dizziness Tachycardia Hypertension Hemolytic anemia Hemoglobinuria Uremia Death	Vomiting Dehydration Electrolyte imbalance Abdominal pain Dizziness Muscular incoordination Acute renal failure	CNS depression Hypotonia Hypothermia Heart block Coma Death		Nausea Vomiting Skin depigmentation Alopecia Lassitude ? Abortion	Growth retardation Anemia Osteoporosis Anosmia Dyspnea Emphysema Fanconi syndrome Pathologic fractures

been described and virtually nothing is known of their mechanisms of absorption. It is possible that small quantities of these elements are absorbed in a form bound to dietary amino acids.

At the serosal surface, these trace metals are picked up by intestinal venous blood for transport to the cells of the body. This process also remains poorly characterized, although it is known that zinc and copper bind to albumin and to transferrin. No specific plasma transport proteins have yet been demonstrated. The mechanisms for cellular uptake and intracellular transport of trace metals are completely uncharacterized, although the exceedingly small quantities of each of these elements would seem to dictate the need for highly specific and organized means of handling. Moreover, the absolute requirement for these metals to confer biologic activity on certain enzymes would contribute further toward indicating such a need.

Excretory routes differ for the various trace metals. Zinc, for example, is returned to the intestine via the pancreatic secretions, although the majority of faecal zinc derives directly from ingested amounts. Magnesium, however, is excreted primarily by the kidney. Because absorption from the gut is not complete, a significant proportion of ingested magnesium is retained in the intestinal lumen and lost in the stool.

The relevance of a better understanding of trace metal metabolism is underscored by disorders like Wilson's disease and Menke's disease, which are conditions of copper toxicity and deficiency, respectively. It is not clear why a patient becomes toxic during long-term ingestion of quantities of copper, which maintains good health in normal individuals; yet, this is precisely what occurs with Wilson's disease. Nonetheless, copper storage can be demonstrated in liver and brain in these patients, although therapy is blindly directed at removing the burden of copper while decreasing absorption. Conversely, it is not immediately clear why an infant with Menke's disease, exposed to normal quantities of dietary copper, is unable to absorb and retain sufficient amounts for normal metabolism. It should be obvious that a complete knowledge of trace metal metabolism is important to our understanding of cellular biochemistry and to clinical medicine, as well.

SUMMARY

Nutrition is an important aspect of medical diagnosis and care. Although the body can interconvert many dietary constituents to meet needs and prevent deficiency, certain materials are beyond its synthetic capacity and must be supplied in the diet. In the absence of adequate quantities of these essential substances, additional quantities of others will not prevent development of insufficiencies. In this respect, one could say that, as with an automobile, adding gasoline to the tank until it overflows will not permit the engine to run without oil for lubrication.

Inadequate nutrition is probably the world's greatest current medical problem and accounts for many diseases related to malnutrition. However, blind advocacy of industrialization of the Third World to alleviate these problems is no answer. In our own highly industrialized nation, not only have we not adequately addressed this issue, but we have managed to foul our environment to the point where new deficiencies, such as those of trace metals, may become major disorders. The truth, which history teaches us clearly, is that as long as there is not equitable distribution of the abundance of the world's food production, starvation and malnutrition will continue to produce disease and human misery as it has through the ages of civilization.

SUGGESTED READINGS

Bender D. Nutritional biochemistry of the vitamins. Cambridge: Cambridge University Press, 1992.

Bender D. An introduction to nutrition and metabolism. London: UCL Press, 1993.

Bouchard C, Perusse L. Genetics of obesity. Annu Rev Nutr 1993;13:337.

Bray GA. Weight homeostasis. Annu Rev Med 1991;42: 205.

Cornelius P, MacDougald OA, Lane MD. Regulation of adipocyte development. Annu Rev Nutr 1994;14:99.

Decker DF. Biosynthesis and function of enzymes with covalently bound flavin. Annu Rev Nutr 1993;13:17.

Drott C, Lundholm K. Cardiac effects of caloric restriction-mechanisms and potential hazards. International Journal of Obesity 1992;16:481.

Eastwood MA. The physiological effect of dietary fiber: an update. Annu Rev Nutr 1992;12:19.

Garrow JS. Treatment of obesity. Lancet 1992;340:409.

Katch FI, McArdle WD. Introduction to nutrition, exercise, and health. 4th ed. Baltimore: Williams & Wilkins, 1994.

Kinney JM, Jeejeebhoy KN, Hill GL, Owen OE. Nutrition and metabolism in patient care. Philadelphia: WB Saunders Co, 1988.

Leibel RL, Rosenbaum M, Hirsch J. Changes in energy expenditure resulting from altered body weight. N Engl J Med 1995;332:621.

Lindpaintner K. Finding an obesity gene—a tale of mice and men. N Engl J Med 1995;332:679.

Ravussin E, Swinburn BA. Pathophysiology of obesity. Lancet 1992;340:8816.

Shils ME, Olson JA, Shike M, eds. Modern nutrition in health and disease. 8th ed. Williams & Wilkins, 1993.

Swinburn BA, Ravussin E. Energy and macronutrient metabolism. Baillieres Clin Endocrinol Metab 1994;8: 527.

Weigle DS. Appetite and the regulation of body composition. FASEB J 1994;8:302.

Wilmore DW. Catabolic illness: strategies for enhancing recovery. N Engl J Med 1991;325:695.

chapter **15**

Lipid and Lipoprotein Metabolism

Concern and, in some cases, preoccupation with obesity and cardiovascular disease in the United States has been a major factor in shaping dietary habits and has spurred development of entire lines of "low-fat" and "no-fat" foods. In this state of heightened concern about fat in the diet, one can forget that lipids and lipoproteins play major and vital roles in maintenance of energy homeostasis and structural integrity in humans. For instance, the fact that the adult human brain is composed of about 23% solid material (the remainder is water) of which more than half is lipid should underscore the structural importance of lipids. Perhaps even more telling, the bilayer structure of all cell membranes is based on phospholipid building blocks, which further emphasizes the axial role lipids play in life.

From a nutritional standpoint, a diet devoid of all lipid makes it almost impossible to achieve a daily caloric intake sufficient to meet the requirements of an average human being and results in a catabolic state. Thus, the energy yield of 9.0 Kcal per gram of fat sustains the energetic requirements of various organs like muscle, heart, and liver, providing a caloric density not easily achieved with carbohydrate and protein, each one of which yields only 4.0 Kcal/g. Furthermore, certain polyunsaturated fatty acids are essential components of the diet, in the same sense that certain amino acids are essential. Therefore, to view dietary fat as indiscriminately "bad" is to place the individual at considerable risk.

A major characteristic of the lipid class is their insolubility in water, which is the solvent that comprises almost 80% of total body weight. Individual lipids exist chiefly as components of macromolecular entities, either in association with protein or carbohydrate. As such, they constitute a key component of membranes, with lipid-protein interactions representing a crucial factor in the expression of the catalytic function of membrane-bound enzymes. The main forces holding lipids together within such supramolecular entities are noncovalent—generally hydrophobic interactions. These hydrophobic interactions make major contributions to lipid-lipid and lipid-protein bonding, and the resulting structures become malleable. The plasicity thus conferred on these supramolecular aggregations of lipids enables them to carry out their in vivo functions, particularly regarding interaction with proteins, as in cell membranes. In addition, because lipids are hydrophobic, triacylglycerol is permitted to be stored in adipocytes without water, resulting in a very high energy yield/weight ratio.

STRUCTURE OF LIPIDS

Unlike the predictable molecular nature of molecules like proteins and nucleic acids, lipids generally do not share a homogeneous structure. Most contain a long hydrocarbon chain, numbering from 14 to 24 carbon atoms, usually in an even-numbered sequence. Straight-chain fatty acids may be either saturated or unsaturated (oleic and palmitic predominate); the polyunsaturated members satisfy the essential dietary requirement mentioned above. Substituted unsaturated fatty acids are almost always in the cis-form rather than the trans-form. This leads to formation of isomers with the substituent on the same side (cis) of the double bond. The presence of a cis-form interrupts the regularity of molecular configuration seen in the trans-form (which can bunch together like saturated fatty acids) and confers distinctive physical properties (Figure 15.1). The "*kink*" in the cis-molecule impairs side-group approximation and, therefore, interchain hydrophobic interactions. This has major functional consequences; for ex-

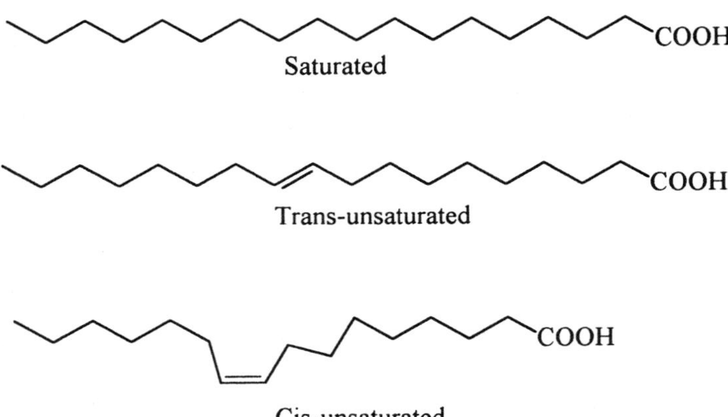

Figure 15.1. Molecular conformation of fatty acids. The saturated fatty acids generally are straight-chain molecules, with their "best-fit" conformation as shown. Insertion of a double bond may result in either a "trans-" or a "cis-" orientation. Note that the difference between these is the "kink" in the molecule introduced by the substituents in the cis-unsaturated molecule.

ample, a cis bond alters fluidity properties of the lipid bilayer in cell membranes. Such an effect may translate into alterations in membrane transport of substrates and catalytic function of membrane-bound enzymes. Moreover, a substantial proportion of lipids stored in adipocytes contain unsaturated fatty acids, ensuring their fluidity and, therefore, ready "mobilizability" to meet energy needs.

Structural Variations on a Lipid Theme

To create larger lipid structures, organisms have evolved means for using molecules bearing several functional groups that serve as bridges for the lipid components (Figure 15.2). The simplest and most commonly used bridge is *glycerol,* a three-carbon polyol in which three functional alcohol groups can be esterified by reaction with fatty acids to form mono-, di- or triglycerides (triacylglycerols). With the formation of a triglyceride, all the functional groups are esterified, resulting in a neutral fat. "Simple" triglycerides contain three uniform fatty acids, whereas "mixed" triglycerides contain one or two different fatty acids. Obviously, triglycerides with fatty acyl components of different chain lengths will possess physico-chemical properties different from simple triglycerides. In general, mixed triacylglycerols predominate.

When a diglyceride is formed, it is possible for the third hydroxyl group of the glycerol backbone to be phosphorylated. This reaction produces a *phosphatidic acid,* which is a molecule that is part hydrophobic because of the neutral ester components and part polar because of the phosphate group. The phosphate group can be used as an additional bridge, thus making phosphatidic acid the parent compound of the extremely important biologic molecules called *phospholipids* (Figure 15.2). In the phospholipids, the substituent added across the phosphate bridge generally also is polar, thus rendering the phospholipids *amphiphilic* as a group. Amphiphilic molecules exhibit both polar and hydrophobic properties. This amphiphilic electrochemical property makes the phospholipids ideally suited for their vital role in cell membrane structure, when their polar heads are directed toward the external and internal aqueous environments and their hydrophobic ends are buried within the interior of the membrane itself. The nomenclature of the substituted phosphatidic acids is based upon the substituent on the phosphate moiety (eg, phosphatidylcholine, phosphatidylethanolamine, etc).

Another bridging compound, *sphingosine,* which is a fatty acid amino alcohol, provides the basis for further variations on a theme. Sphingosine, because of its long fatty acid chain, is lipophilic, and its amide group (Figure 15.2) represents the site of attachment of further acyl residues. This hydroxyl group at the end of the chain is the point of attachment of sugar residues or phosphorylcholine. When phosphorylcholine is linked to sphingosine, the resulting compound is sphingomyelin, which is the only sphingolipid that contains phosphate. Merely on the basis of relative size alone, sphingomyelin is a vital component of cell membranes, adopting a conformation much like that of phosphatidyl choline. Because of the bulk of its polar head group, sphingomyelin is pre-

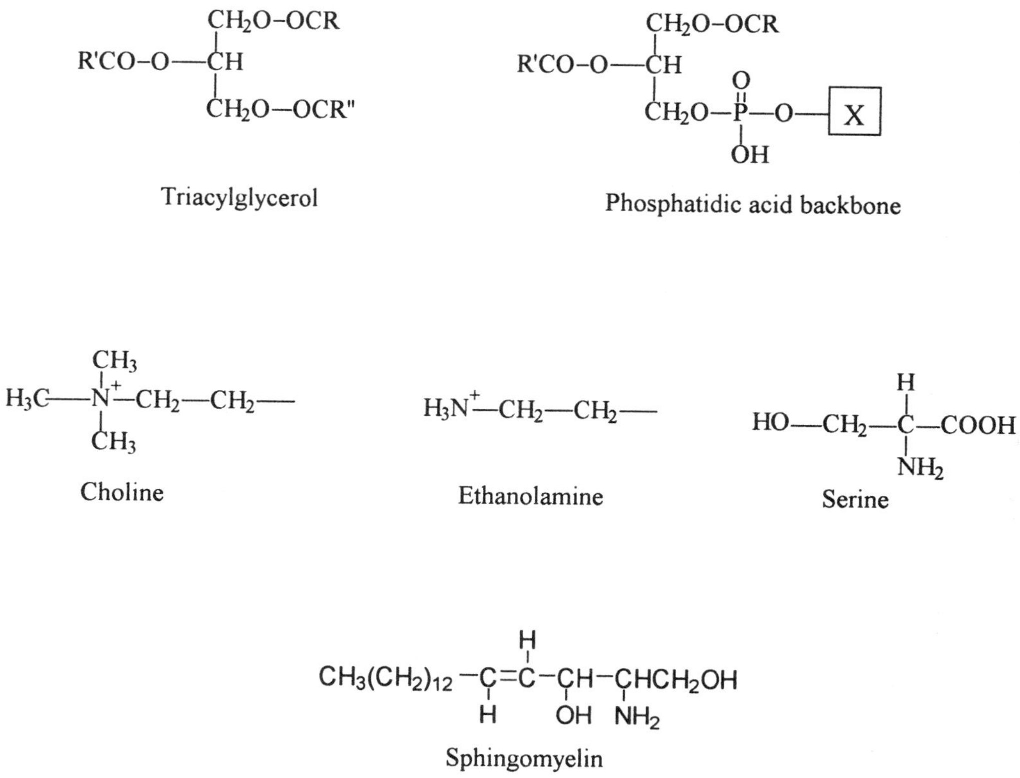

$CH_2O\text{–}OCR$
$R'CO\text{–}O\text{—}CH$
$CH_2O\text{—}OCR''$

Triacylglycerol

$CH_2O\text{–}OCR$
$R'CO\text{–}O\text{—}CH$
$CH_2O\text{—}P(=O)(OH)\text{—}O\text{—}[X]$

Phosphatidic acid backbone

$H_3C\text{—}N^+(CH_3)_2\text{—}CH_2\text{—}CH_2\text{—}$

Choline

$H_3N^+\text{—}CH_2\text{—}CH_2\text{—}$

Ethanolamine

$HO\text{—}CH_2\text{—}C(H)(NH_2)\text{—}COOH$

Serine

$CH_3(CH_2)_{12}\text{–}CH{=}CH\text{–}CH(OH)\text{–}CH(NH_2)CH_2OH$

Sphingomyelin

Figure 15.2. The functional groups of lipids. The simplest of these is the glycerol skeleton of an acylglycerol. These are synthesized in a stepwise fashion, so that instead of a triacyl-substituted glycerol, a diglyceride may be phosphorylated at the third hydroxyl to create phosphatidic acid. To phosphatidic acid, many substituents may be added at the site X (as shown) to form phosphatidylcholine, phosphatidylethanolamine, or phosphatidylserine. An additional "backbone" molecule is sphingosine, which is a fatty acid amino alcohol. The long carbon chain is obviously lipophilic, whereas the highly substituted terminal three carbons offer flexibility in substitutions. An extremely important derivative of sphingosine is sphingomyelin, which is a major component of all cell membranes.

dominantly distributed on the outer lamella of the plasma membrane, helping to shape the greater curvature. In contrast, there is less sphingomyelin in subcellular membranes, which is consistent with the smaller radius of organelle membranes.

If, instead of a phosphate, as in the formation of the ceramide sphingomyelin, a glycosidic bond is established, then a cerebroside is formed (Figure 15.2). Such a molecule is termed a *glycosphingolipid.* The polarity of a cerebroside can be further enhanced by sulfation of the carbohydrate moiety to form a sulfatide. When the carbohydrate moiety of a ceramide is substituted with N-acetylneuraminic (sialic) acid, a ganglioside is the result. Gangliosides are the most polar lipids, being found predominantly within the central nervous system, compared to the less polar phospho- and glycolipid compounds, which are widely distributed in cell membranes. Thus, defects in metabolism of gangliosides are associated chiefly with abnormalities in central nervous system function (see Chapter 26).

LIPIDS IN BLOOD

Because lipids are transported in the blood, which is an aqueous medium, the various lipids must become part of larger water-soluble emulsions that are stable in the blood. These emulsions are the *lipoproteins* and, except for a small percentage of free fatty acids existing in association with albumin, almost all blood-borne lipid is found in some lipoprotein.

To simplify the complexities of lipoprotein metabolism, a few essential concepts should be considered:

1. There are four classes of lipoproteins: chylomicrons, very low density lipoproteins (VLDLs), low density lipoproteins (LDLs), and high density lipoproteins (HDLs). Key to differences in density among classes is the relative proportion of apolipoprotein to lipid (Table 15.1), with HDL understandably containing a greater proportion of protein than lipid.
2. Intestinal cells have limited apolipoprotein synthetic capability, producing only apo A and B, whereas the liver produces representatives of all classes, including apo A, B, C, and E. All apolipoproteins exchange among the various lipoproteins in the blood except for the apo Bs, which are very large proteins intrinsic to the lipoprotein monolayer and which fulfill a mandatory structural role in chylomicrons and VLDLs.
3. Chylomicrons, composed chiefly of dietary lipid, are formed exclusively in the intestine and represent the sole transport modality for dietary triglycerides.
4. VLDLs are synthesized exclusively in the liver, whereas LDLs derive from progressive removal of triglyceride from VLDLs (VLDL → IDL (intermediate density lipoprotein) → LDL). HDLs, formed in both the liver and intestine, carry out reverse transport of cholesterol from the tissues, prompting loss of cholesterol via the bile. Subjects with high HDL levels appear to be resistant to the development of atherosclerosis.
5. Generally, it is the nature of the apolipoprotein(s) present that determines metabolic disposition, rather than the lipid composition. For this reason, metabolic abnormalities of lipoprotein metabolism are related to defects in apoprotein synthesis or their specific receptor sites.

Key to understanding the complexity of the factors involved in lipid metabolism is the relative insolubility of various lipids in the aqueous internal environment of the body. Thus, for the organism to use the high caloric density of lipids, means had to be evolved for their transport from the site of absorption to the metabolic destination. As a consequence, blood-borne lipids always exist in noncovalent association with albumin (as nonesterified fatty acids or NEFA) or as emulsions formed by lipoproteins. Lipoproteins, as a group, are the third most abundant type of plasma protein, with albumin and the immunoglobulins being first and second, respectively. Lipoproteins are supramolecular complexes and are spherical (vesicular) in nature, ranging in size from 8 to 800 nm in diameter. Although lipoproteins are classified according to their relative densities, heterogeneity within each class is a distinctive feature and relates closely to their means of metabolic disposition.

Table 15.1. Physical and Chemical Characteristics of Human Lipoproteins

				COMPONENTS OF LIPOPROTEIN (PER CENT OF TOTAL)				
CLASS	DIAMETER (nm)	DENSITY	M.W.	TG	CHOLESTEROL	CHOLESTEROL ESTER	PHOSPHOLIPID	PROTEIN
Chylomicrons	75–600	0.92–0.96	5×10^8	86	1	5	7	2 Apo C-II Apo B
VLDL	25–75	0.95–1.006–	$5–10 \times 10^6$	50	7	13	20	10 Apo B (50%) Apo C (45%) Apo E (trace)
LDL	17–26	1.006–1.063	$2.2–2.3 \times 10^6$	8	10	30(37)	30(20)	22 Apo B (90%) Apo C-II (10%)
HDL	4–10	1.063–1.125	175,000–360,000	8	4	12	24	52 Apo A-I Apo A-II (80%) Apo C-II (15%)

Lipoprotein Structural Features

In brief, lipoproteins share the following architectural features: (*a*) a core, which mainly comprises triglyceride and cholesteryl ester and is highly hydrophobic; and (*b*) a coat, which comprises a surface film of phospholipids, cholesterol, and specific apolipoproteins, is partially hydrophilic, and confers the property of stable colloid formation (Figure 15.3). Table 15.1 shows the composition of these serum lipoprotein fractions, illustrating the relationship between electrophoretic and ultracentrifugal criteria. The lipoproteins range from chylomicrons and VLDLs with high triglyceride and low protein content to HDLs with the reverse proportions. The spectrum in between is reflected in

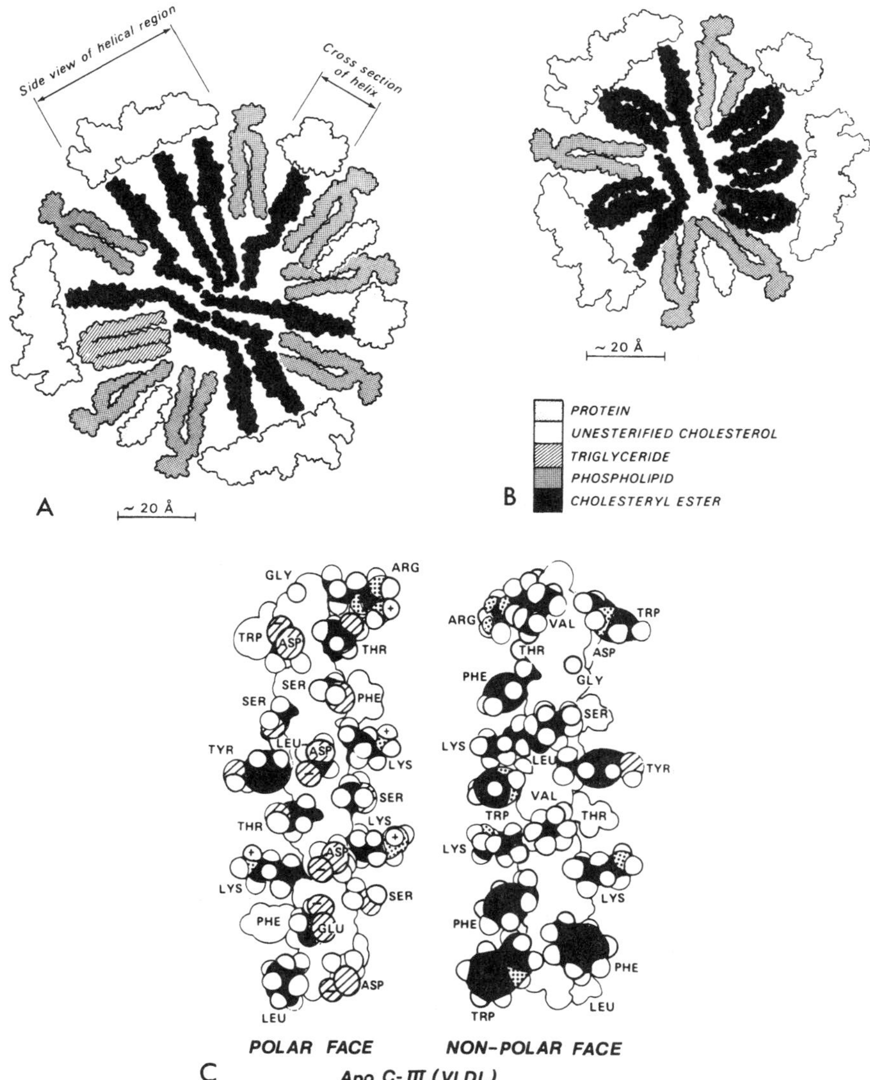

Figure 15.3. Structural features of lipoproteins. (A) Cross-section of a model of HDL_2. (B) Cross-section of a model of HDL_3. Although the core of each is hydrophobic, containing mostly cholesteryl esters and triglyceride, the outer surface is composed of protein, free cholesterol, and polar phospholipid. (C) Polar and nonpolar faces of C-III apolipoprotein. Reprinted with permission from Verdery RB III, Nichols AV. Arrangement of lipid and protein in human serum high density lipoproteins: a proposed model. Chem Phys Lipids. 1975;14:123–134.

increasing content of phospholipid and cholesteryl ester. Overall, therefore, density varies inversely with triglyceride content and directly with protein.

Apolipoprotein synthesis, as mentioned above, occurs mainly in the liver, except for apo B-48, which is produced exclusively in intestinal cells and is unique to chylomicron formation. Hydrophobic interactions provide the major force by which these apoproteins associate with the lipid components of the various lipoproteins. Nonetheless, sizeable hydrophilic segments of these proteins must be present to permit these macromolecules to interact simultaneously with the lipid and aqueous environments in which lipoproteins exist. Beyond this structural role, certain apolipoproteins also function as catalytic activators or mediate receptor-specific endocytosis. For example, although chylomicrons initially contain exclusively apo B-48 (synthesized only by enterocytes), they cannot be metabolized by lipoprotein lipase without apo C-II, which is synthesized only in liver and which acts as a cofactor for the enzyme. Because apo C-II is found predominantly in HDLs, apo C-II must be transferred to chylomicrons. Seen in this light, it should be clear that it is somewhat simplistic to speak of one lipoprotein class in isolation from the others, because they all undergo lipid exchange, furnish cofactors, and interact in the blood to provide for the energetic and structural needs of the cells.

Table 15.1 shows that chylomicrons and VLDLs are the chief source of triglyceride. Although chylomicrons are composed exclusively of resynthesized triglyceride derived solely from dietary sources, those incorporated into VLDLs by the liver represent triglycerides of endogenous origin, packaged for export. A key difference between chylomicrons and VLDLs is the presence of apo B-100, which is confined to VLDLs only, has a molecular weight approximately twice that of apo B-48, and has the additional presence of small amounts of apo C and E. As with the chylomicrons, additional quantities of apo C and E are gained through interaction with HDLs in the blood after secretion. Circulating VLDL also is known as prebeta lipoprotein, according to its electrophoretic mobility. As noted, of all the apoproteins, only apo B-100 and apo B-48 do not exchange with other lipoproteins. This "nonexchangeability" stems from the fact that both of these apo Bs are integral to the phospholipid monolayer of the lipoprotein.

An intermediate species of macromolecule, known as LDL (Figure 15.4), is generated by removal of triacylglycerol from VLDL by lipoprotein lipase. As would be predicted from its increasing density, LDL reflects a lower triglyceride:protein ratio than does VLDL, owing to removal of triglyceride (see following text). LDL has a half-life in the circulation of about 3 days and serves as a transport vehicle for cholesterol from tissues to liver. Free exchange occurs between the lipid of LDL and cell membranes, prompting the suggestion that LDL may have an important role in maintenance of cell membrane integrity. On the basis of electrophoretic mobility, LDL also is termed beta-lipoprotein.

Metabolism of HDLs

The final representative of the lipoprotein macromolecular species is HDL, or alpha-lipoprotein, as it is also known based on its electrophoretic mobility. Although the chief protein component of HDL, apo A, is produced predominantly in liver, we have noted that intestine also is capable of synthesizing small quantities of apo A. Thus, circulating HDL, although largely of hepatic origin, derives in small part from intestine as well. An HDL macromolecule consists of approximately 50% protein and 50% lipid, of which the major species are phospholipid and cholesteryl ester. Beyond the role of supplying requisite apo C and E to other lipoprotein species, HDL plays a major role in mobilizing cholesterol from peripheral tissues for transfer to the liver. It does so in a complex process called reverse cholesterol transport which we will try to outline simply.

Normally, plasma HDL exists in spherical form, although precursor or nascent HDL, isolated from liver cell Golgi, is in the shape of bilamellar discs. The quantitative difference between precursor and circulating HDL particles is the cholesteryl ester content. Hence, it is logical to assume and it has been demonstrated that adding esterified cholesterol to nascent HDL induces conversion of the disc to a sphere. The assembly process that occurs between the Golgi body and the plasma remains poorly understood, but early forms of HDL exist as bilamellar discs in the circulation. Thus, addition of cholesteryl ester must occur in the plasma, a process largely mediated by an

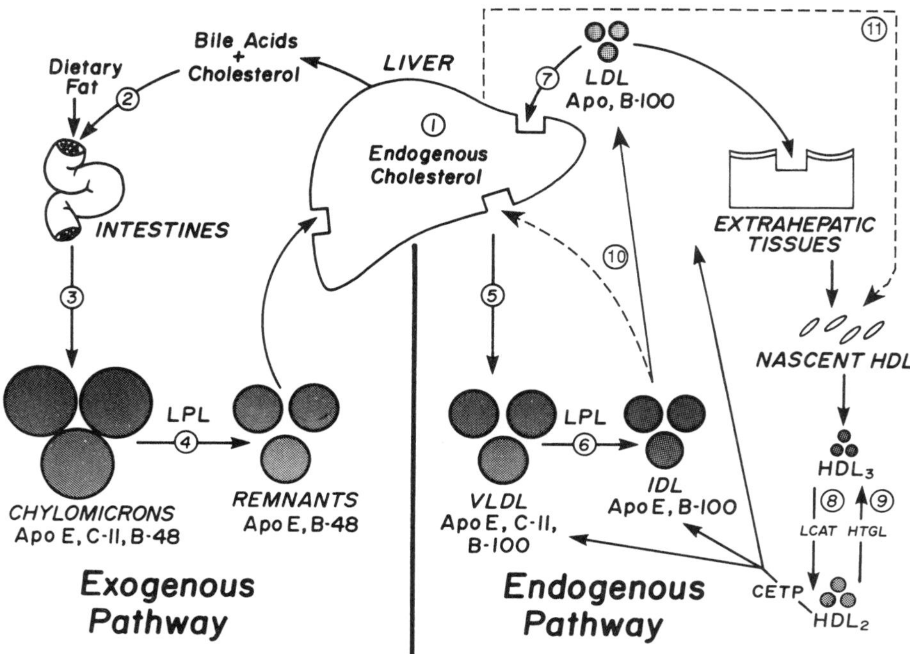

Figure 15.4. Overview of lipoprotein metabolism. Lipoproteins of all classes are represented as circles, with the corresponding apoprotein components listed below each one. In the exogenous pathway, dietary fat leads to chylomicron formation in the intestine (step 3), whereas production of VLDL occurs in liver from triglycerides derived from endogenous sources (reaction 5). Note that chylomicrons contain the intestinally derived apoprotein B-48, whereas all lipoproteins of the endogenous pathway are essentially devoid of B-48 and contain the hepatic apoprotein B-100, instead. Lipoprotein lipase (LPL) acts on each particle (reactions 4 and 6) to produce chylomicron remnants (extrinsic) or IDL and LDL (intrinsic). Both IDL and LDL bind to hepatic receptor sites (reaction 10). Nascent HDL is generated in extrahepatic tissues as well as in liver (reaction 11). HDL_3 is reversibly converted to HDL_2 (reactions 8 and 9) by the enzymes LCAT (lecithin:cholesterol acyltransferase) and HTGL (hepatic triglyceride lipase). Cholesteryl ester transfer protein (CETP) mediates transfer of cholesteryl esters from HDL to VLDL, IDL, and LDL. Cholesterol, an essential component of all lipoproteins, is synthesized de novo in liver (reaction 1). Reprinted with permission from Oberman A, Kriesberg RA, Henkin Y, et al. Principles and Management of Lipid Disorders: A Primary Care Approach. Baltimore: Williams & Wilkins, 1992:89.

HDL-bound enzyme lecithin-cholesterol acyl transferase (LCAT). As noted, a necessary exchange must occur between circulating lipoproteins for activation of LCAT; in this case, requiring transfer of apo A-I from chylomicrons. Upon activation, LCAT begins to transfer an acyl group from phosphatidylcholines to cholesterol, forming acylcholesterol (cholesteryl ester). Continued accumulation of cholesterol and phospholipid from particle interactions ensures a supply of substrate for this reaction. Being very hydrophobic, the cholesteryl ester is either incorporated into the core of the HDL particle, enhancing its spherical shape, or transferred to other particles, such as chylomicrons and LDLs. Cholesterol ester in chylomicron remnants and LDLs is carried to the liver, where receptor-mediated endocytosis admits the particles into the cell for subsequent incorporation into lysosomes. Within the lysosomes, the cholesteryl ester is hydrolyzed and the free cholesterol is made available for bile acid synthesis. The second product of this hydrolysis is, of course, a free fatty acid that can be oxidized to produce ATP or reused for synthesis of phospholipid.

Further Metabolism of Lipoproteins

To this point, we have stated little regarding lipoprotein degradation; our aim thus far has been to explain the distinguishing features of the various classes. Now we want to emphasize the role of lipoprotein degradation as an implicit part of the transformation of one class of particle to another. Chylomicrons and VLDLs, for example, are the major carriers of dietary and endogenous triglyceride, respectively. As mentioned above, transfer of apo C-II and apo E from HDLs to chylomicrons and VLDLs (when these particles collide) is an essential first step, which represents some degree of catabolism of HDL (Figure 15.4). There also is reverse transfer of apo A and some phospholipid from the chylomicrons and VLDLs to HDLs. Acquisition of apo C-II and apo E activates lipoprotein lipase activity at the capillary endothelial surface, leading to rapid hydrolysis of triglyceride and liberation of free fatty acids, which are taken up by cells to provide substrate for energetic needs. Progressive removal of the triglyceride components of chylomicrons and VLDLs reduces the lipid:protein ratio, resulting in transformation to chylomicron "remnants" and cholesterol-rich LDLs (Figure 15.4). These particles are returned to the liver, where they bind to specific receptors (B-48 isn't recognized by the LDL receptor but can be internalized because of the presence of apo E) and are endocytosed for lysosomal degradation. Recall that these cholesterol-rich particles also are a source of cholesterol for cholesteryl ester synthesis in HDL particles. Apo A, the activator of LCAT, which mediates the esterification reaction, thus adds cholesteryl ester to the growing core of HDL.

General Aspects of Lipoprotein Metabolism

Overall, the metabolism of the lipoproteins, as complex as it is, can be simplified by recognizing a few principles. The lipoproteins exist chiefly, but not exclusively, to transport hydrophobic dietary and endogenous lipid in the aqueous medium of blood. Yet another important function is to replenish erythrocyte membrane lipid; this function is well illustrated by the occurrence of acanthocytes (thorns on red cells) in abetalipoproteinemia (see following text). Classification of the lipoproteins is based on the relationship of lipid to protein, which, in turn, determines their relative densities. The protein components contribute not only to density, but to enzyme activation and receptor specificity. Through a series of random collisions with lipid and apoprotein exchanges between particles of different classes, there is a cooperativity between these supermolecules. Finally, understand that the classification system does not explicate that the various classes are actually, in large part, a continuum. In the next section of this chapter, which deals with disorders, it will become clear that disruption of a single aspect of the system has a major impact on the rest, which is consonant with the cooperative nature we have outlined.

DISORDERS OF LIPID AND LIPOPROTEIN METABOLISM

Just as the biochemistry of serum lipid and lipoprotein molecules epitomizes their ceaseless molecular interaction and exchange of components, so too do the clinical phenotypes of their disorders reflect this interactive diversity. Thus, for example, measurement of serum cholesterol and triglyceride levels is not sufficient to make a specific diagnosis, because these are elements of different and interactive composite macromolecules. More studies usually will be required. Lipoproteins can be separated by electrophoresis and stained for identification, thus generating a pattern that provides qualitative data as to the species present. To interpret the electrophoretic data, it is necessary to quantitate lipids and lipoproteins. Lipoproteins also can be separated by ultracentrifugation, using a discontinuous density salt gradient. But such methods are available only in laboratories specializing in lipoprotein metabolism. Precipitation techniques have been developed that allow HDL fractions to be separated from the other lipoprotein species. This method exploits the propensity of apo B-containing lipoproteins to precipitate with polyanions and divalent cations leaving HDL in the supernatant. Many clinical laboratories use this method, but it is not as reliable as density-gradient ultracentrifugation. LDL-cholesterol (LDL-C) usually is estimated by using the following equations:

$$\text{LDL-C} = \text{Total cholesterol} - (\text{HDL-C} + \text{VLDL-C})$$

$$\text{VLDL-C} = \text{TG}/5 \text{ when TG is } < 400 \text{ mg/dl}$$

At a more refined level, immunologic distinctions can be made of the apoprotein components if monogenic defects in protein synthesis are a diagnostic consideration. Note that these monogenic defects constitute a very small percentage of the total lipid and lipoprotein disorders. After considering these inherited disorders, we will examine the larger issue of detection and treatment of multifactorial hyperlipidemia in the effort to forestall or prevent coronary artery disease.

Lipoproteins and Serum Inspection

Notwithstanding the above statements, the importance of accurate measurement of serum triglycerides and cholesterol should not be discounted, because these can help pinpoint a specific diagnosis. A description of plasma, which has been stored overnight at 4°C, in various hyperlipidemic states follows. This method relies on the decreased solubility of already relatively insoluble solids at reduced temperature, as well as their different densities, thus permitting separation by gravity. By way of comparison, blood from a normal individual, under these conditions, will result in a clear and colorless plasma layer.

1. A cream-colored layer resting on clear or just slightly turbid plasma suggests increased chylomicron content of the blood, which is consistent with the extremely low density of these triglyceride-rich particles. Reflecting their high proportion of triglycerides, total serum triglycerides should be markedly increased whereas serum cholesterol is normal or only slightly increased. It is not unusual to find this pattern in normal subjects within a few hours of eating. But because dietary chylomicrons normally are cleared within 12 hours, finding such a creamy supernatant after an overnight fast is definitively abnormal.
2. Although normal plasma will be entirely clear, a plasma sample with an increased serum cholesterol combined with a slight yellow-orange color to the otherwise clear liquid indicates increased LDLs. In such cases, serum triglycerides should be normal.
3. Increased cholesterol and triglycerides, and mild, uniformly distributed turbidity suggest increased VLDLs and LDLs.
4. Familial dysbetalipoproteinemia, or abnormally composed LDLs and VLDLs, is suggested by increase of both cholesterol and triglycerides, in association with plasma manifesting uniformly distributed turbidity of moderate degree, topped by a narrow, creamy band.
5. Grossly turbid plasma of uniform distribution indicates increased VLDLs. Serum cholesterol is slightly increased in proportion to much greater increases in serum triglycerides, consistent with the composition of VLDL particles.
6. Gross turbidity or opacity, topped with a broad creamy layer, suggests combined increase in chylomicrons and VLDLs. Both cholesterol and triglycerides are markedly increased.

It is important to understand that documenting a specific pattern does not, in itself, confirm the diagnosis of a specific disease entity. For example, when uniformly opalescent plasma is present in combination with proportionately increased cholesterol and triglycerides, one could be dealing with a patient who is suffering from one of four primary or more than 30 secondary diseases! This supports the maxim that no laboratory test can supplant a thorough history and physical examination. Some of the more common causes of secondary hyperlipidemias are listed in Table 15.2.

Hyperchylomicronemia

As we have stated, postprandial chylomicronemia is a normal consequence of dietary fat ingestion; the bulk of chylomicrons are cleared within 10 to 12 hours of their entry into the circulation. Thus, with the exception of a sample drawn after a fast of 10 to 12 hours, a normal individual predictably would have a measurable degree of chylomicronemia after a mixed meal. Nonetheless, any sample showing proportionate increases in cholesterol and triglycerides, and a characteristic creamy layer atop clear plasma after overnight storage at 4°C reflects hyperchylomicronemia. Clearance of chylomicrons from the blood stream depends upon: (*a*) presence of normal lipoprotein lipase (LPL) enzyme protein in capillary endothelium, (*b*) presence of HDL particles carrying apo C-II and apo E, (*c*) qualitatively normal apoproteins

Table 15.2. Laboratory Findings and Mechanisms in the Secondary Hyperlipidemias

LIPOPROTEIN PATTERN	PLASMA CHOLESTEROL	PLASMA TRIGLYCERIDE	CAUSES	MECHANISM OF HYPERLIPIDEMIA
Type I: Chylomicronemia	N to ↑↑	↑↑↑	Systemic lupus erythematosus	Ig binds to GAG at capillary endothelium → ↓LPL activity
Type IIa: LDL↑↑↑	↑↑↑	N	Obstructive liver disease Hypothyroidism	↓ catabolism of LDL
			Nephrotic syndrome	↑ secretion VLDL → ↑ formation LDL
Type IIb: LDL ↑↑↑ VLDL ↑	↑↑↑	↑↑	Nephrotic syndrome Cushing's syndrome Growth hormone deficiency	
Type III: LP remnants ↑ (β-migrating)	↑↑↑	↑↑ to ↑↑↑	Monoclonal gammopathies	Igs form immune complexes with VLDL or remnants interfering with their catabolism
Type IV: VLDL↑↑	N to ↑	↑↑ to ↑↑↑	Monoclonal gammopathies	
			Diabetes mellitus	↑ secretion VLDL, ↓LPL activity
			Alcohol Oral contraceptives	↑ secretion VLDL
			Hepatitis Uremia	↓ secretion LCAT ↓ LPL activity
Type V: VLDL ↑↑↑ Chylomicrons ↑↑	↑↑	↑↑↑	Diabetes mellitus Alcohol Oral contraceptives	
LP-X: Cholesterol & phospholipids ↑↑	↑↑	N to ↑	Cholestasis	Biliary cholesterol and lecithin diverted into blood

↑ = mildly; ↑↑ = moderately; ↑↑↑ = markedly; Ig = immunoglobulin; GAG = glycosaminoglycan

and, (*d*) transfer of various apoproteins to chylomicrons for activation of LPL and triglyceride hydrolysis. It follows that the presence of hyperchylomicronemia theoretically can be attributed to a defect at any of these points. Indeed, defects exist at points a (LPL deficiency), b, and c (familial disorders of HDL, apo C-II and apo E deficiencies), and d (cholesteryl ester transfer protein deficiency). Because of the multiple causes of increased plasma chylomicrons, the finding of hyperchylomicronemia delineates a syndrome, not a specific diagnostic entity.

The need for further evaluation is indicated by a fasting triglyceride level greater than 200 mg/dl in a young, healthy individual or in the presence of clinical symptoms at any age. Although much is made in the literature about eruptive xanthomas, representing tissue deposition of lipid, recent memory loss and abdominal pain are by far the more common presenting findings (40%, 85%, and 63% of patients, respectively). In cases when serum triglycerides exceed 4000 mg/dl, "lipemia retinalis" can be seen, representing deposition of lipid in the retina without adverse effects on vision. Morbidity and mortality (due to eventual pancreatic necrosis) can be substantially reduced by lowering serum triglyceride levels. Because chylomicrons are synthesized in intestine from dietary fat, irrespective of the specific etiology of hyperchylomicronemia, a general approach to therapy consists of reducing dietary fat intake. Again, we remind the reader that this is no substitute for appropriate diagnosis, because there are numerous secondary causes of hypertriglyceridemia that may be better addressed with directed treatment.

Hypercholesterolemia

Possibly second in frequency of usage in the American vernacular to "low fat content" is the phrase "high blood cholesterol." Indeed, so attuned has the public become to the dangers, imagined or real, of having an increased blood cholesterol level that cholesterol screening programs have "sprung up" like weeds in a garden. This proliferation has led to several careful studies of the validity of various measurement methodologies and their applications to diagnosis in randomly obtained blood samples. Aside from the effects of dietary lipid intake and the relationship in time to when the sample is obtained, there are interfering chromagens in plasma that may diminish accuracy; even an enzymatic assay method is not entirely specific to cholesterol. Thus, the obvious precautions should be taken to obtain only fasting samples for a lipid profile and to be certain that a single, consistent method of determination is used to provide data. Of note, cholesterol levels per se are affected little by fasting or eating.

Having established a dramatically increased cholesterol under standardized conditions, the value must be viewed in light of the enormous list of drugs and primary illnesses that may cause such an increase. Thus, for example, very significant increases in serum cholesterol are seen in nephrotic syndrome, diabetes mellitus, and alcoholism, to name a few, each of which clearly requires direct and specific therapeutic attention. As with any abnormal laboratory finding, evaluation should be performed methodically and systematically. If all other causes can be excluded, attention should be focused on the possibility of the genetic abnormality, familial hypercholesterolemia (FH), which is inherited as an autosomal dominant trait with very high penetrance (as high as 90%). Individuals carrying a single mutant gene for FH will show an LDL cholesterol level twice that of normal.

The incidence of heterozygotes (carriers) of the gene is estimated to be about 1 in 500 individuals; although, in some populations, such as the South African Afrikkaners, it is as common as 1 in 100. Thus, given the high degree of penetrance of the mutant gene, this defect can account for a substantial proportion of all cases of marked hypercholesterolemia. In the homozygous FH condition, which is far less common, cholesterol levels in plasma may reach five to eight times that of normal. The presence of the increased circulating cholesterol in LDL particles hints strongly at the basic defect, which lies in *defective membrane LDL receptors*. An intricate regulatory balance exists within the cell, involving LDL-receptor binding, which varies depending on the amount of exogenous cholesterol incorporated by this route. As with so many inborn errors, disruption of the finely tuned regulatory balance has major consequences, no matter what the specific cause of the disruption.

Careful studies of homozygous individuals have identified at least 18 different allelic mutations, which generally fall into four major functional classes. These four classes of mutations are those that impair synthesis, transport, binding, or clustering of the LDL receptor. Consequently, biochemical homozygotes actually are most likely to be compound heterozygotes, with each of the two dominant mutations affecting a different aspect of LDL incorporation into the cell. Figure 15.5 shows the loci of the four classes of LDL receptor defects. The essential roles of cholesterol and of the overall process that creates an intracellular pool of cholesterol are underscored by the fact that mammalian cells in culture will die unless they either are supplied with an exogenous cholesterol source or are able to carry out de novo synthesis. There is an absolute requirement for cholesterol as a key structural component of cell membranes, the integrity of which is essential to cell survival. In essence then, when incorporation of LDL cholesterol is impaired, the cell must produce its own or die.

The reader is reminded that LDLs normally are produced as a consequence of the action of lipo-

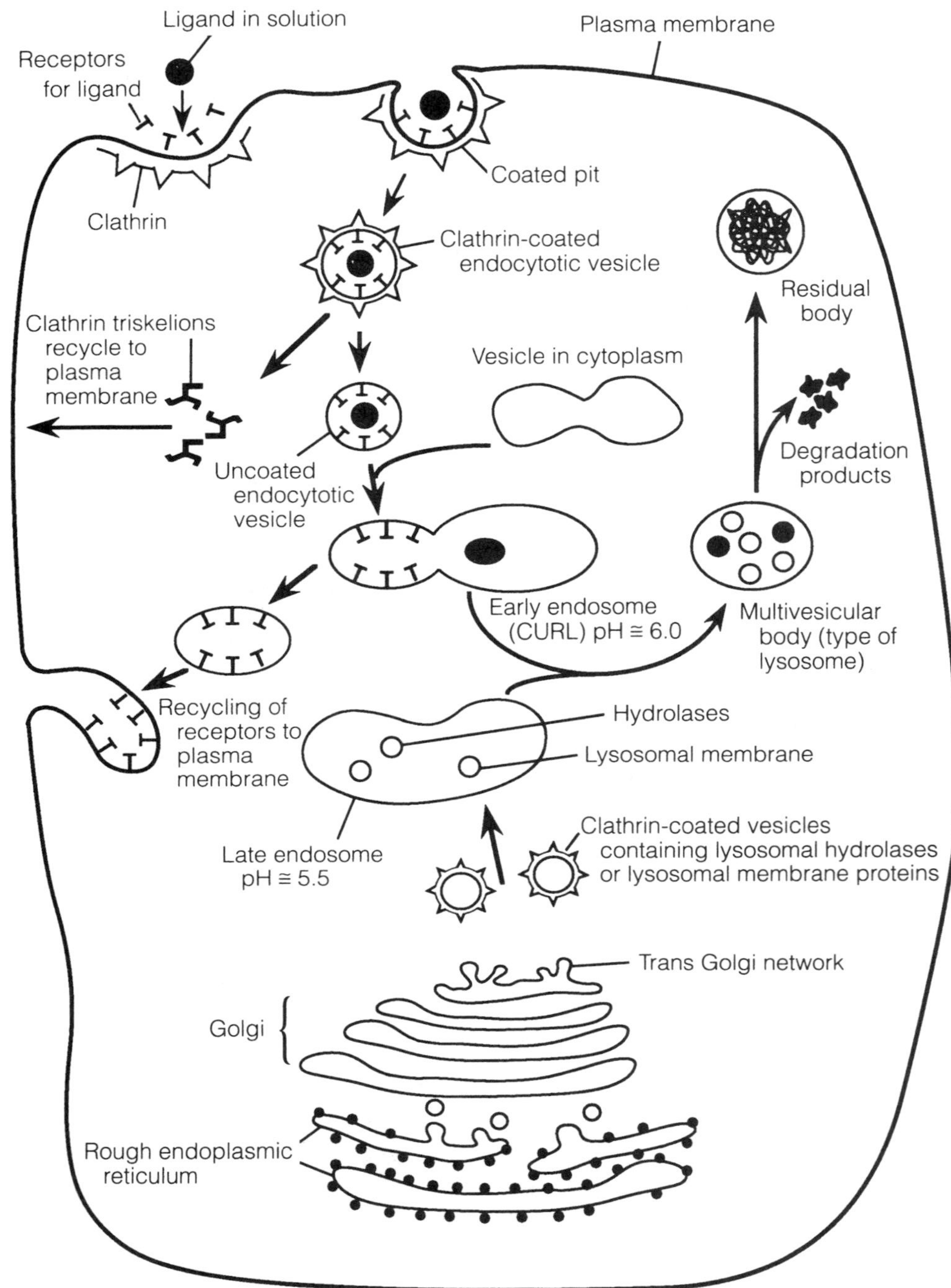

Figure 15.5. Low density lipoprotein (LDL) receptor pathway. LDL in solution binds to a ligand; the complex then is folded into a "coated pit" with the complex protein clathrin surrounding the convexity thus formed within the cell. Endocytosis results in intracellular incorporation of a vesicle completely surrounded by clathrin. As the vesicle approaches the compartment of uncoupling of receptors and ligands (CURL), the clathrin is removed and recycled back to the plasma membrane. Within the CURL, the receptors are removed from the LDL and also recycled back to the membrane. The original ligand then is acted upon by lysosomal hydrolases that are contributed by fusion of the CURL with a mature lysosome within an entity called a multivesicular body. Note that much of this overall process still is somewhat speculative, because the biogenesis of lysosomes is incompletely understood. Reprinted with permission from Gartner LP, Hiatt JL, Strom JM, et al. Cell Biology and Histology. 2nd ed. Baltimore: Williams & Wilkins, 1993: 41.

protein lipase on VLDLs, with consequent removal of triglycerides. There is a progressive increase in particle density as triglyceride is removed, leaving a higher proportion of cholesteryl ester and protein, and eventual emergence of a class of particles termed intermediate density lipoproteins (IDLs). Because we are speaking of a continuum, continued triglyceride hydrolysis will, in the end, produce the final LDL particle. In normal individuals, IDL can bind tightly to LDL receptors. This binding capacity is conferred by the presence of apo E in higher relative proportion in IDL than LDL (20% versus 10%, respectively), as well as apo B-100, which they possess in common (Figure 15.6). Thus, receptor binding favors IDL, which, when bound, follows one of two routes: a significant proportion of bound IDL is endocytosed by the hepatocyte, where triglyceride is added and the particle is released into the circulation as VLDL; the remainder of the bound IDL gives up apo E and is released back into the circulation where further LPL action produces LDL containing only apo B-100.

As a result of the loss of apo E, the LDLs possess a much lower binding affinity for LDL receptors than the IDLs do, and thus have a longer half-life in the circulation. Accordingly, when LDL receptor binding is defective as a consequence of a mutant gene, removal of circulating IDL is impaired. The result is increased conversion of IDL to LDL in the capillary endothelium, which with defective removal of LDL due to the same receptor defect leads to a substantial increase in circulating LDL. It is because of the LDL receptor defect that the hypercholesterolemia of FH is characteristically one of increased LDL-cholesterol.

Given the capacity of the cell to carry out de novo cholesterol synthesis using acetyl CoA as the substrate, a reasonable expectation would be that individuals with FH should show an increased rate of de novo synthesis. Such an increase is not detectable in heterozygotes, presumably because armed with 50% of the typical complement of LDL receptors, these cells can take up sufficient exogenous cholesterol to satisfy cellular demands. But, in homozygous individuals, in vivo stable isotope studies have established a two- to three-fold increase in the daily rate of total body cholesterol synthesis. This increase, which is reflected in additional cholesterol excretion, strongly suggests

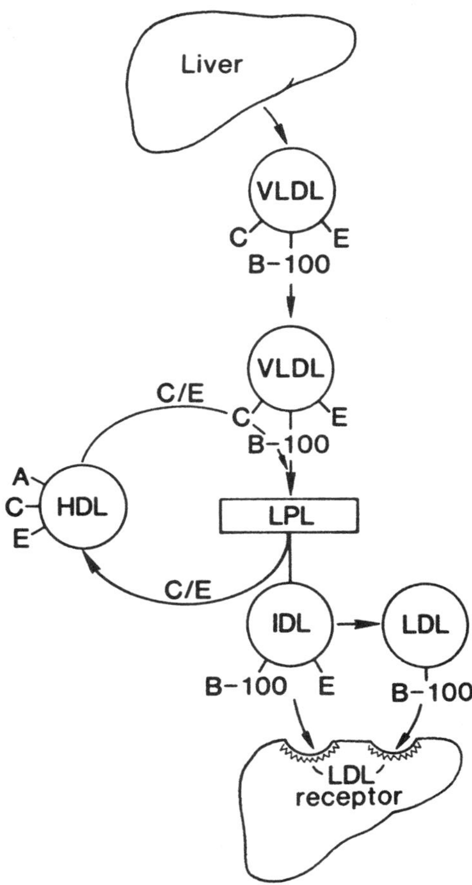

Figure 15.6. Role of LDL receptor in IDL and LDL metabolism. Production of VLDL occurs exclusively in the liver; these particles are clearly distinguishable from chylomicrons by their apoprotein B-100 content. Note the action of lipoprotein lipase (LPL) in transfer of apo C and apo E between VLDL and HDL particles, resulting in IDL and LDL. The latter two classes share apo B-100, but IDL possesses a greater proportion of apo E, which is required for LDL receptor binding. Consequently, under conditions when IDL/LDL is increased, binding sites will tend to be saturated by IDL with diminished rate of LDL clearance by the liver. Reprinted with permission from Hershman JM. Endocrine Pathophysiology: A Patient-Oriented Approach. 3rd ed. Philadelphia: Lea & Febiger, 1988: 331.

disruption of the normally tightly regulated feedback control over the de novo synthetic pathway.

Treatment of Familial Hypercholesterolemia

Based on the above discussion, it should be apparent that treatment for FH will differ, depending upon whether the patient is a heterozygote or a homozygote. Central to the issue is the ability of the hepatocyte, in the presence of a single normal gene, to increase production of LDL receptors under appropriate circumstances. By impairing reabsorption of bile acids in the intestine using cholestyramine, the liver of a normal individual or FH heterozygote can increase the number of LDL receptors to enhance extraction of LDL cholesterol from the circulation and use that cholesterol for increased bile acid synthesis. However, the effectiveness of this approach is partially offset by the contribution made to the intracellular pool through de novo synthesis. Drugs that can suppress de novo synthesis by inhibiting HMG CoA reductase activity as well now are available; therefore, a combined pharmacologic approach can maximize LDL receptor production by the single functional gene. As a result, reduction in circulating LDL cholesterol by 50% to 60% of pretreatment levels can be achieved. The importance of dietary lipid intake should not be overlooked in therapy; particular attention should be paid to cholesterol intake.

Clearly, treatment of FH homozygous individuals cannot be achieved in the same way, because no, or very little, functional capacity exists for LDL receptor production. In homozygotes, it is particularly important that in vitro testing of the residual capacity for LDL receptor activity be carried out. Individuals with greater than 2% of activity may respond favorably to a therapeutic regimen that combines the effects of three drugs: cholestyramine, an HMG CoA reductase inhibitor (for suppression of de novo cholesterol synthesis), and nicotinic acid. Nicotinic acid is thought to inhibit release of VLDL from the liver, thus reducing the load of circulating LDL derived as a result of LPL activity. In combination with dietary cholesterol reduction, such individuals may achieve plasma cholesterol levels approximating those in untreated heterozygotes.

Other forms of treatment for homozygotes are available, including portocaval anastomosis, plasma exchange (using columns that preferentially remove VLDL, IDL, and LDL), and liver transplantation. The relative risk factors are obvious; hopefully, it will be possible in the near future to correct the defect in homozygotes by use of genetically corrected hepatocytes obtained from the patient him- or herself. Such an approach relies on development of recombinant retroviruses that are used to transduce the normal LDL receptor gene.

Combined Hypercholesterolemia and Hypertriglyceridemia—Defect in apo E

The finding of a two-fold increase in plasma cholesterol and 9- to 10-fold increase of plasma triglycerides is distinctly unusual and strongly suggests a diagnosis of *Type III hyperlipoproteinemia (dysbetalipoproteinemia, broad-β disease)*. This unique combination arises from the presence of partially degraded VLDL of both intestinal and hepatic origins in blood. The existence of gut-derived VLDLs is a distinct abnormality, because these particles, identified as such by the presence of apo B-48, actually are chylomicron remnants that have not been normally taken up by the liver. Because clearance of chylomicron remnants from plasma depends upon the acquisition of apo E by interaction with HDL, and subsequent binding to LDL-type receptors via this apolipoprotein, this disorder arises from an abnormality of apo E.

Hepatic synthesis of VLDL renders both apo E and apo B-100 integral parts of the particle. However, as VLDLs are processed by removal of lipid, first to IDL, then to LDL, apo E is lost (see preceding section). Thus, true LDLs are bound to LDL receptors through the lower-affinity apo B-100, which is the only apoprotein remaining in these particles. Hence, abnormal apo E would be expected to adversely affect IDL-binding to the LDL receptor, reflected in an increase above normal in the apo E content of circulating so-called β-VLDLs. These particles account for the name, broad-β disease. The mutant apo E also would be expected to contribute to increased circulating IDLs, which is a finding that also is evident (Figure 15.5).

As a consequence of defective apo E, the total

mass of circulating, lower-density lipoprotein particles largely comprises "*remnants,*" which are partially degraded chylomicrons and VLDLs. Accordingly, the increased total serum cholesterol can be attributed to the cholesterol-enrichment of the β-VLDL in relation to a normal pre-β-VLDL. The increase in total serum triglyceride is accounted for by the increase in circulating chylomicron remnants that cannot be bound and taken up by the liver. These increases are offset, to a degree, by uptake of the β-VLDL particles into macrophages, where this cholesterol is largely esterified and stored. Under normal circumstances, this uptake process is mediated through binding of apo E to LDL-type receptors. In Type III hyperlipoproteinemia, however, it is assumed that a large percentage of total uptake occurs by mass action. Whatever the mechanism, the massive storage of esterified cholesterol leads to formation of "foam cells," which can be found in the xanthomata so characteristic of various defects causing lipid storage.

Unlike Type II hyperlipoproteinemia, which is the prototype of an autosomal, Mendelian dominant disorder, Type III disease is both recessive and atypical. It is well-documented that there is polymorphism of apo E; the most common genetically determined isoform is E3, and the others are designated E2 and E4. The normal biochemical phenotype is E3/E3. Whereas apo E4 has an LDL binding capacity virtually identical to that of E3, that of E2 is less than 5% that of E3. On this basis, it is should be apparent that the biochemical phenotype E2/E2 underlies all of the lipid abnormalities in patients with Type III hyperlipoproteinemia. Oddly enough, although E2/E2 is the phenotype assigned to practically all patients with clinical disease, not all individuals with this phenotype are affected. Another major deviation from the classic Mendelian autosomal recessive disorder is the occasional development of the Type III lipid abnormalities in an E3/E2 individual, who should be endowed with approximately 50% of normal capability for apo E-LDL receptor binding. Thus, it seems clear that hitherto unaccounted for genetic and/or environmental factors are required for clinical expression of the gene defect. These include, but are not limited to, hypothyroidism, obesity, diabetes mellitus, and alcoholism.

Initial treatment should be directed at reduction of dietary fat intake. Given that chylomicrons (their remnants are significant pathogens in this disease) are the carrier of dietary triglycerides, reduction of fat intake most likely will have a salutary effect on the plasma lipid profile. Because the other abnormal remnant derives from hepatic VLDL, a decrease in VLDL remnants can be achieved by inhibiting VLDL synthesis and release using nicotinic acid.

Hypertriglyceridemia

Normal individuals who ingest excess calories or ethanol will produce increased quantities of VLDLs. Some individuals, however, appear to produce increased levels of VLDL without the driving force provided by caloric excess. Unfortunately this area of lipidology is not as well defined as some that we already have considered; therefore, it is important to recognize that the interplay of heredity and acquired factors may be particularly important in the genesis of some forms of hypertriglyceridemia. Two monogenic forms of hypertriglyceridemia are *familial hypertriglyceridemia* (FHT, sometimes called type IV) and *familial combined hyperlipidemia* (also called familial multiple lipoprotein type hyperlipidemia).

Hypertrigylceridemia, defined as a level greater than 250 mg/dl, usually is associated with an increase in only the VLDL fraction. Theoretically, increased VLDL can be caused either by overproduction of VLDLs or by decreased removal of fatty acids from VLDLs, which is a reaction mediated by LPL. Consequently, such patients will have increases in VLDL remnants and IDL and may experience enhanced conversion of VLDL to LDL.

Patients with FHT have increased triglyceride (TG) levels unassociated with increased plasma cholesterol. There is evidence that the defect involves overproduction of VLDL-TG. The VLDL particles in FHT are larger than normal and, therefore, are TG-enriched. There is speculation that defective lipolysis of VLDL also may contribute to the hypertriglyceridemia. Part of the problem in these patients relates to an inability to increase catabolism of triglyceride when VLDL production increases. This is particularly striking in obese individuals and in diabetics.

Many conditions can exacerbate the hypertriglyceridemia in patients with FHT. Paramount among them are diabetes mellitus, nephrotic syndrome, and hypothyroidism. Certain drugs and agents also aggravate hypertriglyceridemia, such as oral contraceptives, ethanol, and β-adrenergic blocking agents.

Restriction of excess sucrose and ethanol, weight reduction, and increased physical activity have been beneficial to many patients. Drug therapy, when the foregoing are not sufficient, include nicotinic acid and gemfibrozil. Of course, secondary causes must be recognized and treated vigorously. And one should be aware that nicotinic acid can increase hyperglycemia in diabetics.

Familial combined hyperlipidemia (FCHL) is a monogenic, autosomal dominantly inherited disorder, characterized by overproduction of apo B, which in turn causes overproduction of VLDL (of normal composition). Patients with FCHL tend to develop premature coronary artery disease. In fact, about 10% of all patients suffering a myocardial infarction before age 55 years suffer from FCHL. If subjects with FCHL are followed longitudinally, the striking finding is the change in the lipoprotein electrophoretic pattern over time. At different times, it is not unusual to find patterns reflecting Types IIb, IIa, IV, or V. Secondary causes of a Type V pattern are diabetes mellitus, nephrotic syndrome, G 6 Pase deficiency, use of oral contraceptives, or ethanol.

Disorders Involving Lipoprotein Deficiency—Abetalipoproteinemia

In contrast to the disorders already considered, in which there is an increase in either triacylglycerol or cholesterol, we now wish to discuss those that are associated with an identifiable deficiency or absence of a specific class of lipoprotein. Inasmuch as such absence may exert a profound influence on other classes, this group of disorders further exemplifies the need for thorough and informed investigation of a clinically affected individual.

A striking example of these deficiency disorders is the entity known as abetalipoproteinemia. Because LDLs are the characteristic components of the electrophoretic "β-band," we may reasonably infer that there is a major deficiency in circulating LDLs. Actually, all apo B-containing classes of lipoproteins are deficient in this disorder, which includes chylomicrons, VLDLs, and IDLs as well. Because these lipoproteins are the chief carriers of both cholesterol and triglycerides in plasma, deficiency of these lipoprotein classes accounts for the very low levels of total lipid, cholesterol, triglycerides, and phospholipid seen in abetalipoproteinemia. Although it is clear that all apo B-containing classes of lipoproteins are adversely affected, the molecular cause of the disease is poorly characterized. Equally obscure is the pathophysiologic link between this abnormality and the varied clinical manifestations of the disease, but progress is being made in explaining some of the findings.

The most straightforward of the clinical manifestations in relation to the biochemical defect is the malabsorption, which usually presents during infancy. Keeping in mind that intestinal epithelial cells are the source of apo B-48, the characteristic apolipoprotein of chylomicrons, a defect in apo B production would seriously impair the incorporation of intestinal triglycerides and other dietary lipids into chylomicrons. As a consequence, there is an associated steatorrhea and a concomitant deficiency of the fat-soluble vitamins, which normally would enter the blood through the agency of chylomicrons. The implications for growth are obvious, and the attendant failure to thrive combined with the steatorrhea may lead to consideration of the diagnosis of cystic fibrosis.

Psychomotor retardation developing during infancy, described in many of the reported cases, may not be a primary aspect of the disease because histopathologic correlates with cerebral disease are lacking. Beyond this, many infants with steatorrhea and multiple nutritional deficiencies from other primary disease processes show delayed development. Independent of the enigma of the cause of the intellectual component of abetalipoproteinemia, there are multiple neuromuscular consequences that are basic to clinical diagnosis and clearly secondary. These include ataxia, proprioceptive loss, loss of deep tendon reflexes, and dysarthria, which frequently lead to consideration of Friedrich's ataxia (see Chapter 26). Myopathy frequently is mentioned, but demonstration that it is a primary process, independent of the neuropathy, is lacking.

A striking feature in laboratory diagnosis is the

presence of characteristic acanthocytes, which may constitute 50% to 100% of the circulating red cell mass, on peripheral smear. When subjected to compositional analysis, it is clear that the lipid abnormalities in the plasma are reflected in the components of the erythrocyte membrane, accounting for their abnormal shape. Of note is the observation that normal cells will develop into acanthocytes when transfused into patients with abetalipoproteinemia. Thus, the membrane lesion is acquired in the plasma and involves an increase in sphingomyelin at the expense of other phospholipids that normally are replenished by exchange with plasma lipoproteins. These cells appear to have an increase in the surface area of the outer aspect of the lipid bilayer, whereas the inner leaflet remains unchanged. In such a situation, this extra outer membrane becomes vulnerable to deformation.

Finally, there is a characteristic finding of retinitis pigmentosa which can lead eventually to complete loss of vision. Taken together, the entire complex of findings bears close relationship to experimental tocopherol deficiency, and treatment with massive doses of vitamin E can arrest and, in some cases, reverse the progress of the disease.

Tangier Disease

Another striking example of a lipoprotein deficiency is Tangier disease, in which there is almost total absence of apo A-I and HDL cholesterol from the serum. Its unusual name derives from the initial case description of an affected individual who resided on Tangier Island, which is located off the eastern shore of Virginia. As with many rare autosomal recessive disorders, the frequency of cases appears to be high on Tangier Island because of the restricted gene pool, and many derive from consanguineous matings. Because normal carriage of lipid in the blood creates a direct link between cholesterol and triglycerides, the finding of an inversely increased serum triglyceride and low cholesterol appears to be unique to Tangier disease. The increased triglyceride is relatively simple to explain because chylomicron (triglyceride-rich) particles normally acquire apo E from interaction with circulating HDL, which are, of course, deficient in Tangier disease. Without apo E, the binding affinity of chylomicron remnants in the liver is decreased, leading to increased circulating quantities. This accumulation of chylomicrons is further enhanced by a relatively low lipoprotein lipase activity. The cause of the low cholesterol remains unexplained.

What also remains somewhat enigmatic is the cause of the decrease in circulating HDL particles. It has been clearly established that the apo A-I gene is normal and, except for increased sialylation compared to controls, circulating apo E molecules also are normal. Radiolabeled, normal HDL particles infused into Tangier disease patients are catabolized much more rapidly than in normal individuals. The same is true of apo A-I and apo A-II proteins. Thus, the basic abnormality leading to plasma deficiency of HDL cholesterol appears to be accelerated removal of normal HDL particles from the circulation, although the mechanism for this remains unclear. Whatever the reason, increased influx of cholesterol-rich HDL particles into macrophages causes an upregulation of the microsomal enzyme acyl-CoA:cholesterol acyltransferase. This increased enzyme activity leads to enhancement of the rate of cholesteryl ester formation and intracellular deposition of lipid droplets; the ultimate result is the transformation of the macrophage into a foam cell.

Histiocytes throughout the body are involved in this storage phenomenon; those with the highest normal macrophage proportion become grossly enlarged. The characteristic tonsillar hypertrophy is directly related to this process, whereas the typical orange tint of the tonsils results from the presence of large quantities of cholesteryl esters. Likewise, the spleen is regularly enlarged and contains 100-fold or greater the normal content of cholesteryl esters. Another area of storage which is easily accessible but not usually considered is the rectal mucosa, which, by proctoscopic inspection, shows orange patches in areas of cholesteryl ester storage.

There also is significant neuropathology associated with Tangier disease. Cholesteryl ester storage can be clearly demonstrated in Schwann cells and neurons of the spinal ganglia and sacral spinal nerves. There is a spectrum of clinical correlates to this storage, including occasional involvement of cranial nerves in isolated fashion, as well as peripheral polyneuropathy. Keeping in mind that cholesterol is the largest single lipid component of myelin (see Chapter 26), it is not difficult to imagine the impact of increased transfer of HDL cholesterol to Schwann cells on myelin formation. The chief cause of morbidity in Tangier disease is the neuropathy, which usually is progressive over many years. There is no known treatment, and palliation by decreased dietary lipid intake has not been shown to be effective.

Hypercholesterolemia and Coronary Artery Disease

Our emphasis thus far on the striking abnormalities encountered in the various inherited defects of lipoprotein metabolism should not mask the reality that the vast majority of individuals manifesting hypercholesterolemia do not suffer from one of these monogenic diseases. Nevertheless, because of the powerful biochemical evidence in familial hypercholesterolemia and the epidemiological evidence of a strong association between increased blood cholesterol and coronary heart disease, expert groups in the United States, Canada, and the United Kingdom have issued guidelines for evaluating and treating adult patients with hypercholesterolemia. Most recently, the National Cholesterol Education Program in the United States has amended its earlier guidelines. This new document:

1. Places emphasis on whether there is preexisting coronary heart disease (CHD) or other arteriosclerotic disease;
2. Takes note of whether there are other risk factors, such as hypertension (or treated hypertension), cigarette smoking, or diabetes mellitus;
3. Considers a positive family history as a further risk factor;
4. Evaluates not only LDL cholesterol, but also HDL-C, viewing an HDL-C of less than 35 mg/dl as a risk factor and one of greater than 60 mg/dl as protective;
5. Considers the effect of age, placing males older than 45 years in a higher risk group, along with females older than 55 years or females who are menopausal and not receiving estrogen replacement therapy; and
6. Recognizes that both increased physical activity and weight loss exert positive effects on risk for CHD.

Using these various guidelines, in conjunction with LDL-C levels, patients are categorized further. For example, individuals without CHD having LDL-C levels of 160 mg/dl or above or those with two or more risk factors and LDL-C levels between 130 and 159 should be considered for dietary modification (see below). Similarly, patients with evidence of CDH and with LDL-C greater than 100 mg/dl also would be candidates for a "Step 1 diet," which is restricted in fat and cholesterol.

Dietary intervention focuses on reducing intake of saturated fats, cholesterol, and total calories. Strategies include sharply curtailing ingestion of red meats, organ meats, regular milk and ice cream, natural cheeses, egg yolks, and baked goods prepared with saturated fats. Substitutions are fish, poultry with skin removed, lean meat cuts, skim and low fat milk and cheeses, fruits and vegetables, and low fat dressings. A recent report cautions against the use of margarine because of its high content of trans fatty acids, which contribute to development of CHD.

Controversy exists in the literature about the efficacy of the Step 1 diet in reducing blood cholesterol and about the efficacy of the more restricted Step 2 diet in a typical living situation. But other studies have shown that a predominantly vegetarian diet will be ingested by a highly motivated subject (generally a patient who has suffered a myocardial infarction). When followed scrupulously, this highly restricted diet has been shown to be effective.

The reason so much emphasis continues to be placed on dietary intervention and increased physical activity is that these two modalities offer the distinct benefit of decreasing the risk for CHD, without side effect. The various lipid-lowering drugs used in hypercholesterolemic states cannot warrant absence of side effects. Many experts have expressed concern that because of vigorous promotion by pharmaceutical companies, these drugs are being urged on patients who might have benefitted from a less aggressive approach. Worse yet, there seems to be an increase in noncardiac related deaths in patients who have been placed on lipid-lowering drugs. Although the reason for this has not yet been discovered, it does suggest that use of these drugs is not entirely innocuous and should not be undertaken without adequate justification.

Consequently, the guidelines of the National Cholesterol Education Program call for a trial of dietary modification of 3 to 6 months before considering drugs, after which several groups of subjects become candidates for lipid-lowering agents. Such patients include: (*a*) those without CHD or with less than two risk factors, whose LDL-C remains 190 mg/dl or greater; (*b*) patients with two or more risk factors whose LDL-C is 160 mg/dl or greater; and (*c*) patients with existing CHD with LDL-C of 130 mg/dl or greater. These National Cholesterol Education Program recommendations limit use of drugs in men less than 35 years and women less than 55 years who have no additional risk factors with LDL-C between 190 and 219 mg/dl.

Many would begin drug therapy sooner in patients with existing CHD, in whom the LDL-C did not decrease to the desired level (ie, less than 130 mg/dl on diet and lifestyle changes), believing that this group is at greatest risk. Of course, in this group, one also might consider daily or every other day low dose aspirin along with an exercise program and vigorous attempts to maintain ideal body weight. Also, in patients who have no contraindications (eg, peptic ulcer disease or addictive personalities), consumption of modest amounts of alcohol increases blood HDL-C and decreases the risk for CHD.

SUGGESTED READINGS

Aviram M. Modified forms of low density lipoprotein and atherosclerosis. Atherosclerosis 1993;98:1.

Cortner JA, Coates PM, Liacouras CA, Jarvik GP. Familial combined hyperlipidemia in children: clinical expression, metabolic defects, and management. J Pediatr 1993;123:177.

Davey Smith G, Song F, Sheldon TA. Cholesterol lowering and mortality: the importance of considering initial level of risk. British Medical Journal 1993;306:1367.

Denke MA, Frantz ID Jr. Response to a cholesterol-lowering diet: efficacy is greater in hypercholesterolemic subjects even after adjustment for regression to the mean. Am J Med 1993;94:626.

Denke MA. Cholesterol lowering diets. Arch Intern Med 1995;155:17.

Friedman GD, Klatsky AL. Is alcohol good for your health? (Editorial) N Engl J Med 1993;329, 1882.

Gaziano JM, Buring JE, Breslow JL, et al. Moderate alcohol intake, increased levels of high-density lipoprotein and its subfractions, and decreased risk of myocardial infarction. N Engl J Med 1993;329:1829.

Genest J Jr. Genetic lipid disorders in cardiovascular disease. Trends in Cardiovascular Medicine 1992;2:140.

Havel RJ, Rapaport E. Management of primary hyperlipidemia. N Engl J Med 1995;332:1491.

Hobbs HH, Russell DW, Brown MS, Goldstein JL. The LDL receptor locus in familial hypercholesterolemia: mutational analysis of a membrane protein. Annu Rev Genet 1990;24:133.

Hornstra G, Saris WHM, eds. Lipids: The continuing challenge. American Journal of Clinical Nutrition 1992;57:703S–832S.

Hunninghake DB, ed. Lipid disorders. Med Clin North Am 1994;78:1–266.

Klag MJ, Ford DF, Mead LA, et al. Serum cholesterol in young men and subsequent cardiovascular disease. N Engl J Med 1993;328:313.

Kreisberg RA, Segrest JP. Plasma lipoproteins and coronary artery disease. Boston: Blackwell, 1992.

Kwiterovich PO Jr. Diagnosis and management of familial dyslipoproteinemia in children and adolescents. Pediatr Clin North Am 1990;37:1489.

Oberman A, Kreisberg RA, Henkin Y. Principles and management of lipid disorders. Baltimore: Williams & Wilkins, 1992.

Paffenbarger RS Jr, Hyde RT, Wing AL, et al. The association of changes in physical-activity level and other lifestyle characteristics with mortality among men. N Engl J Med 1993;328:538.

Sandvik L, Erikssen J, Thaulow E, et al. Physical fitness as a predictor of mortality among healthy, middle-aged Norwegian men. N Engl J Med 1993;328:533.

Scriver CR, Beaudet AL, Sly WS, Valle D, eds. The metabolic and molecular bases of inherited disease. 7th ed. New York: McGraw-Hill, 1995.

Summary of the second report of the National Cholesterol Education Program (NCEP) expert panel on detection, evaluation, and treatment of high blood cholesterol in adults (adult treatment panel II). JAMA 1993;269:3015.

chapter **16**

Purine and Pyrimidine Metabolism and Their Disorders

Purine and pyrimidines are, literally, the building blocks for the foundation of human life. Recall that pyrimidines are six-membered heterocycles, whereas purines are bicyclic heterocycles in which a pyrimidine ring is fused to a five-membered imidazole ring (Figure 16.1). The purines adenine and guanine, with the pyrimidines thymine and cytidine, constitute the genetic code contained within an individual's DNA. Apart from their role in heredity, purines and pyrimidines subserve other vitally important biologic functions, particularly in forming compounds with a high group transfer potential such as adenosine triphosphate (ATP), guanosine triphosphate (GTP), and uridine diphosphate glucose (UDP-glu). As with heme and cholesterol, which are two other molecules with critically important functions, purines and pyrimidines can be synthesized de novo, and the rates of biosynthesis and degradation are tightly regulated. Because synthesis is energetically expensive, salvage pathways for purines and pyrimidines exist that in nondividing tissues contribute these compounds for recycling and, therefore, energy conservation.

Given the complexity of the pathways involved, it is remarkable that genetic defects are not common. This simply may depend on the fact that inability to carry out de novo synthesis of one of these four bases is incompatible with life. Indeed, a fertilized oocyte carrying a mutation that impairs purine or pyrimidine synthesis would be rendered incapable of passing beyond the single-cell stage, because cell replication requires de novo synthesis. Little is known of placental transfer and synthesis of these molecules, as well as the possible role of these processes in regulation of fetal de novo synthesis and growth. Thus, taken together, defects in the overall system that supplies purines and pyrimidines could account for many preimplantation abortions and growth-retarded fetuses. The latter issue has not been explored in a systematic fashion.

Another odd feature of purine and pyrimidine metabolism lies in the vastly disproportionate incidence of abnormalities in purines. Thus, whereas "gout" (idiopathic hyperuricemia) has a firm place in the folklore of history, orotic acid is virtually unknown to most people, including many in the medical community. Given the comparable complexity of the biosynthetic pathways, one would intuitively expect that the number and incidence of disorders in each would be approximately equivalent.

PURINE METABOLISM

De Novo Synthesis

The distinctive feature of the de novo pathway for purines is that synthesis begins from the sugar moiety of the ribonucleotide end product (Figure 16.2). Ribose-5-phosphate is pyrophosphorylated; the product, *phosphoribosylpyrophosphate* (PRPP), then reacts with glutamine, which donates an amino group to form β-5-phosphoribosyl-1-amine. The amino group thus derived serves as the link between the ribose moiety and the growing purine nucleus. Throughout the subsequent nine steps, the elements of the growing purine ring are added from simple building blocks: amino acids, bicarbonate, and folate. The product of de novo synthesis is inosine monophosphate, which is common to both the adenine and guanine nucleotides. The final energetic cost in reaching either final purine nucleotide is a minimum of six ATP

Figure 16.1. Structural formulas for the purines and pyrimidines. Note that the presence of uracil in the triphosphorylated state (UTP) represents a key difference between RNA and DNA, when thymine-triphosphate (TTP) is found instead.

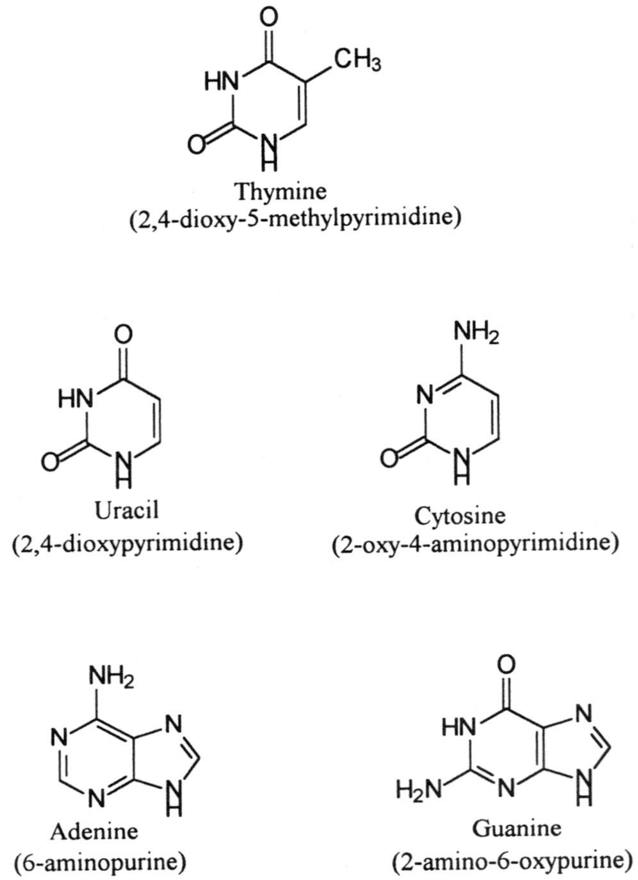

molecules. This is an expensive metabolic process that cannot be "afforded" on a regular basis; the salvage pathway is more economical. Of course, the most important situations demanding net de novo synthesis would be growth and tissue regeneration.

Purine Salvage

The huge energy demand placed on the cell for de novo purine nucleotide base synthesis obviously cannot be sustained throughout the entire period of gestation and early infant growth. Thus, survival has dictated evolution of a pathway to salvage and recycle these expensive molecules. To understand this pathway, it is necessary to define certain terms. The product of the de novo pathway discussed above is defined as a purine nucleotide (eg, inosine monophosphate; Figure 16.2), which consists of the base linked to ribose phosphate. Removal of the phosphate moiety, leaving a base-sugar molecule, yields a nucleoside (eg, adenine nucleoside). Further removal of the sugar leaves a purine base.

The critical step in salvage of purine bases is mediated by one of two enzymes, depending on the base (Figure 16.3): *adenine phosphoribosyltransferase* (APRT) acting on adenine and *hypoxanthine-guanine phosphoribosyltransferase* (HGPRT) acting on hypoxanthine or guanine. The specific activity of APRT, the enzyme acting on adenine, is only a fraction of HGPRT activity, reflecting the relatively small amounts of substrate needing conversion to adenosine nucleotide. Each enzyme requires an additional substrate, *5-phosphoribosylpyrophosphate (PRPP)*, which also serves as the starting compound for purine biosynthesis. In this salvage reaction, PRPP transfers its 5-phosphoribosyl moiety to the free base, liberat-

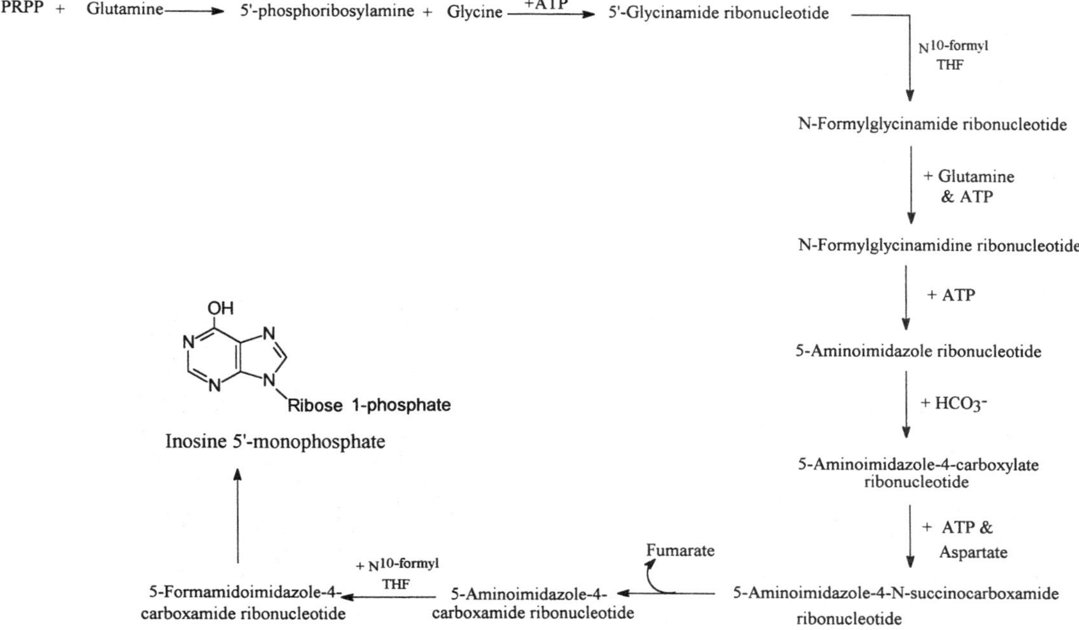

Figure 16.2. The de novo purine synthetic pathway. D-ribose 5-phosphate is derived from the pentose phosphate pathway. Formation of phosphoribosylpyrophosphate (PRPP) occurs via the enzyme ATP phosphoribosyl transferase, which is a critical regulatory step in the overall pathway. Note that at each subsequent step, a simple compound is involved in any addition to the growing purine nucleus. The total energy investment necessary to reach the common nucleoside base, inosine 5′-monophosphate, is six ATP molecules (two are used in production of PRPP). THF = tetrahydrofolate.

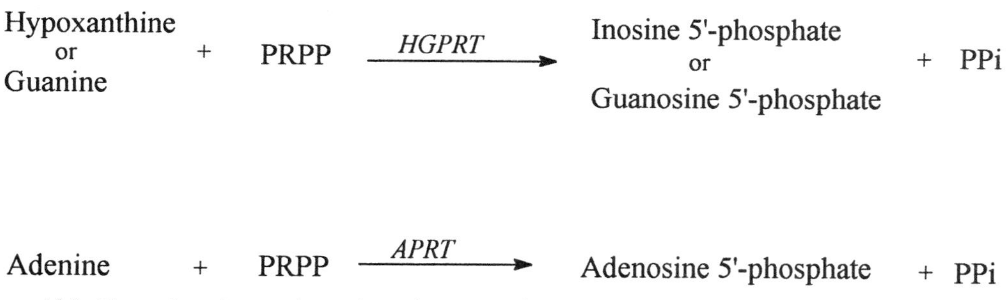

Hypoxanthine or Guanine + PRPP —*HGPRT*→ Inosine 5'-phosphate or Guanosine 5'-phosphate + PPi

Adenine + PRPP —*APRT*→ Adenosine 5'-phosphate + PPi

Figure 16.3. The purine salvage pathway. As in de novo synthesis, phosphoribosylpyrophosphate (PRPP) plays a critical role in purine salvage. Of the two reactions, the one mediated by hypoxanthine-guanine phosphoribosyltransferase (HGPRT) is much more active than that involved in salvaging adenine via adenine phosphoribosyl transferase (APRT). This is a reflection of the relative amount of adenine produced compared to the use and reuse of adenosine in ATP-requiring pathways, thus preventing formation of the free base. Because inosine 5′-phosphate can be used in production of either adenine or guanine nucleotide, its formation in salvage is vital to the well-being of cells that cannot carry out de novo synthesis. Energy consumption in these reactions is one ATP molecule per conserved purine nucleus; this is a much less expensive process than de novo synthesis. PPi = pyrophosphate.

$$\text{Inosine} + \text{Pi} \rightleftharpoons \text{Hypoxanthine} + \text{Ribose 1-P}$$

$$\text{Deoxyinosine} + \text{Pi} \rightleftharpoons \text{Hypoxanthine} + \text{Deoxyribose 1-P}$$

$$\text{Guanosine} + \text{Pi} \rightleftharpoons \text{Guanine} + \text{Ribose 1-P}$$

$$\text{Xanthosine} + \text{Pi} \rightleftharpoons \text{Xanthine} + \text{Ribose 1-P}$$

Figure 16.4. Purine nucleoside phosphorylase reactions. This reaction liberates a free purine base and ribose 1-phosphate, which can be converted to ribose 5′-phosphate by the enzyme phosphoglucomutase. This reaction conserves one of the two molecules of ATP ordinarily required for production of a molecule of phosphoribosylpyrophosphate (PRPP). Pi = inorganic phosphate.

ing pyrophosphate. PRPP can be generated either from the pentose phosphate pathway or directly from ribose-1-phosphate, which is released during conversion of a nucleoside to a free base (Figure 16.4). The energy cost in this direct transfer reaction is 1 mole of ATP per mole of nucleotide product, which is the energy used in generating the PRPP. Thus, salvage of purine bases through this mechanism yields a net energy saving of 5 moles of ATP over the de novo synthetic pathway. Despite this substantial net energy saving achieved through the salvage pathway, it must be recognized that even with 100% efficiency, salvage can maintain only the status quo. Growth or tissue regeneration after destruction can be achieved only in the presence of a net gain in total purines.

Purine Degradation

The end product of degradation of all purine nucleotides is *uric acid,* which is the most oxidized form of all the purines. Catabolism of the purine nucleotides requires: (*a*) removal of the 5′-phosphate, (*b*) deamination, (*c*) cleavage of the glycosidic bond in a phosphorolysis, and (*d*) oxidation of the resulting guanine and hypoxanthine to uric acid (Figure 16.5). Because both guanine and hypoxanthine are intermediates in the salvage pathway, if salvage does not occur, both bases are converted to the common intermediate, *xanthine,* and then are metabolized to uric acid. Notice that xanthine oxidase mediates conversion of hypoxanthine to xanthine and then converts xanthine to uric acid. Guanine must first be deaminated to form xanthine. *Xanthine oxidase* is a flavoprotein found in substantial quantities only in liver and intestine. Significantly, because there is no enzymatic pathway permitting conversion of xanthine to hypoxanthine, guanine cannot be converted through inosine to adenosine monophosphate. As a consequence, all hypoxanthine and guanine not salvaged is converted to uric acid, which causes significant morbidity when the salvage pathway is either overburdened or defective. We will examine these situations more closely below. Finally, note that the xanthine oxidase reaction produces stoichiometric amounts of hydrogen peroxide, which must then be converted to avoid tissue damage from the superoxide radical.

DISORDERS OF PURINE METABOLISM

Synthetic Defects

Ostensibly, it may seem strange that there have been only two defects of the de novo pathway for purines described as causes for clinical disease in humans. Because the ability to synthesize purines de novo is crucial to the survival of the fertilized ovum, it is likely that any genetic defect in the process would render a conceptus nonviable. It also is true that any impediment to ATP production will most likely cause the same end result.

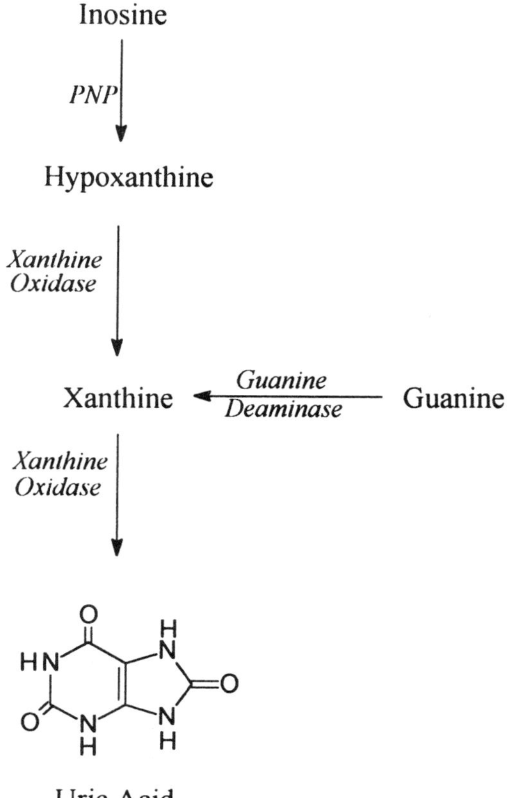

Figure 16.5. Purine degradation pathway. Whereas inosine can be reversibly produced from hypoxanthine, the action of xanthine oxidase results in formation of xanthine, which is an unrecoverable intermediate in degradation. A further oxidation, also mediated by xanthine oxidase, produces uric acid, which is the final compound in purine degradation.

PHOSPHORIBOSYLPYROPHOSPHATE SYNTHETASE SUPERACTIVITY

PRPP synthetase catalyzes the formation of PRPP. PRPP is not only a reactant in the first committed step in de novo purine biosynthesis but also an allosteric regulator of the reaction in which β-phosphoribosylamine is formed from 5-phosphoribosyl-pyrophosphate and glutamine, which is catalyzed by amidophosphoribosyl transferase. This reaction also is regulated in an allosteric fashion by purine ribonucleotides (monophosphate > di- > tri-), which are inhibitory to this reaction. PRPP synthetase, encoded on the X chromosome, is subject to complex regulation, including ADP (acting in competition with MgATP), 2,3-diphosphoglycerate (acting in competition with ribose-5-phosphate), and noncompetitive inhibition by various nucleotides. Thus, reduction in cellular purine nucleotides will cause upregulation, with increased production of PRPP and increase de novo in purine synthesis. Note that PRPP synthesis is critical to purine salvage; therefore, greater availability of PRPP will boost conservation of cellular nucleotides as well. Overall, the initial two steps of purine biosynthesis are tightly controlled by both substrate and cellular purine nucleotide concentrations.

There are various mutations of the gene encoding PRPP synthase that produce abnormal responses to the normal regulatory factors, such as nucleotide or ribose-5-phosphate concentrations; therefore, the enzyme exhibits superactivity. Under these circumstances, purines are synthesized at a rate "more or less" independent of the needs, resulting in an overburdened salvage pathway and ending in increased uric acid production. An analogous situation can be seen in glucose-6-phosphatase deficiency, in which it is theorized that the consumption of ATP to produce phosphorylated intermediates of glycolysis restricts inorganic phosphate availability. This, in turn, leads to increased net purine catabolism in excess of the capacity for salvage, with increased production of uric acid as a result (see Chapter 11).

ADENYLOSUCCINASE DEFICIENCY

Adenylosuccinase is involved in two steps of purine synthesis: (*1*) conversion of succinylaminoimidazole carboxamide ribotide to aminoimidazole carboxamide ribotide, and (*2*) conversion of adenylosuccinate to adenosine monophosphate (AMP). Predictably, the precursors in these reactions accumulate in body fluids. Deficiency of this enzyme is rare and is associated with psychomotor retardation. Presently, it is not clear how the enzyme defect leads to the clinical manifestations.

Salvage Defects

HYPOXANTHINE GUANINE PHOSPHORIBOSYLTRANSFERASE DEFICIENCY

HGPRT catalyzes the transfer of the phosphoribosyl group of PRPP to either guanine or hypoxanthine to form the analogous nucleotides (Figure 16.3). The most extreme example of a salvage pathway defect is *Lesch-Nyhan* syndrome, which is the X-linked genetic condition that is caused by complete deficiency of HGPRT. Lesch-Nyhan disease is characterized by severe neurologic disease and urate nephrolithiasis. This enzyme, of course, is key to the cell's ability to recycle purine bases. In cases of complete deficiency, virtually all purine nucleotide catabolism ultimately flows beyond hypoxanthine and guanine to be converted to xanthine and then is converted to uric acid by the action of xanthine oxidase. Recalling that elevated intracellular PRPP levels enhance production of β-phosphoribosylamine, the first committed step in de novo purine biosynthesis, the increased production of uric acid from unsalvaged bases is compounded by more rapid purine synthesis. Overall, measurements of uric acid in urine from affected individuals show levels approximately 20 times the normal range. Hyperuricemia always is present, with the usual levels at 9 to 12 mg/dl exceeding the limits of urate solubility at normal plasma pH.

In understanding the clinical importance of such plasma urate levels, one must realize that at plasma pH, uric acid is converted to sodium urate, whereas at normal urine pH, it is likely to exist in the acid form. Solubility of uric acid in the urine pH range from 5.0 to 6.0 increases only from 15 mg/dl to 22 mg/dl. Because excretion of uric acid in patients with Lesch-Nyhan syndrome is more than 600 mg/day, a minimum total volume of more than 2700 ml would be required to maintain solubility at pH 6.0!

Thus, although affected infants may show no neurologic manifestations until late in the first year, signs referable to the urinary tract are very likely to be present earlier. In particular, a pink or orange color in wet diapers strongly suggests the presence of uric acid crystals in the urine. This actually may progress to nephropathy before the end of the first year of life and, if untreated, result in death due to renal failure within the first decade. Accumulation of uric acid in interstitial fluid leads to development of tophi, which is the sine qua non of adult gout (see below). Early recognition of hyperuricemia enables treatment with *allopurinol,* which is a competitive inhibitor of *xanthine oxidase,* with resulting prevention of the urate nephropathy and arthropathy.

We purposely discuss the neurologic manifestations of Lesch-Nyhan syndrome last. The chief reason is that, because of the absence of neurologic manifestations in idiopathic gout at comparable plasma uric acid levels, clear evidence exists that hyperuricemia per se is not an etiologic factor in the neuropathy. Neurologic manifestations consist of athetosis as the earliest sign, progressing later to chorea and dystonia. Opisthotonus and spasticity are common later in the course. Dysarthria always is present early and progresses to total aphasia, except for punctuation by screams, making assessment of mental function exceptionally difficult. But the most striking abnormality in Lesch-Nyhan disease is *compulsive self-mutilation.* If extremities are not restrained and teeth not capped or removed, these patients bite away lips, tongue, and finger tips. This destructive behavior does not begin until the second or third year of life. Fortunately, hand and elbow restraints alleviate the agitation that the uncontrollable behavior evokes.

The dysfunctional motor characteristics can be clinically related to abnormalities of the pyramidal and extrapyramidal tracts, yet neuropathologic examination has failed to reveal consistent abnormal findings in these or other areas of the brain. The most promising evidence at this time involves a 70% to 90% reduction of the neurotransmitter dopamine in the basal ganglia. However, dopamine deficiency is not the sole explanation because patients with Parkinson's disease, who suffer from dramatic decrease in dopamine, do not share the strikingly aggressive and self-mutilative behavior manifested by patients with Lesch-Nyhan disease. Of particular note, treatment with allopurinol does not have any positive effect on either the neurologic or the behavioral abnormalities in this disease.

Spontaneous mutations involving the HGPRT gene account for approximately 33% of all cases of Lesch-Nyhan syndrome. It is important to remember that such a new mutation may occur in an asymptomatic, heterozygous mother, thus remaining clinically "silent" until transmitted to a male offspring. Molecular probe studies indicate that there is a considerable degree of heterogeneity among mutations accounting for the clinical phenotype. The common factor among all of these is that they result in complete absence of enzyme activity, with about 70% producing no detectable protein.

There are several variants of complete HGPRT deficiency that result in partial loss of enzymatic activity, only one of which mimics the Lesch-Nyhan phenotype. The other three variants constitute a group of enzyme disorders that produce hyperuricemia, uric acid nephropathy, and gouty arthritis traceable to defective salvage pathway activity. The chief clinical difference between partially deficient HGPRT individuals and the symptomatic hyperuricemia of gout is the earlier age of onset, the former presenting in individuals less than 40 years of age.

IDIOPATHIC HYPERURICEMIA AND GOUT

The vast majority of individuals with serum uric acid levels above the normal range have no known enzymatic defect and will remain asymptomatic throughout at least most of their lives. Considering all people with hyperuricemia together, only about 20% eventually develop gout; the chief determinants are the degree of hyperuricemia and age. Serum uric acid levels bear no gender relationship until puberty, at which time males show an increase of 1 to 2 mg/dl over their prepubertal levels. Because a strong relationship exists between serum uric acid levels and development of clinical manifestations, there is a predictable predilection in males. Moreover, because initial gouty attacks appear with a peak age of onset after 45 years in males, it generally is agreed that exposure to hyperuricemia for roughly 30 years is required. This, however, should be accepted with caution because such an assumption presupposes that uric acid levels were not high prepubertally in diagnosed gouty patients. Data to support such an assumption rarely are available because serum urate is not routinely measured in children.

The pathognomonic lesion of gout is the *tophus*, which typically is found in the distal joints of the extremities, usually the lower limbs. About 90% of all patients with gout will experience an acute arthritis involving a great toe at some point in the clinical course of the disease. Histopathologically, a tophus consists of synovial deposition of uric acid crystals, with a surrounding area of inflammation. The marked propensity of urate to deposit in distal synovial joints is easily explained on physiologic and chemical principles. As discussed above, uric acid solubility diminishes with decreasing pH and temperature. Clearly, the termination of arterial blood flow in the distal extremities, especially in small joints that are relatively poorly vascularized, will contribute to the likelihood of regional acid accumulation. Especially in the toes, which are subjected to the added burden of gravity acting against venous return to the heart, it is not difficult to imagine how this regional acid burden reduces pH in the interstitium with resultant precipitation of uric acid crystals. An additional contribution to the process is the reduced solubility of uric acid with decreasing temperature, which is a situation that occurs during sleep and accounts for the propensity of these attacks to occur after the patient has gone to bed.

Clinically, an acute attack of gout includes obvious signs of inflammation at the affected site, including swelling, erythema, and excruciating tenderness. When present, systemic signs including fever, leukocytosis, and elevated erythrocyte sedimentation rate may be misinterpreted as representing bacterial sepsis resulting from a local infection. Thus, two pieces of information are crucial to the correct diagnosis in a previously well individual: the *serum uric acid level* and identification of *uric acid crystals* in an aspirate of the affected joint. It is important to understand that the pathogenesis of acute gouty arthritis is not related to an acute increase in serum uric acid. Thus, demonstration of hyperuricemia is a necessary, but not sufficient condition to make a diagnosis. The natural course of acute gout includes complete resolution within several hours to weeks without treatment. The mechanism by which this occurs is poorly understood, especially in view of the persistent hyperuricemia that led to the attack. The neutrophil, which migrates in great number to the region involved, phagocytoses the urate crystals, which then leads to oxygen radical formation. These oxygen radicals further enhance the inflammatory reaction. Colchicine inhibits the phagocytotic process, thus reducing superoxide formation. In turn, this antiinflammatory agent reduces lactic acid production by the neutrophil, thus minimizing further uric acid crystal deposition in the area of inflammation. The therapeutic response of acute gouty arthritis to colchicine is so specific that it can be used as a means of diagnosis as well.

The subsequent natural history of gout includes the so-called *interval gout*, commencing upon resolution of the acute attack, which typically is followed by a subsequent acute episode within 2 years of the first one. These recurrences become more frequent, eventually establishing the picture of chronic gout, which results in multiple joint damage and destruction and chronic pain. The ensuing deformities of hands and feet ultimately become crippling. Oddly enough, although logic would suggest that such major morbidity associated with hyperuricemia also should be reflected in renal function, this relationship is far from clear. Indeed, although many gouty patients eventually die from renal failure, they generally do not do so at an age younger than most nongouty patients. Although the relationship of renal failure to gout is clearly established, the role of hyperuricemia in this link remains poorly defined. It is even more odd, in view of this, that uric acid stones occur in primary gout with a prevalence 1000 times greater than that of the general population.

Reduced uric acid excretion is the major mechanism underlying hyperuricemia and the development of gout, according to most major studies. Given the strong evidence that reduced tubular secretion is the chief defect, it is possible to speculate that failure to cross the tubular barrier and enter urine leads to protection of the nephron against uric acid nephropathy. Conversely, however, this also should result in protection against stone formation, which is not supported by the clinical observations. Nonetheless, assessment of uric acid excretion in mg/min versus plasma uric acid demonstrates that gouty underexcretors must have a substantially higher plasma level (ca. 1.7 mg/dl) than normal subjects to achieve the same urinary excretion rate. On the basis of this observation, it is possible to see why the uricosuric agent, *probenecid,* might be suboptimal therapy as a sole drug because its action is based upon inhibition of postsecretory reabsorption.

Most experts do not recommend treating asymptomatic hyperuricemia. But in patients with significant elevation of plasma uric acid, or who are urate underexcretors or have a family history of tophi, the prudent course is to use allopurinol to diminish production of uric acid.

Purine Catabolic Defects

ADENOSINE DEAMINASE DEFICIENCY

Adenosine deaminase is responsible for catalyzing deamination of adenosine and deoxyadenosine. Absence of this enzyme is associated with a life-threatening immune deficiency involving both T- and B-cells called *severe combined immunodeficiency.* T- and B-cells seem to "bear the brunt" of this enzyme defect because, normally, adenosine deaminase activity is highest in lymphoid tissue. Recurrent infections, especially of the skin, respiratory tract, and gastrointestinal tract are the clinical hallmarks associated with striking lymphopenia and hypogammaglobulinemia.

The accumulation of dATP in lymphocytes is believed to exert two noxious biochemical effects on lymphocyte function. First, dATP, formed from deoxyadenosine, inhibits ribonucleotide reductase, blocking formation of deoxyribonucleotides for incorporation into DNA. Second, transmethylation reactions appear to be inhibited because deoxyadenosine inhibits S-adenosylhomocysteine hydrolase. Methylation reactions are important in protecting bases in DNA and RNA.

PURINE NUCLEOSIDE PHOSPHORYLASE DEFICIENCY

Purine nucleoside phosphorylase catalyzes the phosphorolytic degradation of the nucleosides inosine and guanosine and their deoxy congeners to the free base with release of ribose-1-P or deoxyribose-1-P. In the absence of the enzyme, these nucleosides accumulate. T-cells particularly are vulnerable to purine nucleoside phosphorylase deficiency because dGTP, formed from deoxyguanosine, inhibits ribonucleotide reductase and, therefore, DNA synthesis in that cell line. It has been speculated that the sparing of B-cells may be attributed either to the lack of an effect on S-adenosylhomocysteine hydrolase or to the persistence of helper T-cells to direct B-cell function. As with adenosine deaminase deficiency, the clinical manifestations center on recurrent infections.

PYRIMIDINE METABOLISM

De Novo Synthesis

Like the urea cycle (see Chapter 5), entry to de novo pyrimidine synthesis requires formation of *carbamyl phosphate* (Figure 16.6). In contrast to the urea cycle, however, pyrimidine synthesis is initiated in the cytosol through the action of *carba-*

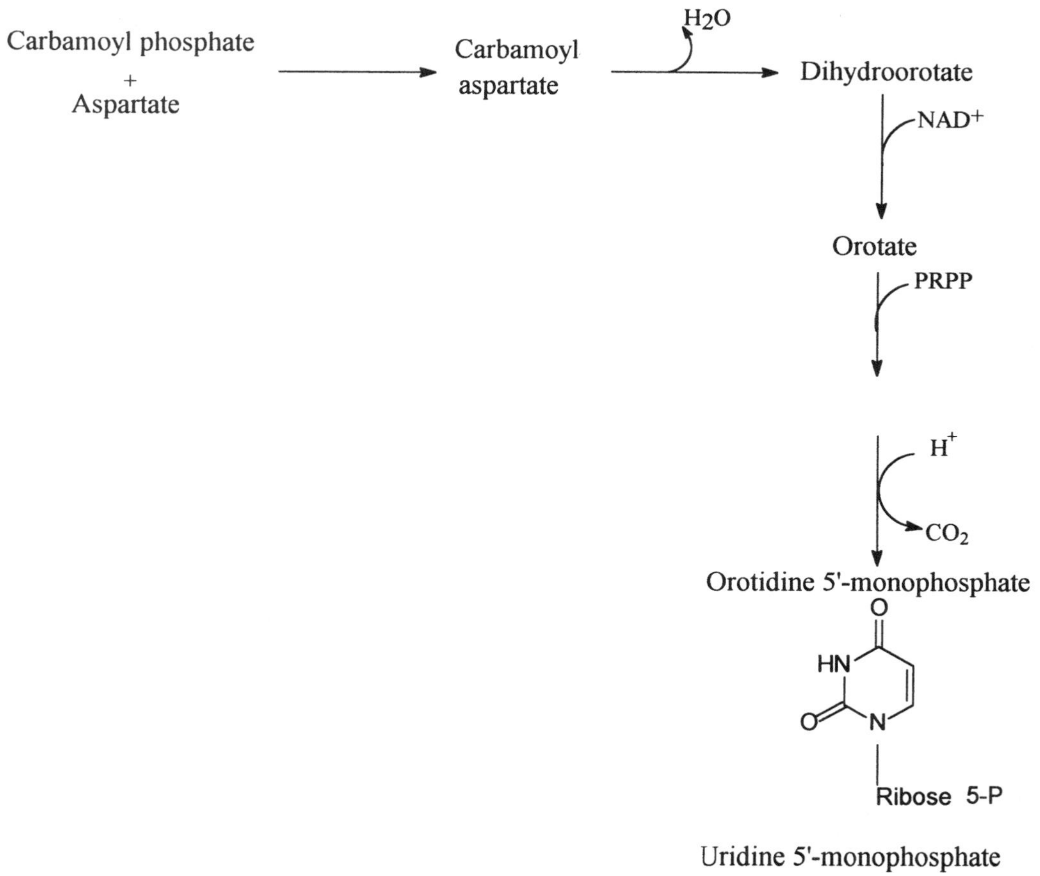

Figure 16.6. The de novo pyrimidine synthetic pathway. The initiating enzyme step, formation of carbamyl phosphate, differs from that of urea synthesis because it is mediated by cytosolic carbamyl phosphate synthase (CPS II), which is a different enzyme from mitochondrial CPS I of the urea cycle. CPS II is a multifunctional enzyme that mediates the first three steps of the synthetic pathway, resulting in formation of dihydroorotic acid. The subsequent step, conversion to the free pyrimidine base orotic acid, takes place through the action of dihydro-orotate dehydrogenase, located on the outer surface of the mitochondrial membrane. A bifunctional enzyme uridine monophosphate synthase produces the common pyrimidine intermediate, uridine-5′-monophosphate (UMP). The net cost is 5 moles of ATP per mole of UMP.

myl phosphate synthase (CPS II), which is an enzyme that is distinct from the mitochondrial protein, CPS I. A second major difference from CPS I is that CPS II is a multifunctional enzyme protein with three distinct catalytic sites mediating the three initial reactions of de novo pyrimidine synthesis. This entry step into pyrimidine biosynthesis also differs regarding the reactants involved in the urea cycle, requiring glutamine rather than ammonia as the donor for the amine group of the carbamyl phosphate. The need for a glutamine donor parallels the requirement in the first committed step in purine de novo synthesis; like that step, formation of CPS is rate-limiting in the process.

The second step, also mediated by CPS II, incorporates aspartate and eliminates phosphate (*aspartate transcarbamylase*) to form carbamyl aspartate. The final product of the multifunctional protein is the closed ring compound, *dihydro-orotic acid,* arrived at through elimination of water (*dihydro-orotase*). Conversion to the free pyrimidine base, orotic acid, occurs through the action of *dihydro-orotate dehydrogenase,* which is a single-function, NAD^+-dependent enzyme that is located on the outer surface of the mitochondrial membrane. Orotic acid then is returned to the cytosol, where it is acted upon by a bifunctional enzyme, *uridine monophosphate synthase.* The first step is conversion to orotidine-5′-monophosphate, which then is converted to form uridine-5′-monophosphate (UMP) through a decarboxylation reaction. UMP is the common intermediate, requiring 5 moles of ATP per mole for its synthesis, from which cytidine, uridine, and thymine nucleotides are synthesized. Overall, the reactions resulting in synthesis of UMP are remarkable because six catalytic conversions are accomplished by three proteins coded for by three genes.

With expenditure of 2 additional moles of ATP, UMP is converted to uridine triphosphate (UTP), which can be converted to cytidine triphosphate (CTP) by amination of the uridine ring, using glutamine as the amine donor and requiring an additional mole of ATP. Although both UTP and CTP are components of RNA, UTP is not used for DNA synthesis. Thus, some of the UMP must be used for thymine nucleotide synthesis, which depends first upon production of UDP by UMP kinase. UDP then is acted upon by ribonucleotide reductase, which reduces the ribose moiety at the 2′-position through a complex, incompletely characterized reaction to form dUDP. This ribonucleotide reductase step is the same enzymatic mechanism used for production of dADP and dGDP. CTP can enter the pathway by initial dephosphorylation to CDP and is subsequently reduced to dCDP by ribonucleotide reductase; the dCDP is either recovered or expenditure of a mole of ATP creates dCMP or dCTP. The former compound can be deaminated by deoxycytidylate deaminase with formation of dUMP.

The conversion of dUMP to dTMP requires methylation of the pyrimidine base. Methylation reactions in biochemistry generally are complex, and this one is no exception. The mediating enzyme, *thymidylate synthase,* requires *5,10-methylene-tetrahydrofolate* as a cofactor and accomplishes transfer of the methylene group plus two electrons to dUMP, leaving dihydrofolate to be regenerated. The importance of folate mediated one-carbon transfer within the present context is as great as deoxyribonucleotide synthesis is to DNA synthesis and cell division.

Given the simplicity of the pyrimidine molecule in relation to the purines, the complexity of the de novo synthetic pathway is impressive. Furthermore, the energy expenditure necessary to reach the common intermediate, UMP, is consistent with the degree of complexity. Viewed in this way, one cannot help but greatly respect the accomplishment of cell division, as well as the "wisdom" of evolutionary forces in finding salvage pathways to conserve such "expensive" and biologically precious molecules.

Pyrimidine Salvage

As with the purine nucleotides, pyrimidine salvage is a means of interrupting what would otherwise be a straightforward and potentially extravagant catabolic process (Figure 16.7). Of the three pyrimidine nucleotides, cytidine monophosphate requires hydrolytic removal of the amino group by cytidine deaminase to form uridine monophosphate. Through this conversion, cytidine enters the mainstream interconversion and degradative pathways to which UMP and TMP are subjected. Degradation of dTTP is reversible at each step up to the point of formation of free thymine base. Thus, each of the degradative enzymes participating in dTTP degradation also legitimately may be considered salvage pathway enzymes. We already have examined the de novo synthesis of UMP, noting that this compound is the common intermediate for synthesis of all three pyrimidine nucleotides. Therefore, conversion of CMP to UMP and stepwise removal of two of the three inorganic phosphate groups from UTP to yield UMP form a pool of this intermediate, which permits recycling to meet cellular needs.

Pyrimidine Breakdown

Cytidine nucleotide catabolism is merged with that of uridine nucleotide after deamination, as discussed previously. After subsequent, stepwise removal of the inorganic phosphate group and then the ribose moiety, free uracil is formed. Thymidine catabolism occurs in a parallel fashion leading to formation of free thymine. In the subsequent step, mediated by the enzyme *dihydropyrimidine dehydrogenase,* which can use either free base as a substrate, two hydrogens are added across the double bond of the ring structure to form either dihydrouracil or dihydrothymine. The saturated

Uracil + Ribose 1-phosphate $\xrightarrow{\textit{Uridine phosphorylase}}$ Uridine + Pi

Uridine or Cytidine + ATP $\xrightarrow[\textit{Kinase}]{\textit{Uridine -cytidine}}$ UMP or CMP + ADP

Thymine + Deoxyribose 1-phosphate $\xrightarrow[\textit{phosphorylase}]{\textit{Thymidine}}$ Thymidine + Pi

Thymidine + ATP $\xrightarrow[\textit{Kinase}]{\textit{Thymidine}}$ dTMP + ADP

Figure 16.7. The pyrimidine salvage pathway. Cytidine 5′-monophosphate differs from the other pyrimidine-forming substrate for this pathway because it must be acted upon by cytidine deaminase to convert it to uridine monophosphate. At that point, it either is recycled or it joins with the degradative pathway for uridine nucleotide. Thymidine degradation can proceed reversibly to the point of free thymine. The next step, resulting in production of dihydrothymine, commits the molecule to complete degradation.

ring is thereby made vulnerable to attack by addition of water, mediated by *dihydropyrimidine cyclohydrolase*, converting dihydrouracil to β-ureidopropionic acid and dihydrothymine to β-ureidoisobutyric acid. These β-ureido compounds are again attacked by a common enzyme, *ureidopropionase*, to liberate CO_2 and $NH4^+$, with the formation of β-alanine or β-aminoisobutyric acid, respectively. Further transfer of the remaining amino group to α-ketoglutarate leads to formation of malonate semialdehyde or methylmalonate semialdehyde, both of which can be completely oxidized to CO_2 through conventional pathways.

DISORDERS OF PYRIMIDINE METABOLISM

Disorders of De Novo Synthesis

OROTIC ACIDURIA

The sole example of a disorder of de novo pyrimidine synthesis is hereditary orotic aciduria. Predictably, the enzyme defect, presumed to be communicated in an autosomal recessive fashion, is a deficiency of the bifunctional UMP synthase activity. In view of the critical role of de novo pyridine biosynthesis in embryogenesis, it should be clear that no such deficiency could be absolute. Indeed, UMP synthase deficient patients all have had detectable, low residual activity. Interestingly, the urinary quantities of orotic acid recovered in these patients is in excess of that normally synthesized per day, suggesting the loss of a regulatory mechanism normally imposed on one or both of the preceding two enzyme proteins in the pathway.

Clinically, defective pyrimidine synthesis has wide-reaching implications. Although these vary from one patient to another, a feature common to all is eventual development of a *megaloblastic anemia*. Given the normal rapid rate of red cell turnover, it is not difficult to imagine the enormous and ongoing demand for nucleotides to permit a normal rate of cell division of the erythrocyte precursors in the bone marrow. A parallel situation occurs with folic acid deficiency, when the restriction of available cofactor impairs purine synthesis, resulting in megaloblastic anemia.

The anemia of orotic aciduria generally is of a moderate degree, with hemoglobin levels ranging from 5 to 8 g/dl, whereas the marrow typically shows a similar degree of megaloblastosis in all cases at the time of diagnosis. An odd feature of the anemia is that it is diagnosed at widely variable ages, ranging from 6 weeks to 7 years. This is contrary to the expectation that impairment of de novo pyrimidine synthesis from conception should affect each patient with a fair degree of consistency. Nonetheless, it usually is the megaloblastic anemia that leads to the diagnosis, because attempts at diagnosis and/or treatment of the more common causes of megaloblastic anemia (see Chapter 18) are without effect.

A second feature common to all cases, of course, is orotic aciduria, which defines the nature of the enzyme defect. The estimated daily synthesis of pyrimidine normally is about 600 mg/day, compared with a normal urinary excretion of orotic acid of less than 10 μmol/mmol creatinine. Patients with orotic aciduria excrete quantities at least three orders of magnitude greater than normal (eg, 3–5 mmol/mmol creatinine). Daily excretions have ranged up to 9.6 mmol/24 hours, or in excess of 1000 mg/day. The difference between daily excretion and estimated de novo production of pyrimidines (hence orotic acid) again suggests that normal regulation of the earlier steps in the pathway is lost. Furthermore, although CPS II activity is the rate-limiting step under normal circumstances, the degree of overproduction of orotic acid in this disease indicates that CPS II usually functions well below its full capacity. The quantities of urinary orotic acid are virtually diagnostic of UMP synthase deficiency; the urea cycle disorders are the only exception to this, specifically *ornithine transcarbamylase deficiency* (see Chapter 5), in which levels as high as 10 mmol/mmol creatinine have been reported. Key differential points are, of course, the blood ammonia, which is normal in UMP synthase deficiency, and the severe neurologic manifestations of OTC deficiency.

The hyperexcretion of orotic acid is not without physiologic consequences, because the majority of reported patients have had orotic acid crystalluria. Several of these children also had urinary tract symptoms consistent with obstructive uropathy, particularly when urinary volume was restricted due to dehydration. To further complicate the problem of uropathy, orotic acid is known to have a uricosuric effect. This is postulated, but not proven, to be a consequence of competition for the same carrier at the tubular level. In any case, however, the enhanced tendency toward stone formation in the combined presence of two insoluble solutes is a legitimate concern that should be addressed by appropriate therapy.

Despite the typically normal birth weight of affected infants, the reader should not be led to believe that impaired pyrimidine synthesis from conception has no effect on prenatal development. Both the *developing nervous system* and the *heart* are major target organs; affected infants evidence a high incidence of intellectual and motor impairment and structural cardiac lesions. These findings are consistent with the chronology and rapidity of nervous system and cardiac development in embryogenesis. Moreover, keep in mind that weight gain in utero occurs most rapidly during the third trimester, chiefly as a result of adipose tissue deposition.

In contrast to normal in utero weight gain, children with hereditary orotic aciduria typically do not thrive during the first year of life. Because growth in the first years of life generally represents ongoing cellular hyperplasia, it is likely that impaired nucleotide synthesis will be reflected in diminished capacity of cells to reproduce themselves. A second, more subtle factor also may influence growth in this period—specifically, an inability to absorb nutrients normally. Like the bone marrow, intestinal epithelium is a tissue with an exceptionally high turnover rate. Hence, there is an imperative for the epithelial cell to sustain a correspondingly high reproductive rate. If this is impaired because of decreased nucleotide availability, intestinal absorption of nutrients is likely to be adversely affected. Although malabsorption has been present in only a few of the reported cases, this aspect of the disease has not been closely examined in all cases.

Finally, immunologic function has been examined in some reported cases, based upon immune dysfunction in other inherited disorders of nucleotide metabolism. Results of these studies have been variable, and the majority of reported cases of hereditary orotic aciduria have presented no evidence of increased susceptibility to infection.

Treatment modalities have been instructive with respect to the basic nature of the disease. *Pyrimidine replacement* circumvents the need for de novo synthesis and is effective in producing remission of the anemia, decreasing orotic acid excretion and improving growth and muscle tone. The decrease in orotic aciduria indicates resumption of normal control over the rate-limiting step in the pathway, at CPS II. The improvements in growth, tone, and general well-being suggest a direct relationship to increased gene and message synthesis, because pyrimidines are not major factors in energy transduction as are purines. An alternative treatment strategy has been administration of *uridine*, which circumvents only the deficient enzyme step and relies upon the integrity of the pyrimidine salvage pathway for nucleotide synthesis. In cases when initially successful treatment was rendered ineffective through patient noncompliance, return to pretreatment levels of orotic acid excretion and recurrence of the anemia required at least 3 weeks. This time frame is consistent with the high degree of efficiency of the salvage pathway in conservation of preexisting pyrimidine nucleotides. This modality has been equally effective compared to pyrimidine replacement and, because of the relative expense, is the better choice.

Disorders of Pyrimidine Salvage

In contrast to disorders of purine metabolism, there are no known disorders of pyrimidine salvage. Because the capacity of de novo synthesis is more than equal to the task of producing daily pyrimidine requirements, it is possible that genetic disorders of the salvage pathway might be unrecognized clinically. This certainly would be true if degradative capacity was equivalent to synthetic capacity, because the end products of pyrimidine degradation are completely oxidized. Thus, there would be no marker compound present in urine or blood to indicate such a defect.

Disorders of Pyrimidine Degradation

Two disorders of degradation have been described. The first, *pyrimidine-5′-nucleotidase* deficiency, results in the inability to cleave inorganic phosphate from pyrimidine nucleotides to form the corresponding nucleosides. The clinical consequence of the defect is a picture of hereditary hemolytic anemia, accompanied by splenomegaly and hyperbilirubinemia. Recent descriptions of isoenzymes could form the basis for an explanation of the tissue-specific expression of the enzyme defect in red cells. Measurement of red cell pyrimidine nucleotides is diagnostic, and it is suspected that accumulated pyrimidine nucleotide triphosphates inhibit pentose phosphate shunt activity, thus contributing to red cell lysis. This, however, has been disputed, and the actual mechanism remains unelucidated. No treatment is available that can deplete the red cells of the accumulated phosphonucleotides, most of which are formed from uptake of circulating pyrimidines. A theoretical treatment strategy would be the use of a compound that would interfere with this uptake.

The second degradative disorder is deficiency of *dihydropyrimidine dehydrogenase*, which is the rate-limiting enzyme in the degradative pathway. The clinical consequences of this defect are poorly defined, although, because of the frequency of neurologically related problems, the disorder cannot be ignored. Diagnosis is based upon the demonstration of elevated plasma levels of the free pyrimidines, uracil and thymine, which are the common substrates for the deficient enzyme. No treatment is available.

In summary, metabolism of purines and pyrimidines is complex and normally equipped to meet demands both by de novo synthesis and through conservation (salvage) of preexisting molecules. The pathways are tightly regulated and integrated; therefore, a molecular defect at any specific point is likely to have many adverse effects overall. It is proposed that many such defects hitherto unreported may adversely affect embryogenesis so much that the conceptus would be rendered nonviable. Hence, their absence in the literature may be attributable to lethal gene defects.

SUGGESTED READINGS

Baldree LA, Stapleton FB. Uric acid metabolism in children. Pediatr Clin North Am 1990;37:391.

Burnstock G. Physiological and pathological roles of purines: an update. Drug Development Research 1993;28:195.

Davidson JN, Chen KC, Jamison RS, et al. The evolutionary history of the first three enzymes in pyrimidine biosynthesis. Bioessays 1993;15:157.

Cross M. Molecular biology of AMP deaminase deficiency. Pharmacy World and Science 1994;16:55.

Hirschhorn R. Overview of biochemical abnormalities and molecular genetics adenosine deaminase deficiency. Pediatr Res 1993;33:S35.

Simmonds HA. Purine and pyrimidine disorders. In: Holton JB, ed. The inherited metabolic diseases. New York: Churchill-Livingstone, 1994:297.

Scriver CR, Beaudet AL, Sly WS, Valle D, eds. The metabolic and molecular bases of inherited disease. 7th ed. New York: McGraw-Hill, 1995.

van den Berghe G. Disorders of purine and pyrimidine metabolism. In: Fernandes J, Saudubray J-M, Tada K. Inborn metabolic diseases. Heidelberg: Springer-Verlag, 1990: 455.

Zimmerman H. 5′-nucleotidase: molecular structure and functional aspects. Biochem J 1992;285:345.

chapter **17**

Disorders of Porphyrin Metabolism

The porphyrias are a complex group of disorders involving heme biosynthesis in liver and erythroid precursors. There are two predominant forms of presentation: *neuropsychiatric,* which is associated with increased excretion of porphyrin precursors, porphobilinogen (PBG), or δ-aminolevulinate (ALA); and *cutaneous,* which is associated with increased excretion of porphyrins, which are photosensitizing agents. Porphyrins (meaning purple) exhibit an intense red fluorescence when exposed to UV light of 400 nm. This fluorescence can be exploited clinically to demonstrate fluorescent staining of teeth (erythrodontia) in patients with congenital erythropoietic porphyria as well as excess porphyrins in feces and fluorescent erythrocytes.

As detailed in Chapter 6 (the text discussing heme biosynthesis), the final product of heme biosynthesis is the porphyrin ring in which the bridge atoms are partially oxidized (Figure 17.1). The intermediates in this pathway are more reduced and are termed porphyrinogens. Unlike porphyrins, the porphyrinogens are colorless and do not fluoresce. They oxidize readily, however, in the presence of air and light and can be converted to porphyrins when they accumulate in affected tissues. Furthermore, although porphyrin precursors are water-soluble, the various porphyrinogens are aromatic compounds with limited aqueous solubility, depending on the number of carboxylic acid residues, and, therefore, are largely excreted via the bile into the feces.

As have many areas of clinical biochemistry, the heme biosynthetic pathway and its disorders have been studied in the context of clinical presentation. Clinical terms such as "hepatic" or "cutaneous," meant to be symptomatically descriptive, have led to focus on study of a particular organ. As a result, little is known of how the pathway may be affected in other organs. This, in turn, has resulted in incomplete understanding of the biochemical processes underlying the clinical diseases. In an attempt to avoid this source of confusion, we have organized the following discussion according to each successive enzymatic step and associated genetic disorders. Finally, we have included a short discussion of acquired defects in the pathway, emphasizing the inadequacy of knowledge in this area of pharmacology and toxicology.

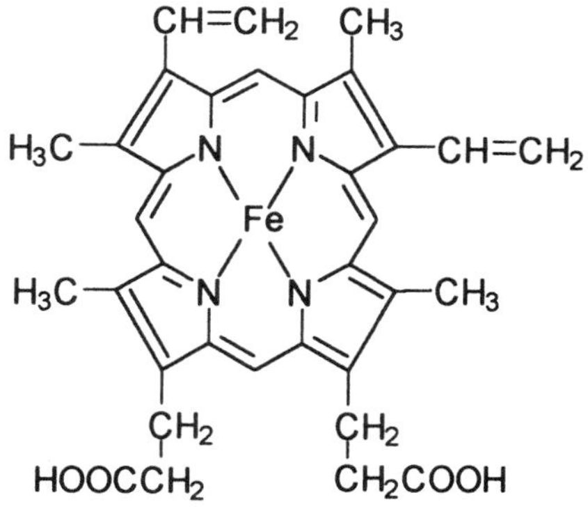

Heme
(Fe-protoporphyrin IX)

Figure 17.1. The structure of the heme molecule. The fundamental structure is that of a cyclic tetrapyrrole (porphyrin): each ring is joined to its neighbors through a methylene bridge. The nitrogen atom of each pyrrole is individually bound to ferrous (Fe^{2+}) iron. Note the asymmetry of the various substituents, the specificity of which is important in differentiating the III from the I series of porphyrin intermediates during the biosynthetic process. Of equal importance is the position of the propionic acid substituents which are critical to the binding of heme oxygenase and bilirubin production.

Table 17.1. Porphyria Variants

	ACUTE INTERMITTENT		VARIEGATE		HEREDITARY COPROPORPHYRIA	
Genetics	AD		AD		AD	
Onset	After puberty		10–30 years		Any age	
Symptoms and Signs	Abdominal pain, nausea, vomiting; hypertension Neuropsychiatric findings No skin findings		Variable pattern of expression Neurologic findings similar to AIP Skin-fragility ≫ photosensitivity		Acute attacks are sporadic—drugs may precipitate Neurologic findings similar to AIP Skin findings rare	
Lab findings						
Urine	**Latent**	**Overt**	**Latent**	**Overt**	**Latent**	**Overt**
Color	N*	Red*	N*	N* or red	N*	N* to red*
ALA	+ to 3+	2+ to 3+	N to 2+	2+ to 3+	N to 2+	3+
PBG	+ to 3+	2+ to 3+	N to 2+	+ to 3+	N to 2+	3+
Uroporphyrin	N to 2+	2+ to 3+	N to 2+	3+	N to 2+	2+
Coproporphyrin	+	+	+ to 2+	3+	N to 2+	2+ to 3+
Feces						
Coproporphyrin	N	+	3+	3+	+ to 3+	3+
Protoporphyrin	N	+	3+	3+	N to +	N to +
Uroporphyrin	+	+ to 2+	N	2+	N	N
Erythrocyte						
Uroporphyrin Coproporphyrin Protoporphyrin	All normal		All normal		All normal	
Enzyme Defect	PBG Deaminase		Protoporphyrin oxidase)—RBC		Coproporphyrinogen oxidase—RBC	
Treatment: Avoid provocative drugs, glucose, hematin			Acute attacks as for AIP Skin—sun screen		Acute attacks as for AIP	

* Color may change to deep brown-red or black on standing.
0 absent; N normal; + increased; 2+ moderately increased; 3+ greatly increased.

Although the common practice of dividing the porphyrins into hepatic (neurologic) and cutaneous (erythropoietic) forms may be faulted on biochemical grounds, it has the advantage of lumping together similar disorders among this heterogenous group. Skin lesions are the result of the photodynamic action of porphyrins that are deposited or generated there, although an additional effect may arise from excitation of plasma and red blood cell porphyrins circulating in dermal blood vessels. Light energy is absorbed by porphyrins creating an excited state, which promptly reacts with dioxygen to form a singlet state. Singlet oxygen is a highly reactive species causing both peroxidative damage of membrane lipids (especially in lysosomes) and cross-linking of membrane proteins. Increased fragility of damaged skin and burning sensations, erythema, and swelling of light exposed skin are the major cutaneous manifestations. Chronic exposure leads to scarring and lichenification.

The neurologic manifestations of the acute hepatic porphyrias include acute attacks of abdominal pain (severe enough to masquerade as an acute abdomen), pain in extremities, peripheral motor deficits, and respiratory paralysis. Such attacks occur in four of the porphyrias (Table 17.1): acute intermittent porphyria, variegate porphyria, hereditary coproporphyria, and ALA dehydrase deficiency. It is not clear what causes this array of neurologic manifestations, but evidence exists that ALA may be the cause because it can cross the blood-brain barrier. Whether a heme deficiency state in neurons also plays a role in the symptomatology is not known. In liver, synthesis of ALA synthetase is suppressed by the end product of the pathway—heme, which acts as an allosteric inhibitor of ALA synthetase. The acute hepatic

Table 17.1 *(continued)*

PORPHYRIA CUTANEA TARDA	CONGENITAL ERYTHROPOIETIC (CEP)	ERYTHROHEPATIC PROTOPORPHYRIA (EPP)
AD Any age—usually after 35 years Skin manifestations No neurologic findings Diabetes mellitus in 1/4 Associated liver disease determines prognosis—alcohol ingestion	AR 0–5 Skin—severe photosensitivity Hemolytic anemia, splenomegaly No neurologic findings Erythrodontia, dark urine	AD 0–5 Early-onset photosensitivity—milder than in CEP No neurologic findings Liver damage
Red*	Red*	N
N to +	N	↓
N	N	↓
3+	3+	↓
2+ to 3+	2+ to 3+	↓
N to 2+	3+	N to +
N to +	N to variable	N to 3+
–	2+	N to 2+
	←Fluorocytes on blood smear→	
All normal	3+	N
	2+	+
	+	3+
Uroporphyrinogen decarboxylase (liver and RBC)	Uroporphyrinogen III cosynthase	Ferrochelatase—RBC
Phlebotomy, oral chloroquine	Splenectomy, oral beta-carotene, hematin	Oral beta-carotene

porphyrias all share increased production of ALA because of induction of liver ALA synthetase activity.

GENETIC DISORDERS

ALA Dehydratase Deficiency

Congenital deficiency of ALA dehydratase was first reported in 1979; relatively few cases have been identified since. Family pedigrees and enzymatic studies of parents and siblings of affected individuals have documented an autosomal recessive inheritance pattern for this disorder. The clinical findings exhibited by these patients have been predominantly neuromuscular in nature, including pain in the extremities, neuropathy (sensory and motor), and paralysis involving extremities and muscles of respiration. Exacerbations have been observed after decreased food intake and metabolic stress. A predictable pattern of massive urinary ALA excretion was found with no change observed in urinary PBG excretion. This may be explained by the fact that, although homozygotes have only about 2% of control ALA dehydratase in their erythrocytes, this residual amount still is fairly large in relation to that of the other, subsequent steps in the pathway under normal circumstances. By contrast, obligate heterozygotes show a 50% reduction in red cell enzyme, which is consistent with an autosomal recessive disease and sufficiently high to prevent clinical consequences.

An interesting and as yet unexplained feature is the finding of 100-fold elevations in urinary and erythrocyte porphyrins, especially the presence of COPRO III in urine. In view of the biochemical defect, it is difficult to conceptualize a reasonable explanation for this without invoking events within nonerythroidal tissues. Indeed, some reports suggest that urinary porphyrin excretion may be related to renal porphyrinogenesis, rather than a simple reflection of total body porphyrin production. ALA dehydratase activity in liver, kidney, or other tissues from affected individuals has not been reported.

With respect to treatment, experience is severely restricted by the small number of patients. However, administration of glucose and hematin have had no significant therapeutic effect during exacerbations in the reported individuals, although the biochemical nature of the defect would suggest they should. This fact, again, draws attention to our lack of understanding of regulation of heme biosynthesis in tissues throughout the body. Recommendations for chronic management must include avoidance of known precipitating factors and adequate carbohydrate intake in conjunction with good dietary practices.

Acute Intermittent Porphyria-PBG Deaminase Deficiency

Although acute intermittent porphyria (AIP) is considered to be the most common of the genetic porphyrias, it is well known that only a small percentage of genetically affected individuals ever experience clinical symptoms. Such an apparent dichotomy could be true only if the disorder were one in which residual enzyme activity was sufficient to prevent symptoms under most circumstances; this situation is most commonly encountered in autosomal dominant disorders, which include AIP. Clinical symptoms are associated with a 50% reduction in PBG deaminase activity. Significantly, however, individuals with the identical genotype and no symptoms also have a 50% reduction in enzyme activity, and both groups show considerable overlap with the lower range of normal genotypic enzyme activity. This has considerable impact upon accurate diagnosis because enzyme activity alone cannot always distinguish clinically affected from latent, or from normal. Hence, diagnosis also must include measurement of urinary ALA and PBG, as well as the medical history.

Several features of the clinical disorder bear emphasizing because these are both inherently odd and may be helpful to diagnosis as well. Most significantly, despite the fact that Mendelian genetic principles predict an equal sex distribution of an autosomal gene, more females than males are clinically affected with AIP. This, added to the relative rarity of clinical onset before puberty, the exacerbation of symptoms coincident with menses, and the moderation of these symptoms after menopause, indicates an interrelationship between the sex steroids and clinical expression of the genotype. In addition, oral contraceptives are prominent among the many drugs known or suspected to precipitate symptoms in a genotypically abnormal person. The specific biochemical mechanisms by which this occurs are complex and beyond the scope of this discussion, as well as still being "worked out"; however, it is fair to state that progesterone has been shown to increase heme breakdown, which alone should cause upregulation of ALA synthase, whereas naturally occurring progesterone metabolites enhance de novo synthesis of the enzyme. Together, these effects might be sufficient to precipitate an attack in a genetically affected individual.

Other peculiar and hitherto unexplained findings characteristic of approximately 50% of AIP patients relate to the central and peripheral nervous systems. Central nervous system involvement can include motor neuropathy, which frequently coexists with sensory neuropathy, and any or all motor innervation including the cranial nerves. The autonomic nervous system may be involved as well, accounting for many of the clinical findings such as tachycardia, hypertension, vomiting, diarrhea, urinary retention, and restlessness. Seizures frequently accompany acute exacerbations of AIP. In addition to all of the above, affected patients often have a major neuropsychiatric component to their disease, ranging from anxiety and paranoia to frank psychosis. As a result of the protean nature of the symptom complex, AIP patients frequently are labelled hysterics and treated as such, while the underlying genetic disorder remains undiagnosed and untreated. Some recent studies have documented a much higher than expected incidence of the AIP gene in patients institutionalized for psychiatric reasons.

Misdiagnosis of AIP as a psychiatric or a seizure disorder puts the patient at substantial medical risk, not including the moral and philosophical issues involved. This becomes immediately apparent when one looks at the many central nervous system active agents used in treatment of these disorders that appear on the list of compounds known or suspected of precipitating an acute porphyric attack. These include all barbiturates, carbamazepine (Tegretol), diphenylhydantoin (Dilantin), meprobamate, trimethadione, and valproic acid. In addition, certain antihypertensives, such as clonidine, and all sulfa drugs may put the individual at great risk. Thus, failure to recognize the underlying genetic disorder while administering drug therapy for psychiatric or convulsive manifestations could compound the severity of the problem and jeopardize the patient's life.

Clinical recognition of AIP demands awareness and heightened suspicion in any patient whose complaints or symptoms or both are multiple, vague, and involve onset during or after puberty. A family history of undiagnosed neuropsychiatric or neurologic conditions should raise suspicion further. Although it would be a clear exaggeration to state that all individuals with a neuropsychiatric diagnosis should be suspect, the physician is well advised to consider AIP in the differential. There is a misconception that all such individuals will have a history of having passed "red" or "port-wine" urine; the color of the urine that contains increased quantities of the inherently colorless PBG depends upon spontaneous conversion to porphobilin, a reaction which is expedited by light, heat, and acidity. It is important to understand that the voided urine is not likely to be colored unless allowed to stand; therefore, the patient is highly unlikely to provide a history of colored urine under normal life circumstances. Moreover, during latent periods, the excretion of PBG may not be elevated sufficiently to cause noticeable pigment by conversion to porphobilin.

Understanding the basic biochemical defect in AIP is essential to appropriate therapy. Given the enzymatic defect at the PBG deaminase step, it is unclear whether the pathogenesis of symptoms is due to heme deficiency or ALA/PBG excess. What is clear, however, is that heme deficiency results from diminished formation distal to the deaminase step, while this deficiency upregulates ALA synthase, in turn elevating ALA/PBG. Because it is known that glucose downregulates ALA synthase, rapid intravenous infusion of large amounts of glucose has been used for many years to abort acute porphyric attacks. It is worth noting that virtually all patients admitted to an emergency room in acute distress are likely to receive such treatment; many undiagnosed AIP patients may be inadvertently treated without diagnosis. A more recent approach to acute therapy in diagnosed patients has involved a more specific means of ALA synthase downregulation—administration of heme, which is directed at both aspects of the biochemical etiology. Chronic treatment is based on an emphasis on good nutrition with adequate carbohydrate supply and avoidance of the known precipitating factors: fatigue, fasting, and specific drugs.

Congenital Erythropoietic Porphyria-Uroporphyrinogen III Synthase Deficiency

This disorder, which results from deficiency of UROgen III cosynthase, is inherited in an autosomal recessive fashion. The nature of the biochemical defect is such that the inevitable consequence is nonenzymatic conversion of hydroxymethylbilane to UROgen I and COPROgen I, which then spontaneously oxidize to the corresponding porphyrins. These latter compounds give the characteristic reddish color to the urine of these patients, which often is detectable in the diaper of a young infant who is affected. Together with this clue, early onset of cutaneous photosensitivity ultimately becomes one of the major complications of the disease.

Although the precise pathogenetic mechanisms remain obscure, it is thought that the cutaneous damage that occurs must be related to the photooxidative process of conversion from porphyrinogen to porphyrin. Bullous lesions appear with light exposure and progress to dermal erosion and healing with scar formation. Over time, repetitive injury with scarring leads to terrible disfigurement. Hypertrichosis is common, and resorption of the distal phalanges with contractures may give a clawlike character to the hands. Key to the clinical diagnosis is the pathognomonic finding of *erythrodontia.* Anemia and splenomegaly also are frequent.

Biochemical diagnosis relies upon demonstration of 20- to 60-fold elevation in erythrocyte, urine, and fecal porphyrins, predominantly of the I series. Measurement of UROgen III cosynthase generally is unavailable; therefore, the physician must base the diagnosis on the early history and clinical course, together with the porphyrin analysis. Treatment must be based upon avoidance of exposure to sunlight; hematin infusion helps much less in this disease than in AIP because the defect is primarily located in erythroid tissue, where the heme biosynthetic pathway is regulated by ferrochelatase activity, beyond the enzyme block. Clinical remission has been reported in an affected individual treated with oral activated charcoal. General efficacy of this form of therapy has yet to be evaluated.

Porphyria Cutanea Tarda-Uroporphyrinogen III Decarboxylase Deficiency

This disorder is the most common among the genetic porphyrias, and, in its acquired form, is a prominent symptom-complex associated with many environmental agents. Because routine measurement of the implicated enzyme UROgen III decarboxylase is not available, distinction between genetic and acquired forms must be based on clinical and family history. Inheritance is believed to be autosomal dominant; therefore, family history can be of great value in differentiation. Moreover, abnormal gene expression occurs in all tissues, whereas environmental agents have been shown to affect the liver predominantly. When the gene defect occurs in the homozygous form, it causes the disorder known as hepatoerythropoietic porphyria, which is clinically indistinguishable from congenital erythropoietic porphyria. Such homozygotes are rare.

The major clinical findings are related to the integument, and consist of vesicular and bullous lesions in areas normally exposed to light. These may heal slowly, with significant scarring and frequent superimposed infection, which may augment the degree of scarring. Pigmentary changes, particularly hyperpigmentation, are common. In genetically affected patients, the liver shows siderosis, with accompanying and variable degrees of fatty metamorphosis and chronic inflammatory changes. Cirrhosis may not be apparent clinically but is a common finding at autopsy. As in congenital erythropoietic porphyria, it is most likely that the photooxidation of the accumulated uroporphyrinogens to uroporphyrins within tissues leads to cellular injury. In this context, it should be recalled that UROgen III decarboxylase also is active on UROgen I as a substrate; therefore, the usual urinary porphyrin pattern is elevation of URO I and III and COPRO I. In addition, it generally is believed that iron has a pathogenetic role in this disease, although knowledge of a specific mechanism is lacking. Nonetheless, serum iron levels frequently are elevated, leading to a suggestion that the mutant UROgen III decarboxylase may be more susceptible to iron inhibition than normal.

Treatment requires protection from light exposure and avoidance of precipitating environmental agents. Beyond this, phlebotomy has been shown to have therapeutic value in these patients; the bulk of evidence suggests that the benefit derives from removal of iron from the total body pool. Maximum therapeutic results usually are not seen until a total of more than 4 liters have been removed, one to two units weekly, reducing the serum iron to the lower limits of normal. This regimen reduces porphyrin excretion, and results in improved liver function and decreased skin lesions. An additional therapeutic modality uses the ability of chloroquine to chelate porphyrins, rendering them water-soluble for easy excretion. In patients who are anemic or for other reasons cannot be phlebotomized, chloroquine in constant low-dose form offers an alternative. Both treatments may be combined, although efficacy of combined therapy beyond that achievable with either alone has not been clearly established.

Hereditary Coproporphyria—Coproporphyrinogen III Oxidase Deficiency

This disease is inherited as an autosomal dominant trait, which results in partial deficiency of COPROgen III oxidase. Striking similarities exist between this disease and AIP, regarding the proportion of genetically affected patients who have clinical manifestations and the clinical manifestations themselves. Acute intermittent porphyria, however, is much more common in the population.

The general clinical manifestations, including neuropsychiatric problems, peripheral neuropathy, acute abdominal symptoms, and precipitating factors are virtually indistinguishable from those seen in AIP. A single difference that can be very helpful, if present, is a component of skin photosensitivity. This distinguishing feature can be traced directly to the different enzymatic bases in AIP and hereditary coproporphyria, because deficiency of COPROgen III oxidase would be expected to result in tissue porphyrin accumulation. As in the other cutaneous porphyrias, therefore, the skin is rendered susceptible to damage resulting from photooxidation of the accumulated porphyrinogens.

Laboratory diagnosis is based upon identification of excessive urinary and fecal excretion of coproporphyrin III, which is the substrate for the defective enzyme. Measurement of PBG deaminase that yields normal values is helpful to diagnosis; direct measurement of COPROgen III oxidase generally is not available. Although urinary ALA and PBG may be found during acute attacks, which is consistent with the demonstration of enhanced ALA synthase activity, these usually normalize during remission, which is not the case with AIP.

Treatment consists of good dietary practices and avoidance of precipitating causes. Acute treatment is the same as that for AIP.

Variegate Porphyria—Protoporphyrinogen IX Oxidase Deficiency

Implicit in its name, this autosomal dominant disorder can primarily affect the skin, the nervous system, and viscera, or all in combination. The enzymatic defect is a deficiency of PROTOgen IX oxidase, which mediates conversion of PROTOgen IX to PROTO IX, which is a reaction that proceeds spontaneously at a substantial rate. Hence, it would be reasonable to expect that the genetic deficiency in enzyme activity might result in attenuated clinical disease, although this is not the case. It has been suggested that George III of England suffered from this disorder; if so, perhaps the neuropsychiatric component of his illness caused his bungled handling of the American colonies, which led to the American Revolution!

As already indicated, the clinical presentation of the disease can closely resemble that of AIP; when cutaneous signs are present, the disease can be indistinguishable from hereditary coproporphyria. Elevated fecal and urinary excretion of COPRO III and PROTO IX (spontaneously produced) are helpful to the diagnosis, which always should be suspected in cases when the clinical picture resembles AIP but PBG deaminase activity is normal.

Treatment of variegate porphyria does not differ from the therapy of AIP and hereditary coproporphyria.

Erythropoietic Protoporphyria-Ferrochelatase Deficiency

Of all the inherited porphyric syndromes, erythropoietic protoporphyria is a clinical name that comes the closest to describing the actual enzyme defect. This is because protoporphyrin exists in the heme biosynthetic pathway exclusively as a substrate for ferrochelatase, which is the deficient enzyme in this autosomal dominant disorder. Protoporphyrin is relatively insoluble in aqueous media, leading to significant tissue deposition. The major source of this protoporphyrin is considered to be the erythrogenic bone marrow cells. However, because heme synthesis in peripheral tissues is necessarily limited by the defect, upregulation of ALA synthase with attendant production and accumulation of intermediate porphyrin analogues would be expected.

These porphyrins probably account for the cutaneous photosensitivity component in this disease, as in many of the other genetic porphyrias. Unlike these others, however, erythropoietic protoporphyria has few, if any, neurovisceral components. In such a clinical presentation, identification of elevated protoporphyrin in erythrocytes, stool, and plasma with normal urinary protoporphyrin (due to insolubility) is virtually diagnostic. Despite the absence of neurovisceral symptoms, however, hepatocellular disease occurs and is progressive, eventually resulting in severe liver dysfunction.

Treatment of the cutaneous component consists of avoidance of light exposure. Some have advocated use of high doses of beta-carotene to provide protection against free radicals liberated during porphyrinogen photooxidation. Efforts to slow or prevent hepatocellular damage, using vitamin E, cholestyramine, and iron, have been reported, but, presently, there is no uniformly accepted means of treatment for this component of the disease.

ACQUIRED DEFICIENCIES

This category of disorder highlights the inadequacy of the present understanding and clinical categorization of porphyrias. Not only is it well known that many drugs interact with the heme biosynthetic pathway to precipitate clinical onset of a genetically determined enzyme deficiency, but many agents interact directly with the various enzyme proteins in a genetically normal individual, interfering with heme biosynthesis. Thus, it is much more accurate to refer to porphyrias, both genetic and acquired, as disorders of heme biosynthesis.

Drugs

Because, in individual cases, the possibility of underlying heme biosynthetic enzyme deficiency frequently remains uninvestigated, so-called drug allergies should be viewed as potential clues to diagnosis. However, animal experiments using barbiturates, halogenated insecticides, steroids, alcohol, and many other exogenous agents have clearly documented the fact that an inherently normal heme biosynthetic pathway can be adversely affected by such compounds. Such studies have shown a multiplicity of biochemical events induced by these agents that impinge on heme biosynthesis; these observations have helped to elucidate the relationship between genomic regulation of the pathway and environmental stress. In summary, an adverse systemic response to administration of a pharmacologic agent, such as barbiturates or steroids, in a previously well individual should alert the physician to institute an investigation of the heme biosynthetic pathway. Considering the relative frequency of clinically unexpressed enzyme deficiencies in this pathway, as well as the independent drug-induced effects, it is important to delineate the diagnosis in each patient individually.

Heavy Metals

Among the several heavy metals, the most common and likely to be encountered in clinical practice is lead. The hematologic and encephalopathic findings of plumbism are part of every physician's store of knowledge and need not be recounted here. A major diagnostic procedure in suspected cases is measurement of urinary ALA excretion, which not only implies an effect of lead on heme biosynthesis but also indicates a locus of its effect on the pathway. Lead is a potent inhibitor of the enzyme ALA dehydratase; therefore, measurement of ALA dehydratase activity in erythrocytes is a sensitive means by which to detect early lead poisoning. However, the existence of ALA dehydratase deficient porphyria on a genetic basis must be excluded by independent means, such as direct measurement of blood lead levels. Lead also is known to inhibit ferrochelatase activity, probably through an indirect means (ie, inhibition of glutathione reduction, which is a process essential for normal enzyme activity). The anemia of plumbism, therefore, can be easily explained by reduced heme synthesis. The neuropathic effects, however, are a matter of some controversy: some believe that ALA itself is neurotoxic, whereas others believe that small decrements in heme generation within the central nervous system cause the clinical problems.

Hereditary Tyrosinemia (Succinylacetone)

Clinical recognition of the similarities in presentation of this rare autosomal recessive disorder and those of acute intermittent porphyria led to examination of the urine from tyrosinemics, with the discovery that they, too, excrete large amounts of ALA. After identification of the urinary compound succinylacetone, which is a biochemical marker for tyrosinemia, it became clear that succinylacetone is a potent inhibitor of ALA dehydratase. Existence of such a physiologic model may assist in addressing the nature of the etiologic agent in neuropathies associated with heme biosynthetic defects.

SUGGESTED READINGS

GENERAL

Houston T, Moore MR, McColl KE, Fitzsimons EJ. Regulation of haem biosynthesis in normoblastic erythropoiesis: role of 5-aminolevulinic acid synthase and ferrochelatase. Biochim Biophys Acta 1994;1201:85.

Kappas A, Sassa S, Galbraith RA, Nordmann Y. The

porphyrias. In: Scriver CR, Beaudet AL, Sly WS, Valle D, eds. The metabolic and molecular bases of inherited disease. 7th ed. New York: McGraw-Hill, 1995:2103.
Moore MR, McColl KEL, Rimington C, Goldberg A. Disorders of porphyrin metabolism. New York: Plenum Medical Book Co, 1987.
Ponka P, Schulman HM. Regulation of heme biosynthesis: distinct regulatory features in erythroid cells. Stem Cells (Dayt) 1993;11(suppl):24.
Rank JM, Straka JG, Bloomer JR. Liver in disorders of porphyrin metabolism. J Gastroenterol Hepatol 1990; 5:573.
Sassa S, Fulita H, Sugita O. Genetic regulation of the heme pathway. Ann N Y Acad Sci 1987;514:15.
Sassa S. Regulation of the genes for heme pathway enzymes in erythroid and in non-erythroid cells. International Journal of Cell Cloning 1990;8:10.

GENETIC

Bloomer JR, Bonkovsky HL. The porphyrias. Dis Mon 1989;35:1.
Bonkovsky HL. Porphyria: practical advice for the clinical gastroenterologist and hepatologist. Dig Dis 1987;5: 179.
Bottomley SS, Muller-Eberhard U. Pathophysiology of heme synthesis. Semin Hematol 1988;25:282.
Elder GH. The cutaneous porphyrias. Semin Dermatol 1990;9:63.
Elder GH, Smith SG, Smyth SJ. Laboratory investigation of the porphyrias. Ann Clin Biochem 1990;27:395.
Elder GH. Molecular genetics of disorders of haem biosynthesis. J Clin Pathol 1993;46:977.
Lip GY, McColl KE, Moore MR. The acute porphyrias. Br J Clin Pract 1993;47:38.
Moore MR. Biochemistry of porphyria. Int J Biochem 1993;25:1353.
Mustajoki P, Tenhunen R, Pierach C, Violin L. Heme in the treatment of porphyrias and hematological disorders. Semin Hematol 1989;26:1.
Straka J, Rank J, Bloomer JR. Porphyria and porphyrin metabolism. Annu Rev Med 1990;41:457.
Tefferi A, Colgan JP, Solberg LA. Acute porphyrias: diagnosis and management. Mayo Clin Proc 1994;69: 991.
Todd DJ. Erythropoietic protoporphyria. Br J Dermatol 1994;131:751.

ACQUIRED

Akagi R, Prchal JT, Eberhart EE, Sassa S. An acquired acute hepatic porphyria: a novel type of delta-aminolevulinate dehydratase inhibition. Clin Chim Acta 1992;212:79.
DeMatteis F. Toxicological aspects of liver heme biosynthesis. Semin Hematol 1988;25:321.
Houston T, Moore M, Porter D, et al. Abnormal haem biosynthesis in the chronic anemia of rheumatoid arthritis. Ann Rheum Dis 1994;53:167.
Wetmur JG. Influence of the common human delta-aminolevulinate dehydratase polymorphism on lead body burden. Environ Health Perspect 1994;102:215.

part **III**

Disorders of Organs

chapter **18**

Hematologic Disorders

The subliminal concept that the sight of blood is indicative of danger has been a part of the human psyche throughout recorded history—and probably before that. Easily accessible and identifiable, blood always has held a fascination for humankind, documented in theological, historic, literary, and medical writings. Moreover, because of its availability, blood has been subjected to intense scrutiny by medical scientists for many years.

Blood is a complex tissue composed of several specialized cell types suspended in an aqueous medium. This medium is the plasma and it contains an array of proteins, electrolytes, and nutrients. Red blood cells (erythrocytes) are adapted for one pre-eminent function: to carry oxygen to the tissues, a function mediated by the remarkable iron-containing protein, hemoglobin. Of course, serving as a transport medium, blood also provides nutrients for the cells of the body, while carrying away waste materials, including CO_2 mostly in the form of bicarbonate.

White blood cells (leukocytes) are involved in defending the host against infection, whereas lymphocytes mount an immune response to foreign invaders, whether they are microorganisms or foreign molecules. An elaborate system of proteins collaborate with the platelets (thrombocytes) to defend the host against life-threatening blood loss from small- and medium-sized vessels. Counterpoised against this blood-clotting system is another enzymatic system aimed at preventing unwarranted clot formation. Finally, the blood plays a role in temperature regulation, ensuring wide dispersal of heat produced by metabolically active organs.

In light of the complexity of blood, it should be clear that maintenance of its various cellular and protein components depends upon a multitude of different organs. As a consequence, systemic disease of virtually any etiology can affect some aspect of the function of blood and lead to confusion regarding the underlying cause, unless the observed changes are assessed in a methodical fashion. It follows that changes in blood may not be representative of primary hematologic disease but rather indicate disruption in homeostatic mechanisms in another diseased organ. One clear example of this is the anemia regularly associated with chronic renal disease. A corollary of this is that primary blood disorders represent a small percentage of the total hematologic abnormalities observed in clinical medicine. Thus, evaluation should not be based on reflexive "panels" of tests, but on sound reasoning.

LABORATORY TESTS TO EVALUATE BLOOD CELLULAR COMPONENTS

As a means of simplifying the approach to blood disorders, it is helpful to first examine the usual means to assess this tissue. Such tests indicate the percentage of whole blood made up of the red blood cell mass (hematocrit); the absolute amount of hemoglobin contained in 100 ml of blood (gms%); the number of red and white blood cells contained in one cubic centimeter (ml) of blood; and a visual inspection of the stained blood smear evaluating cellular size, shape, stage of development, and cellular contents. All of this information is contained in the *complete blood count* (CBC).

Using simple ratios and the values for hemoglobin, hematocrit, and red cell number, additional information can be derived for the following (Table 18.1): mean corpuscular hemoglobin content (MCH) in picograms, mean corpuscular volume (MCV) in femtoliters, and mean corpuscular hemoglobin concentration (MCHC) in g/100 ml packed cells. Key to accurate interpretation of the complete blood count is the recognition that the

Table 18.1. Red Cell Indices

INDEX	REFERENCE RANGE	MEASURES
$MCV = \frac{\text{Hematocrit} \times 1000}{\text{RBC count}}$	80–95 femtoliters	Mean volume of all red cells
$MCH = \frac{\text{Hemoglobin}}{\text{RBC count}}$	27–33 picograms	Amount (weight) of Hb in average rbc
$MCHC = \frac{\text{Hemoglobin}}{\text{Hematocrit}}$	33%–35%	Concentration of Hb in average rbc

MCH = mean corpuscular hemoglobin content, MCV = mean corpuscular volume, MCHC = mean copuscular hemoglobin concentration.

basic parameters (hematocrit, hemoglobin, and number of red cells) are all expressed against whole blood volume. Hence, any factor, such as acute fluid loss through the gastrointestinal tract, which alters volume independent of the cellular elements, will necessarily change these three basic values. Having established this, it becomes clear that visual assessment of cell morphology, particularly the red cell, is essential to accurate interpretation of hematologic abnormalities, because cellular structure, shape, and size ought not to vary directly with the liquid phase of whole blood.

Many red cell disorders can be diagnosed by visually inspecting the cellular elements of a well-prepared coverglass blood film. As listed in Table 18.2, a variety of morphologic abnormalities including spherocytes, elliptocytes, sickled cells, target cells, cells with membrane spicules, and various inclusions (basophilic stippling, Howell-Jolly bodies, Cabot rings, Heinz bodies, and siderocytes) can be recognized on the smear. A fringe benefit of inspection of the smear is the ability to estimate the number of platelets present, thereby confirming the electronic platelet count. Based on this visual estimate, other coagulation studies that may be indicated include bleeding time, prothrombin time, and activated partial thromboplastin time. These coagulation studies are discussed below, included in the section on disorders of hemostasis.

Taking into account the complexity of the blood, it is not surprising that causes of abnormalities frequently must be identified using the diagnostic skill and intuition born of experience. Nonetheless, using simple tests and common sense, even the novice can make significant inroads towards an appropriate diagnosis. In this chapter, we will attempt to underscore this approach, noting fundamentals that enable one to differentiate primary from secondary blood diseases.

SOURCES OF THE CELLULAR ELEMENTS OF BLOOD

The cells inhabiting the blood "turn over" (ie, die and are replenished) at a staggering rate because of short life-span, as in the case of white cells, or because of inability to carry out protein synthesis, as in the case of the red cells. All of these blood cells, which serve widely differing functions, nevertheless, are descendants of a pluripotent *stem cell.* From these cells emerge the erythroid, phagocytic, and megakaryocytic cells. Although lymphoid cells also are derived from these same stem cells, some lymphoid cells do not become terminally differentiated as do the other cells. In the case of the lymphoid cells, some revert to dormant "memory" cells that can be awakened and mobilized on demand.

The stem cells are derived during embryologic development, and retain the genetic apparatus and control mechanisms to permit them to produce more differentiated cell types. Because blood cells turn over, it is clear that "somewhere" there must be one or more of these stem cells retained throughout the life of the individual. It follows that because the normal adult carries out the generation of the cellular elements (hematopoiesis) exclusively in the bone marrow and lymphatic organs, these tissues represent the "somewhere" where stem cells are harbored.

What makes persistence of the hematopoietic stem cell difficult to conceptualize is the necessary qualification that when such a stem cell divides into two daughter cells, one must remain in

Table 18.2. Description and Significance of Various Forms of Red Corpuscles†

TYPE OF CELL	DESCRIPTION	PHYSIOLOGIC SIGNIFICANCE*	CLINICAL DISORDERS
Macrocyte	Larger than normal (>8.5 μm diameter). Well filled with hemoglobin	Young RBC (?skipped generation, early loss of nucleus)	Accelerated erythropoiesis
		DNA synthesis-impaired megaloblastic maturation	B_{12} or folate deficiency
"Thin" macrocyte	Diameter increased but MCV normal; often hypochromic (see target cell)	Membrane cholesterol *and* lecithin increased	Liver disease, postsplenectomy
Microcyte	Smaller than normal (<7.0 μm)	Differs according to whether or not it is: (a) well filled with hemoglobin (b) normal in shape	See below
Hypochromic cell	Exaggeration of normal central pallor; usually also microcytic	Failure of hemoglobin synthesis due to: (a) lack of iron (b) defective globin synthesis (c) defective porphyrin synthesis	Iron-deficiency anemia, anemia of chronic disease (?) Thalassemia, some hemoglobinopathies (C and E) Sideroblastic anemia
Target cell	Hypochromic, with central pigment; thin cell, surface to volume ratio increased	Splenectomy decreases rate and extent of loss of lipids from reticulocytes	As for hypochromic cells; also postsplenectomy in liver disease, especially obstructive jaundice
		Accumulation of both cholesterol and phospholipid on RBC	LCAT deficiency
		Congenital	
Leptocyte	Thin, hypochromic cell, diameter normal, MCV decreased		Thalassemia
Spherocyte	Spherical, not hypochromic; usually also microcytic; surface to volume ratio decreased; no central pallor	RBC membrane abnormality	Hereditary spherocytosis
		RBC lose fragments after impact with fibrin strands, walls of diseased vessels, and artificial surfaces in the circulation	Acquired immunohemolytic anemia
Elliptocyte	Elliptical; not hypochromic	Hereditary abnormality	Hereditary elliptocytosis
		Acquired alteration	In various anemias, especially megaloblastic
Sickle cell	In shape of sickle; form assumed especially on deprivation of oxygen	Molecular aggregation of Hb S	Hb S trait or disease Also seen with Hb I, Hb C_{Harlem}, Hb $C_{Capetown}$
Schistocyte	Triangular or helmet-shaped, fragmented or greatly distorted RBC; smaller than normal	RBC lose fragments after impact with fibrin strands, walls of diseased vessels, and artificial surfaces in the circulation	Microangiopathic hemolytic anemia Hemolytic anemia due to physical agents Also in uremia, malignant hypertension
"Teardrop" RBC	Shape of drop; usually microcytic, often also hypochromic	Distorted or fragmented RBC	Especially in myelofibrosis Less frequently in other forms of anemia (eg, thalassemia)
Spicule cells Acanthocyte ("spur cell")	RBC with spiny projections on surface Has 5 to 10 spicules of various lengths, irregular in spacing and thickness	Ratio of cholesterol to lecithin of RBC membrane increased when associated with liver disease. Can be converted to normal shape by nonionic detergents	In abetalipoproteinemia Liver disease with hemolytic anemia Postsplenectomy (few) Pyruvate kinase deficiency

(continued)

Table 18.2. *(continued)*

TYPE OF CELL	DESCRIPTION	PHYSIOLOGIC SIGNIFICANCE*	CLINICAL DISORDERS
Echinocyte (sea urchin cell, crenated cell, burr cell)	Has 10 to 30 spicules, evenly distributed over surface of RBC	Result of alteration of intra- and extra-cellular environment. Can be brought about by accumulation of fatty acid or lysolecithin on RBC surface, or both, as result of changes in plasma or in RBC metabolism	Uremia Neonates Pyruvate kinase deficiency Phosphoglycerate kinase deficiency
Stomatocyte	Uniconcave, as contrasted with normal biconcave RBC; slitlike instead of circular area of central pallor in RBC	Hereditary. Primary defects in membrane structure or function resulting in abnormalities of cation permeability, content, and flux Acquired alteration in cation content and flux	Hereditary stomatocytosis, several forms Smaller numbers seen in alcoholic cirrhosis, acute alcoholism, obstructive liver disease, malignancies, etc., and perhaps as artifacts
Xerocyte	Dense, dehydrated, irregularly contracted; may have apparent puddling of hemoglobin at periphery	Result of net cation and water loss	Familial xerocytosis

* RBC, red blood cell; MCV, mean cell volume; LCAT, lecithin cholesterol acyltransferase.

† Reprinted with permission from Lee GR, Bithell TC, Foerster J, et al. Wintrobe's Clinical Hematology. 9th ed. Baltimore: Williams & Wilkins, 1993, p. 724.

place and retain its capacity to function as a stem cell, while the other is permitted to differentiate into a mature cell found in the peripheral blood. This is a vastly different scenario from the usual one of division of a mature cell into two daughter cells to replace a single mature cell that has been lost, as in the hepatocyte. Moreover, as in hematopoiesis, the complexity of the genetic and cellular controls involved are underscored by the wide variety of mature cell types involved.

Putting aside the above issues, current theory holds that the "totipotent" stem cell, differentiated from the totipotent fertilized ovum, can function only in hematopoiesis. When such a stem cell divides, it produces either lymphocytic pre-T- or pre-B-stem cells, or a "pluripotent" myeloid stem cell. The pluripotent myeloid cells give rise to stem cells that are more differentiated, each type of which is responsible for generation of the nonlymphocytic cellular elements. It is obvious that this system is competent to respond to demands for a specific mature cell type, both to maintain homeostasis and meet needs when the system is disequilibrated by disease or other stress. However, the signals and controls involved remain poorly understood.

In broad outline, development of the erythroid line is stimulated by a glycoprotein hormone, *erythropoietin* (Figure 18.1). Produced by the kidney, hormonal secretion is governed by tissue oxygen tension. Hence, any cause for decrease in tissue oxygenation, whether it is from any of the anemias or pulmonary or cardiac disease, will trigger an increase in erythropoietin secretion. Similarly, the other cell lines are stimulated to proliferate through the action of a variety of growth factors: colony-stimulating factors in the case of phagocytes and interleukins for the lymphocytes. As a rule, phagocyte proliferation is in response to breaching of the first line of defense against microorganisms, whereas lymphocyte proliferation may be instigated either by a living foreign invader or a xenobiotic.

Taking the erythrocytic cell line as an example, it can be calculated that the equivalent of approximately 1% (1 g/100 g) circulating hemoglobin is excreted daily as bilirubin plus urobilinogen (see Chapter 5). In an average adult male, based on a blood volume of 5 liters and a hemoglobin of 15 g/dl, maintenance of a normal peripheral hemoglobin concentration requires de novo synthesis of 7.5 g of hemoglobin daily incorporated into about 200 million new cells per day. Because each molecule of hemoglobin contains 574 amino acid units,

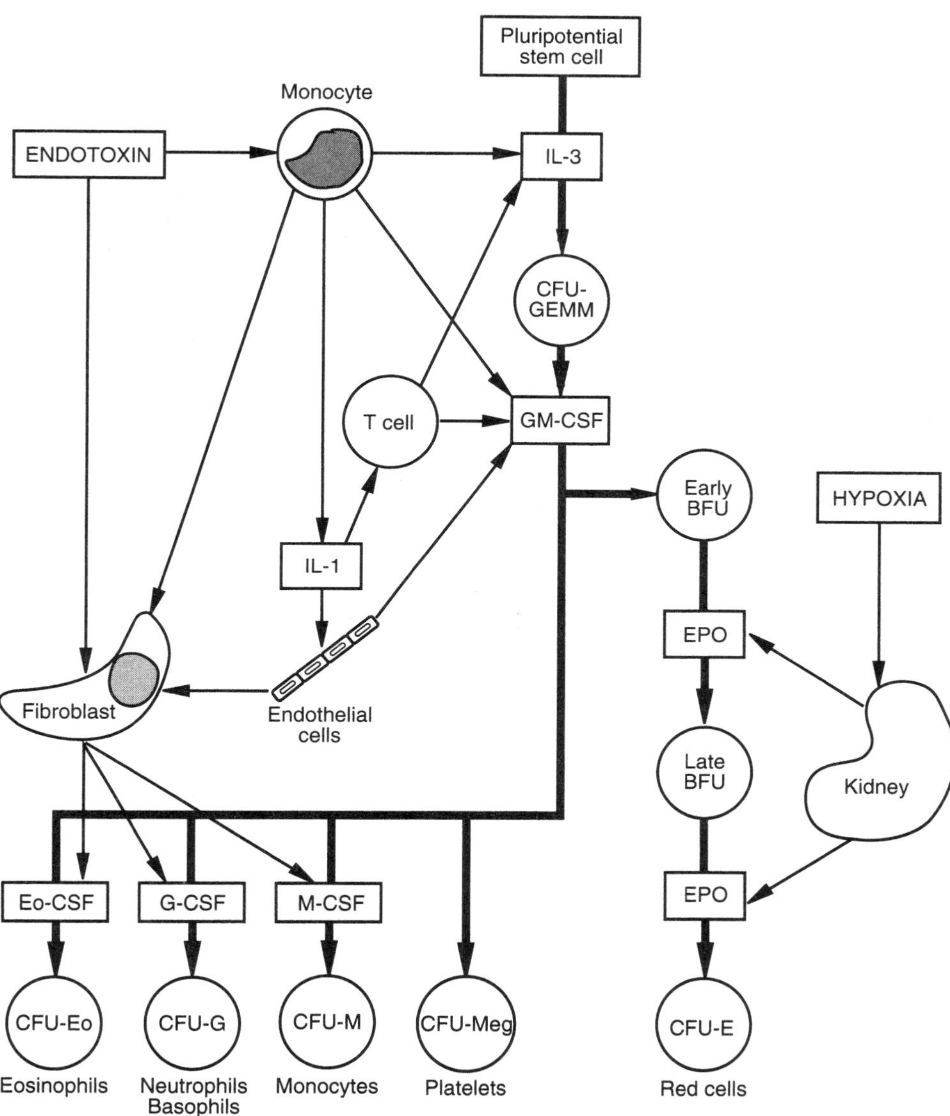

Figure 18.1. The pathways of hematopoiesis. The normal sequence begins with the pluripotential stem cell, which provides a multipotential progenitor cell, or colony-forming unit (CFU) for granulocytes, macrophages, erythroid cells, and megakaryocytes (CFU-GEMM). At this stage, there is a major branch point, with one branch establishing the "burst-forming unit" (BFU), which eventually gives rise to the CFU-E, which is the progenitor of the erythroid line; the other branch leads to progenitors of the leucocytic series. The response scheme of the system to two stress factors also is shown. Bacterial endotoxin stimulates monocytic production of interleukin-1 (IL-1); the subsequent chain involves T-cell production of interleukin-3 (IL-3), and production of colony stimulating factor-1 (CSF-1) by endothelium and fibroblasts. Both of these effects ultimately result in increased numbers of cells of the granulocytic-macrophage lines. Hypoxia, the second stress factor shown, exerts an effect confined to the kidney, resulting in release of erythropoietin (EPO) and a secondary increase in erythropoiesis. Reprinted with permission from Besa EC, Catalano PM, Kent JA, et al. Hematology. Baltimore: Williams & Wilkins, 1992: 15.

it requires little imagination to recognize the awesome metabolic requirements for maintenance of red cell homeostasis alone.

The relative lability of the neutrophil population in the circulating blood, increasing 4- to 5-fold with such "normal" stresses as strenuous exercise, and the short half-life (4–10 hours) of a neutrophil compared to 120 days for an erythrocyte superimpose enormous requirements for basic synthetic elements. From this, it would be easy to realize why a child with leukemia might rapidly develop cachexia, even if the nutrient intake was not decreased because of anorexia. Clearly, diversion of dietary protein into synthesis of literally millions of white cells per day would have a significant effect on protein synthesis in other body tissues.

STRUCTURE AND BIOCHEMICAL FUNCTION OF THE ERYTHROCYTE

Despite its lack of mitochondria, and therefore of oxidative metabolism, the mature erythrocyte can meet its need to generate adenosine triphosphate (ATP) and provide for other housekeeping functions. Given the requirement that the red cell passes through the micro-vessels of the capillary beds to fulfill its oxygen-transfer function, shape and size are key factors in red cell functions because unlike most cells, erythrocytes are subjected to mechanical stresses (in narrow capillaries and in the reticular network of the spleen) throughout their life span. Thus, any deviation from normal shape or ease of deformability will necessarily increase these stresses and likely decrease the average life span. Regarding shape, remember that membrane composition is a major determinant of shape and flexibility. Moreover, because 95% of the intracellular protein content of the erythrocyte is hemoglobin (a 33% solution in cell water), the molecular structure of hemoglobin plays a role in determination of red cell form. This is most dramatically demonstrated in the case of sickle cell hemoglobin (see below).

Morphologically, the mature erythrocyte is a biconcave disc, resembling a doughnut from which the center has not been removed (Figure 18.2). Keeping in mind that in addition to withstanding mechanical stress, the erythrocyte must assume a shape that will provide maximal surface area in relation to volume, this biconcave disk is the ideal shape to provide optimal oxygen exchange. Equally intriguing is how the red cell, devoid of nucleus, mitochondria, and ribosomes, manages to maintain this shape. One clearly demonstrable

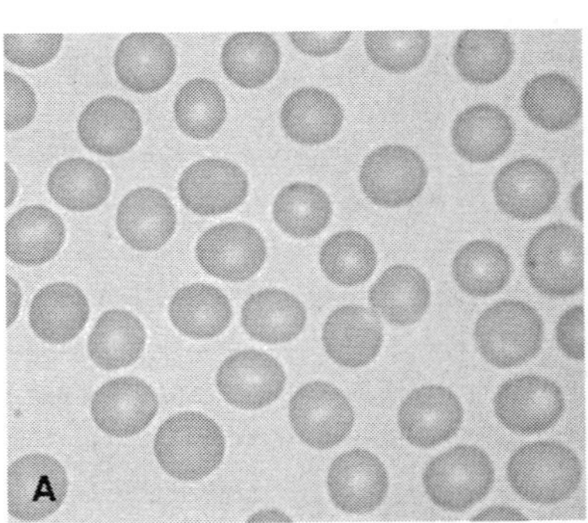

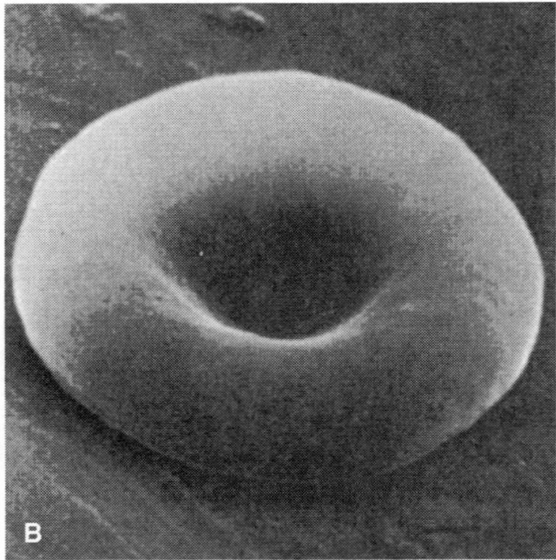

Figure 18.2. (A) Appearance of mature erythrocytes in a peripheral blood smear. (B) Scanning electron micrograph of the mature red cell. The structure as shown permits maximal surface area exposure for efficient oxygen transfer and great flexibility as well (magnification ×9800). Reprinted with permission from Lee GR, Bithell TC, Foerster J, et al. Wintrobe's Clinical Hematology. 9th ed. Baltimore: Williams & Wilkins, 1993: 102.

factor is the osmotic pressure of the suspending medium, because with decreasing osmotic pressure, erythrocytes become progressively more spherical in shape. Exposure of the cell to alkaline pH, increased intracellular calcium, or depletion of intracellular ATP leads to a series of morphologic changes that eventually result in assumption of a spherical shape. The third known factor is acid pH; with progressive decrease (increasing H+ concentration), it causes loss of the center dimple on one side and increased depth on the other, forming a cup-shaped cell and finally a sphere. Thus, what is a typical physical conformation for most cell types represents an abnormal state for the erythrocyte, produced by factors that reflect underlying pathophysiology. It is no exaggeration to state that changes in red cell shape are among the leading factors that initiate splenic degradation of erythrocytes.

Membrane Organization

Red blood cells have the daunting task of navigating the thousands of miles of capillaries, of which their internal diameter (2–3 μm) is considerably less than the red cell diameter of 8 μm. Obviously, for the red cell to withstand the shear forces involved in such a trip, it must be able to deform upon entering the capillaries and resume its biconcave shape upon exiting. Deformability is a consequence of its membrane structure and its associated cytoskeleton—a partnership that echoes the truism "structure determines function." This cytoskeleton comprises an interlocking network of several proteins, affixed at strategic points to the plasma membrane (Figure 18.3). Although the basic form of the red cell membrane is that of a phospholipid bilayer, more than half the mass of the membrane is protein, with 40% accounted for by lipid and the remaining 8% by carbohydrate. Critical differences, however, emerge when the proportions of these lipids are quantitatively examined. Phospholipids and unesterified cholesterol are the major constituents of the erythrocyte membrane. Moreover, within the class of phospholipid, there is wide variation in specific types; the bulk of phospholipid is composed of phosphatidylcholine, sphingomyelin, and phosphatidylethanolamine (Table 18.3). Just as phospholipid distribution in the red cell membrane is asymmetric, the fatty acids also are asymmetrically distributed. Unsaturated fatty acids preponderate in the inner leaflet, making that region of the membrane more fluid than the outer monolayer.

Table 18.3. Lipid Composition of the Erythrocyte Membrane

CONSTITUENT	PERCENT
Cholesterol	25
Phosphatidylcholine	19
Phosphatidylethanolamine	17
Sphingomyelin	16
Phosphatidylserine	10
Glycolipids	5
Phosphatidylinositol	1

As in all membranes, phospholipids are asymmetrically deployed with most of the choline-containing, bulky phospholipids (phosphatidylcholine and sphingomyelin) found on the external surface of the membrane, whereas the charged amino-containing phospholipids (phosphatidylethanolamine and phosphatidylserine) are located on the cytoplasmic face of the membrane. Because the red cell is devoid of organelles, it is incapable of synthesizing lipids. Thus, plasma membrane components of the red cell do not turn over, as a consequence of the lack of endogenous synthetic pathways. Rather, any loss of red cell membrane lipid can be replaced only by exchange with plasma lipoproteins; such interchange occurs predominantly with respect to phosphatidylcholine and cholesterol, the rate of transfer being dependent upon the circulating levels of phosphatidylcholine and cholesterol as they are made available by lipoproteins. Relationships of the various membrane components are critical to cell shape. For example, cholesterol, in combination with phospholipids, forms an "intermediate gel state," which is much more viscous (less fluid) than a pure phospholipid bilayer membrane. Thus, if the ratio of cholesterol to phospholipid increases above the normal, the cell membrane becomes too rigid, the shape becomes distorted, and the cell is destroyed in the spleen. Alternatively, if the ratio decreases, the cell assumes a spheroidal shape and is again destroyed by the spleen. Beyond the physical alterations, the physiologic implications of such changes include increased

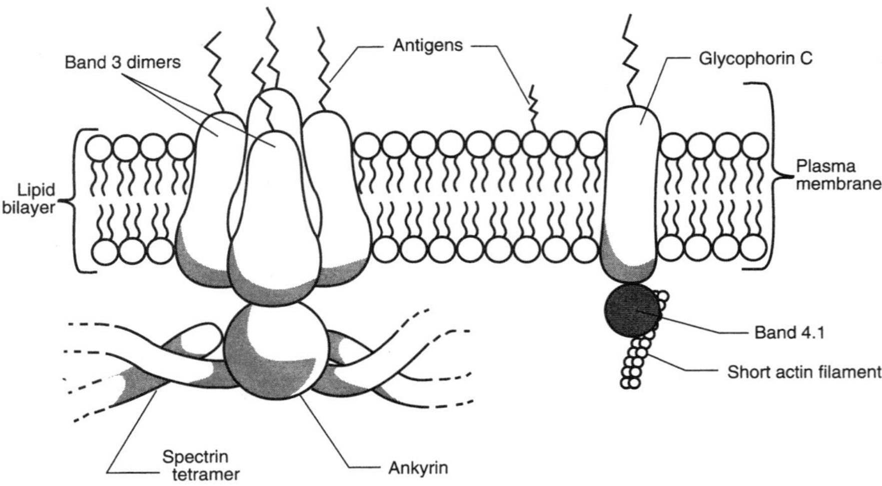

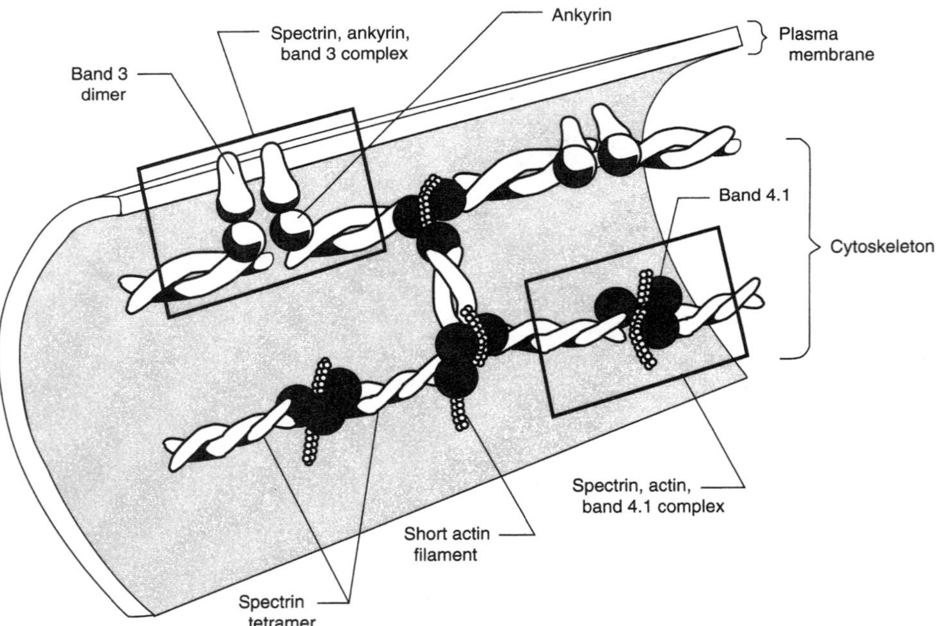

Figure 18.3. Structure of the red cell membrane and cytoskeleton. (A) Erythrocyte plasma membrane exhibits the typical orientation of the component lipids, with the aqueous exposure of the polar heads and the hydrophobic interior. The intrinsic proteins, band 3 and glycophorin C, each play a significant role in joining the membrane with the cytoskeleton, reducing the structure-function relationship to a still finer level. (B) The cytoskeleton is composed of three major proteins (spectrin, actin, and band 4.1 protein) and is anchored to band 3 membrane protein by a fourth cytoskeletal protein named ankyrin and to glycophorin C through band 4.1 protein. The net effect of these "joints" is to provide tremendous elasticity to the structure. Reprinted with permission from Besa EC, et al. Hematology. Baltimore: Williams & Wilkins, 1992: 97.

shear forces in the microvasculature and decreased surface area-to-volume ratios impacting on oxygen transfer.

As noted, much of the strength and resiliency of the red cell membrane stems from the connections between its integral proteins and the attached network of peripheral proteins that form the cytoskeleton. This cytoskeleton, which lies beneath the cytoplasmic face of the plasma membrane, is composed of three proteins: spectrin, actin, and protein 4.1 (so designated because of its migration on sodium dodecyl sulfate-polyacrylamide gel electrophoresis-SDS-PAGE). Spectrin is the main constituent of the cytoskeleton. It is composed of two nonidentical subunits that take the form of a flexible rod. Two heterodimers make a head-to-head connection forming a tetramer, which associates with approximately 12 actin monomers. The result of the spectrin-actin interaction is the formation of a flexible hexagonal lattice of six spectrin molecules joined with actin. Imparting still greater stability to the spectrin-actin junctions is protein 4.1, which is an additional anchor point. Overall, this lattice has rubberlike properties, returning to its original shape after deformation.

How is this cytoskeletal system linked to the lipid bilayer? There are two proteins that induce this connection. Ankyrin connects spectrin to band 3 of the bilayer; the integral membrane protein glycophorin C links up with protein 4.1. When the red cell is in a relatively large diameter vessel, it experiences no deforming stresses and the spectrin molecules of the cytoskeleton are folded in a nonextended conformation. But, when the cell enters a capillary, a deforming stress causes the spectrin molecules to adopt an extended conformation that allows the red cell to undergo the necessary shape change to negotiate the narrow passage.

Given the importance of the spectrin-actin cytoskeleton, it is to be anticipated that many inherited abnormalities of red cell structure would be accounted for by deficiency of one of the following: spectrin, actin, ankyrin, protein 4.1, and glycophorin. Hereditary spherocytosis and hereditary elliptocytosis are the two most well-known disorders of red cell structure attributable to defects in structural elements of the cytoskeleton (see below).

Red Cell Metabolism

As mentioned, energy production by the red cell is restricted by virtue of the absence of mitochondria. Accordingly, the sole sources of energy must be those pathways normally confined to the cytosolic compartment (ie, anaerobic glycolysis with a meager contribution from the hexose-monophosphate shunt). If anything, the prime role of the erythrocyte is to serve as a container for hemoglobin within the circulatory system. Hence, red cell energy requirements include that necessary to maintain membrane integrity, as well as that needed to maintain structure and function of the contained hemoglobin. Unlike most other cells, glucose entry into the red cell occurs by facilitated diffusion, thus eliminating the need for energy for active uptake. Note that the red cell is one of the few cell types that is absolutely glucose-dependent, because it is unable to use alternate fuels that require mitochondrial oxidation.

Turning first to the energy requirement for maintenance of membrane integrity, because de novo synthesis of proteins and lipids for replacement of membrane components is not an option in the absence of endoplasmic reticulum, the focus of energy needs must be upon preserving structure and carrying out active exclusion of cations. Because the maximum net yield of ATP from anaerobic glycolysis is only 2 moles of ATP per mole of glucose, there is little margin for waste. In contrast to glycolysis, energy derived from the hexose-monophosphate shunt is captured as NADPH, which is used as a cofactor in reduction of glutathione, the major antioxidant used to protect integral membrane proteins and cellular enzymes from oxidant stresses. Thus, ATP consumption is severely constrained, being used for two main purposes: (*1*) continued operation of glycolysis (hexokinase, phosphofructokinase); and (*2*) fuel for membrane cation pump, most particularly the Na^+-K^+-ATPase. Formation of 2, 3 bisphosphoglycerate (2,3 BPG [Figure 18.4]), a reaction unique to the red cell and one that is critical to normal function of hemoglobin (see below), circumvents the phosphoglycerate kinase step of glycolysis, a source of ATP. The economy of the cation pump is such that for each mole of ATP consumed, 3 moles of sodium ion leave the cell and 2 moles of potassium ion enter, together with 1 mole of chloride ion to maintain electrical neutrality.

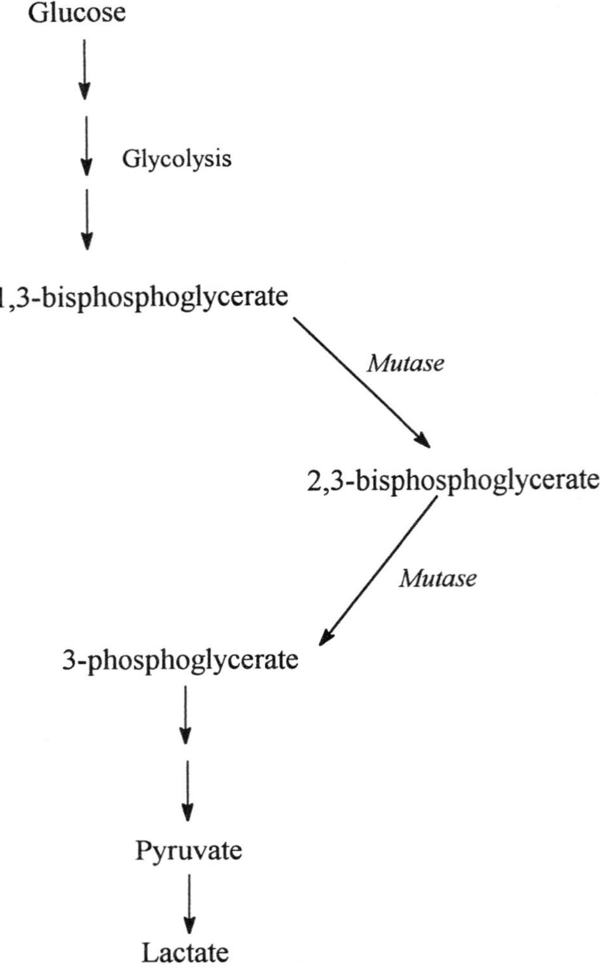

Figure 18.4. Pathway of formation of 2,3-bisphosphoglycerate. The red cell is totally dependent upon glycolysis for energy because it lacks mitochondria. Consequently, it is a marvel of "natural engineering" that the main metabolic pathway would be used to supply a compound (2,3-BPG) that also is a key regulator of the function of the red cell's primary contents, hemoglobin. The enzyme that mediates production of 2,3-BPG and its return to main-stream glycolysis, diphosphoglycerate mutase, is unique to the erythrocyte.

Role of 2,3 Bisphosphoglyceric Acid in Controlling Hemoglobin Oxygen Affinity

A notable biochemical difference between the red cell and other cell types, alluded to above, is the capacity to produce 2,3 BPG as a side-reaction of the glycolytic pathway. Whereas in the red cell, the majority of intracellular phosphate is found as 2,3 BPG, this compound is barely detectable in other cell types. The chief function of 2,3 BPG is as an allosteric effector, to regulate the oxygen affinity of hemoglobin. To better comprehend the mechanism involved, it is necessary to examine the general structure and function of hemoglobin itself. Normal adult human hemoglobin (HbA_1) consists of four globin-heme units, in which two of the units (alpha) differ from the other two (beta) by virtue of a five amino acid difference in length of the globin moieties. Acting in concert, these four subunits bind oxygen through their heme groups in a reversible and cooperative manner so that binding of the fourth O_2 occurs with the least difficulty, whereas binding of the first oxygen occurs with the most. These relative binding affinities result in an oxygen-dissociation curve that has a sigmoid shape in relation to the partial pressure of oxygen (Figure 18.5). The steepest part of the curve occurs within the range of partial pressures found in tissues, so that as the red cell moves into the capillaries, feeding oxygen to hungry cells, it gives off its bound oxygen with increasing ease. It is important to recognize that the sigmoidal pattern of oxygen-dissociation is an intrinsic property of the hemoglobin molecule, related primarily to

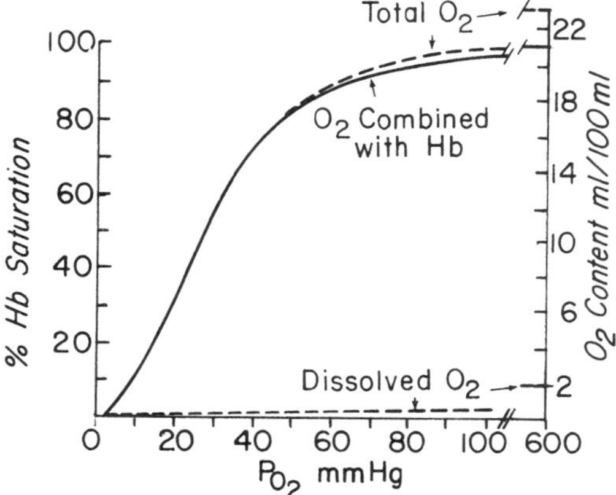

Figure 18.5. Normal oxygen-dissociation curve for hemoglobin. The sequential facilitation of O_2-binding with each of the four monomer units underlies the typical sigmoid shape of the curve. The curve is representative under the following conditions: pH 7.4, pCO_2 40 mm Hg, and temperature 37°C. Also shown are the quantities of O_2 in solution and the total O_2 content of the blood at a hemoglobin of 15 g%. Horizontal axis shows the O_2 partial pressure in mm Hg, whereas the vertical axis portrays the percent O_2 saturation of the hemoglobin. Reprinted with permission from West JB. Best & Taylor's Physiological Basis of Medical Practice. 12th ed. 1990; Baltimore: Williams & Wilkins, 1990: 539.

its molecular structure. However, although the basic form of the O_2 dissociation curve is not changed, the oxygen partial pressure at which the hemoglobin is 50% saturated can be altered by many different factors, including pH and the intracellular concentration of 2,3 BPG. The effect of pH (Bohr effect) on hemoglobin is to reduce its oxygen affinity which, in turn, facilitates oxygen delivery to the peripheral tissues from the red cell. The Bohr effect is mediated through the conformational changes in the hemoglobin molecule induced by changes in hydrogen ion concentration. These conformational changes alter the relationship of the monomeric units to each other, and thus diminish the affinity of hemoglobin for oxygen. However, binding of 2,3 BPG to the hemoglobin molecule occurs as a result of conformational changes stemming from deoxygenation; in the deoxygenated state, one molecule of 2,3 DPG binds to each molecule of hemoglobin. The result of 2,3 DPG binding is to diminish O_2 affinity, thereby providing for increased oxygen delivery to tissues.

Despite the very limited metabolic repertoire available to drive the red cell's function, it is clear that nothing is wasted, all needs are accounted for, and there are margins built in for special needs. Moreover, hemoglobin interacts with crucial ligands to accomplish its purpose, while at the same time contributing to the structural integrity of the cell through its molecular conformation.

DISEASES OF THE ERYTHROCYTE

The extraordinary number of disorders that fall into this general classification precludes an extensive discussion of each. Most erythrocytic disorders involve a decrease in the number of circulating red cells per unit volume, defined by the term *anemia*. Anemia, as defined by a decrease in concentration of circulating red cells, which is reflected in the hemoglobin concentration or hematocrit, should be considered as a sign of other abnormalities and not as a disease in itself. Considering that the chief function of the erythrocyte is carrying oxygen, the extent of physical symptoms will depend upon the degree to which there is hypoxia. At rest, the body's tissues use 250 ml of oxygen per minute. The oxygen-carrying capacity of blood is 20 ml per 100 ml of blood. If one assumes a cardiac output of 5 liters per minute, that provides the tissues with 1000 ml O_2 per minute, supplying a significant margin for exercise and other stresses. To consider biochemical abnormalities within the red cell itself, it is convenient to further subdivide the anemias into those that are: (*1*) macrocytic, (*2*) normocytic, and (*3*) microcytic. Defects in hemoglobin structure or synthesis and defects in the red cell membrane or enzymes are best considered in terms of their underlying biochemistry.

Macrocytic Anemia

Perhaps the most well known of macrocytic anemias is the subgroup known as megaloblastic, macrocytic anemias caused by cobalamin or folate deficiency. Among the entities in this category of megaloblastic anemias, a unifying feature is impaired DNA synthesis without impairment of transcription of DNA into RNA. In this condition, cytoplasmic protein synthesis proceeds "more or less" normally while DNA may increase, but cells do not divide. Consequently, this results in cells of supernormal size. In addition to vitamin B_{12} and/or folic acid deficiency, genetic disorders of DNA synthesis and toxin or drug-induced disorders of DNA synthesis also can cause megaloblastosis.

The mechanism by which DNA synthesis is affected in B_{12} deficiency, for example, remains poorly understood. However, B_{12} is known to function as a cofactor in human biochemistry in only two reactions: the first one we mention is methyl group transfer from methyltetrahydrofolate to homocysteine (resulting in the formation of methionine), and the second is isomerization of methymalonyl-CoA to succinyl-CoA. In each case, the specific form of active B_{12} cofactor is different; the folate-dependent methyl transfer requires methylcobalamin. Indeed, the cooperation between folate and B_{12} in this reaction forms the basis for the postulated mechanism for impaired DNA synthesis. For normal DNA synthesis to occur, all four deoxynucleotides must be present in adequate amounts, each of which can be synthesized de novo. In each case, tetrahydrofolate, generated from dihydrofolate, is required for synthesis. Generation of tetrahydrofolate requires transfer of a methyl group from methyltetrahydrofolate, mediated by N5-methyltetrahydrofolate:homocysteine methyltransferase with methylcobalamin as cofactor (Figure 18.6). Hence, cobalamin deficiency can be expected to result in accumulation ("trapping") of methyltetrahydrofolate, decreased production of tetrahydrofolate, and impaired nucleotide base synthesis. From this, it should be clear that a deficiency of B_{12} produces a functional deficiency of folate as well. The plausibility of this mechanism is further enhanced by the fact that patients who are genetically deficient in their ability to convert cobalamin to adenosylcobalamin but produce normal quantities of methylcobalamin do not show hematologic abnormalities.

The role of folate in DNA synthesis and its relationship to the function of B_{12} as a cofactor makes it possible to understand the basis for development of megaloblastic, macrocytic anemia in many different circumstances. In pernicious anemia, for example, when B_{12} absorption is deficient, folate trapping will occur. Obviously, dietary folate deficiency will have the same effect, as will folate antagonists. Beyond these, any interference with or deficiency of nucleotide synthesis, such as purine antagonists or genetic defects in nucleotide synthesis, will create a similar picture.

Because of the decrease in 5,10-methylene THF, the thymidylate synthetase reaction that converts dUMP to dTMP is impaired. A decrease in dTMP results, but dUMP and dUTP increase. When intracellular levels of dUTP are elevated, DNA polymerase incorporates some uridine residues into DNA instead of the appropriate thymidine residues. This mistake is recognized by DNA uracil glycosylase, which excises the dUTP, but there may not be adequate levels of dTTP to permit the correct thymidine residue to be inserted. In that case, the DNA strand may break, producing an increased amount of fragmented, functionless DNA.

On the peripheral blood smear, there is evidence of an increase in the average diameter of the erythrocytes (macrocytosis), accompanied by corresponding increases in volume (mean corpuscular volume) and hemoglobin content (MCHC) of the cells. Because the MCHC increases in proportion to the size of the cell, this type of anemia is called normochromic. The presence of megaloblasts in bone marrow and peripheral blood distinguishes the megaloblastic subgroup; these cells show a striking discrepancy between the maturational stage of the cytoplasm and that of the nucleus, which appears immature. Such findings are in complete agreement with the postulated deficiency of DNA synthesis in development of the megaloblastic, macrocytic anemias.

Microcytic Anemia

In this group of anemias, each erythrocyte generally contains a decreased amount of hemoglobin; hence, most members of this group also are hypochromic with decreases in mean corpuscular volume (MCV) and, frequently, decreased MCHC as well. Because the major portion of the red cell's content is hemoglobin, when there is decreased hemoglobin synthesis, it is easy to conceptualize the effects on red cell size. Of course, because hemoglobin is the product of the synthesis of the porphyrin heme and the protein globin, hemoglobin synthesis is vulnerable at a number of points. Nevertheless, most cases of microcytic anemia can be attributed to defects in one of the three essen-

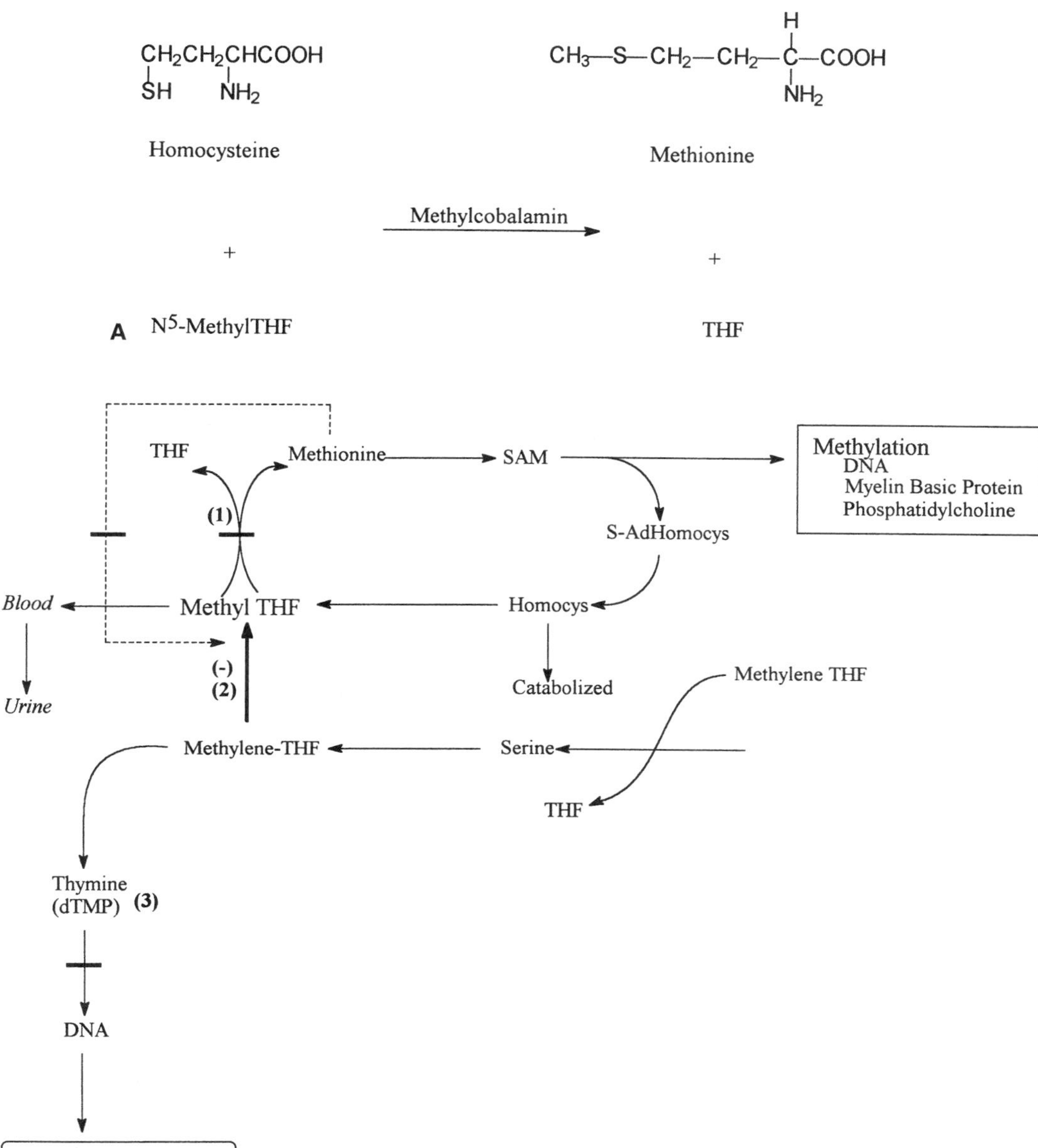

Figure 18.6. The "methyl trap" hypothesis. (A) Methyl group transfer from N5-methyl tetrahydrofolate (THF) to homocysteine, mediated by the methylcobalamin-dependent enzyme N5-methyl tetrahydrofolate:homocysteine methyltransferase, is a critical step in the 1-carbon transfer cycle. In the next step of methionine metabolism, methionine is converted to the methyl-donor compound S-adenosylmethionine (SAM). Therefore, deficiency of methylcobalamin will lead to "trapping" of methyl groups. (B) The mechanism of methyl trapping involves a "block" at step (1) discussed above, with the secondary reduction of SAM slowing the cycle involving homocysteine production. Slowing of the pathway decreases available methylene-THF required to provide thymine (dTMP) for DNA synthesis (3). The hypothesis is advanced to explain neurologic involvement in vitamin B_{12} deficiency, but also can explain the megaloblastic anemia that is characteristic of the disorder.

tial precursors of hemoglobin: iron, protoporphyrin, and globin.

DEFICIENT IRON SUPPLY

Because of the central role of heme iron in the oxygen-transport function of hemoglobin, it is to be expected that iron deficiency will compromise hemoglobin synthesis. Fortunately, because the body tenaciously "holds on" to iron, anemia is a late manifestation of iron deficiency, becoming evident only after body iron stores are depleted. Four moles of iron are required per mole of hemoglobin—on a daily basis, this translates into a requirement for about 15 mg of iron to replace 1/120th of the red cell pool. The bulk of this iron is actually supplied from iron reserves that are banked when red cells are destroyed. Thus, decreased iron intake in an individual experiencing no unusual losses from bleeding will not immediately cause iron deficiency. With time, however, a diet deficient in iron will exert a profound effect on the ability of the marrow to produce sufficient hemoglobin for normal red cell "packaging." Moreover, the degree of hypochromia will be in proportion to the degree and duration of the decrease in intake. The only independent variable in this equation is the remarkable economy of the body regarding its iron stores.

Free Iron is Dangerously Reactive

Normally, the body "goes to great lengths" to guard against loss of iron. From an evolutionary perspective, this stems from the difficulty living cells have in extracting iron from the extensive iron oxide stores found in the earth's crust. Although ostensibly abundant, this iron is virtually unavailable in a readily usable form by living things. The widespread distribution of iron oxides reflects how eagerly oxygen and iron react together. When, however, the iron exists in a form bound covalently or noncovalently to a larger organic molecule, its reactivity is curtailed and becomes subject to modulation. This accounts for the fact that heme-containing proteins (hemoglobin, cytochromes, catalase, and peroxidase) and nonheme forms (ribonucleotide reductase, iron-sulfur proteins, and metalloflavoproteins) are the main intracellular iron species. These iron-containing proteins are at the center of life, mediating oxygen transport, electron transport reactions, and various oxygenations and hydroxylations. When not involved in oxygen transport or some enzymatic role, iron is bound to storage proteins (ferritin and hemosiderin) or is transported in the blood bound to transferrin. In sum, iron is not found free in living things because of its propensity to form toxic free radicals.

IRON LOSS AND REPLACEMENT

Because of menstruation and pregnancy, women, for much of their lives, are at greater liability for loss of iron than are men. Whereas a man may lose about 1 mg Fe/day, mostly by cells sloughed in the stool and urine and from the skin, a menstruating woman will lose about 45 ml of blood during her period. On a monthly basis, therefore, women lose about 0.5 to 1 mg Fe/day more than men.

As we noted previously, inorganic iron compounds are not sufficiently available to meet biologic needs, whereas heme iron (meat) is much more readily absorbed. As eating habits are changing, meat ingestion is decreasing; therefore, most dietary iron increasingly is present in a nonheme form as found in baked goods, egg yolks, vegetables, and nuts. Normally, on a 2500-calorie diet, which contains about 15 mg Fe, enough iron is absorbed (1–2 mg) to replace what is lost. Pregnancy imposes an additional burden for another mg/day, bringing the total requirement in a pregnant woman to about 3 mg/day. Thus, current dietary trends pose a potential problem because nonheme iron is not as well absorbed as is heme iron.

INTERNAL IRON CYCLE

Once ferric iron enters the body through the gastrointestinal tract, it promptly binds to *transferrin*, which is the plasma iron transport protein. Unless unusual losses occur, this iron becomes the possession of the body and is committed to a cycle in which it is repeatedly used to make hemoglobin and other iron-containing proteins. In the case of red cells, after circulating for about 120 days, they are destroyed by macrophages that release this iron and free it to be used again for erythropoiesis. Recycling ceaselessly, any one molecule of iron thus is used repeatedly to make hemoglobin for new red cells. In sum, the daily requirement for new red cells is about 20 mg of iron, taken from the total red cell-associated iron pool of about 2500 mg.

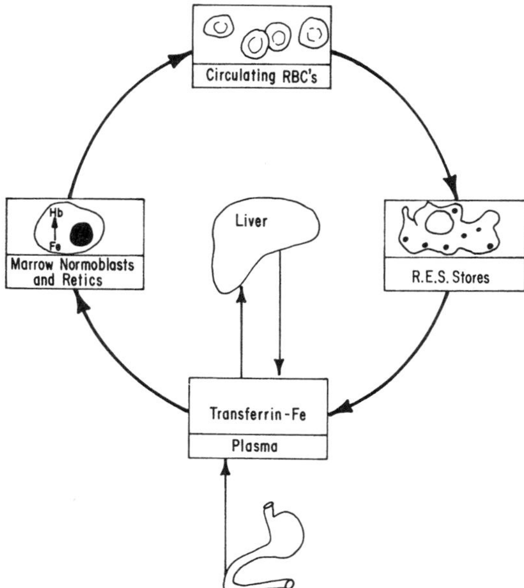

Figure 18.7. Internal iron cycle. The ultimate origin of all body iron (Fe) is the diet and absorption through the gut wall. Upon entering the vascular compartment, the iron is bound to the transport protein, transferrin, which is produced in the liver. Upon delivery to heme-producing cells, the transferrin binds to specific receptors that are present in all nucleated cells, and yields up the bound iron for utilization. In a state of zero balance, the iron is freed from its cellular protein-bound form in the reticuloendothelial system (RES) and recycled by coupling with transferrin. In surplus states, iron is stored within cells bound to ferritin, a storage protein. Reprinted with permission from Lee GR, Bithell TC, Foerster J, et al. Wintrobe's Clinical Hematology. 9th ed. Baltimore: Williams & Wilkins, 1993: 176.

Given the importance of this internal iron cycle (Figure 18.7), we need to consider how iron is transported from the blood to the bone marrow, and how it is stored when there is a surplus. As noted, transferrin is the main plasma iron transport protein. All nucleated cells are outfitted with *transferrin receptors* to facilitate uptake of iron traveling on transferrin. Of course, erythroid precursors are especially well endowed with transferrin receptors, because of the brisk synthesis of hemoglobin during erythropoiesis. Liver also has a substantial number of transferrin receptors. It is possible for males, over a lifetime, to accumulate modest iron stores and for postmenopausal females to store iron as well. Obviously, there must be a way to store iron intracellularly in a manner that will thwart its innate reactivity. That way is through *ferritin*, an iron storage protein that maintains iron in an essentially harmless, but immediately available form for later incorporation into hemoglobin and other iron-containing proteins. Ferritin is a large entity, composed of 24 subunits (combined molecular weight [mw] 500,000) deployed as a hollow sphere that is able to store up to 4500 atoms of iron.

Iron is delivered into the cell via the transferrin receptor, which with other transferrin receptors forms clusters on the cell surface and then fuses with endosomes. The endosome is next internalized and fuses with an acidic vesicle, of which its environment promotes release of iron from transferrin. This iron now is available for hemoglobin synthesis or incorporation into ferritin. After 120 days, senescent red cells are dismantled by macrophages and the iron is released, again affixing itself to transferrin for re-uptake.

Considering the vital and interdependent roles played by transferrin, the transferrin receptor, and ferritin in iron homeostasis, investigators have sought to determine the ways in which biosynthesis or action of these proteins is tied to the availability of iron. First, there is evidence that the rates of synthesis of these three proteins is subject to modulation by iron availability. It has been shown that the mRNA for ferritin and transferrin receptor contain stem-loop regulatory sequences (*iron responsive element* [IRE]) that can bind a protein called iron responsive element-binding protein (IRE-BP, Figure 18.8). When iron supplies are close to exhaustion, the IRE-BP binds to the regulatory sequences in mRNA for ferritin and transferrin receptor. Regarding ferritin, binding of IRE-BP diminishes translation of ferritin mRNA, which is an appropriate response in the iron-deprived state. Equally appropriate, IRE-BP retards degradation of the transferrin receptor transcript, thereby prolonging the biologic life and action of the mRNA for transferrin, with the result that more molecules of the transferrin receptor are available for iron uptake into the cell. Of course, when increased intracellular iron occurs, ferritin production would have to intensify. More ferritin can sequester iron in a haven, protecting the cell from peroxidative damage by iron generated oxidant radicals.

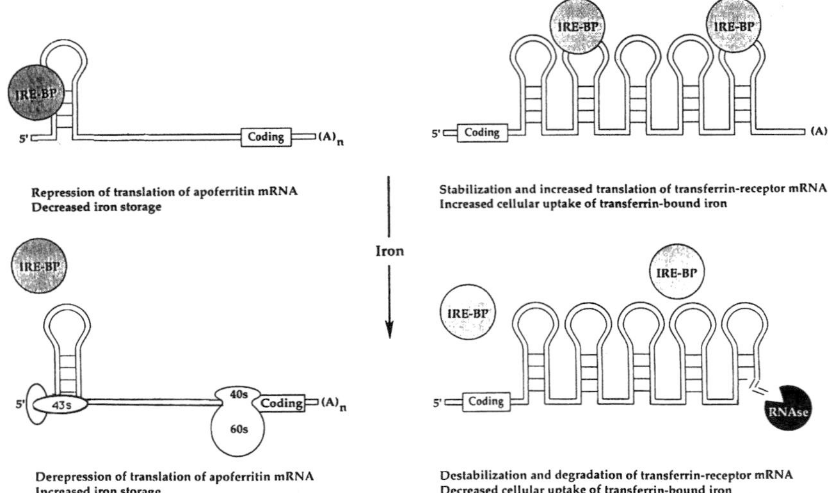

Figure 18.8. The iron-responsive element (IRE) in iron metabolism. The mechanism proposed here can be used to explain the interaction among iron uptake, storage, and elimination by the cell. Control is exerted on the system by a small intracellular "chelatable" iron pool at the level of mRNA. As shown, stem-loop structures, called IREs, exist in the 5′ untranslated region of apoferritin mRNA, and in the 3′ untranslated region of transferrin receptor mRNA. Each of these regions binds a specific regulatory protein IRE-binding protein (IRE-BP) in inverse proportion to cytoplasmic iron concentration. Thus, when iron stores are increased, release of each type of IRE-BP leads to degradation of transferrin-receptor mRNA, decreased receptor sites, and decreased iron uptake. At the same time, apoferritin mRNA moves from the cytoplasm to the ribosome for translation, resulting in increased cellular ferritin. Reprinted with permission from Knisely AS. Neonatal Hemochromatosis in Advances in Pediatrics. Chicago: Year Book Publishers, 1992;39:385.

Although ferritin is mostly confined to the intracellular compartment, trace amounts are secreted into the blood. Because plasma ferritin is proportional to that stored intracellularly, consequently, plasma ferritin is a valuable index of intracellular stores in iron-deficiency anemia.

As discussed in Chapter 6, control of heme biosynthesis in erythroid tissue differs in many of its features from the process in nonerythroidal tissues. A major difference is the role of ferrochelatase as a regulatory enzyme in erythroidal tissue. Unlike other tissues, heme exerts a facilitative effect on aminolevulinate synthase (ALAS) activity in erythroid cells. At the same time, heme curtails further heme formation by blocking iron incorporation into heme at the final step in the de novo pathway, which is called the ferrochelatase reaction. In sum, it stands to reason that limitation of iron supplies constitutes a significant factor in overall production of hemoglobin. Because heme regulates dissociation of iron from the iron-transferrin complex transported into the reticulocyte, heme deficiency should enhance this dissociation. This process, therefore, can explain the decreased serum iron in relation to iron-binding protein that is characteristic of iron-deficiency anemia. Thus, as mentioned earlier, the tenacity with which iron is conserved is reflected in the fact that deficient iron intake does not immediately cause a reduction in hemoglobin synthesis.

At first glance, it would seem reasonable to assume that a deficiency of heme would decrease hemoglobin synthesis merely through simple failure to conjugate normal quantities of globin with adequate heme. It now is clear, however, that heme has a profound regulatory impact on the synthesis of globin proteins, actually decreasing globin mRNA transcription. This effect is mediated by *heme-regulated inhibitor,* which is actually a cAMP-independent protein kinase maintained in an inactive state by heme. This kinase, when activated by heme depletion, phosphorylates a site on the alpha-chain of a key initiation factor eIF-2, which is required for globin synthesis.

This capsular view of events occurring in response to decreased iron intake, makes clear the far-reaching implications of iron deficiency. Beyond the impact on hemoglobin synthesis, note that iron-deficient cells in nonerythroid tissues show decreased quantities of cytochrome oxidase, which is a heme protein exercising a vital role in oxidative phosphorylation. The clinical correlate of this effect on cytochrome oxidase is the muscle weakness that accompanies severe iron-deficiency anemia, because skeletal muscle is replete with mitochondria and relies heavily upon oxidative phosphorylation for its function. Because the predominant use for iron is in erythropoiesis, one might assume that iron deficiency would cause anemia. In reality, however, because of the internal iron cycle, iron stores must be exhausted before erythropoiesis is adversely affected. Consequently, iron-deficiency anemia is actually the last manifestation of iron deficiency, representing the end of a continuum from reduced iron stores to iron depletion to iron-deficient erythropoiesis and culminating in iron-deficiency anemia (Table 18.4). As noted, only when iron-deficiency anemia supervenes does the characteristic microcytic, hypochromic anemia emerge. Biochemical markers for iron-deficiency anemia include low ferritin and plasma iron concentrations, a transferrin saturation of about 15%, and increased free erythrocyte protoporphyrins.

In adults, it is vital to recognize that iron-deficiency anemia often is the result of occult blood loss from the gastrointestinal tract, whereas, in children and adolescents, it may have a nutritional basis. Nevertheless, on a worldwide basis, an estimated 800 million people are thought to suffer from Hookworm infestation, which results in a relentless, slow loss of blood and iron-deficiency anemia. In short, one always should search for the root cause of iron-deficiency anemia, avoiding the trap of treating iron-deficiency anemia as a disease. In fact, iron-deficiency anemia is a sign of some underlying pathologic process and is not a disease per se.

The *anemia of chronic disease* usually is associated with a normocytic, normochromic anemia, but hypochromia and microcytosis are not uncommon and when they are present, this anemia appears morphologically like that of iron-deficiency anemia. However, the pathogenesis of the anemia of chronic disease is different from that of iron-deficiency anemia. First, red cell production is decreased, the defect appearing to reside in the bone marrow. Because bone marrow can augment output of red cells at least six times, the fact that red cell production is not increased suggests that erythropoiesis is not functioning optimally. Second, survival of red cells is slightly decreased to 80 to 90 days. Finally, and most characteristic, macrophages do not release the iron they have acquired from effete red cells, further limiting erythropoiesis.

The anemia of chronic disease develops over 1 to 2 months, and because red cell production is decreased, reticulocyte counts are either normal or low. Like iron-deficiency anemia, serum iron levels are diminished, but unlike iron-deficiency anemia, transferrin saturation also is decreased. It is important to recognize that in anemia of chronic disease, there is abundant iron sequestered in monocytes and macrophages. Evidence is accumulating that this iron is imprisoned there because of the action of various cytokines released by cells of the immune system. Preeminent among these cytokines are interleukin-1 and tumor necrosis factor. A long held view as to why iron is contained

Table 18.4. Stages in the Development of Iron Deficiency†

				IRON-DEFICIENCY ANEMIA	
	NORMAL	PRELATENT	LATENT	EARLY	LATE
Marrow iron	Normal	Reduced	Absent	Absent	Absent
Serum ferritin	Normal	Reduced	<12	<12	<12
Transferrin saturation	Normal	Normal	<16%	<16%	<16%
FEP*	Normal	Normal	↑	↑↑	↑↑
Hemoglobin	Normal	Normal	Normal	8–14	<8
MCV*	Normal	Normal	Normal	N or ↓	↓
Other	—	Increased iron absorption			Epithelial changes

*FEP, free erythrocyte protoporphyrin; MCV, mean corpuscular volume.

† Reprinted with permission from Lee GR, Bithell TC, Foerster J, et al. Wintrobe's Clinical Hematology. 9th ed. Baltimore: Williams & Wilkins, 1993, p. 810.

in the monocyte/macrophage system in chronic disease (especially infection) is to prevent access by microorganisms to that iron. In microorganisms, iron is a trace metal of vital importance to their ability to proliferate. Seen in that light, the cytokine response is an example of the orchestrated response to resist infection.

It also follows that because anemia of chronic disease is mild and, furthermore, because it is reversed when the underlying condition is effectively treated, there is no need to treat the anemia. Instead, the challenges are to ascertain that iron-deficiency anemia is not present and to treat the underlying condition.

IMPAIRED PROTOPORPHYRIN SYNTHESIS

Impaired protoporphyrin synthesis has been discussed in Chapter 17, which covered heme biosynthesis and the congenital porphyrias. With reference to anemia, keep in mind the differences between heme biosynthetic control in erythroidal versus extraerythroidal tissues. Thus, for example, in acute intermittent porphyria, the enhancement of ALAS activity through cellular heme depletion in nonerythroidal tissues is not reflected in the erythroid cells of the marrow. This can be explained by the finding that there are two distinct species of mRNA for ALAS; thus, enzyme activity is regulated at the transcriptional level. This suggests that there are separate genes being expressed in the two tissue types. As a consequence of this and other factors, anemia is not a prominent finding in most of the congenital porphyrias, despite the fact that heme biosynthesis is disordered in some way.

With this last caveat, anemia, when it does occur, usually is hemolytic in nature and accompanied by signs of marrow hyperactivity and jaundice. The precise reasons for the hemolysis are not known; extrinsic causes are excluded by the fact that normal red cells have a normal life span in affected patients, while conversely, abnormal red cells continue to be short-lived when transfused into normal individuals. This implies that intrinsic red cell factors are responsible. Because porphyrins are known to be phototoxic, the high levels of these intermediates that accumulate in genetically affected red cells may create cellular damage that results in splenic trapping and destruction. This, however, remains speculative.

Of all the various porphyric syndromes, the one that is typically associated with microcytic, hypochromic anemia is *erythrocytic protoporphyria*, or erythroidal ferrochelatase deficiency (see Chapter 17). Because erythroidal ferrochelatase is the chief regulatory enzyme step in red cell heme biosynthesis, it should be no surprise that large quantities of protoporphyrin, one of the two substrates for this enzyme (the other being iron), accumulate in young erythrocytes. Of course, deficiency of ferrochelatase will result in decreased heme synthesis. Yet, this does not explain the relatively high frequency of nonhemolytic anemia in these patients, as distinct from individuals with other forms of porphyria.

The most likely common acquired cause of defective protoporphyrin synthesis is *lead intoxication.* Lead causes microcytic, hypochromic anemia through a variety of means, but chief among them is its direct inhibitory effect on the enzymes of the heme biosynthetic pathway. The enzyme most sensitive to lead is ALA dehydratase, which accounts for the presence of excessive amounts of ALA in urine. Ferrochelatase also is sensitive to lead, leading to accumulation of protoporphyrin that can be detected as a zinc conjugate in affected red cells. Although these inhibitory properties of lead certainly can account for deficient heme synthesis, lead affects other red cell properties, such as membrane stability. Hence, the anemia regularly observed in a lead-toxic patient group frequently will have a hemolytic component, just as in the congenital porphyrias.

THE HEMOGLOBINOPATHIES: DEFECTS IN STRUCTURE OR SYNTHESIS OF HEMOGLOBIN

The disorders resulting from structural alterations in hemoglobin or from aberrant globin synthesis are known collectively as the *hemoglobinopathies.* Sickle cell anemia is the best known example of a structural defect in hemoglobin and is the result of a mutation at the sixth position (glu → val) in the β-globin chain. The thalassemias are quantitative disorders in the synthesis of either the α or β chains.

The four polypeptide chains found in human hemoglobins are designated α-, β-, δ- and γ. As expected, there are paired genes on homologous chromosomes for each of these four polypeptides. Actually, there are two pairs of α-genes on each chromosome 16 (as a result of gene duplication during evolution) and one γ-gene, each pair of which codes for a polypeptide chain differing from each other by only a single amino acid (glycine-alanine). Conversely, both β- and δ-chains are coded for by single gene-pairs found on chromosome 11. Thus, each of the hemoglobinopathies can be traced to a mutation in this complex group of genes.

We have noted that heme enhances and coordinates globin chain synthesis by facilitating the chain-initiation step of gene translation. As long as heme synthesis is normal, globin synthesis will proceed at a normal rate. This means that any mutation in globin synthesis will cause the mutant protein to be produced in amounts dictated by the need for globin chains to join with heme and form the hemoglobin tetramer. As a consequence, the increased hemolytic rate that commonly results from the presence of abnormal hemoglobins leads to a cycle of increased catabolism and increased synthesis.

Normal adults possess two forms of hemoglobin, designated HbA_1 and HbA_2, with A_1 predominating in a ratio of approximately 98:2. HbA_1 is composed of two α-chains and two β-chains, each one of which binds heme covalently through two histidine residues in the globin chains. HbA_2 is composed of two α-chains and two δ-chains and has essentially the same oxygen-binding capacity as HbA. Although many molecular variants of HbA_2 have been reported, due to the small relative proportion present in otherwise normal individuals, no clinical consequences arise from point mutations in the δ-Hb gene. As a general rule, point mutations in the alleles coding for α-chains, although numerous, do not result in structural defects in hemoglobin or in significant clinical symptoms. Certainly, a major disease state caused by deficiency of α-chain synthesis is α-thalassemia (see below), but α-thalassemia is not due to mutation in the structural gene. Rather, it is a result of abnormal regulation of synthesis of α-chains. Hence, except for α-thalassemia, for all practical purposes, the hemoglobinopathies involve abnormalities of the genes for the non-α globin polypeptide chains.

Unlike the adult, the human fetus and newborn show a preponderance of HbF, which is a hemoglobin variant composed of two α-chains and two γ-chains. HbF represents 80% or more of the total hemoglobin present in the red cells of neonates. The increased oxygen-affinity of HbF in fetal erythrocytes as compared to HbA provides a distinct adaptive advantage in the relatively hypoxic existence of the fetus.

HbF may be distinguished from HbA by its resistance to alkali denaturation. Another noteworthy property of HbF is the lack of modulating effect of 2,3-DPG on O_2 affinity. This is directly attributable to the fact that the N-terminal amino groups of γ-chains are not available for binding 2,3-DPG as they are in HbA. The same mechanism pertains to the relative lack of effect of chloride on HbF. With respect to pH, HbF has markedly enhanced oxygen-affinity at alkaline pH (alkaline Bohr effect), which is directly related to the substitution at position 143 on the γ-chain of a serine residue for the histidine residue present in the β-chain. The consequent change in polarity and chloride-binding capacity renders HbF better able to bind oxygen at alkaline pH and less able to do so at acid pH. Consequently, as the red cell passes through the relatively alkaline placental circulation, it readily gives up CO_2 in favor of O_2; returned to the high-CO_2, acidic fetal tissues, the red cell easily gives up its bound O_2 in exchange for CO_2. Thus, enhanced in utero survivability is attributable directly to molecular structural differences between HbA and HbF, and exemplifies the capacity of the human organism to adapt its physiology by expressing different genes at different stages of the life cycle.

Given the dramatic differences between HbA and HbF, particularly regarding the changed proportions after birth, the unavoidable question is, "How do we get from there to here?" Because this transition represents an obvious example of gene regulation in development, this question has received enormous attention. Despite this attention, however, the most succinct answer is, "We don't yet know!" But, the fact that most individuals do make the transition without incident makes γ-gene point mutations little more than interesting scientific examples of genetic heterogeneity. In summary, of the hundreds of hemoglobinopathies that have been identified by electrophoretic or other means, clinically the most important ones arise either from point mutations in the α- or β-gene or from abnormalities in synthesis of either the α- or β-chain.

Sickle Cell Anemia

One of the most common of the hemoglobinopathies, world-wide, is sickle cell (HbSS) disease, inherited as an autosomal recessive trait. Note that based on the classic definition of "recessive," there should be no significant phenotypic manifestation of the genetic abnormality in the carrier. Strictly speaking, this is not completely true of the sickle hemoglobin gene, because, under certain circumstances, carriers may show signs or symptoms, including inability to concentrate the urine, hematuria, and splenic infarction. Splenic infarction may occur at high altitude or after heavy exertion, such as during basic training in the armed forces. In the individual with sickle trait, both the normal and abnormal alleles are expressed. Typically, in the heterozygote state of many other autosomal recessive disorders, expression of the abnormal gene may produce either a totally inactive protein or fail to produce any protein at all. In contrast, the abnormal gene product of the sickle gene is clearly evidenced in the heterozygote.

The molecular defect in HbS lies in substitution of a valine residue for a glutamate residue at position 6 of the β-chain. Obviously, a defect expressed in the β-chain will not become clinically apparent until well into the first year of postnatal life. Thus, the newborn who has a homozygous SS genotype will be born with the normal >80% HbF, with the remainder of hemoglobin consisting predominantly of HbS but insufficient to cause clinical symptoms. Until recently, it was not feasible to screen prospectively to select for neonates who either carry or are affected by sickle cell disease. Molecular biologic diagnostic techniques now are being used to make the diagnosis and hopefully will have a positive impact by earlier identification of homozygotes.

One of the most striking observations relating structure to function was the finding that reduced oxygen tension causes red cells containing HbS to assume a sickle shape. Almost 25 years passed before it was discovered that the HbS itself formed a sickle-shaped polymer when deoxygenated, in turn conferring upon the cell the same shape. It is obvious that a large polymer will be less soluble than its monomeric units—so it is with HbS. Indeed, HbS exists in two separate phases, the deoxygenated, polymerized gel and the oxygenated, soluble phase. Because of the substitution of the hydrophobic valine residue at position 6, deoxyHbS tends to form long polymers with other HbS molecules (Figure 18.9). Normally, the approximately 300 million hemoglobin molecules in the red cell are in solution. In the case of HbS, however, when they bind together to form a matrix of fibers, the red cell hemoglobin becomes a gel. The quantitative relationship between the sol-gel phases primarily depends in vivo upon the partial pressure of oxygen in solution. When fully oxygenated, HbS shows no tendency to form aggregates. Accordingly, the tendency of HbS to form a polymeric, sickle-shaped gel can be reversed by increasing oxygen tension. But, when HbS polymerizes, the oxygen saturation curve of HbS in the gel phase loses the characteristic sigmoid shape, indicating loss of the cooperative binding between sequential heme groups and oxygen seen in HbA. With loss of cooperativity also comes diminished solubility of HbS. This loss of cooperativity occurs at O_2 saturations below about 85%, suggesting that only when saturation is above this level is the transition from solution to gel phases minimized. At physiologic concentrations of hemoglobin, there is no discernible difference in oxygen affinity between HbA and HbS when O_2 saturation is above 85%.

Sickle cells are more prone to dehydration than are normal red cells, attaining a MCHC in the range of 50 g/dl. Partial failure of the Na^+-K^+ ATPase in sickled red cells has been implicated in the pathogenesis of cellular dehydration. This dehydration has two important consequences for sickle cells. First, as the concentration of HbS increases within the red cell, the opportunity for interaction among the HbS molecules is enhanced, further exacerbating the likelihood for the cell to adopt a sickle form. Second, increasing the HbS concentration in the cell decreases the oxygen affinity of HbS, further predisposing to sickle cell formation.

In addition to the major roles in sickle cell formation played by changes in O_2 saturation of HbS and the concentration of deoxyHbS within

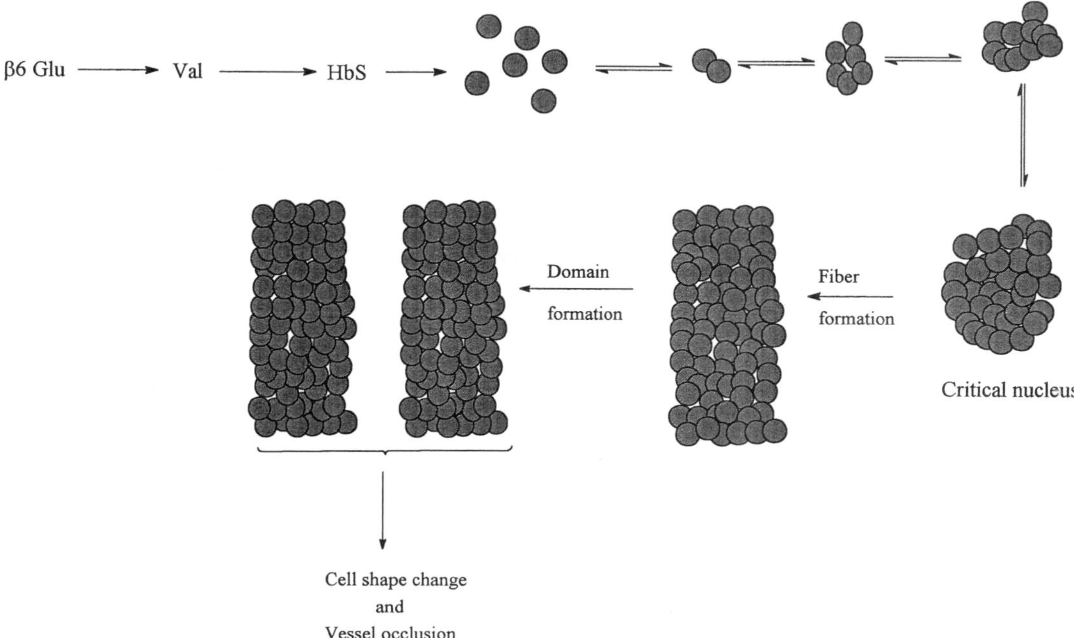

Figure 18.9. Molecular basis for hemoglobin S polymerization. Proposed events in development of venous occlusion in sickle cell disease. The mutation at position 6 of the β-chain substitutes a hydrophobic amino acid (valine) for a hydrophilic amino acid (glutamate). Deoxygenated hemoglobin S (shown as balls) is insoluble and tends to polymerize, forming fibers of HbS molecules. When sufficient polymerization occurs, domain formation induces the characteristic shape change of sickled red blood cells.

the cell, acquired membrane alterations in sickle cell anemia also contribute to the clinical manifestations. To begin, the membrane of sickle cells is less deformable than that of normal red cells. Also, there are differences between the two cell types in the normal asymmetric lipid orientation of the plasma membrane with amino phospholipids, which normally face the cytosol, now moving to the external surface. This increases the chance for inappropriate clotting by intensifying interaction of these cells with the vascular endothelium. Similarly, although protein composition appears relatively normal, HbSS membranes show significant differences in orientation of membrane proteins, with increased intramolecular disulfide bonds, which may be attributable to peroxidant damage as well. And as if this were not enough, after repeated reversible episodes of sickling and unsickling, a cell may become irreversibly sickled. A red cell ghost, prepared from such a cell, rendered entirely free of lipid and intrinsic membrane proteins, retains its sickle shape, strongly implicating the cytoskeleton as the site of irreversible membrane protein changes.

Clinically, these features translate into a tendency for HbS to polymerize while affected red cells are in the capillary beds, where a pO_2 of 80 to 90 mm Hg reduces saturation close to the critical 85% threshold. Further adding to this tendency to sickle is the drop in pH in the capillary beds that enhances polymer formation and further decreases the oxygen affinity, thus accelerating the process. This tendency to form sickle cells within terminal vessels provides an explanation for many of the features of the disease. Considering the need for the normal red cell to be deformable to traverse the course of the capillary bed, it is obvious that a fairly rigid, irregularly shaped body is likely to obstruct flow through the microvasculature. Thus, at least two of the four major categories of manifestations of the disease are directly attributable to vaso-occlusive events: painful crises and the organ damage due to infarction.

The anemia arises from a complex set of interactions, because components of intravascular hemolysis, splenic destruction, increased vascular adhesion, and suboptimal erythropoiesis are involved in its etiology. One would imagine that the anemia would be ameliorated, to an extent, by the characteristic autoinfarction of the spleen; the fact that it is not attests to the presence of other factors. For one thing, intravascular hemolysis derives from mechanical abuse of the misshapen cells, which exhibit an inclination to adhere to vascular endothelium. For another, the increased release of oxygen to peripheral capillary beds characteristic of deoxygenated HbS reduces stimulation of erythropoietin release and leads to suboptimal bone marrow activity in response to the anemia. All the same, it is good to remember that the blood viscosity is inversely related to the anemia; therefore, total correction of the deficit could lead to increased vaso-occlusion and increased tissue damage.

The fourth category of clinical manifestations includes impaired growth and increased susceptibility to infection. Regarding growth, toward late infancy, affected SS children begin to fall significantly behind their control counterparts in weight gain. Linear growth appears less affected than weight, although the pubertal growth spurt occurs later in SS patients than in children who are not affected. This correlates well with the fact that most SS patients experience an onset of puberty 2 or more years later than the control group, although ultimate height achieved is equivalent in both groups. A significant proportion of SS males have impaired fertility, displaying lowered sperm count and abnormal morphology despite full sexual maturation. Reasons for these findings remain unknown. Susceptibility to infection stems from the preoccupation of the reticuloendothelial system with the massive amount of erythrocytic debris; therefore, phagocytic function becomes impaired. The nature of the infecting organisms and the increased incidence of infection are similar in SS children and children asplenic from other causes, further buttressing the view that much of the susceptibility derives from splenic dysfunction. Whether additional resistance factors, such as granulocyte function and immune response, play a role in this problem has not been clarified.

As the genetically affected individual ages, the anemia produces a series of predictable changes, such as cardiomegaly, whereas the hemolytic process results in chronic overproduction of bile pigments, which may affect the gallbladder. Repeat microinfarcts in various organs inevitably affect function, and chronic renal damage invariably occurs in adults. Renal microinfarcts in the relatively hypoxic medulla contribute to the pathophysiology of the disease in at least two ways: (*1*) impaired concentrating ability increases the risk of diminished blood volume and increased blood viscosity; and (*2*) a mild distal renal tubular acidosis enhances the sickling tendency of the SS red cell for reasons discussed earlier. Cerebrovascular accidents are not uncommon and may occur at any age, thus accounting for the frequency of neurologic abnormalities. Consequently, the prognosis for any affected individual, guarded at birth, worsens with age because of the basic pathophysiologic nature of the disease. Treatment modalities vary widely, but none have thus far been proven effective in permanently altering the natural history of SS disease.

Thalassemia Syndromes

Another major group of hemoglobinopathies comprise the thalassemia syndromes. These disorders, although clinically widely heterogeneous, are all a result of absence or unbalanced production of one or more of the globin chains. This causes the relative surplus of normal chains to accumulate because they have no partners to join with to form the hemoglobin tetramer. Consequently, these surplus chains precipitate and damage the membrane of the developing erythrocyte, causing both ineffective erythropoiesis and hemolysis. Because the defect in synthesis of one of the globin chains results in less hemoglobin, this contributes further to the anemia.

The four major subcategories of thalassemia can be designated as follows: (*1*) α-thalassemia, (*2*) β-thalassemia, (*3*) $\Delta\beta$-thalassemia, and (*4*) hereditary persistence of HbF. Each major subcategory comprises multiple entities that represent gene defects resulting in either total or partial absence of the gene product. Thus, the presence in the population of mutant genes that preclude all synthesis of a particular chain, as well as those that dictate reduced protein production, provides the potential for numerous "mixed" heterozygotic states.

Because members of this group are highly diverse in their molecular etiology and the potential for abnormal gene mixing is great, it is more reasonable to approach them clinically than biochemically in a discussion of this length. Thus, we have attempted to condense this section into an overview of the common features and pathophysiology of the thalassemias.

β-THALASSEMIA

Anemia arising from several different pathophysiologic mechanisms is a feature common to all the members of the thalassemia group. Although the root of the anemia, in each case, can be traced back to an imbalance in synthesis of normal α- and, or β-globin chains, the physiologic impact of the defect differs. In the most straightforward case, that of homozygous β-thalassemia, the unbalanced α-chains being produced are incapable of forming a stable tetramer. The result is a deficiency in marrow production of viable erythroblasts and an increased destruction of red cell precursors within the marrow itself, because of intracellular precipitation of the unstable α-chains. Those cells that escape intramedullary destruction and enter the circulation also are destroyed at an accelerated rate because of the inclusions of precipitated hemoglobin. It is this intravascular hemolysis that contributes most to the jaundice seen in this disorder. It should be clear from the above that erythropoietin increase secondary to tissue hypoxia from the anemia will do little to increase production of useful red cells, because of the wanton destruction of erythroid precursors in the marrow. The fact that β-chain synthesis is not required for production of fetal hemoglobin has major significance; the thalassemic fetus suffers no ill effects from the abnormal gene. Thus, the clinical picture of β-thalassemia does not emerge until neonatal life, when the switch from HbF to HbA occurs.

α-THALASSEMIA

In the case of α-thalassemia, however, the situation is different. Because α-globin chains are required for HbF, as well as HbA synthesis, failure to produce the requisite quantity of α-chains results in deficiency of HbF in utero. In its place, the excess γ-chains combine to form γ tetramers called *hemoglobin Bart's.* Recall that HbF, although it has a high oxygen affinity in relation to HbA, functions well within the physiologic range of oxygen tension and pH. Conversely, hemoglobin Bart's shows too high an affinity for oxygen under physiologic conditions, which renders it essentially useless as a means of delivering oxygen to tissues. The basis for this exceptional affinity is the lack of heme-heme interaction, which, in normal hemoglobins, causes reduced affinity for each sequentially bound oxygen molecule. Instead, in Hb Bart's, each γ-chain heme in the tetramer has equal affinity for oxygen. Consequently, in utero, the α-thalassemic fetus experiences severe tissue hypoxia; as a result, a very high rate of stillbirths is due to hydrops fetalis.

Individuals who survive gestation with α-thalassemia will experience more problems when the normal γ- to β-gene switch occurs, because HbA cannot be produced in the absence of α-chains. Thus, in place of Hb Bart's (γ tetramer), these patients produce β tetramers, or HbH. Whereas β-chains join to form a more stable tetramer than do α-chains, HbH still is much less stable than normal HbA; therefore, as the affected red cell ages, HbH tends to precipitate with formation of inclusion bodies. This results in an increased likelihood of trapping in the spleen, with a substantial reduction in the average red cell half-life. The obvious consequence of this is decreased red cell mass, or anemia. The physiologic consequences of the anemia are complicated further by the fact that HbH, like Hb Bart's, has a very high oxygen affinity, which leads to additional tissue hypoxia.

In summary, the pathophysiologic mechanisms underlying the clinical manifestations of the thalassemia syndromes all can be traced back to the molecular defects that result in unbalanced globin chain synthesis. Most important is ineffective erythropoiesis arising from damage from precipitated globin chains to the erythroid precursors; these inclusions also cause intravascular hemolysis of red cells. Finally, those red cells produced are not optimally hemoglobinized because of the genetic defect in globin synthesis.

ANEMIA DUE TO PRIMARY DEFECTS OF RED CELL MEMBRANE

As noted early in this chapter, the red cell membrane is a marvelous structure designed to with-

Table 18.5. Red Cell Membrane Defects and Associated Disorders

PROTEIN AFFECTED	INHERITED ABNORMALITY OCCURS IN
α-spectrin	Hereditary elliptocytosis Hereditary spherocytosis
β-spectrin	Hereditary spherocytosis
Ankyrin	Hereditary spherocytosis
Anion exchanger	Hereditary spherocytosis, ovalocytosis, acanthocytosis
Protein 4.1	Hereditary elliptocytosis

stand tremendous abuse without impairment of its physiologic function. In our discussion of sickle cell anemia, we have noted how the red cell membrane may become permanently distorted in a secondary fashion because of the abnormal shape it is forced to assume and the damage thus sustained. In this section, we are concerned with clinical entities that result from an underlying abnormality of the intrinsic structure of the red cell membrane itself (Table 18.5).

Hereditary Spherocytosis

This disorder is transmitted as an autosomal dominant trait and is considered the most common hereditary hemolytic anemia in individuals of northern European ancestry. It is characterized clinically by hemolysis, jaundice, anemia, and splenomegaly—all of which can be traced back to increased red cell fragility as a consequence of an intrinsic membrane defect. About one-fourth of all cases occur as autosomal recessive traits; in such cases, even though the parents are not affected, the offspring usually is more severely affected than in cases of autosomal dominant transmission.

Morphologically, the structure of the erythrocyte membrane typifies the lipid bilayer structure seen in all biologic membranes. The chemical composition of the overall structure is roughly 55:45 protein to lipid; after detergent removal of lipid, a protein skeleton remains, which is composed of five distinct proteins, with a smaller proportion of three additional ones. The protein skeleton accounts for approximately 50% to 60% of the total membrane protein mass and consists predominantly of spectrin (approximately 27%). Spectrin is a dimeric protein, containing an α- and a β-chain that are aligned in such a way that the chains are parallel in some regions and are helically intertwined in other regions. The molecule has enormous flexibility, which clearly is important to the central structural element of a membrane, which, above all, must be endowed with maximum flexibility. The genes for each of the two chains have been identified and reside on separate chromosomes. Two other proteins, ankyrin and protein 3, are responsible for binding the spectrin to the inner membrane surface, similar to how a suspension bridge roadway is bound to the main suspending cables.

It now is well documented that all patients affected by hereditary spherocytosis, whether autosomal dominant or recessive, have red cells deficient in spectrin relative to normal erythrocytes. Moreover, there is a close correlation between the extent of the deficiency and the clinical severity, as well as the degree of red cell fragility. Referring again to the example of a suspension bridge, what is not yet known is whether the membrane fragility results from intrinsic defects of the roadway (spectrin molecule) or from defects in the vertical cables (ankyrin and/or protein 3). Several mutations have been described in which one of the latter factors has been defective, but the vast majority of spectrin-deficient mutations cannot be explained on this basis.

Structurally, when the red cell shape evolves from the biconcave disc to the spherocyte, a loss of surface area occurs. Biochemically, this change may be attributed to the spectrin deficiency. As explained at the beginning of this chapter, the normal disc shape of the red cell provides maximal surface area for oxygen-CO_2 exchange. Consequently, a change in shape is necessarily related to a decrease in surface/volume ratio. This results in a decrease in the shear force necessary to disrupt the integrity of the membrane, particularly in the spleen, where the spheroidal shape impairs the cell's ability to negotiate the splenic sinusoids. Red cell survival in affected individuals who have undergone splenectomy is extended considerably, underscoring the role of the spleen in destruction of spherocytes.

Hereditary Elliptocytosis

All patients with hereditary elliptocytosis have erythrocyte membrane skeletons that have a characteristic ellipsoid shape. In comparison to normal membrane skeletons, those isolated from elliptocytes are unstable under mechanical stress—an observation that has its clinical correlate in the anemia found in affected individuals. Biochemical investigation has helped to define hereditary elliptocytosis as a heterogeneous group of genetic disorders, virtually all of which are inherited as autosomal dominant traits.

At least a portion of this varied group involves defects related to spectrin, as we have found in hereditary spherocytosis. Referring back to our discussion of spectrin's role in membrane structure, recall that the basic spectrin unit is a dimer composed of an α- and a β-chain. A subgroup of elliptocytotic patients has been identified, in whom there is an abnormally short β-chain that is deficient in the normal carboxy-terminal phosphorylation site necessary for spectrin self-association. By analogy, this leads to a suspension bridge in which the roadway is composed of separate lengths of concrete suspended from the main cables and swinging freely. Only one such genetic defect in β-chain synthesis has thus far been identified.

A total of seven distinct α-chain synthetic defects are now known in hereditary elliptocytosis, six of which involve the amino-terminal end of the molecule. The amino-terminal end of the α-chain in three of these six is now known, each one differing from normal by a single amino acid substitution. All six produce the same effect: impaired spectrin self-association, similar to that seen in the β-chain defect. The seventh α-chain defect derives from a shortened chain, rather than a substitution, also resulting in decreased self-association.

Other molecular defects of the erythrocyte skeleton include abnormalities of either quantity or molecular conformation of several other membrane proteins, such as ankyrin, protein 4.1, glycophorin C, protein 4.2, and protein 3. Most of these abnormalities have been described in a relatively small number of patients.

The precise mechanical mechanism by which a normal juvenile red cell becomes transformed into an elliptocyte is unclear. In most other situations of abnormality, a normal erythrocyte evolves a spheroidal shape, with or without spicules, eventually either rupturing or being trapped within the splenic sinusoids and degraded. However, as in HbSS disease, an inherently normal membrane can assume a permanently abnormal configuration when subjected to ongoing physical deformation. Thus, it is reasonable to imagine that an intrinsically unstable membrane skeletal structure might eventually assume a torpedo-like shape after repeated travel through small capillaries where just such a membrane deformation might be imposed.

STRUCTURE AND BIOLOGIC FUNCTION OF THE LEUKOCYTE

The complexity of cell types categorized as leukocytes necessitates that we simplify our discussion. Thus, we will confine our consideration of each cell type to the mature form only, whenever possible, in an attempt to reduce confusion over various terminologies in use to describe different morphologic appearances, maturational states, etc. It is vital to recall that the circulating blood is an extremely heterogeneous tissue of which its elements are contributed and removed by various organs. Thus, in speaking of peripheral blood leukocytes, keep in mind that the cells present at any given time are in a constant state of flux, some entering while others are leaving the circulation. As a consequence, the absolute and relative numbers of these cell types, as well as their maturity and the duration of their presence within the circulating blood, will be drastically affected by events outside the blood. For these reasons, we will limit our discussion further, at this point, to mature leukocytes present in peripheral blood in a state of health. Changes in these conditions, due to disruptions by disease, will be dealt with according to specific cause.

The Segmented Neutrophil

Normally, the neutrophil is the most common leukocyte in peripheral blood, easily recognized by its multiply-segmented nucleus, clearly visible with Wright's staining (Figure 18.10). In a healthy human, the sole source of the peripheral neutrophil is the bone marrow, within which the neutrophil cell-line normally matures to the polysegmented nuclear stage before release into the blood. It is remarkable that the functional purpose

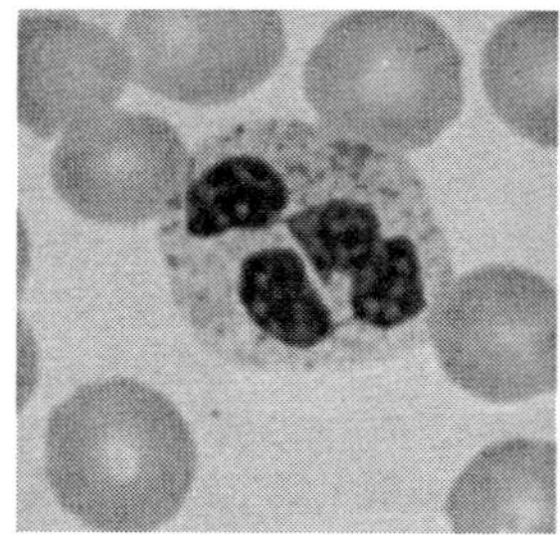
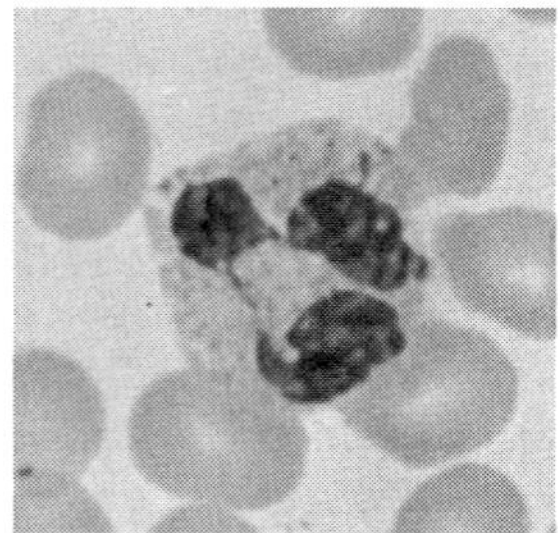

Figure 18.10. (A,B) Morphology of the normal polymorphonuclear neutrophil. Reprinted with permission from Lee GR, Bithell TC, Foerster J, et al. Wintrobe's Clinical Hematology. 9th ed. Baltimore: Williams & Wilkins, 1993, plate VI.

served by the lobulated nucleus is unknown. Under normal circumstances, occasional neutrophils containing nuclei shaped somewhat like a horseshoe and called "band" neutrophils can be seen. These usually represent 10% or less of the total neutrophil count and are representative of a maturational stage one step earlier than that of the true polymorphonuclear cell.

Beyond the striking appearance of the nucleus, the neutrophil contains no nucleolus, a relatively sparse number of mitochondria, numerous cytoplasmic granules of varying electron microscopic density, and a large quantity of glycogen. It is assumed that the electron dense granules correspond to microsomal enzyme aggregates.

An important property of the neutrophil is its motility. Presently, it is uncertain as to how the migratory ability of the neutrophil relates to its disappearance from the circulation. However, the presence of neutrophils in normal urine, saliva, and gastrointestinal tract indicates the variety of ways in which the neutrophil can exit the circulation. As a result of these migratory capabilities, enhanced significantly even by exercise and subclinical infection (see below), it has been difficult to estimate the average time a neutrophil remains in the circulation. However, with an estimated 60 to 400 $\times$ 10^7 neutrophils passing through the blood/Kg/day, the average circulatory life span of a neutrophil will be measurable in hours. In contrast to the 120-day life span of the erythrocyte, this very short period in the circulation does not necessarily indicate rapid destruction, but should be interpreted to represent the propensity of the neutrophil to escape the circulation intact and relocate into various places in the body. In fact, the neutrophil spends most of its short existence outside of the bloodstream.

Although the numbers of circulating neutrophils fluctuate daily, true neutropenia is rarely seen, except in a pathologic state. By contrast, numerous circumstances lead to neutrophilia in the absence of infection. Perhaps the most physiologic is strenuous exercise, with recorded increases in peripheral white cell counts of 25,000 to 30,000/mm^3, the bulk of which is composed of neutrophils. Convulsive seizures can produce a similar picture. Administration of epinephrine as, for example, in treatment of acute asthma, causes a rapid, generalized increase in peripheral cell types, with a longer-lasting neutrophilia. Various other situations, such as noninfectious vomiting, pregnancy, labor, and anesthesia produce leukocytosis and neutrophilia. The common denominator in each of these responses to relatively physiologic stimuli is thought to be stimulation of the adrenal cortex with increased 17-hydroxycorticosteroids. The precise mechanisms involved are not well understood, but the response to steroid secretion may be related to increased bone marrow release, coupled with diminished exit from the peripheral circulation.

Important as they are, the control mechanisms for regulation of circulating neutrophils are poorly understood. Certain requirements for such control are intuitively obvious, but the means by which the control is exerted remain elusive. These must include: a mechanism to increase production of committed stem cells from the pluripotent stem cells of the marrow; stimulation of these committed cells to produce mature neutrophils for release from the marrow; possibly accentuation of the release mechanism itself; and, of great importance, a means of feedback control to dampen the entire process once the initiating factor(s) are no longer present.

Functionally, the neutrophil is important because of its abilities to migrate to the site of infection and ingest foreign organisms as a part of the body's defense against bacterial infection. Clearly, the motility of this cell type is a vital part of this process; therefore, we would expect some means of purposeful movement of the neutrophil toward the point of invasion. A quick examination of the cells present in any minor dermal bacterial invasion should suffice to convince the observer that, however these cells get there, they do so in a hurry. Certain aspects of the process are incontrovertible: neutrophils do not "float" to a site, they adhere to surfaces; neutrophils are "attracted" to a site where they are needed; neutrophils reach such sites by "purposeful" movement. Once there, the neutrophil "recognizes" organisms and cell debris as foreign. Our use of quotation marks is intended to direct attention toward these phenomena as biochemical in nature, but expressed in distinctly anthropocentric terms. Thus, neutrophils respond, as many other cell types do, to biochemical signals that direct them to perform specific tasks. The deficits in our understanding lie in our relative ignorance about these signals. We are uncertain of the way in which these cells adhere to surfaces. The attraction of neutrophils to a specific site occurs through a process loosely termed "chemotaxis," meaning that there is some sort of chemical "scent" leading the cells to the proper place. Two types of agents have been identified in chemotaxis: "*cytoaxigens,*" which are not themselves chemotactic but result in true chemotaxis through interaction with other materials, such as serum or neutrophilic lysosomes; and, "*cytotaxins,*" which are direct chemotaxins, such as low molecular weight peptides contained in bacterial filtrates or derive from split products of serum complement. Although neutrophils in culture can be observed to move constantly, when in the presence of added chemotactic factors, this movement becomes directed (ie, "purposeful"). Precisely how the cell induces the observed reorientation necessary to direct its movements remains unclear.

The ability of the neutrophil to recognize and attack potentially harmful material is both critical to its function in defense of the whole organism, as well as to protection of the body from attack by its own defenses. The recognition process appears to be mediated through neutrophilic cell-surface receptors, which recognize complexes formed between foreign material and attachment to this material by endogenous antibody. Thus, whereas interaction between an organism and an antibody may not be adequate to interfere with the organism, attachment of the antibody to the cell surface triggers neutrophilic receptor recognition of the complex, with resulting binding. Various endogenous molecules that lead to this recognition process are called *opsonins.*

Once binding to its surface has occurred, the neutrophil begins the process of engulfment, or phagocytosis, of the bound complex (Figure 18.11). This cellular activity is energy-requiring, and its initiation begins a cascade of biochemical events within the cell. A rapid increase in glycolysis and lactate production occurs, with a decrease in the pH within the vacuole that contains the engulfed material. A simultaneous "burst" in oxygen consumption occurs, not mitochondrial in nature, which is related to intracellular, bactericidal events (see following text). The phagocytic vacuole enters the cell body and eventually fuses with a lysosome, thus exposing its contents to degradation by the multiple lysosomal digestive enzymes. Membrane lipid synthetic rate increases, probably in response to the loss of cell surface area during formation of the phagocytic vacuole.

The beauty of the biochemical response to bacterial ingestion lies in its integrated and highly functional nature. The initial decrease in vacuolar pH, which may be due to lactate accumulation derived from enhanced glycolysis, also may be an efficient bactericidal event, when the organism is pH-sensitive, as is the pneumococcus; an acid pH also may be permissive for the enzymes of lysosomal degradation. Coordinated with these events, the increase in oxygen consumption results in rapid production of superoxide, hydrogen peroxide, and NADP for reduction to NADPH via the hexose-monophosphate shunt pathway. The generation of superoxide is mediated by an oxidase, using NADPH to reduce molecular oxygen and producing NADP, which activates the HMP shunt pathway. Although superoxide itself is only weakly bactericidal, 80% of the superoxide produced is converted to hydrogen peroxide—a step mediated by superoxide dismutase and requiring $NADH_2$, which is produced during glycolysis. Peroxide

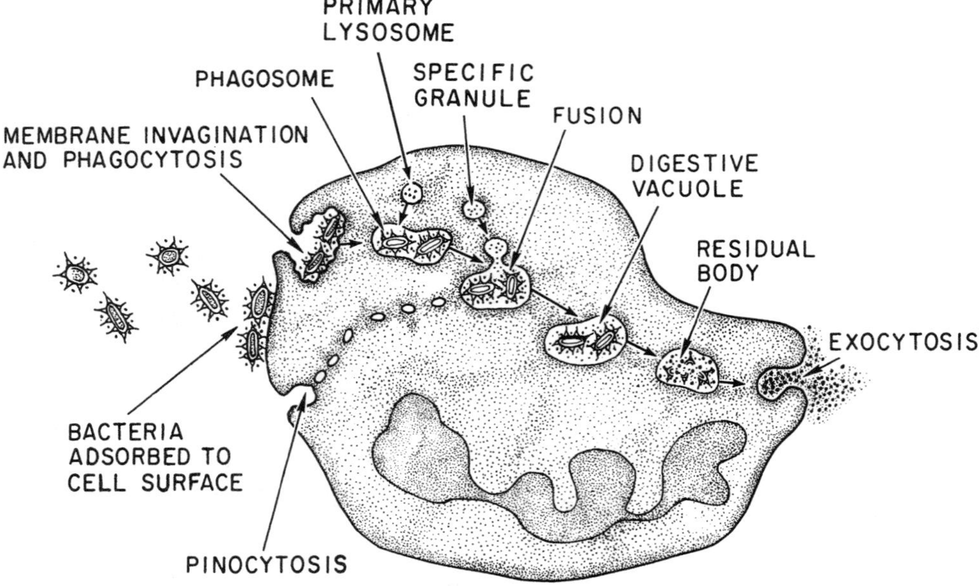

Figure 18.11. Neutrophilic phagocytosis and pinocytosis. Phagocytosis is a key feature of neutrophilic function. Attachment of an organism to endogenous antibody enhances complex binding to neutrophil membrane. The process of engulfment, formation of a phagosome, subsequent digestion, and elimination by exocytosis is energy-requiring. Pinocytosis is a process of which virtually all cells are capable and generally is involved in assimilation of macromolecules rather than organisms. Reprinted with permission from Lee GR, Bithell TC, Foerster J, et al. Wintrobe's Clinical Hematology. 9th ed. Philadelphia: Lea & Febiger, 1993: 251.

alone is an effective bactericidal agent against organisms not able to degrade it, which is an action enhanced by release of myeloperoxidase, contained in the neutrophilic granules, into the phagocytic vacuole. In concert with iodide, known to be concentrated by neutrophils, or the omnipresent chloride ion, myeloperoxidase oxidizes the halide, thus enhancing the cidal effect of peroxide as much as 50 times. Thus, the bactericidal actions of peroxide and iodine, in use in medical practice for approximately 100 years, have been in use by the human neutrophil for millennia!

Unfortunately for the neutrophil, if the phagocytosed organism is resistant to lysosomal digestive enzymes, low pH, and peroxide, multiplication within the cell eventually will result in its death, with release of the bacteria. Alternatively, the bacterium may effect its escape by damaging the vacuolar wall, releasing the digestive enzymes into the cell and causing cell death.

Assuming that the neutrophil is successful in disrupting the integrity of the ingested microorganism, its next task is to digest the bacterial components. Although the ingested bacterium can be seen to undergo morphologic changes as this process proceeds, it also has been demonstrated that bacterial components are released from the cell into the surrounding medium. It is assumed that the mediators of the bacterial dismantling are the lysosomal acid hydrolases.

Other Cells of the Granulocytic Series in Peripheral Blood

There are only two additional, mature granulocytic cells in peripheral blood: basophils and eosinophils, both of which are present in minute proportions relative to the neutrophil. Although each is distinctively different from the neutrophil in morphology, both the basophil and the eosinophil display slight motility and phagocytic properties, probably attesting to their common origins exclusively within the bone marrow. As with the neutrophil, the peripheral blood half-life of each cell type can be measured in hours to days, with emergence from blood into tissue the usual route of escape. Unlike the more mobile neutrophil, neither the basophil nor the eosinophil are highly mobile. Although little is known of the stimuli that attract basophils and eosinophils, it is clear that they do not respond as readily to chemotaxis as do the neutrophils.

The phagocytic properties of eosinophils are stimulated by proximity to antigen-antibody complexes; neither of the reactants alone, even in excess, significantly affects the eosinophil. The relationship between eosinophilia and parasitic infestation is well described; however, the precise function of the eosinophil in this relationship remains enigmatic. The function of the basophil also remains problematic. The dense granules clearly visible on Wright's staining represent, in large proportion, the cellular content of histamine. These cells contain a high specific activity of histidine decarboxylase, and, in humans, this is thought to be the sole source of blood histamine. Despite the similarities between peripheral basophils and tissue mast cells, which also release histamine, the two cell types differ in many significant ways and are not related in development. Finally, an interesting aspect of the basophil is its heparin content, which may be instrumental in regulation of lipoprotein lipase and release of free fatty acids from adipose tissue (see Chapter 15).

The Lymphocyte

In a healthy state, peripheral lymphocytes are only slightly less abundant than granulocytes. However, in their origins, fates, and functions, these cells are much more complex than the granulocytes. A detailed discussion of these issues is beyond the scope of this text; thus, we refer the reader to various sources, which are listed at the end of this chapter, for this information. Nonetheless, it is accurate to state that the lymphocyte is a part of an overall system which, although originating in the bone marrow in common with the granulocyte, functions largely independent of the mechanisms regulating granulocytic function. As will be discussed, several features of the lymphatic system make it difficult to assess the duration of lymphocytic presence in peripheral blood. However, the life span of an average lymphocyte is estimated in terms of years!

Circulating lymphocytes, originating in bone marrow, are classified into two major groups: B- and T-lymphocytes. The designation of B and T, although relating to origin of the cell in bone marrow or thymus, respectively, is to an extent gratuitous, because it generally is accepted that all T-cells arise from the marrow during early fetal life. Thus, although lymphocytes are ultimately traceable in lineage back to the stem cells from which all leukocytes derive, their structure, function, and destinies are entirely different from the granulocytic cells. From the point of their emergence during pluripotent stem cell division in the marrow, lymphocytes assume a distinct morphologic appearance, rendering them easily distinguishable from the immature granulocytes. At about the eighth week of gestation, circulating lymphocytes released from the marrow are captured by the thymic epithelial cells; in the thymus, cell division and differentiation into mature T-cells occur. Within the thymic environment, the lymphocytes undergo several changes that result in irreversible differences between T-cells and their embryonic progenitors, the B-cells. Two of the most important of these changes are: acquisition of cell surface receptors that are complimentary to sites on peripheral lymphoid tissues and expression of a large variety of membrane bound glycoproteins. These T-cells maintain lymphocyte morphology and reproductive capacity throughout their entire life span. In contrast, B-cells spend their lives acquiring the ability to produce antibodies and forming clones, each one of which is capable of production of one specific antibody. The final destiny of a B-cell is its differentiation into a plasma cell that is incapable of division but has enormous capacity for specific antibody production. A restricted number of B-cells avoid plasma cell differentiation, instead retaining their lymphocytic morphology, as well as an antigenic "file," causing them to be named memory B-cells.

Thus, although certain properties of the mature lymphocyte, such as motility, are shared with its commonly derived relation, the granulocyte, lymphocytic function is primarily related to a role in immunologic defense of the body's integrity. A detailed discussion of specific aspects of this role is beyond the scope of this chapter; for present purposes, it is sufficient to note several general features. Fundamental to our understanding is, as discussed above, the presence of two distinct subpopulations of lymphocytes, physically distinguishable as T- or B-cells by their in vitro response in the presence of sheep red cells. After a period of differentiation in thymic tissue, T-cells assume a "supervisory" or "helper" function in relation to B-lymphocytes. T-cells possess immunologic memory, enabling them to interact with B-cells to facilitate antibody production by B-cells. When alone and each exposed to the same antigen, neither T- nor B-lymphocytes can respond effectively to a stimulus against which they can mount a marked response when working together. Another feature of the T-cell is the scope of its memory for antigens, which is broad and relatively permanent. In contrast, although the B-cell memory also is life-long, it is confined to a single antigen. Offsetting its limited repertoire is the B-cell's active antibody production, whereas the T-cell does not release antibody itself. The precise nature of the T- and B-cell interaction is poorly understood, but it is known that initiation of the process at the level of the T-cell requires participation by an additional cell type, the *macrophage*.

Strictly speaking, the macrophage is a member of the reticuloendothelial system, functioning as the "scavenger" unit. The occurrence of macrophages, as monocytes, in the peripheral circulation is inversely proportional to their presence in tissues, where their presence defines the reticuloendothelial system proper. It is important to understand the concept that these cells, as they reside in an organ, constitute a separate and functionally independent organ. Numerically, the majority of these cells are found in spleen, bone marrow, and liver, where they constitute a significant proportion of the total organ mass. Physically, their primary function is to engulf damaged cells and particulate matter, the former for digestion and the latter for storage. Unlike the neutrophil, however, the objective of the macrophage is to process the ingested material, selecting out that which will be immunogenic, concentrating it, and presenting it to T-cells. The nature of this process is not understood, but it can be conceived of as though the T-cells require "jogging" of their immunogenic memory before they can effectively help the B-cell to respond by antibody production. Note that certain antigens can provoke a B-cell response without this complex intercellular communication, but these antigens are a minor fraction of those to which the human organism is normally exposed.

DISORDERS OF HEMOSTASIS

Normal Hemostasis

Blood in the cardiovascular system is pumped at high pressure; therefore, it is vital that there be protective mechanisms to defend against life-threatening hemorrhage if the vessel wall is breached in any way. Of equal importance to preventing hemorrhage, is preventing formation of untimely clots (thrombi) that could block flow to vital organs and also lead to death. Thus, it is clear that the liquidity of the blood and the integrity of the vascular system each must be maintained by opposing processes that normally must exist in a delicate balance.

Three separate but interdependent components constitute the response to vascular damage. First, breached vessels can reflexively vasoconstrict to diminish loss of blood. Second, platelets adhere to the damaged subendothelial fibers at the site of injury, forming a temporary seal. Steps one and two form the basis of *primary hemostasis*. Third, a series of sequential enzyme mediated steps, called the plasma coagulation system, leads to the formation of a fibrin clot. This third process is termed *secondary hemostasis*.

Normally, intact vascular endothelium maintains the fluidity of the blood by shunning interaction with platelets and preventing platelet aggregation. It also synthesizes an array of inhibitors of the coagulation system including prostacyclin, thrombomodulin, and heparan, and produces activators of the fibrinolytic system. In addition, there is a complex system of inhibitors of enzymes of blood coagulation, which are listed in Table 18.6.

Table 18.6. Natural Inhibitors of Coagulation

TARGET	INHIBITOR
Endothelium	Thrombomodulin
Platelet	Prostacyclin
Tissue factor	Tissue Factor Pathway Inhibitor
Factors Va and VIIIa	Proteins C and S
Vitamin K dependent proteases (prothrombin, factors VII, IX, and X)	Antithrombin III

All of these collaborate to ensure that vessels remain patent and that vital blood flow to organs is unimpeded. When elements of this protective system are impaired as in atherosclerosis, coronary artery disease and cerebrovascular disease are two possible outcomes, underscoring the vital importance of the systems that maintain the blood in a fluid state. The fibrinolytic system also carries out digestion of the fibrin clot formed after bleeding has occurred, making possible recanalization of the previously damaged vessel and repair of the wound with collagen.

VASCULAR ENDOTHELIUM

Intact vascular endothelium bears on its surface various glycoproteins and glycosaminoglycans that, in aggregate, impart a marked negative charge that repels the negatively charged platelets. Local damage to the endothelium not only disrupts the repulsive effect, but, more importantly, exposes the blood to deeper structural elements of the vessel wall, including collagen, and the adhesive protein *von Willebrand factor* (vWf), which participate in the coagulation process. As noted, endothelium synthesizes prostacyclin (PGI_2), which is an eicosanoid that blunts platelet responsiveness to various agonists. There also are binding sites on intact endothelium for thrombomodulin and antithrombin III, which are two substances that exert powerful antithrombotic properties.

PLATELETS

Platelets are anucleate cellular fragments 2 to 3 μm in diameter that play two pivotal roles in hemostasis: (*1*) they adhere to and aggregate at sites of vessel wall injury, thus repairing breaches in the vessel—a process that is greatly enhanced by the linkage of numerous platelets by fibrin, which is the end product of the coagulation cascade; and (*2*) platelets provide a phospholipid surface that speeds up the reactions of the coagulation cascade, enhancing both thrombin generation and fibrin formation. Thrombin is the enzyme that converts fibrinogen to fibrin, forming the protein matrix of the clot. Thrombin is a powerful agonist for platelet secretion; such secretory activity by platelets greatly accelerates the development of the clot.

Platelet Structure

Structurally, platelets are less than half the diameter of an erythrocyte, yet they are much more complex. Platelets contain an extensive canalicular system that communicates between other cellular organelles and the surface membrane, two distinct microtubular systems, extensive microfilaments, three distinct classes of granules, glycogen, and mitochondria. The lack of a nucleus is a notable feature that the erythrocyte also possesses, but the resemblance does not extend further.

In the unstimulated state, platelets circulate in the blood as disks; this form is maintained by hollow microtubules deployed directly below the plasma membrane. But when platelets are activated by the binding of various agonists (eg, collagen, thrombin, or ADP to surface receptors), actin (within the platelet cytosol) polymerizes. This polymerization of actin monomers induces the shape change and extension of filopodia characteristic of the stimulated platelet. Secretion of platelet granule contents into the plasma and aggregation of myriad platelets at the site of injury occur promptly after these cytoskeletal changes.

Two platelet membranous systems—the *open canalicular system* and the dense tubular system—are important in platelet activation. The open canalicular system is a series of invaginations that makes contact with the external environment. When platelets secrete their granule contents, they use the channels of the open canalicular system. *The dense tubular system* is a derivative of the endoplasmic reticulum of the precursor megakaryocyte and serves as a Ca^{++} reservoir. Of course, Ca^{++} is an important messenger instigating numerous platelet functions.

In addition to the specialized tubular systems, platelets contain three types of granules—α granules, dense bodies, and lysosomes—that house materials that make important contributions to platelet function. *Alpha granules* contain four proteins that contribute to platelet adhesion and aggregation: fibrinogen, fibronectin, thrombospondin, and von Willebrand factor. *Dense bodies* store Ca^{++}, pyrophosphate, serotonin, and adenine nucleotides. Finally, *lysosomes*, as expected, contain a variety of acid hydrolases. These enzymes are thought to function by clearing the area where platelet aggregation and clotting have occurred, removing debris after hemostasis has been achieved.

Role of Platelets in Hemostasis

Under normal circumstances, it is not unusual for small gaps in capillary and venule endothelium to occur in the high pressure circulatory system. It is the responsibility of platelets to seal these gaps, a role facilitated by platelets circulating next to the vessel endothelium; the smaller platelets are displaced peripherally by the denser erythrocytes. When vessel damage occurs, a sequence of platelet responses ensues (Figure 18.12). First, platelets *adhere* to the denuded endothelium through bridges made by collagen fibers, vWf, fibrinogen, and fibronectin. Von Willebrand factor binds to platelets through a specialized receptor, glycoprotein (GP) Ib/IX complex, whereas platelet membrane GP IIb/IIIa binds to the adhesive proteins. When platelets adhere to the vessel subendothelium, this triggers platelets to undergo a

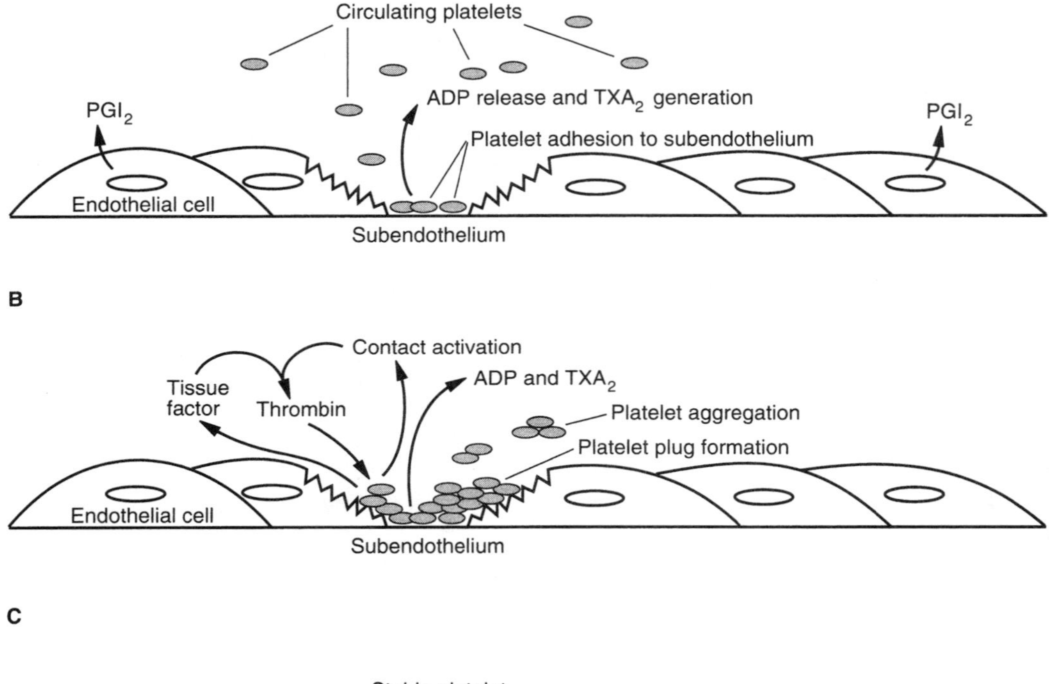

Figure 18.12. Platelet activity at a site of endothelial injury. (A) The initial response is adhesion of circulating platelets to the subendothelial collagen at the injured site. Adhesion to normal endothelium is prevented by surface integrity and prostacyclin (PGI_2). In the process of adherence, ADP and thromboxane A_2 (TXA_2) are released. (B) The next stage is aggregation, which is promoted by the preceding events. During this phase, continued ADP and TXA_2 release promote further accumulation of platelets at the site until a platelet "plug" is generated, which entirely fills the gap. The release of tissue factor and contact activation from the forming plug leads to thrombin formation via the intrinsic and extrinsic coagulation sequences. Thrombin is an important and potent platelet agonist. (C) Fibrin strands that form as a result of the coagulation process initiated in (B) become entwined in and stabilize the structure of the plug. Subsequent endothelial growth and repair, coupled with resorption of the plug, restore the original integrity of the vessel wall. Reprinted with permission from Besa EC, Catalano PM, Kant JA, et al. Hematology. Baltimore: Williams & Wilkins, 1992: 206.

change in shape from the usual disk-like form of quiescent platelets to spheres with extended pseudopodia. These long extensions from the platelet surface enhance the ability of platelets to interact both with other platelets and with the subendothelial surface through fibrinogen, vWf, fibronectin, and vitronectin. This results in platelet *aggregation.* Third, platelet secretory granules fuse with membranes of the platelet canalicular system, discharging their contents into the blood.

Von Willebrand factor is a glycoprotein produced by endothelial cells and by megakaryocytes. Although synthesized as a monomer, the predominant form is as disulfide-linked multimers, which are assembled in the Golgi. vWf has two domains that bind to platelet receptors: one at the amino terminus binds to GP Ib/IX, whereas the other at the carboxy terminus binds to GP IIb/IIIa. In its multimeric form, vWf is effective in crosslinking platelets and linking platelets to the subendothelium. These linkages temporarily anchor the developing platelet "plug" to the site of vessel injury while fibrin formation consolidates the plug, making a more secure seal.

Absence of GP Ib/IX occurs in *Bernard-Soulier disease,* whereas GP IIb/IIIa is deficient in *Glanzmann's thrombasthenia*—two platelet disorders associated with bleeding tendencies. Of course, von Willebrand's disease (actually a group of related diseases) associated with deficiency or defects in vWf is common, and all related diseases are accompanied by some bleeding diathesis.

Important agonists that trigger platelet aggregation and secretion are thrombin, ADP, collagen, arachidonic acid, and epinephrine. G-proteins (see Chapter 1) are familiar mediators that lead to the formation of various second messengers including diacylglycerol, inositol-triphosphate, and the prostanoid thromboxane A_2. Obviously, given the roles of diacylglycerol and inositol-triphosphate, Ca^{++} plays a key role in platelet activation.

Secondary Hemostasis

With the conclusion of the first phase of hemostasis, loosely aggregated platelets adhere to the site of vessel injury. It is now up to the enzymes of the coagulation system to generate fibrin to solidify this mass of platelets into a stable plug or clot, which should be familiar to anyone who has ever cut him- or herself. The coagulation cascade is a series of sequential limited proteolytic enzymatic reactions catalyzed by different serine proteases. These enzymes and cofactors are adsorbed to a lipid surface (usually provided by platelet membranes). The serine proteases are poised in the plasma in zymogenic (inactive) form, and hence do not "spring into action" until the cascade is set off by vessel injury. Each zymogen in the cascade functions both as a substrate that results in its activation and as an enzyme in the succeeding reaction. Normally, platelets adhere only at sites of vessel injury, ensuring that clotting will occur only at those sites and, as a result, safeguarding the general circulation.

Based on work that is decades old, the coagulation cascade has been divided into two pathways: the intrinsic and the extrinsic (Figure 18.13). The intrinsic pathway contains all of the factors necessary to form the fibrin clot, as demonstrated by the fact that blood will clot in vitro. Conversely, the extrinsic pathway was proposed because a substance (*tissue thromboplastin*) external to the blood had to be added to blood to make it clot. Today, tissue thromboplastin is known as *tissue factor.* Tissue factor is widely distributed, being found in membranes of fibroblasts and pericytes of blood vessels, and in many organs including central nervous system, lung, heart, kidney, and gastrointestinal and genitourinary tracts. Such wide distribution ensures that wherever there is tissue trauma, tissue factor will be immediately available to trigger coagulation. Tissue factor is active in the extrinsic pathway only when it is bound to anionic phospholipid (eg, phosphatidylserine). This condition will be met only after tissues have been damaged or platelets have adhered to a site of damage. As another precaution against inappropriate activation, the tissue factor/VIIa complex requires that trace amounts of factor Xa bind to it to achieve full activity.

The Extrinsic Pathway Initiates Clotting

Current thinking is that initiation of blood coagulation is the responsibility of the extrinsic pathway, whereas continued propagation of fibrin formation is designated to the intrinsic pathway. Also, it will become clear that there is considera-

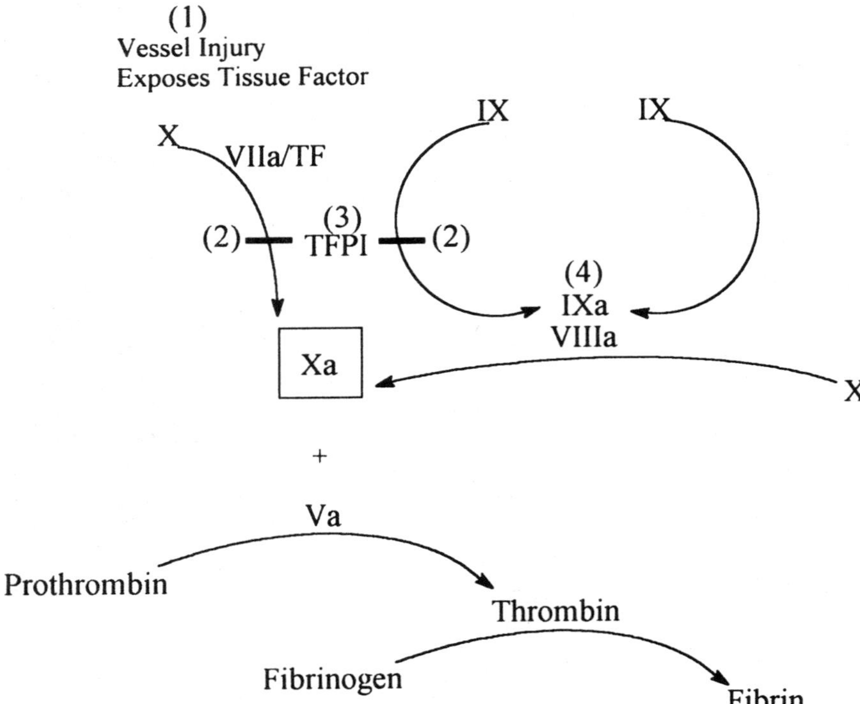

Figure 18.13. The coagulation cascade. Coagulation is initiated (1) when vessel injury exposes tissue factor (TF). Small amounts of circulating factor VIIa bind to TF. The VIIa/TF complex activates small amounts of factors IX and X (2). However, IXa and Xa immediately are inhibited by TFPI (3) through this extrinsic coagulation pathway. Further production of factor Xa, required for generation of thrombin from prothrombin, requires factors IXa and VIIIa (4). In the "common" coagulation pathway, prothrombin, in combination with factors Xa and Va, is converted to thrombin, which catalyzes conversion of fibrinogen to fibrin. Thus, whereas prothrombin time assesses the overall extrinsic pathway function, prothrombin time, together with partial thromboplastin time, provides a measure of the intrinsic pathway integrity.

ble interplay between the two systems; they do not exist in isolation from each other. Instead, they work together to induce fibrin clot formation. Given the fact that clotting should take place only when bleeding has occurred, there are numerous inhibitors that deter the coagulation cascade that, if inappropriately set off, can wreak havoc on the circulatory system.

A plausible view of events leading to formation of a stable fibrin clot is as follows: When a blood vessel is damaged or cut, tissue factor located deep in the vessel wall becomes exposed to the blood and immediately forms a tight complex with factor VII, with which it has a high binding affinity; in the presence of Ca^{++} ions, factor VII undergoes limited proteolysis, converting it to its active form, factor VIIa. The enzyme responsible for this proteolysis has not been identified but possibilities include thrombin, or scanty levels of circulating factor VIIa or factor Xa. The VIIa-tissue factor complex hydrolyzes a single arginine-isoleucine bond in factor X, releasing a small chain of amino acids and producing factor Xa. In both the proteolytic reactions that create factors VIIa and Xa, tissue factor acts as a cofactor accelerating the reaction.

Both The Extrinsic And Intrinsic Pathways Converge On A Common Pathway

Formation of factor Xa represents the beginning of the common pathway of coagulation (Figure 18.13). Next, factor Xa forms a complex with factor Va, Ca^{++}, and phospholipid. Called prothrombinase, this complex converts prothrombin to thrombin, again by limited proteolysis. Throm-

A. Fibrinogen structure

A α B β γ E

D E D

Fibrinogen

B. Fibrin monomer formation

Thrombin

Fibrinopeptide A

Fibrinopeptide B

D E D

Fibrinogen

D E D

Fibrin monomer

C. Fibrin polymerization

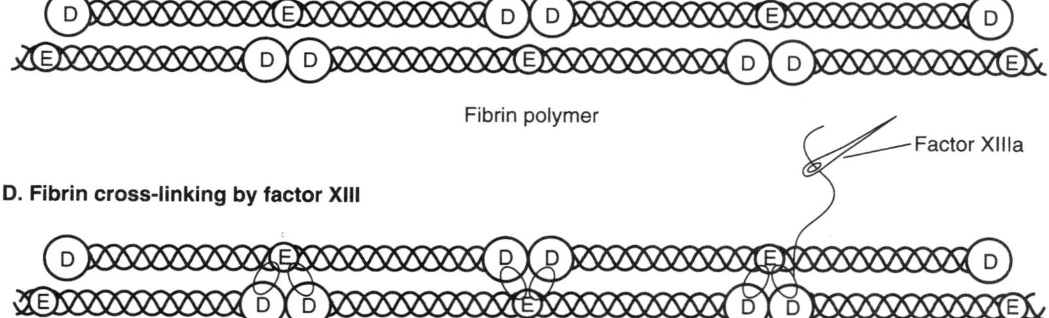

Figure 18.14. Mechanism of conversion of fibrinogen to fibrin. (A) Fibrinogen is composed of three paired polypeptide chains (Aα, Bβ, γ) in a covalent linkage that forms a central E domain; the "tails" are termed the terminal D domains. (B) Through the action of thrombin, fibrinopeptides A and B are cleaved, leaving a fibrin monomer. (C) Linear polymerization of fibrin monomers leads to formation of a fibrin gel. (D) Factor XIII catalyzes formation of lysine-glutamate bonds between E and D domains to form a highly stable structure. Reprinted with permission from Besa EC, Catalano PM, Kant JA, et al. Hematology. Baltimore: Williams & Wilkins, 1992: 226.

bin also is a serine protease. Factor Va is not an enzyme, but a cofactor that accelerates the reaction, probably by instigating a conformational change in factor Xa. Where does factor Va come from? At first, factor Xa probably converts factor V to Va, but once thrombin is formed, it continues the activation by limited proteolysis.

Thrombin next carries out the culminating reaction of the coagulation cascade: conversion of fibrinogen to fibrin. Again, this reaction is a limited proteolysis that cleaves bonds in each of the four chains making up fibrinogen, releasing four fibrinopeptides and forming the so-called fibrin monomers (Figure 18.14). Once the fibrin clot is formed, it is further stabilized by formation of cross-links by factor XIIIa, which is a transglutaminase.

There is a good deal of fibrinogen in plasma: almost 2% to 3% of total circulating proteins. Fibrinogen is composed of three pairs (α_2,β_2,γ_2) of nonidentical polypeptide chains. These chains bear strong negative charges that keep them apart; but, when thrombin cleaves peptides from the center of the molecule, this repulsion is abolished, permitting the chains to approach each other. Polymerization of the fibrin monomers occurs through end-to-end and side-to-side hydrogen bonds. Only after covalent cross links are formed by transglutaminase, however, is the fibrin clot consolidated into a more stable entity.

The Extrinsic and Intrinsic Pathways are Interconnected

A major connection between the extrinsic and intrinsic pathways derives from the ability of the tissue factor/factor VIIa complex to activate not only factor X, as part of the extrinsic path, but also factor IX, from the intrinsic pathway, which also results in activation of factor X. Recall that factor X is the first step in the common path of the coagulation cascade. It is because of the ability of tissue factor/VIIa complex to activate the initial steps of both the extrinsic and intrinsic pathways that it is now believed that *in vivo all coagulation commences with formation of the tissue factor/VIIa complex.* That complex forms when tissue is damaged and is exposed to blood.

Tissue Factor Pathway Inhibitor Modulates Clotting

Why are there two pathways to initiate coagulation? Although a complete answer may not yet be forthcoming, at least a partial answer relates to the presence of an inhibitor of the extrinsic path—*tissue factor pathway inhibitor* (TFPI). TFPI can inactivate both factors VIIa and Xa in the complex they form. Because of the action of TFPI, the duration of action of the extrinsic path is fleeting. Therefore, it is up to the intrinsic path to continue generating factor Xa, via factor IXa, to perpetuate the coagulation cascade. Confirmation for the role of the intrinsic path comes from in vitro studies in which the inhibitory effect of TFPI on fibrin formation is attenuated when the levels of factors IX and VIII are in the normal range. This is in striking contrast to the situation in patients with *hemophilia*, in which either levels of factor VIII (type A-classic) or factor IX (type B or Christmas disease) are decreased or absent. In such patients, the effect of TFPI precludes the possibility of adequate fibrin formation, and these patients experience severe bleeding into joints and sites of trauma. It should now be clear why hemophiliacs bleed. Because TFPI inhibits the activating ability of factor VIIa-tissue factor, continued activation of factor X can occur only through the agency of the factor IXa/factor VIIIa/PL complex. If either factor VIIIa or IXa are ab-

Table 18.7. Gradation of Findings With Inherited Coagulopathies

DEFICIENCY OF	CLINICAL SEVERITY	FEATURES
Factors VIII & IX (Hemophilia A & B)	3+	Hemarthroses, life-threatening bleeding
Deficiency of fibrinogen, factors V, VII, & X	1+ to 2+	Mild to moderate bleeding
Deficiency of factor XI	1+	Bleeding only after surgery or trauma
Deficiency of factor XII, prekallikrein & HMWK (intrinsic pathway factors)	+/− normal	No unusual bleeding even after trauma or surgery

HMWK = high molecular weight kininogen

sent, as in the major forms of hemophilia, then generation of factor Xa is hobbled.

Clinically, patients with deficiency of factor XI suffer from a mild bleeding disorder in which they do not bleed extensively into joints after trauma (Table 18.7). These findings further buttress the view that factor VIIa/tissue factor is the initiator of blood coagulation, assigning a subordinate role to factor XI in propagation of the clotting process.

SUGGESTED READINGS

GENERAL

Beutler E, Lichtman M, Coller BS, Kipps TJ, eds. Williams Hematology. 5th ed. New York: McGraw-Hill, 1995.

Colman RW, Hirsh J, Marder VJ, Salzman EW, eds. Hemostasis and thrombosis: basic principles and clinical practice. 3rd ed. Philadelphia: JB Lippincott, 1994.

Hoffman R, Benz EJ, Shattil S, et al, eds. Hematology: basic principles and practice. 2nd ed. New York: Churchill Livingstone, 1995.

Lee GR, Bithell TC, Foerster J, et al, eds. Wintrobe's clinical hematology. 9th ed. Philadelphia: Lea and Febiger, 1993.

Stamatoyannopoulos G, Nienhuis AW, Majerus PW, Varmus H, eds. The molecular basis of blood diseases. 2nd ed. Philadelphia: WB Saunders, 1994.

ERYTHROCYTES—STRUCTURE AND FUNCTION

Bosch FH, Werre JM, Schipper L, et al. Determinants of red blood cell deformability in relation to cell age. Eur J Haematol 1994;52:35.

Joshi A, Palsson BO. Metabolic dynamics in the human red cell. Part III—metabolic reaction rates. J Theor Biol 1990;142:41.

Kodicek M, Suttnar J, Mircevova L, Marik T. Red blood cells under mechanical stress. Gen Physiol Biophys 1990;9:291.

Lee ID, Palsson BO. A comprehensive model of human erythrocyte metabolism: extensions to include pH effects. Biomedica Biochimica Acta 1990;49:771.

Metcalf D. The molecular control of cell division, differentiation, commitment and maturation in haemopoietic cells. Nature 1989;339:27.

Mohandas N, Chasis JA. Red blood cell deformability, membrane material properties and shape: regulation by transmembrane, skeletal and cytosolic proteins and lipids. Semin Hematol 1993;30:171.

Mohandas N, Evans E. Mechanical properties of the red cell membrane in relation to molecular structure and genetic defects. Annu Rev Biophys Biomol Struct 1994;23:787.

Samaja M, Rovida E, Motterlini R, et al. Human red cell age, oxygen affinity and oxygen transport. Respir Physiol 1990;79:69.

Tanner MJ. The major integral proteins of the human red cell. Baillieres Clin Haematol 1993;6:333.

Valentine WN, Paglia DE. Red cell metabolism, normal and abnormal implications for red cell aging. Adv Exp Med Biol 1991;307:125.

Williamson D. The unstable hemoglobins. Blood Rev 1993;7:146.

DISEASES OF THE ERYTHROCYTE

Allen RH, Stabler SP, Savage DG, Lindenbaum J. Metabolic abnormalities in cobalamin (vitamin B_{12}) and folate deficiency. FASEB J 1993;7:1344.

Baynes RD, Skikne BS, Cook JD. Circulating transferrin receptors and assessment of iron status. Journal of Nutritional Biochemistry 1994;5:322.

Beutler E. Red cell enzyme defects. Hematol Pathol 1990; 4:103.

Beutler E. The molecular biology of G6PD variants and other red cell enzyme defects. Annu Rev Med 1992; 43:47.

Beutler E. G 6PD deficiency. Blood 1994;84:3613.

Brown RG. Determining the cause of anemia. General approach, with emphasis on microcytic hypochromic anemias. Postgrad Med 1991;89:161.

Krantz SB. Pathogenesis and treatment of anemia of chronic disease. Am J Med Sci 1994;307:353.

Leibold EA, Guo B. Iron-dependent regulation of ferritin and transferrin receptor expression by the iron-responsive element binding protein. Annu Rev Nutr 1992;12:345.

Lin CK, Lin JS, Chen SY, et al. Comparison of hemoglobin and red blood cell distribution width in the differential diagnosis of microcytic anemia. Arch Pathol Lab Med 1992;116:1030.

Massey AC. Microcytic anemia. Differential diagnosis and management of iron deficiency anemia. Med Clin North Am 1992;76:549.

Metz J. Cobalamin deficiency and the pathogenesis of nervous system disease. Annu Rev Nutr 1992;12:59.

Oski FA. Iron deficiency in infancy and childhood. N Engl J Med 1993;329:190.

Pollack S. Receptor-mediated iron transport and intracellular iron transport. Am J Hematol 1992;39: 113.

Saxena S, Rabinowitz AP, Johnson C, Shulman IA. Iron-deficiency anemia: a medically treatable chronic anemia as a model for transfusion overuse. Am J Med 1993;94:120.

Sears DA. Anemia of chronic disease. Med Clin North Am 1992;76:567.

Scott RB. Common blood disorders: a primary care approach. Geriatrics 1993;48(4):72.

Tefferi A, Pruthi RK. The biochemical basis of cobalamin deficiency. Mayo Clin Proc 1994;69:181.

Theil EC. Iron regulatory elements (IREs): a family of mRNA non-coding sequences. Biochem J 1994;304:1.

Welborn JL, Meyers FJ. A three-point approach to anemia. Postgrad Med 1991;89:179.

Wymer A, Becker DM. Recognition and evaluation of red blood cell macrocytosis in the primary care setting. J Gen Intern Med 1990;5:192.

THE HEMOGLOBINOPATHIES

Bowie LJ, Reddy PL, Nagabhushan M, Sevigny P. Detection of alpha-thalassemias by multiplex polymerase chain reaction. Clin Chem 1994;40:2260.

Buchanan GR. Sickle cell disease: recent advances. Curr Probl Pediatr 1993;23:219.

Chang JG, Lin CP, Liu TC, et al. Molecular basis of beta-thalassemia minor in Taiwan. Int J Hematol 1994;59: 267.

Charache S. Experimental therapy of sickle cell disease. Use of hydroxyurea. American Journal of Pediatric Hematology Oncology 1994;16:62.

Cima LG, Discher DE, Tong J, Williams MC. A hydrodynamic interpretation of crisis in Sickle cell anemia. Microvasc Res 1994;47:41.

Hebbel RP. Beyond hemoglobin polymerization: the red blood cell membrane and sickle disease pathophysiology. Blood 1991;77:214.

Kulozik AE. β-thalassemia: molecular pathogenesis and clinical variability. Eur J Pediatr 1992;151:78.

Nagel RL, Lawrence C. The distinct pathobiology of sickle cell-hemoglobin C disease. Hematol Oncol Clin North Am 1991;5:433.

Noguchi CT, Schechter AN, Rodgers GP. Sickle cell disease pathophysiology. Baillieres Clin Haematol 1993;6:57.

Olivieri O, DeFranceschi L, Capellini MD, et al. Oxidative damage and erythrocyte membrane transport abnormalities in thalassemias. Blood 1994;84:315.

Powars D, Hiti A. Sickle cell anemia. β^s gene cluster haplotypes as genetic markers for severe disease expression. American Journal of Diseases of Children 1993;147:1197.

Sadiq MF, Huisman TH. Molecular characterization of beta-thalassemia in North Jordan. Hemoglobin 1994; 18:325.

Schiliro G, DiGregorio F, Samperi P, et al. Genetic heterogeneity of beta-thalassemia in Southeast Sicily. Am J Hematol 1995;48:5.

Schrier SL. Thalassemia: pathophysiology of red cell changes. Annu Rev Med 1994;45:211.

Somer T, Meiselman HJ. Disorders of blood viscosity. Ann Med 1993;25:31.

Steinberg MH. The interactions of α-thalassemia with hemoglobinopathies. Hematol Oncol Clin North Am 1991;5:453.

Ting YL, Naccarato S, Qualtieri A, et al. In vivo metabolic studies of glucose, ATP, and 2,3-DPG in beta-thalassemia intermedia, heterozygous beta-thalassemic and normal erythrocytes: ^{13}C and ^{31}P MRS studies. Br J Hematol 1994;88:547.

Viniou N, Georgiou J, Loutradi A, et al. Molecular basis and haplotype analysis of delta, beta-thalassemic chromosome in Greece. Acta Haematol 1994;92:83.

Zipursky A, Chacula DM, Brown EJ. The reversibly sickled cell. American Journal of Pediatric Hematology Oncology 1993;15:219.

PRIMARY DEFECTS OF RED CELL MEMBRANE

Bennett V, Gilligan DM. The spectrin-based membrane skeleton and micron-scale organization of the plasma membrane. Annu Rev Cell Biol 1993;9:27.

Bennett V, Lambert S. The spectrin skeleton: from red cells to brain. J Clin Invest 1991;87:1483.

Cohen CM, Gascard P. Regulation and post-translational modification of erythrocyte membrane and membrane-skeletal proteins. Semin Hematol 1992;29: 244.

Conboy JG. Structure, function and molecular genetics of erythroid membrane skeletal protein 4.1 in normal and abnormal red blood cells. Semin Hematol 1993; 30:58.

Delaunay J, Dhermy D. Mutations involving the spectrin heterodimer contact site: clinical expression and alterations in specific function. Semin Hematol 1993; 30:21.

Kunze D, Rustow B. Pathobiological aspects of cytoskeletal components. Eur J Clin Chem Clin Biochem 1993;31:477.

Lecomte MC, Garbarz M, Gautero H, et al. Molecular basis of clinical and morphological heterogeneity in hereditary elliptocytosis (HE) with spectrin alpha I variants. Br J Haematol 1993;85:584.

Liu S-C, Derick LH. Molecular anatomy of the red blood cell membrane skeleton: structure-function relationships. Semin Hematol 1992;29:231.

Miraglia del Guidice E, Perrotta S, Sannino E, et al. Molecular heterogeneity of hereditary elliptocytosis in Italy. Haematologica 1994;79:400.

Pekrun A, Eber SW, Kuhlmey A, Schroter W. Combined ankyrin and spectrin deficiency in hereditary spherocytosis. Ann Hematol 1993;67:89.

Peters LL, Lux SE. Ankyrins: structure and function in normal cells and hereditary spherocytosis. Semin Hematol 1993;30:85.

Savvides P, Shalev O, John KM, Lux SE. Combined spectrin and ankyrin deficiency is common in autosomal dominant hereditary spherocytosis. Blood 1993;82:2953.

THE NEUTROPHIL

Donnelly SC, Robertson C. Mediators, mechanisms and mortality in major trauma. Resuscitation 1994;28:87.

Ginis I, Tauber AI. Activation mechanisms of adherent human neutrophils. Blood 1990;76:1233.
Johnson KJ, Varani J, Smolen JE. Neutrophil activation and function in health and disease. Immunol Ser 1992;57:1.
Laurent F, Benoliel AM, Capo C, Bongrnad P. Oxidative metabolism of polymorphonuclear leukocytes: modulation by adhesive stimuli. J Leukoc Biol 1991;49: 217.
Yang KD, Hill HR. Assessment of neutrophil function disorders: practical and preventive interventions. Pediatr Infect Dis J 1994;13:906.

EOSINOPHILS AND BASOPHILS

Abu-Ghazaleh RI, Dunnette SL, Loegering DA, et al. Eosinophil granule proteins in peripheral blood granulocytes. J Leukoc Biol 1992;52(6):611.
Dahinden DA, Bischoff SC, Brunner T, et al. Regulation of mediator release by human basophils: importance of the sequence and time of addition in the combined action of different agonists. Int Arch Allergy Appl Immunol 1991;9:161.
Jones DG. The eosinophil. J Comp Pathol 1993;108:317.
Kirchsenbaum AS, Kessler SW, Goff JP, Metcalfe DD. Demonstration of the origin of human mast cells from CD34+ bone marrow progenitor cells. J Immunol 1991;146:1410.
Valent P, Bettelheim P. The human basophil. Crit Rev Oncol Hematol 1990;10:327.

THE LYMPHOCYTE

Burrows PD, Cooper MD. B-cell development in man. Curr Opin Immunol 1993;5:201.
Cioffi WG, Burleson DG, Pruitt BA Jr. Leukocyte response to injury. Arch Surg 1993;128(11):1260.
Coffman RL. Mechanisms of helper T-cell regulation of B-cell activity. Ann N Y Acad Sci 1993;681:25–28.
Goust JM, Bierer B. Cell-mediated immunity. Immunol Ser 1993;58:187.
Goust JM, Jackson A. Lymphocyte ontogeny and membrane markers. Immunol Ser 1993;58:161.
Janeway CA Jr, Golstein P. Lymphocyte activation and effector functions. Editorial overview. The role of cell surface molecules. Curr Opin Immunol 1993;5:313.
Parker DC. T cell-dependent B cell activation. Annu Rev Immunol 1993;11:331.
Vitetta ES. From the basic science of B cells to biological missiles at the bedside. J Immunol 1994;153:1407.
Zanetti M, Sollazzo M, Billetta R. Functions and structures in a regulatory network for self-reactivity. Immunol Ser 1991;55:221.

DISORDERS OF HEMOSTASIS

Bertina RM, Koeleman BPC, Koster T, et al. Mutation in blood coagulation factor V associated with resistance to activated protein C. Nature 1994;369:64.
Bick RL, Murano G. Physiology of hemostasis. Clin Lab Med 1994;14:677.
Bloom AL. Physiology of blood coagulation. Haemostasis 1990;20(suppl):14.
Boon GD. An overview of hemostasis. Toxicol Pathol 1993;21:170.
Brott T, Stump D. Overview of hemostasis and thrombosis. Semin Neurol 1991;11(4):305.
Broze GJ. Tissue factor pathway inhibitor and the revised theory of coagulation. Annu Rev Med 1995;46:103.
Castellino FJ. Human protein C and activated protein C: components of the human anticoagulation system. Trends in Cardiovascular Medicine 1995;5:55.
Furie B, Furie BC. Molecular and cellular biology of blood coagulation. N Engl J Med 1992;326:800.
Gentry PA. The mammalian blood platelet: its role in haemostasis, inflammation and tissue repair. J Comp Pathol 1992;107:243.
Gilbert JA Jr, Scalzi RP. Disseminated intravascular coagulation. Emerg Med Clin North Am 1993;11:465.
Hassouna HI. Laboratory evaluation of hemostatic disorders. Hematol Oncol Clin North Am 1993;6: 1161.
Hoyer LW. Hemophilia A. N Engl J Med 1994;330:38.
Humphries JE. Transfusion therapy in acquired coagulopathies. Hematol Oncol Clin North Am 1994; 8:1181.
Kalafatis M, Swords NA, Rand MD, Mann KG. Membrane-dependent reactions in blood coagulation: role of the vitamin K-dependent enzyme complexes. Biochim Biophys Acta 1994;1227:113.
Lopez JA. The platelet glycoprotein Ib-IX complex. Blood Coagul Fibrinolysis 1994;5:97.
Lusher JM. Transfusion therapies in congenital coagulopathies. Hematol Oncol Clin North Am 1994; 8:1167.
Mann KG, Krishnaswamy S, Lawson JH. Surface-dependent hemostasis. Semin Hematol 1992;29:213.
Mosesson MW. The roles of fibrinogen and fibrin in hemostasis and thrombosis. Semin Hematol 1992;29: 177.
Murray NA, Roberts IA. Circulating megakaryocytes and their progenitors (BFU-MK and CFU-MK) in term and pre-term neonates. Br J Haematol 1995;89:41.
Rapaport SI, Rao LVM. Initiation and regulation of tissue factor-dependent blood coagulation. Arteriosclerosis and Thrombosis 1992;12:1111.
Rubanyi GM. The role of endothelium in cardiovascular hemostasis and diseases. J Cardiovasc Pharmacol 1993;22(suppl):S1.
Sreiff M, Bell WR. Exercise and hemostasis in humans. Semin Hematol 1994;31:155.
Ware JA, Heistad D. Platelet-endothelium interactions. N Engl J Med 1993;328:628.

chapter **19**

Immunity and Infectious Diseases

All of us have endured the common cold—viral and bacterial sore-throats (pharyngitis) and various childhood diseases. These and other infections highlight the fact that humans (and other animals) are in a constant struggle with microorganisms to prevent the inevitable contact with and colonization by these organisms from developing into disease.

These microorganisms not only are found everywhere in our environment but also populate our skin, mucous membranes, and our gastrointestinal tracts. In fact, there are more bacterial cells in our gastrointestinal tract than there are human cells in our body. Despite this enormous indigenous microbial population, most of the time the individual does not display evidence of infectious disease, including *malaise* (a feeling of aches and pains and general discomfort familiar to all), fever, shaking chills, inflammation, cellular destruction, and organ dysfunction. Accordingly, when microorganisms live in harmony with the host, that state is given a special name—colonization. In that state, the host has no symptoms of disease and the immune system may or may not be provoked to respond (depending on the strength of the stimulus) to the invader.

In viewing the factors that account for an individual's susceptibility to infection, three areas of concern exist: *host defenses*, *microbial attributes*, and *environmental factors*. These three are in a constant "see-saw" determining whether the host maintains well-being or whether the microbe gains the ascendancy, causing the host to become infected. For us to make sense of this constant struggle, it is easiest to consider each in isolation, and then to examine how they interact with each other. In that way we will be able to reach an understanding of how someone becomes infected.

Our host defenses include the natural barriers afforded by the skin and mucous membranes, phagocytic cells of the blood, and the immune system with its humoral and cell-mediated arms. These defenses are so effective against most microorganisms that it is fair to say that only when host defenses are compromised or the dose of infecting organisms is large that the individual becomes susceptible to clinical infection. In fact, when immunocompromised because of (*1*) severe malnutrition, (*2*) the use of drugs that suppress white cell or immune function or, (*3*) infectious agents that suppress immune function (as in the acquired immune deficiency syndrome [AIDS]) the individual becomes susceptible to organisms that normally are not considered to be pathogens. Often, such organisms are members of the normal flora and simply are taking advantage of the host when his or her defenses are down. Such organisms are aptly termed *opportunists*.

If, however, natural barriers are breached, as for example from a bite by an insect or animal, or by trauma to the skin, virulent microorganisms can be introduced and active infection may result. In that case, the individual's innate defenses (white blood cells and complement systems) and the adaptive defenses (immune system) will confront the invaders.

Of course, improved public health measures including a safe water supply, sanitation measures to keep rodent populations in check, and improved cleanliness (among others) have made significant contributions to the general health of human beings. Outbreaks of epidemics of water-borne and rat-borne infectious diseases after natural disasters and warfare that disrupt the water supply, aggravate crowding, interrupt sanitation methods, and put an end to personal hygiene illustrate how essential these environmental factors are to normal health. History buffs know, for example, that in the 14th century, the Black Plague eradicated about one-third of the population of Europe and that many armies, including Napoleon's, have been defeated, not by superior force, but by epidemics of infectious disease.

Lastly, some microorganisms are endowed with specific pathogenic biochemical properties. For example, enzymes, toxins, and the ability to alter surface properties or produce a capsule that resists phagocytosis may confer on microbes the ability to elude or kill phagocytes (polymorphonuclear leukocytes), defeat the immune system, or, in the case of toxins, kill the host outright. It would be misleading to imply that the vast majority of microorganisms are endowed with special properties that can render the immune-competent host especially susceptible to disease. Rather, the picture that is emerging is one in which the host and his or her defenses hold the key to whether or not most microorganisms can gain the upper hand in this ceaseless struggle.

HOST DEFENSE MECHANISMS

The skin and mucous membranes lining the nose, mouth, upper respiratory tract, and genitourinary tract represent a formidable barrier to microbial invasion (Table 19.1). But these barriers can be subverted by trauma, chemical agents, and pre-existing disease, thus enabling microorganisms to gain entrance into the body. Some of these organisms will cause only local disease, whereas others gravitate to particular organs (bone, meninges, bladder) and still others are disseminated widely in the blood (septicemia). Not infrequently, infectious agents enter the body in food or water, producing diarrhea, vomiting, and systemic symptoms. Even the developing fetus is vulnerable to viruses that may be transferred in utero via the placenta. Tragically, such fetuses may be severely deformed as occurs with rubella, or manifest widespread infection as with cytomegalovirus or herpes virus.

In fact, we live in a world teeming with microorganisms—present on dust particles in the air; on all inanimate surfaces; in our water; on other living things; and on our skin, mucous membranes, and gastrointestinal tracts. Given the ubiquitous distribution of such potentially infectious agents, we have to ask how it is that most humans enjoy freedom from the clinical manifestations of infectious disease for the bulk of their lives. A general answer recognizes that besides the barriers represented by the skin and mucous membranes, other factors protect the host from overt infection. These defenses include the normal flora of the skin and

Table 19.1. Constitutive Defenses: Barriers to Infection

	PHYSICAL	
SYSTEM OR ORGAN	CELL TYPE	CLEARING MECHANISM
Skin	Squamous	Desquamation
Mucous membranes	Columnar nonciliated (eg, gastrointestinal tract)	Peristalsis
	Columnar ciliated (eg, trachea)	Mucociliary movement
	Cuboidal ciliated (eg, nasopharynx)	Tears, saliva, mucus, sweat
	Secretory	Flow of liquids
	CHEMICAL	
SYSTEM OR ORGAN	SOURCE	SUBSTANCES
Skin	Sweat, sebaceous glands	Organic acids
Mucous membranes	Parietal cells of stomach	Hydrochloric acid, Low pH
	Secretions	Antimicrobial compounds
	Neutrophils	Lysozyme, peroxidase, lactoferrin
Lung	A cells	Pulmonary surfactant
Upper alimentary	Salivary glands	Thiocyanate
	Neutrophils	Myeloperoxidase
		Cationic proteins
		Lactoferrin
		Lysozyme
Small bowel and below	Liver via biliary tree	Bile acids
	Gut flora	Low molecular weight fatty acids

Reprinted with permission from Schaechter M, Eisenstein B, Medoff G, eds. Mechanisms of Microbial Disease. Baltimore: Williams & Wilkins, 1993, p. 91.

gut, the phagocytic cells (granulocytes and monocytes), and the humoral and cellular arms of the immune system. We shall devote some time to discussing the phagocytic cells and the immune system, but we note that the normal flora acts to prevent infection by: (*1*) blocking binding sites for adherence of competing microbes, (*2*) competing for substrates for energy and biosynthetic functions, (*3*) elaborating chemicals that inhibit growth of the interlopers, and (*4*) priming the immune system because the resident flora and invaders may share similar antigenic determinants.

Skin and Mucous Membranes

The skin and mucous membranes lining the various portals to the body (respiratory, gastrointestinal, and genitourinary tracts) are the first barriers encountered by a potential invading microorganism. Normal skin, with its investment of the fibrous protein, keratin, represents an imposing barrier. Burns, dermatitis, cuts, and abrasions, however, can breach that barrier, permitting entry of skin flora and any microbes brought in by the trauma or contamination from hands or clothing. Sebaceous glands secrete long chain fatty acids that also act to restrain bacterial proliferation. When these glands become occluded, as for example when a deodorant prepared in a thick base is applied to the axilla, infection with normal skin residents may result. Finally, propionic acid, a product of metabolism of bacteria making up the normal skin flora, is bacteriostatic.

Mucosal surfaces are protected by hydrolytic enzymes like lysozyme that break down various bacterial cell walls. Another hydrolytic factor, the acid environment of the stomach, is distinctly inhospitable to bacterial growth; it follows that achlorhydria from pernicious anemia or H_2 blockers increases susceptibility to enteric infection by ingested pathogens.

Respiratory passages are defended by a mucociliary blanket that removes small particles that enter with the inspired air. Supplementing this system is the cough reflex, which assists the evacuation of the debris-laden mucous.

Professional Phagocytes Constitute A Potent Defense Against Many Bacteria

Polymorphonuclear leukocytes (polys, neutrophils, or granulocytes) and monocytes/macrophages represent the two cell types in the class of professional phagocytes. Both groups of phagocytes can ingest and destroy a variety of bacteria and fungi, but these distinct types of cells have somewhat different responsibilities in policing the tissue spaces.

Granulocytes are short-lived cells that can go almost anywhere in the body, squeezing out of blood vessels to enter the tissue spaces. *Pus*, a familiar sight surrounding a splinter or boil, is predominantly made up of dead granulocytes. *Macrophages*, however, take up residence in the tissues including lungs, liver, spleen, and skin, where they "ambush" bacteria that have reached those sites either via inhalation or via the bloodstream. Macrophages usually are long-lived cells and their antimicrobial properties are enhanced by the action of local hormones called lymphokines.

We will consider the activities of these two types of cells, comparing and contrasting their different roles in the innate defense system of the body.

Neutrophils

Again, neutrophils function to rid the body of microbial invaders. They do so by engulfing these organisms, killing them through a combination of O_2-dependent and O_2-independent microbicidal strategies. A series of sequential and somewhat overlapping events describes the actions of the neutrophil as it participates in the host defense mechanisms. These steps are exit (diapedesis) from the blood vessel into the tissue (interstitial) spaces, directional migration to the affected site prompted by chemical attractants called chemotaxins, recognition of the invader followed by phagocytosis, degranulation of cytosolic contents, and intracellular killing and digestion.

CHEMOATTRACTANT MOLECULES LURE NEUTROPHILS TO SITES OF MICROBIAL INVASION

Recalling that all cells are endowed with specialized plasma membrane surface receptors to receive information by binding signal molecules, it is expected that neutrophils also would receive information through such receptors. What makes neutrophils unusual is the sheer number of infor-

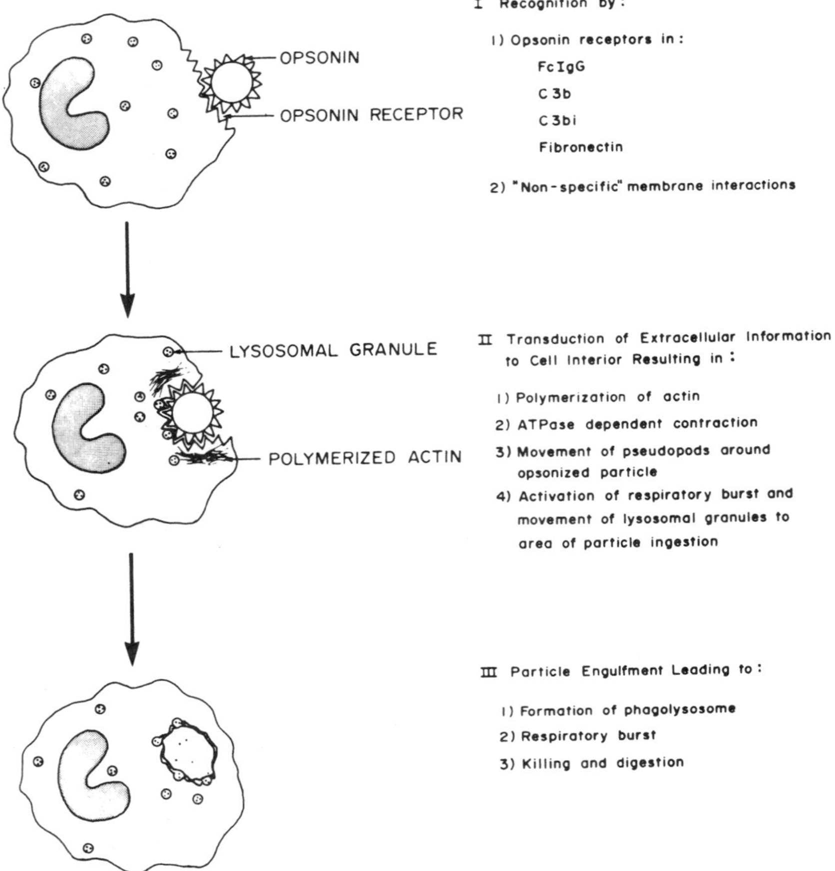

Figure 19.1. Steps in neutrophilic phagocytosis. Opsonin coating of the bacterium assists the cell in recognition and binding of the organism. The process requires energy, but the supply is not derived from mitochondrial metabolism. Reprinted with permission from McCarty DJ, Koopman WJ. Arthritis and Allied Conditions: a Textbook of Rheumatology. 12th ed. Baltimore: Williams & Wilkins, 1993: 356.

mational molecules that can cause them to migrate, in a targeted manner, to the site of invasion. This process, termed *chemotaxis*, is triggered by (*1*) various bacterial products including those bearing N-formyl groups on peptides (a characteristic of prokaryotic protein synthesis); (*2*) components of the complement pathway, especially C5a, C3a, and iC3b and (*3*) a family of secreted compounds produced by neutrophils, lymphocytes, and macrophages—the cytokines.

Although the various chemotactic agents bind to the plasma membrane at distinct receptors, nevertheless, they all trigger activation of a common pathway (Figure 19.1). In the case of neutrophils, this pathway begins with activation of a G protein (see Chapter 1), which in turn awakens a dormant membrane bound phospholipase C that mediates breakdown of the membrane component *phosphatidylinositol* to *diacylglycerol* and *inositol triphosphate* (IP_3). Diacylglycerol, remaining in the plane of the membrane, now activates protein kinase C, which modulates the activity of many neutrophil enzymes. By contrast, IP_3, being water soluble, diffuses into the cytoplasm, triggering both release of intracellular Ca^{++} from storage sites in the endoplasmic reticulum, as well as increased uptake of Ca^{++} through the plasma membrane. This influx of Ca^{++} not only further increases the activity of protein kinase C, but also stimulates many cellular processes acting through the calcium binding protein, *calmodulin* (see Chapter 21).

SHAPE CHANGES AND INGESTION OF FOREIGN MATERIALS BY NEUTROPHILS

Of course, the most conspicuous expression of these biochemical mediators is the purposeful movement toward and ingestion of foreign organisms and particles (Figure 19.1). These morphologic changes depend on reorganization of neutrophil actin and cytoskeletal elements that cause the cell to change in shape from a sphere to an elongated "hand mirror." Polys must squeeze through intercellular spaces in the vascular endothelium to enter the tissue spaces where they do battle with invading microbes. Actual movement of neutrophils requires interaction of actin and myosin fibrils in a sliding filament arrangement, a process powered by hydrolysis of adenosine triphosphate (ATP) (see Chapter 25, which discusses muscle diseases).

Once neutrophils arrive at the "microbial beachhead," they must be able to recognize the foreign organism or particles. This process benefits greatly from coating of these foreign elements with specific antibodies or complement proteins (particularly C3a) called *opsonins*. By opsonization, foreign bodies are made more palatable to neutrophils, because opsonins bind to specific neutrophil membrane receptors, triggering engulfment and ingestion of the coated bodies. Remarkably, even if a randomly moving poly—one for which no chemotactic agent has engendered directional movement—encounters a foreign particle of appropriate size, the poly will engulf the particle. Hence, although chemotaxis is not a precondition to ingestion, chemoattractants typically provoke movement of the poly toward the invader in the first place.

KILLING BY THE NEUTROPHIL RELIES ON O_2-DEPENDENT AND O_2-INDEPENDENT SYSTEMS

When organisms are taken up by neutrophils, these foreign agents are rapidly surrounded by a vacuole derived from a portion of the invaginated plasma membrane. This vacuole merges with a hydrolase-rich lysosome, forming a secondary lysosome or *phagosome*. Before the phagosome is completely enveloped by membrane, cytoplasmic granules discharge their contents into the phagosome, further augmenting the antibacterial arsenal of the phagosome. These agents are all part of the O_2-independent components of antibacterial activity and include bactericidal permeability increasing protein, defensins, cationic proteins, lysozyme, and various proteases and glucosidases. Bactericidal permeability increasing protein exploits a microbicidal mechanism also used by the complement system and natural killer cells—by increasing the permeability of the bacterial or fungal membrane, it effects lysis of the microbe. Defensins, a group of cyclic polypeptides, are cytotoxic to a wide spectrum of bacteria, fungi, and enveloped viruses.

The other arm of the antibacterial assault system of the poly is the O_2-dependent arm. A burst of O_2 consumption promptly follows upon closure of the phagosome. This consumption of O_2 is catalyzed by a "*respiratory burst oxidase*," which, although originally localized to the plasma membrane, becomes part of the membrane of the phagosome. Although short-lived (2 to 20 minutes in duration), this respiratory burst unleashes many potent microbicidal chemical species. Formation of these species begins with the one electron reduction of O_2 to form superoxide anion (O_{2-}), which is a free radical with limited toxicity for bacteria. Two superoxide radicals, however, can form molecular O_2 and H_2O_2 in a reaction catalyzed by superoxide dismutase. Hydrogen peroxide is a familiar and potent microbicidal agent. But the reactions do not stop there. There is evidence that peroxide can react with superoxide in a reaction catalyzed by Fe^{3+} to produce hydroxyl radical (HO.), a species with considerable reactivity and one believed to be particularly microbicidal.

Peroxide also can combine with Cl^- to generate *hypochlorous acid*, the active principle in household bleach. This important reaction is catalyzed by *myeloperoxidase* (MPO), an enzyme found in the primary lysosome.

$$H_2O_2 + Cl- \xrightarrow{\text{MPO}} HOCl + OH-$$

Still another class of toxic agents, chloramine radicals, is generated by reaction of HOCl with primary and secondary amines. These chlorine and nitrogen containing radicals are much more long-lived than the O_2 radicals and are believed to make an important contribution to the microbicidal arsenal of the granulocyte.

Not unexpectedly, these reactive oxygen products and radicals pose a significant toxic hazard to the host's own cells. Endowed with various protective mechanisms, including superoxide dismutase, catalase, peroxidase, glutathione, vitamin E, and selenium, the host can defend against these toxic effects. Still, the damage caused by some infectious processes is, to some degree, the consequence of unrestrained neutrophil microbicidal activity and not the result of the microbe's aggressive actions per se.

Monocytes

Monocytes and macrophages not only possess phagocytic and microbicidal properties like granulocytes, but also play a crucial role in the immune system. They serve as *antigen-presenting cells* (APC) to T-lymphocytes and secrete a variety of cytokines that augment cell-mediated immune function.

It is important to recognize that the monocyte is precursor to the macrophage. Macrophage development unfolds in a wide range of tissues, especially lungs, liver, skin, brain, and kidney, and hematopoietic tissues including bone marrow and lymphoid tissue. Although neither the chemotactic response of monocytes nor their microbicidal properties are equal to those of neutrophils, monocytes, still, figure prominently in the host defense against mycobacteria, fungi, protozoa, and viruses. Macrophages use the same oxygen-dependent chemical species used by neutrophils, but have potent O_2-independent mechanisms at their disposal as shown by their ability to kill microbes under anaerobic conditions. Like granulocytes, monocytes possess lysozyme, lactoferrin, defensins, and various hydrolases. Unlike granulocytes, when monocytes function as APCs, they cease to display any phagocytic or cytocidal properties.

Phagocytic macrophages not only defend against foreign organisms, they also remove dead and dying cells (especially erythrocytes in the spleen), cellular debris, foreign particles, and residua from inflammatory reactions.

THE IMMUNE SYSTEM

The immune system supplements and complements the innate defenses of the body against invasion by bacteria, fungi, parasites, viruses, and foreign chemicals. Immunity is a very specific phenomenon, as illustrated by the fact that once a child has suffered one bout of measles, mumps, or chicken pox, he or she usually will not experience another episode. This adaptive system of defense is so important to survival that an individual could scarcely escape life-threatening infection with a complete defect in one of the arms of the immune system. These arms are the humoral- or *immunoglobulin-based* system on the one hand, and the *cell-mediated* system on the other. Of course, cellular action underlies all of the activities of both of these broad immune functions. Three cell types—thymus-derived lymphocytes (T-cells), bone-marrow derived lymphocytes (B-cells), and tissue macrophages—act in an interdependent fashion to orchestrate the responses of the immune system.

Antibodies produced by B-cells permeate the blood stream and various body fluids. Because their binding affinity is very specific, they attach to complementary sites on microbes or foreign antigens that induced their formation. In some instances, a toxin is neutralized when its specific antibody binds to it (eg, tetanus toxin). In general, the binding of antibody to microbes marks those microbes for uptake by phagocytic cells or induces the complement cascade. *Complement*, as we will discover, is a complicated system of blood proteins and cell membrane receptors that are activated in a sequential fashion (like the coagulation cascade). The endpoint of complement action is destruction of the microbial invader or the host cell, which has become a sanctuary for the invading organism. Destruction by the complement system is achieved by making the cell envelope "leaky," which results in cytolysis.

The other arm of the immune system, cell-mediated immunity, involves T-cell subclasses (helper and cytotoxic cells, Table 19.2) that recognize foreign antigens only when presented to them by specialized cells (APCs) that have specific glycoproteins on their plasma membrane. Cytotoxic T-cells destroy virus-infected cells, preventing further viral replication and dissemination. Helper

Table 19.2. Characteristic Features of Immunoreactive Lymphocytes

	T-CELLS	B-CELLS
% of circulating lymphs	85%	10–20%
Origin	Bone marrow stem cell migrated to thymic cortex	Bone marrow
Life span	Long- and short-lived	Usually short-lived
Humoral response	Helper, Regulator, Suppressor	Production and secretion of antibody
Cell-mediated response	Helper, Regulator, Suppressor	Uncertain
Antigenic specificity	Clonal	Clonal
Cellular products	Lymphokines, Helpers, Suppressors	Immunoglobulin
Cellular memory	Antigen-specific	Antigen-specific

T-cells secrete *cytokines*, a class of signal molecules that activate both B-cells for immunoglobulin secretion and cells of the phagocytic system.

Central to the immune response is recognition of a foreign entity (pathogen, nonself tissue graft, foreign proteins, and other macromolecules) by cells of the immune system, which, acting through of series of steps, culminates in the elimination of the interloper. Most important, because the repertoire of responses of the immune system revolve around recognition and destruction of invading microorganisms and foreign molecules, it is vital to the health of the host that these destructive responses be controlled and confined to nonself only, ensuring that these reactions do not spill over to the host's own cells.

Because B-cells and T-cells use distinct modes of recognition, one of our tasks will be not only to delineate these differences but also to explain why these differences exist. Regardless of whether the response is generated by B-cells or by T-cells, two features that distinguish the action of the adaptive (immune) system from the innate system of host defense are (*1*) its specificity toward particular organisms or foreign antigens and (*2*) its memory as evidenced by the capacity of specific cells to respond in an accelerated fashion to subsequent encounters with the same foreign agent. Such foreign agents are called antigens for *anti*body *gen*erator or immunogens.

Extracellular and Intracellular Antigens

The immune system must be capable of mounting a response to two broad classes of antigens. One class, the *extracellular* antigens, consists of foreign proteins, nucleic acids, polysaccharides, complex lipids, and even small molecules. These entities try to gain entrance into the body through the blood, gut, respiratory tract, and skin, being met at each of these sites by components of the immune system that attempt to restrict or prohibit their entrance. Of course, many microbes are members of the extracellular class of antigens.

The members of the second class, *intracellular* antigens, may be less obvious. One class of intracellular antigens are proteins synthesized within host cells by invading viruses. Another are proteins synthesized by cells that have undergone malignant transformation. Intracellular antigens thus pose a special problem for the host—unless a way can be found to express these proteins on the external surface of the plasma membrane of the involved cells, it would be possible for such infected or transformed cells to escape detection and destruction by the immune defenses. Fortunately, there is an elaborate recognition system that can "home in" on these cells, destroying them and thus depriving the virus of its access to the nucleic acid, replicating machinery of the host. This process of recognition is related to altered expression of cell surface characteristics, such as glycoproteins, synthesis of which is under the control of the invader.

Thymus and Bone Marrow Derived Lymphocytes are the Main Elements of the Immune System

A class of white blood cells, the lymphocytes, which mature in either the thymus gland or the bone marrow, mediates the functions of the immune system. In all, there are more than one trillion lymphocytes deployed throughout the blood and lymphoid tissues, guarding the vulnerable portals of entry to the host. Thymus-derived cells

(T-cells) are the effectors of cell-mediated immunity, whereas bone marrow derived lymphocytes (B-cells) mediate the humoral arm of immunity. But without the production of cytokines by T-cells, the synthesis of immunoglobulins by B-cells will be inadequate. Thus, it goes without saying that interaction between helper T-cells and B-cells is crucial to the mounting of an effective immunoglobulin mediated response to a foreign antigen.

The Clonal Selection Theory

The clonal selection theory lies at the heart of the specificity of the immune system. It posits that during embryologic development, each B-lymphocyte develops a specificity for a particular complementary chemical grouping, without ever having been in contact with that chemical group. Further, during this antigen independent phase, literally millions of different lymphocytes are produced, each with a distinctive antigen recognition specificity on its cell surface receptor. When, for example, a B-cell encounters its complementary chemical grouping on a foreign antigen, the cell then enters the antigen-dependent phase. During this phase, biochemical activation culminates in growth and division, creating a population or clone of *plasma cells* from the initial B-cell. Plasma cells are antibody-secreting cells endowed with enormous synthetic capacity and can produce as many as 2000 molecules per second for several days. Furthermore, clonal selection is not confined to B-cells only, because T-cells also function by clonal selection. Some of the activated cells will not secrete immunoglobulin during this first encounter, but, rather, will be conserved as *memory cells*, remaining poised in the lymphoid tissues to respond to a subsequent encounter with the same antigen.

T-cell Functions

Cell-mediated immunity (a function of T-cells), often in collaboration with a B-cell-mediated antibody response, mounts the most decisive cytotoxic action against intracellular invaders (viruses, mycobacteria, etc). In addition, T-helper-cells, by elaborating cytokines, activate and coordinate much of the B-cell-mediated synthesis of antibodies. Both these cytotoxic and helper functions require that T-cells make contact with their target cells. Most notably, T-cells can bind foreign antigen only when it is presented to T-cells in a macromolecular complex with cell surface glycoproteins (Figure 19.2) encoded by the *major histocompatibility complex* (MHC). The MHC is a group of genes that encode membrane surface proteins that constitute the system for presenting foreign antigens to T-cells. This requirement for "foreign antigen + cell surface glycoprotein" restricts T-cell action to host cells that are displaying either processed extracellular antigen or processed intracellular antigen. In both instances, the foreign protein is expressed on the cell surface so that T-cells can recognize them and take decisive action. Not surprisingly, cellular alterations that do not result in such overt expression are not noticed by these immune mechanisms.

Antigenic Determinants

A bacterial cell wall is composed of many macromolecules, each of which is likely to possess many antigenic determinants. Each antigenic determinant, also known as an *epitope*, will induce generation of an immunoglobulin specific for its unique chemical structure (electron cloud formation). Thus, for example, a bacterium with multiple epitopes will stimulate the formation of multiple different immunoglobulins by the host. Moreover, as the organism triggers a cell-mediated response, various T-cells will respond, arousing B-cells to become antibody-secreting plasma cells. Other specific cell-mediated reactions include cytolysis of infected or foreign cells and secretion of cytokines—molecules that act as signals to trigger and orchestrate various cell-mediated activities.

Antigen Processing And Presentation

Most antigens must be presented to T-cells, which coordinate much of the immune response of other cells, by a specialized group of cells called antigen-presenting cells (APC). What renders this process so closely regulated is that T-cells recognize antigen only when it is presented as an ensemble or complex with proteins on the surface of the antigen-presenting cells. These proteins are encoded by the MHC, which provides the crucial information that allows the immune system to dis-

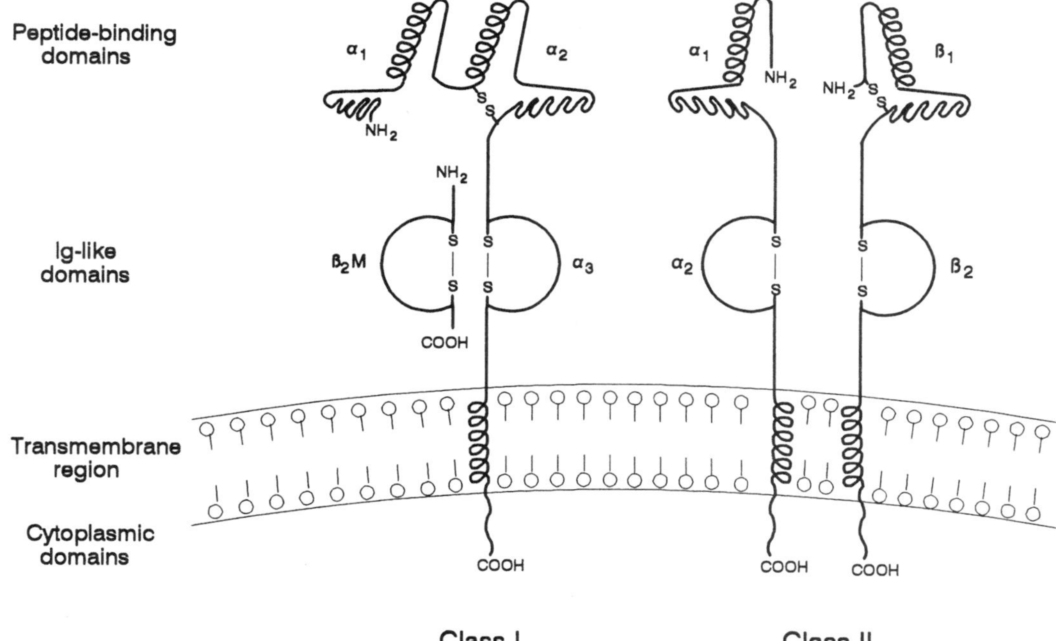

Figure 19.2. Structure of class I and II major histocompatibility complexes (MHC). Both classes of MHC belong to the family of glycoproteins, a group of macromolecules that primarily are found in the role of membrane intrinsic proteins, as shown. Class I molecules are dimeric, composed of an α-heavy chain in combination with a light chain, β2-microglobulin (B_2M), and are found in membranes of virtually all nucleated cells. Class II MHC also are dimeric, but are found only on B- and occasionally on T-lymphocytes. They are composed of two chains (α- and β-), both heavy and roughly equal in size. Reprinted with permission from Noe DA, Rock RC. Laboratory Medicine: the Selection and Interpretation of Clinical Laboratory Studies. Baltimore: Williams & Wilkins, 1994: 84.

tinguish between "nonself" and "self." Although it is true that these histocompatibility proteins came to prominence in the scientific and medical communities because of their role in preventing tissue transplantation from a nonidentical donor, it is now clear that these MHC-encoded proteins play a pivotal role in the defense against viruses and other invaders that take up residence within host cells. After all, it should be obvious that allotransplantation (transplants between different individuals of the same species) is a highly unusual event, whereas parasitism of host cells by viruses occurs frequently. Thus, when evolution found a way to deal with the common problem of intracellular infection, it also complicated the less frequent issue of allotransplantation.

Two classes of proteins (classes I and II) encoded by the MHC are prominently involved in the immune response. Class I molecules are ubiquitously distributed, being expressed on virtually all cells (because all nucleated cells are targets for viral invasion). Class II molecules have a much more limited distribution, being confined to those cells with antigen-presenting capability. These APCs include macrophages, which are specialized cells in skin, liver, and central nervous system, and B-lymphocytes.

Antigen presentation involves two separate phases (Figure 19.3): (*1*) *processing* of the antigen to break it down into smaller peptide fragments and (*2*) *presentation* of those fragments on the surface of the APC conjointly with a glycoprotein encoded by the MHC to form a "macromolecular ensemble" or complex recognized by the T-cell. It is noteworthy that whereas T-cells recognize only fragments of proteins in complex with MHC-coded proteins, B-cells recognize key groupings of the complete protein in its three-dimensional form.

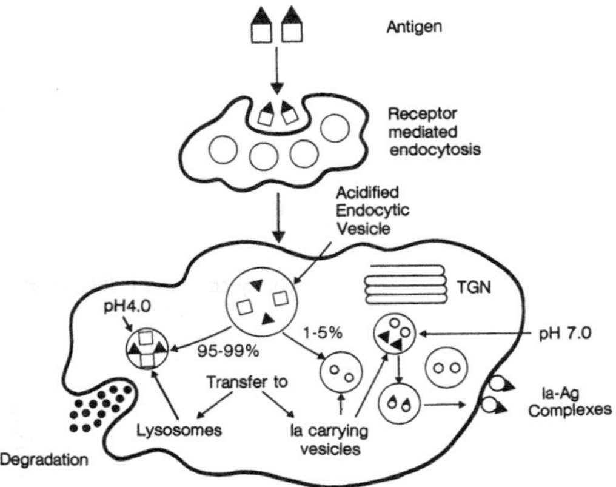

Figure 19.3. Presentation of antigen to T-cells. Antigen must be structurally altered to permit recognition and binding to Ia major histocompatibility complex (MHC). This "processing" may require either fragmentation or unfolding of tertiary structure to expose the "epitope," or binding site. The antigen is phagocytosed into acidified vesicles within the macrophage. Inside these vesicles, the antigen undergoes a degree of proteolysis; the majority of the altered material then is transferred to lysosomes for complete degradation. A smaller portion is conveyed to the trans-Golgi network (TGN) where it is complexed with MHC for cell surface presentation. Reprinted with permission from Lee GR, Bithell TC, Foerster J, et al. Wintrobe's Clinical Hematology. 9th ed. Baltimore: Williams & Wilkins, 1993: 438.

Differences in the Handling of Extracellular and Intracellular Antigens by Antigen-Presenting Cells

To repeat, APCs (also called accessory cells) display fragments of foreign antigens on their cell surface bound to glycoproteins encoded by the MHC. This requirement that foreign antigen be expressed in the context of the MHC encoded glycoprotein is called *MHC restriction*, and its effect is that T- cells will recognize antigen only when presented by these specialized host cells. Hence, T-cells do not recognize soluble antigens or antigens that are not cell bound. Above all, this precaution ensures that T-cells will not unleash their destructive power against cells that are not infected or have not undergone malignant transformation.

For extracellular antigen to be presented to T-cells, it first must be taken up by APCs, either by phagocytosis or receptor-mediated endocytosis, the foreign material being deposited in an *endosome*. Proteolysis of this material follows, with fragments of the antigen binding to class II MHC glycoproteins inside the APCs. Next, the vesicle fuses with the APC plasma membrane so that the antigen fragment-MHC complex is now displayed on the cell surface. In effect, this is phagocytosis in reverse, and uniquely confined to these cells in all of nature. Finally, helper T-cells (class II restricted) recognize the ensemble of protein fragment bound to a groove on the surface of the class II MHC glycoprotein.

Proteins synthesized within the APCs, so-called intracellular antigens, arise from virally directed proteins or from expression of tumor-related antigen, in the case of transformed cells. These antigens also undergo processing within the APC but are expressed in the context of class I MHC glycoproteins, rather than class II. Recognition, in this case, is by cytotoxic T-cells.

Shorn of all details, processing of intracellular antigens begins with the synthesis of viral proteins and class I MHC proteins. Viral proteins then enter a compartment where they undergo proteolysis, and are transported to the rough endoplasmic reticulum (E/R) where they bind to the peptide groove on newly synthesized class I MHC proteins. This peptide-MHC complex fuses with the plasma membrane, permitting expression of this complex on the cell surface, where it can be recognized by cytotoxic T-cells. Once the complex is recognized by cytotoxic T-cells, these T-cells destroy the cells that produced foreign antigen, thus blocking further dissemination of virus. What should be clear is that once a virus appropriates the cell's protein-synthesizing apparatus and causes it to make viral antigen, processing of that antigen by the APC will ensure that the virus will not go undetected. A comparable scenario and fate awaits a deviant cell that has undergone malignant transformation.

B-cells

B-lymphocytes, in their role in antibody production, mount the predominant response to microbial toxins, bacterial polysaccharide capsules, and even to some viral envelopes. A property shared by all of these antigens is that they are extracellular, being found either in the blood stream or the interstitial fluids. On the surface of each B-cell is a

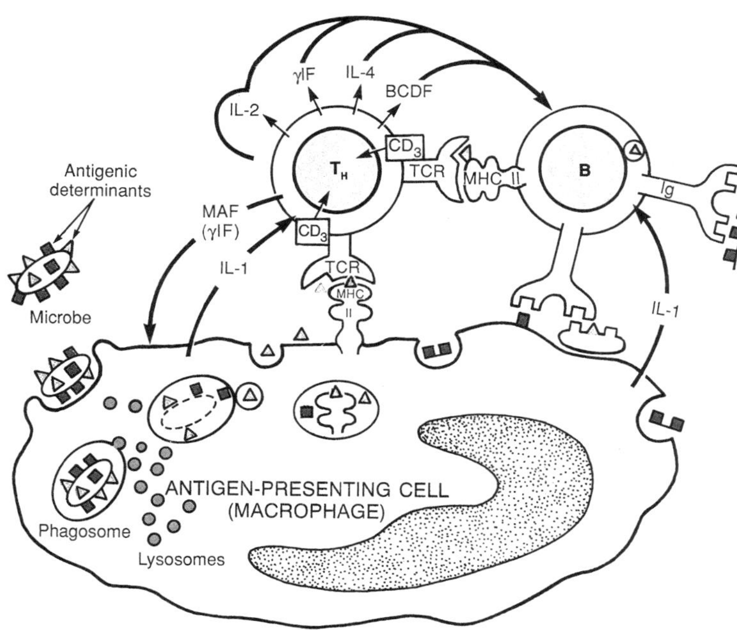

Figure 19.4. The interactions of antigen with macrophages, helper T-cells (T_H), and B-lymphocytes. Macrophagic phagocytosis of an opsonized microbe leads to eventual antigen-presentation on the macrophage cell surface. This presentation is as a complex with major histocompatibility complex (MHC) II glycoproteins and, therefore, can be made by both macrophages and B-lymphocytes. T_H possess specific receptor sites (TCR), which accept the antigen presented and activate the T_H. This activation leads to production of many species of cytokines with lymphocytic proliferation and differentiation. Reprinted with permission from Schaechter M, Eisenstein B, Medoff G, eds. Mechanisms of Microbial Disease. Baltimore: Williams & Wilkins, 1993: 123.

surface immunoglobulin (sIg), specific for the one antigenic determinant for which that B-cell makes complementary antibody, and receptors for fragments of the third component of complement. In all, each B-cell is endowed with about 10^5 sIg receptors, providing an ample number of targets to which antigen can bind. Once antigen binds, it triggers activation of that B-cell, causing expansion of that particular cell into a clone of cells all with the same antigenic specificity.

Unlike the requirement for T-cells to "see" antigen as a macromolecular ensemble with MHC glycoprotein, B-cells bind antigen to their cell surface immunoglobulins (Figure 19.4). These sIgs recognize antigenic determinants of proteins, polysaccharides, and glycolipids in their native three-dimensional state—not as fragments, as with T-cells. Antigen-specific activation of B-cells, triggered by binding of antigen to sIg, must be supplemented by cytokines to induce a complete response of the B-cell. Signal transduction is via the phosphatidyl inositol system generating IP_3 and DG. These two second messengers act in concert to push the B-cell into the G-1 phase of the cell cycle. IP_3, as in other systems, increases intracellular Ca^{++}, whereas DG activates protein kinase C, inducing phosphorylation of various proteins that are believed to function in cell growth and division. Full development of B-cells into plasma cells requires the action of B-cell stimulating factor (BSF1 or IL4), a cytokine produced by T-cells.

ANTIBODIES: STRUCTURE AND ROLE IN INFECTIOUS DISEASES

As we have emphasized, antibodies afford protection against many infectious agents through their ability to bind specifically to an antigenic determinant complementary in structure to that of the antibody. For one thing, this specific binding marks the microbe so that it becomes extremely susceptible to the phagocytic action of neutrophils. And for another, antibody binding functions as a stimulus to initiate the enzymatic reactions of the complement cascade.

Antibody Structure

Antibodies or immunoglobulins are Y-shaped glycoproteins composed of paired identical heavy and identical light chains joined by several disulfide

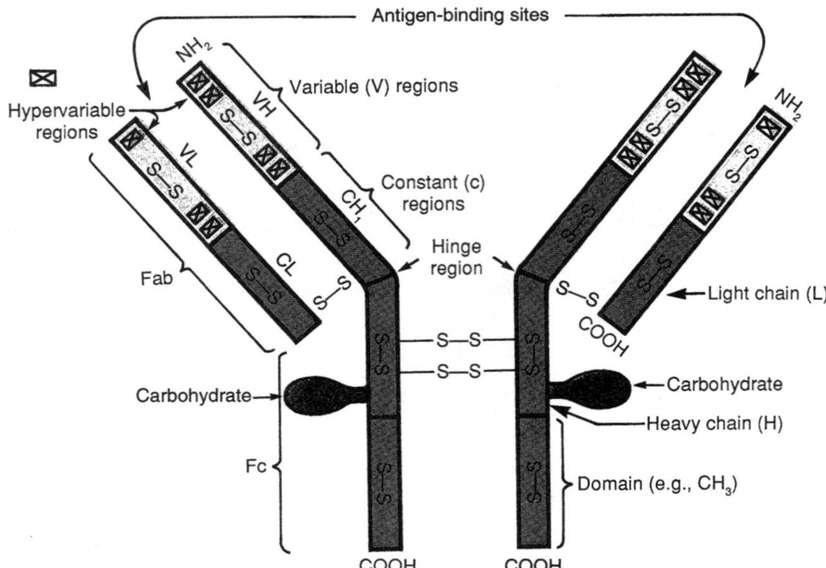

Figure 19.5. The tetrameric structure of IgG immunoglobulins. The overall configuration of the molecule is that of a Y-shape, with the antigen-binding regions contained at the tip of each arm, leading to the designation of bivalent. Digestion of the molecule with papain yields three fragments, of which two (Fab) are identical and bind antigen, and a third (Fc), which represents the tail of the original structure, comprises the effector, directing complement activation and Fc receptor interactions of the intact molecule. The heavy (H) monomer units are the determinants of the Ig class to which the molecule belongs, whereas only two types of light chains (L) are known, kappa and lambda, and any given molecule possesses a pair of one or the other but never both. Note the importance and critical locations of the disulfide bonds in the structure. Reprinted with permission from Schaechter M, Eisenstein B, Medoff G, et al. Mechanisms of Microbial Disease. Baltimore: Williams & Wilkins, 1993: 125.

bonds (Figure 19.5). Each heavy and light chain are further subdivided into domains: (*1*) a *variable* domain, located near the amino terminus, that possesses the complementary structure necessary for antigen binding, and (*2*) a *constant* domain, located near the carboxy terminus, that binds to complement triggering activation of that system or binds to cell surface receptors on monocytes and macrophages.

Each light chain has a mass of about 24 kD (approximately 220 amino acids), whereas each heavy chain is at least twice as large (50–70 kD, about 445 amino acids). X-ray diffraction has demonstrated a series of repeating, homologous structural motifs found in both light and heavy chains. These globular structures are called *immunoglobulin domains* and are comprised of two β-pleated sheets and several antiparallel peptide chains (Figure 19.5).

Located within the variable regions of both the light and heavy chains are discrete regions that possess a unique amino acid sequence and which have been shown to be responsible for binding of a particular antigen. These highly divergent sequences are termed *hypervariable regions* or *complementarity determining regions* (CDRs), because when these light and heavy chain regions assume a three-dimensional shape they become the antigen-binding domain of the immunoglobulin. Just as the active site of an enzyme is made up of amino acids that fold to create a unique three-dimensional structure—one capable of binding stereospecifically to the substrate—the CDR also is a three-dimensional domain that stereospecifically binds antigen.

There is, however, one crucial difference between how these three-dimensional structures are created with enzymes and with immunoglobulins. In the case of enzymes, once an active site structure is achieved, as for example with cytochrome c, the serine proteases and a host of other enzymes, the amino acids making up the active site, show little, if any, variation. But, the scaffolding outside of this delineated region of the enzyme that brings these amino acids constituting the active site together may be permitted significant variability so long as those amino acids making up the active site are able to fold into the required structure. This is not the case with immunoglobulins: the scaffolding or framework of these molecules is highly conserved to provide a stable structure on which to impose a unique antigen-binding site. In short, the active site of an enzyme is conserved, whereas with immunoglobulin the framework is conserved. With antibody, it is the antigen-binding site (CDR) that is varied. Structural diversity of the CDR provides the enormous biologic flexibility for binding to all possible antigens required of immunoglobulins as a class.

More About Antibody Structure

Along each light and heavy chain, hypervariable segments are about only 10 amino acids long, emphasizing that the point of contact is limited relative to the overall size of the foreign macromolecule. Perhaps somewhat unexpected is the finding by x-ray diffraction that the folded shape of each CDR in a wide range of immunoglobulins is rather similar, indicating that specificity for binding to a particular epitope is believed to be a function of the two-dimensional surface of the CDR, rather that its three-dimensional shape.

In addition to the parallel orientation of the light and heavy chains, as seen in Figure 19.5, the two heavy chains also constitute the stem of the Y-shaped immunoglobulin. Consider the region of the heavy chain that connects the stem of the Y with the antigen-binding arms. Predictably, this is called the *hinge region* and, because there are several proline residues in this region, the chain is prevented from folding into a higher ordered structure. The result is that the hinge region manifests greater flexibility than elsewhere in the immunoglobulin molecule, permitting the entire immunoglobulin to achieve greater variability in shape than expected for a Y. For example, if the arms of the Y fan out more perpendicularly, the overall shape of the immunoglobulin now becomes T-like. This change in shape is not merely a curiosity, because a T-shaped immunoglobin furnishes a greater surface for contact between antibody and antigen than the native Y.

Antibody Classes

There are five classes of immunoglobulins: IgG, IgA, IgM, IgD, and IgE, which are distinguished predominantly by the heavy-chain type and number of subunits per molecule (Table 19.3). There are nine different heavy chain types which endow each complete immunoglobulin with different

Table 19.3. Immunoglobulin Classes

	IGg	IgM	IgA	IgD	IgE
Chains:					
heavy	γ	μ	α	δ	ϵ
light	k, λ	k, λ	k, λ	k, λ	k, λ
Monomers	1	5	1–3	1	1
Molecular weight	150,000	900,000	160–500,000	180,000	200,000
Serum concentration					
Mean (mg/dl)	1,200	150	300	3	0.01
% Total	70–80	5–10	10–15	<1	<0.01
First Ab response	−	+	−	−	−
Secondary Ab response	+	−	−	−	−
Crosses placenta	+	−	−	−	−
Complement activation:					
classic	+	+	−	−	−
alternate	−	−	+	±	±
Opsonizes	+	+	−	−	−
Viral neutralizing	+	+	−	−	−

properties. Variation of light chain is limited to just two classes, kappa and lambda. Nevertheless, all antibody classes display the same overall Y-shaped subunit structure.

IgG

Although IgG is the predominant immunoglobulin found in the blood, constituting almost 70% of serum immunoglobulins, a substantial amount of IgG also is found in the extravascular spaces. The generic Y-shaped structure considered above most faithfully represents the composition of IgG. It is important to note that IgG is the major immunoglobulin elaborated after a repeat exposure to an antigen, whereas IgM (see following text) is the first antibody manufactured by the body in response to a new antigen.

Because IgG can cross the placenta, the fetus is passively supplied with antibody. This confers a potent, but not absolute, defense against infection in utero and during the neonatal period. As seen above, an important role for IgG is coating of bacteria to opsonize the microbes, thereby preparing them for ingestion by neutrophils. Another important function of IgG is to activate the complement cascade, triggering complement to bring about cytolysis of invading organisms. Of course, IgG also is capable of binding to bacterial toxins, thereby neutralizing them.

IgM

IgM is the largest of the immunoglobulins with a mass of 900 kD. Because of its large size, IgM is sometimes referred to as macroglobulin. It is the first antibody produced by the fetus in utero, with production beginning at about 5 months of gestation, and continuing in the neonate. Because of its large size, IgM does not cross the placenta. In all age groups, it also is the first antibody produced as a consequence of primary exposure to an antigen.

IgM is a pentameric macromolecule, made up of five Y-shaped subunits (each one like that found in IgG) joined together by disulfide bonds linking the stem regions of the Y and by a connecting piece called the *J chain*. Although there are 10 antigen-binding regions to the pentameric IgM molecule, space constraints lower the number of antigen binding sites from the expected 10 to the observed five. IgM is an efficient activator of the complement system, giving it an important effector role in safeguarding the host.

IgA

IgA exerts its protective action as part of the extravascular secretions found in saliva, tears, mucus on respiratory and gastrointestinal surfaces, prostatic fluid, and human milk. In these locations, it plays the dominant role in local immune defense when exposed tissue sites encounter invaders and foreign antigens. It does so by blocking binding of the microbe to a mucosal surface. Undeniably, its presence in colostrum and breast milk affords the neonate with a substantial, maternally transferred immune repertoire. Like IgM, IgA is a polymer of Y-shaped units, but in the case of IgA, only two to three units are joined by a J chain to form the functional IgA moiety. Unlike IgG and IgM, IgA cannot activate the complement cascade. This is to be expected because complement is localized to the circulatory system, whereas IgA, as we have seen, predominates in the extravascular spaces.

IgE

IgE carries out the major role of immunoglobulin in defense against helminthic parasites. IgE also is found in association with mast cells and basophils, implicating it in allergic reactions. When antigen binds to IgE bound to mast cells and basophils, this triggers release of vasoactive amines that are responsible for the manifestations of the allergic reaction.

Antibody Genes and the Generation of Diversity

Up to now we have alluded to the fact that all the antigen-binding specificities are present in the various clones of B-cells, before any of those B-cells have actually encountered the antigen for which they are specific. Even more startling, we have noted that this diversity runs in the tens of millions of antigen specificities, a number far in excess of the number of genes in the human genome, which contains in the neighborhood of 10^5 different genes. Of course, as we have noted in Chapter 1, if "genes in pieces" make "proteins in pieces," it should be possible to beget an enormous repertoire of different antibodies by varying the pieces used and the manner in which they are combined. This prediction, that DNA rearrangements would lead to antibody diversity, was first made by Dreyer and Bennett and was confirmed experimentally by Tonegawa.

Recall that antibodies are made up of a constant region joined to a variable region. Within the variable region is the hypervariable or complementarity-determining region—the sites where antigen binds to antibody. Because the constant regions carry out effector functions, such as binding to complement, there is little need for variation in the amino acid sequence. And, indeed, that is what is found. Constant regions are remarkably invariant in their amino acid sequences. This is not so in the variable regions because the diversity so important to antibody recognition arises there.

Two Gene Segments Encode the V-region of Light Chains

Analysis of DNA sequences encoding the variable region (V-region) of light chains has shown that two nucleotide segments, a long *V gene* and a short joining or *J gene segment*, together provide the information to synthesize the L chain. In the antibody-synthesizing B-cell, the sequence of L chain genes is V-J-intron-C (Figure 19.6). Transcription of this sequence into RNA is followed by excision of the intron to generate the actual mRNA that encodes the L chain.

Three Gene Segments Encode the V-Region of Heavy Chains

Because heavy chains are considerably larger than light chains, it is not surprising that their synthesis is somewhat more complicated. In addition to V and J genes, a third gene sequence, called D for diversity, participates in encoding heavy chains. Site-specific recombinations, catalyzed by recombinases, permit the joining of 1 of the 20 D_H gene segments to any of several hundred V_H segments and any of the 4 J_H segments.

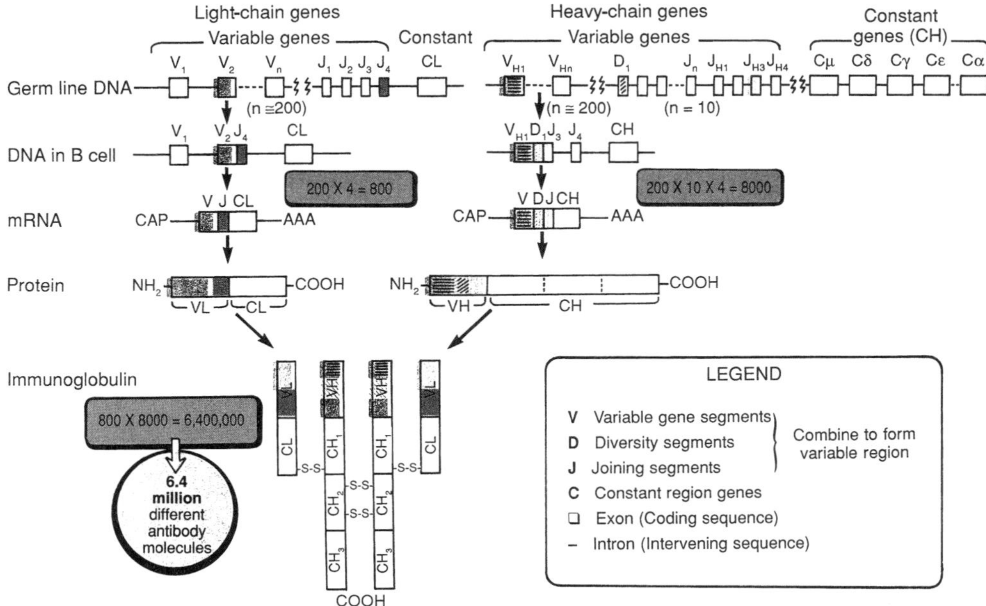

Figure 19.6. The genetic basis of immunologic diversity. Within the antibody-synthesizing B-cell, the sequence of L chain genes is V-J-intron-C whereas that of the heavy chain genes includes a D (diversity) segment. Through spontaneous rearrangements within B-cell DNA, even the relatively limited repertoire of the L chain genes can produce 800 possible mRNA species, whereas that of the H chain genes can account for 10 times that number. Through random association of L and H protein chains, there is potential for more than 6 million possible antibody molecules. Reprinted with permission from Schaechter M, Eisesnstein B, Medoff G, et al. Mechanisms of Microbial Disease. Baltimore: Williams & Wilkins, 1993: 133.

Mechanisms Used to Create Antibody Diversity

Let's now examine the ways in which antibody diversity can be achieved. First, there are hundreds of V_H and V_L gene segments that can combine (in the case of heavy chain) with 1 of the 20 D gene segments and with 1 of the J segments. Second, these various segments can combine in many different ways, generating an estimated 10,000 different heavy chains and 1000 kappa light chains. This type of diversity generated by various V, J, and D combinations is referred to as *recombinatorial diversity*. Third, random combination of these 10,000 heavy chains and 1,000 light chains can produce 10^7 different antibodies. Such diversity is referred to as *combinatorial diversity*. Fourth, imprecise joining of the various gene segments, although creating the likelihood that some non-sense and termination codons will occur, nevertheless creates about a 10-fold increase in diversity. This *junctional* diversity thus increases the diversity to 10^8 unique antigen-binding sites. Fifth, and last, *somatic mutations* occur with high frequency in the hypervariable regions, still further enriching the pool of antigen-binding sites.

Antibodies Serve to Protect Against Infectious Agents in Several Ways

Recall that the Y- or T-shaped antibody molecule provides two different functional domains. Located in the hypervariable domain of the arms of the Y (or top of the T) are the antigen-binding sites, whereas located at the stem is the site that binds to receptors on macrophages or activates complement. By and large, specific binding of an antibody or cell is a prelude to triggering a biochemical response or preventing attachment of the microbe to a host cell. Thus, as we saw when discussing IgA, *blocking* attachment of microbes to a host cell is an important protective function because attachment precedes entry. Such a blocking function is not confined to IgA only: it is manifested by IgG and IgM as well. In each instance, the antibody binds to a bacterial adhesin, preventing the microbe from setting up a beachhead from which to cause further damage.

Another class of antibodies *neutralizes* microbial toxins like those produced by C. tetani and C. diptheriae by preventing their attachment to susceptible target cells. Yet another function of antibody is to *opsonize* microbes by binding to the microbial surface, thereby making them a prime target for ingestion by phagocytic cells. In fact, microbes are made most conspicuous to phagocytes when they are coated with IgG and the complement components derived from C3. Finally, activation of the complement cascade by antibody leads to the generation of a bactericidal membrane lytic complex.

THE COMPLEMENT SYSTEM

Complement is a complicated system of plasma and membrane associated proteins (about 30 in total) that plays a pivotal role in mediating three interlocking functions: (*1*) opsonizing invading microbes, (*2*) lysis of invading microbes or cells infected with these microbes, and (*3*) spurring on the inflammatory response. These three functions all are involved in mounting a *complementary defensive response* (hence, the term complement) to that mounted by the immune system.

From a biochemical perspective, the complement system is very similar to the coagulation cascade, rivaling, and even exceeding, it in complexity. The complement cascade proceeds by a series of sequential proteolytic events, involving serine proteases, in which a peptide fragment is cleaved from a precursor (usually a zymogen) liberating a small fragment designated as "a" and a larger fragment designated as "b." Typically, the smaller piece is cast off into the blood stream where it acts as a mediator of cell function (anaphylatoxin), whereas the larger piece binds to the microbial surface that triggered activation and is itself the target of destruction.

Fragments such as C3a and C5a act as chemoattractants for phagocytic cells and increase vascular permeability; the effect on vessels further enhances the inflammatory response. The larger fragments participate in the mainstream of the cascade of sequential proteolytic reactions that culminates in formation of the lytic membrane attack complex.

Underscoring the importance of the complement system, and again in analogy to the coagulation cascade, there are two pathways by which the complement cascade can proceed. This kind of redundancy ensures that activation of the cascade will occur either by activation by antibody (classic pathway) or by bacterial cell wall components (alternative pathway). Although the alternative pathway is not as efficient as the classic, it is triggered much more readily because it does not require the presence of preformed specific antibody to the invader. Moreover, there is abundant evidence that the alternative pathway always is poised to respond to microbial invasion as a consequence of small amounts of active materials always being formed in the blood. To understand the differences between the classic and alternative pathways, and how they engage in protective interplay, we will consider each pathway in greater detail.

Classic Pathway

Both the classic and alternative pathways of complement activation converge to a common point: activation of plasma protein C3 (Figure 19.7). Hence, the differences between the two pathways of activation relate to what proteins participate in C3 activation, because once C3 is activated, the two paths proceed along the same route. Complement activation by the classic pathways begins when C1 binds to the effector (Fc) portion of an IgG or IgM class antibody bound to its antigen (microbe). Once antibody binds to C1q, one of three proteins constituting the C1 complex, a conformational change ensues which converts the serine protease proenzyme C1s to its active form. Active C1s next acts on C4, forming the major fragment C4b, which also binds to the growing immune complex on the surface of the microbe through the agency of a highly reactive thiolester bond. (Unfortunately, the order in which the proteins involved in the complement cascade were discovered does not coincide with the order in which they act in the host, accounting for the apparent anomaly that C4 comes directly after C1). Next C2 binds to C4b, where it is cleaved into C2b, which dissociates, and C2a, which remains bound to C4b. This *C4bC2a complex* is the required *C3 convertase* of the classic pathway. Now many molecules of C3 are converted to C3b, which bind to the surface of the immune complex, and C3a, which enters the blood stream. *C4bC2aC3b* is the next active enzyme of the cascade acting as the *C5 convertase* of the classic pathway. Additional molecules of C3b act as opsonins, binding directly to the unwelcome microorganism and thus marking it for engulfment by phagocytic cells.

Returning to the C5 convertase, formation of the small mediator fragment C5a, which diffuses into the milieu, is accompanied by formation of the major fragment C5b, which serves as the platform on which to assemble the *membrane attack complex*. This lytic membrane attack complex is assembled by sequential addition of plasma proteins C6 through C9. Once assembled, the C5b-C9 complex inserts into the hydrophobic phospholipid bilayer of the cell membranes, creating a leaky tubular pore which permits unregulated entry of water and ions into the cell, causing it to swell and burst.

Alternative Pathway

As indicated above, the alternative pathway does not depend on interaction with antibody and thus functions independently of the immune system. Although it is more primitive than the classic pathway, it shares its goal of activation of C3 with the classic pathway. C3 contains a reactive thiolester bond that is held in a shrouded or unreactive conformation. However, when C3 is activated to C3b, this thiolester bond can nucleophilically attack proteins, cell membranes, or water. Evidence exists that there is a constant formation of a low level of active C3b, perhaps through the action of plasma trypsin, plasmin, thrombin, and elastin, and, of course, by the C3 convertase of the classic pathway. This constant formation of C3 often is referred to as idling or "tick-over." In any event, this low level of active C3b can bind to bacteria and other activating sites. Three plasma proteins unique to the alternative pathway now come into play: factors B and D, and properdin. C3b bound to a microbe binds factor B to form C3bB. Factor D, a serine protease, now carries out a cleavage of factor B, forming Bb. The combined product, *C3bBb*, is the *C3 convertase* of the alternative pathway, but differs from the C3 convertase of the classic pathway (C4b2b) because it requires another plasma protein, *properdin*, to stabilize it (Figure 19.7).

As occurs with the classic pathway, binding of

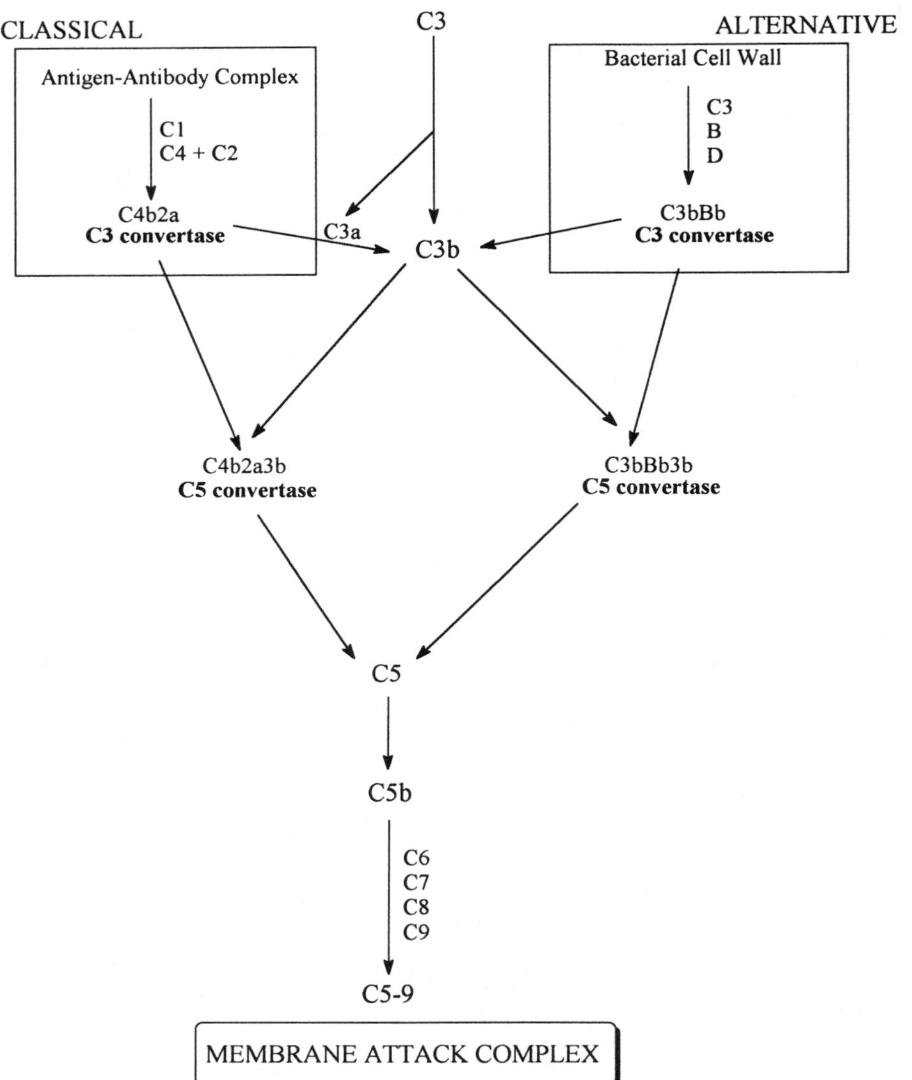

Figure 19.7. Complement activation pathways. In a fashion roughly similar to the coagulation cascade, there are two separate pathways for complement activation, called the classic and the alternative, both merging into a common pathway before becoming active in a functional sense. Each of the two converge at the point of C3 activation; the differences exist in the means by which this is achieved. Whatever the trigger, in both pathways, there is a combination of molecular fragments that combine to form C3 convertase activity (note this is different in each case) which then acts to form a C3b molecule. This C3b is, in turn, used for combination with the C3 convertases to produce C5 convertase activity in a common pathway, based upon production of a C5 fragment. The latter undergoes serial changes to form the so-called membrane attack complex, which is used to assist in lysis of the microbial membrane.

C3b to C3 convertase, (in the case of the alternative pathway C3bBb) yields $(C3b)_2Bb$, the alternative pathway C5 convertase. Once C5 convertase is formed, the subsequent reactions leading to the assembly of the membrane attack complex are identical to those of the classic pathway.

Control of the Complement Cascade

Obviously, the complement system can unleash considerable destructive power. It, therefore, is essential that this series of reactions be tightly regulated, confining the destructive potential to invaders and not against the host. Such regulation is not restricted to limiting initiation of the cascade, but also includes restraints on the action of the membrane attack complex. Because the classic and alternative pathways have different key participants, it is to be anticipated that different controls would be exerted on each. Nonetheless, the general theme is an inhibitory protein binding to a serine protease of the cascade to prevent it from expressing its enzymatic activity.

Control of the Classic Pathway

Because the classic pathway begins with activation of C1, which unleashes its proteolytic activity, inhibition of C1 esterase is an expected site of regulation. In fact, such is the case with C1 being inhibited by *C1 inhibitor*, a serine protease inhibitor that forms a complex with C1s or C1r, preventing expression of its enzymatic activity. Because C1 inhibitor is present in blood at seven times the molar concentration of C1, there is more than ample inhibitor to hold the activity of C1 in check. Of note, it is only when C1 binds to the antigen-antibody complex that the action of C1 inhibitor is nullified.

Recall that C3 convertase is one of the pivotal enzymatic activities formed during the complement cascade. Activity of classic C3 convertase (C4b2a) is inhibited by several proteins including C4 binding protein (C4bp), type 1 complement receptor (CR1), and decay accelerating factor. C4 binding protein, a plasma glycoprotein, and CR1, a membrane protein, act essentially in the same way by binding to C4b in a manner that prevents the binding of C2b, thereby preventing formation of C3 convertase. But C4bp and CR1 act in yet another way, enhancing the action of factor I to cleave C4b into two other fragments, both of which are thus rendered unable to participate in generating C3 convertase activity.

There is yet another protein that inhibits formation of C3 convertase—decay accelerating factor. Decay accelerating factor is one of a family of phosphatidylinositol anchored membrane proteins widely distributed on peripheral blood cells, vascular endothelium, and mucosal epithelium. It too binds to C4b, competitively inhibiting binding of C2 and thus preventing formation of C3 convertase.

Control of the Alternative Pathway

Because the alternative pathway is activated by nonspecific factors, it is vital that there be mechanisms to restrain gratuitous activation with unintended damage to host cells or to set off an inflammatory response by a false alarm. One inhibitor, factor H, acts as a competitive inhibitor of Bb binding to C3b, thereby preventing formation of C3 convertase. As might be expected, CR1 and decay accelerating factor also function in the alternative pathway to prevent formation of C3 convertase; but, in the case of the alternative pathway, these membrane proteins inhibit binding of factor B to C3b.

Factor I catalyzes a limited proteolysis of C3b forming an *inactive C3b (iC3b)* that remains on the cell membrane. Whereas inactive C3b cannot join with Bb to form C3 convertase, iC3b does have important chemotactic properties.

How Do Complement Proteins Distinguish Between Host and Foreign Surfaces?

Because C3 and C4 form covalent bonds with any susceptible groups on cell membranes to create a beachhead for the progression of the complement reactions, it follows that host as well as foreign surfaces would be targets. Of course, equivalent susceptibility to the reactions of the complement cascade by both host and foreign surfaces poses a danger to the host. Because the complement system, however, does not cause indiscriminate damage to the host, there must be recognition phenomena which guide the system to foreign surfaces and away from host cells.

Table 19.4. Bacterial Pathogens

ORGANISM	STRUCTURE AND GRAM REACTION	PATHOGENESIS	VIRULENCE FACTORS AND MECHANISMS OF RESISTANCE TO HOST DEFENSES	ORGANS AFFECTED AND DISEASES CAUSED
Staphylococci	Gram (+) cocci	Hardy, heat resistant. Staph coexist with humans in their environment. Transmission via *fomites*. Enter through breach in skin or mucous membranes.	*Enzymes* (catalase, coagulase, hyaluronidase, β-lactamase) *Toxins*—leukocidin, hemolysins, enterotoxins *Capsule* avoids phagocytosis in absence of specific antibodies Protein A—inhibits opsonization	Local abscess (eg, boils, osteomyelitis) Pneumonia Toxic shock syndrome Food poisoning (toxin is heat stable)—vomiting and diarrhea
Streptococci	Gram (+) cocci	Breach in skin, mucous membranes, or inhalation. Decrease in nonadaptive and adaptive resistance predisposes to infectious disease by previous colonizers.	Capsule to subvert phagocytosis. Enzymes—activate fibrinolysis, hyaluronidase, DNAses, lipoproteinase. Streptolysin—triggers discharge of lysosomal enzymes into cytoplasm → cell death.	Skin—impetigo, erysipelas Mucous membranes—pharyngitis, tonsillitis Heart—endocarditis Septicemia Postinfectious consequences—rheumatic fever acute glomerulonephritis.
Streptococcus pneumoniae	Gram (+) cocci	S. pneumonia can cause pneumonia in individuals who are debilitated or who are immunocompromised Inhalation	Capsule to defeat phagocytosis	Pneumonia—cough, fever, chills, pleural pain Otitis Meningitis
Neisseriae Gonococcus and Meningococcus	Gram (−) cocci	Gonococcus—sexual contact. Meningococcus—respiratory transmission. Dissemination is rare but occurs from blood stream (via lymph) to cerebrospinal fluid (CSF).	*Gonococcus*—pili to adhere to mucosal surfaces. Do not produce exotoxins. Protease splits IgA. *Meningococcus*—capsules resists phagocytosis—they can proliferate in blood stream. Do not produce exotoxins. Complement important in defense against both neisseria species.	Gonococcus—GU tract—gonorrhea. Meningococcus—meningitis and septicemia.
Haemophilus influenza	Gram (−) rod	Respiratory tract multiplication and spread to blood and CSF. Obligate human parasite.	Thick capsule resists phagocytosis. Endotoxins and adhesins.	Meningitis in young children. Pneumonia at all ages.
Escherichia coli	Gram (−) rod LPS is a component of outer membrane.	Contaminated foods.	Adherence factors Enterotoxins Antiphagocytic capsule Iron-binding siderophores	Enteric infections—toxin-induced diarrhea Neonatal meningitis Cystitis and pyelonephritis in women.
Shigella sonnei	Gram (−) rod	Contaminated food or water.	Shiga invade intestinal cells causing ulceration and severe diarrhea. Exotoxin produced, inactivates 60S ribosomal subunit.	Severe diarrhea often with blood and mucous, cramps, fever, significant fluid loss.
Salmonella	Gram (−) rod	Contaminated food or water—fecal-to-oral transmission. Poultry and eggs may be contaminated.	Cholera-like enterotoxin causes some cases of diarrhea. Salmonella able to grow in macrophages.	Enteric fevers—malaise, headache, diarrhea, stepladder fever pattern, rose spots, bradycardia for degree of fever, splenomegaly Septicemia—fever, rigors, local abscesses

Vibrio cholerae	Gram (−) rod with flagellum	Contaminated food or water—fecal-to-oral transmission.	Powerful enterotoxin. Vibrio remain attached to mucosa of intestine.	Gastroenteritis—fever, nausea, vomiting, diarrhea, abdominal pain. Diarrhea with loss of as much as 10–15 L./d.—stool is gray without blood, pus or fecal odor. Risk of death from dehydration.
Brucella	Gram (−) rod	Enters via skin or conjunctiva. Travels to lymph nodes and then into blood stream lodging in reticuloendothelial system (RES).	Able to survive inside monocyte.	Undulant fever—malaise, headache, arthralgia, sweating, intermittent fever, cervical and axillary lymphadenopathy, hepatosplenomegaly.
Yersinia pestis	Gram (−) rod	Transmission by fleas biting infected rodents.	Antiphagocytic capsule	Plague—one of the great killers of all time. Fever, muscular pains, prostration, pneumonia, septicemia. Inguinal adenopathy called bubo.
Francisella tularenis	Gram (−) rod	Transmission via deer fly or wood tick		Tularemia—fever, headache, nausea, localized lesion at site of bite. Regional adenopathy.
Bordetella pertussis	Gram (−) rod	Respiratory route	*Toxin* can activate α subunit of G proteins—inhibits phagocyte chemotaxis and oxygen dependent killing. Adhesions bind to respiratory cilia.	Whooping cough—vaccine available. Paroxsymal coughing with high pitched "whoop" on inspiration. Usually in children <2 years of age. ↑ lymphocytes
Legionella pneumophilia	Gram (−) rod	Respiratory route from contaminated water (eg, air conditioner cooling towers, shower heads). Contaminated dust	Protease, hemolysis Organism finds haven in macrophages. Toxins undermine neutrophils.	Pneumonia—pleurisy, patients toxic, little sputum
Bacillus anthracis	Gram (+) spore former	Skin infected by contact with animal hides or by inhalation of spores.	Exotoxin is an adenylate cyclase that ↑ cAMP levels in polys inhibiting phagocytic action.	Anthrax—localized red papule with blackish center. Regional adenopathy, fever, systemic symptoms occasionally.
Clostridium tetani	Gram (+) rod; spore former	Break in skin	Not invasive. Produces a powerful neurotoxin that prevents release of central nervous system inhibitory neurotransmitters, glycine, and GABA → spastic paralysis	Tetanus—spasms of jaw muscles dysphagia, muscle stiffness → spasm
Clostridium botulinum	Gram (+) rod	Contaminated food—spores are heat-resistant	Potent neurotoxin block release of ACh → flaccid paralysis	Botulism—cranial nerve paralysis, diplopia, dysphagia, dysphonia, respiratory muscle weakness → paralysis Deadly food borne toxin
Corynebacterium diphtheriae	Gram (+) rods	Respiratory route	Potent toxin inhibits EF-2 a factor in protein synthesis.	Diphtheria—grey pseudomembrane in throat, sore throat myocarditis
Listeria monocytogenes	Gram (+) motile diphtheroid	Opportunistic organism	Hemolysin Grows intracellulary in monocytes/ macrophage	Meningitis

(continued)

Table 19.4. *(continued)*

ORGANISM	STRUCTURE AND GRAM REACTION	PATHOGENESIS	VIRULENCE FACTORS AND MECHANISMS OF RESISTANCE TO HOST DEFENSES	CLINICAL MANIFESTATIONS
Mycobacterium tuberculosis	Acid Fast—high lipid content in cell wall—thin rods	Inhalation droplets containing the bacilli	Able to survive and grow intracellularly—resists digestion. Inhibits lysosomes	Pneumonic form Miliary Peritoneal Menigitis
Treponema pallidum	Gram (−) spirochete	Sexual contact	Antiphagocytic capsule	Syphilis—early infectious stage (chancre or ulcer) Secondary—rash, condylomas, papules, osteitis, brain and eyes Tertiary—gummas of skin and bones, aortitis, aneurysms
Borrelia burgdorferi	Gram (−) spirochete	Bite of tick—deer major reservoir.	Undefined	Lyme disease—three stages: (1) erythema chronicum migrans (2) myocarditis, heart block, aseptic menigitis (3) joint pain and arthritis, synovitis
Mycoplasma pneumoniae	Pleomorphic—they have no cell wall	Respiratory route from other infected humans	Tissue toxins hamper normal respiratory ciliary function	Pneumonia with skin rash, otitis media
Rickettsia rickettsii	Gram (−) obligate intracellular parasites	Tick bite—dogs are an important reservoir.	Trophic for vascular endothelia where organisms proliferate. Enter cells by phagocytosis.	Rocky Mt. Spotted Fever—aches, chills, fever, headache, red macular rash
Rickettsia prowazekii	Gram (−) obligate intracellular parasite	Human louse is vector for epidemic typhus. Believed to have caused millions of deaths in war time.	Proliferate in endothelial cells of blood vessels.	Typhus fever—headache, chills fever, maculopapular rash. Serologic tests (+) Also called epidemic typhus.
Chlamydia trachomatis	Gram (−) obligate intracellular parasite	Eye infected by direct contact with fingers or contaminated clothing or towels.	Easy entry into epithelial cells. Inhibit fusion of lysosomes with phagocytic vesicles.	Trachoma Inclusion conjunctivitis Lymphogranuloma venereum

Protecting host cells from indiscriminate damage depends on host cell membranes having complement regulatory proteins, which bind to the membrane. A prime example of such a protein is factor H. Recall that factor H both inhibits formation of alternative pathway C3 convertase as well as hastens its breakdown. Host cells so endowed, therefore, are much more resistant to the initiation of the cascade than are microbial cells that do not possess factor H in their membranes.

Table 19.5. Adherence Mechanisms Used by Various Microbes

Fimbriae
E. Coli, Salmonella, Shigella, Klebsiella, Proteus, Yersinia, Pseudomonas, Bordetella, Hemophilus influenza, Neisseria
Lectins
Chlamydia, Vibrio cholera
Surface Proteins or Projections
Poliovirus, Rhinovirus, Coxsackievirus, Adenovirus, Vesicular stomatitis virus, Mycoplasma pneumoniae, Neisseria gonorrheae

FACTORS THAT ACCOUNT FOR THE ABILITY OF MICROORGANISMS TO CAUSE DISEASE

Portals of Entry of Pathogens

There are five main portals of entry of potential pathogens into the body: respiratory tract, skin and mucous membranes, gastrointestinal tract, genitourinary tract, and blood. It follows from these entry sites that the predominant clinical manifestations will be determined by the site of entry and eventual sites where the organism invades and multiplies within the host. Respiratory pathogens enter through the nose and mouth; scratches and punctures enable organisms to enter through the skin and mucous membranes; several agents capable of causing food poisoning and systemic illness, including hepatitis, enter through the gastrointestinal tract; and sexually transmitted diseases gain a foothold in the genitourinary system. Blood-borne diseases can result either from inoculation of the blood by the bite of an insect or through blood products or contaminated needles. Organisms that gain entrance into the body through these diverse sites and the resultant diseases are listed in Table 19.4.

For bacteria to establish entry into the mucosal cells in the gastrointestinal, genitourinary, and respiratory tracts, they must take advantage of macromolecules and cell surface elaborations that enhance adherence to the various host cells. Many of these adhesins are specifically adapted to interact with site-specific receptors on host cells (Table 19.5). Many microbes are endowed with biochemical mechanisms that enable them to elude one or more of the protective or defensive actions of the host including phagocytic action, the complement system, and B- and T-cell function. A second means by which microbes attempt to defeat the defensive actions of the host is by elaboration of toxins (Table 19.6). A third category involves microbial strategies that interfere with the body's attempt to localize and contain the infection. These are listed in Table 19.4, but broadly involve inhibiting either phagocytic cells, the complement system, or the immune system. We will examine these microbial strategies apart from the countermeasures taken by the host, recognizing that there is a constant interplay between the host and parasite as each struggles to get the upper hand.

Attachment of Microbes to Host Mucosal Surfaces

The first step in the colonization of the host requires that the microbe attach to a particular niche on the host. Because colonization is much more common than actual disease, here again we must invoke the decisive role that host factors play in whether the symbiotic relationship continues or whether it culminates in overt disease. Although our task here is to detail microbial virulence and invasiveness factors that make them potent pathogens, we must remember that, even from the microbe's point of view, death of the host rarely, if ever, describes a favorable outcome.

Ordinarily preferred sites of colonization are on mucosal surfaces such as the mouth and gums, gastrointestinal tract, and genitourinary tract, where bacteria tend to form multilayered biofilms. Such biofilms impose on these microbes an anaerobic life style because of the limited diffusibility of oxygen. Under normal circumstances, the abundant secretions in the oropharynx and gastrointes-

Table 19.6. Bacterial Toxins

ORGANISM	TOXIN	MECHANISM OF ACTION
Clostridium botulinum	Botulinum toxin	Blocks release of acetylcholine at presynaptic vesicles → flaccid paralysis
Corynebacterium diptheriae	Diphtheria toxin	ADP ribosylates protein synthesis factor EF-2. Inhibits protein synthesis → cell death
Vibrio cholera	Cholera toxin	ADP ribosylates the adenylate cyclase regulatory protein Gs. Result: activation of adenylate cyclase → ↑ cAMP → ↑ Cl → secretory diarrhea
Escherichia coli	E. coli enterotoxin	Similar action to cholera toxin
Clostridium tetani	Tetanus toxin	↓ release of glycine and GABA two inhibitory neurotransmitters) → spastic paralysis
Bordetella pertussis	Pertussis toxin	ADP ribosylates Gi → persistent activation of Gs with ↑cAMP production
Shigella dysenteriae	Shiga toxin	Inactivates 60S ribosomal subunit → inhibition of protein synthesis and cell death

tinal tract, as well as pH, proteolytic enzymes, and peristaltic action in the upper GI tract work together to hold bacterial growth in check. Urine flow serves this function in the lower urinary tract. In both the GI and urinary tracts, the protective role of the IgA immunoglobulin class should not be overlooked. Accordingly, any process that impedes these normal housekeeping measures heightens the chance for infection. Thus, any obstruction of a hollow viscus would lead to bacterial overgrowth and infection, as in bladder or kidney infections or blind loop syndrome in the gastrointestinal tract. So, too, the respiratory tract becomes more susceptible to infection when the ciliary action of the airways is impaired.

Host Cell Surface Receptors are Targets for Bacterial Attachment

To colonize tissue surfaces, many bacteria are endowed with proteins called *adhesins*, which bind to host cell surface receptors in a stereochemical manner. The fit of adhesin and receptor is thus like that in a jig-saw puzzle, relying on the same weak forces (see Chapter 1) that underlie enzyme substrate interaction and antigen-antibody interactions. Not infrequently, these bacterial adhesins are deployed on the surface of microbial cell surface extensions termed *pili* or *fimbriae*. Such deployment makes them particularly effective in interacting with host cell surface receptors.

Those host cell receptor molecules, thus far characterized, are either glycolipids or glycoproteins with sugar moieties constituting the binding site for the bacterial adhesin. Bacteria, through mutation and acquisition of plasmids, have developed the ability to recognize and bind stereospecifically to various host cell membrane surface elements. Undeniably, the microbe's ability to bind to host cell receptors is a striking example of genetic adaptation by the microbe to ensure colonization of the host.

Host cell receptors for adhesins are not only confined to cell surfaces, they also are found in secretions of mucosal surfaces. It is speculated that when these soluble forms of receptor molecules bind to adhesins, they drastically decrease the number of microbes remaining to bind to mucosal surfaces. This competitive strategy by the host has been termed "molecular mimicry."

Toxins

Many bacteria secrete exotoxins, proteins which exert powerful biochemical effects on host cells benefiting the microbe at the expense of the host. There are four general classes of toxins: (*1*) those that act as intracellular enzymes; (*2*) those that damage host cell membranes; (*3*) those that act as signal molecules, binding to the cell membrane and setting off a series of intracellular events; and (*4*) those that act systemically.

A-B TOXINS FUNCTION AS INTRACELLULAR ENZYMES

Several bacterial toxins take the form of a dimer with an A-B structure, with the B subunit binding to the external membrane and perhaps facilitating entry of the A (enzymatic) subunit into the host cell cytosol. Although all A-B toxins share this common structural motif, they differ not only in reaction catalyzed but also in receptor specificity and whether the B subunit is single or multiple. Uptake of the A portion into the host cell usually is by receptor-mediated endocytosis.

As seen in Table 19.6, several of the A enzymes catalyze adenosine diphosphate (ADP) ribosylation of intracellular host proteins. As a consequence of ADP ribosylation, the adenosine diphosphate ribose moiety of NAD^+ is transferred to precise residues of the protein. Generally, the target of ADP ribosylation is a protein with a wide reaching regulatory function in the cell's economy. For instance, diphtheria toxin inactivates EF2, which is an important cofactor in mammalian protein synthesis, thereby bringing protein synthesis to a standstill with devastating consequences. Cholera toxin's target is a membrane-bound G-protein responsible for controlling the activity of adenylate cyclase. Unrestrained activity of adenylate cyclase results from the action of cholera toxin, leading to dramatic increase in cAMP levels in intestinal cells. Resultant failure to reabsorb vast amounts of fluid occurs, leading to a life-threatening diarrhea.

Some toxins, for example those of pertussis and anthrax, increase intracellular cAMP levels in so-called professional phagocytes; this increase results in impairment of phagocytic activity. This obviously benefits the microbes that must subvert the protective action of phagocytes.

SOME TOXINS DAMAGE HOST MEMBRANES

Two types of bacterial exotoxins act to damage cell membranes. The first class are *pore formers* or *ionophores*, which, like the membrane attack complex of the host complement system, cause cell lysis. The second class are various phospholipases, which by digesting membrane phospholipids also cause lysis of the host cell.

SOME TOXINS ACT AS SIGNAL MOLECULES

Enteropathic E. coli and related gram-negative enteropathogens secrete an exotoxin that binds to an external protein on the host cell membrane, in turn triggering an increase in guanylate cyclase activity with the expected increase in cellular cGMP. Like the situation with cholera toxin (which increases intracellular cAMP), increased cGMP adversely affects Na^+ and Cl^- transport across the apical face of the intestinal cells, causing diarrhea. Thus, the enteropathogens and Vibrio cholera cause disease by a combination of effects—dramatically accentuating a normal process (secretion in the intestine) and rendering that process impervious to regulation.

SOME TOXINS ACT SYSTEMICALLY

Although evidence exists that both the tetanus and botulinum toxins take the form of A-B toxins, their profound systemic effects on the nervous system warrants placing them in a distinct category. Tetanus toxin acts at presynaptic sites on neurons, blocking release of the inhibitory neurotransmitter, glycine, and spastic paralysis results. Botulinum toxin, however, blocks release of acetylcholine at the myoneural junction, causing a flaccid paralysis. Both the spastic paralysis of tetanus and the flaccid paralysis of botulism represent life-threatening situations for the host.

PLASMIDS, PHAGES, AND TRANSPOSABLE GENETIC ELEMENTS ENCODE MANY TOXINS

Bacteria must adapt to widely different environments including dust, soil, water, and various domains within the host. Many inducible bacterial enzymes are produced only when the appropriate substrate is present in the environment. Also, it is in the bacterium's best interest if toxin production occurs only in those locations where the toxin can exert the desired effect for the microbe. In keeping with the view that toxin be elaborated only when it benefits the microbe, it streamlines matters for the bacterium if toxin production is encoded by forms of DNA, like plasmids and phages, that are external to the bacterial genome. Such foreign DNA can be readily acquired and just as readily discarded as dictated by the composition of the environment the microbe finds itself in.

Expression of other virulence factors frequently is regulated in a coordinate manner with expression of toxins, developing a fully equipped microbial armamentarium. Notwithstanding the power of toxins, most microbes seek to limit the degree of damage they cause the host, to ensure their access to the niche and nutrients afforded by the host. Of course, for many organisms, discharge from the body ensures wider dissemination, a requirement that in some instances makes the presently occupied host less essential to the microbe. In such circumstances, toxin production may advance the microbe's need to disperse.

Microbes Have Ways of Evading the Complement and Immune Systems

Gram-negative bacteria, devoid of the thick peptidoglycan layers that characterize gram-positive bacteria, are susceptible to the lytic action of the membrane attack complex of the complement system. In the case of gram negatives, the paramount feature that enables them to evade the action of the complement system is the surface layer *lipopolysaccharide*, which prevents the membrane attack complex from boring into the membrane by restricting access to the membrane.

Of course, the peptidoglycan cell wall of gram-positive bacteria represents such a formidable barrier to the membrane attack complex that gram positives are not vulnerable to complement's lytic action. An additional means of averting complement is the M protein of certain group A streptococci, which binds to the negative regulatory protein factor H, preventing formation of C3 convertase. In addition, many gram positives have capsules that shield potential activating groups on the cell membrane from triggering the alternative pathway.

Perhaps one of the most clever means of avoiding the recognitive abilities of the immune system is manifested by those organisms that can vary the antigenic targets presented by their surface proteins. For instance, N. gonorrhoeae, Borrelia, and certain trypanosomes possess a bank of genes capable of expressing different surface epitopes.

Microbes Have Ways to Evade Uptake by Phagocytes and Macrophages

We have noted that circulating and fixed phagocytic cells can mount a potent and rapid response to a microbial invader. But many microbes have developed means to avert their uptake by phagocytes. Preeminent among these evasive strategies is the presence of a polysaccharide capsule that (*1*) is nonantigenic, either because of similarity to host cell surface components or because the building blocks are nonimmunogenic, (*2*) is resistant to becoming opsonized, and (*3*) presents a slippery surface making it very difficult for phagocytes to engulf them. In fact, the presence of a capsule probably is the most potent antiphagocytic feature of successful pathogens.

We may add to this the ability of certain bacteria to secrete toxins (see above) that increases intracellular cAMP in neutrophils and monocytes, thereby impairing the migration and response to chemotactic stimuli of these host cells. A prime example of such an organism is Bordetella pertussis. Because of its noxious effect on professional phagocytes, Bordetella provokes a lymphocytic response by the host because phagocytes cannot mount an adequate response.

Some Microbes Can Escape the Killing Action of Phagocytes

We noted above that a "respiratory burst" accompanies the entry of many microorganisms into professional phagocytes. This respiratory burst unleashes production of a series of toxic oxygen radicals that are cumulatively bactericidal. But some bacteria, which are able to thrive in an intracellular environment, can enter neutrophils, monocytes, and macrophages without tripping the switch that sets off the respiratory burst. Some organisms like Legionella and Mycobacterium leprae enter macrophages, not via sites for the Fc immune receptor, but rather via the receptor for C3. Entry via the complement system receptor thus avoids triggering the respiratory burst.

Some microorganisms are endowed with enzymes or cell surface components that inhibit the NADPH oxidase, the first enzyme of the respiratory burst, whereas others produce enzymes that break down the toxic products or aromatic molecules that scavenge the toxic products formed by the phagocyte.

Phagocytes also are equipped with nonoxidative strategies to combat microbes, but some microbes have developed means to avoid these strategies as well. For example, one microbial defense involves inhibiting fusion of the phagosome with the lysosome, thus averting delivery of the microbe to the cidal environment of the lysosome. Another group of microbes can induce rupture of the phagosome into the cytosol, thus providing the microbe with a lavish haven in which to thrive. Finally, and most puzzling, some microbes actually thrive and replicate within the phagolysosome. How they accomplish this feat is as yet unknown.

FEVER AND CYTOKINES

It has long been believed that because fever is exhibited by so many species, including fish, amphibia, reptiles, birds, and mammals, that it must have important biologic value. Indeed, fever as a biologic response to infection and other insults emerged several hundred million years ago. It is no secret that when the body temperature increases, metabolic processes accelerate by about 10% per degree, incurring a significant metabolic cost. For such an expensive process to endure over millions of years, it seems logical that it must play a vital role in survival. Remarkably, it has been only in the past decade or so that experimental data have accumulated to confirm that the ability to mount a febrile response to an invader has survival value. Whereas fish, amphibia, and reptiles transfer to a warmer location when infected, birds and mammals produce fever by increasing metabolic rates and becoming more vasoconstricted.

A group of substances produced by microorganisms, including cell wall constituents and toxins, can provoke a febrile response and, accordingly, these substances are called pyrogens. Best known among these molecules is endotoxin, a lipopolysaccharide located in the outer membrane of gram-negative bacteria. A lipopolysaccharide and other exogenous pyrogens appear to act by triggering the host to produce various *endogenous pyrogens*. These endogenous pyrogens are secreted by monocytes/macrophages, lymphocytes, and other cells and act on the thermoregulatory center of the hypothalamus. Among the endogenous pyrogens are the cytokines IL-1, TNF, INFα, and IL-6. Acting on the hypothalamus, these signal molecules raise the thermoregulatory set point by stimulating synthesis of prostaglandins there, and, in turn, the hypothalamus initiates systemic measures that cause heat to be both conserved and produced. Such measures include stimulating peripheral vasoconstriction, shivering, and intermediary metabolism. Recall that much of the heat produced by the body arises from exothermic reactions occurring both in metabolic pathways (especially in skeletal muscle and liver) and as a consequence of active transport across cell membranes. Preeminent among transport mechanisms is the Na^+-K^+ ATPase, which is vital not only to maintaining osmotic balance of the cell but also to power other secondary transport mechanisms. Notably, this transporter is sensitive to regulation by thyroid hormones. Consequently, in hypothyroidism, basal body temperature falls, providing further evidence for the role of this transporter in maintaining body temperature.

As more has been learned about the cytokines produced in response to microbial invasion, it has become clear that the generation of fever is just one aspect of the orchestrated inflammatory response by which the body mobilizes its forces to repel an invader. For instance, when body temperature rises, both neutrophil phagocytic and bactericidal activity are enhanced and T-cell proliferation and resultant cytotoxicity are intensified.

Although fever clearly provides survival value to the individual, still there are instances when the body temperature rises to greater than 41.1°C (106 °F), a threshold which constitutes a life-threatening level and must be remedied. Therefore, the febrile response, like the inflammatory response in sepsis (see following text), can sometimes exceed what is a safe homeostatic response, sliding instead into a pathologic region. In that region, the body's response actually may be more harmful than the initial infection.

SEPTIC SHOCK

In the past, it was believed that sepsis or septicemia was a potentially life-threatening state induced by the presence of pathogenic bacteria in the bloodstream. Yet, it also was known that bacteremia commonly occurred after everyday events, such as brushing one's teeth or straining at stool, and caused no clinical manifestations. Sepsis, however, scarcely is a benign condition, usually being associated with fever, shaking chills, increased heart rate, a decrease in blood pressure, and an alarmingly high mortality rate. As research into the cause and manifestations of sepsis have advanced, it has become clear that two important host factors contribute to the picture of sepsis: (*1*) production of cytokines by macrophages, through which the bacterial presence impinges on, (*2*) the endothelial lining of vessels throughout the body. In this scenario, certain bacterial products (exotoxins and endotoxins) prompt an inflammatory response, but once the process is set in motion, the bacterial products no longer need to be present because the body's response can become self-perpetuating. Hence, the manifestations of sepsis stem from the body's deployment of many mediators and does not arise directly as a consequence of the action of the bacterial products. Rather, these bacterial products act by inducing monocytes/macrophages, T-cells, neutrophils, and platelets to produce various cytokines. In turn, these cytokines act on vascular endothelium, the heart, and coagulation and complement cascades; if the response is excessive, the situation created can be life-threatening. Nor is this all, because the vascular endothelium may respond to these provocations by producing more cytokines, platelet activating factor, nitric oxide, and eicosanoids that further advance the process to produce the shock state.

By virtue of the generalized involvement of blood vessel endothelium, sepsis is now regarded as a generalized process and is referred to as *septic shock*. It also is viewed as being synonymous with *multiple organ failure syndrome*. Consonant with the involvement of multiple organs, it has become clear that the manifestations of sepsis are far ranging and involve the heart and vasculature, coagulation cascade, brain, lungs, and kidney (Table 19.7). There also are substantial metabolic consequences to sepsis.

Most cases of sepsis occur in debilitated hospitalized patients who, because of various indwelling lines or tubes, are at heightened risk for entry of organisms that normally would be repulsed by intact skin and mucous membrane barriers. These hospital acquired organisms are called *nosocomial* agents. Because of the emergence of antibiotic resistant organisms there is a preponderance of gram-negative organisms responsible for sepsis. But it would be incorrect to conclude that only gram-negative organisms cause sepsis; so too do gram positives (in increasing numbers), rickettsiae, fungi, and some viruses. Again, the key factor is the release of bacterial products that, in turn, trigger release of various cytokines from macrophages. The crucial event in the pathogenesis of sepsis occurs when some of these agents act on endothelial cell to kindle and perpetuate the septic process.

Table 19.7. Consequences of Septic Shock

Vasculature—peripheral vasodilation → ↓B.P. → inadequate perfusion of kidney, liver, and gastrointestinal tract
Heart—although myocardial contractility ↓s, cardiac output ↑s because the heart dilates and beats faster
Brain—confusion, delirium → coma
Hemostatic system—disseminated intravascular coagulation with consumption of platelets and clotting enzymes and factors
Lung—capillary endothelial damage → leakage of fluid and adult respiratory distress syndrome
Kidney—acute renal failure
Liver—liver damage and juandice
Gastrointestinal tract—mucosal hemorrhage
Metabolic derangements—release of cytokines → proteolysis, lipolysis, and gluconeogenesis.
Poor perfusion or intracellular biochemical derangements → lactic acidosis

Paramount among the cytokines that trigger septic shock is *tumor necrosis factor*, but other signal molecules participate, including interleukins, platelet activating factor, and various eicosanoids. As is the case with fever, the cytokines produced, for the most part, are identical to those that mount the orchestrated acute phase response to microbial invasion. With sepsis, however, at some critical threshold the multiplicity of responses engendered by the cytokines becomes chaotic, ceasing to protect the host. In effect, the body overreacts, releasing a welter of signal molecules that trigger many dangerous or destructive responses. Of course, when deployed in a controlled fashion, the inflammatory response has distinct survival value. Providing a throttle to the inflammatory response are products of the neutrophil myeloperoxidase system, endogenously secreted glucocorticoids, and prostaglandin E_2. But if secretion of the inflammatory mediators is unchecked or becomes widely disseminated, these downregulators may not be able to brake the process sufficiently. It is as if the body overreacts in attempting to eradicate the pathogen and in the process destroys itself.

Again, although most organs are damaged in septic shock, the underlying focus of such widespread destruction begins with injury to the vascular endothelium throughout the body. Prompting blockage of the micronutrient capillaries, the endothelial damage deprives tissues of oxygen and nutrients. This is the essential lesion in all forms of shock (see Chapter 24 on cardiovascular physiology).

We have noted that many infectious agents can trigger release of signal molecules that collectively produce the inflammatory response. Past a certain threshold, however, this protective response unfolds into the septic syndrome. It follows that therapeutic agents directed against the perpetuation of the inflammatory cascade should prove valuable in abolishing this over-response. This is not to suggest that antibiotics and hemodynamic monitoring and support are not necessary, but, because septic shock is attended by a 50% mortality rate, new approaches are required.

Meningitis

Meningitis is one of the most dread of medical conditions, affecting the membranes and cerebrospinal fluid (CSF) that invest and protect the brain. Further heightening the concern about meningitis is its preponderance in children and the elderly, with about 70% of cases occurring before the age of 5 years. Although brain itself is not directly invaded by the infectious process, the occurrence of cerebral edema and inflammation in the confined space of the cranial vault puts the brain at grave risk. Symptoms arising from compression of brain structures include obtundation, seizures, coma, and cranial nerve palsies.

Four routes account for seeding of the meninges with bacteria: (*1*) via the blood; (*2*) via a defect in the barrier between the respiratory tract and brain; (*3*) via venules in the nasopharynx; and (*4*) spread from a neighboring infection (eg, the paranasal sinuses). By far, spread through the bloodstream from respiratory tract (more rarely, gastrointestinal and genitourinary tracts and heart valves) is the dominant mode by which bacteria reach the meninges.

Although the blood-brain barrier prevents passage of bacteria into the brain and CSF, this tight barrier also limits access of complement and immunoglobulins into the CSF. In this environment, the brain is less able to defend against microbial invasion than in most other sites in the body.

PATHOGENESIS

Steps required for the development of bacterial meningitis are believed to be the following: (*1*) initial mucosal colonization of the nasopharynx; (*2*) invasion of mucosal epithelial cells; (*3*) transient bacteremia; (*4*) seeding of the meninges; and (*5*) mounting an inflammatory response by the host. It turns out, now that physicians are armed with potent antibiotics, that it is step 5, the inflammatory response, that poses the greatest problem in improving the outcome of bacterial meningitis.

Those bacteria that commonly cause bacterial meningitis (S. pneumoniae, H. influenzae, N. meningitidis, and E. coli) use adhesins and surface extensions to attach to host nasopharyngeal mucosa. To sustain their foothold at these sites, these bacteria must subvert the action of secretory IgA, doing so by secreting IgA proteases. Those pathogens that make it to the bloodstream must next evade the neutrophils and avoid setting off the alternative complement cascade, because it is this arm of the complement system that can be triggered without specific antibody. As we have noted before, the presence of a capsular polysaccharide provides protection from phagocytosis and a shield against the alternative cascade for some microbes. But the capsule of S. pneumoniae can activate the alternative cascade, causing C3b to become attached to the bacterial surface and thus opsonizing the microbe, making it more attractive to phagocytes.

Still a puzzle is how bacteria cross the blood-brain barrier to reside in the CSF, although, as we will see below, there is now evidence that the blood-brain barrier becomes more permeable when microbes arrive at that barrier. Obviously, this is an uncommon outcome but one with devastating consequences for the infected individual.

PATHOPHYSIOLOGY

Perhaps the most important insight gained from research into the causation and abnormalities caused by meningitis is that its most devastating clinical manifestations result not from the actions of the pathogens, but rather from actions of the host as it mobilizes the inflammatory and specific responses to the invader. This is a sobering prospect and has led some to suggest that improving the outcome of bacterial meningitis now depends on modulating the response of the body, rather than developing another generation of antibiotics. This echoes the concerns raised about septic shock.

Experimental evidence supports the view that gram-negative lipopolysaccharide provokes the inflammatory reaction in CSF and contributes to the breakdown of the blood-brain barrier. Once provoked by bacterial products, host mediators of the inflammatory process include interleukin-1 and tumor necrosis factor.

Another target for therapy may be adhesion molecules that facilitate the transfer of white cells into the infected space. Selectins are cell surface binding proteins that permit white cells to bind to the vessel wall. Another class of adhesion molecules, the integrins, further retard white cell movement in the blood stream, making it possible for these to slip through the vessel wall into the infected tissue space.

VIRAL INFECTIONS

Viruses are minute (18–450 nm) intracellular parasites that can replicate their nucleic acid only by appropriating the host's biochemical machinery. From the simplest to the most complex, viruses are composed of nucleic acid, either DNA or RNA, surrounded by a protein coat. Because they require the host's replicative apparatus, they have neither ribosomes nor the enzymes necessary for replication of DNA or RNA.

Viral nucleic acid codes for two classes of proteins: (*1*) those that are involved in further nucleic acid replication, and (*2*) those that form the viral coat or enable the virus to take over the host's biochemical machinery for its own benefit. Because, at most, the viral genome encodes several hundred proteins, it is predictable that the protein coat or capsid is made up of repeating, identical units that are capable of self-assembly. In addition to their protein coat, some viruses also possess an envelope. This envelope arises from host cell membranes through which viral glycoproteins are inserted. Often, these viral glycoproteins are the site of interaction of the virus with host cell receptors and are targets for the host antibody response.

What are the Steps by Which a Virus Infects a Host Cell?

A viral particle makes contact with a host cell by random collision, and if that host cell has an appropriate receptor for that virus, attachment ensues. Accordingly, the initial step in the pathogenesis of viral diseases depends on the "goodness of fit" of viral surface proteins for cell surface receptors on target cells in the host. The cell surface receptors used by viruses clearly are not meant to be sites of attachment for viruses. Rather, they are receptors for hormones, neurotransmitters, and other substances that must be able to bind stereospecifically to host cells. By mutation, viruses have developed surface structural elements that can bind to host plasma membrane proteins, gangliosides, or carbohydrates, like sialic acid and heparan sulfate.

In some instances, the virus can enter the cell by exploiting the receptor-mediated endocytosis mechanism typically used to take up various particulates. In such an instance, the cell is tricked into "seeing" the virus as something the cell desires, prompting its uptake. In other instances, uptake of the virus is by direct translocation through the plasma membrane. In either case, the virus is internalized into an endosome, within which the acidic environment facilitates release of the virus from the attached plasma membrane. This paves the way for replication of the viral genome, because the virus expropriates the host replicative apparatus.

Understandably, great interest exists concerning the nature of the nucleic acids and the method of replication of the different viruses. This interest is not limited only to concerns about viruses because many of the leaps in understanding the eucaryotic genome, including discovery of intervening sequences and splicing, were the result of studies with viruses that infect animal cells. Moreover, work with recombinant DNA was built on a foundation of studies with bacteriophages. As we noted above, from the viewpoint of entry into a particular target cell, it is not the nature of the viral nucleic acid that matters—rather, it is the presence of the appropriate receptor on the surface of the host cell for some viral surface element. We will consider the replication of the viral genome below.

After the viral proteins are synthesized in the host cell at the behest of the viral genome, viral components then can be assembled within the host cell. Once assembled, release of viral particles occurs either by budding (enveloped viruses) or cell lysis (nonenveloped viruses). It is at this stage that the infection becomes disseminated to other sites in the body. Depending on host defenses, when enough cells have been injured or destroyed, overt disease occurs. Many viruses induce cell death by lysing the host cell. In some instances, however, it is the host immune response that eventuates in cell death, either through the action of the complement system or via cell-mediated killing of an infected cell. Obviously, when the body responds in this manner, it is attempting to confine the infection.

Of course, not all viral infections culminate in cell death. Many viruses can trigger *transformation* of cells, causing them to proliferate continuously. In Chapter 2, we noted that *viral oncogenes* can induce neoplastic transformation with the development of malignant tumors. Still other viruses remain latent within the host cell genome for years.

Mechanisms of Viral Replication

In contrast to all other forms of life, viruses can replicate their nucleic acid and form more viral particles only when harbored within the living cells of a host they infect (Table 19.8). As a rule, target host cells furnish the synthetic apparatus, including ribosomes, tRNA, and cofactors, for replication of viral nucleic acid and synthesis of viral proteins. Thus, whereas the proteins are viral, synthesized according to the information encoded in the viral genome, the synthetic apparatus is provided by the host.

As is the case with protein synthesis in procaryotes and eucaryotes, the synthesis of protein is directed by mRNA, which by convention is designated (+) sense or strand, meaning that it participates directly in protein synthesis. That RNA with a sequence complementary to mRNA is designated (−) strand, and such RNA must be transcribed into a (+) strand for viral protein synthesis to ensue. Typically, viruses with (−) strand RNA carry their own RNA polymerase to synthesize (+) mRNA. Of course, viruses with ds (double-stranded) DNA follow the typical eucaryotic pattern of transcription into mRNA, using DNA-dependent RNA polymerase.

This relatively straightforward picture was made more complex when it was demonstrated that there are a group of viruses that possess an RNA-dependent DNA polymerase that synthesizes viral DNA from viral RNA. These viruses have been named *retroviruses* because they reverse the so-called central dogma (DNA → RNA → protein) to RNA → DNA → RNA, and their polymerases have been named *reverse transcriptases* in recognition of this fact. Aside from providing insights into the workings of the retroviruses, the reverse transcriptases have been pivotal in developing strategies for recombinant DNA work (see Chapter 1).

Host Defenses Against Viruses

Because viruses must enter cells to replicate, they are not left as vulnerable to the phagocytic action of neutrophils as are bacteria. In addition, the antibody response to viral infection is more effective in preventing reinfection than it is in moderating a primary infection. But, as we have seen above, the role of cell-mediated immunity and antigen presentation (which unmasks a virus harbored within a cell) are among the most potent induced defenses that can be marshalled against a viral infection. Elements of cell-mediated immunity include not only cytotoxic T-cells and natural killer cells, but also macrophages that are capable of destroying cells infected with a virus.

Antibodies

The most potent antibodies raised against a viral infection are *neutralizing antibodies*, which recognize antigenic determinants of viral proteins situated on the surface of the virion. For the most part, steps leading to infection that occur outside of the host cell, that is, attachment and penetration, are most susceptible to the action of neutralizing antibodies. Secretory IgAs are of utmost importance in blocking attachment of viruses that enter via a mucosal surface. Activation of the complement cascade further augments the potency of the antibody response. Finally, when a virus-infected cell presents antigen on its surface, those epitopes may

Table 19.8. Strategies of Nucleic Acid Transcription by Various Viruses

TYPE OF NUCLEIC ACID	INTERMEDIATE FORMS	EXAMPLES	SEQUENCE OF EVENTS IN TRANSCRIPTION AND EVENTUAL VIRAL PROTEIN SYNTHESIS
(+) ss RNA	± ds RNA	Picornaviruses (eg, polio)	(+) mRNA binds to ribosomes and is translated into a polyprotein. Polyprotein is cleaved—one product is a polymerase (RNA replicase). Viral (+) mRNA is template for synthesis of complementary (−) mRNA. (−) mRNA is template to synthesize more (+) mRNA which directs protein synthesis.
(−) ss RNA	None	Orthoviruses (eg, influenza) Paramyxoviruses (eg, parainfluenza, mumps, measles)	(−) RNA is complementary to (+) mRNA, which must be transcribed into mRNA. Host lacks necessary enzyme; therefore, viral particle carries a viral transcriptase.
(±) ds RNA segmented	None	Reoviruses (eg, Rotavirus)	Virion carries a polymerase that transcribes ds RNA into (+) ss RNA using the viral (−) sense strand. mRNA formed then directs protein synthesis.
(+) ss RNA	− DNA, ± DNA	Retroviruses (HIV-1)	Viral RNA is a template for synthesis of viral DNA. Virion endowed with reverse transcriptase (RNA-dependent DNA polymerase). DNA formed can be integrated into host DNA. Host DNA-dependent RNA polymerase makes viral mRNA along with host mRNA.
(±) ds DNA		Adenoviruses Herpesvirus Poxvirus	For many of this group the viral genome is transcribed and replicated in host nucleus. But poxviruses carry out transcription and replication in host cell cytoplasm. Poxvirues carry their own DNA-dependent RNA polymerase, which directs synthesis of viral proteins and mRNA to effect continued synthesis of viral particles.

All viruses ultimately synthesize (+) strand mRNA to carry out protein synthesis.

be available for the combined action of antibody and complement.

Cell-Mediated Immunity

Cell-mediated destruction of viral-infected cells occurs through both antibody-independent and antibody-dependent pathways. Natural killer cells are large lymphocytes that function without antibody, being deployed within 2 to 3 days of infection. These natural killer cells attach to virus-infected cells and secrete cytotoxic agents into the target cell. The objective is to lyse the infected cell and thereby deprive the virus of both its "shelter" and its "incubator."

One type of antibody-dependent cell lysis involves interaction of virus-specific antibody on the surface of an infected cell with the Fc receptors for IgG on neutrophils. This mechanism is called *antibody-dependent cell-mediated cytotoxicity* and the activated leukocytes are the lethal agents.

Most well known and most effective are the cytotoxic T-cells, which interact with antigen-presenting cells, unmasking a virus that has entered the cell.

Interferons

Many viruses can induce leukocytes to produce a variety of agents called *interferons*. Once bound to

Table 19.9. Pathogenic Viruses

VIRUS	STRUCTURE AND NUCLEIC ACID	PATHOGENESIS	TISSUE TROPISM AND DISEASES	TREATMENT OR PREVENTION
Picornavirus (Small RNA) Polio	Nonenveloped, ss (+) RNA. Message translated into a polyprotein. Viral RNA replicated by a virally encoded RNA-dependent RNA polymerase.	Entry by fecal-oral route. Replicates in lymphoid tissue of mouth and gut. Spreads via blood but causes only minor disease. Even before vaccines only a minority of those infected developed nervous system disease.	Lymphoid tissues Neurons in brain and spinal cord → cell lysis and paralytic poliomyelitis.	Vaccines are effective.
Enteroviruses-Coxsackie	Nonenveloped, ss (+) RNA	Spread by fecal-oral route or oral secretions. Like polio grow in pharynx and intestine.	Respiratory disease Herpangina Epidemic pleurodynia Aseptic meningitis Myocarditis/pericarditis	Most coxsackie illnessses are benign, but neural and cardiac forms may be serious.
Rhinovirus	Nonenveloped, ss (+) RNA	Transmitted by sneezing and coughing (aerosols) and by hand contact.	Common cold-virus binds to respiratory epithelial cells via intercellular adhesion molecule-1 (ICAM-1).	
Caliciviridae Norwalk virus	Nonenveloped, ss (+) RNA	Contaminated water or seafood, or infected food preparers.	Gastroenteritis	
Togaviridae Rubella	Enveloped, ss (+) RNA	Spread by respiratory secretions or across placental wall to fetus.	Mild respiratory illness. Congenital infection can → Rubella syndrome with multiple defects including mental retardation, hearing loss, cardiac defects and cataracts.	Vaccine
Flaviviridae Yellow fever	Enveloped, ss (+) RNA	Vector is the mosquito Aedes aegypti.	Mild to life-threatening liver disease.	Vaccine Eradicating of vector with insecticides.
Dengue	Enveloped, ss (+) RNA	Vector is mosquito from genus Aedes.	Break-bone fever—severe headache and backache, exhaustion, fever	
Rhabdoviridae Rabies	Enveloped, ss (−) RNA	Bite of infected raccoon, skunk or bat.	Rabies—neurotropic virus that if it reaches the central nervous system produces a fatal encephalitis. Not all bites → clinical disease.	Mandatory vaccination of dogs. Rabies vaccine to subject if bitten by rabid animal.
Paramyxoviridae Measles	Enveloped, ss (−) RNA	Transmission by respiratory secretions—highly contagious.	Measles—fever, upper respiratory infection, rash, conjunctivitis. In malnourished unimmunized individuals measles can be fatal.	Vaccine Immune globulin within 6 days of exposure will prevent or modify.

(continued)

Table 19.9. *(Continued)*

Paramyxoviridae *Parainfluenza*	*Enveloped, ss (−) RNA*	*Transmission by respiratory secretions.*	*Upper respiratory infections in adults.* *Laryngotracheobronchitis (croup) in infants from swelling of tracheal mucosa.*	
Mumps	*Enveloped, ss (−) RNA*	*Transmission by respiratory droplets.*	*Mumps—painful swollen parotid or other salivary gland. In adolescent males and men orchitis occurs in 25%. Aseptic meningitis can occur.*	*Vaccine*
Respiratory syncytial virus	*Enveloped, ss (−) RNA*	*Highly infectious—patients in hospital pose risk to immunocompromised individuals. Epidemics occur in winter and spring. Transmission by respiratory secretions or hands.*	*Respiratory tract—causes pneumonia and bronchiolitis.*	
Orthomyxoviridae Influenza	Enveloped, ss (−) RNA Multisegmented genome	Transmitted by respiratory secretions, cases usually part of an epidemic. Undergoes frequent antigenic change from point mutations and genetic reassortment.	Generalized aches, chills, fever, "grippe" out of proportion to respiratory symptoms (coryza, cough). May cause secondary pneumonia.	Polyvalent vaccine provides partial (temporary) immunity, especially for elderly individuals with chronic disease.
Reoviridae Rotavirus	Unenveloped, ds RNA	Transmission by fecal-oral route and possibly via infectious aerosols.	Viral gastroenteritis—causes one million deaths worldwide from dehydration resulting from diarrhea. Oral rehydration is effective.	
Retroviridae HIV-1	Enveloped, ss (+) RNA Uses reverse transcriptase to replicate genome.	Transmitted sexually or by introduction into bloodstream. Virus may exist in latent state for years in helper T lymphs (CD4+). Eventually, these T cells are drastically reduced in number → severe immunodeficiency (AIDS)	ARC—AIDS related complex AIDS—acquired immunodeficiency syndrome: multiple organ system involvement.	
Hepadnaviridae Hepatitis-B	Enveloped, ds DNA with ss regions. Uses reverse transcriptase.	Transmission by infected blood or blood products or by sexual routes.	Viral hepatitis Chronic carriers at risk for primary hepatocellular carcinoma.	Hep B immune globulin within 7 days of exposure. Hep B vaccine for high risk individuals.
Adenoviridae Human adenovirus	Unenveloped, ds DNA	Respiratory secretions, contaminated swimming pools and instruments can lead to infection.	Common cold Pharyngitis with exudate Keratoconjunctivitis may → opacities Acute hemorrhagic cystitis Juvenile gastroenteritis	

Herpesviridae Herpes simplex virus (HSV)	Enveloped, ds DNA that codes for 50–80 proteins	HSV1 causes oral, skin, and eye infections. It is acquired early in life by oral contact. HSV2 is usually transmitted sexually.	Herpes Simplex Type I • Gingivostomatitis—gums inflammed and oral mucosa ulcerated • Eczema herpeticum—multiple skin sites • Keratoconjunctivitis • Recurrent Herpes labialis • Meningoencephalitis Herpes Simplex Type 2 • Neonatal Infections → genital herpes	Acyclovir Foscarnet (phosphonoformic acid)
Herpesviridae Varicella-Zoster virus	Enveloped, ds DNA	Varicella (chickenpox) spread by respiratory route or contact with lesions. Zoster-reactivation of latent varicella virus (sensory neurons)	Chickenpox—fever, malaise, pruritic papular to vesicular lesions. Zoster (shingles)—painful skin lesions resembling those of chickenpox and following nerve root distributions.	Varicella-Zoster immune globulin for exposed individuals. Acyclovir, Vidarabine
Cytomegalovirus	Enveloped, ds DNA	Multiple routes of transmissions: sexual, congenital, blood products, transplanted organs, close personal contact (eg, day care). Eighty percent of adults older than 35 years have antibodies.	Congenital infection—generalized infection. Infectious mononucleosis like illness. Disseminated disease in immune suppressed hosts.	Ganciclovir Foscarnet
Epstein-Barr virus	Enveloped, ds DNA	Transmission is by saliva (kissing). Latency in B lymphocytes and salivary gland cells.	• Infectious mononucleosis—fever, severe sore throat, exhaustion, lymphadenopathy, splenomegaly (frequent). • Burkitt's lymphoma—EBV believed to play a role in develpment of this cancer.	
Poxviridae Smallpox	Enveloped, ds DNA	Transmission by inhalation and spreads via the bloodstream.	Smallpox—malaise, prostration, headache, muscle aches. Rash evolves from macular to papular to pustular.	Vaccination has eradicated smallpox—effective since humans were the only reservoir.

the appropriate cell surface receptor, interferons trigger many valuable antiviral measures. For one, it induces formation of a protein kinase that phosphorylates a protein initiation factor, handicapping viral protein synthesis. For another, it elicits formation of 2,5-oligoadenylates, which activate a host ribonuclease that, in turn, dismantles the viral mRNA. Still another effect of interferons is to intensify the activity of natural killer cells. Of note, administration of interferon to normal subjects produces many signs and symptoms that typically accompany viral infections—fever, myalgias, and leukopenia—suggesting that these findings are at least, in part, attributable to the interferon and not to the infection per se.

Properties of clinically important viral pathogens are listed in Table 19.9.

LABORATORY TESTS TO DIAGNOSE INFECTIOUS DISEASES

The most effective therapy of an infectious disease relies on identification of the causative agent. This especially is true for bacteria, fungi, and parasites, but, even in the case of some viral disease, specific treatment is now a reality. Three avenues of approach can provide the clinician with the specific information as to what organism is the culprit: (*1*) growing the organism in culture, (*2*) demonstrating the organism at a focus of infection, and (*3*) showing that antibodies to the organism rise in response to the infection.

If a specific site of infection can be identified and a pathogenic organism isolated from culture, the physician may obtain firm evidence on which to base a therapeutic approach. When susceptibility to antimicrobial agents can be added to this, the clinician should be able to proceed with some confidence. Unfortunately, culture and sensitivity takes at least 24 hours and usually longer. But techniques involving monoclonal antibodies and DNA detection by polymerase chain reaction and hybridization techniques are reaching clinical feasibility and will dramatically shorten the time to definitive diagnosis. Rapid and time-honored techniques include direct microscopic examination of gram stained or acid-fast stained infected material. Although such methods may not permit unequivocal identification of the offending organism, they can quickly establish the class of pathogen involved.

If a specimen is to be obtained from a suspected site of infection, including the bloodstream or the cerebrospinal fluid, great care must be exercised to avoid contamination during specimen collection. It behooves the clinician to be apprised of the preferred techniques (swabs, aspirates) and transport media recommended by the laboratory serving his patients. Although practices differ in various institutions, all procedures are directed to optimize recovery of suspected pathogens. For the laboratory to do its best work, the specimen it receives must be optimal. In collaboration with the clinical laboratory, this end can be realized. These admonitions are particularly relevant to the collection of viral specimens.

Tests based on antigenic determinants on the pathogen or on DNA hybridization techniques do not depend on maintaining organism viability and, therefore, broaden the range of specimens that can be submitted. These techniques are only now emerging as important means by which to diagnose infectious diseases.

As we have noted above, the immune response can be an important element of the body's defense against a microbe. Because the initial response takes 1 to 2 weeks to mount, demonstrating an immune response usually is more useful as a means of confirming infection than as an element in choosing a therapy. Typically, acute and convalescent sera are obtained several weeks apart.

SUGGESTED READINGS

GENERAL

Gorbach S, Bartlett J, Blacklow N, eds. Infectious diseases. Philadelphia: WB Saunders, 1992.

Mandell GL, Bennett JE, Dolin R, eds. Principles and practice of infectious diseases. 4th ed. New York: Churchill Livingstone, 1995.

Salyers AA, Whitt DD. Bacterial pathogenesis: a molecular approach. Washington DC: American Society for Microbiology, 1994.

Schaechter M, Medoff G, Eisenstein BI. Mechanisms of microbial disease. 2nd ed. Baltimore: Williams & Wilkins, 1993.

Volk WA, Benjamin DC, Kadner RJ, Parsons JT. Essentials of medical microbiology. Philadelphia: JB Lippincott, 1991.

PHAGOCYTIC ACTION

Anderson DC, Kishimoto TK, Smith CW. Leukocyte adhesion deficiency and other disorders of leukocyte adherence and motility. In: Scriver CR, Beaudet AL, Sly WS, Valle D, eds. The metabolic and molecular bases of inherited disease. 7th ed. New York: McGraw-Hill, 1995:3955.

Babior BM. The respiratory burst oxidase. Advances in Enzymology 1992;65:49.

Curnutte JT, Orkin SH, Dinauer MC. Genetic disorders of phagocyte function. In: Stamatoyannopoulos G, Nienhuis AW, Majerus PW, Varmus H, eds. The molecular basis of blood diseases. 2nd ed. Philadelphia: WB Saunders, 1994:493.

Forehand JR, Nauseef WM, Curnutte JT, Johnston RB Jr. Inherited disorders of phagocyte killing. In: Scriver CR, Beaudet AL, Sly WS, Valle D, eds. The metabolic and molecular bases of inherited disease. 7th ed. New York: McGraw-Hill, 1995:3995.

Roos D. The genetic basis of chronic granulomatous disease. Immunol Rev 1994;138:121.

Rosen GM, Pou S, Ramos CL, et al. Free radicals and phagocytic cells. FASEB J. 1995;9:200.

Segal AW, Abo A. The biochemical basis of the NADPH oxidase of phagocytes. Trends Biochem Sci 1993;18: 43.

Yang KD, Hill HR. Neutrophil function disorders: pathophysiology, prevention, and therapy. J Pediatr 1991;119:343.

IMMUNE SYSTEM

Abbas AK, Lichtman AH, Pober JS. Cellular and molecular immunology. 2nd ed. Philadelphia: WB Saunders, 1994.

Golub ES, Green DR. Immunology: a synthesis. Sunderland, MA: Sinauer Associates, Inc, 1991.

Paul WE, ed. Fundamental immunology. 3rd ed. New York: Raven, 1993.

Roitt I, Brostoff J, Male D, eds. Immunology. 3rd ed. St Louis: CV Mosby, 1993.

Sigal LH, Ron Y, eds. Immunology and inflammation. New York: McGraw-Hill, 1994.

Stites DP, Terr AI, Parslow TG, eds. Basic and clinical immunology. 8th ed. Norwalk, CT: Appleton and Lange, 1994.

COMPLEMENT SYSTEM

Colten HR, Rosen FS. Complement deficiencies. Annu Rev Immunol 1992;10:809.

Farries TC, Atkinson JP. Evolution of the complement system. Immunol Today 1991;12:295.

Frank MM, Fries LF. The role of complement in inflammation and phagocytosis. Immunol Today 1991; 12:322.

Hostetter MK, Gordon DL. Biochemistry of C3 and related thioester proteins in infection and inflammation. Reviews in Infectious Disease 1987;9:97.

Moffitt MC, Frank MM. Complement resistance in microbes. Springer Semin Immunopathol 1994;15:327.

Muller-Eberhard HJ. Molecular organization and function of the complement system. Annu Rev Biochem 1988; 57:321.

Nicholson-Weller A, Halperin JA. Membrane signaling by complement c5b-9, the membrane attack complex. Immunol Res 1993;12:244.

Reid KBM. Activation and control of the complement system. Essays Biochem 1986;22:27.

Winkelstein JA, Sullivan KE, Colten HR. Genetically determined disorders of the complement system. In: Scriver CR, Beaudet AL, Sly WS, Valle D, eds. The metabolic and molecular bases of inherited disease. 7th ed. New York: McGraw-Hill, 1995:3911.

MICROBIAL PROPERTIES

Aktories K, Wenger A. Mechanisms of the cytopathic action of actin-ADP-ribosylating toxins. Mol Microbiol 1992;6:2905.

Barua D, Greenough WB III. Cholera. New York: Plenum Publishing Co, 1991.

Cheney CP, Wong RKH. Acute infectious diarrhea. Med Clin North Am 1993;77:1169.

Falkow S. Bacterial entry into eukaryotic cells. Cell 1991; 65:1099.

Field M, Semrad CE. Toxigenic diarrheas. Congenital diarrheas and cystic fibrosis: disorders of intestinal ion transport. Annu Rev Physiol 1993;55:631.

Hasty DL, Ofek I, Courtney HS, Doyle RJ. Multiple adhesions of streptococci. Infect Immun 1992;60:2147.

Johnson HM, Russell JK, Pontzer CH. Staphylococcal enterotoxin microbial superantigens. FASEB J 1991;5: 2706.

Kaslow HR, Burns DL. Pertussis toxin and target eukaryotic cells: binding, entry, and activation. FASEB J 1992;6:2684.

London E. Diphtheria toxin: membrane interaction and membrane translocation. Biochim Biophys Acta 1992; 1113:25.

Tarr PI. Escherichia coli O157:H7: clinical, diagnostic, and epidemiological aspects of human infection. Clin Infect Dis 1995;20:1.

Tesh VL, O'Brien AD. The pathogenic mechanisms of shiga toxin and the shiga-like toxins. Mol Microbiol 1991;5:1817.

Verlinde CLMJ, Merritt ET, Van Den Akker F, et al. Protein crystallography and infectious disease. Protein Sci 1994;3:1670.

FEVER

Cooper KE. The neurobiology of fever: thoughts on recent developments. Annu Rev Neurosci 1987;10: 297.

Dinarello CA. Interleukin-1 and its biologically related cytokines. Adv Immunol 1989;44:153.
Kluger MJ. Fever: role of pyrogens and cryogens. Physiol Rev 1991;71:93.
Mackowiak PA. Fever: blessing or curse? A unifying hypothesis. Ann Intern Med 1994;120:1037.
Saper CB, Breder CD. The neurologic basis of fever. N Engl J Med 1994;330:1880.
Sim E, ed. Humoral factors. New York: Oxford University Press, 1993.
Styrt B, Sugarman B. Antipyresis and fever. Arch Intern Med 1990;150:1589.

SEPTIC SHOCK

Bone RC. The pathogenesis of sepsis. Ann Intern Med 1991;115:457.
Bone RC. Gram-positive organisms and sepsis. Arch Intern Med 1994;154:26.
Faist E, Meakins JL, Schildberg FW, eds. Host defense dysfunction in trauma, shock and sepsis. Berlin: Springer-Verlag, 1993.
Glauser MP, Zanetti G, Baumgartner J-D, Cohen J. Septic shock: pathogenesis. Lancet 1991;338:732.
Mizock BA, Falk JL. Lactic acidosis in critical illness. Crit Care Med 1992;20:80.
Mizock BA. Alterations in carbohydrate metabolism during stress: a review of the literature. Am J Med 1995;98:75.
Parillo JE. Septic shock in humans: advances in the understanding of pathogenesis, cardiovascular dysfunction, and therapy. Ann Intern Med 1990;113:227.
Parillo JE. Pathogenetic mechanisms of septic shock. N Engl J Med 1993;328:1471.
Rackow EC, Astiz ME. Pathophysiology and treatment of septic shock. JAMA 1991;266:548.
Raetz CRH. Biochemistry of endotoxins. Annu Rev Biochem 1990;59:129.
Tracey KJ, Cerami A. Tumor necrosis factor, other cytokines and disease. Annu Rev Cell Biol 1993;9:317.
Tracey KJ, Cerami A. Tumor necrosis factor: a pleiotropic cytokine and therapeutic target. Annu Rev Med 1994;45:491.
van der Poll T, Sauerwein HP. Tumor necrosis factor-α: its role in the metabolic response to sepsis. Clin Sci 1993;84:247.

MENINGITIS

Bell WS. Bacterial meningitis in children. Selected aspects. Pediatr Clin North Am 1992;39:651.
Bevilacqua MP, Nelson RM, Mannori G, Ceccioni O. Endothelial-leukocyte adhesion molecules in human disease. Annu Rev Med 1994;45:361.
Durand ML, Calderwood SB, Weber DJ, et al. Acute bacterial meningitis in adults: a review of 493 episodes. N Engl J Med 1993;328:21.
Kornelisse RF, deGroot R, Neijens HJ. Bacterial meningitis: mechanisms of disease and therapy. Eur J Pediatr 1995;154:85.
Quagliarello V, Scheld WM. Bacterial meningitis: pathogenesis, pathophysiology, and progress. N Engl J Med 1992;327:864.
Saez-Llorens X, Ramilo O, Mustafa MM, et al. Molecular pathophysiology of bacterial meningitis: current concepts and therapeutic implications. J Pediatr 1990;116:671.
Tunkel AR, Wispelwey B, Scheld WM. Bacterial meningitis: recent advances in pathophysiology and treatment. Ann Intern Med 1990;112:610.
Tunkel AR, Scheld WM. Pathogenesis and pathophysiology of bacterial meningitis. Annu Rev Med 1993;44:103.

VIRAL INFECTIONS

Doms RW, Lamb RA, Rose JK, Helenius A. Folding and assembly of viral membrane proteins. Virology 1993;193:545.
Fields BN, Knipe DM, eds. Virology. 2nd ed. New York: Raven Press, 1990.
Lanzrein M, Schlegel A, Kempf C. Entry and uncoating of enveloped viruses. Biochem J 1994;302:313.
Levy JA, Fraenkel-Conrat H, Owens RA. Virology. 3rd ed. Englewood Cliffs, NJ: Prentice-Hall, Inc, 1994.
Suzuki Y. Gangliosides as influenza virus receptors. Variation of influenza viruses and their recognition of the receptor sialo-sugar chains. Prog Lipid Res 1994;33:429.
Pereira L. Function of glycoprotein B homologues of the family herpresviridae. Infect Agents Dis 1994;3:9.
Ring CJA. The B cell-immortalizing functions of Epstein-Barr virus. J Gen Virol 1994;75:1.
Sen GC, Lengyel P. The interferon system: a bird's eye view of its biochemistry. J Biol Chem 1992;267:5017.
Voyles BA. The biology of viruses. St. Louis: CV Mosby, 1993.
White DO, Fenner FJ. Medical virology. 4th ed. San Diego: Academic Press, 1994.
Whitely RJ, Gnann JW Jr. Acyclovir: a decade later. N Engl J Med 1992;327:782.

chapter **20**

Endocrine and Reproductive Disorders

Four far-reaching processes are vital to the perpetuation of the species and to the maintenance of the well-being of the individual. They are: (*1*) providing for the individual's ability to reproduce; (*2*) ensuring normal growth and development; (*3*) maintaining the integrity of the internal milieu by defending fluid and electrolyte homeostasis and; (*4*) orchestrating the metabolic responses to eating, fasting and starvation, infection, trauma, and stress in general. These four complex processes require the participation of billions of cells from various organs. Coordinating the activity of so many cells requires a signal that can be recognized by the cells to synchronize their activities.

Two systems are specially adapted to drive the actions of other cells: the nervous system and the endocrine system. The nervous system exerts most of its influence via localized synaptic connections in which a specific neurotransmitter is released and bound to a receptor on a proximate neuron. Thus, the functional integrity of the nervous system relies on structural continuity. By contrast, the endocrine system has more wide-spread influences because it can exert influence over target cells throughout the body, disseminating its signal via the circulation. Specificity of response to a particular hormone then relies on a target cell endowed with the complementary receptor for that hormone. In that way, cells will not react to the myriad other hormones being carried in the blood, unless, of course, the cell is endowed with the appropriate receptor. Ultimately, of course, the nervous system acting through the hypothalamus controls much of the endocrine system by pacing the activity of the pituitary gland. In that role, the pituitary serves as the relay between the nervous system and the various target glands including the thyroid, adrenal, and gonads.

A moment's reflection will reveal that the four processes listed above require such a high degree of coordination that more than one hormone or signal molecule must be involved. For example, in the case of the defense of the blood glucose concentration, a sensor resides in the pancreas, which secretes insulin when the blood glucose increases above 90 mg/dl. This causes glucose to enter cells for storage as glycogen or fat. Another hormone, glucagon, is secreted when the blood glucose falls. Thus, it is plain to see that these metabolic processes depend on coordination by hormones exerting counter-regulatory control.

At a minimum, a hormonally regulated system must include a secretory gland, a receptor for the hormone on or within the target cell, and some feedback mechanism that regulates the secretion of the hormone in response to the function being regulated. For instance, in the cases of the blood [glucose](Figure 20.1), plasma [Ca^{++}], and plasma [Na^{+}], it is clear that the particular metabolite is being regulated by oscillating around a physiologic set-point. But with processes such as growth and development or signaling the onset of puberty, there is no simple set-point to establish the focal point of the oscillations. In the case of these developmental programs contained within the genome, full expression can occur only in collaboration with the secretion of various hormones, and feedback typically involves more than one hormone.

As informational or signal molecules, hormones carry out the primary function of modulating cellular activity in one or more organs in a selective fashion. In some cases, this effect is an end in itself, whereas in others, it is a stimulus to the cells to release a different, but complementary hormone. Hence, release of hormones must be directed by a signal from a higher center and the inhibition of their secretion must depend upon recognition by the higher center that the desired change in cellular activity has been accomplished. Typically, secretion and suppression of hormones

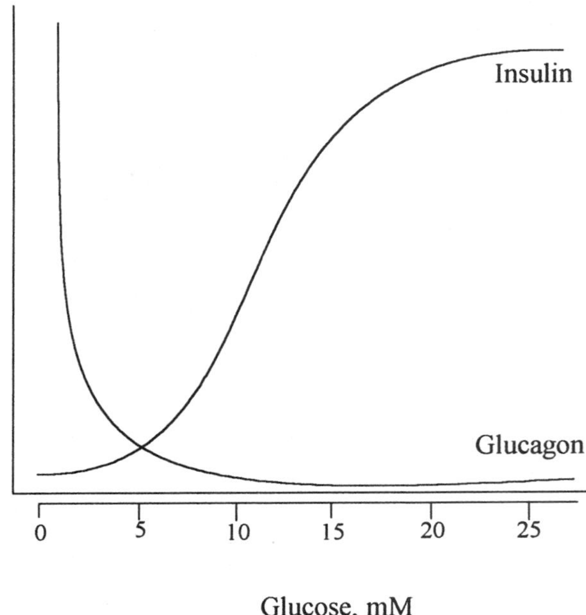

Figure 20.1. Feedback regulation of blood glucose. The relative secretion rates of the major glucose counter-regulatory hormones insulin and glucagon are shown. Note the intersection of the two at a point roughly equivalent to the normal average blood sugar of 5 mM.

is carried out under control of a "feedback loop," wherein the absence of some factor elicits secretion of a hormone to stimulate cellular production of the factor. Secretion continues until the increased levels of the hormones causes secretion to cease because of operation of the feedback loop. It follows that circulating level of many hormones tend to fluctuate. When estimating hormone levels, this requires pooled specimens, obtained every 20 to 30 minutes over 1 1/2 hours to compensate for the fluctuations.

NEUROENDOCRINE INTERACTIONS

The pituitary gland is responsible for production and secretion of many of so-called tropic hormones, which promote, in turn, the hormonal secretions from the target organs for which each trophic hormone is specific. The pituitary can be conveniently discussed, according to its anatomy, as the neurohypophysis (posterior pituitary), which is under direct control of the central nervous system (CNS), and the adenohypophysis (anterior pituitary), which is controlled by the brain through more indirect, humoral factors. The portion of the CNS directly responsible for pituitary secretory control is the hypothalamus; the hypothalamic-pituitary anatomic unit functions as what is commonly thought of as a neuroendocrine system. In the case of the neurohypophysis, the evidence shows that the principal hormones secreted by the posterior pituitary (vasopressin and oxytocin) actually are synthesized in the axons of nerves originating in the hypothalamus; therefore, the glandular portion of the system is principally a storage and secretory, rather than synthetic, organ. Release of these hormones occurs under direct neural stimulation.

Neural control over the adenohypophysis is less direct: the several hormones actually synthesized by the various cell types the anterior pituitary comprises are secreted in response to neurally produced "releasing factors" (hypophyseotrophic hormones). These releasing factors are carried to the adenohypophysis from the hypothalamus by means of the vascular hypophyseal-portal complex. Ultimately, the entire pituitary is controlled by the brain through the hypothalamus.

GENERAL CELLULAR RESPONSE TO HORMONES—ROLE OF RECEPTORS

As solubility considerations are central to biologic phenomena, it is apt to consider the general cellular responses to hormones by dividing them into water-soluble and lipid-soluble groups. Because cell membranes typically are lipid in nature, members of the lipid-soluble group (steroid and thyroid hormones) generally enter cells, thus exerting their influences intracellularly. Members of the water-soluble group (peptides and catecholamines) cannot traverse the membrane easily, thus being forced to interact with the cell surface receptors anchored to the plasma membrane. Thus, modulation of cellular activity by water-soluble hormones requires some means to link binding of the hormone to the outside of the cell membrane to production of an intracellular message to trigger the hormone mediated action. One common way that this translation step is mediated is by the G-proteins (see Chapter 1) (Figure 20.2) and the enzyme adenylate cyclase, which converts adenosine triphosphate (ATP) to cyclic adenosine monophosphate (AMP) at the inner surface of the cell membrane. Cyclic AMP then diffuses through the cell, activating various protein kinase which, in turn, phosphorylate multiple enzymes of which their activity is thus modified. In contrast, the lipid-soluble hormones bind directly to receptors within the cell that, in turn, bind to regions of the genome of which its function is thereby modulated directly.

Above all, hormonal actions at the cellular level require some means of specific recognition. Clearly, if hormones are secreted into blood, most cells of the body are exposed to equal concentrations, yet only specific cell types may react to the hormones' presence. Such specific recognition depends upon specificity of the cell surface receptor sites, in the case of water-soluble hormones, or intracellular molecule-specific binding sites, in the case of lipid-soluble hormones. Although the genetic endowment of all body cells is identical in a given individual, through the process of differentiation, parts of the genome are repressed in favor of cellular specialization; hence, hormonal-responsiveness of a particular cell will depend ultimately upon whether its genome is directing synthesis of specific binding sites for that hormone. It should be evident that even if a hormone is produced, when the receptor for it on the target cell is absent or defective, no biochemical response will ensue.

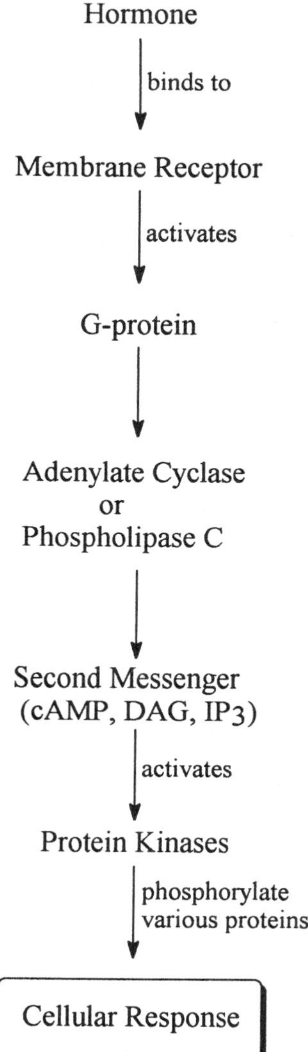

Figure 20.2. Membrane hormone receptor-mediated cellular response. The mechanism shown is a general one for water soluble hormones that cannot enter the cell easily through the lipid barrier. Activation of adenylate cyclase or phospholipase C depends upon G- protein activation at the membrane receptor site, which initiates the cascade and produces the cellular response.

Principles of Feedback Inhibition

With the above in mind, the principles of a feedback loop should become clear. In general, it is obvious that sustained release of a given hormone is undesirable for overall homeostatic control. This is so because hormonal secretion normally is episodic, rather than constant, reflecting the waxing and waning of the target analyte. If it was constant, there would be no "information gathering step"—the essence of a feedback loop. For instance, the CNS would be at risk for severe hypoglycemia if the person experienced 24-hour continuous secretion of insulin. Hence, it also is obvious that there must be some means of regulating secretion, such that there is a balance established between hormonal output and attainment of the desired cellular response. In the case of insulin, it is the glucose level that varies directly with the insulin level and causes regulation of insulin release by pancreatic β-cells. Other feedback loops are somewhat more complex in nature, but all function in essentially the same way. Interruption of the loop will result in unregulated hormone secretion, with potential effects on organs not normally targets for that hormone. This especially is true of the lipid soluble hormones.

Factors that may impact on the feedback mechanism include: (*1*) presence of secretory cells not under feedback control (eg, cells of a thyroid nodule that lead to clinical hyperthyroidism because of sustained responses by the target cells); (*2*) inadequate target-organ response causing sustained hormone release (eg, thyroid dysgenesis leading to sustained elevations in thyroid-stimulating hormone [TSH] because of failure of the thyroid gland to respond); (*3*) a defect in hormone synthesis that may result in formation of a biologically inactive molecule appearing clinically to be a deficiency of secretion (eg, vitamin D-dependent rickets, a deficiency of the capacity to 25-hydroxylate 1-OH-vitamin D, resulting in a relatively inactive form); (*4*) end-organ unresponsiveness due to lack of specific binding receptors or an appropriate adenylate cyclase response to hormone-receptor binding (eg, pseudohypoparathyroidism, in which circulating levels of parathyroid hormone are elevated due to lack of cellular response). Thus, although endocrinopathies typically are classified as either hyperfunction or hypofunction of secretion, it now should be clear that the underlying cause actually may be remote from the affected endocrine gland. Moreover, because of the feedback loop, hypofunction of one aspect of the loop may result in hyperfunction of another.

PITUITARY GLAND

In the introduction, we highlighted the fact that the pituitary functions as a relay between the hypothalamus and various target glands, thereby influencing a wide range of metabolic and developmental processes. By convention, the hormones elaborated by the anterior pituitary are placed in three groups on the basis of structural homologies: (*1*) growth hormone (GH) and prolactin, which act on nonendocrine target tissues; (*2*) the glycoprotein hormones, TSH, follicle-stimulating hormone (FSH), and luteinizing hormone (LH); and (*3*) adrenocorticotropic hormone (ACTH) and related peptides. Members of groups two and three act on other endocrine glands and, accordingly, secretion of those pituitary hormones are under feedback control by the product of its target gland.

GH, as the name implies, is essential to realizing the full growth potential (as encoded by the genome) of the individual's skeletal system, muscles, and viscera. Prolactin is crucial to the development of the mammary gland's synthetic capacity for milk production, the food that nourishes the neonate. The glycoprotein hormones TSH, FSH, and LH are members of the second group. They are heterodimers that share a common α-subunit but are distinguished by their unique β-subunits. TSH stimulates the thyroid to produce and secrete thyroxine and tri-iodothyronine. In women, FSH is responsible for inducing maturation of ovarian follicles, whereas in men, it stimulates spermatogenesis by the testes. The other pituitary gonadotropin, LH, participates in development of the corpus luteum, which secretes progesterone. In men, LH stimulates the ability of the interstitial cells of the testes to secrete male hormones. The third group is marked by the presence of ACTH, which is the hormone responsible for stimulating the adrenal cortex to synthesize cortisol both under normal circumstances and, even more importantly, during times of stress. The ability to augment ACTH secretion and consequently cortisol production during times of stress is a biologic attribute necessary for the individual's survival.

Tests of Anterior Pituitary Function

Situated at the base of the brain, just below the optic chiasm in a cavity called the sella turcica,

Table 20.1. Tests of Pituitary Function

HORMONE	STIMULATION	SUPPRESSION
ACTH	Insulin-induced hypoglycemia Metyrapone CRH	Dexamethasone
TSH	TRH	T_3 or T_4
LH/FSH	GnRH Clomiphene	
GH	Insulin-induced hypoglycemia Arginine infusion L-dopa GRF	Glucose tolerance test
Prolactin	TRH Chlorpromazine Metoclopramide	

the pituitary is in a strategic location to disrupt a variety of brain functions if it undergoes enlargement (eg, as with an adenoma). Consequently, any evaluation of a patient with suspected anterior pituitary disease must not be limited to the testing of endocrine function but also demands a quest for evidence of anatomic distortions in the region of the gland. Such a search should begin with a painstaking neurologic and ophthalmologic exam, but must also include appropriate radiographic studies.

In probing the endocrine function of the anterior pituitary, it is important to measure secretions by the target glands because endocrine symptomatology will stem from hypo- or hyperfunction of one or more target glands. Provocative studies are used to stimulate pituitary hormone production in cases when hypofunction is suspected (Table 20.1). Insulin-induced hypoglycemia is the most widely used test to assess the ability of the pituitary to augment GH secretion. Various hypothalamic releasing hormones (CRH, GnRH, and TRH) provide specific stimulation for secretion of its target pituitary hormone. By contrast, when hyperfunction is suspected, tests of suppressibility are warranted.

Hypopituitarism

Pituitary tumors, other mass lesions that invade the pituitary gland, and ischemic necrosis all can lead to varying degrees of hypopituitarism. Radiation therapy of brain tumors also can damage the pituitary. Because adrenal cortical function is essential to life, ACTH deficiency manifests the signs and symptoms of adrenocortical deficiency. These are discussed in the section on the adrenal. One feature, however, distinguishes ACTH deficiency from adrenocortical deficiency: no hyperpigmentation is seen with ACTH deficiency whereas it may be striking in adrenocortical deficiency.

TSH deficiency manifests the features of hypothyroidism. During childhood, because thyroid hormones participate in normal growth, retardation of growth will ensue. Notably, only thyroid replacement will suffice in this case. LH and FSH deficiency cause a variety of hypogonadal manifestations that are discussed in the section on reproductive function.

GH deficiency in children results in growth retardation (discussed in Chapter 2 on growth and development), whereas in adults, GH deficiency usually is asymptomatic. It is important to emphasize that despite all the notoriety of GH deficiency in childhood, it is not a leading cause of growth retardation. Instead, chronic disease, emotional deprivation, and chromosomal abnormalities account for the "lion's share."

Pituitary Hormone Excess

In contrast to the situation with hypopituitarism, hypersecretory states of pituitary hormones generally are confined to only one hormone. GH-secreting tumors cause acromegaly in the adult and gigantism in the child before epiphyseal fusion, whereas ACTH-secreting tumors cause Cushings disease. These syndromes are discussed below. Prolactin-secreting tumors are associated with amenorrhea and galactorrhea and, therefore, are considered in the section on reproductive function.

GROWTH HORMONE EXCESS

Chronic hypersecretion of GH results in gigantism or acromegaly or both, depending upon the degree of epiphyseal closure at the time of onset. The specific cause of this dysfunction usually is a pituitary adenoma. This includes cells responsible for production of GH that have become unresponsive to feedback inhibition by somatostatin and are independent of hypothalamic secretory command.

When hypersecretion of GH commences in childhood, it is manifested chiefly by markedly increased growth velocity. Growth of the adenoma with associated destruction of the gonadotropin-secreting cells causes either delayed puberty or hypogonadotropic hypogonadism.

If onset of the GH hypersecretion occurs after epiphyseal closure, acromegaly is the result. Signs and symptoms of acromegaly due to GH hypersecretion usually begin insidiously and may evolve over many years. Patients may notice a change in ring, glove, or shoe size, whereas acquaintances may detect coarsened facial features from soft tissue overgrowth of the nose and mouth. In time, the skin becomes thickened, from edema and deposition of hyaluronic acid, and oily. Hair growth increases, and skin tags and acanthosis nigricans occur. Mandibular enlargement becomes a problem with malocclusion while vocal cord hypertrophy causes the voice to deepen. Visceromegaly and bony overgrowth are prominent features. Males may suffer from impotence and females may experience menstrual irregularities including amenorrhea and reproductive failure.

ADRENOCORTICOTROPIC HORMONE EXCESS

In the vast majority of cases, primary ACTH hypersecretion is due to primary pituitary adenomas, in turn, producing hypersecretion of adrenal corticosteroids and resulting in the clinical picture of Cushing's disease. Signs and symptoms include central obesity ("buffalo hump"), muscle wasting, osteopenia, cutaneous atrophy, diabetes mellitus, and hypertension. It is worth mentioning that, although Cushing's disease is uncommon in children, when it does occur, growth arrest is a prominent finding. The effects of the adrenal androgen hypersecretion causes masculinization in females. In Cushing's disease associated with feminization of a male, the cause is almost always an adrenal tumor, suggesting that the genes coding for the enzymes necessary for ovarian steroid biosynthesis are derepressed in such tumors.

Pituitary Hormone Deficiency

Because the anterior pituitary secretes six hormones, loss of all defines panhypopituitarism. If onset is caused by ischemia or infarct, the results can be both abrupt and catastrophic. But when loss of secretion stems from a mass lesion, onset may be more gradual. As a rule of thumb, pituitary hormones are lost in the reverse order of how essential they are to sustaining life. Accordingly, the order is as follows: GH, then gonadotropins, then TSH, and finally ACTH. But as a practical matter, one should not rely too heavily on this clinical pearl. Rather, appropriate stimulatory tests are necessary to probe pituitary reserve when hypopituitarism is suspected (Table 20.1). We consider the effects of deficiency of GH and ACTH below.

GROWTH HORMONE DEFICIENCY

Although growth hormone deficiency is the single most common pituitary hormone deficiency state, it actually is not a leading cause of growth retardation. Nevertheless, its importance stems from the fact that it is a treatable cause of short stature and from the insights that studies of the mechanism of action of growth hormone have provided. Because these aspects have been considered in detail in Chapter 2 on growth and development, we will not repeat them here.

There are several different etiological entities grouped under the generic term "GH deficiency," among which isolated GH secretory deficiency is one of the rarest. Retrospectively, newborns with an isolated GH deficiency are within normal limits for birth length and weight, although micropenis may be present in the male, and GH-deficient infants are prone to hypoglycemia. Depending upon the degree of deficiency, the growth velocity slows within the first 6 months of life or later in infancy with a concomitant retardation in bone age. Both long bone and cranial bone growth are affected, causing not only short stature but a characteristic facies, including frontal bossing, flattened nasal bridge, and small chin. Puberty is delayed, but the normal pubertal growth spurt is attenuated. Normal reproduction is possible.

Tests of GH reserve include brisk exercise, insulin-hypoglycemia (not without risk to the patient), L-dopa, or arginine. Because in any particular subject any one of these tests may fail to provoke GH secretion, it is necessary to use more than one test and to collect multiple samples to establish the diagnosis of GH deficiency.

ADRENOCORTICOTROPIC HORMONE DEFICIENCY

Because the primary function of ACTH is the support and stimulation of the adrenal cortex, deficiency of ACTH will result in adrenocortical hypofunction. Pituitary and hypothalamic tumors can cause ACTH deficiency, but usually in association with deficiency of other pituitary hormones. Clinical manifestations will be those associated with deficiency of adrenal corticosteroids, classically termed Addison's disease, with the single exception that hyperpigmentation is not present. It is not at all clear that failure of ACTH secretion is due to primary pituitary dysfunction, rather than hypothalamic disease, and cases meeting the clinical criteria for this entity are rare. Of course, chronic treatment with glucocorticoids is the most likely reason for ACTH deficiency, with persistent elevation of corticosteroids suppressing ACTH secretion.

If the adrenals produce adequate amounts of cortisol or if they respond with a surge of cortisol to an injection of cosyntropin (a synthetic fragment of ACTH), then the adrenals are not suppressed. No increase in plasma cortisol in response to cosyntropin implicates either the adrenals or the hypothalamic-pituitary axis. The next step is to measure plasma ACTH levels, which will be elevated in adrenal disease because of lack of feedback, whereas in pituitary or hypothalamic dysfunction, the ACTH levels will be low or apparently normal. Needless to say, when cortisol levels are low, low or normal levels of ACTH are abnormal.

NORMAL REPRODUCTIVE ENDOCRINOLOGY

Menarche, the time of the first menses, heralds the onset of reproductive capability in the female. At that time, the ovaries release ova (oocytes or gametes) in an episodic fashion, adhering to a cycle that recurs on average every 28 days. The ovaries also secrete estradiol, androstenedione, and progesterone, a biosynthetic function that is a property of the ovarian follicle. Human females are born with about two million oocytes (germ cells), some 450 of which will be lost during ovulation over a woman's reproductive lifetime. But the bulk of the oocytes will disappear by atresia, leaving essentially no remaining ova by the onset of menopause around age 50 years. At that time, the reproductive life of the woman comes to an end. During each reproductive or menstrual cycle, only a small number of follicles are recruited toward the goal of ovulation, but normally only one follicle, the dominant follicle, actually is extruded.

Like all steroid hormones, female sex steroids are made from cholesterol, largely supplied in the form of low density lipoproteins (LDL) cholesterol. In the first step of ovarian steroid synthesis (Figure 20.3), the cholesterol side chain cleavage enzyme removes the side chain from cholesterol (C-27), forming pregnenolone (C-21). By various routes, progesterone, 17-OH progesterone, and 17α pregnenolone are formed. Removal of the C-20,21 side chain from 17-OH progesterone yields androstenedione, which can be converted to testosterone or estrone. Both testosterone and estrone can go on to form estradiol, catalyzed by an aromatase that desaturates the A ring of the androgen steroid nucleus. The aromatase catalyzes three sequential hydroxylations involving O_2 and NADPH.

The ovarian follicles are embedded in the stroma of the ovarian cortex. Each follicle contains one oocyte enclosed in a layer of granulosa cells. Concentric layers of theca cells surround the granulosa cells. Granulosa and theca cells work together to synthesize estradiol: the theca cells synthesize androstenedione, which is converted to estradiol by the granulosa cells that have abundant aromatase activity. As seen, aromatase is essential to desaturate the A ring of the precursor, androstenedione. However, theca cells, although possessing only meager levels of aromatase activity, can convert 21-carbon steroid precursors to the 19-carbon androgen, androstenedione.

As females near the onset of puberty, feedback sensitivity of the hypothalamic-pituitary unit to sex steroids lessens, resulting in a surge of the pituitary gonadotropins FSH and LH. FSH and LH arouse the ovaries to secrete the sex steroids that will drive the development of secondary sexual characteristics according to the information contained within the genome of the normal female. FSH stirs the biosynthetic capabilities of the granulosa cells, whereas LH stimulates theca cell activity. Thus, from a biochemical point of view, it is clear why two gonadotropins are required to elaborate the female sex steroids.

Production of gonadotropin hormone-releasing hormone (GnRH) is an inherent property of the cells in the medial basal hypothalamus and is the stimulus for the secretion of FSH and LH at

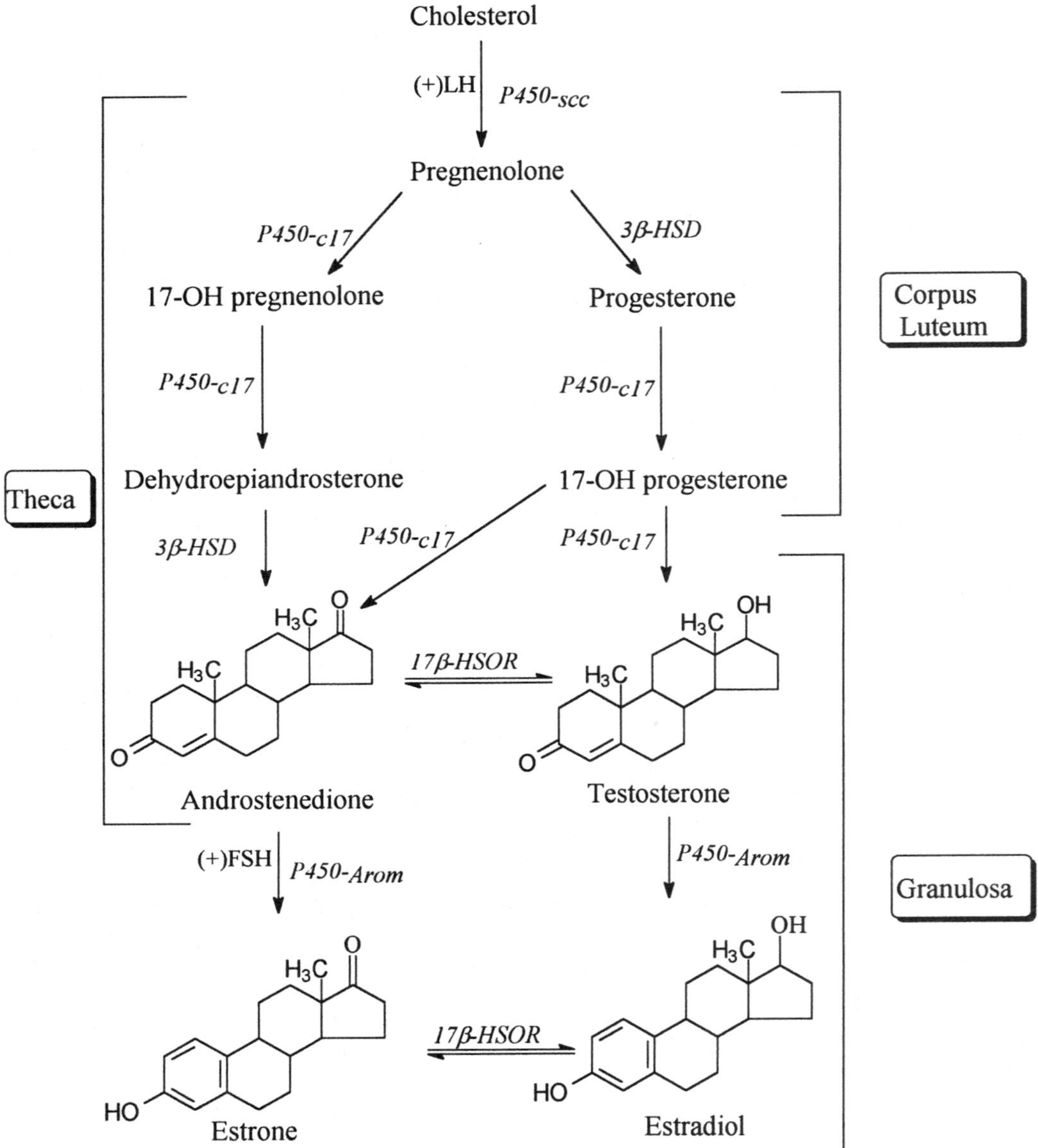

Figure 20.3. Ovarian steroidogenesis. The common substrate for steroid synthesis is cholesterol, with conversion to pregnenolone under positive feedback control of luteinizing hormone (LH). Testosterone is a normal intermediate in synthesis of estradiol from progesterone, a fact of significance in diagnosis of female masculinization disorders. The major route of conversion of progesterone to estradiol through androstenedione is controlled by follicle-stimulating hormone (FSH). P450-$_{scc}$ = cholesterol side chain cleavage enzyme; P450-$_{c17}$ = 17-α hydroxylase; 3β-HSD = hydroxysteroid dehydrogenase; 17β-HSOR = hyroxysteroid oxido-reductase; P450-$_{Arom}$ = aromatase. Note that there is some degree of overlap in the capacities of different segments of the ovary to carry out these reactions.

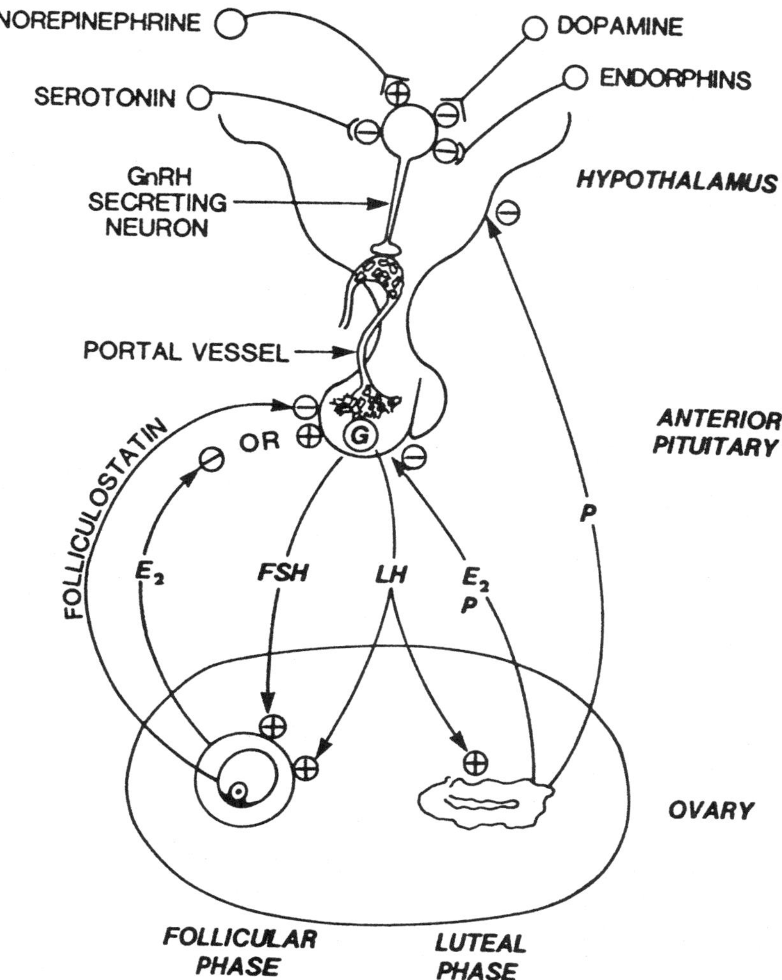

Figure 20.4. Hormonal relationships during normal menstrual cycle. Note the multiplicity of positive and negative feedback control sites involving several different organs. GnRH = gonadotropin releasing hormone; G = gonadotrope; E_2 = estradiol; FSH = follicle stimulating hormone; LH = luteinizing hormone; P = progesterone. Reprinted with permission from Hershman JM. Endocrine Pathophysiology: A Patient-Oriented Approach. 3rd ed. Philadelphia: Lea & Febiger, 1988: 156.

the onset of puberty. Communication between the CNS and the anatomically distant ovaries occurs via the circulation through feedback loops, involving the basophilic cells of the anterior pituitary that produce LH and FSH. GnRH normally is secreted in pulses, separated by 1 to 3 hours; its secretion is regulated primarily by norepinephrine, dopamine, and serotonin, as well as by endorphins. LH and FSH release from the pituitary follows within minutes of a pulse of GnRH. FSH and LH also are under feedback control, both from the hypothalamus and from estradiol and progesterone levels in the female and testosterone in the male. These complex relationships are illustrated in Figure 20.4, from which it can be seen that the neurosecretory, primary, and secondary glandular components all are essential for normal sexual development.

The Menstrual Cycle

By convention, the menstrual cycle is divided into three stages (Figure 20.5): the preovulatory or follicular phase, ovulation, and the luteal phase. The

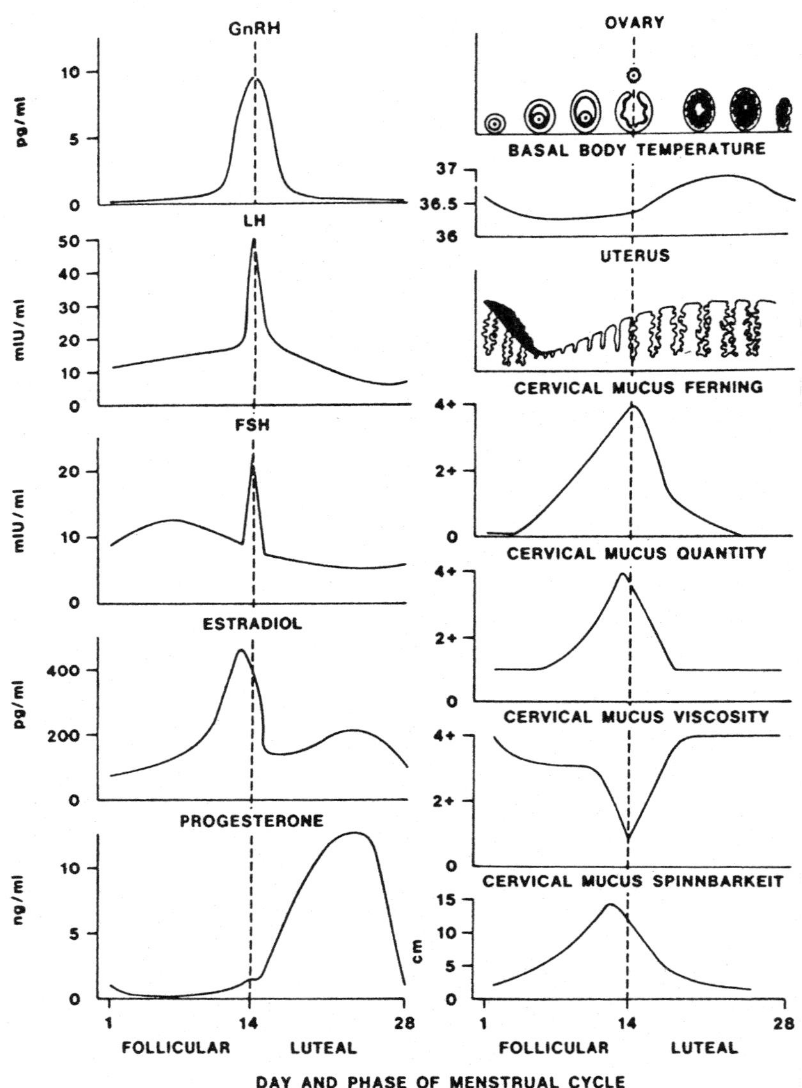

Figure 20.5. Hormonal changes and the physiologic changes of menstruation. Reprinted with permission from Hershman JM. Endocrine Pathophysiology: A Patient-Oriented Approach. 3rd ed. Philadelphia: Lea & Febiger, 1988: 155.

cycle usually unfolds over 28 days, with a range of 21 to 40 days, with the follicular and luteal phases occupying approximately 14 days each and ovulation requiring about 1 day. During the preovulatory phase of the menstrual cycle, FSH secretion induced by both GnRH and low circulating estrogen levels stimulates growth of a collection of preovulatory follicles. From among this cohort, one follicle—the dominant ovarian follicle—will ovulate. It is not known how a particular follicle is selected during each cycle. The resulting increase in intrinsic ovarian estrogen synthesis triggers a negative feedback response in FSH secretion, while also inciting a positive response in LH secretion. The LH "surge" thus induced stimulates maturation of the dominant follicle. During the ovulatory phase, which lasts about a day, rupture of the follicle with release of the oocyte occurs. Attendant upon ovulation, there is a rapid decrease in the luteal estrogen production, thought to provoke a corresponding decrease in LH secretion through a negative feedback loop. The reason for release of only a single oocyte with each cycle is unclear, but that it is the rule rather than the exception is attested to by the relatively uncommon occurrence of dizygotic twinning in human pregnancies.

The third or luteal phase of the menstrual cycle usually lasts about 14 days and is coordinated in time with passage of the oocyte from the follicle into the uterus, a trip that requires approximately 8 to 9 days. During this time, the slow decline in LH levels provides sufficient LH to support the luteal production of increasing quantities of progesterone and to sustain high estrogen levels in ovarian venous blood. High circulating levels of these hormones, particularly of progesterone, exerts a negative feedback effect on pituitary secretion of LH. If fertilization of the ovum does not occur, luteal production of progesterone and estrogen begins to wane because of the decline in pituitary secretion of LH, the corpus luteum becomes atretic, and menstruation ensues. Thus, a new cycle is initiated.

Menstruation itself is a consequence of the uterine changes induced by the cyclic sequence of estrogen and progesterone secretion. Estrogen supports proliferative changes in the endometrium, causing epithelial and stromal cell division, mucosal thickening, and linear elongation of the tubular glands. As progesterone levels increase, these changes are amplified by increasing edema and vascularity of the endometrium, and coiling of the tubular glands. Consequently, the uterus is readied to receive a fertilized ovum for implantation and development of a placenta. But, if implantation does not occur, the luteum becomes atretic, bringing with it sloughing of the endometrium. Menses then can be thought of as the "outraged cry of a frustrated uterus." Before passing on to a consideration of changes that occur as a consequence of fertilization, a brief discussion of clinical abnormalities of the menstrual cycle is in order.

Menstrual Disorders

Normal menses is the visible result of the highly ordered and complex interaction of the above-described hormonal influences. It follows that abnormal menses implies some disruption in this order, at one or more points. Key to appropriate diagnosis is a determination of whether the menstrual disorder is a primary or secondary event; that is, whether a previously normal pattern has ever been established by the individual, and at what age. If no anatomic abnormalities of the female outflow tract or of the uterus are present, the most common cause of amenorrhea is lack of adequate stimulation by the hypothalamic-pituitary-ovarian axis.

PRIMARY AMENORRHEA

Menarche typically occurs at about 12 to 13 years in American females. Thus, primary amenorrhea is defined as the absence of menses in a phenotypic female 16 years of age or older. Because increased growth velocity and physical maturation normally precede menarche, absence of these two changes in body dimensions occurring in conjunction with amenorrhea in an adolescent female should be considered abnormal. Painstakingly taking a history and conducting a physical examination are the pillars of diagnosis in any patient with suspected primary amenorrhea. Because primary amenorrhea is relatively rare among all amenorrheic patients, an intensive investigation can be extremely rewarding diagnostically.

Etiologies of primary amenorrhea are wide-ranging, extending from genetic, through acquired or congenital glandular dysgenesis, to simple or complex anatomic causes. For instance, a thorough physical examination might reveal something as easily remedied as an imperforate hymen. It goes without saying, however, that such a relatively straightforward etiology should be suspected beforehand if the patient has exhibited normal growth and secondary sexual development. Establishing evidence for secretion of endogenously secreted sex steroid hormones by end organ effects can be very helpful to diagnosis. These effects include the distribution and extent of development of axillary and pubic hair, breast development, pattern of adipose tissue distribution, and velocity of growth versus age. Also, one should determine whether there is evidence of undue androgen effect as reflected by hirsutism, deepening of the voice, vaginal atrophy, and clitoromegaly. The various syndromes and disorders associated with pri-

Table 20.2. Primary Amenorrhea

Defects of Genitourinary Tract and Uterus
Vaginal aplasia or atresia
Imperforate hymen
Congenital absence of uterus—may be associated with other anomalies
Ovarian Disorders
45,X (XO) gonadal dysgenesis (Turner's syndrome)—25% to 40% of patients with primary amenorrhea: short stature, gonads replaced by fibrous tissue, somatic abnormalities
XX gonadal dysgenesis—fibrotic gonads but do not have phenotypic features of Turner's syndrome
Congenital absence of ovaries
Testicular feminization—resistance to circulating androgens but responsive to estrogens produced by testes
Hormonal and Hypothalamic Disorders
Congenital adrenal hyperplasia
Hypothyroidism
Hypopituitarism
Nutritional disorders

mary amenorrhea are listed in Table 20.2. It should be noted that, as in disorders of growth (see Chapter 2), there is an entity known as delayed menarche that corresponds to constitutional growth delay. Although this is a diagnosis of exclusion, it is important because premature initiation of estrogen therapy may result in premature closure of the epiphyses, with suppression of growth potential.

SECONDARY AMENORRHEA

Whereas secondary amenorrhea is defined by cessation of menses in a female who has undergone menarche, the distinction between this and primary amenorrhea is somewhat artificial. This artificiality arises because several of the disorders classified as primary amenorrhea depend upon the number of normal or near-normal follicles that can respond to and be cycled by the pituitary messengers. Hence, some patients will experience menarche only to undergo cessation of normal menses after a few cycles.

In general, patients with secondary amenorrhea will have experienced normal pubertal growth and undergone appropriate secondary sexual changes with onset of menarche. Because the hypothalamic-pituitary-ovarian axis lies at the heart of the female reproductive cycle, it is entirely predictable that hypothalamic, pituitary, ovarian, and uterine disorders account for the majority of disorders causing amenorrhea (Table 20.3). Secretion of GnRH by the hypothalamus is a delicate function easily disrupted by various stresses such as malnutrition, severe weight loss, a vigorous and sustained exercise program, psychological distress, and chronic disease. Thus, it is plain to see that after pregnancy itself, hypothalamic disorders lead the list, accounting for at least two-thirds of patients with secondary amenorrhea.

Pituitary prolactinomas may account for as many as 20% of patients with amenorrhea. Here again, the effect on the menstrual cycle actually is exerted on the hypothalamus, because excessive prolactin secretion can disrupt the normal pulsatile secretion of GnRH by the hypothalamus. Less common pituitary causes of amenorrhea are Cushing's disease, acromegaly, and post-partum pituitary infarction (Sheehan's syndrome).

Ovarian causes of amenorrhea are broadly divided between *anovulatory* states, which include *polycystic ovary disease* (PCOD), Cushing's disease, late onset congenital adrenal hyperplasia, and *premature ovarian failure*. Of these disorders, polycystic ovary disease (PCOD) is the most common, representing the phenotypic expression of several different disorders of ovarian, adrenal or hypothalamic function. Hence, PCOD, like anemia or hypoglycemia can come about from multiple causes. Subjects with PCOD usually have

Table 20.3. Secondary Amenorrhea

Pregnancy —↑ estrogen effect
Hypothalamic
Psychogenic: stress, anxiety—variable estrogen effect
Strenous exercise—↓ estrogen
Chronic disease—variable estrogen
Pituitary
Prolactinoma — ↓ estrogen
Acquired hypopituitarism
Ovarian
Anovulatory states: polycystic ovary disease—↓ estrogen effect
Premature ovarian failure
Adrenal
Cushing's syndrome
Late onset congenital adrenal hyperplasia
Adrenal insufficiency
Uterine
Infection or surgical procedures causing scarring
Thyroid
Hypothyroidism
Hyperthyroidism

signs of excessive androgen secretion including hirsutism, acne, and oily skin, but usually do not show evidence of virilization (clitoral enlargement, male pattern baldness, and deepening of the voice). In patients with PCOD, excessive androgens are elaborated by the ovaries leading to a distorted LH/FSH ratio in which LH predominates. In such a hormonal setting, normal follicular growth and ovulation are blocked. Further contributing to the increase in LH levels is disrupted feedback of estrogen on the hypothalamus which increases pulsatile GnRH release. Some of the androgens are converted to estrogens, but, for the most part, the excessive estrogens are not of ovarian origin. Rather, estrogens are formed in adipose tissue (many patients are obese) from androgens.

Another factor contributing to ovarian androgen production in these patients is *insulin-resistant hyperinsulinemia*. Theca cells in the ovary possess receptors for IGF-1, which are further stimulated to produce androgens by high insulin levels. Evidence exists, at least in some patients, that the adrenals also participate in elaboration of excessive amounts of androgens. Recently, Rodin et al have presented evidence that adrenal androgen secretion is increased in a cohort of patients with PCOD in whom urinary excretion of cortisol was increased. They reasoned that cortisol wastage stimulated steroidogenesis, including augmented production of androgens, by the adrenal. They further implicated 11β-hydroxysteroid dehydrogenase, which converts cortisol to cortisone, as another factor contributing to decrease in cortisol levels, thereby evoking still further secretion of androgens and other adrenal steroids.

In contrast to the relatively common PCOD, disorders associated with premature ovarian failure fortunately are rare. Symptoms suggestive of menopause, especially hot flashes, suggest premature ovarian failure. Causes include anomalies of the X chromosome, ovarian destruction from infection, neoplasm, or autoimmune process. Diagnosis is confirmed by demonstrating elevated gonadotropins in association with low estrogens. This is the classic situation wherein the absence of the target hormone creates a setting in which trophic hormone secretion cannot be suppressed.

Finally, uterine damage sufficient to cause amenorrhea is the result of surgical or other trauma, for example dilatation and curettage, to the uterus. Pregnancy associated with infection is another setting in which sclerotic changes to the uterine wall may occur.

The estrogen-dependent tissues are breast, vagina, cervix, and vulva. In the absence of adequate estrogen, the vagina and vulva will atrophy and breast size will diminish. Cervical mucous, which is watery and clear in the presence of estrogen, will become sparse, thick, and opaque in hypoestrogenic states. Furthermore, in hypoestrogenic states, patients will report dyspareunia and hot flashes.

RATIONALE FOR DIAGNOSTIC EVALUATION OF AMENORRHEA

In our overview of the events occurring during a normal menstrual cycle, it is clear that the reproductive cycle depends upon multiple loops that maintain control over the cooperation among the hypothalamus, pituitary, and ovaries. For example, interruption of the hypothalamic-pituitary axis as occurs in prolactinoma, with psychologic stress, or in PCOD will render otherwise functional glands dysfunctional. A second example, involving a normally functioning endocrine system, is the amenorrhea associated with obesity and PCOD. Recalling that androstenedione, produced by the adrenal glands, is converted to estrone by adipose tissue, some cases of gross obesity in endocrinologically normal women may result from high circulating levels of estrone that interfere with the normal feedback mechanisms between pituitary and ovary.

Keeping the above in mind, it is important to consider where in the hypothalamic-pituitary-ovarian axis the interruption may lie before embarking on a laboratory investigation. For example, diagnosis of pregnancy clearly obviates the need for further evaluation, whereas postpubertal development of hirsutism mandates an orderly, but vigorous workup. A laboratory finding of note includes elevated FSH levels, which are the most helpful in diagnosing primary ovarian failure, a diagnosis bolstered by finding low serum estradiol levels. Other FSH and LH patterns are noted in Figure 20.6. Further useful tests are serum prolactin levels (even in the absence of galactorrhea), thyroid studies, and serum estradiol. Opinion is divided as to the usefulness of a progesterone chal-

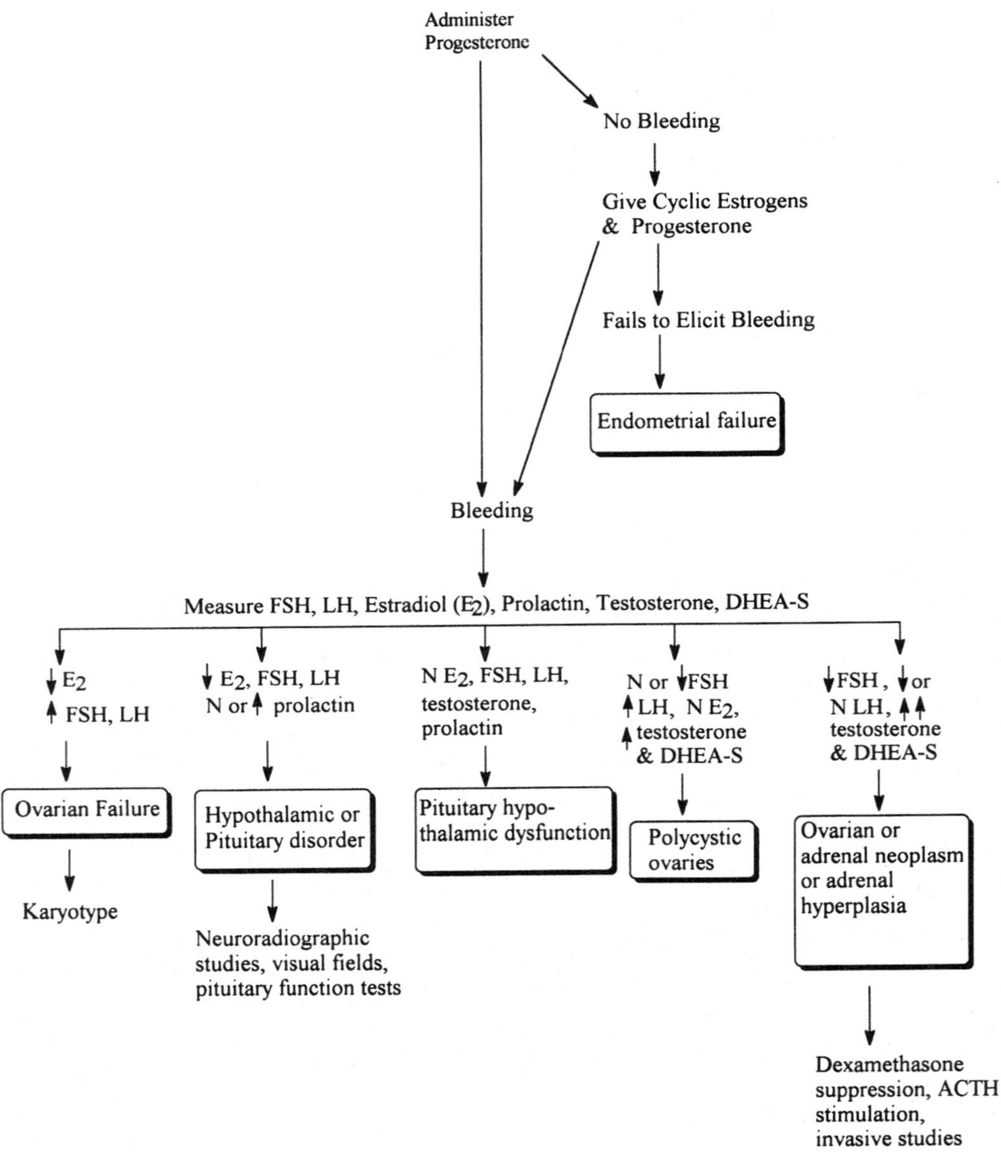

Figure 20.6. Flow sheet for methodologic approach to diagnosis of secondary amenorrhea. FSH = follicle stimulating hormone; LH = luteinizing hormone; DHEA-S = dehydroepiandrostenedione-sulfate; N = normal; ACTH = adrenocorticotropic hormone. (Based on Hershman JM. Endocrine Physiology: A Patient-Oriented Approach. 3rd ed. Philadelphia: Lea & Febiger, 1988: 174.)

lenge to determine whether adequate estrogen effect has been exerted on the endometrium. This test relies on the fact that secretion of both estrogen and progesterone are necessary for the endometrium to proliferate (estrogen) and differentiate for secretion (progesterone). If the endometrium has been prepared by estrogen, a single injection of progesterone (or oral progesterone for several days) will induce sloughing and bleeding. Various protocols for evaluation of amenorrhea are discussed in the texts listed in the suggested readings section at the end of this chapter.

FERTILIZATION AND ENDOCRINE FUNCTION OF THE FETO-PLACENTAL UNIT

In the event that fertilization of the ovum occurs, a very different scenario takes place from that outlined above. Taken together, the endocrinologic events instigated by pregnancy are quite profound and account for the most common cause of secondary amenorrhea. Hence, in the evaluation of amenorrhea, pregnancy should be considered first among diagnostic etiologies.

Maternal Events

Conception alters the course of the normal menstrual cycle, as described above, primarily by maintaining the endometrium as a fertile site to nourish the embryo. Thus, although the road is smoothed to accept the fertilized ovum by the changes that normally occur in the first half of the menstrual cycle, only successful implantation can accomplish the subsequent hormonal alterations that take place with pregnancy. The presence of a normal corpus luteum is essential to accomplish the transition from free blastocyst to the "master of ceremonies" for events yet to come over the next 40 weeks.

Feto-Placental Events

The placenta is unique among organs because it contains elements supplied by both the fetus and the mother. The fetal contribution consists of the syncytiotrophoblast and the closely associated cytotrophoblast. Maternal endometrial cells interdigitate with microvilli from the fetal trophoblastic layer. Implantation of the fertilized ovum follows ovulation by 8 to 9 days, at which time the trophoblast infiltrates the endometrium. Expansion of the trophoblast coincides with the earliest hormonal sign of pregnancy, secretion of human chorionic gonadotropin (hCG), produced by the cellular anlage of the placenta. Maternal blood levels of hCG increase rapidly thereafter, doubling every other day until the 10th gestational week when they decline slightly, maintaining a plateau for the duration of pregnancy. As a result of this rapid increase, the corpus luteum is prevented from undergoing its normal involution. It thus continues to produce estradiol and progesterone and so maintains the integrity of the uterus to sustain the embryo. Accordingly, it is evident that continued luteal function becomes independent of the pituitary, which normally supplies LH and FSH for this purpose.

In a very real sense, then, pregnancy causes an inversion of the usual orderly sequence of events, initiated in the hypothalamus. Indeed, by virtue of a negative feedback loop, hCG causes the frequency and amplitude of hypothalamic gonadotropin-releasing hormone to decrease, as well as causing the pituitary to become refractory to its presence. These events result in virtual absence of LH and FSH in maternal circulation throughout the pregnancy. Luteal support of placental secretory function continues over the first 7 weeks after conception. After that, the placenta is capable of producing sufficient quantities of estradiol and progesterone (see following text). These hormones increase progressively throughout pregnancy so that by term they are more than 10-fold their nonpregnant levels, the lion's share of both being placental in origin.

After about 8 weeks gestation, responsibility for progesterone synthesis passes from the corpus luteum to the placenta. Among progesterone's important functions in maintaining the conceptus, none may be more important than its role in inhibiting T-cell-mediated rejection of a foreign graft—in this case, the fetus itself. Progesterone also suppresses myometrial contractions, preventing premature expulsion of the fetus.

Estrogen synthesis during pregnancy, like that during the menstrual cycle, is a collaborative affair. In the case of the menstrual cycle, both granu-

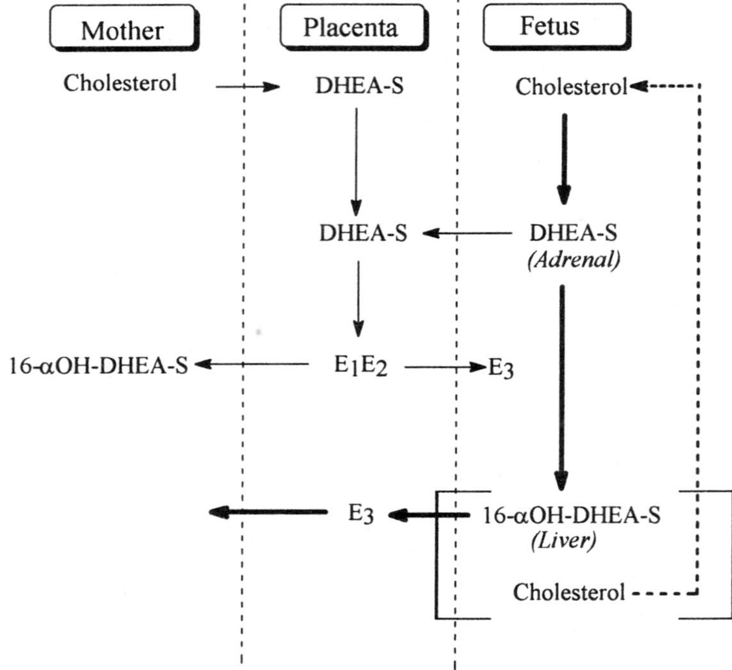

Figure 20.7. Materno-fetal-placental synthesis of estrogen. The unique product of this multiorgan cooperative pathway is estriol, produced by the fetal adrenal gland. In addition, note that the chief source of estrogen in pregnancy is the placenta, not the maternal ovary. $P_{450\text{-}c17}$ is required to convert progesterone to estrogens. Because placenta lacks this enzyme, it depends on androgens (DHEA-S) produced by maternal and fetal adrenal glands to produce estrogens. DHEA-s = dehydroepiandrostenedione sulfate; E_1 = estrone; E_2 = estradiol-17β; E_3 = estriol.

losa and thecal cells participate in the biosynthesis of estradiol, whereas in pregnancy, cells from the placenta and maternal and fetal adrenal glands all are required (Figure 20.7). Because the placenta cannot convert progesterone to estrogens, because of meager activity of 17α-hydroxylase and 17,20 desmolase, the placenta requires dehydroepiandrosterone sulfate (DHEA-S) produced by maternal and fetal adrenals. Once supplied with sufficient DHEA-S, the placenta induces conversion to estrogens, a task that requires several enzymes including the "all important" aromatase. Because the placenta has ample aromatase, it can convert all androgenic steroid precursors it receives to estrogens. One advantage of this cooperation of various cell types to produce estrogen is that any maternal androgen promptly will be converted to estrogen, thereby nullifying any potential virilizing effect on a female fetus.

Although estradiol is the major estrogen produced during the normal reproductive cycle, estriol becomes the predominant estrogen during pregnancy. As noted, all three estrogens derive from DHEA-S, which is produced by the fetal and maternal adrenals. Formation of estriol requires 16α hydroxylation of estrone, a reaction that is largely, if not entirely, confined to fetal adrenal and liver. Thus, the ability to elaborate large amounts of estriol during pregnancy depends on the integrity of the fetus. Consequently, estriol levels represent a fairly sensitive index of fetal well-being.

Early production of hCG forms the basis of the most commonly used pregnancy tests, being detected in the mother's serum within a week of ovulation. Besides interrupting the hypothalamic-pituitary-ovarian loops and supporting luteal function, hCG also maintains and stimulates placental steroidogenesis, which results in the very high maternal steroid levels referred to above; hCG does this by enhancing conversion of cholesterol to pregnenolone, the precursor of both estradiol and progesterone. Fetal adrenal synthesis of dehydroepiandrosterone sulfate (DHEA-S) also is enhanced by hCG. In addition, the fetal testis possesses specific receptors for hCG, resulting in stimulation of testosterone production during early pregnancy. Recall that the placenta does not possess the enzyme systems necessary to convert pregnenolone or progesterone to 17-hydroxylated compounds; in other words, the inability of the placenta to carry out these reactions protects the fetus against autovirilization, because these compounds have androgenic actions.

An additional placental peptide hormone, human placental lactogen, further illustrates the dominance of the fetus over the mother. Human placental lactogen appears in the 5th-6th week of gestation and increases by 80-fold over the next 30 weeks, reaching a peak between 34 and 40 weeks. Secreted into the maternal blood, human placental lactogen produces a glucose-sparing effect, causes mobilization of fat from maternal depots, and exerts an anti-insulin effect, all of which are beneficial to the rapidly growing fetus nearing term, while exacerbating any latent tendency in the mother to develop gestational or true diabetes mellitus.

The Fetus

In considering reproductive endocrinology, two facts should be kept in mind: (*1*) the fetus, through the placenta, orchestrates a multitude of maternal endocrine changes to maintain its viability within the uterus while remaining essentially protected from the direct effects of these hormonal changes; (*2*) fetal growth, except for the last trimester, consists primarily of increasing cell numbers and types, rather than size; such increases are largely under the direction of the genome. Hence, although the fetal endocrine organs develop relatively early in gestation, there is no compelling evidence that they play a major role in fetal growth. This is vividly illustrated by fetuses with anencephaly, or congenital absence of the thyroid or agonadism—none of which significantly affect intrauterine growth. Most notably, it also may be surmised that human growth hormone has a negligible role in support of fetal growth.

Fetal effects of hCG can be seen primarily in development of the adrenals and the gonads. The adrenal glands develop by 8 weeks of gestation into organs capable of de novo steroid synthesis from acetate, as well as metabolism of cholesterol, pregnenolone, and progesterone to cortisol and DHEA-S. During the first half of gestation, support for the growth and function of the adrenals is provided by the high levels of hCG. As hCG levels decrease in later gestation, fetal ACTH becomes the predominant sponsor. Fetal ACTH levels are highest in midgestation, thus complementing the decrease in hCG production that occurs at the same stage. Release of ACTH from the pituitary at 15 to 16 weeks coincides in gestation with development of the hypophyseal-pituitary portal system.

Testicular development is largely enhanced by hCG during early gestation, as manifested by increasing Leydig cell numbers and fetal testosterone levels that peak at 15 to 17 weeks. Amniotic fluid levels of testosterone are considerably higher if the fetus is a male rather than a female, although at term, fetal sex cannot be distinguished on this basis. Conversely, a female fetus produces a significantly higher level of estradiol in the amniotic fluid at midgestation. These differences caused by genetic endowment of the fetus are reflected in differences in pituitary LH and FSH levels, which are greater in the female than in the male fetus. In turn, this finding strongly implies the existence of a feedback loop, the high circulating level of testosterone in the male, driven by hCG, causing a negative effect on pituitary production of LH and FSH; however, minimal female gonadal function early in gestation causes stimulation of FSH production and release, and the rising estradiol levels then stimulate LH release. In the female fetus, this sequence is similar to that which induces each menstrual cycle in the mature individual. The requirement for these gonadotropins for normal fetal development is attested to by the presence of micropenis in a hypopituitary male newborn and hypoplastic ovaries in the anencephalic female fetus. Thus, as with ACTH, development of pituitary-hypothalamic intercommunications permit fetal gonadotropin regulation of gonadal development in a fashion coordinated with the decrease in placental hCG support.

Fetal thyroid hormone synthesis begins as early as 10 weeks gestation, whereas pituitary TSH is identifiably present by the 12th week. However, until the hypothalamic-pituitary portal communication is established at 15 to 17 weeks, pituitary TSH content and circulating T_4 levels remain low. Thereafter, under hypothalamic direction, TSH and T_4 levels increase rapidly. After 30 weeks gestation, TSH levels decrease while T_4 levels remain high, suggesting that the feedback loop has been established. During all of this, the fetus is rendered immune to the metabolic effects of thyroid hormone by virtue of the fact that fetal tissues convert T_4 to a compound known as "reverse T_3," which is metabolically inactive. But, within hours of birth, the term infant becomes capable of converting T_4 to 3,5,3,'-T_3, the optimally active form of thyroid hormone.

In summary, then, fetal endocrine development is carried out under the direction of both placental and endogenous factors. The primary placental factor is hCG, which induces gonadal and adrenal development, whereas the endogenous factors primarily are genetic/embryologic in nature and involve development of the hypothalamic-pituitary axis and synthesis of trophic hormones and releasing factors. However, fetal endocrinopathies are rare, and usually derive from failure of structural development. All things considered, the primary mission of the fetal endocrine system is to support fetal well-being through placental hormone production while readying itself for an extrauterine existence.

Disorders of Reproduction

The most likely and inevitable cause of failure of insemination to culminate in the birth of a neonate is the physiologic consequence of aging in the female known as *menopause*. Besides the menopause, there are a multitude of reasons for reproductive failure; what follows is a brief treatment of these disorders.

MENOPAUSE

At menopause, permanent cessation of menstruation results from decreased ovarian production of estrogen in the presence of adequate or increased gonadotropin stimulation. Embodied in this definition is the implication that the central event in menopause is the eventual decline of ovarian function. For one thing, ovarian follicles are almost completely exhausted at menopause from successive cycles of ovulation and atresia of follicles. For another, a few years before menses cease, a woman's ovaries become less responsive to gonadotropin stimulation, so that circulating FSH and LH levels are higher in women of perimenopausal age who are still having ovulatory cycles than in younger women, while estrogen and progesterone levels are lower. As aging progresses, the follicular cells of the ovary degenerate, causing diminishing estrogen production and release of the negative feedback loop, which explains the increase in gonadotropin release. Eventually, with degeneration of the follicular cells, ovarian estrogen production is drastically reduced and circulating levels of estrogen mainly reflect conversion of adrenal androgens by peripheral tissues, principally adipose tissue. Menopause is inevitable and irreversible, although conception is potentially possible early in the process, when sporadic ovulatory cycles may occur. Once accomplished, reproduction is no longer possible.

NEUROENDOCRINE CAUSES

Emotional disorders and/or stress can impair release of gonadotropins or growth hormone, as exemplified by psychogenic amenorrhea or psychosocial dwarfism. Organic lesions and space-occupying masses within the cranium also frequently will impact upon the pathways leading to normal endocrine function. As we have discussed, endocrine expressivity by the CNS is channelled through the hypothalamus, resulting in secretion of "releasing factors," which reach the pituitary by a venous portal system. Clearly, diseases involving the hypothalamus and/or causing interruption of the portal system will interfere with the transport of releasing factors and the consequent secretion by the pituitary of trophic hormones.

Primary pituitary dysfunction may involve a single messenger or several and may be manifested as either deficiency or excess, both types of disorder being associated with tumors as well as genetic disease. In considering the clinical manifestations of these diseases it should be kept in mind that the pituitary gland is the "facilitator" of messages initiated from the CNS; as such, the pituitary hormones direct the activities of the peripheral endocrine glands without exerting direct effects on other tissues (except for GH and prolactin). Hence, clinical signs and symptoms of pituitary deficiency or excess are related to hypo- or hyperactivity of the respective target endocrine glands.

PROLACTIN

Deficiency

The usual condition in which prolactin deficiency is found is postpartum pituitary necrosis (Sheehan's syndrome), a situation involving all of the pituitary hormones. Isolated prolactin deficiency has not been described.

Excess

Although prolactin-secreting tumors are the most common form of pituitary tumor, there are many other possible causes of hyperprolactinemia, including neurogenic, hypothalamic, and pharmacologic factors. The common effect of prolactin excess is suppression of gonadotropin secretion, resulting in menstrual irregularities in the female. The resulting decrease in testosterone in affected males leads to loss of libido, possible impotency, and decreased sperm count.

DISORDERS OF OTHER ENDOCRINE GLANDS

Thyroid

Disorders of the thyroid gland are the most common of endocrine abnormalities worldwide, affecting individuals of all ages. Congenital deficiency of thyroid hormone is estimated to occur in 1 of 4000 live births, whereas chronic lymphocytic thyroiditis is seen in 3% to 4% of the older population. Chemically, thyroid hormones are the simplest of humoral agents, composed of various iodinated derivatives of two tyrosine molecules linked through the p-hydroxyl group of one of the two (Figure 20.8). No hormones affect such a wide range of cells and tissues, exhibiting such a diversity of actions, as do thyroxine (T_4) and tri-iodothyronine (T_3). These actions are vitally important to the regulation of basal metabolism of all tissues, to the development of the CNS, and to the growth and differentiation of bone.

Working together with the developmental and morphogenetic program dictated by the individual's DNA, the thyroid hormones play a vital role in the early development of the CNS in the neonate. In stark contrast to the situation with the older child and adult, in which administration of replacement thyroxine promptly reverses the effects of hypothyroidism, in the neonate and infant, deprivation of thyroid hormone for a period of several months results in irreparable damage to the CNS. During the vulnerable period of brain development, when arborization of neural connections are proceeding at a rapid pace and myelination is proceeding in tandem, lack of thyroid hormone will permanently impair the normal wiring process. Thus, there is a crucial period for thyroid action during brain development. Undeniably, if that opportunity is missed, the brain can never be repaired. It is for this reason that screening of neonates for congenital hypothyroidism is such a high priority.

Thyroid hormone secretion is stimulated by TSH release from the pituitary; TSH binds to spe-

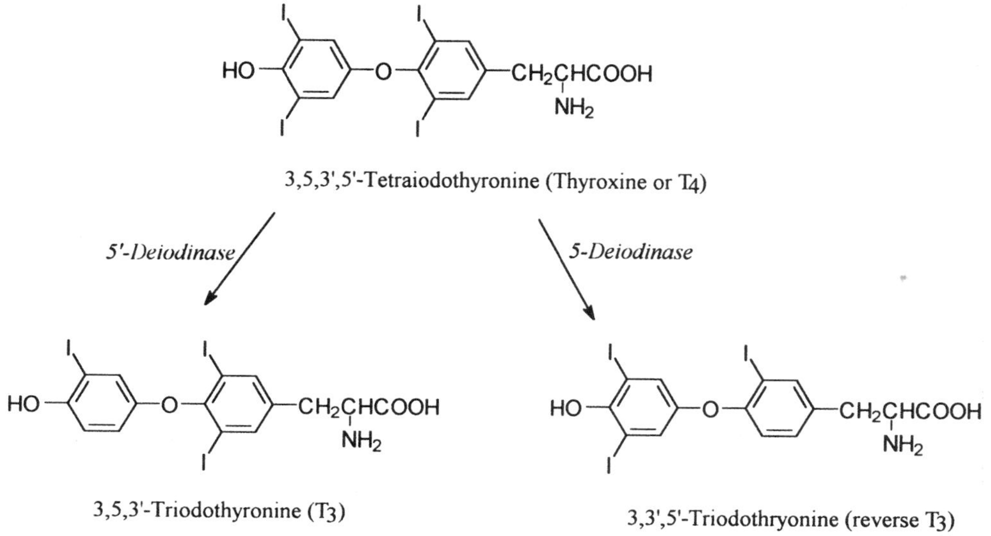

Figure 20.8. Molecular structures of the various thyroid hormones. Note the relative differences in location of the iodide substituents in the two T_3 molecules, resulting from two separate enzymes acting upon the common T_4 substrate.

cific receptor sites on the thyroid gland and stimulates thyroid hormone synthesis and release. This stimulatory effect is, in turn, mediated by adenylate cyclase and cyclic AMP levels within the cell. Moreover, thyroid hormone also enters the cell and binds to nuclear and mitochondrial membranes, influencing gene transcription and mitochondrial oxidation. Through an enhancement of membrane NA^+-K^+-ATPase activity, uptake into the cell of sugars and amino acids is increased, thus providing the energy substrate for increased mitochondrial activity and protein synthesis. Beyond all of this, T_4 and its more active product T_3 also affect protein, carbohydrate and lipid metabolism, amino acid and electrolyte transport, and modulate sympathetic nerve function through interaction with the adrenergic endocrine system. It is not difficult, then, to understand the far-reaching consequences of either deficiency or excess of these simple but enormously influential dipeptides to overall function of the organism.

LABORATORY TESTS OF THYROID FUNCTION

In ordering and interpreting thyroid tests, it is vital to recognize the importance of integrating the clinical history and physical examination with the results of these tests. In the neonate, however, in whom congenital hypothyroidism may not reveal any signs or symptoms, or in the elderly, when findings may be subtle or misleading, it may be appropriate to order tests of thyroid function on the basis of the odds rather than clinical findings. Surely, in the case of screening for congenital hypothyroidism, this strategy has had a major impact on preventing the otherwise devastating mental retardation that would ensue. In all cases, one must correlate the TSH level with the other test results, because TSH levels reflect the feedback loop with the pituitary. For example, in primary hypothyroidism, the gland does not produce adequate thyroid hormones for the body's needs and the feedback loop to the pituitary is not active, causing a surge of TSH to drive the reluctant thyroid gland. However, in hyperthyroidism, with the typically high circulating levels of thyroid hormones, pituitary secretion of TSH will plunge to very low levels (Table 20.4).

In addition to providing a sensitive assay for TSH, the laboratory must be able to measure the free T_4 and T_3 levels, because it is only the free hormones that exert the physiologic effects attributed to the thyroid. Likewise it is only the free hormones that participate in the feedback loop modulating TSH secretion. Free thyroid hormones, however, are only a minute fraction of the total thyroid hormones carried in the blood; the fraction bound to protein accounts for over 99% of the plasma hormones. Most of the T_3 found in the blood (80%) is produced as a consequence of conversion of T_4 in the periphery. This is noteworthy because T_3 is, depending on the biologic effect assessed, 5 to 10 times more active than T_4.

Table 20.4. Thyroid Function Studies

Hypothyroidism
↓ Free T_4
↑ sTSH
Hyperthyroidism
↑ Free T_4
↓ sTSH
Nodules
Fine needle aspiration

sTSH = sensitive TSH assay able to detect TSH concentrations <0.1 μU/ml

Although equilibrium dialysis methods are the "gold standard" for measuring free T_4 and free T_3, they are not suitable for running multiple specimens in a clinical laboratory setting. The *thyroid hormone binding ratio* or resin T_3 uptake (RT_3U) is a satisfactory alternative procedure to assess free thyroid hormone levels. The thyroid hormone binding ratio reflects the percentage of unoccupied binding sites on thyroid binding globulin (TBG), the major plasma protein carrier of thyroid hormones. Normally, 25% to 35% of the binding sites on TBG are occupied by T_4 or T_3. In the assay, a fixed amount of ^{125}I-T_3 is added to the test serum, with a portion of the radioactive hormone binding to the unoccupied TBG sites. There thus will be some remaining unbound ^{125}I-T_3 in the test tube. If now one adds a resin, the remaining unbound label will bind to the resin. In hypothyroidism, thyroid hormone levels are decreased and, consequently, fewer sites on TBG will be occupied. With increased numbers of unoccupied sites on TBG, there is more opportunity for ^{125}I-T_3 to bind to TBG, with the result that less label is taken up by the added resin. By contrast, in hyperthyroidism as thyroid hormone levels are increased, more hormone will bind to TBG. Accordingly, less radiolabeled material will bind to TBG and there thus will be more label to bind to the resin. Results of such tests are compared to the percentage uptake of a normal serum (euthyroid and normal amounts of TBG).

Provided with values for total T_4 and the thyroid hormone binding ratio, the laboratory can calculate the free thyroxine index (FT_4I), a value that correlates with, but is not expressed in the same units as, free serum T_4.

Hypothyroidism

Hypothyroidism is the result of inadequate support of peripheral tissue metabolism by thyroid hormone; this can be due, as we have noted, to dysfunctions arising proximal to the thyroid gland itself, to intrinsic thyroid disease, or to peripheral tissue unresponsiveness. Because the scope is so broad, for our purposes, we will confine ourselves to the most common causes of hypothyroidism.

CONGENITAL HYPOTHYROIDISM

The most common form of congenital hypothyroidism is somewhat misleadingly, termed "sporadic" cretinism. In this context, sporadic is intended to imply that there is no heritable factor involved. In this disorder, thyroid tissue is virtually absent except for a small amount of residual tissue that is present, often in an ectopic location. Recall that in utero the fetus rapidly converts T_4 to an inactive form of thyroid hormone. It follows that absence of thyroid tissue will have little effect upon in utero growth and development. However, to meet the environmental stresses of extrauterine existence, it is critical to accelerate metabolic processes. Homeothermic extrauterine existence relies, at least partially, on rapid conversion of T_4 to the active form of T_3 in the term infant. Without adequate thyroid hormone, the neonate cannot maintain a constant body temperature. Otherwise, the newborn affected by absent thyroid function shows few characteristic signs, although the fontanelles may be abnormally large and there may be constipation which in itself demands clinical attention. In the subsequent neonatal period, the following occur: poor feeding with hypocaloric intake, failure to thrive, hypothermia, bradycardia, marked hypotonia, persistent hyperbilirubinemia, and enlargement of the tongue. All but the tongue hypertrophy can be related to the absence of up-regulation of cellular metabolism to meet the requirements for growth. Because of the absence of thryoid hormone effect on development of bone ossification centers, a neonate who has not been treated will develop the facial features of cretinism with depressed nasal bridge, narrowed forehead, and mandibular underdevelopment.

Enlargement of the tongue (macroglossia) and thickening of the skin are results of accumulation of interstitial glycosaminoglycans (mucopolysaccharides), creating the picture of myxedema, from which the disease derives its name. But, although macroglossia is prominent in infants with athyrotic cretinism, true myxedema is much less pronounced than in severely hypothyroid adults. There are many other congenital hypothyroid states, all of which manifest themselves in ways that combine many of the above findings (Table 20.5).

Above all, it is vital to remember that clinical diagnosis of the affected newborn can be extremely difficult, accounting for the programs to screen newborns in the United States and throughout much of the industrialized world. One also must recognize that with a mass screening program, specimens can be mixed up or perhaps never collected. Hence, testing is imperative in any infant in whom congenital hypothyroidism is suspected. It is not prudent to assume that testing was done and that it was negative. In any case, once the diagnosis of hypothyroidism is made, the need for immediate treatment is urgent. Mental retardation progresses inexorably in the hypothyroid neonate: it has been estimated that such an infant loses 3 to 5 I.Q. points for each month treat-

Table 20.5. Hypothyroidism

Congenital
- Thyroid dysgenesis
- Inborn errors of thyroid hormone biosynthesis or metabolism
  - Defects in iodide trapping, organification, coupling, etc.
  - Peripheral receptor defect
- Pituitary or hypothalamic

Acquired
- Hashimoto's thyroiditis
- Idiopathic atrophy—lymphocytic thyroiditis
- Surgical thyroidectomy, radiation to neck
- Endemic regions of iodine deficiency
- Pituitary or hypothalamic disease

ment is delayed during the first year of life. The importance of prompt replacement therapy cannot be overemphasized because, in utero, a modest maternal-to-fetal transfer of T_4 exerts some protective effect on the developing CNS in the athyroid infant. At birth, however, even this limited thyroid hormone now is denied to the neonate.

ACQUIRED HYPOTHYROIDISM

The most common form of acquired hypothyroidism (Table 20.5) in both children and adults is Hashimoto's disease (chronic lymphocytic thyroiditis). The true incidence is unknown, but it is suspected that it is much more common than believed. High circulating levels of antithyroid antibodies can be demonstrated in most affected individuals, together with cell-mediated immunity against thyroid antigens. Hence, the etiology of the lymphocytic infiltrate is believed to be autoimmune in nature. The mechanism by which autoimmunity is triggered, as well as the means by which the tissue damage is produced, are poorly understood. However, the strong familial pattern, including demonstrability of increased circulating antibodies in clinically unaffected relatives, suggests a genetic contribution.

The cardinal clinical finding in Hashimoto's disease is a *goiter*. In the majority of patients, this enlargement occurs gradually and may be found incidentally on physical examination, although a small percentage of cases are heralded by fairly rapid development of the goiter. Typically, the thyroid is uniformly increased in size, although it may be asymmetric, and is smooth without nodules. Development of the goiter usually precedes appearance of the signs and symptoms of hypothyroidism, often by years. Pathophysiologically, this makes sense because as glandular function diminishes, TSH secretion increases, thus driving residual functional tissue to compensate and encouraging glandular hypertrophy earlier than appearance of functional loss.

Clinical manifestations of thyroid hormone deficiency in individuals beyond the neonatal period of life depend upon the age of onset (Table 20.6). Thus, acquired hypothyroidism in the prepubescent child will have a marked effect on linear growth, whereas onset after adolescence will not influence stature. Prepubescent onset also will guarantee delayed sexual maturation. In all cases, mentation is slowed to the extent that the individual appears dull, but such changes in the older child and adult are reversible with treatment. In adults, menstrual abnormalities and impotence frequently are seen as equivalent manifestations to the delayed sexual maturation in the child. Fatigue, lethargy, cold sensitivity, hoarseness, loss of appetite with a paradoxical modest weight gain, hoarseness, and dry skin constitute the major findings; development of the full blown myxedematous picture may require years. Ultimately, aside from the growth failure and mental retardation seen in neonates and young children, severe adult hypothyroidism will produce a picture very similar to that seen in athyrotic cretinism. The major difference, however, is the reversibility of all the effects. Untreated, such a patient may succumb to infection.

Table 20.6. Frequent Clinical Findings in Acquired Hypothyroidism

Weakness
Dry, course skin and hair
Lethargy
Slow, thick speech
Cold intolerance
Thick tongue
Impaired memory
Constipation
Weight gain

Hyperthyroidism

Hyperthyroidism is reserved for those disorders that result from exposure of the peripheral tissues to greater than normal levels of thyroid hormone derived from thyroid glandular dysfunction. With this definition we can confine our discussion to etiologies of hyperthyroidism due to primary disease of the thyroid gland. Such disorders are almost never seen in infancy, are rare in childhood, and are much less common in adults than is hypothyroidism. The various causes of hyperthyroidism are listed in Table 20.7.

THYROTOXICOSIS (GRAVE'S DISEASE)

This disorder is the most common form of spontaneous hyperthyroidism in adults under 40 years of age, occurring in 0.3% to 0.5% of Americans with a frequency in females 10-fold that in males.

Table 20.7. Causes of Hyperthyroidism

Graves' disease
Hot thyroid adenoma
Lymphocytic thyroiditis
Administration of thyroid hormones
TSH-producing pituitary adenoma
Thyroid carcinoma

The specific etiology is almost certainly autoimmune in nature—the IgG immunoglobulin class antibodies react with thyroid cellular membrane receptor for TSH, activating adenyl cyclase and triggering the sequence of events normally reserved for the tightly controlled levels of TSH itself. The overall result is that the thyroid is under the aberrant control of an immune system gone awry, rather than the feedback regulatory loop originating in the CNS. There is strong familial incidence, with excellent evidence for association with specific HLA-haplotypes in various racial groups. With its predilection for females, the most common times of onset are during puberty, pregnancy, and menopause, thus significantly impacting on reproductive capacity. With sufficient time, the hyperactive thyroid gland in Grave's disease tends to "burn out"; therefore, patients eventually may become hypothyroid, although the time frame for this may be up to 20 years.

Beyond diffuse thyroid enlargement (the sine qua non of the disease), clinical presentation may begin insidiously. The complex of symptoms includes nervousness, heat intolerance, palpitations, tremor, irritability, weight loss, fatigability, menstrual abnormalities, and/or increased libido (Table 20.8). The combination of nervousness and irritability which drives the individual to constant activity conflicts with the weakness and fatigability, leading to frustration and emotional lability. The classic sign of thyrotoxicosis, *ophthalmopathy*, may occur coincidental with the clinical onset, or may develop later in the course. Emergence of this sign is a consequence of several factors: increased hyaluronic acid in the retrobulbar connective tissue leads to edema because hyaluronate is hydrophilic in nature, the extraocular muscle tissue is swollen with lymphocytic infiltration, and the lacrimal glands may contribute by similar involvement. There is a corresponding increase in the retrobulbar fat tissue, which is somewhat paradoxical to the known effects of thyroid hormone on fat metabolism, which typically are lipolytic. The net result is to cause an anterior protrusion of the globes (exophthalmos), partially accounting for the so-called "lid-lag" sign. In cases when the major changes are due primarily to accumulation of retrobulbar fat and minimal infiltration, the findings regress with treatment, whereas extensive infiltrative changes are not reversible and pose serious problems, such as corneal ulcerations due to incomplete closure of the lids.

Table 20.8. Clinical Manifestations of Hyperthyroidism

Excess Thyroid Hormone
↑ O_2 consumption (↑ BMR)—heat intolerance, sweating
↑ appetite but weight loss
Muscle weakness
Increased Tissue Sensitivity to Catecholamines
Tremor
Palpitations, angina, arrhythmias
Agitation, nervousness, anxiety, depression
Increased defecation without diarrhea
Lid lag and eyelid retractions (Graves' disease)
Immunologic Features (Graves' disease only)
Goitre
Exophthalmos

An additional infiltrative process, due to the same underlying mechanisms, is dermatopathy, which occurs much less frequently than the ophthalmopathy in this disease. Paradoxically, the characteristic lesion is termed pretibial myxedema and consists of reddened, indurated areas in the pretibial and dorsal pedal regions. Infiltrative dermatopathy occurs in less than 10% of thyrotoxic patients, but is almost always associated with infiltrative ophthalmopathy of severe degree.

The most frequent presenting symptoms, those of nervousness, tremor, and heat intolerance, are due to poorly understood interactions between thyroid hormone and endogenous sympathetic mediators (ie, catecholamines). Although adrenergic activity is increased generally, secretion rates and plasma concentrations of catecholamines are unchanged. However, thyroid hormone can be shown to increase the number of beta-adrenergic receptor sites in some peripheral tissues. Together with the previously mentioned enhancement of adenylate cyclase activity exerted by thyroid hormone, it is possible that the net effect is to enhance end-organ responsiveness to adrenergic agents. Parenthetically, it is thought that the activation of adenylate cyclase by thyroid hormone mediates thryoid hormone's lipolytic effects, because glycerol release is in proportion to accumulation of cAMP in fat cells. The net lipolysis would partially account for weight loss in this disorder.

Muscle weakness, also a prominent symptom, can be related to electron microscopic changes in muscle tissue, represented by fat cell and lymphocytic infiltrations, mitochondrial abnormalities, and myocytic atrophy. Alterations such as these add an additional component to weight loss. Functionally, these changes are thought to result in decreased myocytic ability to generate creatine phosphate, the reservoir of high-energy phosphate bonds within muscle tissue. Another factor contributing to muscle weakness may be the increased loss of calcium and phosphate induced by excess thyroid hormone. The relationship of these substances to muscle function is discussed in Chapters 21 and 25. The mechanisms underlying the calciuria and phosphaturia are poorly understood; parathyroid hormone levels are low to normal in thyrotoxic patients, and the interaction of thyroid hormone with vitamin D metabolism is not well understood.

Despite the disruptive effect of thyrotoxicosis on menstrual regularity, there is no evidence that levels of the regulatory pituitary messengers, LH and FSH, are affected. Indeed, as shown by the presence of secretory endometrium in the majority of thyrotoxic premenopausal patients, the cycles are ovulatory in nature. There are, however, demonstrable and significant alterations in metabolism of gonadal steroids, involving both the relationship between bound and free fractions, as well as enzymatic conversions of ovarian and testicular steroids. These changes may have a role, yet to be delineated, in the reproductive problems experienced in thyrotoxic patients.

Finally, in addition to the above symptoms and signs, which typically develop into a thyrotoxic syndrome over many years, there is a fulminant form, combining all of these findings known as "thyroid storm" or thyrotoxic crisis. Onset typically is abrupt, in association with an underlying Grave's disease, the overall picture being that of a markedly hypermetabolic organism. All of the typical findings are exaggerated, including delirium or psychosis or both, lapsing into stupor, and finally coma. If the disorder is not promptly diagnosed and treated, it is invariably fatal.

Thyroid Adenoma

According to the current terminology, adenomas are, by definition, benign neoplasms. Thyroid adenoma presents as a nodular enlargement of the gland that is discrete from the rest of the surrounding tissue and is slow-growing. Because these adenomas are follicular in origin, it follows that they are composed of functioning thyroid tissue. In this respect, the distinguishing feature of an adenoma is functional independence from TSH control. Hence, the elevated circulating thyroid hormone levels suppress TSH secretion, which, in turn, reduces function of the normal thyroid tissue without affecting the adenoma. This process occurs over long periods; therefore, hyperthyroidism evolves insidiously and generally is milder in degree than that seen in Graves' disease.

The major importance of the toxic adenoma, aside from the endocrinologic consequences, is the great difficulty in distinguishing such a lesion from a thyroid carcinoma. Given the caveat that no diagnostic test is 100% reliable short of histologic examination, the most generally reliable distinguishing feature is the functional ability of the tumor. Whereas adenomas function, by definition, as endocrine organs, thyroid carcinomas generally do not. Hence, thyroid adenomas are known as "hot" nodules when studied by radioactive iodine, whereas carcinomas typically are "cold" nodules. It is important, however, not to extrapolate beyond this statement by assuming that all cold nodules, therefore, are malignant. In fact, the majority of these cold lesions ultimately are found to be benign, degenerated adenomas.

Adrenal Gland

The importance of the adrenal steroid hormones to influencing a wide range of biochemical processes in the maintenance of normal homeostasis is out of all proportion to the diminutive size of the glands that synthesize these hormones. Functionally, the adrenal cortex is the source of three separate classes of hormones: glucocorticoids, mineralocorticoids, and sex hormones. All members of each of the three classes are steroid mole-

Table 20.9. Actions of Glucocorticoids

↑ Protein catabolism ⟶ gluconeogenesis
↑ Glycogenolysis
Sensitize arterioles to norepinephrine helping to maintain blood pressure
Exert permissive effect on water excretion by kidneys
Exert permissive effect on lipolysis

cules. Thus, each has an identical mode of action, entering the cell by diffusion and binding to a specific protein receptor. The steroid-receptor complex interacts with the specific nuclear receptor, thus effecting regulation of messenger RNA transcription and enzyme synthesis. Histologically, the adrenal cortex consists of three zones, although, in humans, the distinction between the two innermost zones is blurred; the outer, or zona glomerulosa, is the source of production of mineralocorticoid, whereas the glucocorticoids and sex hormones are produced by the inner cortex. Although pituitary ACTH secretion is necessary for functional support of the adrenal cortex and to evoke glucocorticoid secretion, secretion of mineralocorticoids by the zona glomerulosa is much less under the influence of ACTH than is secretion of the other two classes of steroids. Teleologically, regulation of renal fluid and electrolyte homeostasis independent of the complex functions of the glucocorticoids and sex hormones makes a good deal of sense, and its achievement represents an evolutionary triumph.

As their name suggests, the glucocorticoids have notable effects on glucose metabolism, especially through their ability to promote gluconeogenesis (Table 20.9), whereas the mineralocorticoids are named for their effects on Na^+, K^+, and H^+ ion balance. Moreover, the glucocorticoids are vital to survival during times of stress.

Glucocorticoids not only promote gluconeogenesis in liver by stimulating protein catabolism, they also promote additional gluconeogenesis from glycerol by encouraging lipolysis in adipose tissue and they induce de novo synthesis of enzymes involved in gluconeogenesis. It generally is believed that during stress (eg, trauma, fever, severe dehydration), glucocorticoids stimulate cardiovascular functions by improving cardiac performance and by sensitizing the arterial system to the action of catecholamines. Another component of the role of glucocorticoids in stress probably involves attenuating the effects of various other hormones, eicosanoids, and enzymes that are produced during stress and inflammation; these latter substances, if unopposed, might precipitate vascular instability and even shock.

To add further to the remarkably complex picture presented by the adrenal cortex, we must consider the adrenal medulla, which is primarily under neural control and is responsible for production and secretion of the catecholamine messengers. Medullary function is independent of cortical function; indeed, the embryonic tissue from which each is derived is utterly distinct and their combined presence in the adult is more an accident of anatomy than commonality of function. Thus, to serve the need for brevity, we will consider only major examples of hypo- and hyperadrenal cortical and adrenal medullary dysfunction.

Adrenal Cortex

HYPOADRENALISM (ADRENOCORTICAL INSUFFICIENCY, ADDISON'S DISEASE)

The initial description of this disorder by Addison in 1855 included cases due to tuberculosis, metastatic infiltration, and unknown causes. With improvement in public health, idiopathic causes have replaced tuberculosis as a primary etiology in this relatively rare disease. As with thyroid disorders, idiopathic hypoadrenalism is most commonly associated with an autoimmune phenomenon; hence, the clinical onset typically is insidious and is termed chronic adrenal insufficiency (Table 20.10). However, a form of acute adrenal insuffi-

Table 20.10. Causes of Adrenal Insufficiency

Acute Adrenal Insufficiency
Adrenal hemorrhage
Meningococcus
Anticoagulant therapy
Adrenal vein thrombosis or artery embolus
Chronic Adrenal Insufficiency
Autoimmune
Infections
Tuberculosis
Histoplasmosis
Crytococcosis
Drugs
Metyrapone
Aminoglutethimide
Ketoconazole
Hemochromatosis

Table 20.11. Clinical Findings in Primary Adrenal Insufficiency

Weakness, fatigue
Anorexia, weight loss
Hyperpigmentation over pressure areas
Postural hypotension and dizziness
Nausea, vomiting
Salt craving (in about ⅕ of patients)

ciency can occur either as a long-term consequence of neglected chronic insufficiency or because of acute insult such as hemorrhage into the glands. In the chronic form, signs and symptoms are referable to deficiencies of all three adrenal steroid classes, whereas in the acute form, deficiency of glucocorticoids (cortisol, primarily) causes the earliest clinical findings. The normal adrenal gland has a large reserve capacity to produce and secrete hormones; therefore, the gland must suffer extensive functional disturbance before clinical manifestations become apparent.

Chronic adrenal insufficiency most commonly presents with fatigue, anorexia, and weight loss, and frequently is accompanied by hyperpigmentation and hypotension. Early medical complaints usually are diagnosable as neurosis: weakness, lethargy, inability to concentrate, irritability, and occasional depressive periods (Table 20.11). As a consequence, early diagnosis of chronic adrenal insufficiency often is obscured by the frequency of such complaints in the usual medical practice. With the passage of time, decreased release of adrenal corticosteroids leads to enhancement of ACTH release from the pituitary together with a coupled secretion of beta-lipotropin; the latter is hydrolyzed to beta-melanocyte stimulating hormone (MSH). These events lead to the characteristic hyperpigmentation seen in Addison's disease, beginning as a generalized phenomenon and eventually becoming most marked in the axillae, perineum and mucous membranes of the oral cavity, the vagina and anus. Preexisting scars may appear striking by virtue of their failure to darken as much as the surrounding area of skin.

As the disease progresses further, hypotension develops as a consequence of loss of myocardial contractility and diminished vascular tone, both of which are substantially supported in health by adrenocorticoids. Because this hypotension is refractory to catecholamines, the earliest clinical indication of its presence may be postural—dizziness or fainting episodes. Unfortunately, unless the clinician is astute enough to note the hyperpigmentation, the hypotensive symptoms may only serve to enhance the initial impression of neurosis. Electrolyte disturbances are the rule, the usual ones involving hyponatremia, hyperkalemia, and hypercalcemia. Because chronic adrenal insufficiency develops slowly over months to years, the bouts of nausea and vomiting that cause dehydration and hyponatremia may be counterbalanced by increased salt intake. Thus, in this setting, the anticipated hyponatremia may not be particularly striking. The muscle weakness so common in this disease is a likely consequence of such electrolyte abnormalities and should be clinically recognized as such. Nevertheless, it would be a mistake to dismiss the possibility of the diagnosis of adrenal insufficiency in an individual presenting the clinical manifestations of adrenal insufficiency but lacking the serum electrolyte abnormalities. Such patients demand further endocrine evaluation.

In the absence of adrenocorticoids, muscle protein breakdown in response to fasting is significantly impaired. In this setting, catabolism to sustain gluconeogenesis is restricted when loss of adipose tissue and decreased intake occur, making the individual susceptible to fasting hypoglycemia. Thus, as we have made clear elsewhere (see Chapter 7), although true hypoglycemia is a relatively rare phenomenon, it represents an important diagnostic clue when it can be documented.

Sexual potency in males is reduced, although women of reproductive age with early Addison's disease may conceive. Once pregnant, the fetal and placental hormones serve to protect the mother from her own deficiency. In the immediate postpartum period, however, the rapid withdrawal of this hormonal supplement may precipitate an Addisonian crisis. It is worth noting again that lethargy, fatigue, anorexia, and vomiting are so commonly seen in routine obstetrical practice that the diagnosis of impending adrenocortical insufficiency may be overlooked.

Diagnosis of primary adrenocortical insufficiency is relatively simple to make if the patient has not been previously treated with steroids. All that is required is to document failure of the adrenals to increase plasma cortisol in response to a

Table 20.12. Cushing's Syndrome and Adrenal Function Tests

	BASAL CORTISOL	EFFECT ON PITUITARY ACTH SECRETION	DEXAMETHASONE SUPPRESSION
Normal	Normal range	Negative feedback intact	Suppresses
Cushing's syndrome	↑	Negative feedback only at higher level of cortisol	Suppresses only at high dose
Adrenal tumor	↑ but may fluctuate	High cortisol inhibits ACTH secretion	Autonomous
Ectopic ACTH secretion	↑↑	Cortisol inhibits ACTH secretion	Does not suppress unless tumor has glucocorticoid receptors

standard dose of ACTH. Conversely, of course, if there is an adequate adrenal response, the diagnosis of Addison's disease should be rejected.

ADRENOCORTICAL HYPERSECRETION (CUSHING'S SYNDROME)

The only primary form of adrenocortical hypersecretion is attributable to adrenal tumors that autonomously secrete corticosteroids, the primary one being cortisol. The other major causes of Cushing's syndrome are either pituitary hypersecretion of ACTH or tumor in another tissue with ectopic ACTH-like secretion; thus, they are secondary causes of adrenal hypersecretion. Statistically, the most common cause of Cushing's syndrome is excess release of ACTH from the pituitary (Table 20.12), due either to a pituitary tumor or to undetermined causes of hyperactivity of the hypothalamus. Pituitary and hypothalamic causes account for approximately 80% of affected patients. However, about 70% of children with Cushing's disease are found to have a primary adrenal tumor, usually an adenoma. In both forms of the disease, there is a propensity toward females, whereas ectopic production of ACTH by nonendocrine tumors occurs equally in both sexes, affects almost exclusively adults, and accounts for approximately 15% of the total cases.

Because glucocorticoids affect intermediary metabolism, function of striated and cardiac muscle, immunologic mechanisms, and wound healing, it can be appreciated that excess cortisol has significant and far-reaching consequences (Table 20.13). With respect to intermediary metabolism, glucocorticoids promote gluconeogenesis, thus diverting amino acids into glucose and glycogen. The increased net synthesis of glucose eventually leads to elevation of blood glucose, together with insulin, whereas provision of gluconeogenic amino acids from muscle results in the decreased muscle strength that constitutes a very early part of the clinical picture. The genesis of the unusual fat distribution (face and back of neck) so characteristic of Cushing's disease is at present unexplained, but may stem from the unusual state in which both cortisol and insulin are elevated.

Effects of hyperadrenocortical function on sex-related characteristics are more easily discerned early in the female, due to hypersecretion of adrenal androgens and their disruption of normal menses. Eventually, the affected female may become amenorrheic and show signs of virilization. Loss of body and facial hair in affected males is the result of adrenal feminization, and may be accompanied by loss of potency and gynecomastia.

Cortisol enhances activity of Na^+-K^+-ATPase in the distal tubule, an effect which works together with that of mineralocorticoid and leads to enhanced potassium excretion; hence, hypokalemia frequently is seen in Cushing's disease. The hypokalemia may contribute significantly to the profound and early muscle weakness seen in such patients. This potassium loss is promoted further by the action of cortisol in the small intestine, which enhances potassium secretion into the lumen. Similarly, glucocorticoids enhance cal-

Table 20.13. Clinical Manifestations of Cushing's Syndrome

Obesity—moon facies, truncal, buffalo hump
Hypertension
Hirsutism, acne
Skin—atrophic and fragile with purple striae—fungal skin infections
Weakness—especially of proximal muscles
Osteoporosis and back pain
Virilism in female patients
Glucose intolerance

cium excretion by the kidney and decrease calcium absorption by the gut, thus creating a negative calcium balance. These actions, combined with the protein catabolic effect which decreases collagen synthesis for bone matrix formation, creates the dual problem of decreased bone formation and increased resorption. Consequently, affected individuals frequently develop osteoporosis with the potential for pathologic fractures, with the vertebral bodies being common loci of compression fractures. The major cardiovascular effect of hyperadrenalism is hypertension. Cortisol, which possesses slight mineralocorticoid properties, when secreted in very large excess causes sodium reabsorption, water retention, and volume expansion. In addition, cortisol is thought to act synergistically with adrenal medullary vasopressors, causing exaggerated pressor effects of endogenous directly vasoactive substances.

The known effects of corticosteroids are sufficient to explain the occasionally bizarre, frequent infections and poor wound healing common to patients with hyperadrenalism. The common use of steroids in a clinical context to produce immunosuppression derives from their multiple effects on the immune system; steroids reduce lymphocytic proliferation in response to antigen and reduce both B- and T-cell numbers, thus diminishing circulating antibody response to infection. Moreover, steroids depress the typical inflammatory response, impairing vasodilation and reducing cellular exudative and fibrin-secretory response, thus delaying wound healing. As a consequence of these multiple effects, minimal trauma to the integrity of the skin can result in significant infection in a patient with hyperadrenalism.

An additional clinical problem that may cause significant distress, either to the patient or to the family, is the frequent emotional disturbance seen in hyperadrenalism. This may involve paranoid or frank psychotic states, although exogenously administered doses of glucocorticoids can cause euphoria. The incidence of serious emotional problems approximates 50% of hyperadrenal patients. However, it is not possible to predict which individuals are susceptible to this manifestation of the disease. Moreover, it is unclear what effects of corticosteroids on the CNS are responsible for eliciting psychological disturbances.

CONGENITAL ADRENAL HYPERPLASIA

A group of inborn errors of adrenal steroidogenesis have been described that collectively are called the congenital adrenal hyperplasias. Almost all of the enzymes involved in steroid biosynthesis are members of the cytochrome P450 family, except for 3-β-OH-steroid dehydrogenase (Figure 20.9). The cytochrome P450 enzymes are monooxygenases because they incorporate only one of the two oxygen atoms into their substrate. These-heme containing enzymes require NADPH and flavoproteins as cofactors. Because all of the defects in steroid synthesis drastically reduce formation of cortisol, which normally suppresses ACTH secretion, a marked increase in ACTH secretion is induced by a lack of feedback to the pituitary. Spurred on by high levels of ACTH, the patient's adrenals become hyperplastic, pouring forth steroid precursors that occur before the metabolic block in the pathway. Treating such patients with cortisol (or a congener) will suppress ACTH secretion and the adrenal will no longer elaborate large amounts of precursors, some of which possess mineralocorticoid or androgenic activity. The various defects in steroidogenesis are summarized in Table 20.14.

Adrenal Medulla

The adrenal medulla derives embryologically from neural crest cells, and release of the primary medullary catecholamine, epinephrine, normally is entirely under neural control. Diseases of the adrenal medulla tend to become clinically apparent as dysfunction of the sympathetic nervous system. Symptoms are most often caused by excessive adrenal medullary secretion. Symptoms tend to resemble those which all normal individuals experience when barely escaping a life-threatening, acute situation such as being almost hit by a car while crossing a street—tachycardia, profuse perspiration, tremors, headache, and overwhelming anxiety.

It is worth noting that 10% of the American adult population is estimated to experience these symptoms spontaneously, due to acute anxiety (panic) attacks with or without agoraphobia. Hence, the frequency of such experiences among the population at large causes great difficulty in the clinical diagnosis of adrenal medullary dys-

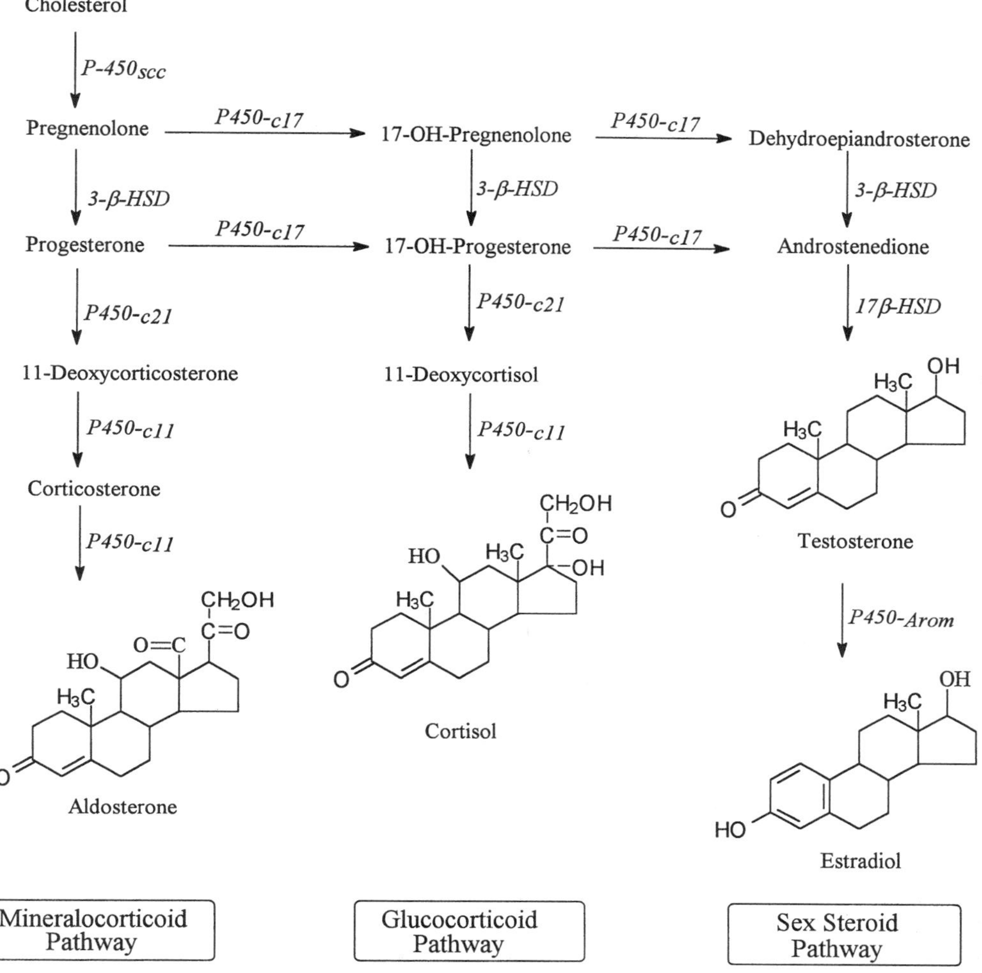

Figure 20.9. The pathways of adrenal steroidogenesis. In the adrenal, as in the ovary, the common precursor is cholesterol, which is utilized for the synthesis of three separate classes of steroids, as shown. Of particular note is the adrenal capacity for testosterone synthesis, which significantly contributes to the masculinization experienced in postmenopausal women. (See Figure 20.3 for abbreviations.)

function. Although hypertension also is among the most common of adult disorders, it is estimated that only 0.1% of hypertensive individuals suffer from pheochromocytoma, the most common pathologic primary disorder of the adrenal medulla.

As stated in the introductory section of this chapter, the small, water-soluble second-messengers typically require membrane surface receptor binding by which to convey their message to the cell interior. The catecholamine molecule is a prime example of such a molecule, binding to so called alpha- and/or beta-adrenergic receptors in various tissues, thus activating adenylate cyclase and influencing intracellular levels of cyclic AMP. The adrenal medulla secretes both norepinephrine and epinephrine; the former has special binding affinity with the alpha receptors present in greatest number in peripheral vasculature and gut wall, whereas epinephrine has affinity for both the alpha- and beta- receptors (present in heart, intestine, pulmonary bronchi, and peripheral vasculature).

Thus, the manifestations of a pheochromocytoma are predictably those involving the above tissues. Because, as with other primary glandular

Table 20.14. Features of Common Types of Disorders of Adrenal Steroidogenesis

DEFECTIVE ENZYME	CHOLESTEROL DESMOLASE SYSTEM (CHOLESTEROL 20α-HYDROLASE	3β-HYDROXYSTEROID DEHYDROGENASE	17α-HYDROXYLASE	11β-HYDROXYLASE	21α-HYDROXYLASE SALT WASTING	21α-HYDROXYLASE NONSALT WASTING
Neonatal XX	0	+	0	+	+	+
Ambiguous		(Clitoromegaly)				
Genitalia XY	+	+	+	0	0	0
Postnatal virilization	0 (Sexual infantilism at puberty)	0	0 (Sexual infantilism at puberty)	+	+	+
Salt-wasting	+	+	0	0	+	0
Hypertension	0	0	+	+	0	0
Deficient production of cortisol	+	+	+	+	+	+
Increased serum deoxycortisol	0	0	0	+ +	0	0
Increased serum DHEA	0	+ + +	0	+	±	±
Increased renin	+	+	0	0	+ +	±

From Nyhan WL, Sakat: NA. Diagnostic Recognition of Genetic Disease. Philadelphia: Lea & Febiger, 1987.

disorders, this adrenal tumor tends to function independently of the normal control mechanisms, it might be anticipated that clinically associated findings are either sustained or paroxysmal, depending upon the whim of the abnormal tissue. Hypertension often is severe and is the most common sign of the disease, although the paroxysmal presentation may be extremely difficult to document. Profuse perspiration and heat intolerance are important signs, especially in conjunction with postural hypotension and tachycardia.

Biochemical effects of epinephrine include blocking insulin release, increased gluconeogenesis, activation of the glycogenolytic cascade, and lipid mobilization, with increased free fatty acid levels in blood. Hence, patients with pheochromocytoma may experience hyperglycemia, diminished glucose tolerance, glucosuria, and weight loss. Moreover, epinephrine increases basal metabolic rate, which may accentuate the rate of this weight loss.

The diagnosis of a pheochromocytoma is relatively straightforward and involves measurement of basal levels of catecholamines and their metabolites in urine. The primary metabolite is vanillymandelic acid; this metabolite is less accurate as a diagnostic measurement than the 3-methoxy metabolites, metanephrin and normetanephrin, because it is measured by a technique that does not discriminate the phenolic acids present in many foods. Treatment is surgical removal of the tumor.

The importance of hyperadrenal medullary function lies in the fact that this is one of very few definitively treatable causes of severe hypertension. Despite its rarity and the frequency of the clinical picture in conjunction with other very common disorders, it is a disease that, nevertheless, needs to be considered in all such patients.

SUGGESTED READINGS

GENERAL

DeGroot LJ, ed. Endocrinology. 3rd ed. Philadelphia: WB Saunders, 1995.

Greenspan FS, Baxter JD, eds. Basic and clinical endocrinology. 4th ed. Norwalk, CT: Appleton and Lange, 1994.

Hung W, ed. Clinical pediatric endocrinology. St. Louis: CV Mosby, 1994.

Lavin N, ed. Manual of endocrinology and metabolism. 2nd ed. Boston: Little, Brown and Co, 1994.

Wilson JD, Foster DW, eds. Williams textbook of endocrinology. 8th ed. Philadelphia: WB Saunders, 1992.

RECEPTORS AND OVERVIEW OF ENDOCRINE SYSTEM

Beato M. Transcriptional control by nuclear receptors. FASEB J 1991;5:2044.

Combarnous Y. Molecular basis of the specificity of binding of glycoprotein hormones to their receptors. Endocr Rev 1992;13:670.

Logan MA. Thyroid hormone receptors: multiple forms, multiple possibilities. Endocr Rev 1993;14:184.

Lucas PC, Granner DK. Hormone response domains in gene transcription. Annu Rev Biochem 1992;61:1131.

Reichlin S. Neuroendocrine-immune interactions. N Engl J Med 1993;329:1246.

Smith D, Toft DO. Steroid receptors and their associated proteins. Mol Endocrinol 1993;7:4.

Spiegel AM, Shenker A, Weinstein LS. Receptor-effector coupling by G proteins: implications for normal and abnormal signal transduction. Endocr Rev 1992;13:536.

PITUITARY

Casaneuva FF. Physiology of growth hormone secretion and action. Endocrinol Metab Clin North Am 1992;21:483.

Davis JRE, Belayew A, Sheppard MC. Prolactin and growth hormone. Baillieres Clin Endocrinol Metab 1988;2:797.

Frasier SD, Lippe BM. The rational use of growth hormone during childhood. J Clin Endocrinol Metab 1990;71:269.

Hartman ML, Iranmanesh A, Thorner MO, Veldhuis JD. Evaluation of pulsatile patterns of growth hormone release in humans: a brief review. American Journal of Human Biology 1993;5:603.

Klibanski A, Zervas NT. Diagnosis and management of hormone-secreting pituitary adenomas. N Engl J Med 1991;324:822.

LeRoith D, Clemmons D, Nissley P, Rechler MM. Insulin-like growth factors in health and disease. Ann Intern Med 1992;116:854.

Melmed S. Etiology of pituitary acromegaly. Endocrinol Metab Clin North Am 1992;21:539.

Oelkers W, Diederich S, Bahr V. Diagnosis and therapy surveillance in Addison's disease: rapid adrenocorticotropin (ACTH) test and measurement of plasma ACTH, renin activity, and aldosterone. J Clin Endocrinol Metab 1992;75:259.

Vance ML. Hypopituitarism. N Engl J Med 1994;330:1651.

Wilson DM. Clinical actions of growth hormone. Endocrinol Metab Clin North Am 1992;21:519.

REPRODUCTIVE ENDOCRINOLOGY

Auchus RJ, Fuqua SAW. The oestrogen receptor. Bailleres Clin Endocrinol Metab 1994;8:433.

Barnes R, Rosenfield RL. The polycystic ovary syndrome: pathogenesis and treatment. Ann Intern Med 1989;110:386.

Burgoyne RD, Wilde CJ. Control of secretory function in mammary epithelial cells. Cell Signal 1994;6:607.

Cowan BD, Morrison JC. Management of abnormal genital bleeding in girls and women. N Engl J Med 1991;324:1710.

Goldzieher JW, Young RL. Selected aspects of polycystic ovarian disease. Endocrinol Metab Clin North Am 1992;21:141.

Hillier SG, ed. Ovarian endocrinology. Oxford: Blackwell Scientific Publications, 1991.

Loprinzi CL, Michalak JC, Quella SK, et al. Megestrol acetate for the prevention of hot flashes. N Engl J Med 1994;331:347.

McElreavey K, Vilain E, Cotinot C, et al. Control of sex determination in animals. Eur J Biochem 1993;218:769.

McKenna TJ. Pathogenesis and treatment of polycystic ovary syndrome. N Engl J Med 1988;318:558.

Richards JS. Hormonal control of gene expression in the ovary. Endocr Rev 1994;15:725.

Rodin A, Hansa T, Taylor N, Clayton R. Hyperandrogenism in polycystic ovary syndrome. N Engl J Med 1994;330:460.

Schlaff WD, Roch JA, eds. Reproductive endocrinology. Cambridge, MA: Blackwell Scientific Publications, 1993.

Shangold MM, Tomai TP, Cook JD, et al. Factors associated with withdrawal bleeding after administration of oral micronized progesterone in women with secondary amenorrhea. Fertil Steril 1991;56:1040.

Speroff L, Glass RH, Kase NG. Clinical gynecologic endocrinology and infertility. Baltimore: Williams & Wilkins, 1994.

Turner RT, Riggs BL, Spelsberg TC. Skeletal effects of estrogen. Endocr Rev 1994;15:275.

THYROID

Bahn RS, Heufelder AE. Pathogenesis of Graves' ophthalmopathy. N Engl J Med 1993;329:1468.

Bayer MF. Effective laboratory evaluation of thyroid status. Med Clin North Am 1991;75:1.

Brent GA. The molecular basis of thyroid hormone action. N Engl J Med 1994;331:847.

Burch HB, Wartofshy L. Graves' ophthalmopathy: current concepts regarding pathogenesis and management. Endocr Rev 1993;14:747.

Burrow GN, Oppenheimer JH, Volpe R. Thyroid function and disease. Philadelphia: WB Saunders, 1989.

Burrow GN, Fisher DA, Larsen PR. Maternal and fetal thyroid function. N Engl J Med 1994;331:1072.

Fisher DA, Polk DH. Development of the thyroid. Bailleres Clin Endocrinol Metab 1989;3:627.

Fisher DA. Management of congenital hypothyroidism. J Clin Endocrinol Metab 1991;72:523.

Helfand M, Crapo LM. Screening for thyroid disease. Ann Intern Med 1990;112:840.

Heyerdahl S, Kase BF, Lie SO. Intellectual development in children with congenital hypothyroidism in relation to recommended thyroxine treatment. J Pediatr 1991;118:850.

Ledent C, Parma J, Dumont J, et al. Molecular genetics of thyroid diseases. Eur J Endocrinol 1994;130:8.

Mazzaferri EL. Management of a solitary thyroid nodule. N Engl J Med 1993;328:553.

McDougall IR. Thyroid disease in clinical practice. Oxford: Oxford University Press, 1992.

Ross DG, Daniels GH, Gouveia D. The use and limitations of a chemiluminescent thyrotropin assay as a single thyroid function test in an out-patient endocrine clinic. J Clin Endocrinol Metab 1990;71:764.

Samuels HH, Forman BM, Horowitz ZD, Ye Z-S. Regulation of gene expression by thyroid hormone. Annu Rev Physiol 1989;51:623.

Surks MI, Chopra IJ, Mariash CN, et al. American thyroid association guidelines for use of laboratory tests in thyroid disorders. JAMA 1990;263:1529.

Thorpe-Beeston JG, Nicolaides KH, Felton CV, et al. Maturation of the secretion of thyroid hormone and thyroid-stimulating hormone in the fetus. N Engl J Med 1991;324:532.

Toft AD. Thyroxine therapy. N Engl J Med 1994;331:174.

Woeber KA. Thyrotoxicosis and the heart. N Engl J Med 1992;327:94.

Yen PM, Chin WW. New advances in understanding the molecular mechanisms of thyroid hormone action. Trends in Endocrinology and Metabolism 1994;5:65.

ADRENAL

Addison GM. Inherited disorders of steroid biosynthesis. In: Holton JB, ed. The inherited metabolic diseases. New York: Churchill Livingstone, 1994.

Azziz R, Dewailly D, Owerbach D. Nonclassic adrenal hyperplasia: current concepts. J Clin Endocrinol Metab 1994;78:810.

Burnstein KL, Cidlowski JA. The down side of glucocorticoid receptor regulation. Mol Cell Endocrinol 1992;83:C1.

Chin R. Adrenal crisis. Crit Care Clin 1991;7:23.

Danese RD, Aron DC. Cushing's syndrome and hypertension. Endocrinol Metab Clin North Am 1994; 23:299.

Dickstein G, Shechner C, Nicholson WE, et al. Adrenocorticostimulation test: effect of basal cortisol level, time of day, and suggested new sensitive low dose test. J Clin Endocrinol Metabol 1991;72:773.

Guengerich FP. Cytochrome P450 enzymes. American Scientist 1993;81:440.

Kannan CR. The adrenal gland. New York: Plenum Medical Book Co, 1988.

Levine LS, Pang S. Prenatal diagnosis and treatment of congenital adrenal hyperplasia. J Pediatr Endocrinol 1994;7:193.

Miller WL. Congenital adrenal hyperplasias. Endocrinol Metab Clin North Am 1991;20:721.

Miller WL. Genetics, diagnosis, and management of 21-hydroxylase deficiency. J Clin Endocrinol Metab 1994; 78:241.

New MI. 21-hydroxylase deficiency congenital adrenal hyperplasia. J Steroid Biochem Mol Biol 1994;48:15.

Orth DN. Cushing's syndrome. N Engl J Med 1995;332: 791.

Rosner W. Plasma steroid-binding proteins. Endocrinol Metab Clin North Am 1991;20:697.

Speiser PW, Agdere L, Ueshiba H, et al. Aldosterone synthesis in salt-wasting congenital adrenal hyperplasia with complete absence of adrenal 21-hydroxylase. N Engl J Med 1991;321:145.

Speiser PW, New MI. Prenatal diagnosis and management of congenital adrenal hyperplasia. Clin Perinatol 1994; 9:631.

Strachan T. Molecular pathology of 21-hydroxylase deficiency. J Inherit Metab Dis 1994;17:430.

White PC, Curnow KM, Pascoe L. Disorders of steroid 11β-hydroxylase isozymes. Endocr Rev 1994;15:421.

Yanase T, Simpson ER, Waterman MR. 17α-hydroxylase/17,20-lyase deficiency: from clinical investigation to molecular definition. Endocr Rev 1991;12:91.

chapter **21**

The Skeleton—Disorders of Bone, Connective Tissue, and Ground Substance

We have chosen the above title to emphasize that the framework of the human body consists of more than one's disarticulated bones. Connective tissues include a wide variety of structures including bone, cartilage, tendons, joint capsules, fascia, and the supporting structures of the walls of blood vessels and hollow organs. Deployed throughout the body, these materials give form and shape to the organs that make up the individual. What distinguishes connective tissue from other tissues is that in addition to the specialized cells constituting these tissues, there is an extracellular matrix secreted by these cells. Components of the extracellular matrix or ground substance are collagen, elastin, glycoproteins, and carbohydrate polymers (glycosaminoglycans [GAGs]). Not infrequently, the GAGs are bound to protein to create still larger entities called proteoglycans. But, of all the specializations of connective tissue, perhaps the most remarkable is that achieved by the deposition of a mineral phase in the extracellular matrix to form bone.

The physicochemical interaction of these macromolecules determine the distinctive characteristics of a particular connective tissue. Because of this interdependence, disorders affecting collagen, elastin, GAGs, and glycoproteins may affect connective tissues and bone, making those derangements a prominent part of their clinical manifestations.

Anyone who has ever sprained an ankle can appreciate the importance of the connective tissue that "binds the bones together" to skeletal function. Most dramatically, clinical and radiologic findings in a patient with osteogenesis imperfecta underscores the vital role of normal ground substance (in this instance collagen) to the formation of strong bone. True, the skeleton was not essential to the emergence of life itself, because our ancestors, the unicellular organisms, have existed (and continue to exist) very nicely without one. But, locomotion in an environment in which the effects of gravity are not mitigated by the natural buoyancy of water requires an alternative means of support—one that provides a firm anchor for the muscles that effect movement.

Virtually all unicellular organisms exist in an aqueous milieu—the only exceptions are those that can encapsulate to prevent water loss. In such an environment, many of the small molecular nutritional requirements, such as NaCl and Ca^{++} and Mg^{++} ions are ubiquitous; the remaining essentials, such as amino acids, are obtained by engulfing smaller organisms. Multicellular organization does not necessarily demand a skeleton (eg, jellyfish) nor, for that matter, a means of locomotion; but, in such cases, survival depends upon an aqueous milieu and availability of a continuous food supply in the immediate environment. Much farther along the evolutionary scale is the shark family, which includes some of the oldest creatures on earth and has remained essentially unchanged over several million years. Sharks are particularly notable for the fact that their skeletons are cartilaginous, underscoring the important point that large, powerful multicellular organisms do not necessarily require rigid, calcified frameworks to survive. Yet sharks, like the unicellular animals, depend upon an aqueous milieu containing electrolytes and other small molecules within a fairly narrow concentration range. In this respect, the shark gains little advantage from its enormous power and mobility compared to the most primitive barnacle.

Thus, only at the point when life emerged from the oceans onto land, with a concomitant loss of buoyancy and cutting off access to a continuous bath of electrolytes, was it necessary to evolve a rigid skeleton for support, one that also provided a way to internalize an electrolyte storehouse. If, indeed, it is true that ontogeny recapitulates phylogeny, then study of the evolution of the kidney from fish to humans details the story of how the requirement to conserve electrolytes was satisfied. Nature, always extremely parsimonious, eventually found a means by which to integrate the two requirements for terrestrial life: (*1*) construction of a calcium phosphate-reinforced, cartilaginous-based framework, (*2*) provision of a reservoir of electrolytes vital to all cells, a function also performed by the skeleton. Moreover, the kidney, which already had evolved primitive regulatory functions to maintain this electrolyte pool in aqueous animals, could be further refined to regulate and defend the pool against depletion. So kidney and bone, in conjunction with several hormones, together constituted an elaborate system to maintain the constancy of the internal fluid compartment. With this evolutionary stroke of good fortune, terrestrial life began in earnest; the existence of dinosaurs which weighed several tons attested to the success of the strategy. Therefore, our discussion of the skeleton, which is the primary subject of this chapter, must also examine the interrelationship with the regulatory components.

COLLAGEN AND ITS DISORDERS

Collagen is an aggregate of three left-handed polypeptide chains containing about 1000 amino acids, with approximately three amino acids per turn of the helix, 1.5 nm in diameter and 300 nm in length. The three helices twist around each other like a rope to form a right-handed helix. Finally, these triple helices associate to form fibrils, such association depending upon hydrophobic interactions, interchain hydrogen bonds, and specific side-chain interactions (all noncovalent forces).

Collagen is unique among proteins, because every third amino acid is glycine. Apparently, approximation of the three chains precludes the presence of an amino acid with a side chain, a stereochemical requirement that can be satisfied only by glycine (Figure 21.1). As we will shortly

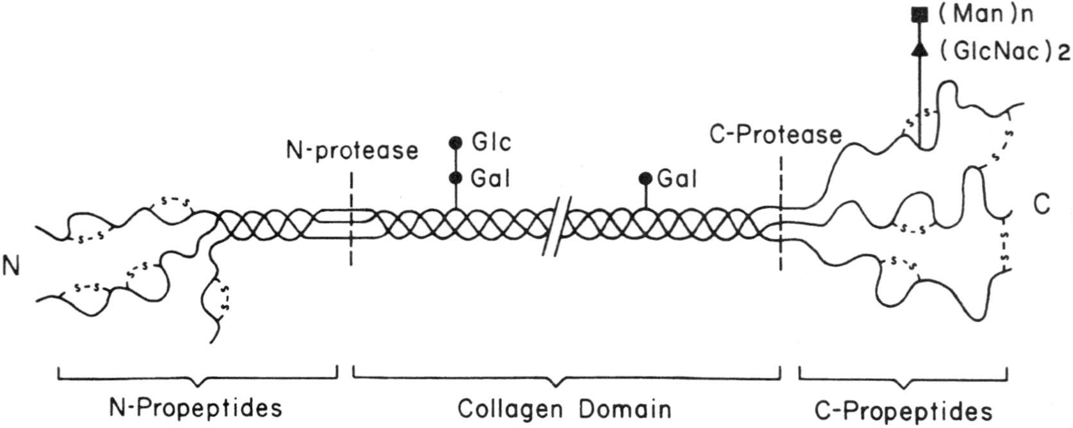

Figure 21.1. Schematic representation of type I procollagen. The amino acid sequence of each of the three chains shown is a variation of the general formula $(\text{-Gly-X-Y-})_{333}$, where the presence of proline and hydroxyproline in the X and Y positions favor formation of a triple-helical structure. The rigid ring substituents of these two amino acids prohibit the molecule from folding upon itself, while the presence of hydroxyproline is essential to crosslinking between chains, as is the occasional hydroxylysine residue. Glycosylation of hydroxylysine residues occurs prior to formation of the triple helix, as does attachment of a mannose-rich oligosaccharide at the C-terminus. The latter site initiates association of the individual chains, with subsequent interchain crosslinking through hydroxylyine, hydroxyproline and disulfide bonds. Cleavage of the propeptide domains at both N- and C-termini is an extracellular event. Reprinted with permission from Nyhan WL, Sakati NA. Diagnostic Recognition of Genetic Disease. Philadelphia: Lea & Febiger, 1987: 496.

see, a mutation that substitutes a bulkier amino acid for glycine can have devastating consequences for the stability of the collagen formed. The general formula $(X\text{-}Y\text{-}Gly)_{333}$ describes the composition of collagen. Other unusual aspects of collagen include the presence of approximately 100 proline residues in the X position and 100 hydroxyproline residues in the Y position. Both proline and hydroxyproline are rigid rings, which favor the formation of a triple helix. They do so because proline and hydroxyproline form inflexible peptide bonds and, being linked to glycine which has a flexible peptide bond, the collagen precursors (called pro α- chains) cannot fold into a three-dimensional structure as does a globular protein. Furthermore, hydroxyproline is crucial to stabilizing the triple helix. Finally, hydroxylysine also is found in collagen, serving both as a site for formation of covalent cross-links as well as for attachment of carbohydrate residues. Hydroxylation of proline and lysine occur as a posttranslational event in the elaboration of collagen.

Biosynthesis

As implied in the introductory section above, the "all important" structural protein, collagen, preceded bone in the process of evolution, imposing a logical sequence to approach the subject at hand. A priori, we may assign an important function to the collagen molecule, because it constitutes approximately 25% of total body protein. Distribution of collagen throughout the body is widespread with collagens of different composition serving distinctive functions (Table 21.1). Examination of Table 21.1 reveals a gamut of vital structural as well as more subtle discriminatory functions, for example, tendons, ligaments, bone, cartilage, basement membrane (glomeruli), and cornea (light transmission).

Until the early 1970s, collagen was assumed to be a single type of molecule but it has since turned out to be a group of at least 15 different types, composed of at least 23 different polypeptides, designated "α-chains." There are three polypeptide chains constituting a specific type of collagen molecule, in an arrangement that results in formation of an α-helix (Figure 21.1). So-called "fibril" formation is the result of an extracellular process of aggregation of multiple triple helices in a specific alignment.

In the body, there are four broad categories of collagen molecules: (*1*) those that characteristically form fibrils, (*2*) nonfibrillar collagens, similar in size to their fibrillar counterparts, but composed of α-helices that are segmentally interrupted, (*3*) collagens that are shorter than the fibrillar collagens in which the helix may or may not be discontinuous, and (*4*) a long-chain anchoring molecule with an interrupted helix. In its final form, a given collagen molecule represents the product of a very complex process involving genes on different chromosomes, as well as many posttranslational and extracellular events. So complicated is this process that, despite emerging evidence that quantitatively minor types of collagen are important components of various pathophysiologic responses to injury, we will limit discussion to the fibrillar (Types I–III) collagens, which represent 95% of the total. The importance of Types

Table 21.1. Collagen Types

TYPE	TISSUE DISTRIBUTION	PROTEIN UNITS	CHEMICAL COMPOSITION
I	Bone, tendon, skin, ligament, fascia, cornea, arteries, uterus, heart valves	Two identical chains plus one nonidentical fiber; bundles in parallel	67% hydroxylysine; 1% carbohydrate; no cysteine
II	Cartilage, nucleus pulposus, neural retinal tissue, vitreous body	Three identical chains	Abundant hydroxylysine and carbohydrate
III	Skin, arteries, uterus, lung, liver, intestine	Three identical chains: forms circumferential helical network in hollow tissues	High hydroxyproline; hydroxylysine and carbohydrate content similar to type I; interchain disulfide bonds
IV	Basement membranes (glomeruli, cornea)	Three identical chains	High hydroxylysine; hydroxyproline; three hydroxyproline and carbohydrate interchain disulfide bonds

I–III derives from their roles in load-bearing tissue throughout the body and their presence in cartilage, bone, and blood vessel walls.

Of the three types of fibrillar collagen, Type I is distinct in having two different types of α-chains, designated α1I and α2I, present in a ratio of 2 : 1, respectively. Type III, however, is distinct in possessing cysteine in the three homologous α-chains, designated α1(III)3. Type II is, of course, a distinct species of molecule because these molecules have three homologous α1II chains, each with the same, unique amino acid sequence. It should be clear that there must be separate genes that code for the sequences of each of the distinct α1 chains. As a corollary, synthesis of Type I collagen must require two separate genes with pro α1I chains being directed from chromosome 17 and pro α2I from chromosome 7. Finally, it follows that if mutations occur in any of these genes, tissues in which the corresponding type of collagen normally occurs will be selectively affected and abnormalities will be manifested at a clinical level.

Table 21.2 reveals the complexity of the biosynthetic process leading to a mature collagen molecule, with processing of collagen beginning intracellularly but being completed extracellularly. Setting aside discussion of regulation of transcription of multiple genes leading to synthesis of multiple forms of α1 chains simultaneously in appropriate quantities and at rates consistent with demand, many other steps remain. Key among these is the process of association between α1 chains to form a triple helix. Triple helix formation depends, in turn, upon the action of three separate hydroxylases acting on proline and lysine residues in the sequences to form hydroxyproline and hydroxylysine, respectively. As interaction of the active site with a substrate is dominated by steric fit, so the amino acid sequence containing the proline or lysine residue also is a significant factor in providing a binding site for the enzyme mediating enzymatic hydroxylation. All three hydroxylases require ascorbate, α-ketoglutarate, Fe^{++} and O_2, producing succinate through sequential decarboxylation and oxidation of α-ketoglutarate, in the process consuming one atom of oxygen. The second oxygen atom is installed into the proline or lysine residue of the chain. In addition to the crucial (-X-Y-Gly-)n triplet sequence of the α1-chains, hydroxylation is the second critical step in permitting formation of the triple helix through proper "fit."

These hydroxylation reactions begin as the pro α-chains enter the cisternae of the endoplasmic reticulum (E/R), where about 100 proline residues are converted to hydroxyproline. Many lysine residues are also hydroxylated to hydroxylysine. Following termination, the chains fold and intrachain disulfide bonding is established, mediated by an enzymatic disulfide exchange. This disulfide bonding is restricted to the C- and N-termini regions of the chain, thereby creating "globular" domains. The association of the C-termini of the three pro α-chains is vital, because it sets up the proper registration along the length of the three pro α-chains so that they can adopt the correct orientation to create a stable triple helix (Figure 21.2). If the chains are out of register, as can occur with some mutations, then the triple helix cannot form properly with devastating consequences.

Prior to formation of the triple helix, some of the hydroxylysine residues undergo glycosylation with glucose or galactose. Addition of each carbohydrate requires a specific glycosyl transferase and, it should be noted, does not occur on every hydroxylysine residue. Once again, the "goodness" of steric fit probably constrains enzyme activity and is determined by other residues adjoining the hydroxylysine to be glycosylated. The purpose served by the glycosylation is not known. Moreover, glycosylation occurs only on separate α1 chains, so that those that are further modified and have associated to form a triple helix are rendered immune to the process. A mannose-rich oligosaccharide (Figure 21.2) is enzymatically added to the carboxy-terminal end of the chain, as well, the linkage established through one or more asparagine residues, depending upon the species of α-chain. Although not yet certain, it is likely that the number and conformation of these oligosaccharides play a role in further Golgi recognition and processing of the peptide chains.

The α1 chains initially associate at the C-termini, first by noncovalent forces and then by disulfide bond formation, so that the mannose-asparagine configuration probably plays a role in creation of a specific domain, permitting only certain types of α1 chain associations. These interchain associations are further enabled by the

Table 21.2. Steps in Biosynthesis of Collagen and Associated Disease States

PROCESS	COMMENT	ASSOCIATED DISEASE STATE
Intracellular		
Protein synthesis of pre-procollagen	Determines linear sequence (primary structure), which contains information for higher order folding (see Part I)	Regulation of synthesis deranged in osteogensis imperfecta, Ehlers-Danlos type IV (ecchymotic)
Processing		
1. Removal of peptide sequences from pre-procollagen	Proteases remove "signal" sequences to form procollagen from pre-procollagen	
2. Hydroxylation		
Proline residues	Most hydroxylated by prolyl-4-hydroxylase (requires ascorbate, acts only on residues in Y position) Smaller percentage by prolyl-3-hydroxylase (residues in X-position only if Y position is 4-hydroxyproline)	Ehlers-Danlos type VI Osteogenesis imperfecta Scurvy ?Alcaptonuria
Lysine residues	Lysyl hydroxylase—sites for addition of carbohydrates—required for cross-link formation (see below)	
3. Glycosylation of hydroxylysine	Mediated by glycosyl and galactosyl transferases	
4. Association of three pro α chains with formation of interchain disulfide bonds	Process may be spontaneous or enzyme mediated (not known)	
5. Formation of triple helix	Spontaneous association (information inherent in primary structure)	
6. Secretion into extracellular space	Procollagen must be in triple helix conformation; may involve microtubules	
Extracellular		
1. Procollagen → Collagen	Removal of additional sequences at amino and carboxy termini by proteases	Ehlers-Danlos, type VII
2. Collagen molecules assemble into fibrils	Spontaneous process—these fibrils lack tensile strength of final collagen	Ehlers-Danlos, type I
3. Cross-link formation to achieve tensile strength	Formation of reactive aldehydes at certain lysyl and hydroxylysyl residues—mediated by lysyl oxidase (Cu-containing protein) Synthesis of covalent cross-links (condensation of two aldehydes; or condensation aldehyde and amino group of lysine or glycosylated hydroxylysine)	Cutis laxa, X-linked Ehlers-Danlos, type V Menke's syndrome Homocystinuria Alcaptonuria

characteristic folding of the $\alpha 1$ propeptide, such folding generated through intrachain disulfide bonds spoken of above. As formation of the triple helix begins, it is propagated toward the N-terminus of each $\alpha 1$ chain. With completion of the association process, the three pro α chains of the triple helix thus formed is called procollagen, and requires further posttranslational modifications prior to release from the cell. These posttranslational events occur in the Golgi body and for example include removal of some saccharide units from Type I procollagen to enhance the exposure of the mannose-asparagine domain. The functions of these modifications are not known.

Now the procollagen molecule is secreted from the cell into the extracellular space, where it must undergo still further processing. Removal of the C- and N-termini occurs through the action of C- and N-proteinases, resulting in a loss of approximately one-third of the mass of the original procollagen triple helix. It is thought that as the triple helix is extruded, proteolytic action begins in very

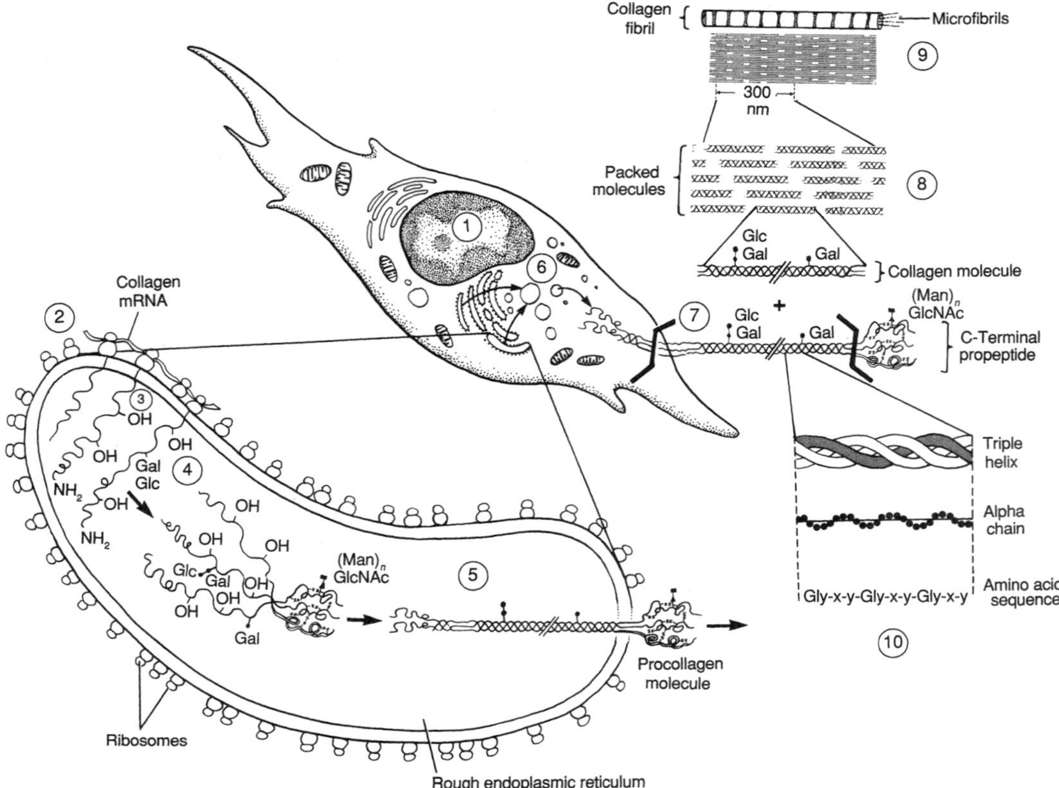

Figure 21.2. Biosynthesis of Type I collagen. Transcription of α1 (I) and α2 (I) genes occurs within the nucleus (1). The product, collagen mRNA, is shown at site (2) being translated on ribosomes within the endoplasmic reticulum. Hydroxylation (3) and glycosylation (4) are posttranslational events which require enzymes and are necessary for pro α chain aggregation (5) to form procollagen. The procollagen molecule is relayed by the Golgi system (6) to the surface of the cell, where cleavage of the N- and C-terminal propeptides (7) results in formation of the mature collagen molecule. These molecules self-aggregate, with enzymatic mediation of the formation of intra and intermolecular crosslinking (8), leading to a macromolecule with substantial tensile strength, called a fibril (9). The relationship between the molecular information presented in Figure 21.1 and the final macromolecular fibril is shown (10). Reprinted with permission from Kaplowitz N. Liver and Biliary Diseases. Baltimore: Williams & Wilkins, 1992: 120.

close proximity to the cell membrane. After cleavage of the terminus that emerges first, adjacent triple helices present in high density at the cell surface associate to form fibrils. This association occurs in a highly ordered fashion, culminating with cleavage of the final terminus to emerge, resulting in the formation of a collagen fibril. The manner in which this association occurs is nonenzymatic and illustrates self assembly of a higher ordered structure. Naturally, this specificity derives from the information inherent in the amino acid sequence of the protein. Thus, ordering of the fibril depends on the sequence and distribution of the hydrophilic and hydrophobic residues projecting from each individual collagen triple helix.

Although the spontaneous association of collagen molecules within a fibril is so highly ordered that it is predictable, there is a further order imposed within the fibril, so that tensile strength and insolubility are increased. This additional processing requires the generation of reactive aldehydes from specific lysyl and hydroxylysyl residues through the action of the enzyme lysyl oxidase. Pyridoxal phosphate and copper are cofactors for the enzyme. The aldehydes thus created undergo spontaneous conversion to aldimines, prerequisite to formation of stable cross-links between these reactive groups and amino acids on contiguous collagen molecules. An additional cross-link involving two dehydrodihydroxylysinonorleucine residues and resulting in formation of a 3-hydroxypyridinium derivative has been described. The mechanism for formation is shown in Figure 21.3. It is thought that this constitutes the most stable cross-link in formation of the collagen fibril.

Biodegradation

Because collagen is a key component of bone formation, and because bone can be remodeled in response to stress, breakage, and the like (see following text), it follows logically that collagen also must be susceptible to biodegradation. At present, however, the specifics of collagen breakdown are incompletely understood.

Inasmuch as the extensive, stable cross-linking of fibrillar collagen confers remarkable resistance to solubilization, it follows that cleavage of these bonds must be central to degradation of the molecule. Moreover, the inherent stability of these linkages implies, even demands, the need for enzymatic mediation of the process. Yet, these specific enzymes have not been identified. Those that are known to be involved in collagen degradation are collectively described as the collagenases. These enzymes attack the peptide sequence, rather than the cross-links, resulting in fragments that are more soluble than the parent molecule. These fragments are thought to be phagocytosed and degraded further in lysosomes, where all but the hydroxylated residues are recycled. Keep in mind that hitherto undescribed diseases may be associated with enzymatic deficiency of one or more of the enzymes of collagen degradation. Of course, there is ample precedent for this from other categories of disease involving catabolism of structural molecules, such as the glycogen, mucopolysaccharide, and lipid storage diseases.

Disorders of the Fibrillar Collagens

Of the three predominant molecular species (Types I–III), which are involved in disorders of fibrillar collagen, Type I is the most plentiful and widely distributed. Type I collagen, as the product of two separate species of α-peptides and, therefore, of at least two separate genes, is also likely to be subject to the greatest molecular variation. Thus, it is no surprise that many disease entities have been linked to abnormalities of Type I collagen. In addition, the rather extensive posttranslational modifications necessary to form a mature collagen fibril from the α-peptides, processes that, in some cases, are not specific to a single type of α-peptide, further broadens the range of possible biochemical defects. Taken together, all of these factors lead to a wide spectrum of clinical phenotypes, as exemplified by the definition of four distinct types of osteogenesis imperfecta.

OSTEOGENESIS IMPERFECTA

Few human diseases have been so appropriately named, because the pathophysiologic basis for the clinical presentations of osteogenesis imperfecta is a direct result of abnormal collagen formation and hence, ground substance. All four types of osteogenesis imperfecta, in themselves heterogeneous, derive from defects in Type I collagen synthesis (Table 21.3). Given that collagen constitutes about 90% of demineralized bone on a weight-to-weight basis (w/w), it is easy to imagine the ramifications of abnormal Type I collagen for bone formation, Type I accounting for almost all of the collagen present in bone. To simplify, in what follows we will refer to Type I collagen only as "collagen," to avoid the confusions that might arise from nomenclature of the disease entities, also referred to in terms of types.

The unifying feature of all forms of osteogenesis imperfecta is bone fragility stemming from abnormalities in the collagen molecule forming the bone matrix. As we will see, depending on the nature of the defect, there is variation in the degree of severity of the brittle bones. To a large extent, the fragility can be related to the molecular defect, and the degree to which the resulting collagen structure is abnormal. It also should be noted that there is variability in the mode of inheritance between the types, although most are transmitted as autosomal dominant traits. A dominant inheritance pattern has extremely important implications for understanding the pathophysiology, primarily because the collagen of bone is a macromolecule normally formed from triple helices that are composed of two different α-chains. Thus, a mutation

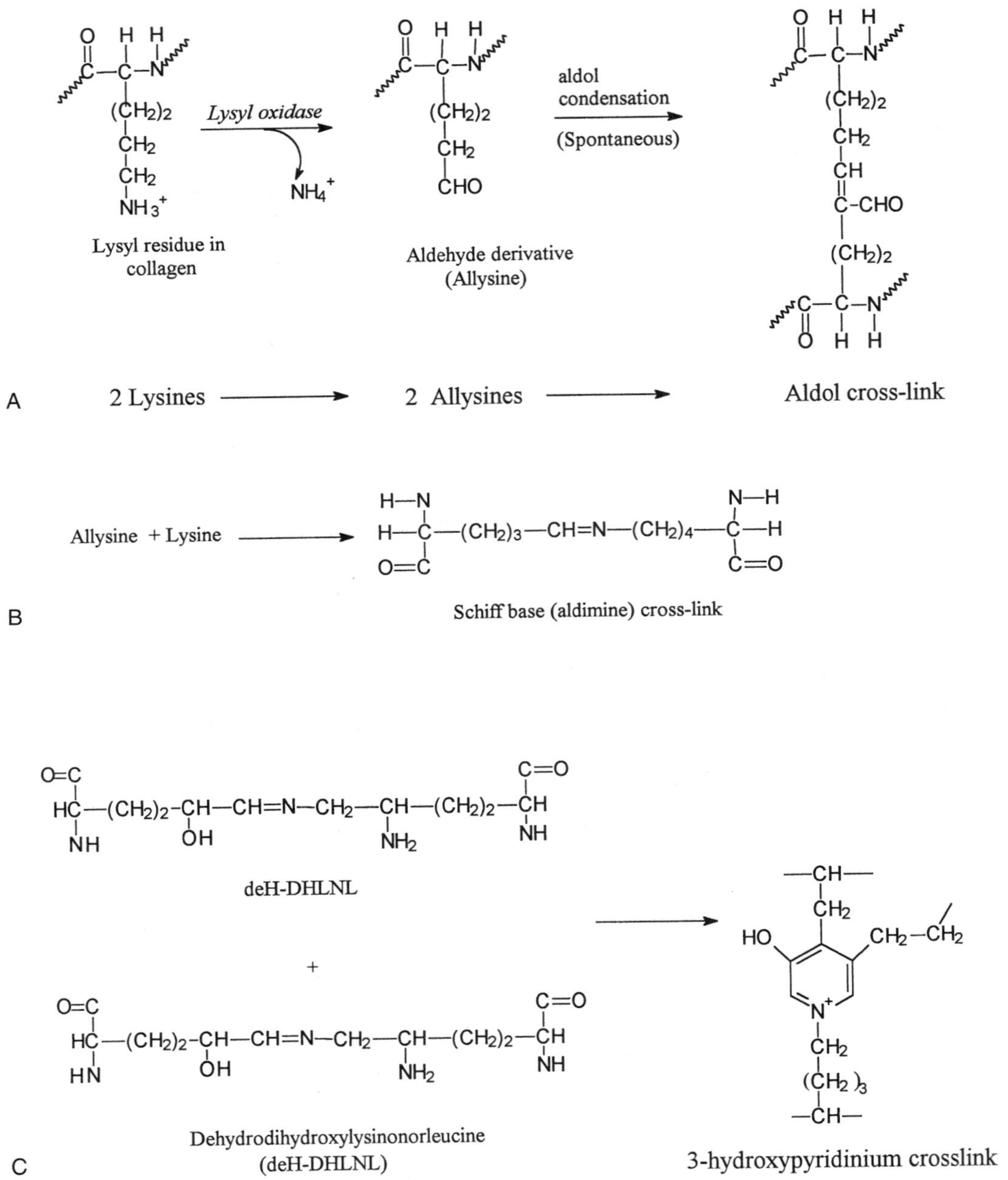

Lysyl residue in collagen — *Lysyl oxidase* (NH_4^+) → Aldehyde derivative (Allysine) — aldol condensation (Spontaneous) → Aldol cross-link

A 2 Lysines → 2 Allysines → Aldol cross-link

Allysine + Lysine → H—N / H—C—$(CH_2)_3$—CH=N—$(CH_2)_4$—C—H / O=C ... N—H / C=O

B Schiff base (aldimine) cross-link

deH-DHLNL + Dehydrodihydroxylysinonorleucine (deH-DHLNL) → 3-hydroxypyridinium crosslink

C

Figure 21.3. The formation and nature of collagen crosslinks. (A) Formation of aldol crosslinks begins with production of allysine (or hydroxyallysine) through the action of lysyl oxidase, a copper and pyridoxal phosphate dependent enzyme which mediates an oxidative deamination and an increase in oxidation state of the terminal methylene group to an aldehyde. Cross linking between two allysine residues occurs by a spontaneous aldol condensation reaction. (B) Formation of aldimine crosslinks requires prior production of allysine (or hydroxyallysine); further reaction to form a Schiff base occurs spontaneously between the aldehyde of the former compound and the É-amino group of a lysine residue. (C) Two dehydrodihydroxylysinonorleucine crosslinks on collagen react to form a 3-hydroxypyridinium crosslink.

Table 21.3. Osteogenesis Imperfecta

TYPE	CLINICAL FEATURES	FRACTURES AT BIRTH	INHERITANCE	ADDITIONAL FEATURES	BIOCHEMISTRY	MOLECULAR DEFECT
I	Scoliosis, "codfish" deformity of vertebrae, deformity fractured and bowed long bones, hyperextensible joints, blue sclera, normal dentition, deafness	No	AD	Easy bruisability	↓ Type I collagen relative to type III	All in COL1A1: multiple point mutations in coding region: deletions
II	Low birth weight, often premature, multiple fractures (most intrapartum), disordered cranial ossification, femurs misshapen ("crumpled"), deep blue sclera	Yes	AR	Invariable fatal in infancy	↓ Synthesis of type I collagen; ↑ bone -OH-lysine content	gly211 → arg211 in alpha 1 (I) triple helical domain
III	Normal birth weight, scoliosis, long–bone deformities, hypertensible joints, poor dentition, blue sclera in infancy, normal sclera in adult years	Yes	AR (sporadic)	Easy bruisability, occasional deafness	Altered ratio of type I: type III collagen	gly427 → arg427 in alpha 1 (I) triple helical domain
IV	Normal birth weight, fractures generally uncommon, osteoporosis with variable bony deformities, sclera normal, dentition strikingly abnormal	No	AD	Normal auditory acuity	Altered ratio of type I: type III collagen	gly883 → ser883 in pro alpha 1 (I) triple helical domain

N.B. Study of these disorders is ongoing at a molecular level, and there is every reason to expect that many more mutations will be described for each clinical phenotype.

in a structural gene coding for one of these chains need only be present on one member of a pair of chromosomes to impair synthesis of normal collagen. In this respect, there is a close similarity to the molecular basis of several hemoglobinopathies (see Chapter 18).

Clinically, Type II osteogenesis imperfecta is the most dramatic of the four general types and, perhaps for this reason, the most thoroughly studied. Inheritance has been reported as both autosomal dominant and recessive, although most cases appear to derive from new dominant mutations. In pedigrees with a recurrence of the disease, it is proposed that germ cell mosaicism can account for such events. Accordingly, the prudent course is to offer prenatal diagnosis to all families with a previously affected pregnancy. Affected newborns are relatively easy to identify because they exhibit macrocephaly with absence of mineralization clearly seen radiographically. In addition, the extremities are shortened and the thoracic cavity is disproportionately small. Remarkably, significant fractures are uncommon in the immediate newborn period, perhaps because of the tendency toward prematurity combined with decreased mineralization. Most such infants expire by 1 month of age, and virtually all die by 1 year. The chief cause of death is respiratory, either pulmonary insufficiency, secondary congestive heart failure, or infection. In infants surviving the newborn period, frequency of fractures increases, probably related more to essentials of handling during normal care than from causes intrinsic to the abnormal bone itself.

Molecular studies in cells and tissues from Type II patients have presented us, yet again, with the lesson that a single phenotype may be common to numerous genotypes. Three separate structural gene modifications have been identified, two in the gene coding for α1I on chromosome 17, the other (located on chromosome 7) in the gene coding for α2I. The first of these mutations is an intron-to-intron deletion which resulted in loss of three exons in between and led to synthesis of an abnormally short pro $\alpha1$ peptide. The second mutation described was an insertion that resulted in duplication of a portion of the amino acid sequence and led to synthesis of an abnormally long pro $\alpha1$ peptide. Finally, a deletion in the pro $\alpha2$ structural gene has been shown to result in a pro $\alpha2$ peptide which was 180 residues shorter than normal. Given the complexities of posttranslational modifications, such as enzymatic hydroxylation and folding, which are dependent upon the correct peptide sequence and proper side chain orientation and charge, it is not difficult to imagine how such mutations might impact upon ultimate gene product. Indeed, the abnormally short procollagen formed as a result of either the first or the third of these mutations was found to be more slowly secreted than normal, because it was subjected to overmodification inside the osteoblast. Because assembly of the triple helix begins at the C-terminus moving toward the N-terminus, mutations located at the C-terminus will have a profound effect on formation of the entire triple helix. Furthermore, as posttranslational modification can occur only on pro α-chains that have not yet folded into the triple helix, interference in folding will lead to excess posttranslational modification. Overmodification is both believed to decrease secretion from fibroblasts and osteoblasts into the extracellular space and to further destabilize the secreted product.

Further examination of the genetic defects in Type II patients has made clear the fact that the majority of affected individuals derive from point mutations involving base-pair substitutions, rather than deletions involving thousands of such pairs. In some cases, there has been a base-pair substitution resulting in insertion of a bulky cysteine residue in place of a glycine within the $\alpha1$ chain molecular domain that forms the triple-helix, thus hobbling the normal process of molecular association. Other point mutations leading to substitution of arginine or aspartic acid for glycine have had a similar effect, both with respect to abnormal collagen formation and to manifestation as Type II osteogenesis imperfecta. The presence of abnormal collagen molecules would be expected to trigger increased turnover. The role of increased rate of degradation in the pathogenesis of the disease remains undetermined. Furthermore, keep in mind that both $\alpha1$ and $\alpha2$ propeptides are coded by pairs of allelic genes, only one of which is mutant, and that Type I collagen is a composite of two $\alpha1$ and a single $\alpha2$ chain. Thus, both normal and abnormal α-chains are synthesized, and a coding defect for $\alpha2$ would be expected to result in fewer normal triple helices than a similar defect in $\alpha1$ synthesis. It remains to be determined whether there are subtle differences in phenotype that reflect the molecular defects.

The osteoblasts, as the chief architects of bone collagen, reflect both a retarded secretory rate and increased catabolism of abnormal collagen. The endoplasmic reticulum of these osteoblasts is dilated and engorged. Of those collagen fibrils that are present, many can be identified as having smaller diameters than normal. In osteogenesis imperfecta, there is no question that there is markedly poor mineralization of bone—the real problem is why. As pointed out above, to a varying extent, there is always likely to be some normal collagen present. How much of the abnormal, in relation to normal, is required for development of the abnormal phenotype is not known.

Clinically, Type III disease is equally dramatic, differing from Type II in having frequent perinatal fractures, yet a much longer survival, on average. Types I and IV are, in general, milder with respect to fractures; Type I has little effect on stature or bone deformity and Type IV causes detectable bony deformity and some degree of short stature. Each of these types is, in a way, similar to Type II—biochemically heterogeneous and the result of either frameshift or point mutations in a structural gene. Thus, it is fair to say that, mutations that lead to any of the forms of osteogenesis imperfecta are confined to structural genes. Subsequent aberrant cellular and/or extracellular events leading to abnormal bone formation are a consequence of the abnormal interaction of normal posttranslational mechanisms acting on abnormal substrate.

EHLERS-DANLOS SYNDROME

Having already discussed osteogenesis imperfecta, a disease with multiple genotypic variations confined to collagen structural genes, it is logical to focus on examination of a syndrome that represents many different genotypes, some of the manifestations of which can be attributed to posttranslational abnormalities. Because these posttranslational modifications are essential to fibril formation from structurally normal triple helices, it can be assumed that where abnormalities in posttranslational processing exist, some or all of the fibrillar collagens will show some abnormality as well. Currently, there are 10 known phenotypes of Ehlers-Danlos syndrome, differing from each other in terms of heredity pattern, primary tissue involvement, and severity (Table 21.4). Of these, the biochemical etiologies are unknown for Types I–III, V, and VIII, although the shared characteristics of the skin and other involved tissues suggest abnormal collagen.

Ehlers-Danlos syndrome Type IV, inherited as an autosomal dominant trait, is the extreme example of abnormalities common to the other Types as well. Phenotypic manifestations are chiefly referable to the vascular system; extensive bruising with ecchymoses beneath a thin and hyperlucent skin is the most common finding. Thus, Ehlers-Danlos syndrome (EDS) IV always should be included in the differential diagnosis of a suspected coagulation disorder. In contrast to many of the other forms of EDS, patients with Type IV show no evidence of skin or joint hyperextensibility, correlating closely with the nature of the biochemical defect (see following text). Although the unifying biochemical feature of EDS IV is the abnormal synthesis of Type III collagen, there is wide heterogeneity in the molecular defects underlying the biochemical phenotype. Of the three fibrillar collagen types, Type III is present in very low quantities in normal skin and bone. However, Type III collagen is the quantitatively dominant form of collagen in normal blood vessels and hollow organs, such as intestine and uterus. Thus, the normal pattern of distribution of Type III collagen determines the clinical phenotype in EDS IV. Yet, there are several genetic mutations that have been identified in different pedigrees that can result in the phenotype of EDS IV. In some families, it has been shown that fibroblasts from affected individuals secrete Type III procollagen at a rate less than 20% of normal. The sequestered, nonsecreted molecules are degraded at a slow rate and are totally excluded from the extracellular space, which has made molecular characterization of the abnormalities difficult. In other pedigrees, shortened α1 (III) chains are synthesized because of deletion of several exon regions in the corresponding gene. The shortened chain is inefficiently secreted, leading to a proportion of Type III collagen fibrils that are completely abnormal, others that are hybrid varieties of normal and shortened chains, as well as a small proportion that will be normal as a consequence of the activity of the normal synthetic gene. Other abnormalities have been identified, but are less well-characterized than the foregoing examples.

The potential for abnormalities of posttranslational modification of collagen is further illustrated by EDS VI. The clinical picture in this disorder includes joint hyperextensibility, hyperextensible skin, keratoconus, and scoliosis. The biochemical basis for these abnormalities is a deficiency of lysyl hydroxylase, the hydroxylase responsible for modification of lysine residues in the polypeptide. It should be recalled that formation of hydroxylysine is required for α-chain glycosylation, as well as to set the stage for active aldehyde formation to further stabilize the triple helix by creating cross-links. Thus, defects in formation of such hydroxylysine residues lead to formation of abnormal fibrillar collagen. As with most other monogenic disorders, and in contrast to most other forms of EDS, the inheritance pattern is autosomal recessive. Affected individuals show less than 10% of normal lysyl hydroxylase activity, obligate heterozygotes retaining the predicted 50% of control levels. Nonetheless, because of the variation in residual enzyme and extent of substrate hydroxylation in affected individuals, as well as the lack of consanguinity among such families, it is thought that many patients represent a compound heterozygous state. Obviously, therefore, the prediction is that there must be more than one mutant allele at the same locus that codes for an abnormal enzyme protein. There is great potential for this, because the enzymatic reaction is complex and requires many cofactors, including ascorbic acid (see previous text). Accordingly, high doses of ascorbic acid are recommended in treatment, although results of such therapy are not yet certain. Lack of adequate normal cross-linking affects primarily Type I collagen, reflected in a disorganized branching which is apparent on microscopic examination.

To further illustrate the diversity of disruptions in collagen formation, we can point to EDS IX, which is inherited in an X-linked recessive (a

Table 21.4. Ehlers-Danlos Syndromes

TYPE	MAJOR CLINICAL MANIFESTATIONS	SKIN	BRUISING	JOINT MOBILITY	INHERITANCE	BIOCHEMICAL DEFECT
I Gravis	Musculoskeletal deformities, prematurity due to membrane rupture, venous varicosities, heart valve abnormalities	3+ extensibility 3+ fragility Velvet feel, cigarette paper scars	2+, hyperpigmentation from heme	3+	AD	Undefined
II Mitis	Rarely mitral valve prolapse	2+ extensibility 2+ fragility	2+	2+	AD	Undefined
III Benign; Hypermobile		2–3+ extensibility + fragility Soft, not velvety	+	3+	AD	Undefined
IV Ecchymotic	Arterial rupture, intestinal perforation; skin torn easily	+ extensibility 2+ fragility	3+	0–+	AD AR	Undefined Deficient synthesis of type III collagen
V X-linked	Cigarette-paper, floppy cardiac valves, short stature, inguinal hernias	2+ extensibility + fragility	+	Digits only	X-linked	Lysyl oxidase, deficiency of type III collagen cross-link formation
VI Ocular	Musculoskeletal deformity, marfanoid habitus, ocular fragility, keratoconus, rupture of globe	3+ extensibility 2+ fragility	2+	3+	AR	Lysyl hydroxylase—interferes with cross-link formation
VII	Short stature, hip dislocation (arthrochalasis multiplex congenita)	2+ extensibility + fragility	2+	3+	AR	Structural mutation pro $\alpha 2$ chain-inhibits cleavage of aminopeptide → poor tensile strength ?Procollagen peptidase

+—mild
2+—moderate
3+—marked

questionably significant term) pattern. Not only is the inheritance unusual among EDS syndromes, but so too is the nature of the deficiency of lysyl oxidase activity. Even more interesting is the fact that this deficiency derives, not from an apoenzyme defect, but from abnormalities in intracellular copper metabolism. Because lysyl oxidase is a copper-dependent protein, it is likely that the extremely low levels of holoenzyme activity in affected individuals may be due to instability of the apoprotein in the absence of the metal cofactor. Although mutant cells show a normal rate of copper uptake, release of the copper-protein complex is grossly abnormal. In view of the basic defect, it is likely that other copper-dependent enzymes are also abnormal in this disorder, making it very similar in both inheritance and biochemistry to Menkes disease (see Chapter 14). Lysyl oxidase is an extracellular enzyme, acting to establish crosslinking, which creates the final triple helix conformation of fibrillar collagen. Accordingly, abnormalities in this process will affect Types I–III collagen and significantly impair the strength of the resulting abnormal molecules. Similar collagen defects are seen in Menkes disease, although the latter is a consequence of deficient intestinal copper absorption rather than of a failure to release copper-protein complexes.

GLYCOSAMINOGLYCANS (MUCOPOLYSACCHARIDES) AND THEIR DISORDERS

Functions and Biosynthesis

Apart from collagen, which constitutes the primary fibrous element of bone, the other major category of organic molecule is the GAG, the key element in formation of bone matrix. GAGs are heterogeneous carbohydrate polymers (Figure 21.4), composed of amino and sulfate substituted hexoses in covalent association with proteins, thus constituting a polyanionic proteoglycan (Figure 21.5). A proteoglycan is a macromolecule with the higher order structure and binding specificity of a protein endowed with the mechanical strength of a polysaccharide. Not unexpectedly, because of their strength, GAGs are widely distributed throughout the body, subserving important structural and binding functions beyond their vital role as the ground substance for ossification. GAGs occur in cartilage, bone, blood vessels, heart valves, skin, tendons, and cornea and in smaller amounts in liver and brain.

In contrast to glycogen, which is a homogeneous glucose polymer, differing only by virtue of the position of linkage points between units, GAGs are heterogeneous in their carbohydrate composition. Structurally, these heterogenous carbohydrate polymers may extend for more than 1000 residues, anchored at one end to the protein, as a branch is attached to the trunk of a tree. A single proteoglycan macromolecule contains many such branches, each of different carbohydrate sequence. Indeed, there is a degree of randomness to the carbohydrate sequence of these chains which, at least on the surface, appears to run counter to the usual fundamental orderliness of biologic processes. Underlying this apparent contradiction, however, is the fact that GAG function ultimately depends upon the binding and steric properties of the finished molecule, as determined by the substituent groups. Hence, the biosynthetic enzymes are group-specific, rather than hexose-specific, permitting a wide range of heterogeneity in the linear sequence of monomer units.

The backbone of GAGs is composed of alternating uronic acid and hexosamine residues (Figure 21.6). The uronic acids β-D-glucuronic acid and α-L-iduronic acid are C-5 epimers, whereas the amino sugars are acetylated derivatives of the parent hexoses glucose (N-acetyl-β-D-glucosamine) and galactose (N-acetyl-β-D-galactosamine). In keratan sulfate, underivatized D-galactose residues are present, but the amino sugars are further modified by addition of sulfate residues at position 4 or 6. This results in a polyanionic molecule containing both acidic sulfate and carboxyl groups, thus permitting electrostatic interactions with other molecules. Hyaluronic acid and the chondroitin sulfates have relatively simple structures, but dermatan sulfate, heparan sulfate, and heparan species manifest wide compositional heterogeneity. Table 21.5 summarizes the major properties and biologic distribution of proteoglycans in mammalian tissues.

Although, as we have stated, GAGs figure prominently in ossification, we also have seen that collagen (especially Type I) is a major component

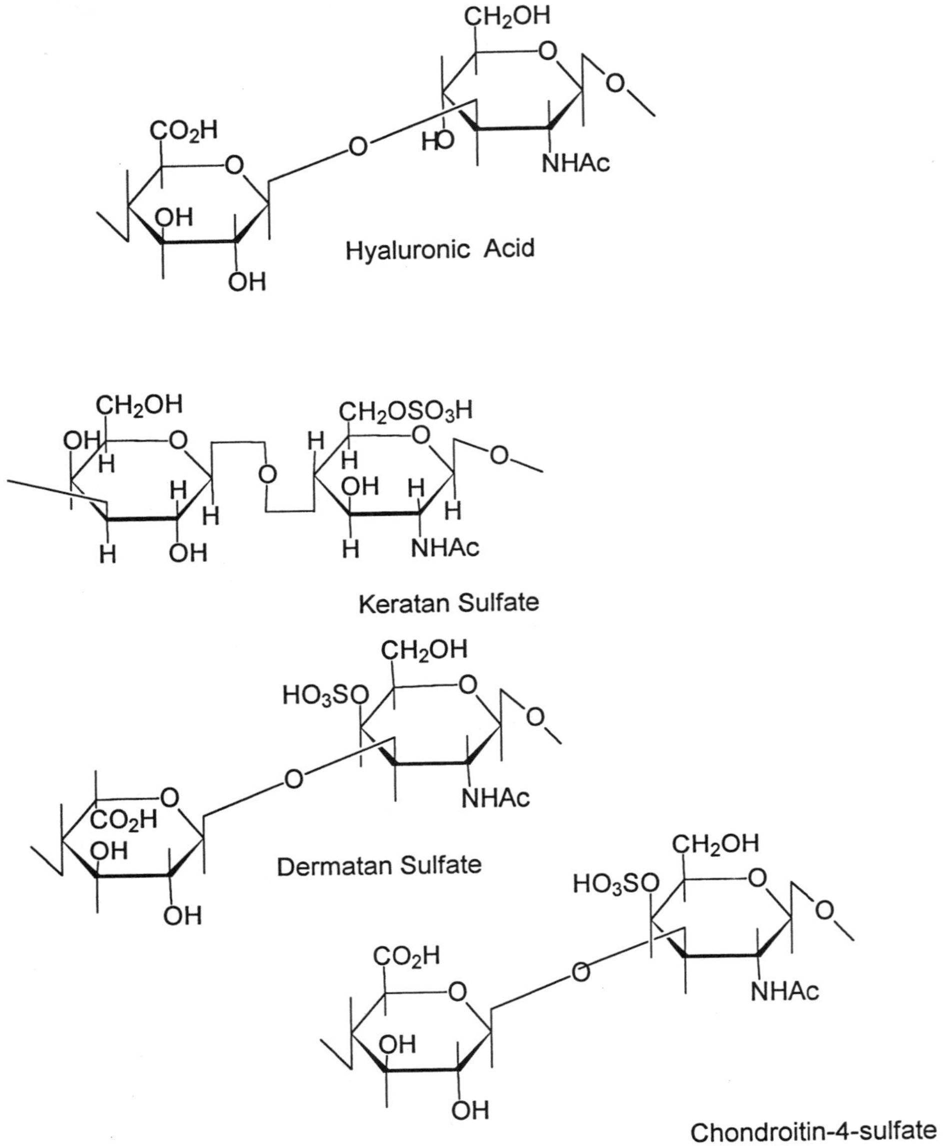
CH2OH
CO2H
O
O
O
HO
NHAc
OH
OH
Hyaluronic Acid
CH2OH
CH2OSO3H
OH
H
O
O
O
NHAc
Keratan Sulfate
CH2OH
HO3SO
NHAc
CO2H
OH
Dermatan Sulfate
CH2OH
HO3SO
CO2H
NHAc
OH
Chondroitin-4-sulfate

Figure 21.4. The various types of repeating disaccharide units found in glycosaminoglycans.

of bone. How, then, should we define the relationship of GAGs to both collagen and bone? The GAG molecule, by virtue of its polyanionic and physical structural properties, traps water in solution and thus increases greatly in volume. This increased volume lends itself to provision of a major structural property—the ability to cushion against mechanical stress. The resistance to damage thus conferred is further enhanced by the tensile strength of fibrillar collagen, embedded in the GAG matrix. So, in large part, the mechanical nature of bone is determined by the relative proportions of GAG matrix and collagen, as well as their complementary structural relationship.

Biodegradation

Although the potential for enzyme defects in GAG biosynthesis clearly exists, to date no such disorders have been described. In contrast, however,

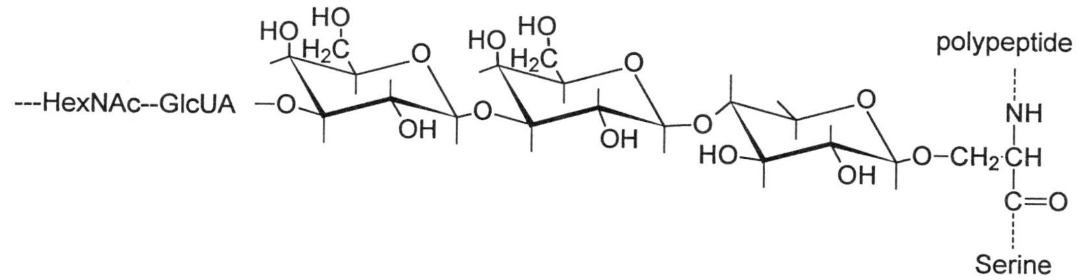

---HexNAc--GlcUA

polypeptide

Serine

Figure 21.5. The structure of chondroitin sulfate. By definition, a proteoglycan, the polysaccharide chain is linked to the polypeptide chain through a heterogeneous sequence of galactose and xylose monomers. HexNAc = N-acetyl hexosamine; GlcUA = glucuronic acid.

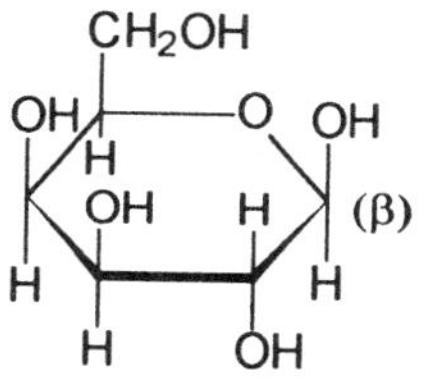

β-D-Galactose

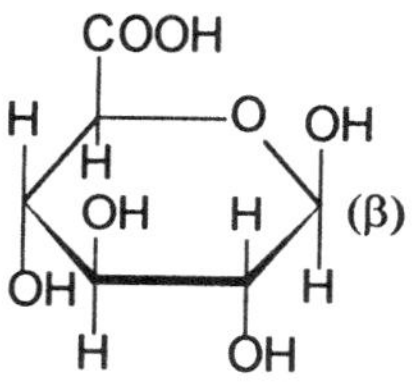

β- D-Glucuronic acid

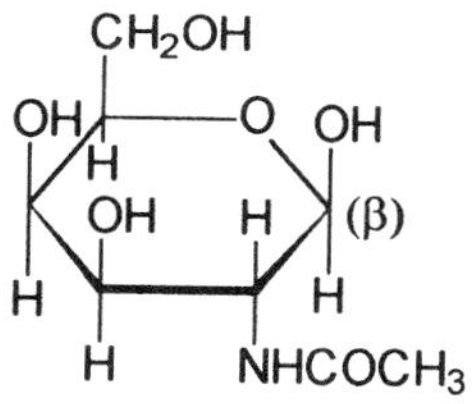

N-Acetyl-β-D-Galactosamine

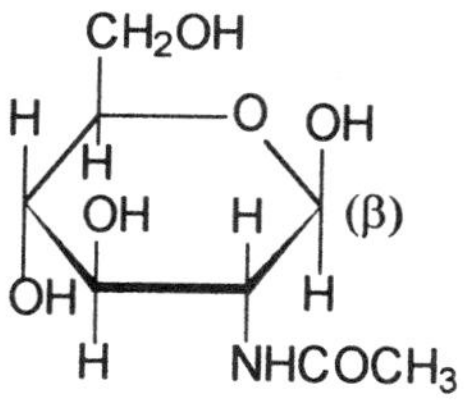

N-Acetyl-β-D-Glucosamine

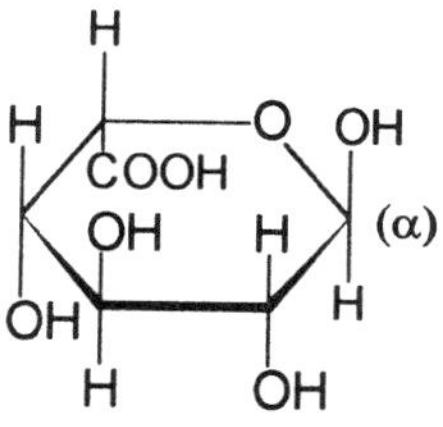

α-L-Iduronic acid

Figure 21.6. The monosaccharide units that form the backbone of glycosamino-glycans.

Table 21.5. Composition and Distribution of Structural Glycosaminogoglycans

GLYCOSAMINOGLYCAN	BUILDING BLOCKS	OCCURRENCE
Hyaluronic acid	D-Glucuronic acid N-Acetylglucosamine	Umbilical cord Joint fluid Vitreous humor
Chondroitin sulfate	D-Glucuronic acid N-Acetylgalactosamine-4-sulfate	Cartilage Bone Aorta
Dermatan sulfate	L-Iduronic acid N-Acetylgalactosamine	Skin Lung Heart valves
Keratan sulfate	Galactose N-Acetylgalactosamine-6-sulfate	Cartilage Cornea Intervertebral discs
Heparan sulfate	D-Glucuronic acid L-Iduronic acid N-Sulfate glucosamine N-Acetylglucosamine	Lung Liver Muscle

the biodegradative pathway for GAGs is replete with known enzymatic abnormalities, known collectively as the mucopolysaccharidoses (MPS syndromes). These disorders involve storage of GAGs, in specific stages of degradation (depending on the defect) in nearly all cells of the body. Each defect represents an abnormality in a specific lysosomal hydrolase participating in the sequential degradation of GAG. Thus, the MPS syndromes are a group of storage disorders in which the stored material is incompletely catabolized quantities of normal substrate, in direct analogy with most other monogenic metabolic disorders. Also in direct analogy, many refined studies have documented a variety of phenotypes in association with each enzyme defect and, conversely, more than one genotype producing the same phenotype.

We have summarized the features of the many MPS syndromes in Table 21.6, from which it can be seen that most, if not all, clinical findings are shared among the clinical entities. For extensive treatment of the individual defects, the reader is referred to the works cited at the end of this chapter. Of significance to the present discussion is the fact that an invariable feature, shared by all MPS syndromes, is *dysostosis multiplex*. Dysostosis multiplex consists of morphologic abnormalities of the skull, the vertebral bodies, the thoracic ribs, pelvis, the long bones, and the bones of the hands and feet. Such extensive involvement of the skeleton implies a common factor, which can be inferred from the functional importance of GAGs to bone formation. Indeed, morphologic study of involved vertebrae shows nodules of fibrous material replacing and deforming bone trabeculae. Given the enormous amounts of storage materials present in lysosomes, it is easy to imagine that there would be interference with normal cell function, including synthesis of ground substance and collagen for normal bone formation. What is not understood, however, are the specific ways in which this interference actually occurs.

At an intuitive level, it is possible to see how the different types of defects lead to the distinctly separate bone disorders of osteogenesis imperfecta and MPS syndromes. We have seen that osteogenesis imperfecta (OI) in its most severe form derives from abnormal Type I collagen formation. Because the function of collagen in bone is to contribute tensile strength, much in the same fashion as do the steel rods in concrete bridge piers, defects in the reinforcing structures make the structures themselves prone to breakage. In contrast, proteoglycans are the material of bone ground substance, without which there is no matrix for hydroxyapatite deposition. Thus, in the MPS syndromes, we would anticipate undermineralization and increased radiolucency. In fact, however, both OI and MPS syndromes show decreased mineralization, although the propensity for breakage, so evident in OI, is absent in the MPS disorders. There is evidence for increased bone turnover in OI, but the reasons for dysostosis multiplex in the mucopolysaccharidoses remain problematic. In

Table 21.6. Mucopolysaccharidoses and Mucolipidoses*

DISEASE	ENZYME DEFECT	URINARY GAG EXCRETION	MENTAL RETARDATION	COARSENED FEATURES	DYSOSTOSIS MULTIPLEX	HEPATOSPLENO-MEGALY	CARDIOVASCULAR FINDINGS	OCULAR FINDINGS	DEAFNESS	SURVIVAL
Mucopolysaccharidoses										
IH Hurler	α-L-Iduronidase	DS:HS 3:1	3+	3+	3+	2+ to 3+	2+ to 3+	3+	2+	5–10 years
IH/S Hurler-Scheie compound	α-L-Iduronidase alleles	DS:HS	+	2+	2+	+	2+	3+	+/–	20's
IS Scheie	α-L-Iduronidase alleles	DS:HS 1:1	–	+	+	+/–	Aortic valve	3+	–	50's
II Hunter	Iduronate sulfatase	DS:HS† 1:1	3+	2+	2+ to 3+	2+ to 3+	2+ to 3+	Corneal clouding rare	2+	10–15 years
III Sanfilippo forms (clinically indistinguishable) A B C	*N*-Sulfamidase *N*-Acetylglucosamidase Acetyl CoA:α-glucosaminide-N-acetyltransferase	HS	3+	+	+	+ to 2+	–	–	+	Puberty
IV Morquio	Gal-6-sulfate sulfatase	KS:CS† 1:1	–	+/–	3+	+/–	+	+	+	20–40 years
V (unoccupied, currently classified as Scheie)										
VI Maroteaux-Lamy	*N*-Acetylgalactosamine-4-sulfatase (arylsulfatase-B)	DS:HS 4–5:1	–	3+	3+	2+	2+	3+	+	Adulthood
VII β-Glucuronidase deficiency	β-Glucuronidase	HS, DS C-4/6-S	+ to 2+	2+	2+	2+	Aortic valve	Appear late +	–	Variable
VIII	Glucosamine-6-sulfatase	KS:HS	2+ to 3+	–	2+	+	–	–	+	Unknown
Mucolipidoses										
I	Neuraminidase	Normal	+	3+	3+	2+	–	Cherry-red macula	+ to 2+	10 years
II I-Cell	Incorporation of hydrolases into lysosome	3+ Oligosaccharides	3+	3+	2+	3+	3+	–	+/–	2–8 years
III Pseudo-Hurler	Milder variant of I-cell	Oligosaccharides	+ to 2+	+/–	+ to 2+	+	Aortic valve	+	–	Adulthood
IV	Not known	Normal	2+ to 3+	–	–	–	–	3+	–	Unknown
Mannosidosis	α-Mannosidase	3+ Oligosaccharides	3+	+ to 3+	+ to 2+	2+	–	– to +	+	Variable to adulthood
Fucosidosis	α-Fucosidase	3+	3+	+ to 2+	2+	+ to 2+	+ to 3+	+/–	+/–	

* All are inherited as autosomal recessive traits except Hunter's syndrome, which is X-linked.

† Age-dependent.

+/– variable; + minimal; 2+ moderate; 3+ marked.

the final analysis, the intuitive view is not accurate, despite the accuracy of our understanding of the biochemical abnormalities.

CALCIUM AND PHOSPHORUS HOMEOSTASIS AND BONE

Biosynthesis and Function

One of the most remarkable features of bone is how it combines such high tensile strength with such light weight. Viewed simplistically, the skeleton functions like the steel girders of a skyscraper, supporting the overall structure. However, such a simple view of the function of bone utterly overlooks one essential function of bone, which is to act as a reservoir for calcium and inorganic phosphate, as well as other ions (sodium, magnesium) required by the organism in many complex cellular reactions (Table 21.7). Accordingly, it is obvious that any conception of bone as a static structure is misleading, because any reservoir must have both inflow and outflow. It follows that the dynamic nature of bone is an important, even vital, part of the body's overall mechanisms for control of ion homeostasis.

Table 21.7. Functions Served by Calcium and Phosphorus

FUNCTIONS SERVED BY CALCIUM
Extracellular ionized Ca controls membrane excitation, neural excitability, and muscle contraction
Coupling of excitation to secretion; neurotransmitter release
Activation of enzymes in clotting (glycogenolysis, gluconeogenesis, amylase, lipases, trypsinogen, ATPase)
Cell-cell interactions
Decreased extracellular calcium associated with decreased cell adhesion
Biologic messenger
Information molecule for many processes
FUNCTIONS SERVED BY PHOSPHORUS
Formation and metabolism of the following constituents of the cell depend upon availability of adequate phosphate:
Nucleic acids
High-energy organic phosphate compounds for group-transfer reactions and coupling ATP
Phospholipids (membrane components)
Phosphorylated intermediates in metabolism (predominantly carbohydrate)
Phosphorylation of key serine and threonine residues in certain proteins is a major factor in covalent regulation of metabolism
Signal molecules—cAMP, 2-3,BPG
Urinary buffer system (titratable acid)

From the foregoing, it is clear that means must exist by which to control both the input and output of calcium and phosphorus as the major inorganic constituents of bone. Keeping in mind that the role of calcium and phosphorus in cell biochemistry antedated their skeletal function by billions of years, regulatory priority can naturally be assigned to biochemical over skeletal functions. Thus, bone disease often occurs in a setting in which perturbation in calcium and phosphorus homeostasis are buffered by bone, at the expense of bone. To understand the process by which this takes place, it is necessary to examine the specific control mechanisms through which the integrity of both cell and bone is defended.

Of the two ions, calcium appears to be under more stringent control than phosphorus. Nonetheless, because much of what impinges on calcium ultimately affects phosphorus, the two must be viewed as being loosely coupled. In addition, the two hormones exerting the greatest influence on calcium homeostasis, parathormone (PTH) and vitamin D, have direct effects on phosphorus homeostasis as well. Considering the importance of calcium and phosphorus, multiple regulatory factors would be anticipated, making divalent ion homeostasis a rather complicated affair. Immediate control of bone mass is exerted by the remodeling cell system, whereas plasma calcium is regulated by a separate system in which bone is responsive to hormonal signals. The kidney, through reabsorption of phosphate and calcium, exerts the major regulatory influence on these ions; in so doing, it assures that calcium levels will be maintained without requiring a significant contribution from the skeletal reservoir.

The major effects of the three chief regulatory hormones on divalent ion homeostasis are summarized in Table 21.8. PTH is charged primarily with defense of the extracellular ionized calcium concentration. Decreases in ionized calcium are buffered by augmentation of bone resorption and increased renal tubular reabsorption of calcium. Increased circulating PTH also stimulates production of active vitamin D (a steroid hormone, dihy-

Table 21.8. Hormones Affecting Mineral Homeostasis and Bone

		FUNCTIONS			
HORMONE	CHEMISTRY	BONE	INTESTINE	KIDNEY	BIOCHEMICAL MECHANISM OF ACTION
Parathyroid hormone Main determinant of ionized calcium in extracellular fluid—increases plasma Ca and decreases plasma P	Protein Prohormone cleaved to hormone (84 amino acids) Residues 1–34 have biologic activity	Regulates activation of bone metabolic units Increases rate of skeletal remodeling and resorption Principal effect is marked increase in number of osteoclasts Short-term effects—↑ osteolytic activity of osteoclasts and osteocytes and ↓ osteoblastic activity	Increases GI absorption of Ca, secondary to stimulating synthesis of 1,25-Vit D by kidney ↑ P, Mg absorption	Prompt onset of phosphaturia Regulates conversion of 25-Vit D to 1,25-Vit. D. Believed to ↑ tubular reabsorption of Ca, Mg	Activation of adenylcyclase in target tissues
Calcitonin Hypocalcemic agent—more effect in young than in old individuals	Polypeptide (32 amino acids) synthesized as prohormone	Inhibits osteoclastic activity—decreases brush border, which leads to ↓ bone resorption	Inhibitis GI secretion but stimulates intestinal secretion—results in delayed absorption of Ca from gut	Decreases tubular reabsorption of P, Ca, Mg Inhibits conversion of 25-Vit D to 1,25-Vit D	Acts through adenylycyclase
"Vitamin D" Enhances mineralization of bone by increasing Ca and P concentration in serum	Sterol—synthesized in skin (UV light) with subsequent processing in liver (25-Vit D) and kidney (1,25-Vit D)	Stimulates bone resorption Question of a direct effect of 1,25-Vit D on mineralization Mobilizes Ca into circulation—used in mineralization	Increases absorption of Ca Increases phosphate absorption by a system that is distinct from the one mediating Ca uptake	Increases proximal tubule reabsorption of Ca and P	Intestine—binding to cytosol receptor, which is transported to nucleus where it activates mRNA transcription

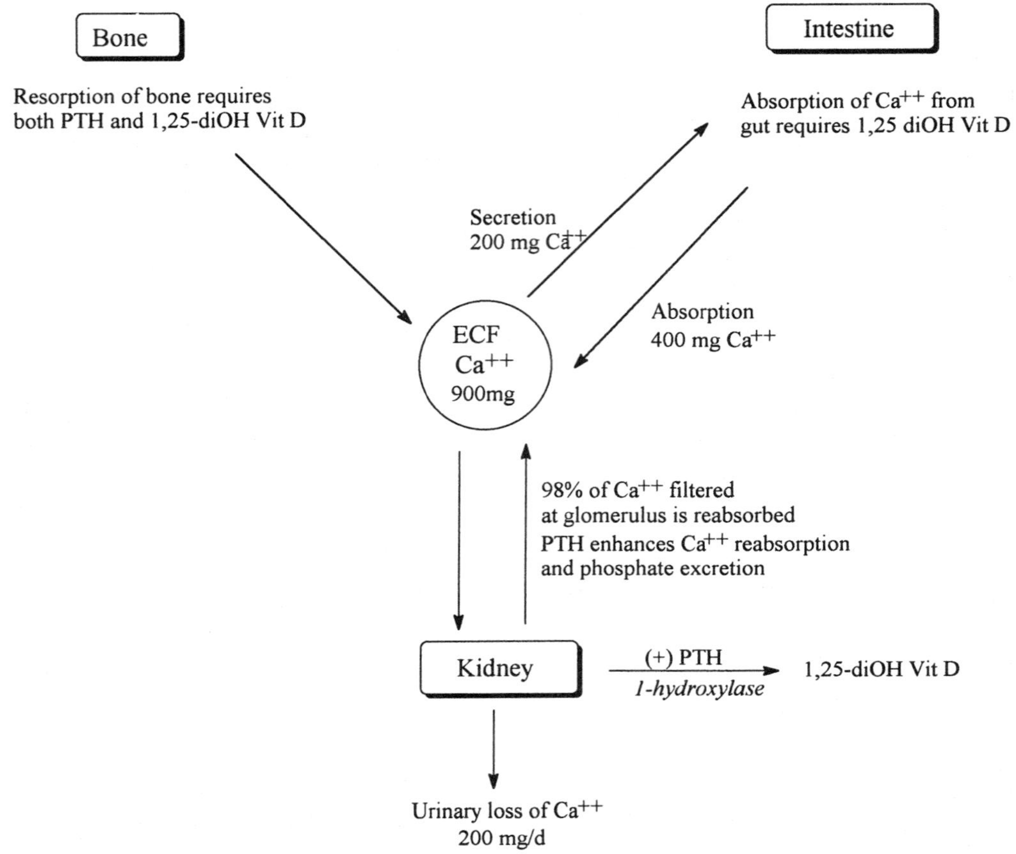

Figure 21.7. Regulation of calcium homeostasis. The chief regulatory hormones are parathyroid hormone (PTH) and 1,25-dihydroxyvitamin D (Vit D). Vit D enhances intestinal calcium and phosphate absorption, acting also as a cofactor in suppression of osteocytic osteogenesis and enhancing osteocytic osteolysis. However, Vit D also exerts a positive effect on osteoclastic bone reabsorption, which is required for bone remodeling. PTH acts directly upon the nephron to enhance calcium reabsorption and phosphate excretion. The effect of PTH on bone is overall to suppress formation and enhance resorption, also acting in concert with Vit D in the remodeling process. The third regulatory hormone, calcitonin, is not shown here, but acts as a PTH antagonist by suppressing bone resorption and enhancing renal calcium excretion.

drocholecalciferol), which directs increased intestinal calcium absorption. Protection against generalized calcification throughout the body is provided through the phosphaturic effect of PTH (Figure 21.7).

The role of vitamin D in prevention of rickets is well-known to the general public. A precursor to vitamin D, cholecalciferol, is produced in skin, but requires metabolic alterations by both liver and kidney for synthesis of biologically active vitamin D (Figure 21.8). The initial hydroxylation takes place in liver to form 25-hydroxycholecalciferol, followed by 1-hydroxylation in the kidney and production of dihydrocholeciferol, or active vitamin D. The 1,25$(OH)_2$D3 hormone maintains bone mass indirectly through provision of adequate calcium and phosphorus for mineralization of new bone. As mentioned above, there is a direct gut wall effect of vitamin D which enhances calcium and phosphate absorption. Active vitamin D also exerts a synergistic effect on bone resorption, acting in concert with PTH, an effect that, in turn, stimulates bone mineral turnover with no net loss. When the individual ingests foods containing calcium and phosphorus, vitamin D stimulates uptake of both from the intestine. But if the diet is

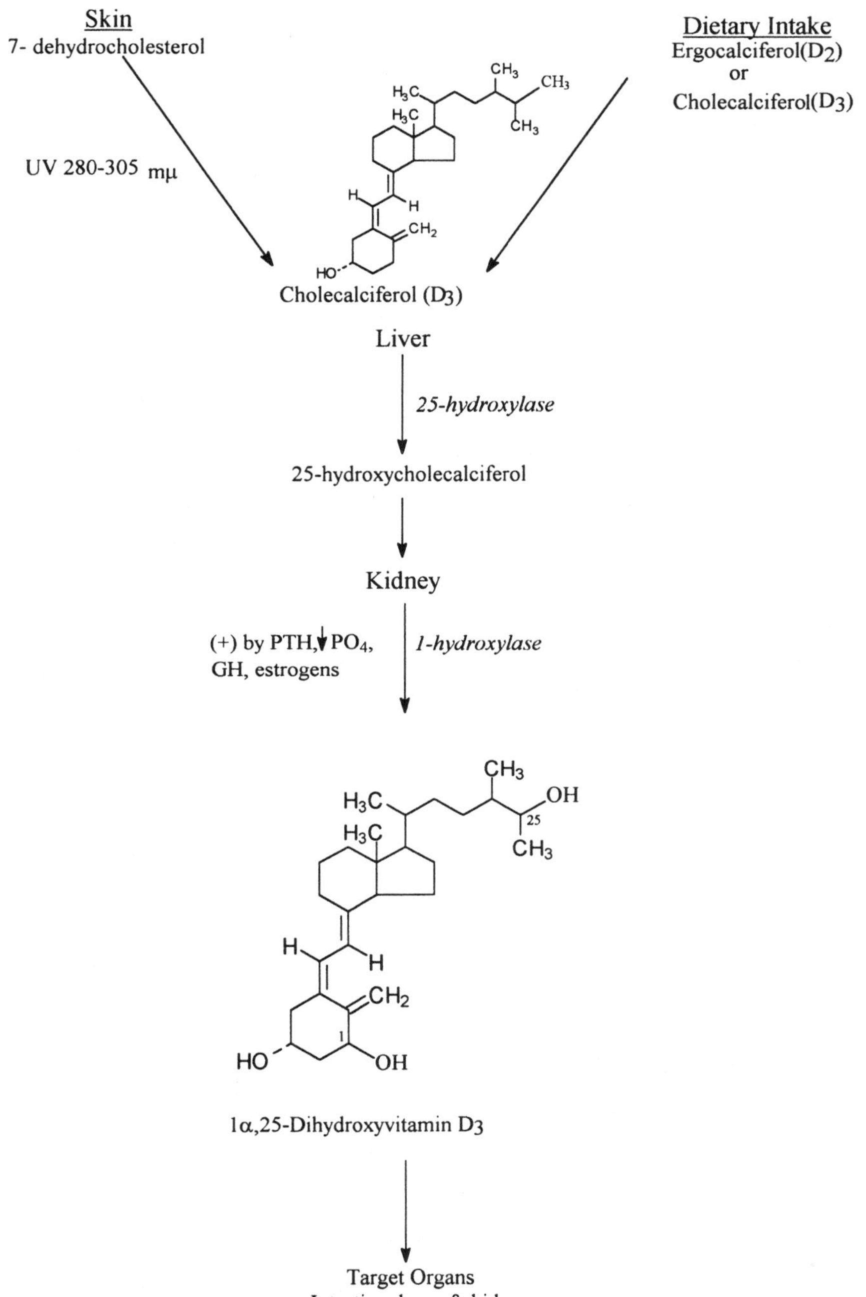

Figure 21.8. Metabolism of vitamin D. Cholesterol synthesis in skin produces a normal intermediate, 7-dehydrocholesterol (5,7-cholestadienol), which is converted to cholecalciferol (vitamin D_3) by exposure to ultraviolet radiation. An alternative source of vitamin D is dietary ergocalciferol (vitamin D_2) present in plants. Cholecalciferol is then transported in the blood, in combination with a specific transport globulin, and taken up by the liver for storage and/or further metabolism. In the liver, cholecalciferol is 25-hydroxylated by a microsomal monooxygenase to form 25-hydroxy vitamin D (25-OHD). The monooxygenase requires NADPH as an electron donor and is feedback regulated, which leads to a relatively low rate of product formation. 25-OHD is transported by the same transport globulin to the kidney, which contains a 1α- and a 24-hydroxylase, both of which are mitochondrial and utilize the 25-OHD as a substrate. The 1,25-dihydroxyD is the biologically active product, whereas the 24,25-dihydroxyD is inert and the trihydroxy compound is intermediate in biologic activity. 1α-hydroxylase is positively regulated by PTH and negatively by inorganic phosphate, whereas the 24-hydroxylase is regulated in the reverse fashion.

impoverished in these ions, then the major effect seen with vitamin D will be to stimulate bone resorption thereby increasing serum calcium and phosphate. In either case, plasma calcium and phosphate, not adequacy of bone formation, is what drives the vitamin D response.

The third hormone that plays a role in calcium-phosphorus homeostasis is calcitonin, which functions as a PTH antagonist. Thus, calcitonin suppresses bone resorption and increases calcium excretion by the kidney, in direct response to plasma calcium levels. Calcitonin also inhibits secretion of gastric acid, at the same time stimulating secretions of the small intestine and resulting in an overall decrease in calcium absorption and circulating plasma calcium.

We already have emphasized that bone is a dynamic tissue. It is worth noting that what makes bone unique is the turnover of cellular secretions, rather than of the cells themselves. The constant resorption of the crystalline elements, coupled closely with formation, results in a process known as remodeling. The "remodeling units" that carry out this process consist of osteoclasts, mitotically active mesenchymal cells, a capillary loop, mononucleocytes, and osteoblasts—all carry out independent functions in an orchestrated fashion (Table 21.9). From what already has been said, it

Table 21.9. Cellular Elements of Bone

CELL TYPE	MICROSCOPIC ANATOMY	ELECTRON MICROSCOPIC (E/M) FEATURES	FUNCTIONS	FACTORS THAT INFLUENCE FUNCTION
Osteoblast life span—few days–weeks	Situated on surface of growing bone Cuboidal to fusiform, 15–20μ	Well-developed endoplasmic reticulum (E/R), Golgi, mitochondria High-content alkaline P-ase	Formation of bone matrix—secretes collagen, glycosaminoglycans, glycoproteins Matrix laid down as osteoid and becomes calcified thereafter, taking about 5 to 10 days to complete the process Mineralization (in vesicles) occurs in two steps: nucleation and crystallization.	PTH, CT, estrogen, vitamins A, C, and "D"
Osteocyte ca. 26,000/mm^3 of bone tissue	Entombed osteoblasts that have become included in lacuna and are subsequently buried in the mineralized matrix Fusiform cell body with many projections	Similar to osteoblast with less elaborate E/R	Short-term regulation of Ca homeostasis—exist as part of elaborate canalicular systems, which in concert with osteolysis feed Ca from bone resorption into the blood	PTH, CT, vitamin A, vitamin D
Osteoclast life span—few hours–days	Large multinucleated cell on surface of bone Striking feature is brush border (ruffled border) of irregular microvilli in contact with matrix of bone	Numerous lysosomes, vesicles, and phagocytic vacuoles serve in resorption Little E/R, large numbers of mitochondria	Long-term Ca homeostasis—maintenance of normcalcemia Bone resorption Remodeling of bone By exocytosis excrete H^+ ions, which dissolve bone mineral, and lysosomal hydrolases and collagenases, which degrade bone matrix	PTH stimulates osteoclast formation and therefore resorption (+)PTH, T_4, $1,25(OH)_2D_3$, GH, (−)CT, estrogens, glucocorticoids

Table 21.10. Comparison of Spongy and Compact Bone

	SPONGY	COMPACT
Synonyms	Woven, trabecular	Cortical, lamellar
Characteristics	Three-dimensional lattice-work of trabeculae that are highly branched and surround vascular marrow	Consists of haversian systems (onion skin-like)
		Solid calcified matrix
	Osteocytes scattered randomly in the matrix	Osteocytes oriented in relationship to vascular channels
	Bone laid down without directionality (impermanent)	Formed only at an existing surface
	Less responsive to hormonal stimulation than compact	Responsive to hormonal stimulation
Locations	Vertebrae, flat bones, ends of long bones	Shafts of long bones
	Embryonic bone (fetal bone)	Accounts for about 80% of skeleton
Functions	Transmits compressive load across a joint	Resistance to bending and torsion
	Serves as a temporary structure en route to more permanent lamellar bone	

is clear that a part of the regulatory control over the process must rest with the humoral mechanisms, including PTH, vitamin D, and calcitonin. But, as these factors obviously affect all remodeling units simultaneously, this leaves unexplained the means by which a specific area of a long bone, for example, undergoes structural alteration in response to abnormal vectors of stress or to fracture. It is logical to conclude that there are also local controls, which enable the affected remodeling units to respond to specific needs to adjust structure. Evidence points to transforming growth factor (TGF-β) as the most potent local factor promoting bone formation. TGF-β acts by stimulating differentiation of osteoblast precursors into mature bone, forming osteoblasts.

It is important to note that bone possesses varying architectural characteristics to serve different needs. The general types of adaptations to these needs are summarized in Table 21.10. The specific arrangement of compact cancellous bone with layers of mineralized collagen, for example, provides the combination of strength and density necessary for support of the vertebrate organism. At the same time, by analogy with common principles of mechanical engineering, this type of architecture is found in bone that is characteristically tubular and reinforced by outgrowths that resemble the flying buttress of Gothic structures. Just as the flying buttress permitted construction of massive cathedral walls, the combination of the inherent strength of a tube reinforced by flying buttresses at special stress points provides maximum strength with minimum weight. Trabecular, or woven bone, however, is typically located at the ends of long bones or as the major architectural form in flat bones, such as those of the skull. The weblike or spongy structure of trabecular bone allows it to change conformation in response to compression or tensile stress. Thus, in the long bones, it functions partially as a shock absorber across joints. In the skull, for instance, it confers an ability to "fold" or become deformed in response to a blow without breaking.

We have consistently emphasized the concept that the functional properties of a macromolecule or a tissue are derived from its structural organization. This principle is superbly illustrated by bone, in which the extracellular components are related as follows: a solid mineral phase exists in close association with a predominantly collagenous matrix, admixed with a variety of glycoproteins and some proteoglycans. The major components of the mineral phase are microcrystals of hydroxyapatite [$3\text{-}Ca_3(PO_4)_2.Ca(OH)_2$] and "amorphous" calcium phosphate. In addition, there are other ions, such as magnesium and sodium, present in the external layers. Deposition of the mineral phase of bone occurs in apposition to the collagenous fibrils, within the spaces between adjoining fibrils. Thus, the structural organization of mineral and matrix generates a two-phase material possessing tremendous mechanical stability combined with significant flexibility. As pointed out in our earlier discussion of osteogenesis imperfecta, it is essential that the matrix be properly synthesized and oriented, so that the assembly of the mineral phase proceeds normally. Secretion of the organic matrix

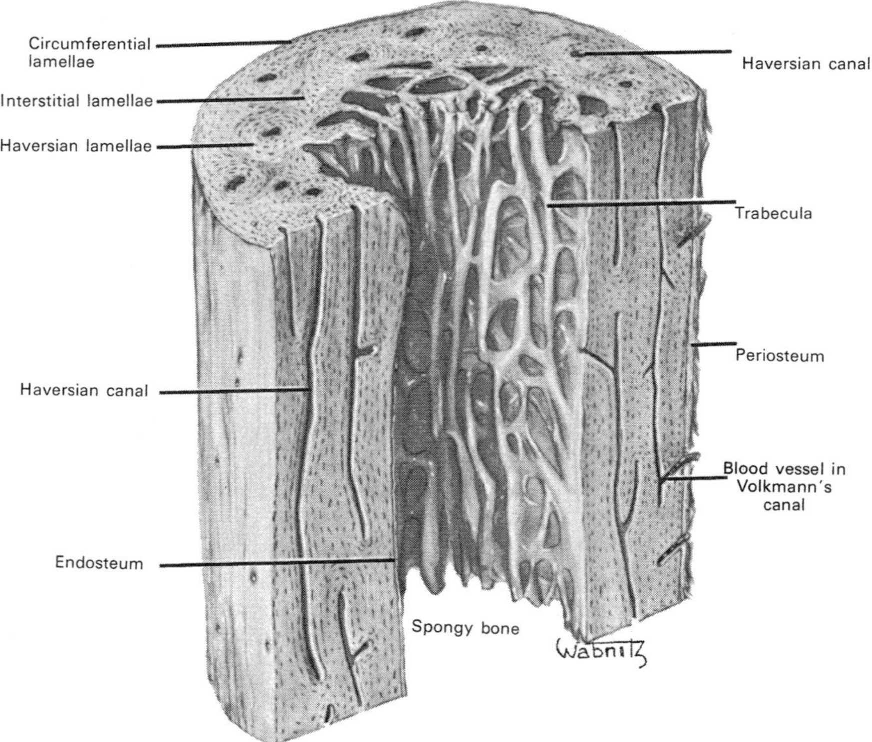

Figure 21.9. The structure of bone. The cortex of compact bone contains living cells, called osteocytes, which are mature osteoblasts entombed within the mineral matrix which they were responsible for laying down. The osteocytes remain viable by virtue of the oxygen and nutrients brought to them via the extensive canicular network running throughout the cortex. Reprinted with permission from Gray H. Anatomy of the Human Body. 30th ed. Philadelphia: Lea & Febiger, 1985: 316.

is a responsibility of mesenchymal cells, and is followed by mineralization occurring in two phases (primary and secondary), the entire process requiring several weeks. As the events proceed, the osteoblast responsible for provision of the mineral phase becomes entombed and is transformed into an osteocyte. The extensive canal system (Figure 21.9) provides oxygen and nutrients to the entombed osteocytes.

Resorption

Because bone remodels itself and provides a reservoir for divalent ions, it follows that there must be carefully regulated means for removal (resorption) of existing bone. During the process of resorption, calcium and phosphorus ions, derived from the mineral phase, are released into the extracellular fluid. Subsequently, the organic matrix is hydrolyzed. Resorption is a life-long process, but achieves its greatest importance during growth and development, when the bones assume their normal contours according to the dual influences of genetic direction and mechanical stress factors. Because this process is mediated by intracellular enzymes released into the matrix, it must necessarily begin in proximity to osteocytes and osteoclasts. With respect to the organic matrix, collagen is degraded by collagenases, whereas lysosomal hydrolases are responsible for degradation of the glycoproteins and mucopolysaccharides.

Cellular elements involved in resorption include both mononuclear cells and multi-nucleated osteoclasts. Osteoclasts possess a brushborder at which mineral resorption takes place, an event which precedes dissolution of the matrix. Although osteocytic mineral resorption occurs as well, this event is primarily involved in calcium

Table 21.11. Functions Served by Skeleton (Bone)

Mineral Reservoir
Ca and phosphorus are so essential to the biochemistry of the body that this function takes precedence over structural functions of bone
Support Body and Protect Internal Organs
Bone marrow and hematopoiesis enjoy protected status
Acidosis Defense
After physicochemical (immediate) buffering by lungs and kidney, bone serves as a defense against acidosis in chronic states
Acts as a trap for blood-borne ions
Pb can exchange with Ca in lead intoxication

homeostasis rather than bone remodeling. It is important not to lose sight of the fact that there is an intimate relationship between the activity of remodeling units, hormonal regulation of divalent ion homeostasis and the input and output of calcium within the gut. To clarify these relationships, it is necessary to examine calcium and phosphorus metabolism from a general perspective.

Calcium

Given that approximately 98% of the 1 to 2 kg of calcium in the human body is located in the skeleton, the function of the skeleton as a mineral bank and structural support (Table 21.11) should be evident. Yet, the functional morbidities of the human organism associated with the extremes of hypo- and hypercalcemia make it clear that calcium plays vital metabolic roles critical to normal function. These roles are directly related to the presence of ionized calcium in extracellular fluid and within the cells. As seen from Table 21.12, there is a normal distribution of calcium between the ionized and bound forms in both the extracellular and intracellular fluids. Moreover, it should not escape mention that there is much more calcium in the extracellular fluid than there is within cells. From this alone, we can be sure that there is a selectivity at the level of the cell membrane for the transfer of calcium, and further that this distinct gradient can be exploited to use calcium as a signal molecule.

Of the 500 to 1000 mg of daily dietary calcium available to most Americans, less than 50% is absorbed by healthy adults, whereas considerably more is absorbed by growing children and by women during pregnancy and lactation. Under all circumstances, availability of vitamin D is an important determinant of the extent of calcium absorption. The bulk of calcium absorption occurs in the jejunum and ileum, where active transport processes are present. Although a normal fecal loss of ingested calcium is unavoidable, reduction of oral intake to less than 200 mg/day will trigger a decrease in urinary loss below normal levels of 100 to 300 mg/day. Given the very tightly regulated circulating calcium levels, this decreased urinary loss points directly to the role of kidney in homeostasis.

With renal filtration of approximately 10,000 mg of calcium/day, daily urinary losses are only about 1% of that filtered. But, the impressive ability of the kidney to conserve calcium is not matched by its ability to excrete the excess in the face of hypercalcemia. Because phosphorus is both reabsorbed and excreted by the renal tubule, the primary role of the kidney in augmenting phosphorus excretion required an imposition of a ceiling on the quantity of calcium which could be simultaneously excreted so as to avoid precipitating calcium phosphate in the tubule. It stands to

Table 21.12. Distribution of Calcium, Phosphorus, and Magnesium Species

	Ca (mg/100 ml)	P	Mg
Serum Concentration			
Total	10.0 (100)*	3.5 (100)	1.9 (100)
Ionized	4.7 (46.9)	1.9 (53)	1.1 (55)
Complexed	1.3 (13.6)	1.2 (35)	0.2 (13)
Protein-bound	4.0 (39.5)	0.4 (12)	0.6 (32)
Intracellular Concentration			
Total	4 mg% (2 mEq/l)	140 mEq/l	30–40 mEq/l
Ionized	0.4 mg% (0.2 mEq/l)		

* (per cent of total).

reason that with a daily adult urinary phosphate loss in the range of 500 to 1400 mg/day, absence of a limit on calcium excretion would result in widespread precipitation of calcium phosphate in the tubules at normal urinary pH.

CALCIUM AS A SIGNAL MOLECULE

At a physiologic level, the many roles of calcium as coupling agent for excitation-transmission in the central nervous system, excitation-contraction in muscle, and stimulation-secretion in glands, as well as in blood coagulation, have been known for many years. Additionally, calcium is now known to play a role in many metabolic pathways, including glycogenolysis and gluconeogenesis. Its actions in such a wide variety of physiologic responses suggest general and specific features shared by all these systems that provide for the appropriate response to calcium when the stimulus is applied.

Intracellular total calcium concentration is in the range of 2 mM. In muscle and nerve, for which the most accurate data exist, the free (ionized) concentration varies between 0.01 and 1 μM. Obviously, then, the bound calcium fraction predominates within the cell, probably as phosphate complexes within mitochondria and microsomes, with the remainder bound to protein and organic ions. Thus, with such compartmentation of unionized calcium within the cell, there is potential for shifts between the ionized and unionized cellular pools, buffering any small fluctuations and preventing abnormalities of function. Once more, we draw attention to the fact that calcium serves as an informational cation in the range of 0.01 to 1 μM when an external ionized calcium concentration is at least 1000 times higher (1–2 mM). Maintenance of this enormous concentration gradient has been shown to depend on an adenosine triphosphate (ATP)-requiring calcium "pump." The sequestration of calcium within mitochondria and microsomes is also related to the presence of these pumps in the organellar membranes. Most strikingly, the exceedingly narrow range of calcium concentration used to signal the onset of a biochemical response depends on the ability of a specific protein to bind calcium preferentially over other ions. In most cells, this protein, named *calmodulin*, exists either independently or as a subunit of an enzyme protein. Each calmodulin molecule must bind four calcium ions, at specific binding sites, before activity is conferred on the molecular complex. This constant is inversely related to the fourth power of the calcium ion concentration. Such a relationship easily explains how tiny changes in ionized calcium can trigger major functional alterations within the cell. In this fashion, a micromolecule like calcium functions as a biochemical lever to induce a conformational change in a macromolecule, which then initiates a series of events at a biochemical level. When millions of cells respond simultaneously to the applied stimulus, the event is expressed at a macroscopic or physiological level. Again, we point to the theme that small molecules affecting the activity of macromolecules lies at the center of control of life processes.

Phosphorus

It must be recognized, that although calcium and phosphorus are intimately associated at the level of bone metabolism, their general metabolic roles in cells are vastly different. Whereas calcium plays a vital role in activation of metabolic pathways, phosphorus (in its role in ATP) is the currency of energy conservation and transfer. Unlike the oxidation of wood in a fire, during which all available energy stored in the wood is given up as heat energy and increased entropy, combustion of metabolic fuel proceeds with sequential generation of high energy phosphate bonds as metabolism progresses toward production of CO_2 and H_2O, products common to both combustion of wood and catabolism of metabolic fuels. Storage of energy derived from metabolic oxidation in the ATP molecule permits ATP to be used in temporally and spatially (within the cell) unrelated biosynthetic reactions. Thus, despite the common reservoir through which calcium and phosphorus flow in bone, it is predictable that regulation of body phosphorus pools would be under somewhat different, and in some respects, independent controls from those that affect calcium.

Lipmann and others have emphasized that the uniqueness of the class of high energy phosphate compounds is not their high group-transfer potential. Rather, what is unique about these biologic high energy compounds is their resistance to reaction in the aqueous cellular medium in which they exist, in contrast to the fleeting existence of acid anhydrides and acid halides in water. It is truly remarkable and fortunate for living creatures that the energy stored in these compounds is unleashed only in the presence of specific enzymes and under suitable conditions. This orderly system of energy release stands in stark contrast to the havoc wreaked on a cell by free radicals, for example, which also represent a class of high-energy molecules.

In addition to its well-known role in energy metabolism, phosphorus also shares with calcium an important function in information transfer. Indeed, the part played by phosphorus in this respect is so fundamental that, in its absence, the cell would cease to exist! The presence of phosphorus is intrinsic to the formation of the nucleotide sequences of both DNA and RNA, each of which is a component of the most basic, yet complex form of information transfer in human cells. Moreover, intracellular phosphate concentration plays a vital role in regulation of synthesis and turnover of these macromolecules. In addition, the presence of phospholipids in cell membranes facilitates communication between the cell and its external environment. Thus, despite the usual eponym, "calcium-phosphorus metabolism," used in clinical medicine, each of the two subserve vastly different metabolic and physiologic roles.

Reflecting this functional diversity between calcium and phosphorus, it is evident that serum phosphorus concentrations are not maintained within the same narrow range as are those of calcium. This diversity is further reflected in the fact that intracellular phosphate concentration is approximately 140 mEq/l, in contrast to calcium which is generally present in the range of 2 mEq/l within the cell. At a physiologic level, an acute, two-fold increase in serum calcium would approach the lethal point and would be clearly manifested in abnormalities of neuromuscular function, whereas a similar two-fold increase in serum phosphorus would produce no clinical signs referable to the phosphate level. Such an increase would, however, tend to cause hypocalcemia and ectopic calcification in extraosseous tissues.

The bulk of serum phosphorus is found in the organic form, chiefly bound to serum lipids (Table 21.13). Most of the inorganic form of phosphorus in serum is present in combination with monovalent or divalent cations. Yet another key distinction between calcium and phosphorus metabolism is the extent to which they are bound to protein. Whereas 40% of serum calcium exists in the protein bound form, only 20% of serum inorganic phosphorus is protein bound.

Table 21.3. Plasma Phosphorus*

Organic Phosphorus	
Lipid phosphorus	2.58
Other organic phosphorus	0.19
Total	2.77
Inorganic Phosphorus	
Diffusible phosphorus	0.86
HPO_4^{2-}	0.44
$NaHPO_4^-$	0.26
$H_2PO_4^-$	0.10
$CaHPO_4$	0.04
$MgHPO_4$	0.02
Protein bound	0.22
Total inorganic	1.08
Total plasma	3.85

* In mmol/l.

Phosphorus absorption from the gut is much more efficient than that of calcium. On a phosphate-restricted diet almost 90% is absorbed, whereas even on a normal diet, about 70% of the load (700 mg) is absorbed. Hence, the burden of plasma phosphorus regulation falls more heavily on the kidney than is the case with calcium regulation. Of the 6200 mg of phosphorus/day filtered, approximately 90% is reclaimed at the level of the proximal tubule, in a fashion that is sodium cotransport-dependent. Thus, the net phosphorus turnover in an adult is close to zero under normal conditions.

In view of the high degree of ultrafilterability of phosphate in the glomerulus, the chief mechanism of plasma phosphate regulation must lie with alterations in tubular reabsorption, which is greatly influenced by PTH. Overall, this regulatory system is rather unique, because secretion of PTH from the parathyroid glands is controlled by calcium and magnesium, whereas levels of calcium are partially regulated by the effect of PTH on tubular reabsorption of phosphate, which may be "loosely" considered an antagonistic ion. In humans, acute administration of PTH results in a prompt and sustained increase in urinary phosphate excretion. In contrast to the permissive action of PTH on renal phosphate excretion, 1,25-dihydroxyvitamin D enhances tubular reabsorption of phosphate when the hormone is present in physiologic amounts. Administration of vitamin D in small doses to vitamin D-deficient rats will cause marked reduction in urinary phosphate losses. It should be emphasized that, despite the apparently simple, antagonistic effects exerted by PTH and vitamin D under defined experimental conditions, their combined regulatory effects under physiologic conditions is much more complex and less well-defined. There is also recent evidence to suggest that insulin-like growth factor-1 (IGF-1), a growth hormone stimulated polypeptide produced chiefly in liver, but also in kidney, plays an important role in increasing tubular phosphate reabsorption. Indeed, it may also enhance enzymatic conversion of 25-OH-vitamin D to the active 1,25-dihydroxy form. Thus, although much has to be learned about the interaction of IGF-1 and phosphate excretion, IGF-1 may actually play a more pivotal role than either PTH or vitamin D on phosphate excretion.

Metabolic Bone Disease

Thus far, we have considered disorders affecting bone integrity as a consequence of underlying abnormalities of collagen or noncollagenous ground substance (matrix). Still remaining to be considered are those entities that result in abnormalities of bone due to disordered mineral turnover, in the presence of normal matrix. In common clinical parlance, this is the category of metabolic bone disease.

To best understand this group of disorders, it should be noted that, to date, there are no reported primary abnormalities associated with the osteoblast-osteoclast system. Rather, dysfunctional mineralization, as we currently understand it, must arise from inadequate supply or over-supply of mineral substance or from disordered humoral factors regulating this supply. Under normal circumstances, dietary intake of calcium and phosphorus is such that no excess in plasma levels of either component is seen. Yet, it must be recognized that even if intake is adequate, gastrointestinal pathology interfering with normal absorption will cause depletion with compensatory effects on the humoral controls. Thus, in any calcium or phosphate deficiency state, a search for malabsorptive causes is mandatory.

RICKETS AND OSTEOMALACIA

Among the most well-known metabolic bone diseases is vitamin D-deficient rickets, or osteomalacia. This disorder involves an abnormality of humoral regulation, and its presence may herald dietary vitamin deficiency in a broader sense. Furthermore, the marked negative impact of vitamin D deficiency on bone clearly underscores the importance of this sterol in the mineralization process. Because the precursor of vitamin D, 7-dehydrocholesterol, is normally synthesized in skin, exposure to the sun's ultraviolet rays is sufficient for nonenzymatic conversion to the substrate required for hepatic conversion to 25-OH-vitamin D. Once more, we are reminded of the relationship between humans and their environment throughout evolution, right up to the present. When social circumstances are interposed between humans and nature, as in 19th century industrial-revolution England, we see the negative effects on the environment exemplified in widespread rachitic disease in the children of that period. Events such as these serve to highlight the interplay of sociologic phenomena and the practice of clinical medicine.

Remarkably, despite all of the circumstantial evidence that points to a direct effect of vitamin D on mineralization of bone, such an effect remains to be demonstrated. The prevailing view of vitamin D's role continues to be one of a facilitator of a process which is, itself, directly dependent on circulating calcium and phosphorus levels. Given our present detailed level of understanding of the biochemical effects on cells of other humoral factors (eg, epinephrine on glycogen metabolism), such a view of vitamin D's action on bone is particularly unsatisfying. But, the available experimental evidence does not support a direct role for vitamin D in mineral deposition or, for that matter, in initiation of matrix synthesis.

Phenomenologically, rickets results from a reverse in the ratio between calcified and uncalcified matrix. Histologically, this is seen as osteoid material in excess of mature bone, and radiologic studies of the long bones show bowing with widening and irregular margins of the growth plates. The bowing is a result of mechanical stress on the poorly mineralized diaphyses. Widening and irregularities of the metaphyses derive from under-mineralization of the expanding cartilaginous growth plates.

Given that marked enhancement of intestinal calcium absorption occurs by virtue of the presence of adequate vitamin D, a decrease in plasma calcium would logically be expected to ensue promptly. In fact, however, the typically long-delayed onset of hypocalcemia in rickets vividly illustrates the enormous calcium reservoir function of the skeleton. Despite the presence of visually obvious skeletal deformities consistent with the diagnosis, serum calcium is likely to be normal or near-normal in any such patient. Correspondingly, however, there will be a compensatory parathyroid response, resulting in enhanced renal phosphate excretion, so that serum phosphate may be low in relation to the calcium concentration.

We should not ignore the significance of the hypophosphatemia. Because phosphate is chiefly an intracellular ion, it may be assumed that when hypophosphatemia is present, there will be a gradual depletion of the intracellular phosphate pool. Also, because phosphate is critical to so many active metabolic processes, it should not be surprising that a cardinal sign of rickets is muscle hypotonia and weakness. These effects on muscle tone and strength (see Chapter 25) are reflected visually in development of a "pot-belly," due to flabby abdominal musculature. Despite this, tetany is relatively rare in rachitic disease, because serum calcium is maintained in the normal range. But one should be aware that initiation of vitamin D treatment may cause a rapid shift of calcium from serum into bone, leading to a precipitous fall in serum calcium and clinical signs of tetany. For this reason, it is advisable to insure adequate calcium intake and close serum calcium and phosphate monitoring, especially when therapy is initiated.

In uncomplicated, vitamin D-deficiency rickets, appropriate treatment can be expected to result in full recovery. As the depleted pools of calcium and phosphate are replaced, bone mineralization accelerates and muscle tone improves. The bony deformities so characteristic of the rachitic state, however, require considerable time for resolution, because bone remodeling is a process that takes place over many weeks. In severe cases of long bone bowing, for example, resolution may require months and even years to fully resolve. In this context, we once again caution that in dietary vitamin D deficiency, in individuals who get little or no exposure to sunlight, other deficiencies may coexist, so that uneventful resolution of rachitic disease in response to D administration may uncover other equally severe but less dramatic clinical disorders.

Thus far, we have dealt with rickets that occurs as a result of a simple dietary deficiency of vitamin D. However, it should be kept in mind that, as with many disorders, the symptoms and signs are the "final common pathway" of deranged biochemical processes. Thus, the same clinical findings may be produced by many different mechanisms, a statement vividly illustrated by the multiple causes of rachitic bone disease (Table 21.14). For instance, the mechanisms by which significant liver or kidney disease might produce rickets is fairly simple to imagine, because each of the two organs is involved in production of biologically active dihydroxyvitamin D through successive enzymatic hydroxylations. Therefore, if either organ's cellular function is significantly impaired, a secondary consequence will be decreased production of active vitamin D.

As with diseases associated with many other humoral factors, deficient end-organ response to vitamin D predictably will result in a clinical pic-

Table 21.14. Disorders of Bone Mineralization

Rickets

- I. Deficiency of 25-HCC or 1,25-DHCC accompanied by secondary hyperparathyroidism
  - A. Deficiency of Vitamin D
    - 1. Lack of adequate intake
    - 2. Lack of sunlight
    - 3. Malabsorption
      - a. Sprue
      - b. Hepatic or biliary dysfunction
    - 4. Chronic renal insufficiency
    - 5. Vitamin D dependency
    - 6. Drugs that enhance conversion to inactive forms
      - a. Diphenylhydantoin
      - b. Phenobarbital
- II. Phosphaturic states
  - A. Fanconi syndrome
    - 1. Cystinosis
    - 2. Wilson's disease
    - 3. Galactosemia
    - 4. Hereditary fructose intolerance
    - 5. Hereditary tyrosinemia
  - B. Renal tubular acidosis
  - C. Oculo-cerebral-renal syndrome

Hypophosphatasia

- I. Pseudohypophosphatasia

ture similar to that seen in nutritional D deficiency. Such a state is present in the entity known as vitamin D-dependent rickets Type II. The major distinguishing characteristic between Type II and the nutritional form of rickets is the high circulating level of dihydroxyvitamin D seen in Type II. Studies in a variety of different types of cells from patients with Type II have shown a generalized decrease in 1,25-dihydroxyvitamin D binding to receptor protein or in migration and binding within the nucleus. Functionally, this is reflected in inadequate intestinal absorption of calcium.

A second inherited disorder underlying development of clinical rickets is the Type I variety of vitamin D-dependent rickets. This entity is the result of a specific deficiency of the enzyme, 25(OH)D 1α-hydroxylase, which is essential to the conversion to the active form of vitamin D. It goes without saying that, in this disorder, circulating levels of 1,25-dihydroxy vitamin D are lower than normal, and may even be undetectable in some patients. The clinical findings in this disorder are the same as in the D-deficient and D-resistant types of rickets, and once again illustrate that phenotype alone cannot always provide the basis for specific diagnosis. It is also worthwhile to point out that in modern societies, where most infants receive daily vitamin D supplementation in formula or multivitamin preparations, D-deficiency rickets has become almost nonexistent, leading to a narrower differential diagnosis.

Just as decreased calcium absorption due to inadequate vitamin D leads to rickets, increased phosphate excretion can create the same clinical picture. The best example of this situation is that found in X-linked (primary) hypophosphatemic rickets, a disorder in which renal tubular phosphate reabsorption is chronically reduced. Although the specific tubular mechanism at fault remains unelucidated, it is clear that urinary phosphate loss is excessive in the presence of normal dietary intake. This, in turn, leads to a characteristic moderate hypophosphatemia, probably reflecting abnormally reduced total body phosphate. This is very likely to be the case, because inorganic phosphate is primarily an intracellular ion, except where present in bone. Thus, because these patients evidence poor mineralization due to lack of phosphate, the hypophosphatemia is reflective of an inability to maintain normal levels during the cellular struggle to maintain its essential pools. In contrast to vitamin D-deficient rickets, patients with X-linked hypophosphatemia have normal PTH levels, a finding that provides a key to the differential diagnosis.

Many other disorders of phosphate homeostasis can result in rachitic bone disease, but virtually all of these are diseases in which bone metabolism is affected in a secondary fashion. A primary example of this group is the renal Fanconi syndrome, known to be associated with a wide variety of primary disorders, both genetic and acquired (see Chapter 3). In the Fanconi syndrome, renal tubular reabsorptive function is abnormal, causing urinary losses of phosphate, glucose and amino acids, as well as other small molecules. In addition to the bone demineralization attributable to the phosphate losses, the abnormality thus created is enhanced further by the proximal tubular acidification defect, which is also characteristic of the syndrome. In cystinosis, one of the many primary causes of the renal Fanconi syndrome, the overall process is still further complicated by progressive renal damage, which can result in decreased 1 α-hydroxylation and reduced levels of active vitamin D.

OSTEOPOROSIS

The final general category of metabolic bone disease, osteoporosis, has received widespread attention in recent years for its impact on postmenopausal orthopedic morbidity. Osteoporosis is distinguished from osteomalacia by the fact that although bone mass is reduced in both, in osteoporosis the mineral to osteoid ratio remains normal. Hence, in osteoporosis, there is a decreased bone density, but that bone that is present is normal in composition. This points to a chronic imbalance between new bone formation and its resorption, with the balance tipped in favor of resorption. However, this disequilibrium does not need to be very large, because a calcium loss of 30 mg/day from bone resorption extended over a 30-year period can and does produce clinical osteoporosis. Although postmenopausal estrogen administration has been conclusively demonstrated to prevent loss of bone mass, there has been no demonstration of estrogen receptors in mammalian bone. It is believed that the protective effect on bone mass exerted by estrogen is related to nullifying the resorptive effects of PTH on bone. In support for this view is a decreased incidence of postmenopausal osteoporosis in women with hypoparathyroidism. It also has been speculated that estrogen may exert an additional indirect effect on intestinal calcium absorption and calcitonin secretion. As pointed out earlier, such indirect effects would not have to be quantitatively large to prevent the cumulative calcium losses leading to postmenopausal osteoporosis.

Regarding treatment, although there is as yet no definitive regimen for postmenopausal osteoporosis, certain measures can help alleviate various aspects of this problem. To begin with, patients should get adequate sun exposure (unless coexisting dermatologic problems preclude this), increase dietary or pharmacologic intake of calcium, and try to institute a modest weight bearing exercise program. The role and dose of estrogens, fluoride, bisphosphonate compounds, and other hormones are in a state of flux and the reader is encouraged to consult the texts listed in the suggested reading section at the end of this chapter for guidance in this area.

SUMMARY

In summary, it is interesting to compare the general causes of disorders of bone mineral metabolism with those of collagen and GAGs. Based upon past experience, although there are no known intrinsic defects of the osteoblast-osteoclast class of cells, it is extremely likely that diseases of this system do exist. Nonetheless, disorders of bone mineral metabolism are distinct from the other two groups by virtue of the absence of any known intrinsic cellular defect. Thus, all described entities in this group are the result of various disordered processes extrinsic to bone tissue itself. It follows logically from this that bone mineral metabolic disorders are likely to be responsive to treatment of the underlying primary cause. In contrast, disorders of collagen and GAG metabolism derive from intrinsic defects in cells that are directly responsible for generation of the framework in which bone mineralization takes place. Hence, in these two groups of disorders, the impact on bone is a necessary consequence of these defects and unlikely to respond to any treatment modality short of alteration of the genetic defect itself.

SUGGESTED READINGS

Addadi L, Weiner S. Control and design principles in biological mineralization. Angewandte Chemie International Edition English 1992;31:153.

Anderson JJB. Nutritional biochemistry of calcium and phosphorus. J Nutr Biochem 1991;2:300.

Bickle DD, Pillai S. Vitamin D, calcium, and epidermal differentiation. Endocr Rev 1993;14:3.

Byers PH. Osteogenesis imperfecta. Annu Rev Med 1992; 43:269.

Byers PH. Disorders of collagen biosynthesis and structure. In: Scriver CR, Beaudet AL, Sly WS, Valle D, eds. The metabolic and molecular bases of inherited disease. 7th ed. New York: McGraw-Hill, 1995:4029.

Centrella M, Horowitz MC, Wozney JM, McCarthy TL. Transforming growth factor-β gene family members and bone. Endocr Rev 1994;15:27.

Coe FL, Favus MJ, eds. Disorders of bone and mineral metabolism. New York: Raven Press, Ltd, 1992.

Dempster DW, Cosman F, Parisien M, et al. Anabolic actions of parathyroid hormone on bone. Endocr Rev 1993;14:690.

Edelson GW, Kleerekoper M. Hypercalcemic crisis. Med Clin North Am 1995;79:79.

Engel J, Prockop DJ. The zipper-like folding of collagen triple helices and the effects of mutations that disrupt the zipper: Annu Rev Biophys Biophys Chem 1991;20: 137.

Fensom AH, Benson PF. Recent advances in the prenatal diagnosis of the mucopolysaccharidoses. Prenat Diagn 1994;14:1.

Finkelstein JS, Klibanski A, Schaefer EH, et al. Parathyroid hormone for the prevention of bone loss induced by estrogen deficiency. N Engl J Med 1994;331:1618.

Gertner JM. Disorders of calcium and phosphorus homeostasis. Pediatr Clin North Am 1990;37:1441.

Hamdy NAT. Role of bisphonates in metabolic bone diseases. Trends in Endocrinology and Metabolism 1993;4:19.

Hsu HHT. Mechanisms of initiating calcification. ATP-stimulated Ca- and Pi-depositing activity of isolated matrix vesicles. Int J Biochem 1994;12:1351.

Manolagas SC, Jilka RL. Bone marrow, cytokines, and bone remodeling: emerging insights into the pathophysiology of osteoporosis. N Engl J Med 1995; 332:305.

Marx SJ. Vitamin D and other calciferols. In: Scriver CR, Beaudet AL, Sly WS, Valle D, eds. The metabolic and molecular bases of inherited disease. 7th ed. New York: McGraw-Hill, 1995:3091.

Neufeld EF, Muenzer J. The mucopolysaccharidoses. In: Scriver CR, Beaudet AL, Sly WS, Valle D, eds. The metabolic and molecular bases of inherited disease. 7th ed. New York: McGraw-Hill, 1995:2465.

Nordin BEC, Need AG, Morris HA, eds. Metabolic bone and stone disease. 3rd ed. Edinburgh: Churchill Livingstone, 1993.

Pike JW. Vitamin D_3 receptors: structure and function in transcription. Annu Rev Nutr 1991;11:189.
Reid IR, Ames RW, Evans MC, et al. Effect of calcium supplementation on bone loss in postmenopausal women. N Engl J Med 1993;328:460.
Riggs BL, Melton LJ. The prevention and treatment of osteoporosis. N Engl J Med 1992;327:620.
Rowe PSN. Molecular biology of hypophosphataemic rickets and oncogenic osteomalacia. Hum Genet 1994; 94:457.
Tilstra DJ, Byers PH. Molecular basis of hereditary disorders of connective tissue. Annu Rev Med 1994; 45:149.
Sebastian A, Harris ST, Ottaway JH, et al. Improved mineral balance and skeletal metabolism in postmenopausal women treated with potassium bicarbonate. N Engl J Med 1994;330:1776.
Vandenberg P. Molecular basis of heritable connective tissue disease. Biochemical Medicine and Metabolic Biology 1993;49:1.
Walters MR. Newly identified actions of the vitamin D endocrine system. Endocr Rev 1992;13:719.

chapter **22**

Gastrointestinal Pathobiochemistry

The gastrointestinal tract is, in essence, a continuous mucous membrane lined tube extending from the oral cavity to the anus. In health, with the single exception of the entry of the common bile duct into the jejunum, the wall of this cylinder constitutes a continuous barrier. Absorption of materials from the gut into the rest of the body, therefore, normally takes place only by transfer across biologic membranes.

Living organisms need hexoses, amino acids, and fatty acids not only as fuels to generate ATP, but also as building blocks to fashion macromolecules. For the most part, however, the food we eat consists of very large molecules like polysaccharides, proteins, nucleic acids, and triacylglycerols. Such molecules cannot be efficiently transferred across the gut membrane barrier. Instead, it is necessary to dismantle these macromolecules into their monomeric building blocks for them to be absorbed by the organism. The process by which this is accomplished is called digestion, a process that for all practical purposes takes place in the stomach and small intestine. There ingested macromolecules are broken down by a variety of hydrolytic enzymes. The most important source of these hydrolases is the pancreas, but the small intestine also contributes enzymes that help complete digestion. Digestion of fat poses a physicochemical problem, because they are apolar compounds in an aqueous environment. To solve this problem, the liver secretes bile salts into the intestinal tract, which by virtue of their detergent action, facilitates attack by lipolytic enzymes on fats. Once the larger molecules in the meal are broken down into their simpler forms, the resulting monomers can be absorbed from the lumen into the bloodstream by mucosal cells of the small intestine, from whence they are taken up by the liver and other organs of the body. Monomers gaining entrance into the bloodstream include amino acids, hexoses and pentoses, fatty acids, glycerol, and purines and pyrimidines. These familiar compounds are the fuels that undergo the various enzyme-mediated reactions which, in aggregate, constitute intermediary metabolism. Certain mechanical actions like the chewing of food and the churning actions of the stomach and small and large intestines aid the enzymes in cleaving the chemical bonds that hold the macromolecules together. Both the autonomic nervous system and complicated hormonal interactions exert important controlling effects on gastrointestinal mixing and propulsive actions. At the conclusion of the digestion and absorption of a meal, indigestible materials remaining accompanied by billions of bacteria from the lower gastrointestinal tract pass out as feces.

DISORDERS OF THE OROPHARYNX

Setting aside anatomic and neoplastic disorders, the oropharynx is most commonly affected by acquired conditions, either infectious or nutritionally related. The general response to infection is one of inflammation, which is dealt with in Chapter 19, and can be associated with gum and tooth disease. The oropharynx frequently mirrors the nutritional status of the individual.

Color

The oropharyngeal mucosa is the most accessible window on the gastrointestinal tract. The vasculature that supplies the tissues of the oropharynx are close to the surface, so that changes in hematocrit are apparent upon visual inspection. Anemia from any cause will produce pallor of the oropharyngeal mucosa, the gingiva, and the vermillion border of the lips. The most likely cause of this finding in children and adolescents is iron-deficiency anemia related to poor nutrition. But in older individuals, blood loss from sites further down the gastrointestinal tract must be considered. Conversely, a more intense color of the oropharyngeal mucosa would be noted in conditions such as carbon monoxide poisoning or other conditions that cause methemoglobin formation.

Increased pigmentation of the buccal mucosa and gums is typical of adrenal insufficiency, but is generally preceded by hyperpigmentation of sun-exposed surfaces. These findings may also be an early signal of the presence of adrenoleukodystrophy (see Chapter 26) preceding the neurologic degeneration by months or years.

Absence of the fungiform papillae of the tongue, which are normally reddish, is replaced by a gray appearance of the lingual mucosa in familial dysautonomia (Riley-Day syndrome).

Non-Infectious Lesions of the Mucosa

In many respects, the oropharyngeal mucosa is subjected to as much trauma as the skin—abrasion, temperature extremes, and the occasional puncture or laceration are all hazards to which this surface is daily exposed. Repair of these injuries is extraordinarily swift in the well-vascularized area of the mucosa, relying on rapid cell division and replacement. This requirement for rapid cell division and repair renders the process vulnerable to deficiencies of materials needed for cell turnover, especially protein and certain vitamins.

In particular, ulcerative lesions involving the mucosa and the lingual surface are typical of B-vitamin deficiencies (thiamine, niacin, pyridoxine, and riboflavin). Although such disorders are less common in the normal pediatric population and in most adults, they are being found with increasing frequency in the geriatric age group and some adolescents. Antimetabolite therapy in neoplastic disease may cause deficiencies of agents needed for repair and renewal, either as a result of diminished oral intake or as metabolic antagonists of one or more of the B-vitamins.

Heavy metal poisoning causes mucosal inflammation and ulceration, probably by virtue of their marked tendency to cause protein denaturation. Thus, the combination of repeated trauma and cellular protein denaturation is bound to lead to an inability to adequately replace damaged tissue.

DISORDERS OF THE ESOPHAGUS

The esophagus is a tubular structure that conveys ingested solids and liquids from the mouth to the stomach. It is composed of four layers, which beginning at the lumen are the mucosa, submucosa, muscularis, and connective tissue envelope (tunica adventitia). In the upper third of the esophagus, the muscularis is composed of striated muscle only, whereas in the middle third, there is both striated and smooth muscle, and in the last third, (which attaches to the stomach) there is only smooth muscle. Normally, prolonged reflux of gastric contents into the esophagus is prevented by the lower esophageal sphincter, a segment of smooth muscle 3 to 4 cm in length. This is vital because the esophageal mucosa, unlike the gastric mucosa, is vulnerable to the effects of the HCl and pepsin of gastric juice.

Esophageal Reflux

Judging from the number of advertisements on television and the statistics for use of antacids for heartburn, esophageal reflux must be very common. In fact, many studies confirm that most individuals experience some degree of reflux, especially when recumbent, but in the vast majority these episodes are brief and cause no damage to the esophageal mucosa.

As noted, heartburn, variously felt as heat or burning in the area above the sternum, is the accompaniment of reflux. Some experience a sour taste in the mouth, evidence of *water brash*. Although an occasional episode of reflux is unlikely to cause any damage to the vulnerable esophageal mucosa, repeated episodes can produce esophagitis and in long-standing cases metaplasia of the squamous epithelium to columnar epithelium. This finding is called *Barrett's epithelium* and is sometimes a precursor of malignant transformation.

From the foregoing it should be clear that esophageal reflux is the result of the interplay of two events: intermittent or continual incompetence of the lower esophageal sphincter and damage to the esophageal mucosa from the acid and hydrolytic enzymes (pepsin) in the gastric juice.

TREATMENT

Measures that can combat reflux begin with simple strategies such as raising the head of the bed, or placing a right angle-shaped foam wedge under the subject's head. Food and fluid intake should end within 3 to 4 hours before bedtime. If the patient is overweight, weight reduction can be helpful (in this as well as many other conditions). To increase the competence of the lower esophageal sphincter, certain foods should be avoided including, fats, chocolate, mints, caffeine, and alcohol. Antacids and histamine-2 antagonists are effective in more resistant cases. Omeprazole, a drug that covalently inactivates the H^+-K^+-ATPase that secretes gastric acid (see following text), is the most powerful drug presently available for suppressing gastric acid secretion. But chronic use of omeprazole is at present discouraged because prolonged suppression of acid secretion by the stomach is a stimulus to secretion of gastrin. Gastrin is a hormone with potent acid-stimulating action that has caused carcinoid tumors in animals.

STOMACH

The stomach is a conspicuously dilated J-shaped region of the gastrointestinal tract, with a potential capacity of about 1 L, attached to the esophagus at the cardia and to the duodenum at the pylorus. Intervening between these extremes is the bulk of the organ, concave in shape and richly endowed with glands that secrete a variety of materials. For example, parietal or oxyntic cells secrete hydrochloric acid. This acid functions in protein digestion by denaturing the ingested protein thereby making its peptide bonds more vulnerable to the action of the hydrolytic enzyme pepsin. The parietal cells also secrete intrinsic factor, a glycoprotein required for the absorption of vitamin B_{12}. Another type of cell, the chief cell secretes the proteolytic zymogen, pepsinogen, that is converted to its active form, pepsin, when it is exposed to H^+. Still another cell secretes the glycoprotein rich mucoid covering that invests the mucosa with a surface resistant to the acid environment. In addition, endocrine cells secrete gastrin, somatostatin, glucagon, and several other hormones (Table 22.1).

The stomach is the site where tangible digestion of foodstuffs begins. Proteolysis is begun by the collaborative action of hydrochloric acid and pepsin, aided by the mixing action of gastric peristalsis. Fat digestion relies on lingual lipase that arrives from salivary secretion and carbohydrate digestion proceeds to a degree based on residual salivary amylase.

Table 22.1. Gastrointestinal Hormones

HORMONE	LOCUS OF ACTION	FUNCTIONS
Stomach		
Gastrin	Stomach	Stimulates acid secretion
Small Intestine		
Secretin	Pancreas	Bicarbonate secretion and fluid release
Cholecystokinin	Gall bladder, pancreas	Contraction of gall bladder Stimulates pancreatic enzyme secretion Potentiates actions of secretin
Gastric inhibitory peptide	Pancreas	May play a role in stimulating postprandial insulin release
Motilin	Stomach, intestine	Inhibits pyloric sphincter May play a role in normal G.I. motility
Enteroglucagon	Small intestine	Released after feeding—may have a role in G.I. motility—linked to "dumping syndrome"
Vasoactive intestinal peptide	Stomach, intestine	Inhibits gastric acid secretion Stimulates insulin release Stimulates production of fluid by pancreas and intestine
Somatostatin	Stomach, intestine, and hypothalamus	Inhibits gastrin release and pancreatic enzyme and bicarbonate secretion Inhibits release of growth hormone, TSH, insulin, glucagon, motilin, GIP, secretin, enteroglucagon

Acid Secretion and Peptic Ulcer

Hydrochloric acid, secreted by the parietal cells of the gastric mucosa, is essential to hydrolysis of the peptide bonds in dietary protein. An acid pH is also necessary for conversion of pepsinogen, secreted by chief cells, to active pepsin. The mechanism of HCl secretion is unique to the parietal cell, and is attributable to a specific H^+; -K^+-ATPase present (Figure 22.1) in the apical surface, which permits exchange of hydrogen for potassium ions. Moreover, it has been shown that this specific ATPase acts in concert with a carrier which is not present in unstimulated parietal cells. Chloride, moving inward with K^+, is available to restore electrochemical balance, hence forming HCl within the gastric lumen.

Acid secretion by the stomach is under the control of three local mediators: gastrin, acetylcholine, and histamine. *Gastrin* is released by cells situated in the antrum of the stomach, especially in response to the presence of aromatic amino acids. *Acetylcholine*, a neurotransmitter, is released from cells emanating from the vagus and parasympathetic roots. *Histamine* is the most potent mediator of the three, behaving as a go-between for gastrin and acetylcholine. Actually, it was not until the advent of the H_2-receptor blockers that histamine's central role in acid secretion was appreciated.

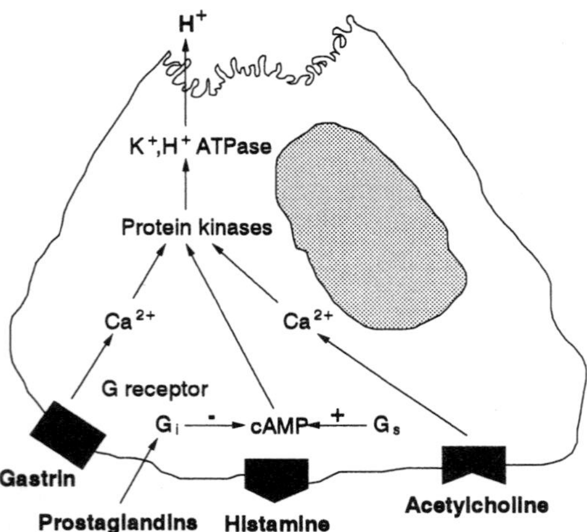

Figure 22.1. Secretion of H^+ by the gastric parietal cell. The parietal cell is responsive to at least three separate influences: gastrin, histamine, and acetylcholine, for which surface receptors exist. Through various intracellular mechanisms, each of these stimulatory influences eventually is mediated through the K^+,H^+-ATPase with secretion of H^+. Reprinted with permission from Roe DA, Rock RC. Laboratory medicine: the selection and interpretation of clinical laboratory studies. Baltimore: Williams & Wilkins, 1994: 385.

Histamine acts through cAMP as its second messenger, leading to the phosphorylation of various intracellular proteins. Among them is the protein, ezrin, that is believed to participate in recruiting the H^+-K^+ ATPase to the secretory canaliculus.

Secretion of acid by the parietal cells makes enormous metabolic demands, a fact reflected by the presence of more mitochondria in that cell than any other in the body. The H^+-K^+ ATPase, like the ubiquitous Na^+-K^+ ATPase acts through a phosphorylated intermediate. These two enzymes are members of the family of *P-enzymes*, a designation that recognizes the obligatory phosphorylated form.

Ulcer Disease

Peptic ulcers involve junctional areas in the stomach and duodenum, which are more vulnerable to acid, proteolytic enzymes (pepsin), and other factors (eg, Heliobacter pylori). Ulcer formation requires, as a minimum, acid and pepsin, but there are other factors categorized as decreased mucosal integrity that also contribute to development of ulcer disease. The integrity of the mucosa is defended by mucus (a group of glycoproteins that invest the lining), bicarbonate, adequate blood flow, and the capacity to replace damaged cells by cell proliferation. Prostaglandins also contribute to the integrity of the mucosa, an effect highlighted by agents like aspirin and nonsteroidal anti-inflammatory drugs (NSAIDs), which inhibit prostanoid synthesis and are associated with ulcers in some individuals.

Perhaps the most interesting, and probably unanticipated, factor in ulcer formation is the role of chronic infection with *H. pylori* as a predisposing element in mucosal damage. This organism is a gram-negative curved bacillus and has been found in biopsy specimens of gastric mucosa in virtually all patients with duodenal ulcer and approximately 80% of patients with gastric ulcer. Notably, the organism does not enter gastric cells. Studies with human volunteers have confirmed the role of H. pylori in the pathogenesis of chronic gastritis. Because the organism is endowed with considerable urease activity, this may create a local environment relatively free of acid because of the basic properties of NH_3.

Although classic ulcer therapy has relied on suppression of acid secretion or neutralization of acid, it is possible to heal ulcers with sucralfate and bismuth compounds that exert no influence on acid secretion, but may inhibit the effects of harboring H. pylori. Therapy with these agents and antibiotics can eradicate the organism—however, it is not a simple matter. In sum, H. pylori, like other factors, cited above is not in itself sufficient to cause ulcer disease, the propensity to gastric or duodenal ulcer being dependent on a multiplicity of factors including genetics, stress, drugs, smoking, and the presence of H. pylori.

Hypersecretion of HCl, rare in childhood and relatively common in adults, is must strikingly illustrated in the Zollinger-Ellison syndrome. Caused by a gastrin-secreting tumor, the syndrome is manifested by acid hypersecretion and multiple gastric and duodenal ulcerations. It is also worth mentioning that the extremely low pH of the stomach guarantees the virtual absence of bacteria in the proximal small intestine.

Hypochlorhydria

Hypo- or achlorhydria are also uncommonly seen in children, with a higher frequency in the adult population. Perhaps the best-known association between achlorhydria and clinical disease is seen in pernicious anemia. Because intrinsic factor, required for vitamin B_{12} absorption, is secreted by the parietal cells, significant reduction or total loss of parietal cell mass would predictably result in intrinsic factor deficiency, as well. Apart from the hematologic and neurologic manifestations of pernicious anemia, the finding that may draw attention to the achlorhydria is the overgrowth of bacteria in the small bowel. As noted above, the normally acidic pH of the stomach should prevent bacterial growth.

Vomiting

Vomiting is among the most common complaints in all of medicine. Notably, the basis for virtually all of clinically significant vomiting does not lie within the function of the stomach itself, but rather with superimposed abnormalities, such as viral infections, local irritation, or systemic factors like ketosis. An important cause of vomiting is hyperammonemia. Another frequent cause of gastric motility abnormalities lies in the central nervous system, either because of emotional or organic causes. Remote though it may be anatomically, the central nervous system always should be included in the differential diagnosis of vomiting.

SMALL INTESTINE

The small intestine is the site where most of digestion is completed. It is the longest part of the digestive tract and is divided into three parts: duodenum, jejunum, and ileum. The mucosal surface area in contact with the ingested intestinal contents is multiplied several hundred times by a series of surface specializations. In aggregate, these anatomic refinements to the mucosa create a total absorptive surface area in the small intestine of about 200 M^2, an impressive area equivalent to that of a doubles tennis court. Three surface specializations of the mucosa account for most of this increase in surface area, over what would be expected if the surface were entirely flat. First, the surface of the small intestine is arranged in concentric folds that create a series of transverse ridges. Second, the villi project 0.5 to 1 mm into the intestinal lumen and are covered with a single layer of columnar epithelium, just as are the mucosal glands (crypts of Lierberkuhn) that sit between adjacent villi. Third, the villi are themselves further subdivided into microvilli, each cell possessing as many as 1000 microvilli. Not only do the microvilli enhance the absorptive surface area, but because digestive enzymes (disaccharidases, peptidases) are located in these microvilli, contact between intestinal contents and enzymes is further enhanced.

Much like the proximal renal tubule, the intestinal mucosal cell must exist in a state of readiness to absorb a wide variety of nutritionally valuable materials. Some of these materials are thought to be absorbed by facilitated diffusion, whereas others are transferred by active transport processes. Active transport requires membrane carrier proteins specific for the materials to be transferred, just as in the renal tubules.

Because very few dietary components can be absorbed in their original form, the task facing the digestive tract is to reduce each polymer to simple monomers facilitating absorption while the overall mass moves inexorably towards the anus. Thus, the gastrointestinal tract may be likened to a carefully regulated conveyer belt that transfers materials at a rate appropriate to optimize uptake of nutrients into the body.

Similarities between intestinal and renal tubular epithelium include the presence in each of the brushborder surfaces endowed with microvilli, and of specialized membrane carrier proteins. Perhaps the most compelling factor in considering the kinship of these two cell types is that they are often simultaneously affected by genetic disorders of membrane transport. This underscores not only their similarities of function, but also the common genetic control exerted over their membrane functions.

The secretions of the embryologic derivatives of the gut, the pancreas, and the liver play an important role in digestion. The ducts of the pancreas and the gallbladder open into the duodenum at a point just distal to the pylorus. Pancreatic and gallbladder secretions are basic and neutralize the acidic chyme entering the duodenum and change the pH slightly to the alkaline side of neutral. Stomach contents are introduced piecemeal into the duodenum, so that it takes chyme 2 to 4 hours to vacate the stomach. It is necessary to switch to alkalinity for the intestinal enzymes to express optimal activity. This alkaline secretion, also rich in mucus, is elaborated by Brunner's glands, the distinctive histologic feature of the duodenum.

Introduction of HCl, fats, proteins, carbohydrates, and partially digested foodstuffs into the first part of the duodenum prompts the secretion of at least five hormones elaborated by the glands of the duodenum and upper part of the jejunum (Table 22.1). These hormones are carried via the portal blood to the pancreas, liver, and gallbladder.

The *succus entericus*, elaborated by the intestinal wall itself, contains a variety of digestive enzymes (Table 22.2). It should be obvious, therefore, that the small intestine is eminently able to digest a wide variety of foodstuffs. In fact, the diversity of enzymes present in intestinal juices, along with water as co-reactant for hydrolysis, enables the intestine to degrade a wide assortment of biologic materials to monomeric components for absorption.

Secretions of the pancreatic exocrine glands contain enzymes (Table 22.2) that supplement those of the succus entericus, further enhancing the digestive tract's ability to dismantle almost any substance likely to be ingested. Pancreatic juice includes a variety of inorganic substances, mainly sodium, potassium, bicarbonate, and chloride. Calcium and zinc are present in small amounts, and the pH is distinctly alkaline (in the range of 7.5 to 8).

In addition to all of these digestive factors present in the intestinal lumen, we should underscore the presence of bile acids and bile salts. Bile is synthesized by the liver and stored in the gallbladder. One of the major functions of the gallbladder is to concentrate the bile by removal of some of the water content. Release of bile from the gallbladder during digestion is stimulated by the hormone cholecystokinin. This hormone, is secreted by the upper intestine in response to the presence of various foodstuffs. Another hormone, hepatocrinin, also secreted in response to the presence of food by the upper intestine, is a stimulant for the production of bile by the liver.

Bile acids are important end-products in the metabolism of cholesterol, which is removed from the blood by the liver for the synthetic process. It should be noted, however, that cholesterol is also present in the bile. Bile acids are not excreted into the intestinal lumen in their free form but are conjugated by the liver with glycine or taurine to form glycocholic or taurocholic acids (Figure 22.2). Conjugation increases the water solubility of the bile acids. Because bile is alkaline, the conjugated bile acids are usually neutralized by reaction with sodium or potassium. These compounds are "bile salts," and exert powerful surface tension and emulsifying effects on the intestinal contents, thus aiding in the digestion of fats, most probably through micelle formation. In addition, the presence of bile in the small intestine activates many pancreatic enzymes, perhaps due to its alkaline nature and effect on the pH of the intestinal contents. Thus, the process of digestion, a complex enzymatic process animated by hor-

Table 22.2. Enzymes of the Gastrointestinal Tract

ORIGIN	ENZYME	SUBSTRATE	PRODUCT
Intestine			
("Succus Entericus")	Sucrase	Sucrose	Fructose + Glucose
	Maltase	Maltose	2 Glucose
	Lactase	Lactose	Glucose + Galactose
	Phosphatase	Organic phosphates	Organic molecule + P_i
	Polynucleotidase	Nucleic acids	Nucleotides
	Nucleosidase	Nucleosides	Adenine or Guanine + Ribose
	Lecithinase	Lecithin	Glycerol, fatty acids, phosphoric acid, choline
	Enterokinase	Trypsinogen	Trypsin
Pancreas			
	Trypsinogen*	Proteins	Polypeptides
	Chymotrypsinogen*		
	Peptidases		
	Carboxypeptidase	Terminal peptide bond at carboxyl end of chain	Peptide + Amino Acid
	Aminopeptidase	Terminal peptide bond at amino end of chain	Peptide + Amino acid
	Dipeptidase	Dipeptides	2 Amino acids
	Amylase	Starch	Maltose
	Lipase	Fat	Fatty acids, glycerol, monoglycerides, diglycerides
		Cholesterol	Cholesterol esters
	Cholesterol esterase	Cholesterol esters	Cholesterol
	Ribonuclease	RNA	Pyrimidine-containing nucleoside-3'-phosphate Oligonucleotides ending with pyrimidine nucleotide
	Deoxyribonuclease	DNA	Oligonucleotides ending with nucleotide Oligonucleotides ending with 3'-phosphate

* Activated by trypsin.

mones, is "fine-tuned" and partially regulated by the liver through its control of bile metabolism. Small bowel dysfunction, therefore, must be looked upon as resulting from possible abnormalities of other systems as well, a view that we will attempt to incorporate in what follows.

Abnormal Small Bowel Motility

Like any mechanical function involving flow of material through a cylindrical structure, maintaining patency of the tube is critical to its function. In the case of the intestines, patency depends to a large extent upon propulsion of contents by coordinated muscular contractions primarily directed distally toward the cecum. Because these contractions, although still poorly understood, are known to derive from coordinated depolarization and contraction of the intrinsic musculature of the gut wall, it stands to reason that electrolyte imbalance will affect the process of muscle cell depolarization and thus the contractile process. The clinical entity that results is termed "*ileus*," and normalization of electrolyte balance will result in restoration of normal contractility. Trauma and/or general anesthesia can also cause an ileus, which normally resolves spontaneously.

Hastening bowel transit time is a more complex situation, and may stem from congenital as well as acquired causes. One of the most common of these is infection, usually thought to impair absorption and resulting in increased intraluminal solute and water content. There is evidence, however, to suggest that bacterial endotoxin may directly affect the intrinsic musculature, producing a more rapid peristaltic wave and decreased transit time. Certain viral pathogens, such as rotavirus, show a preference for infection of the small bowel. The pathogenesis of the contractile abnormalities is still less clear for viruses than for bacteria. But, because ro-

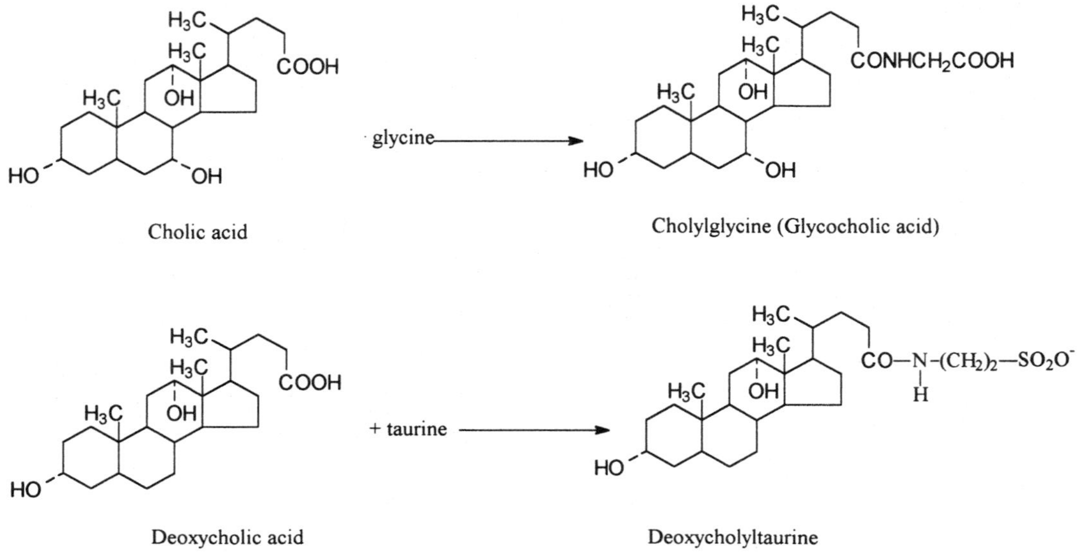

Cholic acid — glycine → Cholylglycine (Glycocholic acid)

Deoxycholic acid + taurine → Deoxycholyltaurine

Figure 22.2. The molecular structure of conjugated bile acids. The amide linkage of the taurine or glycine to the bile acids is resistant to pancreatic carboxypeptidase, thus facilitating the role of these compounds in digestion by preventing their hydrolytic breakdown.

tavirus results in death and shedding of the jejunal villar cells, certainly decreased absorptive capabilities play a role in the diarrhea that results. Congenital causes of diarrhea are addressed below.

Genetically Determined Disorders of Nutrient Absorption

This group of entities has shed considerable light on how nutrients are absorbed in the human gut. As we have gained an understanding of each of these disorders, we have learned the site in the gut where specific substances are absorbed, the nature of the interactions with other substrates, and the importance of those nutrients because impaired absorption produces deprivation syndromes. From a clinical perspective, disorders of sugars and lipids are of greatest significance, because disorders of these materials most adversely affect small bowel function and overall nutritional status. It should be understood that absorptive disorders of amino acids, although they exist, would be incompatible with life if they involved extensive malabsorption of essential amino acids.

Disaccharidase Deficiency

Carbohydrate digestion occurs mostly in the upper jejunum, due primarily to the secretion into the pylorus of pancreatic amylase. When, because of an enzyme defect or a transport defect, the small intestine fails to digest complex sugars or absorb monosaccharides resulting from such digestion, this creates a potent *osmotic load*. Hence, water and electrolytes are drawn into the gut lumen, causing a laxative effect and diminishing small bowel transit time. Once this sugar enriched fluid reaches the cecum, the microbial flora of the large bowel delight in fermenting this unexpected wealth of sugars to volatile short-chain organic acids (including butyric and propionic), which, in turn, exert a cathartic effect on the large bowel. Thus, defects in digestion or absorption of carbohydrates can be manifested clinically by abdominal distension and cramps, copious flatus, hyperactive bowel sounds, and explosive diarrhea following an ingested carbohydrate load.

The predominant disorders of intestinal carbohydrate handling are attributable to deficiency of mucosal disaccharidase activity. The chief entities in this category are *lactase* and *sucrase-isomaltase* deficiencies, each of which results in increased intraluminal disaccharide concentrations and, therefore, the clinical picture typical of carbohydrate malabsorption. Sucrase-isomaltase deficiency is inherited as an autosomal recessive trait and appears with an incidence of about 1% in

North America. Because neither breast milk nor the standard cow's milk-based infant formulas contain sucrose or isomaltose, clinical symptoms are not seen until these sugars are introduced into the diet at about mid to late infancy. However, congenital lactase deficiency, although very rare, will cause severe diarrheal disease from the earliest days of life in an affected infant, unless fed a nonlactose-containing formula. A remarkable feature of lactase deficiency is that, although it is rare as a congenital disorder, it occurs with an estimated frequency of 15% in Caucasian Americans and 80% in African Americans. From a teleologic view, this makes sense, because humans are the only members of the animal kingdom who insist upon milk consumption beyond the time of weaning.

Finally, it is important to note that the presence of normal gut mucosal disaccharidase activities is dependent upon normal mucosal structure. Thus, infectious diarrhea of either bacterial or viral origin can cause shearing and sloughing of the intestinal microvilli with consequent loss of disaccharidase activities. In such an acquired disaccharidase-deficient state, attempts to reinstitute feeding with a regimen high in disaccharide content may reaggravate a resolving diarrheal disorder. Particularly in young infants, full recovery of intestinal disaccharidase activity may require weeks to months, a fact that should dictate caution during convalescent treatment.

Fat Digestion and Absorption

Fat contributes 20% to 40% of calories in a typical Western diet. Although only essential fatty acids (arachidonic, linoleic, linolenic) must be ingested, fat provides concentrated calories and adds palatability to food. Digestion of fat, however, is not as straightforward a process as that for carbohydrates and proteins because fats are not water-soluble. How does the body deal with the challenge of dismantling energy rich hydrophobic molecules like triglycerides, phospholipids, and cholesterol? The general answer is that it emulsifies the lipid by subdividing the material so that microscopic droplets of fat can be dispersed in the aqueous medium greatly increasing the surface area. Usually, this depends on the churning and agitating actions of the stomach and small intestine. Milk is an example of an emulsion in which fat droplets are dispersed in an aqueous medium. Lipolytic enzymes can adsorb to the emulsion and thus gain access to the ester bonds that have to be severed. During lipolysis of triglycerides, monoacylglycerols and free fatty acids are generated, molecules that are amphipathic and, therefore, can also further help solubilize lipids to be digested. These free fatty acids and monoacylglycerols are incorporated into micelles made up of bile salts and phosphatidylcholine, the micelles exiting the gut lumen and entering the enterocytes for further processing, ultimately to emerge in chylomicrons.

As indicated above, for lipases to gain access to the ester bonds, the fats have to be emulsified. Lipolysis appears to take place on the surface of the emulsion at the water-lipid interface. As a particular triglyceride is dismantled, another triglyceride situated in the core of the emulsion moves to the surface for digestion. Some lipolysis begins in the stomach but the bulk takes place in the small intestine.

In the small intestine, pancreatic lipase needs an auxiliary protein, called *colipase* (Figure 22.3), to anchor it to the emulsion, as well as to offset the inhibitory effects of bile acids on lipase action. In the absence of bile acids, colipase is not needed by lipase to exert its lipolytic activity.

Complete hydrolysis of triglycerides produces glycerol and fatty acids. But, sequential removal of the first, second, and third fatty acids from the triacylglycerol occurs with increasing difficulty; removal of the third fatty acid requires special conditions provided only within the intestinal epithelial cell. Thus, intraluminal hydrolysis of the tri- and diglyceride is facilitated by lipase, the removal occurring preferentially at the 1 and 3 bonds, leaving a 2-monoglyceride. Free fatty acids thereby released enter the intestinal epithelial cell carried to the cell surface in micelles composed of bile acids and lipid hydrolysis products. The 2-monoglyceride remaining undergoes a slow, spontaneous preabsorptive isomerization to form 1- as well as 3-monoglycerides. Upon entry into the epithelial cell, the two isomers follow different paths; the newly isomerized monoglyceride undergoes further hydrolysis to free fatty acid and glycerol. The 2-monoglyceride, which predominates because of the slow rate of isomerization, is used for reconstruction of

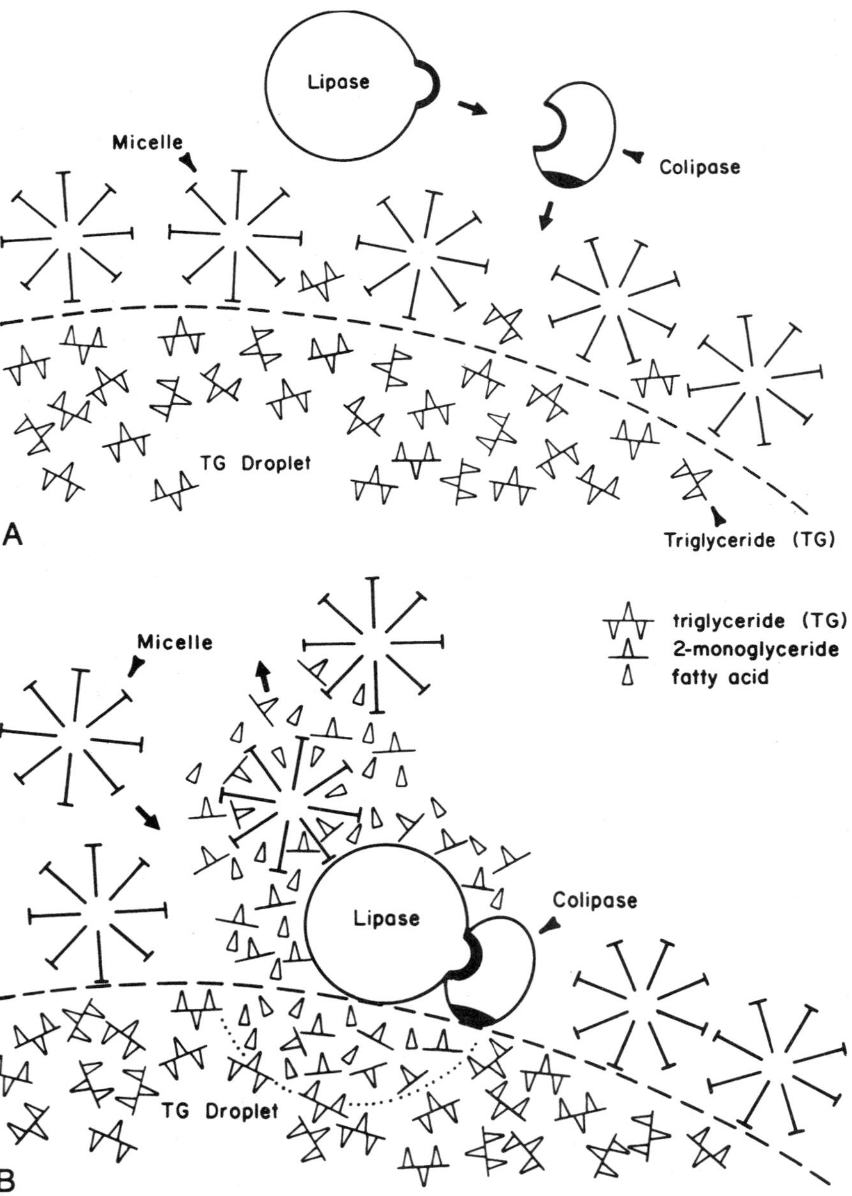

Figure 22.3. Action of lipase on triglycerides. (A) Bile micelles effectively shield triglycerides from hydrolysis by pancreatic lipase because of surface adhesion between the two. (B) The high affinity of colipase for triglyceride causes dispersion of the adhesive surface, displacing and complexing with the micelles and the oil phase simultaneously. Reprinted with permission from Shils ME, Olson JA, Shike M, et al. Modern Nutrition in Health and Disease. 8th ed. Baltimore: Williams & Wilkins, 1994: 53.

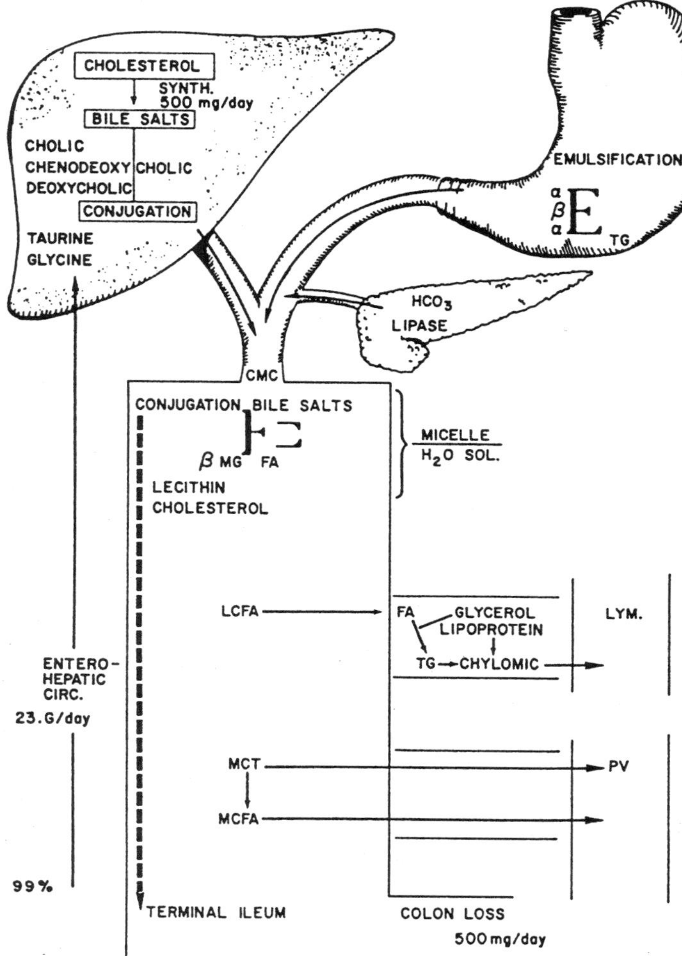

Figure 22.4. Absorption of fat. Digestion of lipid begins in the stomach with the process of emulsification. Upon entering the proximal jejunum, the emulsion is acted upon with hydrolysis of the triglycerides (TG) to β-monoglycerides (β-MG) and free fatty acids (FA). The long chain fatty acids (LCFA) are absorbed and enter the lymphatic circulation (LYM) as chylomicrons (CHYLOMIC). In contrast, the medium chain triglycerides (MCT) and the medium chain fatty acids (MCFA) are absorbed and enter the portal circulation (PV). The return of the bile salts to the liver via the enterohepatic circulation is shown, as well as the colonic loss of fat, which approximates 0.5 g/day on a normal diet. Reprinted with permission from Achkar E, Farmer RG, Fleshler B, et al. Clinical Gastroenterology. 2nd ed. Baltimore: Williams & Wilkins, 1992: 302.

triglyceride in an ATP-dependent reaction mediated by fatty acid CoA ligase. Triglycerides endogenously synthesized, from long chain fatty acids (> 12-C), in this way are then incorporated into chylomicrons in the intestinal cell and make their way to the intestinal lymphatics (Figure 22.4). Most notably, dietary triglyceride neither enters the circulation in the form of fatty acids, nor are the triglycerides that reach the systemic circulation (via the lymphatics) in their original ingested form. In contrast, medium chain fatty acids (6-12 C) pass through the intestinal wall into the portal vein without modification. This offers an important therapeutic opportunity in a patient with fat malabsorption.

More complex lipid, such as cholesterol esters and phosphatidylcholine follow a roughly similar pathway (Figure 22.4). In each case, fatty acid is hydrolyzed and absorbed into the epithelial cell; the remaining portion of the original molecule is absorbed intact. Within the enterocyte, cholesterol ester and phosphatidylcholine are resynthesized in the endoplasmic reticulum. Thereafter, the molecules join apoproteins, also synthesized in the endoplasmic reticulum (E/R) in an orderly migration to the Golgi apparatus. At that site, the lipid is "packaged" for shipment to the antiluminal surface, where the definitive formation of chylomicrons takes place.

In a complex system such as that described above, the potential exists for both genetic and acquired defects at one or more points. The rarity

Table 22.3. Causes of Fat Malabsorption

PANCREAS	LIVER AND BILIARY TRACT	INTESTINE
Cystic fibrosis (1,2)*	Cirrhosis (1)	Blind loop syndrome (1)
Schwachman's syndrome (1,2)	Biliary atresia or obstruction (1)	Chronic infection (1)
Lipase deficiency (1)	Bile acid abnormalities (1)	Short-bowel syndrome (1,2)
		Immune deficiency (2)
		Celiac disease (2)
		Enterokinase deficiency (1)
		Abetalipoproteinemia (3)
		Acrodermatitis enteropathica (2)
		Severe malnutrition (1–3)
		Intestinal lymphangiectasia with protein-losing enteropathy (4)
		Wolman's disease
		Parasites (1,2)
		Radiation damage (2)

* *Stage of process deranged:* 1—hydrolysis of lipids or micelle formation impaired; 2—absorption of products of hydrolysis impaired; 3—chylomicron formation impaired; 4—lymphatic drainage impaired.

of such conditions does not warrant lengthy treatment here, but these are listed in Table 22.3.

Immune-Mediated Protein Intolerance—Celiac Disease

The malabsorptive conditions considered here differ from those already discussed, because the primary defect is not absence of intraluminal digestion or intracellular processing of the normal hydrolytic products of dietary protein. Instead, the pathologic process derives from an untoward and atypical response to an intact and specific protein molecule. It is vital to make this distinction, because both diagnosis and treatment depend on its recognition.

The most well-known member of this category of immune-mediated protein intolerance is *gluten-sensitive enteropathy* (celiac disease). In celiac disease, the wheat protein gliadin initiates a cascade of immunologic events impacting directly on intestinal integrity and function. Because intact proteins are not normally absorbed through the gut wall, except specifically at the location of Peyer's patches, which is where lymphoid tissue is deployed in the gut, it follows that initiation of an immunologic reaction to gliadin must occur at the point of contact between the gut epithelium and the inciting protein. An alternative possibility is that a peptide fraction of gliadin is absorbed and provokes an intracellular reaction to its presence. Much about the precise mechanism by which this occurs remains poorly understood.

Direct examination of the jejunal mucosa from a gluten-sensitive individual reveals a striking increase in the plasma cell population. Humoral antibody assessment of such a patient shows marked increase in gliadin antibodies of the IgG and IgA classes, suggesting increased mucosal permeability as the initiator of a systemic antibody response. There is also evidence of cell-mediated immune response in celiac patients. A significant increase in mast cell numbers occurs; amplification of this greatly T-cell dependent cell type suggests the presence of cell-mediated immune mechanisms in gluten-sensitive mucosa. These and other data unequivocally attest to the involvement of immunological mechanisms in gluten-sensitivity, but beg the question as to why all humans do not react in this way when exposed to gluten.

DISORDERS OF THE LARGE INTESTINE

Under typical dietary conditions, the gastrointestinal tract handles copious amounts of fluid each day. For instance, when eating three meals, about 9 L of fluid enter the duodenum: 2 L from ingested foods and liquids and the other 7 L from secretions of the pancreas, small intestine, and stomach.

As food undergoes digestion in the small intestine, the bulk of hydrolytic products (amino acids, sugars, fat, and liquid) are absorbed. By the conclusion of these absorptive processes, about 1 L of fluid remains, which enters the colon. Normally, the colon, which has a considerable reserve capacity to absorb fluid, removes about 0.9 L from the fluid it receives from the ileum.

As anyone who has ever had diarrhea knows, large amounts of fluid can issue forth from the rectum when one contracts an acute enteric infection. There are, however, other causes of diarrhea that may be less dramatic than enteric infections, but because all forms of diarrhea carry the potential for severe dehydration, especially in the young, fluid replacement is essential to survival. Indeed, an adult who suffers from cholera, and who receives fluid to keep pace with losses can be purged of 1 L of fluid per hour. Worldwide, acute infectious diarrhea accounts for over 4 million deaths/year, most of them in children less than 5 years of age.

Mechanisms of Diarrhea

Because the intestine carries out a vital absorptive and transport function, moving substances from the lumen into the blood (or lymph), most causes of diarrhea can be traced to one of four basic mechanisms (Table 22.4): (*1*) presence in the gut lumen of unusual amounts of poorly absorbable, osmotically active substances, (*2*) augmented intestinal secretion, (*3*) damage to the mucosal absorptive surface, and (*4*) disturbed intestinal motility. It should be realized that many diarrheal states are caused by elements from more than one of these categories.

Osmotic diarrhea, caused by the presence of large amounts of nonabsorbed solutes in the gut lumen, ceases when the offending agent is no longer ingested. Ingestion of large amounts of lactose, in a subject with lactase deficiency is a common cause of occasional diarrhea in such individuals. Other causes are noted in Table 22.4.

Table 22.4. Diarrheal Mechanisms

Osmotic: excess of poorly absorbable or unabsorbable solute in gut
- Disaccharidase deficiency
- Malabsorptive states
- Cathartics
- Immune deficiency states

Abnormalities of Active Transport Processes: chloride losing diarrhea; glucose galactose malabsorption

Secretory: increased secretory activity of gut—persists despite cessation of oral feeds
- Enteric infections (invasive and toxin producing)
- Accumulation of secretogogues—bile salts, hydroxy fatty acids

Motility Abnormalities: hypocalcemia, hyperthyroidism, adrenal insufficiency, carcinoid syndrome; cholinergic drugs

The most common cause of *secretory diarrhea* is enterotoxin-induced secretion, the most striking abnormality being that caused by V. cholera which alters the state of activation of a G-protein causing, in turn, a persistent increase in cAMP levels in the gut. The train of events culminates in explosive active ion secretion by gut cells. Another common secretory diarrhea, is that caused by enterotoxigenic E. coli, which is believed to be the main cause of so-called "travelers diarrhea." Fecal contamination of food or water, usually by food handlers who fail to practice handwashing are at the source of travelers' diarrhea. Foods and drinks that are not adequately heated or fruits and vegetables that are not peeled are the usual source of infection. Ofttimes a salad is prepared on the same surface that was contaminated with meats (beef, pork, or poultry) that were the original source of contamination.

Two features of secretory diarrhea are striking: first, the diarrhea does not abate with fasting, and second, the fluid losses can be striking, approaching 1 L per hour. *Oral rehydration solutions*, containing a liberal ration of glucose, Na^+, K^+, Cl^-, and citrate have considerably reduced mortality. Provision of glucose in the rehydration solution allows glucose-Na^+ cotransport to continue to enhance both Na^+ and fluid absorption despite the concomitant secretory abnormalities. In other words, while fluid loss will continue replacement can also be effected. The original oral rehydration solution contained 90 mmol/L of Na^+, a level that although appropriate for initial rehydration is too high for maintenance therapy. Other commercial solutions provide Na^+ at 45 to 50 mmol/L. Cooked rice cereal has been used as a substitute for glucose where the hexose was in short supply, and this refinement has turned out to be efficacious.

Damage to the mucosal absorptive surface is a common finding with those viral and bacterial agents that invade the mucosal surface or enterocytes themselves. Disturbed intestinal motility is found in irritable bowel syndrome, the most common gastrointestinal complaint bringing patients to primary care physicians. It is also a feature of thyrotoxicosis, advanced diabetes, and carcinoid syndrome.

SUGGESTED READINGS

GENERAL

Gitnick G. Principles and practices of gastroenterology and hepatology. 2nd ed. Norwalk, CT: Appleton Lange, 1994.

Johnson LR, ed. Physiology of the gastrointestinal tract. 3rd ed. New York: Raven Press, 1994.

Yamada T, Alpers DH, eds. Textbook of Gastroenterology. Philadelphia: JB Lippincott, 1995.

GASTROESOPHAGEAL REFLUX

DeVault KR, Castell DO. Current diagnosis and treatment of gastroesophageal reflux disease. Mayo Clin Proc 1994;69:867.

Gelfand MD. Gastroesophageal reflux disease. Med Clin North Am 1991;75:92.

Peters JH, DeMeester TR. Gastroesophageal reflux. Surg Clin North Am 1993;73:1119.

PEPTIC ULCER

Berardi RR, Dunn-Kucharski VA. Peptic ulcer disease: an update. Am Pharm 1993;NS33(6):26.

Graham DY, Go MF. Helicobacter pylori: current status. Gastroenterology 1993;105:279.

Hersey SJ, Sachs G. Gastric acid secretion. Physiol Rev 1995;75:155.

Hopkins RJ, Morris JG Jr. Helicobacter pylori: the missing link in perspective. Am J Med 1994;97:265.

Katz J. The course of peptic ulcer disease. Med Clin North Am 1991;75:831.

Kozol, Robert A, Dekhne N. Helicobacter pylori and the pathogenesis of duodenal ulcer. J Lab Clin Med 1994; 124:623.

Mertz HR, Walsh JH. Peptic ulcer pathophysiology. Med Clin North Am 1991;75:799.

Rabon EC, Reuben MA. The mechanism and structure of the gastric H,K-ATPase. Annu Rev Physiol 1990;52: 321.

LIPID DIGESTION AND ABSORPTION

Erlanson-Albertsson C. Pancreatic colipase: structural and physiological aspects. Biochim Biophys Acta 1992; 1125:1.

Johnson LR, ed. Intestinal lipid absorption. New York: Raven Press, 1994.

Wang C-S, Hartsuck J. Bile salt-activated lipase. A multiple function lipolytic enzyme. Biochim Biophys Acta 1993; 1166:1.

DISACCHARIDASE DEFICIENCY

Arola H. Diagnosis of hypolactasia and lactose malabsorption. Scand J Gastroenterol 1994;Suppl 29(202):26.

Aroloa H, Tamm A. Metabolism of lactose in the human body. Scand J Gastroenterol 1994;Suppl 29(202):21.

Hoffman LR, Chang EB. Regional expression and regulation of intestinal sucrase-isomaltase. Journal of Nutritional Biochemistry 1993;4:130.

Lebenthal E, Khin-Maung U, Zheng BY, et al. Small intestinal glucoamylase deficiency and starch malabsorption: a newly recognized alpha-glucosidase deficiency in children. J Pediatr 1994;124:541.

Rings EH, Grand RJ, Buller HA. Lactose intolerance and lactase deficiency in children. Curr Opin Pediatr 1994; 6:562.

Tamm A. Management of lactose intolerance. Scand J Gasteroenterol 1994;Suppl 29(202):55.

COELIAC DISEASE

Bock SA, Sampson HA. Food allergy in infancy. Pediatr Clin North Am 1994;1:1047.

Collin P, Maki M. Associated disorders in coeliac disease: clinical aspects. Scand J Gasteroenterol 1994;29:769.

Collin P, Reunala T, Pukkala E, et al. Coeliac disease—associated disorders and survival. Gut 1994; 35:1215.

Sprue C. Medical progress. N Engl J Med 1991;325:1709.

DIARRHEA

Cheney CP, Wong RKH. Acute infectious diarrhea. Med Clin North Am 1993;77:1169.

Donowitz M, Kokke FT, Saidi R. Evaluation of patients with chronic diarrhea. New Engl J Med 1995;332:725.

Echeverria P, Sethabutr O, Serichantalergs D. Modern diagnosis (with molecular tests) of acute infectious diarrhea. Gastroenterol Clin North Am 1993;22:661.

Field M, Semrad CE. Toxigenic diarrheas, congenital diarrheas, and cystic fibrosis: disorders of intestinal ion transport. Annu Rev Physiol 1993;55:631.

Moran BJ, Jackson AA. Function of the human colon. Br J Surg 1992;79:1132.

Park S, Giannella RA. Approach to the adult patient with acute diarrhea. Gastroenterol Clin North Am 1993; 22:483.

chapter **23**

Respiratory Disease

The respiratory system is charged both with ensuring uptake of adequate oxygen to meet the metabolic needs of the body's cells and disposing of the carbon dioxide produced during metabolism by these cells. Oxygen is the final electron acceptor for all of the metabolic processes taking place within the mitochondria, including fatty acid oxidation, the citric acid cycle, and the electron transport chain, the last of which generates adenosine triphosphate (ATP) for the energy needs of the cell. In aggregate, these metabolic processes consume a considerable amount of oxygen: approximately 250 ml/min under resting conditions. To meet this ceaseless demand for oxygen, three systems must interact in a seamless manner so that the individual can promptly adjust to varying metabolic demands. These three systems are: (*1*) the lungs and associated muscular pumping mechanisms which take in oxygen from the air and exhale carbon dioxide into the atmosphere; (*2*) the blood and circulatory system with hemoglobin rich red blood cells that transport O_2 and CO_2; and (*3*) the nervous system which controls the rhythmic action of the respiratory system including the lungs, airways, and muscular bellows in response to the body's needs.

BREATHING DEPENDS ON MUSCLES CREATING PRESSURE DIFFERENCES BETWEEN ALVEOLI AND ATMOSPHERE

Muscles in the chest (the intercostals) and abdomen (diaphragm) determine the pressure in the chest cavity in which the lungs are housed (Figure 23.1). Tensing these muscles expands the chest and abdominal cavity, causing the pressure within the alveoli (air sacs) of the lungs to fall below atmospheric pressure permitting air to enter (inspiration). With relaxation of these muscles, the chest cavity contracts, alveolar pressure increases, and expiration occurs. Not only are muscles vital to respiration, but so also is the elasticity of the lungs and chest. In fact, the lungs are resistant to expansion much the way a balloon resists inflation. Unless there is a pressure difference maintained between the inside and outside of the lungs, their natural tendency is to collapse. Hence, during quiet breathing, muscle contraction powers inspiration, but expiration is actually passive depending primarily on the elastic recoil of the lung.

The lung is covered by a membrane (visceral pleura), and the inner chest wall abutting the lungs is also covered by a membrane (parietal pleura). Surface tension between these two membranous layers results in the lungs hugging the chest wall. Should air enter this potential space as might occur from perforation of the chest wall by trauma or surgery, the lung will collapse. Such a condition is termed a *pneumothorax*.

SURFACTANT AND SURFACE TENSION

Even though surface tension is crucial to maintaining the intimacy of the two pleural surfaces, this same physical force could obliterate the alveolar spaces if there was not some substance to mitigate alveolar surface tension. Fortunately, a group of proteins and phospholipids, collectively referred to as *surfactant*, decreases the surface tension in the alveoli, thus maintaining their patency, much as soap bubbles maintain themselves.

Surface tension arises because atoms or molecules of a liquid exert a powerful force of attraction on each other causing the surface they occupy to contract to a minimal value (Figure 23.2). This cohesive or attractive force between adjacent molecules of the liquid is greater than the force of attraction between liquid and gas molecules lo-

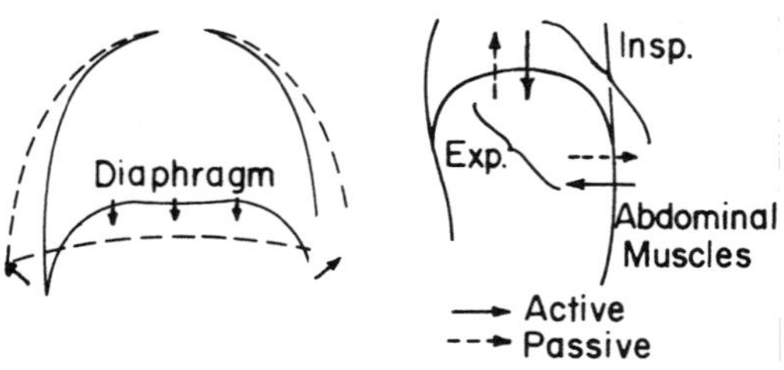

Figure 23.1. The action of the muscles of respiration. The chief muscle of respiration is the diaphragm, of which its action is assisted by the abdominal musculature. During inspiration (Insp) the diaphragm contracts; as a result of its anatomic structure, contracture results in downward (flattening) movement of the normal dome-shaped muscle. This, in turn, expands the volume of the thoracic cavity by lifting the rib cage and forcing the abdominal musculature anteriorly over the compressed abdominal contents. During expiration (Exp), the process is reversed, with relaxation of the diaphragm and contraction of the abdominal musculature. Reprinted with permission from West JB. Best & Taylor's Physiological Basis of Medical Practice. 12th ed. Baltimore: Williams & Wilkins, 1990: 561.

cated at the gas-liquid interface. Such a gas-liquid interface is present in the alveoli and minimizing the surface tension in the alveoli is crucial to promoting lung expansion. Two common examples of surface tension are soap bubbles and the beads of water that form on a highly polished automobile surface.

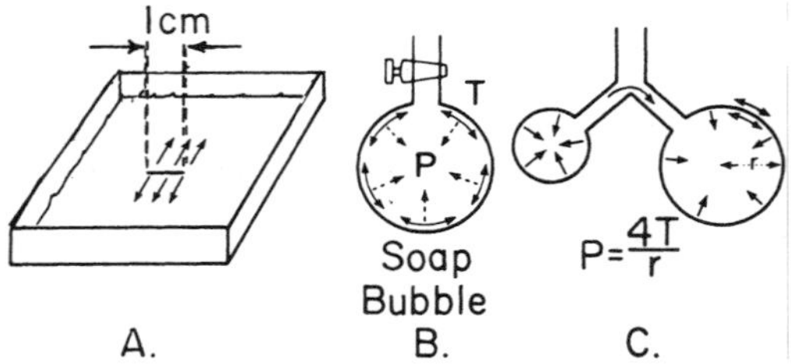

Figure 23.2. Relationship of surface tension to surface area. (A) Surface tension (T) is defined as the force (measured in dynes) exerted across a line 1 cm in length in a liquid surface. (B) The nature of the forces within a soap bubble is to reduce the area of the surface, in turn, generating a pressure (P). (C) Because the pressure within the smaller bubble is greater, it increases the size (r = radius) of the larger bubble. Reprinted with permission from West JB. Best & Taylor's Physiological Basis of Medical Practice. 12th ed. 1990; Baltimore: Williams & Wilkins, 1990: 563.

Gas trapped in such bubbles (or alveoli) is under pressure, with the pressure developed within small bubbles exceeding that of larger bubbles. In fact, if these bubbles are connected, a smaller bubble will empty its gas content into a larger bubble. Such an event would be undesirable in the lung, because it would cause many alveoli to collapse into other alveoli, producing in their place a few enormous hyperinflated alveoli. Clinically, development of *emphysema* involves just such a pathophysiologic mechanism.

To prevent alveolar collapse, the alveolar wall contains a specialized, Type II, pneumocyte which is responsible for synthesis and secretion of surfactant into the extracellular space interposed between the alveolar air and the epithelial cell surface. Surfactant functions to lower the surface tension at the gas-liquid interface. Surface tension decreases because the surfactant molecules not only attract each other, but other molecules at the interface, with less force than do the molecules making up the liquid phase. From what has been said so far, it should be clear that there are two distinct pools of surfactant (intracellular and extracellular), and that the extracellular pool must be "turned over" to prevent accumulation which might cause as many problems as deficiency.

Approximately 90% of the composition of surfactant is lipid in nature, of which virtually 90% is phospholipid. The remaining fraction consists chiefly of surfactant-associated proteins, which are thought to play a significant role in surfactant homeostasis, as well as in its function. *Dipalmitoylphosphatidylcholine* (DPPC) constitutes 70% to 80% of the phospholipid. This molecule is unusual because its fatty acids are saturated. Possessing two saturated fatty acid groups, DPPC orients itself at the gas-liquid interface in the alveolus so that the hydrophobic saturated fatty acid tails of the lipids pack closely. This close packing optimizes mutual repulsion of the tails. It follows that if high surface tension depends on optimizing attraction, then surfactant decreases surface tension by optimizing repulsion. This is precisely the effect of DPPC at the alveolar surface.

By lowering the surface tension, surfactant prevents alveolar collapse and reduces the effort necessary to expand the lungs after each expiration. When, because of prematurity, surfactant is not manufactured, *respiratory distress syndrome* of the neonate results. And when, in any age group, sepsis or other serious disease damages the endothelial lining of the alveolus (and consequently synthesis of surfactant), so-called *adult respiratory distress syndrome* results. In both cases, without ventilatory support, the work of inflating the lungs is more than the individual can sustain.

The routes of removal of surfactant from alveoli are poorly understood. As with other biologic processes, homeostasis demands a balance between secretion and removal. Although much of the available evidence suggests that this equilibrium is maintained by an efficient recycling between the extracellular and intracellular compartments, knowledge of the molecular mechanism is lacking. As noted, the protein component of natural surfactant is thought to be intimately involved in this recycling process. Thus, instillation of artificial, protein-deficient surfactant in therapy of respiratory distress in the newborn has at least two unaccounted-for potential hazards: (*1*) administration of exogenous surfactant may lead to accumulation in excess in a system where the extracellular components for removal are inadequate in number; and (*2*) if the surfactant solution administered is artificial and lacks the protein components, those cells that are present may not respond to its presence by recycling, contributing further to accumulation.

Finally, another mechanism contributes to the stability of the lung—the interdependence of the alveolar units. These alveolar units gain additional structural support because each is attached to and takes part in a "chicken wire"-like structure composed of other alveoli (Figure 23.3). This structure helps alveoli resist the tendency to collapse, thus averting atelectasis.

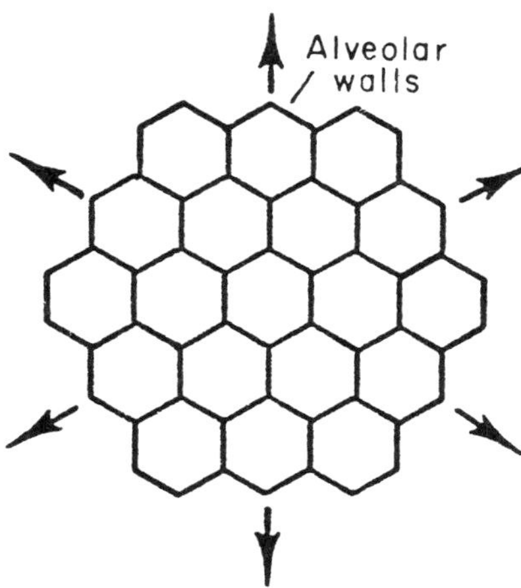

Figure 23.3. Alveolar interdependence. Conceived as a honeycomb-shaped entity, the figure demonstrates the structural support rendered by each alveolar unit to its neighbors. Given the relationship of alveolar radius to pressure, it is apparent that disturbance of the integrity of the wall (as in emphysema) could lead to alveolar units of vastly different size and surface area, because the major vector is directed against the alveolar surface. Reprinted with permission from West JB. Best & Taylor's Physiological Basis of Medical Practice. 12th ed. Baltimore: Williams & Wilkins, 1990: 566.

FOUR INTEGRATED PROCESS MAKE UP RESPIRATION

Normal respiration ensures uptake of O_2 from the atmosphere and delivery of that O_2 to the blood while providing for the concomitant elimination of CO_2 from the body's cells. Four integrated processes—ventilation, diffusion, perfusion, and control of breathing—are required for normal respiration.

Ventilation refers to the entry of air into the lungs, with its ultimate arrival in the alveoli where gas exchange with the blood takes place. As emphasized, gas exchange is a function not only of the muscles of respiration, but also of the *compliance* (distensibility) of the lung, patency of the airways, and integrity of the chest wall. Typically, at rest, a normal adult takes in 500 ml of air per breath about 12 to 16 times per minute. Of course, not all of this air reaches the alveoli, because a portion is wasted in filling the conducting tubes of the airways. This volume is called the *anatomic dead space* and amounts to about 150 ml. Thus, to maintain the oxygen partial pressure sufficiently high within this dead space to effect inward oxygen transfer across the alveolar wall, the lungs must take in approximately 1000 ml of O_2 (contained in 5 L of air) per minute at rest. In view of this, it is truly remarkable that we have any capacity for exercise at all!

Diffusion is a mass action phenomenon during which molecules travel down a gradient from higher to lower concentration. In the case of the lung, the molecules of interest are the gases O_2 and CO_2. The importance of CO_2 to acid-base homeostasis cannot be overstated and is illustrated by the fact that CO_2 diffusion is approximately 40 times faster than that of O_2. The initial diffusion phenomenon occurs between the inspired air and the anatomic dead space, whereby oxygen from the inspired air replenishes the relatively oxygen-poor gas content of the dead space. Without this constant replenishment, the oxygen gradient would dissipate at the level of the alveolus. The next site of diffusion is across the *alveolar-capillary membrane* and red blood cell membrane. Diffusion across these barriers permits gas exchange between the alveoli and the blood in the network of pulmonary capillaries that serve the alveolus as well as in the capillaries that supply the cells of the body.

Perfusion entails the distribution of venous blood to the capillaries serving the alveoli and return of that blood to the pulmonary veins. Because there are approximately 300 million alveoli with a total surface area of about 150 m^2 (about the size of a tennis court), there is ample surface for gas exchange. To guarantee that there is sufficient opportunity for the blood to come in contact with the alveoli, there are about 280 billion capillaries deployed so that, on average, 80 capillaries criss-cross the surface of each alveolus. Furthermore, capillaries are so narrow that they permit only one red cell to pass through at a time, making sure that gas exchange takes place over a minimum distance. This is especially important, because the rate of diffusion is inversely proportional to the square of the radius and oxygen must diffuse throughout the cell to fully saturate hemoglobin. Further ensuring adequate gas exchange is the red cell residence time in the capillaries of about 0.75 seconds, with only 0.25 seconds required for gas exchange. Hence, there is a margin of safety which is only taxed during vigorous exercise when cardiac output is substantially increased and residence time is decreased.

Control of breathing involves changes in the ventilatory rate in response to varying metabolic demands and is a function of the respiratory centers in the brainstem.

VENTILATION AND PERFUSION ARE CLOSELY MATCHED UNDER NORMAL CONDITIONS

Things would be a lot simpler for the lung and for students working to understand the function of the lung, if there were a one-to-one correspondence between alveoli ventilated with air and capillaries perfusing those alveoli. But, in actuality, blood flow to the lung is decisively influenced by gravity so that more blood flows to the dependent rather than the upper regions of the lung. This should not be cause for surprise, when we recall that pulmonary arterial pressure is a mere fraction of that in the aorta, although the reduced perfusion pressure is enhanced in efficiency by the negative intrathoracic pressure.

So too, ventilation favors the more dependent regions of the lung, but the preference is not as conspicuous as for perfusion. When, for example, an alveolus receives no ventilation but perfusion is undiminished, the ventilation/perfusion (V/Q) ratio approaches infinity and that alveolar-capillary unit represents a *shunt*. And when, the alveolus is well ventilated but receives no blood supply, the V/Q ratio approaches zero and that alveolar-capillary unit behaves as a *dead-space*. Even though these extremes of pathologic alveolar-capillary behavior do not occur in the normal lung, nevertheless, regional differences of ventilation and perfusion throughout the lung produce a V/Q ratio of between 0.8 to 1.0, rather than the expected ideal of 1.0. To make matters worse, in many disease states, mismatching of ventilation and perfusion causes further deterioration in oxygenation of the blood and removal of CO_2.

SYMPTOMS OF LUNG DISEASE

A wide variety of diseases can potentially afflict the lungs. This propensity to disturbed function is caused by several facets of lung physiology. In the first place, the lungs are exposed to the atmosphere and, therefore, are vulnerable to damage from toxins, organisms, and environmental hazards. In addition, some of these foreign agents can elicit allergic phenomena in susceptible hosts. In both respects, the lungs are similar to the gastrointestinal tract and possess similar defense mechanisms. Finally, because the lungs receive the entire cardiac output (in keeping with the need for all blood to undergo O_2-CO_2 exchange), any disorder of the small vessels is likely to involve small vessels in the lung.

Cough is a symptom of lung and upper airway

disease and is so common that only when it is prolonged or productive of sputum is it likely to elicit concern on the part of the patient. Of course, if the sputum is blood-tinged or frankly bloody the cause must be determined. And although it is true that paroxysms of coughing can cause hemoptysis, so too can chronic pulmonary disease and lung neoplasms.

Another important symptom of lung disease is shortness of breath or *dyspnea*, especially when not associated with exertion. Certainly, most of us will experience shortness of breath after vigorous exercise, but individuals with pulmonary disease such as emphysema may do so with minimal exertion or even at rest because they have no respiratory reserve.

Pain may be prominent during an acute attack of pneumonia and will be aggravated when the pleura is inflamed. Sometimes malignancies—primary and secondary—will evoke chest pain. Because of the increased metabolic demand in patients with chronic obstructive pulmonary disease, profound fatigue and a general ill-feeling are common. Weight loss and anorexia accompany lung disease, but of course are not specific enough to pinpoint a respiratory cause.

OVERVIEW OF WAYS IN WHICH RESPIRATORY FUNCTION MAY BE IMPAIRED

Respiratory function may be compromised because of (*1*) direct damage to the lungs; (*2*) neuromuscular disease or trauma that affects nerves or muscles of respiration; or (*3*) interference with delivery of O_2 and removal of CO_2 because of cardiac disease or severe anemia. In each of these instances, the predictable outcome will be a decrease in the O_2 carried by hemoglobin and, depending on circumstances, an increase in CO_2 in the blood as well. Diseases like asthma and chronic bronchitis, in which there is narrowing of the airways, pose an *obstruction* to the flow of air. In asthma, the cause of this narrowing is bronchospasm and chronic inflammation, but in chronic bronchitis, the narrowing arises from edema of the mucosal cells and accumulation of secretions resulting from chronic irritation and infection.

Another class of lung disease affecting O_2 delivery to the blood are the so-called *restrictive* disorders, characterized by a decrease in the lung volumes (especially vital capacity, see below). The term restrictive connotes a decrease or restriction in the amount of air held within the lungs. Still another class of disorders affecting gas exchange are those in which there is *ventilation-perfusion mismatching*. Recall that mismatching of ventilation and perfusion means that areas of lung being ventilated are not perfused, whereas other areas of lung being perfused with blood are not ventilated. In either circumstance of V/Q mismatch, the result is a decrease in gas exchange between the affected alveoli and the capillaries supplying it.

Neuromuscular disease can also cause failure of adequate gas exchange, not because the lungs per se are abnormal, but because the bellows controlling respiration is not functioning. Examples of such conditions are suppression of the ventilatory drive by sedatives or anesthetics, cerebrovascular accident, high spinal cord injuries, muscular dystrophy, and myasthenia gravis.

LABORATORY EVALUATION OF PULMONARY FUNCTION

Arterial Blood Gases

The most commonly performed test of pulmonary function is measurement of the arterial blood gases: PCO_2, PO_2, and pH (pH, although not a gas, is customarily considered part of the test). It should be emphasized that gases in solution are measured in terms of their partial pressures (mm Hg), not in units of concentration. Arterial blood gases dominate the assessment of lung disease because they can be rapidly performed, blood usually being obtained from the radial artery. They provide a measure of the end point of lung function (ie, the overall effect on gas exchange). Blood must be drawn as painlessly as possible (local anesthesia is recommended) so as not to agitate the patient and cause hyperventilation. The specimen must then be collected in a heparinized syringe excluding all air and must be promptly transported on ice to the lab to minimize red and white cell metabolism. In the setting of an intensive care unit, where an indwelling arterial line may be in place, blood for arterial blood gases (ABGs) may be sampled several times a day. This facilitates gauging the response of the patient to various therapeutic measures. And although there are other tests of pulmonary function (see below) that assess lung volumes and airflow dynamics, none of those tests are as easy to perform; therefore, the ABGs provide a vital, although incomplete, picture of pulmonary function.

The *alveolar gas equation* assesses whether the lungs are effectively transferring oxygen into the blood. The most common form of this equation, when the fractional concentration of inspired O_2 (FIO_2) is less than 0.6, is:

$$PAO_2 = PIO_2 - 1.2\ (PaCO_2)$$

when PAO_2 is the mean alveolar PO_2; PIO_2 is the partial pressure of inspired air under standard conditions, and the P_aCO_2 is the arterial PCO_2, which is 40 mm Hg.

This simple and powerful equation shows that the PAO_2 will increase as the PIO_2 increases and will decrease as more CO_2 is delivered into the blood. Reference ranges for arterial pO_2 decrease with age, unlike P_aCO_2, which is relatively fixed throughout the decades. In normal individuals under age 25 years, P_aO_2 is about 95 mm Hg, but in octogenarians, it is 80 to 85 mm Hg.

As noted, arterial pCO_2, unlike pO_2, is not age-dependent, with a relatively tight reference range between 36 and 44 torr. As seen by a simplified version of the Henderson-Hasselbalch equation:

$$pH \sim kidney/lungs$$

blood pH is a function of the ratio of the P_aCO_2, determined by the lungs, and the plasma bicarbonate, determined by the kidneys. It follows that a decrease in the P_aCO_2, referred to as hypocapnia, causes respiratory alkalosis, whereas an increase in P_aCO_2, or hypercapnia, causes respiratory acidosis. Of course, as discussed in Chapter 4 on acid-base balance, the kidneys will attempt to compensate for changes in P_aCO_2 to mitigate the effect on hydrogen ion concentration of a decrease or increase in P_aCO_2.

Because the lungs are the only exit route for the 15,000 or so mmoles of CO_2 produced daily by metabolism, it is evident that hypoventilation will result in respiratory acidosis whereas hyperventilation will result in respiratory alkalosis. But it is important to recognize that, just as with oxygen transport in the blood, only a negligible amount of CO_2 (8%) is dissolved in plasma. Another 10% is carried as a carbamino compound bound to hemoglobin, whereas the dominant fraction (> 80%) is carried as HCO_3^-, formed as a result of the action of red cell carbonic anhydrase. That familiar reaction is:

$$CO_2 + H_2O \rightleftharpoons H_2CO_3 \rightleftharpoons H^+ + HCO_3^-$$

The impact of carrying 90% of CO_2 in a nongaseous state is that the enormous metabolic load of CO_2 can be carried in a form that does not perturb the P_aCO_2. As can be seen from the P_aCO_2 equation, the arterial PCO_2 is directly

$$P_aCO_2 = K \times VCO_2/\ VA$$

related to VCO_2, the amount of CO_2 produced by metabolism (most coming from the TCA cycle), and indirectly related to VA, the alveolar ventilation. In turn, VA is determined by VE-VD, where VE is the minute ventilation and VD is the dead space ventilation. Minute ventilation, the total volume of gas entering and leaving the lungs in 1 minute, is about 5 L or 3 to 4 L/min/m^2 of body surface area. Because dead space is not available for gas exchange, the minute ventilation is reduced to 2 to 2.5 L/min/m^2, a number that reflects the VA. Except under conditions of strenuous exercise, the amount of CO_2 produced/min is relatively stable. Consequently, the P_aCO_2 generally will be governed by the rate of alveolar ventilation. It should be evident then that hypercapnia (>45 mm Hg) occurs when alveolar ventilation is unable to adjust to the increased CO_2 produced by metabolism.

Alveolar-Arterial Oxygen Gradient

Under ideal circumstances, the P_aO_2 should be equal to the PAO_2. But ideality is not physiologically possible, even in normal lungs, because of a degree of pulmonary arteriovenous shunting and perfusion of regions of the lung that are underventilated. Consequently, there is a slight alveolar-arterial (A-a) oxygen gradient. In individuals under 30 years of age breathing room air, this gradient is between 5 and 10 mm Hg, increasing to 15 to 20 mm Hg in the elderly.

In patients with intrinsic pulmonary disease,

characterized by even a modest degree of V/Q mismatch, the (A-a) oxygen gradient will be increased. In contrast, patients suffering from extrapulmonary disorders involving the respiratory pump, (eg, central nervous system), neuromuscular system, or chest wall, although manifesting increased P_aCO_2 and decreased P_aO_2, will nonetheless have a normal (A-a) oxygen gradient. Sometimes, however, patients with respiratory pump abnormalities will suffer from a degree of atelectasis. In that case, the atelectasis will contribute to an abnormal (A-a) oxygen gradient.

Oxygen Content

With emphasis on the partial pressure of O_2, it is easy to assume the bulk of O_2 carried in the blood is reflected by that value. But that would be a mistake. Obviously, hemoglobin, which can carry 1.34 ml of O_2/g, transports most of the O_2 in the blood. In fact, hemoglobin carries about 65 times as much O_2 as can be dissolved in plasma. Plasma can hold 0.3 ml of O_2/dl—a puny amount relative to that clinging to hemoglobin. This is not to discount the P_aO_2, because this value is the tension of oxygen that sets the driving force for O_2 to leave the alveoli into the erythrocyte and thence into the cells.

The total oxygen content of the blood can be calculated as follows: An individual with 15 g/d of hemoglobin can carry (15 × 1.34) 20.1 ml of oxygen/dl of blood and a small increment of 0.3 ml dissolved in plasma for a total of 20.4 ml of O_2 in 100 ml of blood. Because the O_2 dissolved in plasma alone could scarcely meet the incessant demand for oxygen, the key to providing adequate oxygen is hemoglobin.

Under resting conditions, in a normal individual, cardiac output is about 5 L/min. With an oxygen content of about 20 ml/dl, the blood transports about 1 L of oxygen/min. And because, at rest, O_2 utilization is about 250 ml/min, a significant reserve of unextracted O_2 remains—about 750 ml/min. If one adds to this reserve the ability to increase cardiac output, it is clear that the individual can greatly augment oxygen delivery when metabolic needs so demand.

Ventilation/Perfusion Mismatch

Recall that the oxyhemoglobin dissociation curve describes a sigmoid shape (Figure 23.4). From a physiologic point of view, the importance of the sigmoid shape is that at a P_aO_2 of 60 mm Hg, hemoglobin is 90% saturated. Thereafter, as oxygen tension increases, there is only a modest increase in hemoglobin saturation so that at a P_aO_2 of 120 mm Hg saturation is at 100%. Obviously, raising the inspired O_2 to increase the oxygen tension will have no effect on the hemoglobin saturation once hemoglobin is 100% saturated with oxygen. In effect, as with an enzyme active site, once hemoglobin is saturated with O_2, it cannot bind any more. From a practical point of view, an area of lung with significant V/Q mismatch will impair O_2 delivery sufficiently so that increasing the FIO_2 cannot offset the decrease in O_2 transfer.

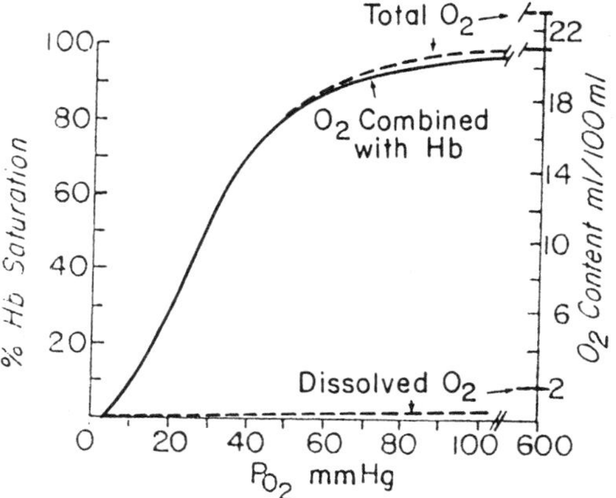

Figure 23.4. Hemoglobin (Hb)-oxygen (O_2) dissociation curve. The curve shown represents the amount of oxygen bound to hemoglobin (%Hb saturation) at various partial pressures of oxygen (PO_2), measured at a pH of 7.4. The quantity of O_2 dissolved in blood is minimal at all PO_2 in comparison to the quantity bound to Hb. The total O_2 content of blood is calculated as: {(1.39) × (Hb) × %saturation)} + $0.003PO_2$. Reprinted with permission from West JB. Best & Taylor's Physiological Basis of Medical Practice. 12th ed. Baltimore: Williams & Wilkins, 1990: 539.

In contrast to the sigmoid oxyhemoglobin dissociation curve, the relationship for CO_2 is nearly linear (Figure 23.5). Thus, increasing the ventilatory rate will improve CO_2 elimination by those alveoli with normal V/Q relationships, or those with V/Q mismatch which favors ventilation over perfusion. It is for this reason that patients with V/Q mismatch will evidence hypoxemia long before they show hypercapnia.

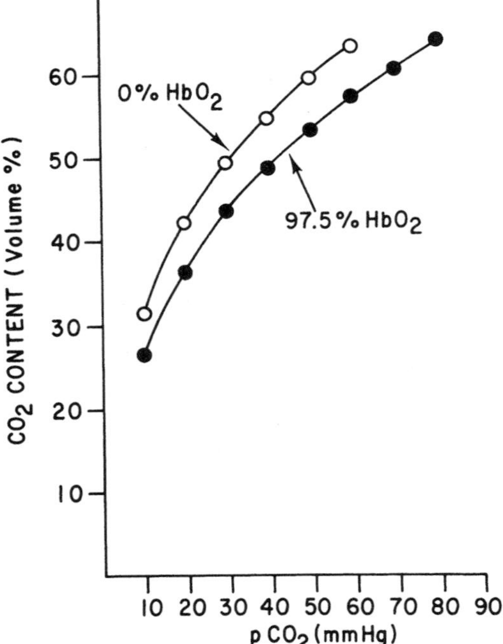

Figure 23.5. Hemoglobin-carbon dioxide dissociation curve. Deoxygenated whole blood (0% HbO_2) has a higher affinity for CO_2 than oxygenated blood (97.5% HbO_2). Both curves are relatively linear in the physiologic range (40 to 60 PCO_2), and the difference is known as the Haldane effect, which facilitates transfer of CO_2 from tissues to blood for excretion via the lungs. Reprinted with permission from Lee GR, Bithell TC, Foerster J, et al. Wintrobe's Clinical Hematology. 9th ed. Baltimore: Williams & Wilkins, 1993: 122.

SHUNTING

In a right-to-left shunt, deoxygenated blood (about 75% saturated) enters the systemic circulation without going through the lungs and thus fails to replenish its O_2 content and release CO_2. This is the most extreme form of V/Q mismatch and is caused by: (*1*) congenital cardiac or large vessel disease, (*2*) pulmonary AV malformations, or (*3*) pulmonary parenchymal disease. Shunting because of pulmonary parenchymal disease is the most common of the three and is the result of alveoli that have collapsed or are filled with inflammatory or edema fluid (as in pneumonia, adult respiratory distress syndrome [ARDS], and pulmonary edema).

Administration of 100% O_2 can differentiate V/Q mismatch in which P_aO_2 will increase, from right-to-left shunt, in which the P_aO_2 will remain fixed or improve only slightly.

Interpreting Blood Gases

A practical strategy for assessing the clinical significance of blood gas data and acid-base consequences is presented in the monographs by Malley, Martin, and Shapiro et al. Here we summarize the essential aspects of that evaluation. In short, the process entails three issues: ventilation, acid-base balance, and oxygenation.

First, assess the P_aCO_2 to evaluate ventilatory status. Next, relate the P_aCO_2 to the pH to determine whether there is an acidosis or alkalosis and, further, whether the process is respiratory or metabolic. Additionally, one should determine whether there is evidence of compensation. Finally, assess the P_aO_2 for evidence of hypoxemia or normoxemia. Oxygenation must be considered in light of the FIO_2.

Pulmonary Function Testing

Although there are a large number of tests that can be categorized as pulmonary function tests (PFTs), many are specialized. Consequently, we want to concentrate here on those few tests that are generally available and that are most commonly used in assessing the degree of impairment of pulmonary function. In particular, the tests discussed here are used to distinguish between two broad categories of respiratory disease: *obstructive disease* (chronic bronchitis, emphysema, and asthma) and *restrictive disease* (in which lung volumes are decreased as in pulmonary edema, ARDS, pneumothorax, kyphoscoliosis, and neuromuscular disease).

Figure 23.6 shows the most important lung volumes and capacities that figure prominently in the interpretation of compromise of pulmonary function. As can be seen, the sum of the IRV + TV + ERV (inspiratory reserve volume + tidal volume + end respiratory volume) equals the VC (vital capacity), which is the maximal amount of air the individual can exhale after taking a maximal inspiration. Note, too, that the sum of the VC + RV (reserve volume) is the total lung capacity (TLC), the total amount of gas the lungs can contain. Several of these volumes and capacities can

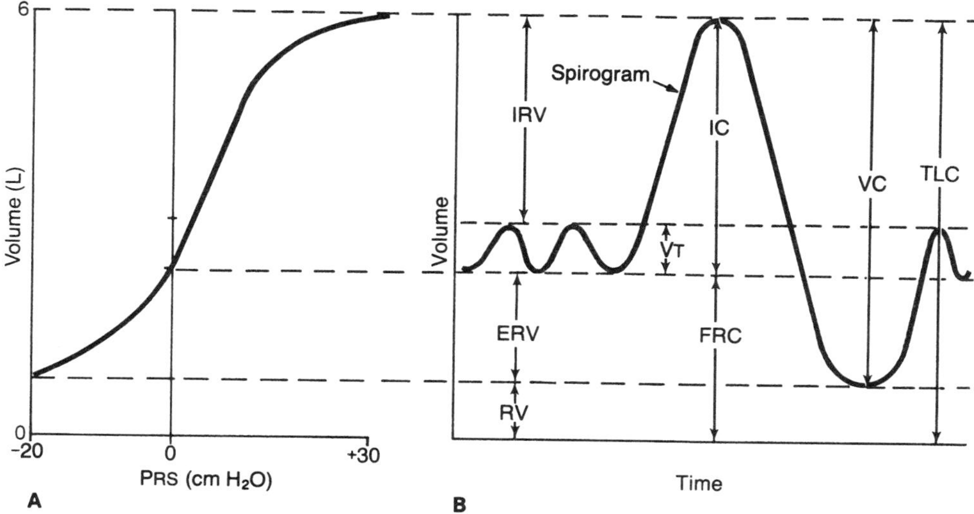

Figure 23.6. Pressure-volume relationships in the respiratory system. (A) Pressure-volume curve, showing that residual volume (RV) and total lung capacity (TLC) are limited by decreasing compliance as represented by the decreasing slope in relation to increased or decreased volume. The functional residual capacity (FRC) is determined by finding the volume corresponding to a zero transrespiratory pressure (PRS). (B) Spirogram tracing illustrating normal tidal volume (VT), followed by maximal inspiration capacity (IC) with a subsequent maximal expiratory capacity, the combination being termed vital capacity (VC). The difference between the minimal tidal volume and the residual volume is called the expiratory reserve volume (ERV), whereas the difference between the maximal tidal volume and the inspiratory capacity is called the inspiratory reserve volume (IRV). Reprinted with permission from Bullock J, Boyle J III, Wang MB, et al. Physiology. 3rd ed. Baltimore: Williams & Wilkins, 1995: 221.

be assessed by spirometry, an apparatus that (with cooperation of the subject) can measure the volume of air exhaled or inhaled. But the volume of air remaining in the lungs after maximal exhalation requires other means to be estimated.

Perhaps the most useful data garnered from spirometry are the forced vital capacity (FVC), which is the maximal amount of air the patient can exhale after inhaling maximally, and the forced expiratory volume in 1 second (FEV_1), the maximal amount of air exhaled in 1 second (again after inhaling maximally). The VC must be added to these two. Armed with values for the FVC, FEV_1, and VC, the clinician can determine whether there is restrictive disease (the VC is normal), whereas the FVC and FEV_1 determine whether there is obstruction to airflow.

Another important measure of pulmonary function, the TLC, cannot be gauged by spirometry. Instead, it is usually evaluated by gas dilution or body plethysmography. In the gas dilution technique, an inert gas of known volume (helium or neon) is inhaled by the patient and is allowed to equilibrate with the gas in the lungs. The lung volume in which the test gas was diluted (ie, the total volume) can be calculated using the concentration of inspired and expired gas and the volume of inspired test gas.

Body plethysmography, the other method to determine the TLC, depends on Boyle's law (ie, holding the temperature constant, pressure varies inversely with volume—a relationship reflected by a piston in a cylinder). Body plethysmography entails placing the patient in an airtight box and measuring pressure changes in the box as the patient breaths in and out through a mouthpiece.

With these test results, the physician can determine whether a patient demonstrates an obstructive pattern or a restrictive pattern (Figure 23.7). Needless to say, some patients may show evidence of both obstructive and restrictive disease.

Obstructive pulmonary disorders (Table 23.1) include asthma, chronic bronchitis, and emphy-

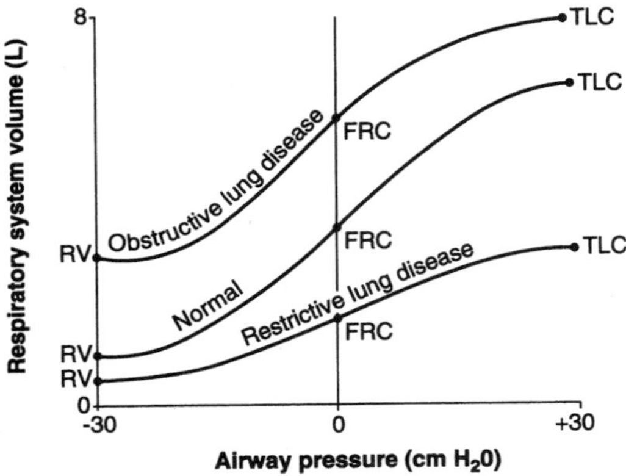

Figure 23.7. Obstructive versus restrictive lung disease. The pressure-volume relationships are shown for normal, obstructive, and restrictive lung disease, without regard for etiology. Note that although total lung capacity (TLC) increases in obstructive disease, it does so at the price of increased residual volume (RV), which is a functional liability. Conversely, the decreased RV in restrictive disease which should be functionally advantageous is offset by the decrease in TLC. The vital capacity, calculated as the difference between TLC and RV, is greatest for the normal lung. FRC = functional residual capacity. Reprinted with permission from Bullock J, Boyle J III, Wang MB, et al. Physiology. 3rd ed. Baltimore: Williams & Wilkins, 1995: 221.

sema and, in these conditions, the FEV_1/FVC ratio is decreased. If one adds the hyperinflation found in emphysema and active asthma to these findings, one can appreciate why the TLC of such patients is increased.

Restrictive disease (Table 23.2) is set apart by decrease in lung volumes with preservation of normal airflow dynamics. In patients with restrictive disease, it follows that the VC and TLC are diminished, but tests of airflow will remain in the normal range.

Table 23.1. Obstructive Pulmonary Disease

Acute Obstructions
Asthma
Acute bronchitis
Chronic Obstructive Pulmonary Disease
Chronic Bronchitis—narrowing of airways
Emphysema— ↓ elastic recoil → ↓ driving pressure to expel air
Cystic fibrosis
Bronchiectasis

ASTHMA

Over the past few years, a change in the conception of the fundamental nature of the disorder in asthma has been taking place. Whereas, in the past, emphasis was placed on airway hyperreactivity secondary to an allergic or other trigger, asthma is now viewed as primarily a chronic inflammatory disease. This change in emphasis is by no means a semantic issue, because anti-inflammatory agents now assume center stage. Accordingly, bronchodilators are assigned a secondary role in symptomatic relief of the bronchoconstriction that remains an important feature of bronchial asthma. Moreover, despite strides in treating asthma, morbidity and mortality have been increasing. Workers in the field now believe that earlier introduction of antiinflammatory agents, for example, inhaled corticosteroids and cromolyn sodium or nedocromil sodium, along with better recognition by patients and their families of worsening airway obstruction, will turn the tide against this distressing trend.

Asthma is common among children and young adults and is among the most common diagnoses requiring admission to the hospital in those age groups. Overall about 3% to 5% of the population suffer from asthma at some time. Features pointing to a diagnosis of asthma are recurrent episodes of cough, shortness of breath, chest tightness, and wheezing, which are typically reversible with treatment and which sometimes reverse spontaneously. Bronchial lavage and biopsies have demonstrated increased numbers of inflammatory cells. Most notably, evidence of inflammation has been found in all types of asthma whether the triggers are immune, nonimmune, or occupational.

What Causes Asthma and Why do the Airways React by Constricting?

Although there is a clear tendency of many patients with asthma to have an allergic history, by no means does every patient with asthma manifest an allergic diathesis. Those patients without an allergic trigger for asthma attacks most often are thrust into an attack by an upper respiratory infection, by inhalation of respiratory tract irritants, and sometimes by exercise if it is associated with cooling of the air passages. As emphasized, both groups, the allergic and the nonallergic, share in-

Table 23.2. Restrictive Lung Disease (↓ TLC and ↓ VC—i.e., diminished lung volumes with normal expiratory airflow)

CLASS	CLINICAL EXAMPLES	CAUSES OF RESTRICTION	CLINICAL FINDINGS
Depression of respiratory center	Narcotic or sedative overdose Trauma to central nervous system	Direct effect on respiratory center	↓ respiratory rate; hypoventilation
Neuromuscular	Guillain-Barre syndrome	Toxic polyneuritis → intercostal paralysis	Hypoventilation → hypercapnia
	Duchenne muscular dystrophy	Paralysis of all muscles of respiration	Late onset respiratory symptoms. Hypercapnia.
Movement of thorax impaired			
Skeletal deformity	Kyphoscoliosis, pectus excavatum	Lung tissue compressed. Chest movement limited.	↑ work of breathing because of ↓ compliance, TLC, Vc, ERV. Hypoxemia.
Trauma to chest with rib fracture	Flail chest	Chest wall unstable. ↓ intrathoracic pressure on inspiration causes chest wall on affected side to pull in	Evidence of trauma, unequal chest movement. ↓ TLC and Vc.
Severe obesity	Pickwickian syndrome	Abdominal fat limits diaphragmatic excursion; ↓ thoracic movement.	Somnolence, periodic breathing, ↓ PO_2, ↑ PCO_2
Disorders of lung	Occupational lung disease with fibrosis	Silicosis, asbestosis, 2° emphysema	↓ Compliance, ↓ PO_2, ↑ PCO_2
	Atelectasis	Collapse of lung tissue—2° to retained secretions	Dyspnea, ↓ chest wall expansion, ↓ PO_2
	Adult respiratory distress syndrome	Atelectasis, ↓ surfactant, interstitial edema 2° to sepsis and other serious conditions	Dyspnea, hypoxemia → respiratory failure
	Pulmonary edema	CHF → interstitial and alveolar edema	Hypoxemia, congestive heart failure (CHF)

flammation of the airways with denudation of the epithelial lining as the underlying cause of the bronchial hyperresponsiveness.

Various mediators and cytokines liberated by inflammatory cells are believed to create the conditions that poise the airways on the verge of bronchoconstriction. These mediators include the kinins, leukotrienes, acetylcholine, and tachykinins—a group of small peptides which include substance P, and neurokinins A and B.

Clinical and Laboratory Findings

Asthmatic attacks include shortness of breath with difficulty breathing and anxiety, cough, and audible wheezing. An increased respiratory rate (25–40 per minute) is typical, and is associated with tachycardia. Striking is the use of accessory muscles during inspiration, although there is greater difficulty encountered during expiration than during inspiration. Distress on expiration is a feature of asthma because during expiration the intrapleural pressure increases causing lung parenchyma and airways to contract. A particularly ominous finding is breath sounds that are muffled or absent, because it means that the airway obstruction is so severe that wheezing is not possible.

Although breathing is labored during an asthmatic attack, as long as the airways are at least partially unobstructed, the increased respiratory rate will maintain the $PaCO_2$ in the low to normal range, whereas the PaO_2 will reflect hypoxemia because of mismatch of ventilation and perfusion. However, if the pCO_2 is higher, in the normal or high normal range, this is cause for alarm because the increased ventilatory rate cannot compensate and eliminate CO_2. In such circumstances, the patient may be on the brink of respiratory failure, while the continued metabolic production of CO_2 will superimpose itself on the already severe respiratory acidosis. Thus, it is essential not to be complacent about asthma, because any attack, in any patient, bears the potential for becoming life-threatening. The only protection is careful observation and vigilance.

Treatment

Bronchodilators, especially beta-adrenergic agents, administered by inhaler are effective as the first line of treatment in most patients with asthma. Some patients with moderate to severe asthma (those using an inhaled β_2-agonist more than three times per week benefit from the addition of inhaled corticosteroids to their regimen, as a measure to decrease the inflammatory component of airway hyperreactivity. Disodium cromoglycate or nedocromil sodium, agents that stabilize the mast cell membrane, have a role in the prophylaxis of asthma and is administered during asymptomatic periods. An important feature of therapy is to educate the patient as to what factors trigger an acute attack. This measure should lead to earlier treatment with the expectation that morbidity and mortality will decrease.

A controversial issue in acute asthma therapy is determining the end-point for discharge. In older individuals who are cooperative, careful pulmonary function testing will frequently reveal continued outflow obstruction after the audible wheezing has disappeared and blood gas values have returned to normal. In young children, such measurements are not routinely performed. Thus, considerable skill and experience are required to determine the appropriate time for discharge in a pediatric asthma patient. Finally, it should be mentioned that individual variations in drug metabolism and/or absorption from the gut lead to wide variability in effective doses of some of the therapeutic agents used in asthma. This is particularly true of theophylline, of which the best criterion for effective dosage is the blood level at the "trough," midway between doses.

CHRONIC OBSTRUCTIVE PULMONARY DISEASE (COPD)

Chronic obstructive pulmonary disease exacts a terrible toll in terms of mortality and morbidity. About 10 million Americans suffer from COPD, with almost 75,000 per year dying as a consequence of respiratory failure. Another large group of individuals with COPD succumb to acute pneumonia, superimposed on their chronic lung disease. Add to these statistics the admissions to the hospital (21 million) and workdays lost (31 million) and it is readily apparent that COPD is an important public health problem. Most notably, this tragic toll in lives lost and suffering is the result of smoking—a potentially preventable cause for so much misery. Two diseases, chronic bronchitis and emphysema, are classified as COPD. *Chronic bronchitis* is associated with excessive secretion of mucus and chronic cough, whereas *emphysema* (a pathologic diagnosis) refers to destruction of alveoli with creation of enormous dilated airspaces and decrease in the lung's elastic recoil. We shall begin by considering the role of smoking in the pathogenesis of these disorders.

How Does Smoking Cause COPD?

Smoking is an irritant and increases the number and size of bronchial mucous glands and evokes an inflammatory reaction. Acting in concert the excessive mucus and inflammatory cells that are attracted to the airways decrease the diameter of those airways. Cilial function is also adversely affected by inhaled smoke, hampering the function of the mucociliary escalator.

In the case of emphysema, it is believed that smoking causes an imbalance in the function of the *protease-antiprotease enzyme system*. Normally, routine housekeeping functions of the lung require the removal of effete cells and denatured and damaged elements of the connective tissue matrix. An important component of this matrix is *elastin*, a structural protein which, like rubber, can undergo significant stretching, reverting to its normal size when the stretching is discontinued. This elasticity is a pivotal factor in creating compliance of the lung. Thus, any process that would put these elastic fibers at risk for wholesale destruction would have profoundly negative effects on pulmonary function. Smoking is a perturbation that has a negative effect on the elastin of the alveolar walls. It exerts this noxious effect (*1*) by increasing the amount of elastase in the lung and

(2) by interfering with the function of the antiproteases. Elastase concentrations in the lung increase because of polymorphonuclear leukocytes (PMNs) and alveolar macrophages that congregate in regions damaged by smoke. Antiprotease function is compromised because a toxic oxygen radical found in cigarette smoke damages a pivotal methionine residue in a_1-antitrypsin, impairing its ability to bind to and inhibit elastase.

Alpha$_1$-Antitrypsin Deficiency

It follows from the restraining role of antiproteases on the action of elastase that an inherited defect in an antiprotease could predispose to the development of emphysema. In the inherited absence of a_1-antitrypsin, elastase can dismantle alveolar walls when its action is unimpeded by the antiprotease. The result is premature development of emphysema.

Emphysema-Clinical Manifestations (Table 23.3)

Patients with emphysema have little respiratory reserve, evincing dyspnea with minimal exertion. These patients must use accessory muscles to aid in breathing and experience tachypnea and expiratory grunting. Because arterial blood gases show normal $PaCO_2$ and low normal PaO_2, these patients are not cyanotic. In fact, because of the absence of cyanosis and the presence of such pronounced respiratory effort, they are often referred to as "pink puffers."

Due to destruction of many alveoli and loss of elastin, the lung suffers a decrease in its elastic recoil. This decreased elasticity, in turn, causes a decrease of the pressure head (during expiration) that drives air from the lungs. Further exacerbating the tendency to airway collapse is the loss of the tethering effect of adjacent alveoli, an effect that in the normal lung helps maintain the patency of the alveoli during expiration.

Chronic Bronchitis-Clinical Manifestations (Table 23.3)

Individuals whose COPD is dominated by chronic bronchitis experience chronic cough which is productive of mucopurulent sputum. Arterial blood gases reveal hypercapnia and hypoxemia and this is reflected clinically by the presence of cyanosis. At any rate, these patients are more likely than those with emphysema to develop cor pulmonale and consequently have edema. Taken together, the presence of both cyanosis and edema have led to dubbing these patients "blue bloaters."

Hypoxemia arises because there is significant mismatching of ventilation and perfusion. A major contributor to this mismatching is the plugging

Table 23.3. Features of Chronic Bronchitis and Emphysema

CLINICAL FEATURES	CHRONIC BRONCHITIS	EMPHYSEMA
General appearance	"Blue bloater"	"Pink puffer"
History	Recurrent infections after age 35 years	Insidious onset of dyspnea after age 50 years
Chest exam	Rhonchi, wheezes	Quiet but barrel chest, hyper-resonant
Sputum	Copious, purulent	Scanty, mucoid
Weight loss	Minimal, may be overweight	Often marked
Chest radiograph	Pulmonary markings evidence of old inflammatory disease	Bullae, blebs, depressed diaphragm
Hypoxemia	Moderate to severe ($\dot{V}/\dot{Q}$ mismatch)	Mild
Hypercapnia	Moderate to severe	Unusual
Respiratory acidosis	Present	Absent
TLC	Normal	↑
RV	↑↑	↑
EKG	RAD, RVD, evidence of cor pulmonale	Normal (cor pulmonale unusual)

TLC = total lung capacity
RV = residual volume
EKG = electrocardiogram
V/Q = ventilation/perfusion ratio
RAD = right axis deviation
RVD = right ventricular dilation

and narrowing of airways in chronic bronchitis, so that many alveoli are poorly ventilated while their blood supply remains intact. Hypercapnia in obstructive lung disease stems from: (*1*) inspiratory muscle fatigue from increased work of breathing; (*2*) V/Q mismatch so severe as to behave as a dead space; and (*3*) in some patients, abnormal central ventilatory drive.

Treatment of COPD

Although it is useful to lay out the features that distinguish emphysema from chronic bronchitis, it is certainly true that most patients with obstructive lung disease manifest features of both emphysema and chronic bronchitis. And although therapy for all patients with COPD must be individualized with respect to underlying disease and lifestyle expectations, still, certain therapeutic modalities form the mainstay of treatment. Paramount among them is the use of bronchodilators and chest physiotherapy. As circumstances warrant, corticosteroids by inhaler and supplemental oxygen by nasal cannula also may be required by these patients. Not to be overlooked in such patients is adequate nutrition to try to forestall the weight loss that so often attends obstructive lung disease. By the same token, obesity will substantially increase the work of breathing and must be avoided.

PNEUMONIA

Pneumonia, which is infection of the alveoli, interstitium, and terminal airways, is the most common of all serious infectious diseases and for that matter of all diseases affecting the lungs. It continues to cause the death of about 50,000 persons in the United States per year. Colonization of the respiratory mucosa is prerequisite to development of frank infection of the lungs and this occurs most readily in a setting in which lung defenses (or, more generally, host defense mechanisms) have become impaired. Factors that predispose to depressed lung defenses are fairly common and include a recent or concurrent viral upper respiratory infection, smoking, abuse of alcohol, and COPD. Needless to say, individuals who are immunocompromised are at particular risk for developing pneumonia.

Given our continual need to breathe, it is not surprising that one route of entry of microbes into the respiratory tract is by inhalation. But, this is not as common a route to pneumonia as one might imagine, because, in general, only those microbes that are invasive (plague bacillus), able to survive in stagnant water (Legionella), or adapted to an intracellular existence (M. tuberculosis) are likely to cause pneumonia when inhaled. The outstanding exception to this is the pathogenesis of the viral pneumonias, which generally require inhalation of the inoculate into the upper respiratory tract, whence the agent spreads by contiguity to involve the lower tract as well. There are a few viral agents that reach the lower respiratory tract by hematogenous spread—these include rubella, varicella, and herpes viruses.

But, a second way, aspiration of oropharyngeal secretions, is an even more common cause of pneumonia. Although aspiration poses the greatest threat for development of pneumonia to individuals with swallowing dysfunction or who are comatose, nevertheless, during sleep, all of us aspirate small amounts of these secretions. Happily, for those who have intact glottic function and who can cough, the chance of developing pneumonia from aspiration is remote.

Lung Defense Mechanisms

There are two broad classes of lung defense mechanisms (Figure 23.8): (*1*) those that attempt to exclude microbes and particulates from entering the lower airways and; (*2*) those that defend against microbes that reach the lower airways and alveoli.

Measures used by the lung to exclude material from the lung include: (*1*) filtration of inspired air in the naso-oropharynx and trachea and bronchi; (*2*) immobilization of inspired materials on the surfaces of the highly branched airways; (*3*) the presence of secretory IgA in the upper airways; (*4*) coughing; and (*5*) the mucociliary escalator. The efficacy of the mucociliary escalator derives from the collaborative effect of ensnaring particulates in the mucus produced by airway epithelium and the remarkably effective beating action of the cilia lining these passages. Other than the ciliated

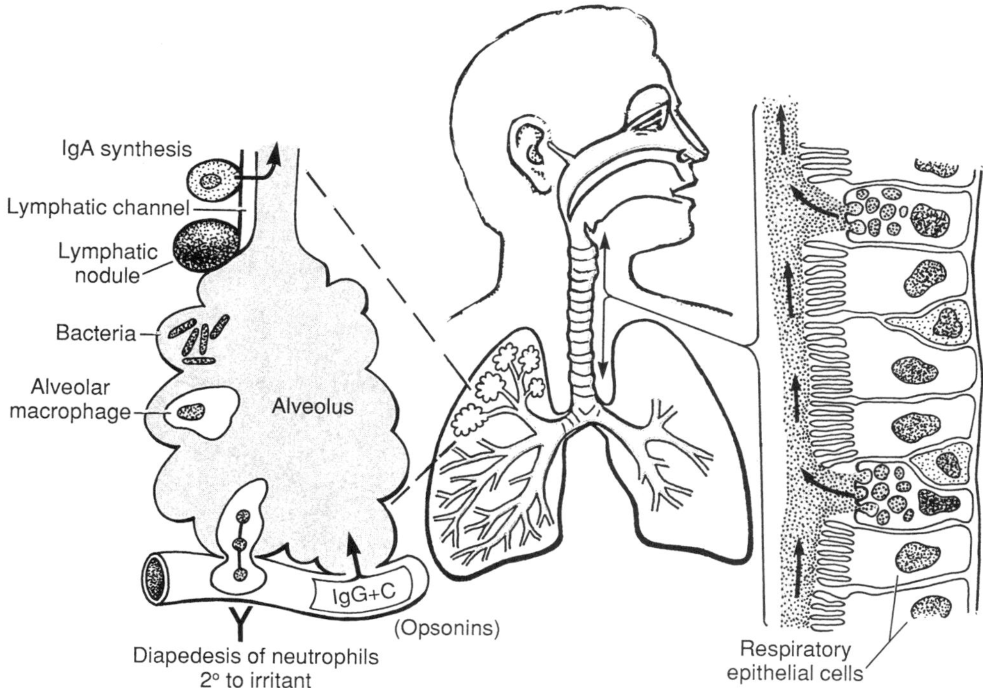

Figure 23.8. The defense mechanisms of the respiratory tract. The presence of very fine hairs (vibrissae) in the anterior nares and rapid changes in air flow direction are important to normal toilet of the upper airway. The upper and lower airways are separated anatomically and functionally by the epiglottis and the cough reflex, respectively; together, these two factors prevent introduction of particulate matter into the lungs. The cilia of the respiratory epithelium assists in this effort by propelling the surface mucus layer, containing trapped particulates, toward the oropharynx. Alveolar macrophages, neutrophils responding to inflammatory factors, and immunoglobulins and complement are all features that enhance resistance to or help in fighting infection. Reprinted with permission from Schaechter M, Eisenstein B, Medoff G, et al. Mechanisms of Microbial Disease. 2nd ed. Baltimore: Williams & Wilkins, 1993: 687.

cells of the inner ear, the respiratory tract is the only place in the human body in which ciliated cells are found. Their presence in humans reminds us of our remote origins in the unicellular and invertebrate organisms, in whom cilia are common. Nonetheless, it is obvious that cilia are much more than vestigial remnants of our distant past.

Yet, potent as these protective measures are, microbes do gain entrance to alveoli; therefore, there are defenses that immobilize, kill, and remove these intruders. These defenses are deployed at the alveoli and include: (*1*) surfactant that possesses antibacterial properties probably acting as a membranolytic agent; (*2*) complement that possesses both opsonizing and membrane destructive actions; and (*3*) phagocytosis by roaming alveolar macrophages and PMNs.

Clinical Manifestations

During a bout of pneumonia, the alveoli become filled with phagocytic cells, edema, and blood. And although the host must mount a vigorous defense against the invader, the negative consequence of this alveolar engorgement is decrease in ventilation to the affected regions of the lungs leading to ventilation-perfusion mismatch and consequent hypoxemia. Even though different microorganisms cause pneumonia, patients with acute bacterial pneumonia manifest certain typical clinical findings that point to a pneumonic process. These include fever and shaking chills, chest pain, cough and purulent or blood-tinged sputum, a marked shift to left on the peripheral smear, and patchy or lobar infiltrates on radiographs. In evaluating such patients, it is important to obtain blood for culture and to make an attempt to secure sputum (not saliva) for Gram stain and culture as well.

Treatment

Ideally, the Gram stain will give sufficient information to indicate what antibiotic should be administered, but in some instances broad coverage will be required until the cultures give definitive information. Supportive measures in the patient with bacterial pneumonia include rest, supplemental oxygen if hypoxemia is present, and adequate calories to sustain the individual during this decidedly catabolic event.

CYSTIC FIBROSIS

Cystic fibrosis, inherited in an autosomal recessive pattern, is usually a cause of premature death in those afflicted. It has over the years, however, displayed a remarkable heterogeneity of clinical manifestations and severity, which permits us to temper the earlier bleak outlook. Just the same, the life expectancy for most patients is still less than 30 years. Although much more common in Caucasians (1:2000), it does occur in African-Americans (1:17,000) but is very rare in American Indians and Orientals. Particularly exciting have been advances in the last few years that have led to improved understanding of the root cause of cystic fibrosis.

Genetic Defect and Biochemical Lesion in Cystic Fibrosis

Dramatic progress has been made in unraveling the basic defect in cystic fibrosis. We now know that the gene for cystic fibrosis is located on the long arm of chromosome 7 and that this gene, comprised of 24 exons, encodes a protein of 1480 amino acids. A wealth of evidence points to the gene product functioning as a Cl^- channel in epithelial cells, bearing the name *cystic fibrosis transmembrane conductance regulator (CFTR)*. The most common defect, accounting for 70% of the patients with cystic fibrosis, results from loss of three base pairs that normally code for phenylalanine at position 508. This lesion is referred to as ΔF_{508}. Many other alleles that cause cystic fibrosis have been identified, underscoring the substantial heterogeneity in the genetic defects causing the other 30% of cases of cystic fibrosis.

For over 40 years, it has been known that the sweat produced by patients with cystic fibrosis was more salty than that of normal subjects. The sweat gland is a classic exocrine gland, which produces a primary secretion that is delivered to the lumen. This primary secretion is then further modified by withdrawal of some of the ions, decreasing the tonicity of the final sweat. Although the primary sweat elaborated by patients with cystic fibrosis is similar in ionic content to that generated by normal individuals, the sweat duct epithelium is relatively impermeable to Cl^- in patients with cystic fibrosis (Figure 23.9). This impermeability decreases the reabsorption of Cl^- in the duct and with it diminishes Na^+ reabsorption as well. The result, in patients with cystic fibrosis, is elaboration of a final sweat with Cl^- and Na^+ concentrations three to five times normal. Once again, the genetic defect involves the handling of Cl^-, with Na^+ traveling along to maintain electroneutrality.

Chloride channels of epithelial cells specialized for transport are situated on the luminal face of the cell. Such cells populate the airways, and although Cl^- exits the cell through the channel into the lumen of the airway, Na^+ exits via a paracellular pathway. When Cl^- and Na^+ move into the lumen, water follows passively, with the overall result being hydration of the mucus lining the respiratory airways. In patients with cystic fibrosis, these mucus secretions, deprived of sufficient water to maintain just the right thickness (because of the defect in the CFTR), become overly viscous. These viscous secretions, which are difficult for patients to clear from the respiratory tract, contribute to plugging of airways with recurrent infection a predictable consequence of the blockage.

Evidence reviewed by Riordan and Welsh et al supports the view that the CFTR is a Cl^- channel with complex regulatory properties, and not merely the regulator of the Cl^- channel. Moreover, evidence is now accumulating that, at least in the case of the ΔF_{508} mutation, the genetic defect impairs the normal incorporation of the Cl^- transporter into the apical membrane. This strongly suggests that the Cl^- channel is itself functional,

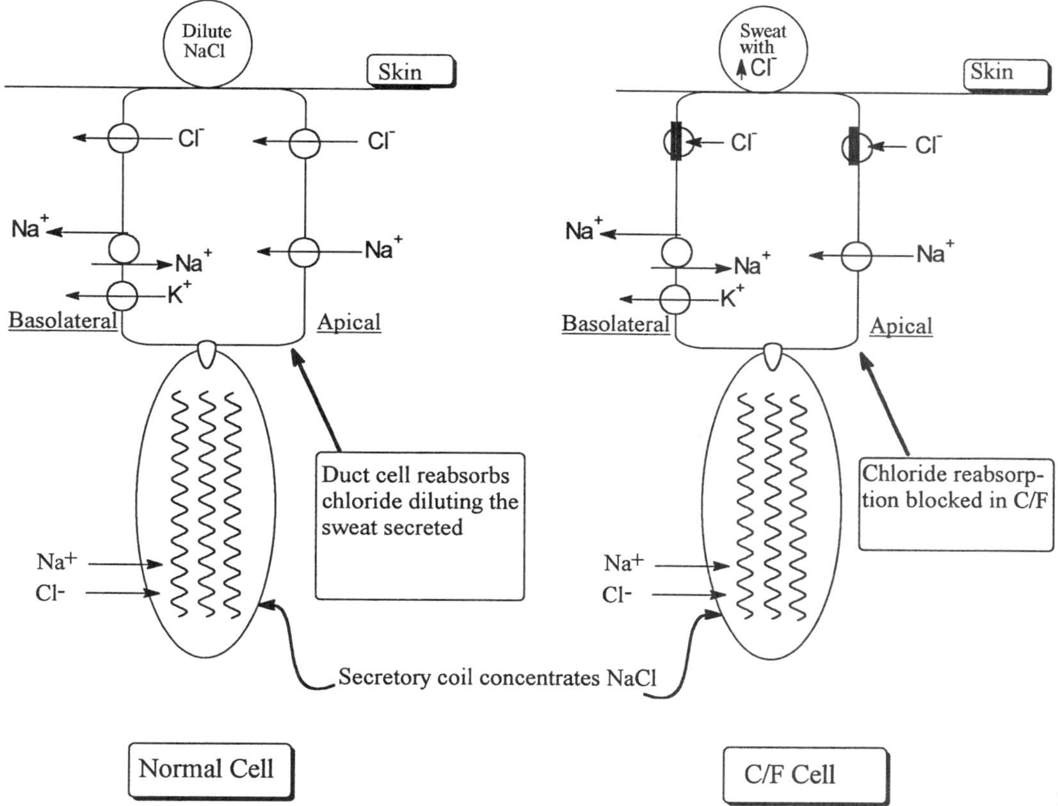

Figure 23.9. Electrolyte transport in sweat gland ductal cells. NaCl is concentrated within the secretory coils of the sweat gland in normal (left) and cystic fibrosis (right) individuals. Reabsorption of chloride by the duct cell through normal chloride channels results in production of dilute sweat, whereas a nonfunctioning chloride channel in cystic fibrosis prevents dilution, with resultant production of sweat with a typically high chloride concentration.

but that failing to arrive at its normal location it cannot exert that function.

The CFTR defect appears to be at the root of this abnormality in regulation of the Na^+ and Cl^- channels. Production of dehydrated secretions in lung airways, pancreas, gastrointestinal tract, liver, and genitourinary tract lead to obstruction of various tubular structures with consequent impairment of function and tissue destruction. Of all the organs affected, the inability to clear viscous secretions is most ominous. The toll on lung anatomy and function from the recurrent infections with Pseudomonas and other agents eventually causes the demise of many of these patients.

Clinical Findings

Clinical manifestations arise from obstruction of organ ducts by thick secretions, with the main symptoms being those of chronic obstructive pulmonary disease. Insufficiency of pancreatic enzymes and secretions causes malabsorption and failure to thrive (Table 23.4). Even with advances in defining the DNA lesion in 70% of patients, the diagnosis still depends upon demonstrating abnormal sweat Cl^- (> 60 mEq/l) or Na^+ concentrations. Because of increasing recognition of milder forms presenting in adolescence and adulthood, the indications for sweat testing are fairly broad; hence, older individuals with chronic cough and bronchitis (especially without a history of smoking) or minimal malabsorption should have cystic fibrosis considered in the differential diagnosis. Several diseases are also associated with abnormal sweat electrolytes, but they should be easily distinguished from cystic fibrosis. These include Addison's disease, nephrogenic diabetes in-

Table 23.4. When to Consider Cystic Fibrosis

Neonate and Infant
Meconium ileus; rectal prolapse
Steatorrhea
Recurrent pulmonary infections
All Ages
Siblings of patients with cystic fibrosis or child or a patient with cystic fibrosis
Failure to thrive
Chronic cough
Recurrent pulmonary infections and complications
Intestinal obstruction
Nasal polyps
Liver disease
Salty taste to skin
Undue sensitivity to heat exposure

sipidus, glucose-6-phosphatase deficiency, hypothyroidism, fucosidosis, ectodermal dysplasia, and severe malnutrition. Clinical situations that warrant quantitation of sweat electrolytes are listed in Table 23.4.

So variegated are the manifestations and complications of cystic fibrosis, a team approach is essential. This is best accomplished in a regional center for care of patients with cystic fibrosis. These centers are engaged in several clinical research studies, one of which involves the use of recombinant human DNAase to liquify the DNA from neutrophils that accumulate in infected areas. Work is also progressing on replacing the missing gene.

PULMONARY EMBOLISM

Pulmonary embolism denotes the lodging of a clot in one or more branches of the pulmonary artery. Although most physicians think of pulmonary embolism as a manifestation of disease of the pulmonary circulation, in reality the embolus that lodges in the pulmonary artery arises, not in the lung, but most frequently in the lower extremities. Consequently, pulmonary embolism is a disorder affecting the propensity of blood to clot, under conditions that from the patient's point of view must be seen as inappropriate.

In patients developing venous thrombi of the lower extremities, there is a considerable risk that the clot will detach and enter the pulmonary circulation. Needless to say, preventing the formation of venous thrombi in the first place is by far the most effective way of preventing pulmonary embolism. Prevention is more likely to be successful than treating the embolus once it imperils pulmonary function. No doubt the reader is aware that this preventive approach is analogous to measures taken to prevent myocardial infarction, rather than to have to treat an acute myocardial infarction. Curiously, physicians and the public are more attuned to the need to act aggressively to prevent coronary artery disease than they are to prevent pulmonary embolism. Indeed, workers in the field are frustrated that their call for a vigorous assault on the causes of pulmonary embolism has not been heeded, with the result that the incidence of pulmonary embolism in the United States (500,000 cases per year) and of fatal episodes (50,000 cases per year) has not changed in a quarter of a century. This is certainly cause for concern.

Pathogenesis

As noted, serious or even fatal outcomes can attend the formation of deep venous thromboses, especially in the iliac and femoral veins. Over 100 years ago, Virchow proposed a triad of factors that predispose to venous thrombosis: (*1*) stasis of blood in the veins, (*2*) a tendency for the blood to coagulate more readily (hypercoagulability), and (*3*) damage to the endothelial lining of the vessel wall. Individuals who are immobilized in bed after surgery or because of serious disease, as well as individuals whose extremities remain in a dependent position for long periods as on airplanes and during prolonged trips in vehicles are prone to stasis. So, if clotting is activated, because of what appears to be innocuous trauma, stasis will impede clearance and permit progression. Several medical conditions can contribute to intimal damage of the vessel wall, including trauma, congestive heart failure, immobilization, pregnancy, estrogen therapy, and malignancy.

Pathophysiology and Clinical Features

It should be clear from our earlier discussion of ventilation-perfusion matching that when an embolus occludes an artery, perfusion to the alveoli served by that vessel will cease. Furthermore, if those alveoli continue to be ventilated without blood supplying them, these alveoli will constitute a dead space. Remarkably, pulmonary emboli, in an undefined manner, increase the ventilatory rate of such patients so that despite the fact that the affected alveoli are not perfused, hypercapnia does not occur. But, whereas $PaCO_2$ does not increase, pulmonary emboli cause the PaO_2 to decrease. Ventilation-perfusion mismatching (early on) and shunting (after 48 hours) is believed to account for the hypoxemia. Platelets entrapped in the thrombus are believed to release histamine, serotonin, and prostaglandins—all agents that cause bronchoconstriction thus further exacerbating the hypoxemia. And if this were not enough, because of the mechanical blockage of the regions affected by the thrombus, pulmonary arterial pressure increases acutely. In patients with tenuous cardiovascular status, sudden increase in pulmonary arterial pressure can precipitate acute cor pulmonale.

Pulmonary embolism is a diagnosis for which the physician must maintain a high level of suspicion, especially in patients with the acknowledged risk factors and who have suggestive symptoms and signs. But no group of clinical manifestations can ensure the diagnosis with certainty. Dyspnea and chest pain occur in over 80% of patients with pulmonary embolism, and tachycardia and tachypnea are also common, but they point to the need to evaluate such patients with more definitive studies. Apprehension, perhaps due in part to endogenous epinephrine release, associated with cor pulmonale is the most ominous finding of pulmonary embolism. Because of the increased inotropic load on the myocardium, cor pulmonale is associated with the most rapidly fatal presentation of pulmonary embolism. Of course, patients with other serious causes of chest pathology may also experience apprehension. Tragically, about 50,000 patients per year in the United States suffer an episode of pulmonary embolism that is fatal within several hours of the lodging of the thrombus in the pulmonary circulation. For the majority of patients who survive a pulmonary embolus, after about a day, surfactant synthesis decreases. This comes about because of decrease in the supply of building blocks for surfactant to the affected regions. Decreased surfactant has the effect of making the affected alveoli more liable to collapse and thus become atelectatic.

Establishing the diagnosis of pulmonary embolism requires radionuclide perfusion lung scanning and in selected patients pulmonary angiography, because there are no routine laboratory or radiologic procedures adequate to make that diagnosis. Details of these procedures and strategies for their use can be found by referring to the texts listed in the suggested reading section at the end of this chapter.

Treatment and Prevention

Prophylaxis against deep venous thrombosis in patients at risk involves use of intermittent venous compression pneumatic devices on the lower extremities and low dose heparin.

Treatment for a patient who suffers a pulmonary embolism demands a higher dose of heparin (than for prophylaxis) to maintain the activated partial thromboplastin time at 1.5 times the control value. In some patients, thrombolytic therapy with streptokinase or urokinase have been used. Urokinase is an enzyme produced by and isolated from human kidney which has thrombolytic effect. This action is exerted by catalyzing the conversion of plasminogen to plasmin, an enzyme that degrades fibrin clots and fibrinogen. Advances in recombinant DNA technology have led to commercial production of a serine protease (altepase) from a human gene introduced into a Chinese hamster ovary cell line. This enzyme has a very similar action to that of urokinase. Rationale for this mode of therapy derives from the action of the bacterial enzyme, streptokinase, elaborated by β-hemolytic streptococci as one of that bacterium's invasive strategies. Long-term prevention in a patient who has suffered a prior pulmonary embolus usually entails oral therapy with a coumarin derivative or low dose subcutaneous heparin.

LUNG CANCER

Lung cancer is notorious not only for being the leading cause of death from cancer in men and women in the United States, but also for the role of cigarette smoking in its causation. Although the causative role of cigarette smoking has been established beyond any doubt, the carcinogenic agents in cigarette smoke that bring on this tragedy have

Table 23.5. Features of the Four Major Types of Lung Cancer

CELL TYPE	%	INITIAL SITES	SPREADS TO	TREATMENT	COMMENTS
Squamous cell	30 to 35	Central bronchi	Regional lymph nodes	Surgery or palliation	10% cavitate
Small cell	20	Central bronchi	Local nodes and distant sites	Chemotherapy and radiation	Many produce ADH or ACTH Chromosomal abnormality 3p14 → 23
Adenocarcinoma	35	Peripheral	Local nodes, other lung, brain, adrenal	Surgery or palliation	Escape detection on sputum exam
Large cell	15 to 20	Peripheral	Local nodes and distant sites	Surgery or palliation	Escape detection on sputum exam

ADH = antidiuretic hormone
ACTH = adrenocorticotropic hormone

not been clearly identified. Candidates include nitrosamines, benzopyrenes, and other aromatic hydrocarbons. Duration of exposure and the number of packs smoked are crucial to assessing the risk and are estimated as "pack years" smoked. The bronchial mucosal lining is most vulnerable to the carcinogens in cigarette smoke because these agents are likely to be concentrated there.

There have been major strides made in the application of genetics to an understanding of the pathogenesis of certain tumors, such as retinoblastoma. Despite this, however, the potential relationship between carcinogenic substances and a common genetic mutagen effect in the etiology of lung cancer remains unelucidated. Consequently, classification of these tumors has advanced little in 50 years, while treatment has virtually no biochemical basis and is largely empirical. No doubt this vast area of ignorance contributes significantly to the extremely high mortality. Four cell types account for about 95% of lung neoplasms: squamous cell carcinoma, adenocarcinoma, large cell carcinoma, and small cell carcinoma (Table 23.5).

Clinical Features

Symptoms suggestive of lung cancer are cough, dyspnea, weight loss, anorexia, and hemoptysis. Tumors that obstruct bronchi can cause atelectasis and pneumonia. Most of these tumors metastasize both locally and distantly. Those metastasizing locally within the mediastinum cause clinical findings by impinging on a nerve or vessel as in recurrent larnyngeal nerve palsy and the superior vena cava syndrome. Not infrequently, tumors arising in the lung apices can press on the brachial plexus or cervical sympathetic chain producing Horner's Syndrome and Pancoast's syndrome (Table 23.6). Additionally, remote extrapulmonary manifestations termed *paraneoplastic syndromes* occur in approximately 15% to 20% of patients with lung cancer. These paraneoplastic syndromes are not limited to the well-known endocrine effects of ectopic hormone production, but also include cutaneous, neuromuscular, cardiovascular, hematologic, and connective tissue manifestations (Table 23.7).

Diagnosis and Staging

In approaching the diagnosis and treatment of lung cancer, it is important to recognize that the presence of co-existing respiratory impairment, as in COPD, may seriously limit the vigor with which treatment can be pursued. And the finding of widespread metastases generally means that the physician can offer the patient only palliative measures with little hope of cure.

A nodule or mass found on chest radiograph requires further evaluation to determine whether that lesion is lung cancer. Bronchoscopy provides the expert with the ability not only to observe an intrabronchial lesion but also to obtain samples

Table 23.6. Syndromes Associated with Intrathoracic Growth of Lung Cancer

CONDITION	STRUCTURE AFFECTED	FINDINGS
Horner's syndrome	Cervical sympathetic chain	Ptosis, miosis, enophthalmos and ↓ sweating on involved side
Pancoast's syndrome	Brachial plexus	Pain, loss of strength in upper arm ± Horner's syndrome
Recurrent laryngeal nerve syndrome	Recurrent laryngeal nerve branch of vagus	Vocal cord paralysis with hoarseness
Superior vena cava syndrome	Superior vena cava	Edema of upper extremities and face 2° to obstruction of superior vena cava (SVC)

for histologic examination and diagnosis. CT scanning is valuable for detection of possible metastatic lymph nodes within the mediastinum. However, it is imperative in understanding the natural history of any malignant tumor that the reader realize the limits of resolution of each diagnostic technique used. Thus, rather than being related to therapeutic efficacy, a successful 5-year survival could, just as well, be the time required for one or two undiscovered metastatic cells to establish themselves as a recurrent tumor mass. Although this may be a disturbing thought, it certainly underscores the importance of developing markers for detection of malignant cells. This can be accomplished only through a more fundamental understanding of the biology of malignant transformations.

Table 23.7. Paraneoplastic Syndromes

SYSTEM	SYNDROME
Endocrine and metabolic	Cushing's syndrome
	SIADH
	Hypercalcemia
	Carcinoid syndrome
	Gynecomastia
Cutaneous	Acanthosis nigricans
	Chronic erythema multiforme
	Scleroderma
Neuromuscular	Peripheral neuropathy
	Subacute cerebellar degeneration
	Myasthenia
	Seizures
	Dermatomyositis
	Psychosis
Cardiovascular	Thrombophlebitis and arterial thrombosis
	Non-bacterial endocarditis
Hematologic	Anemia
	DIC
	Eosinophilia
	Thrombocytosis
Connective tissue and osseous	Digital clubbing
Liver	Jaundice and abnormal liver function tests

SIADH = syndrome of inappropriate antidiuretic hormone
DIC = disseminated intravascular coagulopathy

Staging of the tumor is based on three criteria: (*1*) the primary tumor—its size, location, and evidence of compression of adjoining structures, (*2*) hilar and mediastinal lymphs nodes (Are they involved with tumor?), and (*3*) metastases to distant sites including brain, adrenal, bone, and liver.

Treatment

In the case of a localized tumor, surgery offers a chance of cure. But in all other forms of lung carcinoma, with evidence of local or widespread metastases, the therapeutic options are mostly palliative, with 5-year survival a grim 13%.

DISORDERS OF VENTILATION

At the outset of this chapter, we saw that an intact (*1*) chest wall, (*2*) diaphragm and (*3*) neuromuscular connections are all required to animate the chest bellows that carries out inspiration and expiration. It follows that ventilatory disorders can arise as a consequence of dysfunction of any one of these three components.

Disorders of the chest wall that cause deficient respiratory function are *kyphoscoliosis* and obesity. Kyphoscoliosis, a deformity of the spine manifested as an abnormal backward and lateral curvature of the spine, causes increased stiffness of the chest wall with the consequence that breathing becomes more difficult. This defect is often referred to as *decreased compliance*, compliance referring to the ease with which the chest wall can be stretched. Further aggravating the situation is the presence of ventilation-perfusion inequality because of underventilated regions of lung.

Table 23.8. Disorders of Ventilation

Chest Wall Disorders
Kyphoscoliosis
Obesity
Ankylosing spondylitis
Diaphragmatic Fatigue
Disorders increasing work of breathing—COPD, status asthmaticus
Neuromuscular Disorders
Guillain-Barre syndrome
Myasthenia gravis
Amyotropic lateral sclerosis
High spinal cord injury
Muscular dystrophy

Obesity, because of the excess adipose tissue on the chest wall, renders the chest wall stiffer or less compliant. Of course, there is even more adipose tissue accumulation in the abdominal wall and this makes it exceedingly difficult for the diaphragmatic excursion to meet the requirements for air exchange. Both the less compliant chest wall and the restricted diaphragmatic movement conspire to impair lung expansion with the result that ventilation-perfusion mismatch results.

Diaphragmatic fatigue occurs in two common situations: in patients with increased work of breathing as in COPD and in patients with severe malnutrition where diaphragmatic muscle, among others, is used to sustain gluconeogenesis.

Finally, *neuromuscular disorders* affecting the ventilatory apparatus act by blocking neural transmission to the muscles of respiration causing weakness or paralysis. Selected neuromuscular disorders are listed in Table 23.8.

RESPIRATORY FAILURE

Respiratory failure occurs when the respiratory system is unable to meet the needs of the body for oxygen uptake and carbon dioxide disposal. Although many clinical situations can lead to respiratory failure, many of which have been discussed in this chapter, the diagnosis of respiratory failure rests not on clinical impression but on the arterial blood gases (Table 23.9a). Criteria for respiratory failure in an individual without pre-existing respiratory condition is a $PaCO_2$ greater than 50 torr and a PaO_2 of less than 60 torr on breathing room air

Table 23.9a. Respiratory Failure

Hypoventilation
Usually caused by failure of nervous or muscle function
Treatment usually requires intubation and mechanical ventilation
Ventilation-Perfusion Mismatch
Usually involves airway disorders with:
copious secretions
mucosal edema
bronchospasm
Results in less air supply to affected region while blood flow remains unchanged
Right to Left Shunts (Perfusion of totally nonventilated area)
Atelectasis closes respiratory exchange units
Edema, pus, or blood fills the alveoli
Circulatory Disturbances
Acute left heart failure → pulmonary edema → acute respiratory failure

(Table 23.9b). Of course, the caretaker must be on the lookout for deterioration of respiratory function in patients with pre-existing chronic conditions. A high index of suspicion will permit a rapid response to reverses in respiratory function in patients whose function was already diminished.

There are Two Types of Respiratory Failure: Hypoxemic and Hypercapnic/Hypoxemic

In the course of this chapter, we have noted those conditions in which hypoxemia was the major blood gas abnormality, distinguishing them from those in which both hypercapnia and hypoxemia were present together. Conditions in which hypoxemia predominates share ventilation-perfusion inequality and shunting as contributing factors. Examples include severe pneumonia and adult respiratory distress syndrome in which the affected alveoli are partially or completely filled with fluid. But because these patients are able to breath at an adequate rate, they are able to provide for disposal of CO_2 and so hypercapnia is not a feature.

Hypoxemia alone can be chronically tolerated for months and years. As evidence of this, one need only look at the child with cyanotic congenital heart disease. In the absence of pulmonary disease, arterial blood gases in such a patient will show only relative hypoxia, with a normal P_aCO_2. This is not, of course, to say that hypoxemia is

Table 23.9b. Respiratory Failure

TYPE	LABORATORY FINDINGS	CAUSES
Inadequate alveolar ventilation	$PaCO_2 >$ mm Hg	Asthma, COPD, neuromuscular diseases, sedatives or narcotic overdose
Inadequate oxygenation of arterial blood	$PaO_2 <$ 50–60 mm Hg	Pneumonia, asthma, COPD
Inadequate O_2 delivered to the tissues	$PaCO_2 \uparrow$ and $PaO_2 \downarrow$ Lactic acidosis	Anemia, carbon monoxide poisoning, hypovolemic or cardiogenic shock, cardiorespiratory arrest
Inadequate uptake of O_2 by peripheral tissues	Low oxygen consumption $\downarrow$ (arterial-mixed venous oxygen content difference) Lactic acidosis	Adult respiratory distress syndrome Distributive shock Multiple organ system failure Cyanide poisoning

COPD = chronic obstructive pulmonary disease

without effect, because restriction of oxygen will cause enhanced lactic acid production from glycolysis. But, so long as lactate production rate can be offset by gluconeogenesis and renal excretion, arterial pH will remain normal, albeit compensated by enhanced CO_2 excretion through the lungs.

In contrast, hypercapnia/hypoxemia occurs in those conditions in which there is both a significant imbalance in ventilation and perfusion plus an inadequate level of alveolar ventilation to remove CO_2. Thus, enhanced lactate production due to hypoxemia cannot be compensated by increased rate of transfer of metabolically produced CO_2, leading to a decrease in plasma pH. Examples of conditions with this degree of mismatching and hypoventilation are diseases of the ventilatory apparatus, including the chest wall and neuromuscular system, and depression of the brain's control of breathing (most often by drugs). V/Q mismatching is also a feature of cerebrovascular accidents and COPD, severe congestive heart failure and fulminant ARDS. As seen from this list, patients suffering from both hypercapnia and hypoxemia usually suffer from chronic lung disease, the compensation of which is no longer adequate to maintain gas exchange.

Clinical findings that point to respiratory failure include: dyspnea, mental confusion, headache, sometimes obtundation or even coma, tachycardia, and central cyanosis. These findings should prompt the caretaker to evaluate the patient's arterial blood gases.

Treatment of Respiratory Failure

Essential for the patient in respiratory failure is ventilatory support, both to improve air exchange and also to reduce the work of breathing. All therapeutic approaches share the goal of maintaining positive pressures in the lungs to maximize the functional residual capacity (FRC), from which several benefits accrue. By keeping alveoli patent, even during expiration, V/Q inequality and shunting decrease. In addition, positive pressure improves pulmonary compliance and retards loss of surfactant. Specific aspects of such therapy cannot be discussed here, but references are provided for the student wishing to delve into this area.

ADULT RESPIRATORY DISTRESS SYNDROME

Adult respiratory distress syndrome or shock lung refers to a constellation of findings that are most often associated with multiple organ failure. Hence, lung involvement is often only one of the life-threatening manifestations. Regarding the lung, many underlying conditions including septic shock, severe trauma, smoke inhalation, diffuse pneumonia, and cardiac arrest damage either the endothelial lining of the pulmonary capillaries or the alveolar epithelial cells, causing fluid to enter the alveoli. Predictably, fluid-filled alveoli encounter profound interference in gas exchange.

Pathogenesis

Because so many varied conditions can result in ARDS, an attempt has been made to reconcile these various precipitating causes. This has led to the proposal that neutrophils, alveolar macrophages, and platelets in the course of their protective functions liberate compounds that damage the capillaries and type I alveolar cells in the lung. Included in this list of mediators are toxic oxygen radicals, endotoxin, thromboxanes and prostaglandins, complement (C5a), and tumor necrosis factor.

Pathophysiology and Clinical Features

In ARDS, there is extensive damage to the lungs but by no means are the entire lungs typically involved. It follows then that those alveoli, engorged by interstitial and alveolar edema, are not ventilated at all, causing true shunting with consequent hypoxemia. Other alveoli may not be as severely affected, yet a degree of ventilation-perfusion mismatch exists for these alveoli too, further contributing to the hypoxemia. An additional hindrance to ventilation is the development of atelectasis and a decrease in the compliance of the lung.

Diagnosis depends on recognizing the conditions with which ARDS is associated, recognizing that dyspnea, tachypnea, crackles (rales), and hypoxemia are present and recognizing interstitial and alveolar edema on chest radiograph. Use of the Swan-Ganz pulmonary artery catheter can differentiate cardiac edema (pressure elevated) from the noncardiogenic edema of ARDS when the pressure is normal.

In practice, treatment is complex and requires: (*1*) a vigorous assault on the precipitating cause, (*2*) measures to combat the fluid leak, and (*3*) support of ventilation. These issues are discussed in the texts listed in the suggested reading section at the end of this chapter.

FINAL COMMENT

Although there are elaborate descriptive details of the pathophysiologic and histopathologic effects of pulmonary disease, as yet there is only rudimentary comprehension of the cellular mechanisms at work. Only with their elucidation is medicine likely to make significant impact on the substantial morbidity and mortality attributable to lung disease. But on the brighter side, cessation of smoking has been shown to have a major positive effect on the incidence of chronic lung disease and lung cancer. Preventive measures should also result in decreased incidence of pulmonary emboli. Hence, there is much that physicians can do to lessen the burden of some forms of pulmonary disease while awaiting more powerful specific therapies.

SUGGESTED READINGS

GENERAL REFERENCES AND RESPIRATORY PHYSIOLOGY

Baum GL, Wolinsky E, eds. Textbook of pulmonary diseases. 5th ed, Boston: Little Brown, 1994.

Crystal RG, West JB, et al, eds. The lung: scientific foundations. New York: Raven Press, Ltd, 1991.

George RB, Matthay MA, Light RW, Matthay RA. Chest medicine. 3rd ed. Baltimore: Williams & Wilkins, 1995.

Leff AR, Schumacker PT. Respiratory physiology: basics and applications. Philadelphia: WB Saunders, 1993.

Levitzky MG. Pulmonary physiology. 3rd ed. New York: McGraw-Hill, 1991.

Murray JF, Nadel JA, eds. Textbook of respiratory medicine. 2nd ed. Philadelphia: WB Saunders, 1994.

Nunn JF. Nunn's applied respiratory physiology. 4th ed. Oxford: Butterworth-Heinemann Ltd, 1993.

Staub NC. Basic respiratory physiology. New York: Churchill Livingstone, 1991.

West JB. Pulmonary pathophysiology: the essentials. 4th ed. Baltimore: Williams & Wilkins, 1992.

West JB. Respiratory physiology: the essentials. 5th ed. Baltimore: Williams & Wilkins, 1994.

Weinberger S. Principles of pulmonary medicine. 2nd ed. Philadelphia: WB Saunders, 1992.

SURFACTANT

Batenburg JJ. Surfactant phospholipids: synthesis and storage. Am J Physiol 1992;262:L367.

Caminiti SP, Young SL. The pulmonary surfactant system. Hospital Pract 1991;Jan 15:57.

Hamm H, Fabel H, Bartsch W. The surfactant system of the adult lung: physiology and clinical perspectives. Clinical Investigator 1992;70:637.

Kuroki Y, Voelker DR. Pulmonary surfactant proteins. J Biol Chem 1994;269:25943.

Van Golde LMG, Batenburg JJ, Robertson B. The pulmonary surfactant system. News in Physiological Science 1994;9:13.

ARTERIAL BLOOD GASES AND PULMONARY FUNCTION TESTING

Bates DV. Respiratory function in disease. 3rd ed. Philadelphia: WB Saunders, 1989.

Connett RJ, Honig CR, Gayeski TEJ, Brooks GA. Defining hypoxia: a systems view of VO_2, glycolysis, energetics, and intracellular PO_2. J Appl Physiol 1990;68:833.

Crapo RO. Pulmonary-function testing. N Engl J Med 1994;331:25.

Lane EE, Walker JF. Clinical arterial blood gas analysis. St Louis: CV Mosby, 1987.

Malley WJ. Clinical blood gases. Philadelphia: WB Saunders, 1990.

Martin L. All you really need to know to interpret arterial blood gases. Philadelphia: Lea and Febiger, 1992.

Shapiro BA, Harrison RA, Cane RD, Templin R. Clinical application of blood gases. 4th ed. Chicago: Yearbook Medical Publisher Service, 1989.

Weinberger SE, Schwartzstein RM, Weiss JW. Hypercapnia. N Engl J Med 1989;321:1223.

ASTHMA AND CHRONIC OBSTRUCTIVE PULMONARY DISEASE

Badgett RG, Tanaka DJ, Hunt DK, et al. Can moderate chronic obstructive pulmonary disease be diagnosed by historical and physical findings alone? Am J Med 1993;94:188.

Barnes PJ. Anti-inflammatory therapy for asthma. Annu Rev Med 1993;44:229.

Bernstein JA, Bernstein IL. Cromolyn and nedocromil. Immunology and Allergy Clinics of North America 1993;13:891.

Ferguson GT, Cherniack RM. Management of chronic obstructive pulmonary disease. N Engl J Med 1993; 328:1017.

Goldstein RA, Paul WE, Metcalf D, et al. Asthma. Ann Intern Med 1994;121:698.

Kikuchi Y, Okabe S, Tamura G, et al. Chemosensitivity and perception of dyspnea in patients with a history of near-fatal asthma. N Engl J Med 1994;330:1329.

McFadden ER Jr, Gilbert IA. Asthma. N Engl J Med 1992; 327:1928.

Murphy TF, Sethi S. Bacterial infection in chronic obstructive pulmonary disease. American Reviews Respiratory Diseases 1992;146:1067.

Skorodin MS. Pharmacotherapy for asthma and chronic obstructive pulmonary disease. Arch Intern Med 1993; 153:814.

Stempel DA, Redding GJ. Management of acute asthma. Pediatr Clin North Am 1992;39:1311.

Stempel DA, Szefler SJ. Management of chronic asthma. Pediatr Clin North Am 1992;39:1293.

Van Oosterhout AJM, Nijkamp FP. Role of cytokines in bronchial hyperresponsiveness. Pulm Pharmacol 1993; 6:225.

LUNG DEFENSES AND PNEUMONIA

Gee MH, Albertine KH. Neutrophil-endothelial cell interactions in the lung. Annu Rev Physiol 1993;55: 227.

Guerra LG, Verghese A. New pathogens in pneumonia. Med Clin North Am 1994;78:967.

Mason CM, Nelson S, Summer WR. Bacterial colonization: pathogenesis and clinical significance. Immunology and Allergy Clinics of North America 1993;13:93.

Pison U, Max M, Neuendank A, et al. Host defence capacities of pulmonary surfactant: evidence for "non-surfactant" functions of the surfactant system. Eur J Clin Invest 1994;24:586.

Salinas F, Pine JR, Riemersma LJ. Approach to pneumonia in adults and the elderly. Immunology and Allergy Clinics of North America 1993;13:171.

Skerrett SJ. Host defenses against respiratory infection. Med Clin North Am 1994;78:941.

Teague WG. Approach to pneumonia in infants, children, and adolescents. Immunology and Allergy Clinics of North America 1993;13:159.

CYSTIC FIBROSIS

Aitken ML, Fiel SB. Cystic fibrosis. Dis Mon 1993;39:1.

Boucher RC. Human airway ion transport. Am J Respir Crit Care Med 1994;150:271,581.

Fuchs HJ, Borowitz DS, Christiansen DH, et al. Effect of aerosolized recombinant human DNase on exacerbations of respiratory symptoms and on pulmonary function in patients with cystic fibrosis. N Engl J Med 1994;331:637.

Haas M. The Na-K-Cl cotransporters. Am J Physiol 1994; 267:C869.

Hamosh A, Corey M, et al. Correlation between genotype and phenotype in patients with cystic fibrosis. N Engl J Med 1993;329:1308.

Konstan MW, Byard PJ, Hoppel CL, Davis PB. Effect of high-dose ibuprofen in patients with cystic fibrosis. N Engl J Med 1995;332:848.

Pencharz PB, Durie PR. Nutritional management of cystic fibrosis. Annu Rev Nutr 1993;13:111.

Ramsey BW, Boat T. Outcome measures for clinical trials in cystic fibrosis. J Pediatr 1994;124:177.

Riordan JR. The cystic fibrosis transmembrane conductance regulator. Annu Rev Physiol 1993;55:609.

Sferra TJ, Collins FS. The molecular biology of cystic fibrosis. Annu Rev Med 1993;44:133.

Tizzano EF, Buchwald M. Cystic fibrosis: beyond the gene to therapy. J Pediatr 1992;120:337.

Welsh MJ, Tsui L-C, Boat TF, Beaudet AL. Cystic fibrosis. In: Scriver CR, Beaudet AL, Sly WS, Valle D, eds. The metabolic and molecular bases of inherited disease. 7th ed. New York: McGraw-Hill, 1995:3799.

Wine JJ. Basic aspects of cystic fibrosis. Clin Rev Allergy. 1991;9:1.

PULMONARY EMBOLISM

Carson JL, Kelley MA, Duff A, et al. The clinical course of pulmonary embolism. N Engl J Med 1992;326:1240.

Goldhaber SZ. Managing pulmonary embolism. Hospital Pract 1991:Sept 15:41.

Kelley MA, Abbuhl S. Massive pulmonary embolism. Clin Chest Med 1994;15:547.

Moser KM. Venous thromboembolism. American Reviews Respiratory Diseases 1990;141:235.

Stein PD. Acute pulmonary embolism. Dis Mon 1994;40: 467.

Wolfe MW, Skibo LK, Goldhaber SZ. Pulmonary embolic disease: diagnosis, pathophysiologic aspects, and treatment with thrombolytic agents. Curr Probl Cardiol 1993;18:587.

LUNG CANCER

Kalemkerian GP. Biology of lung cancer. Curr Opin Oncol 1994;6:147.

Lyubsky S, Jacobson MJ. Lung cancer: making the diagnosis. Chest 1991;100:511.

Rabbitts PH. Genetic changes in the development of lung cancer. Br Med Bull 1994;50:688.

Sorensen JB, Hansen HH. Recent advances in diagnosis and treatment of small cell and non-small cell lung cancer. Curr Opin Oncol 1994;6:162.

ADULT RESPIRATORY DISTRESS SYNDROME

Jobe AH. Pulmonary surfactant therapy. N Engl J Med 1993;328:861.

Kollef MH, Schuster DP. The acute respiratory distress syndrome. N Engl J Med 1995;332:27.

Lewis JF, Jobe AH. Surfactant and the adult respiratory distress syndrome. American Reviews Respiratory Diseases 1993;147:218.

Schuster DP. ARDS: clinical lessons from the oleic acid model of acute lung injury. Am J Resp Crit Care Med 1994;149:245.

Seeger W, Gunther A, Walmrath HD, et al. Alveolar surfactant and adult respiratory distress syndrome: pathogenetic role and therapeutic prospects. Clinical Investigator 1993;71:177.

chapter **24**

Cardiovascular Pathophysiology

As defined by the pioneering work of William Harvey in the 17th century, the cardiovascular system is a closed tubular system in which the heart, acting as a muscular pump, propels blood through vessels that dispatch blood to all parts of the organism. Blood is conveyed to the cells through ever narrowing vessels—arteries, arterioles, and finally capillaries. A capillary is a tube, a single cell thick, of which its permeability to O_2, CO_2, and waste products renders it the functional point of distribution and collection in the circulatory system. After leaving the tissues, blood is depleted of about 25% of its O_2 and now carrying waste products it returns to the heart in a sequence involving capillaries, venules, and veins.

The heart is a cone-shaped muscular structure, about the size of a clenched fist, located behind the sternum. It is divided into right and left halves, so that in reality it is a double pump, the right side pumping to the lungs and the left side pumping to the rest of the body. The upper chambers of the heart, called atria, serve to receive blood from the lungs and body, whereas the ventricles pump blood to the lungs and body. To ensure that blood flows in one direction and thereby prevent backflow, the entrance to the ventricles and to the aorta and pulmonary arteries are guarded by valves.

It should be clear then that the effects of all disorders of the heart—a remarkably sturdy and complex pump—are far-reaching. Indeed, these effects, at the least, deprive all or part of the cells of the body of sufficient oxygen and nutrient supply for normal metabolism. Under various physiologic situations (eg, exercise, cold, and digestion), neurohumoral mechanisms help the circulatory system redistribute the cardiac output to meet these demands. Similarly, in pathologic states like hemorrhage or myocardial infarction, these same neurohumoral mechanisms induce redistribution of blood so that the brain and heart continue to receive blood at the expense of other organs.

STRUCTURE AND FUNCTION OF THE MYOCARDIUM

The myocardium of the ventricles is composed of cells about 15 μm in diameter and 125 μm in length. These cells are replete with interconnecting fibers of which their lengths vary from 30 to 60 microns and diameters vary from 10 to 20 microns. Thus, although cardiac fibers are functionally similar to skeletal muscle fibers, they are smaller than the latter. Like skeletal muscle fibers, cardiac fibers are composed of a few thousand cross-banded strands or bundles, termed *myofibrils*, that traverse the length of the fibers. The myofibrils are, in turn, composed of thousands of sarcomeres that are themselves composed of contractile proteins (actin and myosin) arranged as myofilaments (Figure 24.1). In cardiac muscle, the sarcomeres occupy only about 50% of the mass of the cardiac cell (in contrast to approximately 90% of skeletal muscle) and are aligned end to end, giving the entire fibers a banded or striated appearance. The molecular mechanisms involved in muscle contraction are similar to those for skeletal muscle and are discussed in Chapter 25.

Considering that the normal heart beats ceaselessly, it is not surprising that its energy requirements are high. Indeed, mitochondria constitute 25% to 30% of the entire mass of the cell. These mitochondria appear to be located in proximity to the contractile filaments, which may facilitate transfer of ATP from its site of production in the mitochondria to its site of utilization during contraction.

Membranes Involved in Contraction

The sarcolemma is the surface membrane that invests individual myocardial fibers. Functions served by the sarcolemma include (*1*) mainte-

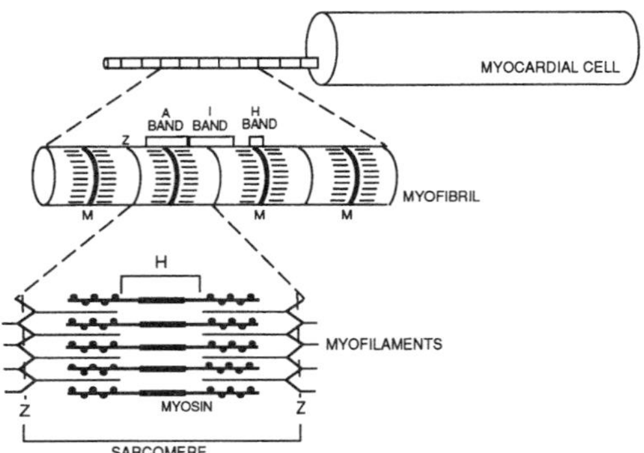

Figure 24.1. Organization of myocardial contractile elements. The primary unit of contractility is the myofibril, multiples of which comprise the myocardial cell. The myofibril is, in turn, composed of units called sarcomeres, which are delineated by two sequential Z lines, visible under an electron microscope. Within each sarcomere, there are thin (actin) and thick (myosin) myofilaments; the length of the latter is delineated by the A bands, whereas the lighter I band is representative of the actin filament length from the Z line which is not overlapped by myosin. The most dense, or H band is the region containing the portion of myosin not overlapped by actin. Reprinted with permission from Lilly LS. Pathophysiology of Heart Disease. Baltimore: Williams & Wilkins, 1993: 9.

nance of the intracellular environment, (*2*) depolarization, and (*3*) propagation of electrical depolarization from one fiber to the next, producing generalized activation. Hence cardiac muscle is an "excitable" tissue with some special properties. Like all excitable cells, at rest there is a resting membrane potential difference across ventricular and atrial cells of about −90 mV (inside negative). This resting potential is largely determined by the distribution of K^+ across the cell membrane. The normal trigger for the heart beat is the sinus node which has a resting potential of only −65 mV. It is, therefore, more excitable than the rest of the cardiac cells and conducting system, causing it to function as the pacemaker for the rest of the heart.

Generation of the Cardiac Action Potential

As a pump, the heart must have a phase during which it fills with blood, called *diastole*, and a phase during which it propels the blood through the vascular system, called *systole*. In the resting state, the myocyte cell membrane is fully polarized and it is during this phase that filling occurs. But, in the specialized conduction tissue of the heart, the resting membrane potential spontaneously tends to approach the threshold for depolarization. At threshold, depolarization occurs and promptly spreads throughout the cardiac muscle via the specialized conducting bundles. For the myocyte, the sodium channels are the dominant factor in rapid depolarization, permitting the sudden movement of Na^+ ions into the cell. In the case of the SA and AV nodes, however, slower calcium channels are the major factor in the pacing action, but they are also the source of the calcium that triggers further calcium release by the sarcoplasmic reticulum. Recall that the thin filament of cardiac muscle, like that of skeletal muscle, has in addition to actin, several polypeptides that prevent actin from interacting with myosin (Figure 24.2). They are tropomyosin and three polypeptide chains that together make up troponin. Troponin C binds calcium, troponin T links troponin to tropomyosin and troponin I inhibits actin-myosin interaction. When this additional calcium binds to troponin C, it lifts the inhibition on actin-myosin interaction permitting the muscle to contract. Thus, calcium sets the sliding filament mechanism into motion. Not surprisingly, these calcium channels are susceptible to pharmacologic intervention.

A distinguishing feature of cardiac muscle, as opposed to skeletal muscle, is the prolonged depolarization (ca. 100 ms) of cardiac tissue, allowing it ample time to pump blood, while making it refractory to another signal that would hamper its pumping efficiency.

The effectiveness of the muscle contraction of the heart as a unit is dependent on three elements. First is the *preload*, the initial length of the muscle, which is described by the Frank-Starling mechanism. This mechanism reflects the fact that within limits the greater the muscle is stretched the greater will be the tension generated. Second, is the *afterload*, the head of pressure that the heart must overcome to force blood into the arterial system. And third, is its intrinsic *contractility* or inotropic state.

Assuming normal cardiac muscle function, the major factor governing cardiac output is how much blood is in the ventricles at the end of diastole, the so-called end-diastolic volume.

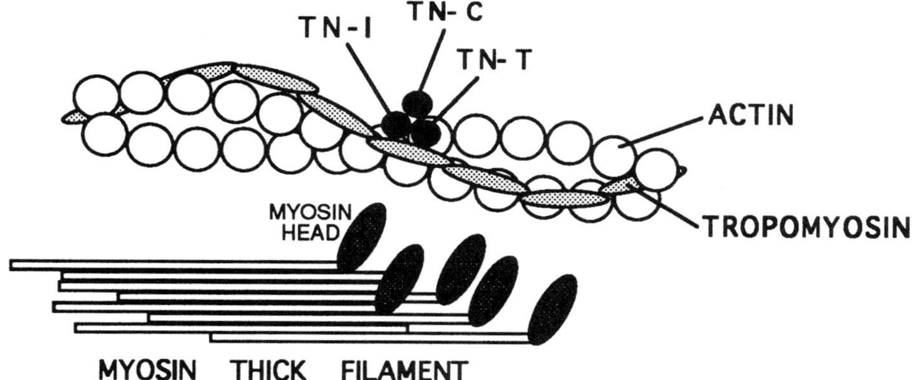

Figure 24.2. Organization of contractile proteins of the myocardium. The globular protein, actin, is arranged longitudinally along the regulatory protein tropomyosin, together with a cluster of subunits (TN-I, TN-C, TN-T) of another regulatory protein, troponin. This complex interacts with myosin heads which protrude from the myosin thick filaments. Reprinted with permission from Lilly LS. Pathophysiology of Heart Disease. Baltimore: Williams & Wilkins, 1993: 16.

Metabolic Requirements of Cardiac Muscle

Myocardial oxygen demand is determined by the mechanical load on the muscle cell (termed wall stress), the rate of contraction and how efficiently the muscle is able to contract. For example, catecholamines and digitalis increase the efficiency of myocardial contractility, whereas acidosis and myocardial ischemia or intrinsic disease decrease its efficiency. Unlike all other organs, extraction of 0_2 from the blood perfusing the heart is near maximal, meaning that the only way to increase 0_2 delivery is by augmenting the amount of blood delivered. Adenosine, one end product of an exhausted supply of ATP, has been shown to be a powerful vasodilator in the coronary bed. Adenosine is believed to play a major role in augmenting the blood delivered to the stressed heart.

THE CONDUCTION SYSTEM AND CARDIAC ARRHYTHMIAS

Cardiac muscle is endowed with the ability to generate an action potential without external stimulation. This property of inherent rhythmicity is referred to as automaticity. Normally, the sinoatrial (SA) node, located in the posterior wall of the right atrium near the entrance of the superior vena cava, acts as the pacemaker for the heart. The SA node has an inherent rhythmicity of about 70 beats/minute, which is faster than any other potential pacemaker in the heart. This node comprises specialized muscle cells of which their resting membrane potential spontaneously inches toward the threshold for depolarization.

Specialized fibers carry the action potential to the atrioventricular (AV) node, located in the lower portion of the right atrium. Before the impulse passes on, it is briefly delayed to permit the atria to contract and contribute an additional portion of blood to the ventricles. The conducting system now divides into right and left bundle branches, ramifying into numerous subbranches that serve the lower reaches of the ventricular myocardium. The presence of gap junctions between cardiac myocytes ensures that all cells are recruited for contraction.

Essentials of the Electrocardiogram

As we have seen, cardiac excitability rests on cycles of depolarization and repolarization of individual cells. The sum total of these forces can be measured on the skin by an electrocardiogram (ECG). Various leads are attached to the extremities and across the precordial area to observe and measure the electrical events in a cardiac cycle from various vantage points. Six limb leads are shown in Figure 24.3, consisting of three unipolar leads and three bipolar limb leads. In addition, there are six precordial leads shown in Figure

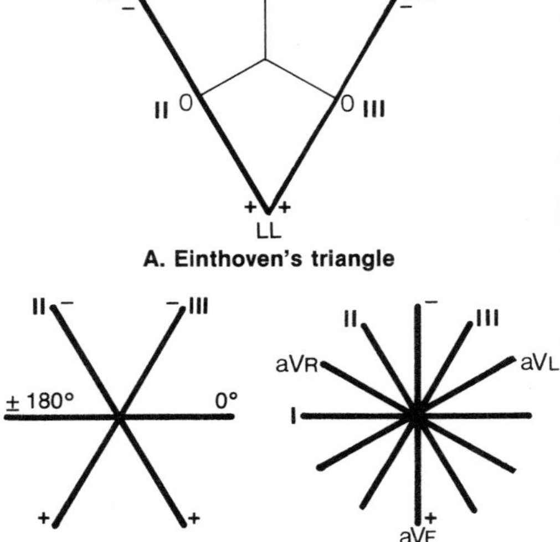

Figure 24.3. Principles of electrocardiogram. (A) Einthoven's triangle is shown, as represented by leads mounted on the right arm (RA), left arm (LA), and left leg (LL), together with the polarities of each. Termed bipolar limb leads, lead I measures the potential difference between the LA and RA, lead II is the potential difference between LL and RA, and lead III is the difference between LL and LA. Lines drawn perpendicular to each of the leads represent the zero potential lines for each. (B) The triaxial reference system, in which the three limb leads are collapsed onto their respective zero potential points. (C) With elimination of the electrode of interest from the bipolar limb lead system, one converts the system to a unipolar one, at the same time increasing (augmenting) the strength of the signal. For these reasons, the potentials so recorded are named according to the eliminated electrode, as aVR, aVL and aVF (a = augmented, F = left leg). By superimposing these unipolar leads over the triaxial system, one obtains the hexaxial system shown here. Reprinted with permission from Bullock J, Boyle J III, Wang MB, et al. Physiology. 3rd ed. Baltimore: Williams & Wilkins, 1995: 139.

24.4. To interpret an ECG tracing, one must realize that when a wave of depolarization proceeds towards the (+) pole, there will be an upward deflection on the ECG. It follows that when an electric force is traveling away from the (+) pole, the deflection will be downward. Also, one should recognize that the deflection will be greater the more parallel the wave is to the position of the lead. Of course, if the deflection is perpendicular to the lead the ECG will be isoelectric, evidencing a flat line. Normally, the SA node is the pacemaker of the heart and because it is located in the top of the right atrium, the first evidence of depolarization on the ECG is the *P wave* which reflects atrial depolarization. There is a slight delay of further conduction at the AV node, registered on the ECG as a return to baseline. Next the ventricles depolarize, recorded on the ECG as the *QRS complex*. After a brief return to baseline, repolarization commences (a process that takes longer than depolarization because of the need to restore the transmembrane potential) and this is manifested as the *T wave*. Because the various leads are deployed in such a way as to view the same process from differing positions, the electric forces will approach the (+) electrodes in some leads and move away from them in others. Thus, some leads present almost mirror images of each other.

CARDIAC ARRHYTHMIAS

Cardiac arrhythmias are usually clinically significant deviations in the normal rate of impulse generation either by the SA node, or by another excitable focus that preempts the normal pacemaker duty of the SA node. This other focus may be within the specialized conduction system or within the heart muscle itself.

Normally, the cardiac impulse, which arises in the SA node, activates the atria and is manifested on the electrocardiogram (ECG) as a P wave. A slight delay of the impulse occurs in the A-V node, seen on the EKG as the P-R interval. Now the wave of depolarization proceeds down the remainder of the conduction system, including the bundle of His and the right and left bundle branches, and ramifies out to the periphery of the ventricular musculature. This entire activation takes place in about 0.10 seconds and generates the QRS complex on the ECG.

Arrhythmias may arise from two broad categories of abnormalities (Table 24.1): (*1*) alterations in generation of the impulse, and (*2*) alteration in propagation of the impulse. Slowing of impulse generation or propagation can lead to bradyarrhythmia, whereas increasing the frequency of impulse generation or formation of an ectopic focus with reentry (see below) can produce a tachyarrhythmia. Specialized cardiac cells in the sinus

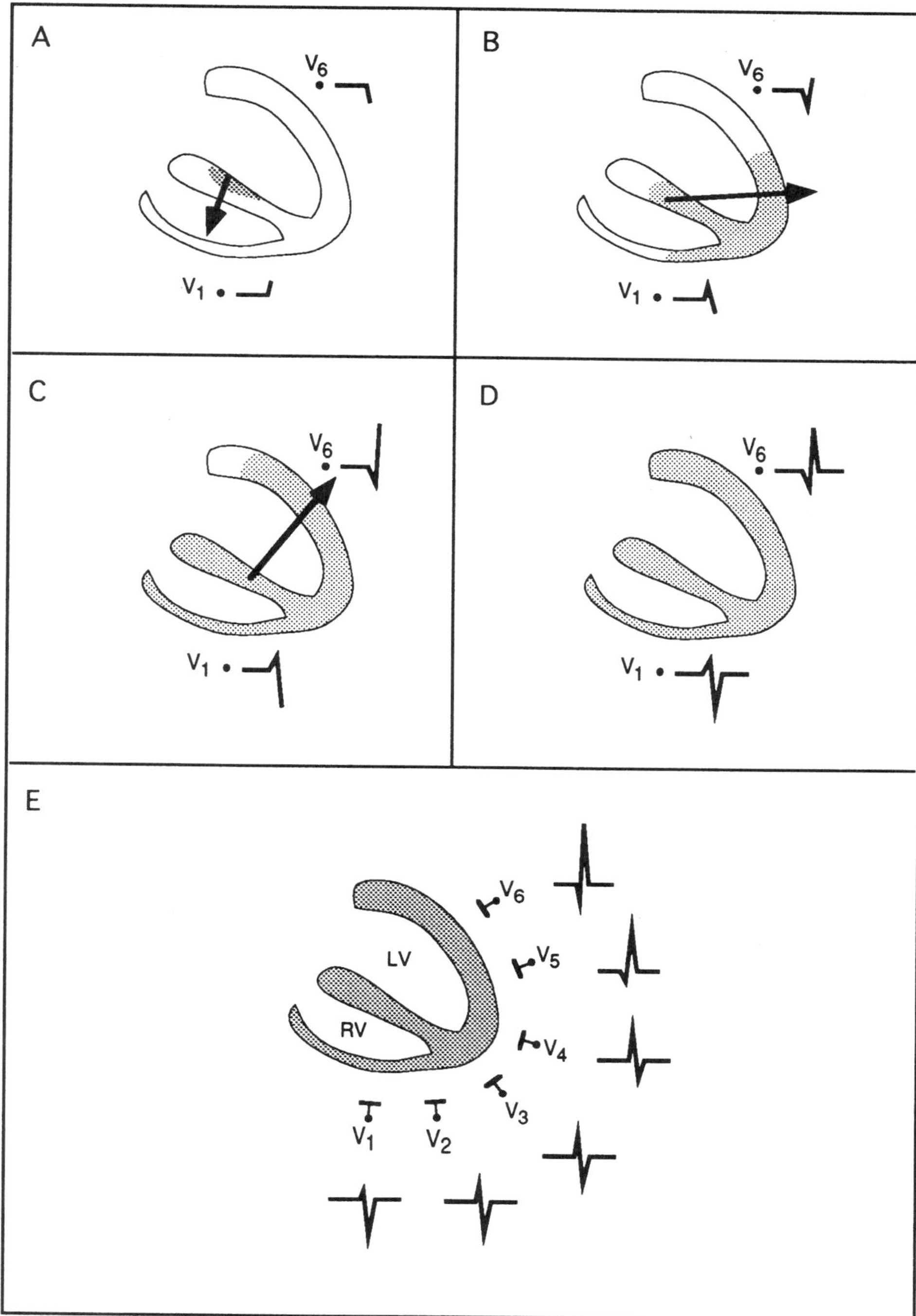

Figure 24.4. Cardiac depolarization recorded by precordial leads. In contrast to the standard leads, which represent electrical forces recorded in a frontal plane, the precordial leads (V1-V6) record electrical vectors in a horizontal plane. Thus, in panels A and D, it can be seen that V1 and V2 are anterior and posterior leads, respectively, based upon the polarity of the deflection. A-D show the tracings obtained from V1 and V6 as depolarization proceeds. Panel E shows the normal QRS complex obtained from each of the six precordial leads. Reprinted with permission from Lilly LS. Pathophysiology of Heart Disease. Baltimore: Williams & Wilkins, 1993: 64.

Table 24.1. Arrhythmias

ABNORMALITY	MECHANISM	CLINICAL EXAMPLES	TREATMENT AND COMMENTS
Bradyarrhythmias			
Altered impulse formation Decreased automaticity	Cholinergic stimulation → ↓ slow phase depolarization of SA node	Sinus bradycardia	No treatment required unless it produces symptoms. Not infrequent in trained athletes.
Altered impulse propagation Conduction blocks	Conduction system damaged or drug-induced impairment	AV Blocks—1°, 2°, 3° 1°—Conduction is prolonged, ECG-PR interval > 0.20 sec. 2°—Some atrial impulses not conducted to ventricles—two types I—Wenckebach or Mobitz I—PR lengthens until 1 P wave fails to be conducted II—Mobitz II—AV conduction stops without the warning of progressive lengthening of PR interval—usually associated with underlying cardiac disease 3°—No impulses conducted from atria to ventricles—P waves do not result in QRS complexes. Latent pacemaker generates an escape rhythm	
Tachyarrhythmias			
Altered impulse formation Enhanced automaticity SA node	Sympathetic stimulation → ↑ slow phase depolarization of SA node	Sinus tachycardia	Usually normal response to exercise, excitement, fever, hypotension
Triggered activity → ectopic focus			
Early after depolarization	Early depolarization believed to stem from ↓ K^+ efflux during repolarization. Usually drug induced (eg, quinidine, sotalol).	Torsade de pointes ECG-wide QRS complexes with sinusoidal pattern	
Delayed after depolarization	↑ intracellular Ca^{++} from digitalis	Atrial premature beats—ectopic focus fires before SA node → P wave that differs from normal P	Exercise abolishes
		Ventricular premature beats—wide QRS with different shape than normal QRS. Bigeminy—every other beat is premature	Exercise abolishes
Altered impulse propagation			
Reentry	Unidirectional block with delay in retrograde conduction → repeat depolarization at site of origin	Paroxysmal supraventricular tachycardia—abrupt onset, heart rate 160–220/minute and regular. P waves differ in contour. Atrial fibrillation—atrial rate 400–600/minute, ventricular rate 80 to 180/minute and irregularly irregular. Risk of emboli and heart failure Atrial flutter—atrial rates 250 to 300/minute with lower ventricular rate due to transmission of only some of impulses	Reentry can be terminated by a spontaneous or induced premature beat
		Ventricular tachycardia—three or more consecutive VPBs, rate 160 to 240/minute	Carotid sinus pressure has no effect
		Ventricular fibrillation—often fatal, disorganized motion of ventricles so that heart does not pump	Defibrillation

SA = sinoatrial
AV = atrioventricular
ECG = electrocardiogram
VPBs = ventricular premature beats

node, atrioventricular node, and the ventricular conducting system (including the bundle of His, bundle branches, and Purkinje fibers) all manifest automaticity. These specialized cells are endowed with cation channels that open when the membrane potential approaches −60 mV, a value considerably less negative than the −90 mV evident in myocytes. With the opening of these cation channels, Na^+ predominantly, but also K^+, slowly enter the cell moving the potential toward threshold at about −40 mV. When the potential reaches threshold, voltage-gated Ca^{++} channels open (opening and closing of these channels is dependent on the membrane potential), and the Ca^{++} ions enter the cells to trigger the action potential. Unlike the situation with myocytes and neurons, where Na^+ rushes into the cell, in the case of pacemaker cells, entry of Ca^{++} is more deliberate. Repolarization in pacemaker cells, like myocytes and neurons, depends largely on K^+ efflux from the cell.

Because the sinus node has the fastest intrinsic beat (70 to 80 beats/minute), it sets the pace for all other cells in the heart, including other specialized conducting cells which normally have slower automatic rates than the sinus node. As an added safeguard against one of these other sites determining the heart rate, the sinus node is able to suppress the automaticity of other specialized sites exerting a restraining effect termed *overdrive suppression*.

Arrhythmias May Arise From Altered Impulse Formation

The normal automaticity of the sinus node may be altered by vagal (cholinergic) stimulation which slows the rate of firing or by sympathetic stimulation which steps up the rate of firing. These two situations are variants of normal and occur commonly, with vagal stimulation attending a Valsalva maneuver and sympathetic stimulation occurring during emotional or physical stress. From the perspective of abnormal function, a latent pacemaker may develop an intrinsic firing rate that exceeds that of the SA node, becoming the site of an ectopic focus that now governs the heart rate. Formation of an ectopic focus is most likely to occur after cell injury, which is often associated with membrane damage and inability to sustain the resting potential. In effect, these injured cells take on the property of specialized pacemaker cells.

Another way in which altered impulse generation can lead to arrhythmias is through the phenomenon termed triggered activity, which, although not strictly a change in the automaticity of cells, can nevertheless spawn a faster rate. In the setting of *triggered activity*, the cell depolarizes normally but somehow triggers an oscillation of the membrane potential called an *afterdepolarization*. These afterdepolarizations come in two varieties: early and late. Early afterdepolarizations are secondary depolarizations that occur before repolarization is accomplished and are seen in the setting of myocardial hypoxia, as in angina pectoris. However, late afterdepolarizations occur only after repolarization is complete, being found in digitalis toxicity when intracellular Ca^{++} is abnormally elevated.

Arrhythmias May Arise From Altered Impulse Propagation

Abnormalities of impulse conduction can arise from (*1*) slowing of conduction or block, (*2*) reentry, and (*3*) bypass pathways. Although it should be obvious that conduction delay or block leads to a bradyarrhythmia, it will become clear from our discussion why reentry and bypass pathways cause tachyarrhythmias.

Conduction blocks can result from ischemia, anatomic damage, or anomalies, and probably most commonly from drugs. *Reentry* is a self-sustaining, but not self-initiated, electrical discharge that forms a closed loop. Repetitive firing of the impulse over this closed loop can generate a tachyarrhythmia. How does such a closed loop form in the first place? Reentry can occur when a normal impulse is blocked in one of the branches of the conduction system (Figure 24.5). The conducted impulse now must travel in a retrograde direction, but at a slower rate, through the pathway that was blocked from above. Such a situation could easily arise in damaged myocardium because scar tissue would be nonconducting, forcing the impulse to traverse a different route. Because conduction is delayed over the retrograde pathway, this gives the initial pathway time to repolarize, preparing it to be stimulated by the retrograde route. This

Figure 24.5. The reentry phenomenon. (A) Normal conduction involves travel of an action potential (AP) down conduction pathways α and β which originated at branch point x. At more distal branch points, the AP is expected to again divide as shown. (B) Unidirectional block is shown in path β, following which the AP travels through α to more distal conduction pathways, until at point y the AP enters β and travels retrograde to the point of the block. (C) Normal retrograde conduction occurs when a portion of the conduction system has not had adequate time for repolarization (α), in which case the impulse conducted from point y retrograde through β dies out. (D) If conduction velocity along β is abnormally slow, when the AP reaches point x it can once again travel down α, establishing a reentry loop. This phenomenon may prevent normal AP conduction from point x. Reprinted with permission from Lilly LS. Pathophysiology of Heart Disease. Baltimore: Williams & Wilkins, 1993: 188.

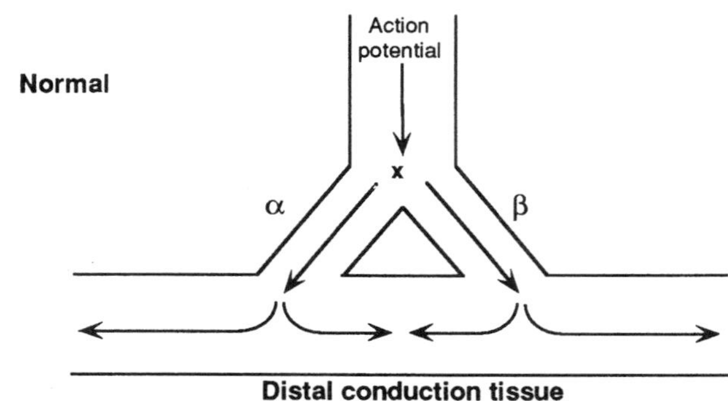

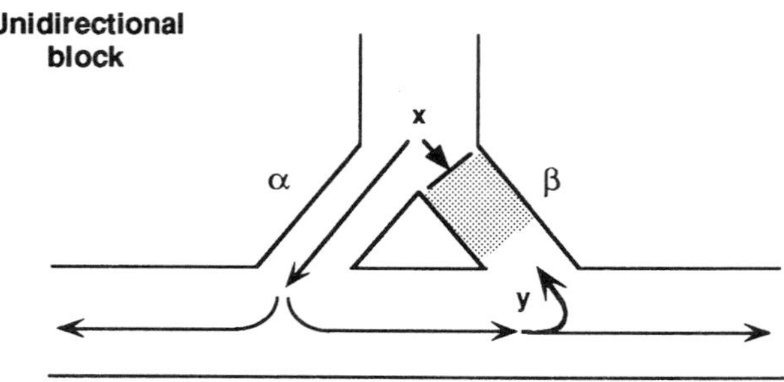

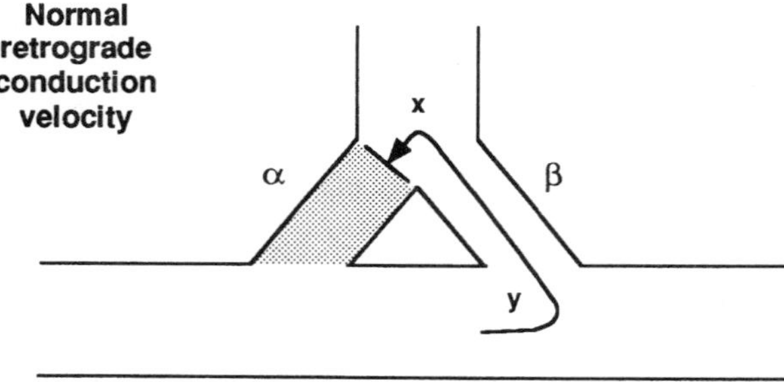

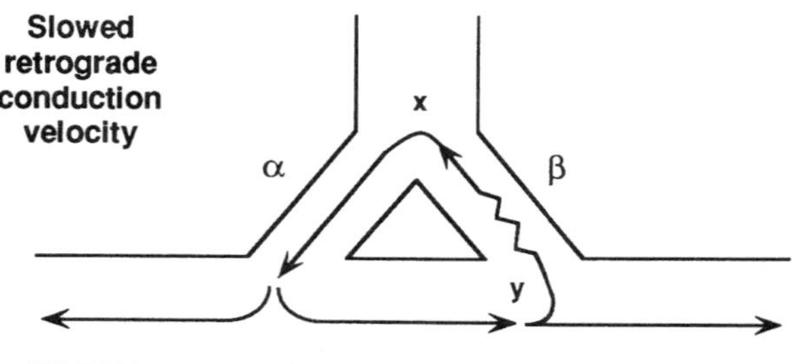

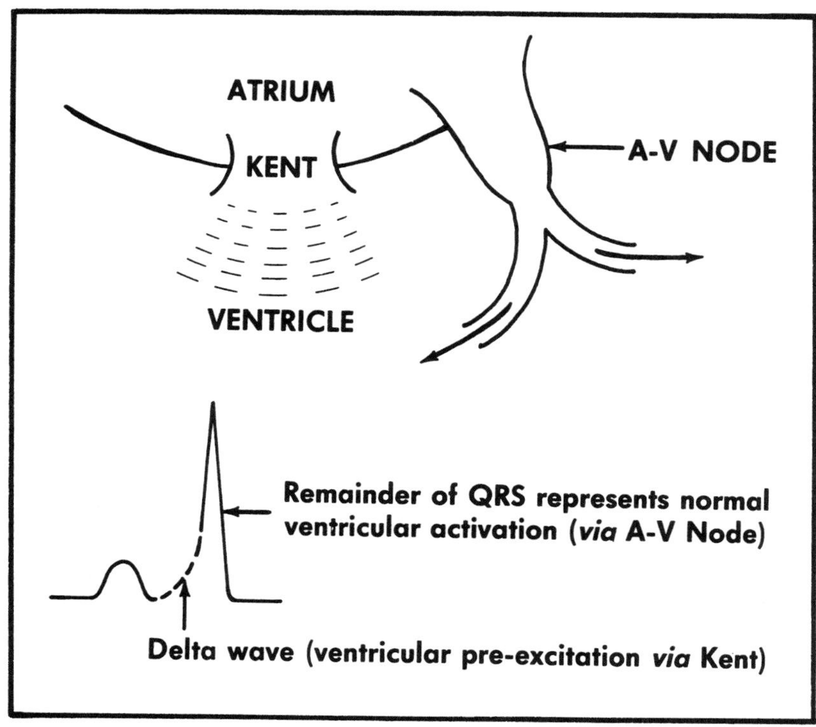

Figure 24.6. Aberrant atrial-ventricular (A-V) conduction. Persistence of an atrioventricular myocardial bundle can result in ventricular preexcitation which shortens the PR interval and produces a "delta wave." Reprinted with permission from Stein E. Electrocardiographic Interpretation: A Self-Study Approach to Clinical Electrocardiography. Baltimore: Williams & Wilkins, 1991: 470.

creates a loop of excitation that can recur indefinitely.

Finally, with a *bypass tract*, normal conduction through the AV node is supplemented by conduction through an additional pathway (usually the Bundle of Kent) so that the ventricles are depolarized via two routes. This results in earlier than normal stimulation of the ventricles, because the normal delay operative at the AV node does not occur in the accessory pathway. Moreover, in this setting, ventricular activation is a composite of the normal and bypass tracts which widens the QRS complex and depolarizes the ventricles sooner than normal. The evidence for this early activation is an upstroke on the QRS complex, called the delta wave (Figure 24.6).

Although an ECG tracing is the best way to document and diagnose an arrhythmia, it may not help in the situation when the arrhythmias occur infrequently, thus being missed during the limited time that the ECG was obtained. Ambulatory ECGs can usually resolve that limitation. But it should be realized that missed beats can be identified during physical examination if one pays particular attention to the presence of a pulse deficit in which cardiac beats by ausculation are not matched by an equal number of radial pulse beats.

Therapeutic Approaches to Cardiac Arrhythmias

From a clinical perspective, various measures can be used to combat formation or propagation of arrhythmias. One approach is to inhibit automaticity in an ectopic focus, or to render the membrane of such a focus less excitable. As for re-entry, which is believed to underlie most tachyarrhythmias, therapeutic measures involve prolonging the refractory period, further slowing conduction or using a strong electrical stimulus to normalize the aberrant rhythm. This last method is called cardioversion, and has been made familiar because of its portrayal on television and in the movies. The goal of cardioversion is to present a powerful electrical stimulus to the heart, compelling all cells to respond to this irresistible inducement to take up a normal rhythm.

Anti-arrhythmic drugs fall into five categories: (*1*) membrane stabilizers that inhibit Na^+ channel activation, thereby slowing the pace of depolarization. Quinidine and lidocaine are examples of these agents. (*2*) Ca^{++} channel blockers that inhibit the normal slow influx of Ca^{++} that maintains the plateau of the action potential. They thus decrease automaticity and slow AV conduction. (*3*) Beta-adrenergic antagonists that, by blocking binding of norepinephrine and epinephrine, prolong AV conduction. (*4*) Digitalis glycosides that increase the refractory period of specialized conduction tissues and (*5*) agents that block K^+ channels thereby decreasing automaticity and prolonging conduction and the interval that the muscle remains refractory.

PATHOPHYSIOLOGY AND BIOCHEMISTRY OF THE FAILING MYOCARDIUM

Many authorities have defined congestive heart failure as a clinical syndrome in which the function of cardiac muscle is impaired so that the pumping action of the heart is incompetent, decreasing the volume of blood ejected and impeding venous return. This impaired myocardial function involves both abnormalities in contraction as well as of relaxation. Most notably, evidence is accumulating that some of the biochemical responses of the failing heart lead to the synthesis of proteins that further hasten the decline in myocardial function, and may even be the proximate cause of myocardial cell death.

Congestive heart failure is synonymous with pump failure and consequent venous congestion that results from various insults to the heart. Such insults include diverse conditions such as coronary artery disease, hypertension, valvular lesions, and the cardiomyopathies. When heart failure ensues from any of these conditions, the ability of the heart to pump the blood is severely impaired with the result that cardiac output cannot match the metabolic requirements of the body. Because coronary arteriosclerosis and hypertension exact a much greater toll on the left ventricle, and because they are the most common causes of heart failure it is the left ventricle that is usually the first to fail. Clinically, this translates into the inability of the individual to maintain a reasonable level of activity, so that, for example, a patient in heart failure may be out of breath while at rest. When the right ventricle fails, as it usually does when there is prior left ventricular failure, systemic venous congestion and peripheral edema become additional clinical findings.

Of course, it is possible to produce overfilling and congestion of the circulation without heart failure, from excessively large or rapid intravenous infusions or in severe anemia. If the excessive rate of infusion was to continue, it is likely that the ventricular muscle fibers will elongate beyond their range of efficient contractile length (Frank-Starling mechanism), ventricular end-diastolic pressures will increase, and the heart will fail as a pump.

Compensatory Responses to Reduced Cardiac Output Eventually Impair Cardiac Function

Early on in heart failure, the blood pressure is decreased, the body responding first by peripheral vasoconstriction and then by salt and water retention. This maintains blood flow to the brain and heart, using much the same neurohumoral reflexes that attempt to maintain the effective circulating blood volume after hemorrhage. As an immediate response to hemorrhage or heart failure, such measures by the body contribute to survival, but in the setting of heart failure they further exacerbate the worsening cardiac and circulatory performance. Peripheral vasoconstriction increases the afterload confronting the already failing ventricles, whereas salt and water retention further exacerbates the systemic and pulmonary venous congestion.

Alterations in Mechanical Function

Adaptation of the myocardium to changes in workload is governed by the relationship, defined by Starling, between the resting myocardial fiber length and the force of contraction and extent of fiber shortening. Thus, within limits, the longer

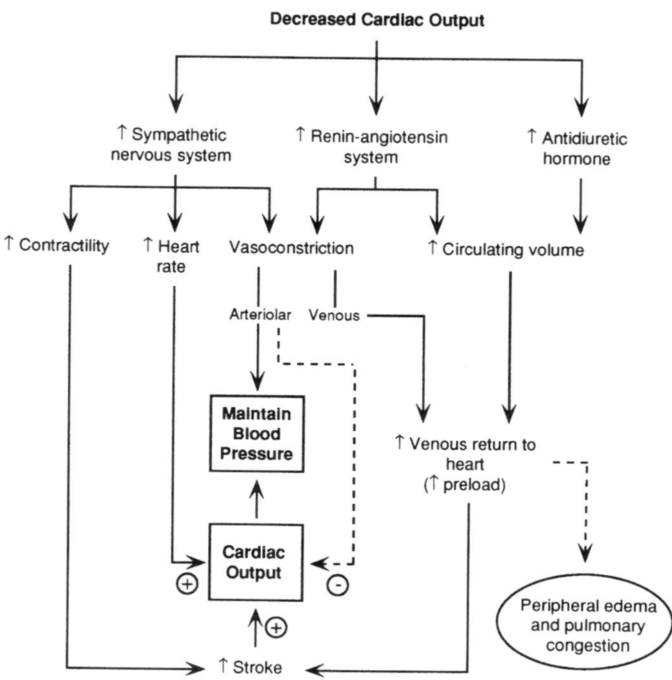

Figure 24.7. Neurohormonal response to congestive heart failure. Maintenance of blood pressure and cardiac output (boxes) are the common factors at which all responses are directed. The sympathetic nervous system acts directly to increase contractility, heart rate, and blood pressure. However, the renin-angiotensin system and antidiuretic hormone are actually "systems gone awry," because they each result in an absolute increase in circulating blood volume, which only superimposes an additional load on an already compromised pump. Reprinted with permission from Lilly LS. Pathophysiology of Heart Disease. Baltimore: Williams & Wilkins, 1993: 157.

the resting fiber length, the greater the force exerted by the fiber. This relationship is traceable, at a molecular level, to progressively more favorable orientation of actin and myosin filaments, in a sense engaging more "gear teeth" to deliver more power. In this respect, under normal circumstances, the myocardium can be viewed as intrinsically self-regulating, adjusting its output per stroke (or beat) according to the volume entering under low pressure. As we have seen, this is commonly termed the ventricular end-diastolic pressure or "preload." Clinically, preload is usually measured in terms of right and left atrial pressures as reflected by central venous (right atrial) and pulmonary capillary wedge (left atrial) pressures. These relationships are illustrated in Figure 24.7.

As with any mechanical system, the ability of the myocardium to compensate for increased ventricular volume has finite limits. These limits, when exceeded, will cause the myocardial fibers to become elongated to the degree that the "gear teeth" cannot effectively engage, reducing the efficiency of contraction and resulting in decreased stroke volume. Such a situation results in congestive heart failure.

Alterations in Contractility

Contractility may be thought of simply as the biochemical status of the myocardial cell that confers functional status upon the sarcomere. Thus, contractility may be profoundly influenced by hypoxia, types of fuels supplied to the myocardium, acidosis, ionic balances, endotoxins, and a variety of other factors. For instance, acidosis increases the resistance to impulse conduction at gap junctions. This slows the rate at which the action potential propagates, creating the conditions for conduction delay or block.

As noted earlier, energy requirements of the myocardium are very high; to subserve these demands, mitochondrial density of the myocyte is correspondingly high. Given the fact that oxidative mitochondrial metabolism generates ATP which is used to establish the actin-myosin bridges that bring about contraction, any significant decrease in myocardial oxygenation is apt to affect contractility. When cardiac muscle hypertrophies, mitochondria more distant from the source of oxygen will not get their fair share, impairing cardiac function. Thus, as we will see below, hypertrophy is in some ways maladaptive. If one administers oxygen to a patient in heart failure this will not only improve myocardial contractility but peripheral tissue oxygenation as well.

Another factor important in determining myocardial contractility is the role of calcium. We have emphasized elsewhere (see Chapter 21) the vital role calcium plays in both general cellular metabolism and in muscle contraction. We have seen that, one of the three protein subunits, troponin-C, of the trimeric regulatory protein troponin, has a specific calcium-binding site. Interactions between troponin-C and calcium are regulated by a second inhibitory subunit of troponin, troponin-I. Binding of calcium to troponin-C induces conformational changes in a separate regulatory protein, tropomyosin. Tropomyosin is normally bound to a third subunit, troponin-T, which blocks actin-myosin interaction (Figure 24.2). But the conformational changes induced in tropomyosin, by the Ca-troponin-C complex, favors this interaction allowing the formation of cross-links. In this fashion, the development of force of contraction will be proportional to the number of Ca-troponin-C complexes formed which, in turn, is partially related to the calcium concentration in the surrounding milieu of the sarcomere. Dissociation of the Ca-troponin-C complex initiates relaxation.

It should be clear that changes in the intracellular calcium concentration regulates muscle contraction and relaxation. The major intracellular calcium pools include those in the mitochondria and sarcoplasmic reticulum. Extracellular calcium can enter by (*1*) calcium-specific, time- and voltage-dependent "slow channels" subject to selective blockade by calcium-blocking agents; and (*2*) nonspecific ionic channels; or, (*3*) via a Na^+-Ca^{++} exchange system.

As seen above, when the action potential causes rapid Na^+ influx as part of membrane depolarization, there is a concomitant calcium influx through the voltage-dependent slow channels with a resultant abrupt modest increase in intracellular calcium concentration. Through a mechanism not entirely understood, this initial increase induces a secondary release of large quantities of calcium sequestered in the sarcoplasmic reticulum. These two coupled events then initiate the cascade of troponin-related actions, considered above, leading to myocardial contraction. Thus, the entry and exit of calcium from the myocardial cell is a target for the pharmacologic action of various inotropic and calcium-blocking agents.

Alterations in Energy Relationships in the Failing Heart

Because the failing heart is confronted with both the problems of circulatory overload (Na^+ and water retention) and elevated head pressure (peripheral vasoconstriction) even if a normal amount of ATP were generated it would not be sufficient to meet these unusual demands. Unfortunately, however, there is an absolute decrease in production of ATP by the heart in failure, whereas the requirements of the hypertrophied heart are even greater than those of a normal heart. In addition, remember that oxygen delivery to the myocardium depends largely upon aortic flow, which is also reduced in heart failure. Thus, many factors conspire against efficient use of substrate and oxygen by the failing myocardium.

Hypertrophy of Cardiac Muscle

Because cardiac muscle cells are unable to divide, their biologic response to various stresses, including hypertension, ischemia, infarction, or heart failure is hypertrophy of individual cells. Factors that can stimulate hypertrophy include pressure (resistance to flow), neurotransmitters, and several growth factors. Acting through G proteins and membrane tyrosine kinases, these agents stimulate production of nuclear oncogene encoded proteins (especially products of c-myc, c-jun, and c-fos) which incite the genome to augment production of various cardiac cell *oncoproteins*.

Unfortunately, hypertrophy itself and the product of these signalling molecules does not extend the life of the heart. Rather, connective tissue replaces necrotic myocytes impairing the contractility of the heart by increasing the mechanical load on surviving sarcomeres. The combination of cardiac enlargement and fibrosis increases the propensity to develop arrhythymias because conduction slows and the cardiac impulse must traverse a longer path. Worse yet, the cardiac cell oncoproteins produced during the hypertrophic response to heart failure somehow hasten the deterioration of the heart. It is speculated that the capacity of the failing heart to turn on protein synthesis rests on the recruitment of certain oncogenes that normally are expressed only during fetal life. When heart failure triggers this oncogenic response, to augment protein synthesis, the trade-off is that the proteins synthesized actually accelerate the decline of cardiac function. This has been called the *cardiomyopathy of overload*.

It is important to distinguish between the normal hypertrophy that attends exercise and the pathologic hypertrophy that attends the chronic overload of heart failure. Hypertrophy that follows an exercise program does not culminate in the dramatic decline of cardiac muscle lifespan that attends the cardiomyopathy of overload. In fact, as an initial response to overload in early cardiac failure, hypertrophy exerts a positive influence reducing the total amount of energy that must be expended to bring about contraction and relaxation by reducing the contribution of each sarcomere to contraction. But, because overload persists for months to years, growth factors and oncogenes participate in a process that centers on production of fetal isoforms of proteins normally represented in the mature heart by a different isoform. These fetal isoforms apparently are a biochemical Trojan horse, hastening cardiac muscle death. This is clearly an important area for further research, if the devastation caused by these isoforms is to be prevented.

Treatment of Congestive Heart Failure

Treatment of heart failure centers around three objectives: reducing the metabolic demands of the body, enhancing ventricular contractility, and decreasing cardiac filling pressures. Metabolic demands can be reduced by instituting physical and psychologic rest, ending smoking, restricting salted foods, and eating small frequent meals rather than larger meals. For over 200 years, digitalis has been the mainstay of therapy to improve the force of cardiac contraction. This cardiac glycoside (and its congeners) are believed to act by augmenting intracellular calcium by inhibiting the actions of the Na^+, K^+ ATPase. The primacy of digitalis in treatment of heart failure is now being supplanted by the angiotensin-converting enzyme inhibitors, which by blocking formation of angiotensin, a powerful vasoconstrictor, lower peripheral vascular resistance. Thus, they mitigate the afterload that faces the failing heart. The popularity of ACE inhibitors stems from their ability to extend life in patients suffering from moderate to severe heart failure. Finally, diuretics can help reduce the volume of the venous return by ridding the body of excess fluid.

SHOCK

Shock is a broad term that signifies the inability of the cardiovascular system to provide adequate O_2 and nutrients for the body's cells. Although many different etiologies can result in shock (eg, hemorrhage, cardiac dysfunction, vascular obstruction, and sepsis), the thread common to all of them is failure of the microcirculation to meet the metabolic needs of cells. Bereft of O_2 and substrate, cells rapidly deplete ATP, membrane dysfunction ensues, intermediary metabolism is thrown into disarray, and cells swell. Cell death can result if this progression is not halted before changes become irreversible. It is the interplay of three major factors that governs the adequacy of the perfusion of peripheral tissues: cardiac output, vascular resistance, and the state of the microcirculation. We will consider each in turn.

At rest in normal adults the *cardiac output* is about 6.5 L per minute (72 beats/minute × 90 ml/beat). The major determinant of the stroke volume, the amount of blood ejected per contraction, is the circulating blood volume. Thus, hemorrhage, third-space sequestration of fluid, or severe external fluid loss can lead to a *hypovolemic* state. This is not the only factor, however, as one can have a blood volume that is ample but inappropriately distributed. Inadequate venous tone or inadequate intrathoracic pressure are two factors that can cause inadequate perfusion because of maldistribution of blood. Not to be overlooked is the role of the power and rate of the cardiac contraction, referred to as the inotropic state of the heart. Factors such as sympathetic stimulation, coronary artery perfusion of the heart muscle, metabolic demands of the heart, and abnormal conditions such as hypoxia and acidosis, all influence the force of cardiac contraction.

Resistance to blood flow is predominantly a function of the cross-sectional area of the arteriolar bed (itself a function of vascular smooth muscle tone). The arterioles are the portals to the nutritional capillaries that feed the cells. Too great a resistance at the level of the arterioles can greatly impair flow to the capillaries. Vascular smooth muscle tone is governed by neurogenic, humoral, and local metabolic factors.

Ultimately, the locus of malfunction in shock resides at the level of the *microcirculation* or capillary network, because it is at that level that cells receive their ration of O_2 and nutrients. No matter how satisfactory the delivery of arterial blood to an organ, it is the distribution via arterioles and capillaries that determines cell survival.

Pathophysiology of Shock

From both a conceptual and therapeutic perspective, it is useful to visualize shock as proceeding along a continuum of derangements. Compensated hypotension characterizes early shock, ensuring that the brain and heart receive adequate blood. During this stage, blood flow through the microcirculation is nonuniform in response to a sympathetically mediated vasoconstriction, being ill-matched to cellular O_2 requirements of many organs other than brain and heart. This stage of early shock can progress rapidly to one of decompensation in which the classic clinical findings of hypotension, increased heart rate, and weak pulse are associated with confusion, oliguria, and evidence of myocardial ischemia. The critical role of sympathetic stimulation in compensating for circulatory derangements is evidenced by cold clammy extremities. At this stage, perfusion in all microvascular beds is borderline and requires rapid and decisive intervention to restore cardiac output and tissue perfusion.

If restorative measures are not adequate, or if the process progresses downhill at too rapid a pace, then the unrelenting sympathetic stimulation further compromises flow to vital organs ending in cell death. Sequelae such as acute renal failure, ulceration of the GI tract, damage to the vascular endothelium with consequent disseminated intravascular coagulation, further myocardial ischemia, and liberation of lysosomal hydrolases all conspire to make this stage of shock irreversible.

Deranged Cellular Biochemistry In Shock

The wide range of organ dysfunction in shock involving the kidneys, liver, lungs, vascular endothelium, and ultimately the heart and brain all reflect profoundly altered cellular biochemistry. Hypoxia, from microcirculatory failure, sets off a vicious cycle of events that begins with crippling of aerobic metabolism, causing lactate and H^+ to accumulate intracellularly. With diminished ATP levels, membrane transport suffers, especially the Na^+-K^+ ATPase which can no longer reverse the incessant entry of Na^+ into the cell along its concentration gradient.

Calcium homeostasis is also adversely affected, perhaps directly by effects on the Na^+/Ca^{++} exchanger, but most forcefully by H^+ blocking Ca^{++} entry into myocardial cells by the slow Ca^{++} channel. H^+ also impairs release of Ca^{++} from the sarcoplasmic reticulum. Because Ca^{++} plays such a critical role in promoting myocardial contractility, intracellular acidosis interferes with the effectiveness of the heart as a pump. Obviously, such detrimental effects on the myocardium further reduce the adequacy of the circulation. If this continues, protein synthesis shuts down, cells swell, and lysosomes leak out their potent hydrolytic enzymes, bringing about the cell's demise.

Causes of Shock

There are four main categories that account for most cases of shock. We already have encountered several of them in our earlier discussion. They are: (*1*) hypovolemic shock, (*2*) cardiogenic shock, (*3*) neurogenic shock, and (*4*) vasogenic shock caused by maldistribution of blood in the vascular system as, for example, occurs in sepsis (see Chapter 19).

Hypovolemic shock is attributable to hemorrhage or fluid loss (external or internal) and causes profoundly decreased cardiac output, because the blood volume is inadequate. Although a normal subject can easily sustain a loss of 5% of his blood volume (equivalent to donating a unit of blood), a loss of 10% will cause a moderate decrease in cardiac output with a slight but measurable decrease in blood pressure. If acute blood loss approaches 20%, hypotension and further decrease in cardiac output become evident. A sudden loss of 40% of the circulating blood volume is at the extreme of this continuum, putting the individual into a state of profound hypotension attended by a dramatic decrease in cardiac output. At this point, neurohumoral mechanisms, including norepinephrine, epinephrine, renin, and adrenocorticotropic hormone (ACTH) make a valiant effort to compensate with tachycardia, tachypnea, and extreme peripheral vasoconstriction. The vasoconstriction decreases the size of the vascular bed, especially on the venous side (which carries the greater blood volume) and maintains flow to the heart and brain. To preserve blood flow to the heart and brain, flow to the kidneys, gastrointestinal tract, skin, and skeletal muscle must decrease drastically. In addition, transcapillary filling attempts to replace the fluids lost from the circulation. Sometimes the expected sympathetic response is blunted by activation of ventricular mechanoreceptors which cause bradycardia instead of tachycardia. Whatever the response, in the setting of such severe volume loss and hypotension, one must act swiftly to prevent progression of the shock state.

In *cardiogenic shock*, the heart fails as a pump. It is most often the result of an acute myocardial infarction (see below), but may also occur with advanced heart failure, severe arrhythymias, and other processes that impair function of cardiac muscle like tamponade. In each instance, there is decreased cardiac output because of decreased cardiac contractility; neck vein distension reflects the high filling pressure. Consequently, the metabolic needs of the body cannot be met. It is noteworthy that the sympathetic compensatory responses, so beneficial in hypovolemic shock, can actually be harmful in cardiogenic shock. Although raising the peripheral vascular resistance may maintain the effective circulating blood volume and increase the force and rate of contraction, in cardiogenic shock, it will be at the expense of increasing the pressure head against which the already damaged heart must pump blood.

Neurogenic shock is associated with loss of vascular tone, creating the inability to maintain adequate peripheral resistance. In effect, the pipes are too large for the contained blood volume. It is most often associated with central nervous system or high spinal cord injury or with spinal anesthesia. Although blood pressure may be low, the patient is bradycardic with warm, sometimes flushed extremities.

Vasogenic or distributive shock is characterized by a decrease in vascular resistance that is not offset by an increase in cardiac output. The most common cause of distributive shock is septic shock, and in this and other states of distributive shock some vascular beds may be adequately perfused, whereas other beds will be drastically deprived of O_2 and nutrients. Early septic shock differs from the other forms of shock considered in that cardiac output is elevated, systemic vascular resistance is diminished, hypotension may or may not be present, and the extremities are warm. Associated findings that point to sepsis include fever, hyperventilation and respiratory alkalosis. Even with the apparent preservation of perfusion, patients who have reached the age of cognition will manifest confusion or frank hallucinations.

There is evidence that the local vasculature loses its autoregulatory properties and that not only is the metabolic capacity of the vascular endothelium affected but so too are ventricular myocytes. As septic shock progresses, cellular consumption of available O_2 declines, leading some to speculate that there is a deficit in the ability of mitochondria to use O_2. The earlier preservation of cardiac output gives way to worsening cardiac performance, so that advanced septic shock looks clinically like other forms of shock.

CORONARY ARTERY DISEASE AND MYOCARDIAL INFARCTION

Inadequate coronary blood flow to the ventricular myocardium can cause ischemia and pain (*angina pectoris*) and if severe enough can cause the death of cardiac muscle (*myocardial infarction*). Angina can be brought on in an individual whose coronary circulation is narrowed, by such common events as exercise, emotional stress, or any other condition where sympathetic stimulation is intensified. Recall that there is little margin for further O_2 extraction by the heart, because the heart extracts about 75% of the O_2 brought to it by the coronary arteries. This high O_2 extraction distinguishes the heart from most other organs, making it peculiarly vulnerable to ischemia. Consequently, the only way to increase myocardial O_2 supply is by increasing the rate of coronary blood flow.

Most cases of angina pectoris and myocardial infarction are attributable to underlying severe *coronary atherosclerosis*. The role of abnormal lipoprotein homeostasis and cholesterol metabolism in the pathogenesis of atherosclerosis has been considered in Chapter 15. In individuals who consume a diet rich in meats and other cholesterol rich foods, fatty deposits and fibrous plaques accumulate over time on the walls of arteries, causing a narrowing of the vessel lumen. Although such processes go on throughout the body, plaque formation is most pronounced at branch points in the coronary and cerebral arterial systems. Not only do plaques cause local stenosis, but worse yet, they are often friable. Friable plaques may fracture, liberating a piece that lodges in a vessel causing occlusion. In other instances, if the plaque surface is breached, the exposed site serve as a nidus for further thrombus growth with vessel occlusion.

The prevailing theory on how atherosclerosis progresses envisions the initial event as injury to the vascular endothelium and is called the *response-to-injury hypothesis* (Figure 24.8). A site of endothelial injury, caused by hypercholesterolemia, hypertension, cigarette smoking, or diabetes mellitus attracts monocytes and platelets which adhere to the damaged vessel. Monocytes migrate deeper into the vessel wall, become transformed into macrophages, which liberate oxygen radicals

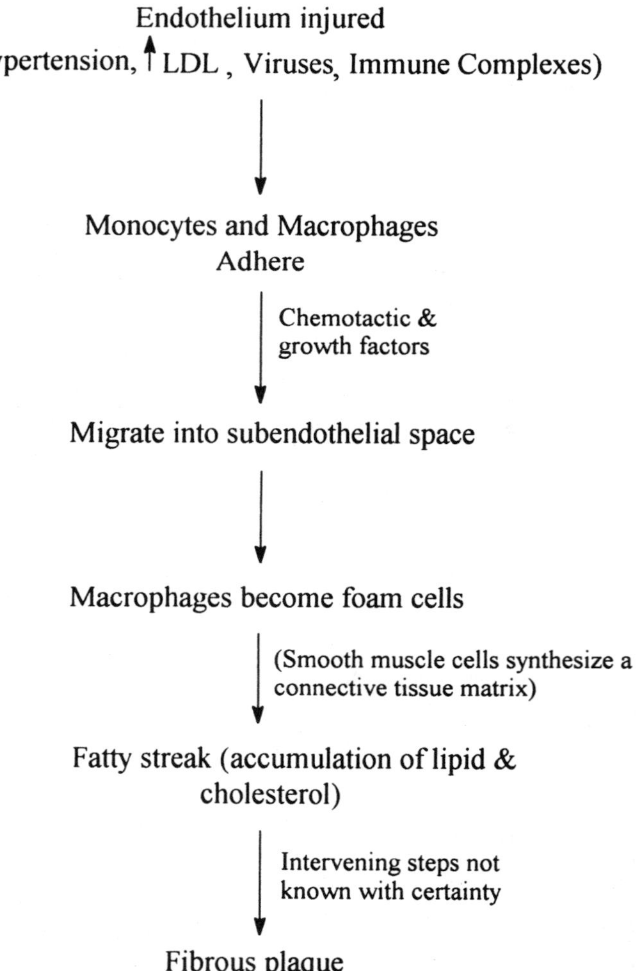

Figure 24.8. Hypothetical response-to-injury mechanism causing atherosclerosis. The common factor of endothelial injury (by multiple factors) leads to adhesion of platelets and monocytes at the site of damage. Through chemotaxis the monocytes migrate subendothelially and are converted to macrophages, releasing oxidative metabolites which enhance the damage and oxidize low density lipoproteins. The macrophages then express surface receptors for and take up the modified low density lipoproteins (LDLs), thus converting to foam cells. Simultaneously, there is migration of smooth muscle cells from the arterial media to the intima, where the smooth muscle cells produce extracellular matrix and ingest ambient lipid to become foam cells. The proliferation of extracellular matrix material together with the formation of foam cells in a concentrated area of initial damage leads to fatty streaks and fibrous plaque formation.

and alter LDL-cholesterol to an oxidized form. These macrophages also express LDL receptors and take up this modified LDL-chol becoming foam cells. Smooth muscle cells, which can express a synthetic, rather than the more familiar contractile phenotype, are drawn to the intima by platelet derived growth factor (PDGF) and other chemotactic agents. Spurred on by a variety of mitogens, derived from platelets, macrophages, and damaged endothelium, these smooth muscle cells proliferate secreting excessive collagen, elastin, and glycosaminoglycans which contribute to the formation of the fibrous plaque.

Normal endothelium is armed with many agents that maintain a nonthrombogenic state, and normal coronary arteries are no exception. First, when a clot forms, the fibrinolytic system is set in motion by tissue plasminogen activator (t-PA) which generates plasmin from plasminogen. Plasmin is a potent enzyme which strikes fibrin clots and dissolves them. Second, procoagulants like thrombin are inactivated by antithrombin III (AT III) so that unwarranted clotting is stopped in its tracks. Activated coagulation factors V and VIII are degraded by another inhibitor of coagulation, protein C. Third, endothelial cells secrete prostacyclin, a prostanoid that blocks platelet aggregation. Finally, various agents—adenosine, thiolated NO (endothelium-derived relaxing factor), and bradykinin—cause vasodilatation when markers of hypoxia like lactate and CO_2 accumulate.

But, vascular endothelium on which a fibrous plaque has formed is no longer nonthrombogenic. The foci of foam cells and elements of the extracellular matrix are particularly thrombogenic, especially when the surface is broken so that collagen and other activators of the coagulation cascade are now uncovered. By the same token, endothelium that harbors a fibrous plaque no longer secretes antithrombogenic substances like prostacyclin and thrombomodulin or vasodilators like NO.

Myocardial Infarction

Myocardial infarction is the leading cause of death in industrialized countries, accounting for over one million attacks per year in the U.S. alone. Worse yet, in the U.S., an estimated 300,000 die of massive myocardial infarction or from the attendant complications, most commonly fatal arrhythmias, before reaching the hospital. When perfusion of the myocardium is so severely compromised as to cause death of the muscle, infarction occurs. Clinically, many but not all patients experience the well-known symptoms of crushing retrosternal chest pain with radiation down the left arm and perhaps the lower jaw, profuse sweating, nausea, vomiting, restlessness, and a premonition of imminent death. Some, however, experience "indigestion" and do not realize (until too late in some cases) that the lack of effect of antacids and progression of pain announces the occurrence of a myocardial infarction.

For many patients, there is preceding history of vague symptoms—fleeting chest pain with exertion, breathlessness, or undue fatigue or severe indigestion—that is too often discounted by the subject. Not infrequently, several weeks later such individuals suffer a myocardial infarction, and in those who do not succumb, this antecedent history can sometimes be elicited. In short then, myocardial infarctions in patients at risk do not always come without warning. Without a doubt, it is in such patients that the personal physician must be alert to symptoms and be prepared to recommend various measures to ameliorate known risk factors, like hypertension, hypercholesterolemia, and smoking.

Pathophysiology of Myocardial Infarction

Left ventricular muscle is most vulnerable to ischemia and coronary occlusion because of its greater thickness than the right ventricle, the greater wall stresses that it braves, and the pressure against which it pumps. Infarcts can extend the full thickness of the myocardium (transmural or Q infarcts) or may involve only the subendothelium (nontransmural or non-Q infarct). Full thickness infarcts usually are attributable to prolonged occlusion of a coronary artery or a branch, whereas subendothelial infarcts are not usually associated with such extensive impairment of the blood supply. Nevertheless, because the subendothelium is perfused by vessels that pass through contracting muscle and because its blood supply has few collaterals, blood flow to the subendothelium is always somewhat at risk. And if these vessels are atherosclerotic, then the risk for myocardial infarction is, if anything, greatly enhanced.

If the blood supply carrying O_2 and nutrients is completely cut off from a zone of heart muscle, irreversible cell injury occurs within 20 minutes. This injury causes membranes to become leaky and mitochondria to swell impairing both the integrity of the cell and the ability to generate ATP. Anoxia also depletes the modest cardiac stores of glycogen and causes lactic acid to accumulate. The Na^+-K^+ ATPase malfunctions and cellular edema and loss of K^+ into the extracellular compartment ensue. This hyperkalemia may be one factor in the propensity of infarcted myocardium to arrhythmias like ventricular fibrillation.

Finally, intracellular Ca^{++} levels increase in ischemic cells because of loss from storage compartments (sarcoplasmic reticulum and mitochondria) and increased uptake through various pumps and channels. Persistently elevated intracellular Ca^{++} sparks activation of lipases and proteases which set the cell on a course to degradation and death, but even short-lived elevation of Ca^{++} can cause serious damage.

If the patient survives the early period with its heightened risk for fatal arrhythmia a collagen scar eventually forms, replacing the necrotic muscle cells with a patch that maintains the integrity of the ventricle wall, but is otherwise nonfunctional being neither able to conduct an impulse nor contract. As already pointed out, this nonfunctional area increases the work-load of the surviving myocardium.

Electrocardiographic Findings in Myocardial Infarction

The ECG manifestation of transmural myocardial infarction is an abnormal Q wave (Figure 24.9), recognized by a duration of >1 small box on the ECG and a depth >25% of the height of the entire QRS complex. These abnormal Q waves are found in leads that reflect the distorted electrical activity of the infarcted ventricle, because dead myocytes do not undergo depolarization. Instead, the only electrical forces recorded are those from normal myocardium, which because they travel away from the infarcted zone cause a downward deflection. There is one caveat, however, if a pathologic Q wave is seen in only one lead it is probably not indicative of a myocardial infarction.

Of course, many myocardial infarctions are not transmural, involving the subendocardial tissues only. In that case, no Q wave will be generated, but ST and T wave abnormalities reflecting ischemia and injury will often attend nontransmural myocardial infarctions.

Laboratory Findings

Because myocardium is damaged or destroyed as a result of infarction, it is to be expected that various intracellular proteins will leak out into the interstitial space, being transported by the lymphatic system into the general circulation. Armed with a characteristic or suggestive history, ECG changes, the addition of elevation of creatine kinase isozyme MB (CK-MB) within hours of the event strongly supports the occurrence of a myocardial infarction. CK-MB reaches its peak serum concentration within 24 hours and takes another 48 to 96 hours to return to the reference range.

Other proteins that are useful in diagnosis and monitoring the progress of a myocardial infarction are LDH, myoglobin, and troponin-I.

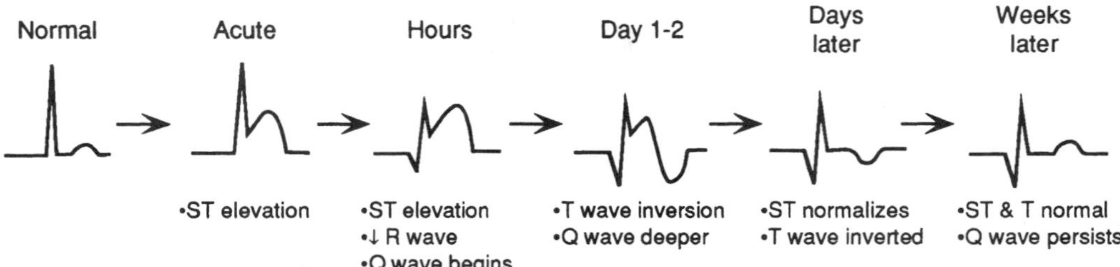

Figure 24.9. Electrocardiographic changes during acute myocardial infarction. The earliest and most definitive EKG change is ST elevation, typical of significant myocardial hypoxia. Within hours of the initial insult, a Q appears, which becomes larger with time and remains for years a part of the cardiogram. Reprinted with permission from Lilly LS. Pathophysiology of Heart Disease. Baltimore: Williams & Wilkins, 1993: 77.

Treatment

Because almost 65% of deaths from myocardial infarction occur before the subject reaches the hospital, treatment in the period before arriving at the hospital by individuals trained to use a defibrillator can exert a very favorable effect on survival. Treatment of ventricular arrhythmias with lidocaine also contributes to survival before reaching the hospital.

Once in the hospital setting, care in a cardiac ICU has further augmented survival from myocardial infarction—again predominantly by providing immediate therapy for ventricular fibrillation.

In principle, there are two avenues to treat the coronary occlusion and consequent ischemia that are at the root of a myocardial infarction. One way, used for many years, was to decrease myocardial O_2 consumption and increase the concentration of O_2 inspired. Unfortunately, because of the extensive blockage that attends most myocardial infarctions, this approach has not proved very effective in increasing long-term survival.

The other approach is to open the blocked vessel. Although this approach attacks the problem directly, it was not until the availability of various thrombolytic agents that it became feasible. It is now clear that if a thrombolytic agent can be administered within 3 to 6 hours of the onset of the actual myocardial infarction it is possible to achieve a significant reduction in mortality. From a practical standpoint, if a thrombolytic agent is to be given so soon after the onset of symptoms, then a new approach is necessary to counter the time lost by delays before reaching the hospital. Such delays are attributable to failure of the patient to recognize that the chest pain may be a myocardial infarction, to time for transport to the hospital and to evaluation in the emergency department. This new approach requires that physicians rely on history, ECG, and response to nitrates to arrive at a diagnosis in time so that thrombolytic agents be administered during the 3 to 6 hours (perhaps up to 12 hours) therapeutic window when such intervention is likely to be effective. This means that in most instances cardiac enzyme analyses and other ancillary studies will not be available to buttress the decision. Presumably, with development of diagnostic and treatment protocols, errors in diagnosis can be held to a minimum. Although thrombolytic treatment and anti-arrhythmic measures have greatly enhanced the outcome of myocardial infarction, the time-honored measures to relieve pain (morphine) and reduce myocardial O_2 consumption with rest, decrease in emotional stress, and provision of supplemental O_2 still have a place in therapy. Aspirin and heparin are helpful in consolidating the gains achieved by the thrombolytic agents and ACE inhibitors and β-blockers may improve survival. Again, because the treatment of myocardial infarction is of national and international concern, new measures and protocols can be expected to emerge with the data garnered from the numerous multi-institutional studies being conducted both in the U.S. and Europe.

SUGGESTED READINGS

GENERAL

Braunwald E, ed. Heart disease: a textbook of cardiovascular medicine. 4th ed. Philadelphia: WB Saunders, 1992.

Cheitlin MD, Sokolow M, McIlroy MB. Clinical cardiology. 6th ed. Norwalk, CT: Appleton and Lange, 1993.

Hurst J, ed. The heart: arteries and veins. 8th ed. New York: McGraw-Hill, 1994.

Lilly LS, ed. Pathophysiology of heart disease. Malvern, PA: Lea and Febiger, 1993.

CARDIAC FUNCTION

Fliegel L, Frohlich O. The Na^+/H^+ exchanger: an update on structure, regulation and cardiac physiology. Biochem J 1993;296:273.

Grant AO. Electrophysiology of the cardiac sodium channel. Trends in Cardiovascular Medicine 1991;1: 321.

Katz A. Physiology of the heart. 2nd ed. New York: Raven Press, 1992.

Lompre A-M, Anger M, Levitsky D. Sarco(endo)plasmic reticulum calcium pumps in the cardiovascular system: function and gene expression. J Mol Cell Cardiol 1994; 26:1109.

Milnor WR. Cardiovascular physiology. New York: Oxford University Press, 1990.

Opie LH, ed. The heart: physiology and metabolism. 2nd ed. New York: Raven Press, 1991.

Reeves JP, Condrescu M, Chernaya G, Gardner JP. Na^+/Ca^{2+} antiport in the mammalian heart. J Exp Biol 1994;196:375.

ARRHYTHMIAS

Josephson ME. Clinical cardiac electrophysiology: techniques and interpretations. 2nd ed. Baltimore: Williams & Wilkins, 1993.
Orchard CH, Cingolani HE. Acidosis and arrhythmias in cardiac muscle. Cardiovasc Res 1994;28:1312.
Pritchett ELC. Management of atrial fibrillation. N Engl J Med 1992;326:1264.
Prystowsky EN, Klein GJ. Cardiac arrhythmias. New York: McGraw-Hill, 1994.
Roden DM, Tamkun MM. Toward a molecular view of cardiac arrhythmogenesis. Trends in Cardiovascular Medicine 1994;4:278.
Stein E. Rapid analysis of arrhythmias: a self-study program. 2nd ed. Baltimore: Williams & Wilkins, 1992.
Waldo AL, Wit AL. Mechanisms of cardiac arrhythmias. Lancet 1993;341:1189.
Wilde AAM, Janse MJ. Electrophysiological effects of ATP sensitive potassium channel modulation: implications for arrhythmogenesis. Cardiovasc Res 1994;28:16.

CONGESTIVE HEART FAILURE

Cody RJ, Kubo SH, Pickworth KK. Diuretic treatment for the sodium retention of congestive heart failure. Arch Intern Med 1994;154:1905.
Gaasch WH, LeWinter MM, eds. Left ventricular diastolic dysfunction and heart failure. Philadelphia: Lea and Febiger, 1994.
Greenwald L, Becker RC. Expanding the paradigm of the renin-angiotensin system and angiotensin-converting enzyme inhibitors. Am Heart J 1994;128:997.
Gwathmey JK, Briggs GM, Allen PD, eds. Heart failure: basic science and clinical aspects. New York: Marcel Dekker, Inc, 1993.
Harris P. Evolution and the cardiac patient. Cardiovasc Res 1983;17:1,8,14.
Hosenpud JD, Greenberg BH, eds. Congestive heart failure: pathophysiology, diagnosis, and comprehensive approach to management. New York: Springer-Verlag, 1994.
Klug D, Robert V, Swynghedauw B. Role of mechanical and hormonal factors in cardiac remodeling and the biologic limits of myocardial adaptation. Am J Cardiol 1993;71:46A.
Mann DL, Young JB. Basic mechanisms in congestive heart failure: recognizing the role of proinflammatory cytokines. Chest 1994;105:897.
Nagano M, Ohkubo T, Arino T, et al. Growth factor for cardiac hypertrophy. Mol Cell Biochem. 1993;119:17.
Neyses L, Vetter H. Molecular biology of oncogenes and cardiovascular hypertrophy. J Hypertens 1992;10:1447.
Parker TG, Schneider MD. Growth factors, proto-oncogenes, and plasticity of the cardiac phenotype. Annu Rev Physiol 1991;53:179.
Simpson PC. Proto-oncogenes and cardiac hypertrophy. Annu Rev Physiol 1989;51:189.

SHOCK

Alpert JS, Becker RC. Cardiogenic shock: elements of etiology, diagnosis, and therapy. Clin Cardiol 1993;16: 182.
Baue AE. The horror autotoxicus and multiple-organ failure. Arch Surg 1992;127:1451.
Geller ER, ed. Shock and resuscitation. New York: McGraw-Hill, 1993.
Lefer AM, Lefer DJ. Pharmacology of the endothelium in ischemia-reperfusion and circulatory shock. Annu Rev Pharmacol Toxicol 1993;33:71.
Parillo JE. The cardiovascular pathophysiology of shock. Annu Rev Med 1989;40:469.
Rackow EC, Astiz ME, Weil MH. Cellular oxygen metabolism during sepsis and shock. JAMA 1988; 259(13):1989.
Teba L, Banks DE, Balaan MR. Understanding circulatory shock: is it hypovolemic, cardiogenic, or vasogenic? Postgrad Med 1992;91:121.

CORONARY ARTERY DISEASE AND MYOCARDIAL INFARCTION

Anderson HV, Willerson JT. Thrombolysis in acute myocardial infarction. N Engl J Med 1993;329.
Brown BG, Zhao X-Q, Sacco DE, Albers JJ. Atherosclerosis regression, plaques disruption and cardiovascular events: a rationale for lipid lowering in coronary artery disease. Annu Rev Med 1993;44:365.
Eisenberg MS, Aghababian RV, Bossaert L, et al. Thrombolytic therapy. Ann Emerg Med 1993;22:417.
Fuster V, Badimon L, Badimon JJ, Chesebro JH. The pathogenesis of coronary artery disease and the acute coronary syndromes. N Engl J Med 1992;326:242,310.
Goode GK, Miller JP, Heagerty AM. Hyperlipidemia, hypertension, and coronary heart disease. Lancet 1995;345:362.
Hennekens CH, Jonas MA, Buring JE. The benefits of aspirin in acute myocardial infarction. Arch Intern Med 1994;154:37.
Homeister JW, Lucchesi BR. Complement activation and inhibition in myocardial ischemia and reperfusion injury. Annu Rev Pharmacol Toxicol 1994;34:17.
Hugenholtz PG. How late is too late and how early is early: the clinician's view of the first 100 minutes. Postgrad Med J 1994;70:S50.
Jang Y, Lincoff AM, Plow EF, Topol EJ. Cell adhesion molecules in coronary artery disease. J Am Coll Cardiol 1994;24:1591.
Jennings RB, Reimer KA. The cell biology of acute myocardial ischemia. Annu Rev Med 1991;42:225.

Kinch JW, Ryan TJ. Right ventricular infarction. N Engl J Med 1994;330:1211.

Levine GN, Keaney JF Jr, Vita JA. Cholesterol reduction in cardiovascular disease. N Engl J Med 1995;332: 512.

Marber MS. Stress proteins and myocardial protection. Clin Sci 1994;86:375.

Ross R. The pathogenesis of atherosclerosis: a perspective for the 1990s. Nature 1993;362:801.

Roth GJ, Calverley DC. Aspirin, platelets, and thrombosis: theory and practice. Blood 1994;83:885.

Rozenman Y, Gotsman MS. The earliest diagnosis of acute myocardial infarction. Annu Rev Med 1994;45:31.

Siegmund B, Schluter K-D, Piper HM. Calcium and the oxygen paradox. Cardiovasc Res 1993;27:1778.

Woodward DA, Limacher MC. The impact of diet on coronary heart disease. Med Clin North Am 1993;77: 849.

chapter **25**

Muscle: Normal and Abnormal Biochemistry and Function

Our skeletal muscles endow us with the ability to move, an ability controlled by the central nervous system. A vivid example of how dysfunction of the central nervous system affects muscle function is the generalized, or grand mal seizure. A seizure is a striking event, and illustrates the many factors that we will need to consider in this chapter: the means of communication from nerve to muscle, the translation of the nerve impulse into the "language" of muscle, the events within the muscle that bring about contraction, and the distinguishing features between contraction and relaxation. Nor is this all, because the inherent regularity of cardiac muscle contraction, as opposed to the volitional control that we exercise over our hands, feet, etc points to the existence of different types of muscle tissue. There are, in fact, three major categories of muscle (voluntary, cardiac, and smooth), each one subserving distinct functions; herein we will consider common features.

Muscle function, like that of nervous tissue, depends upon the ability of its membrane to reversibly depolarize. Unlike nerve, however, muscle must translate the electrochemical energy that results from this depolarization into mechanical energy to carry out its physiologic role. This process requires not only the means by which to translate the message, but also the equipment with which to carry it out. Hence, distinguishing features of the muscle cell are the vast interconnecting network of intracellular tubules overlying a characteristic "banded" pattern of fibrils (Figure 25.1). Approximately 75% of skeletal muscle is found in the myofibrils. Two filaments—thick and thin—make up each myofibril. The thick filament contains myosin, whereas the thin filament is composed of actin, troponin, and tropomyosin. This tubular system is a reservoir for Ca^{++}. As we shall see, the T system couples depolarization to contraction by releasing Ca^{++} into the myofibril, thereby altering the relationships of the various proteins within the fibrils. It is noteworthy that restoration of the relaxed state is an energy-requiring process. One aspect of this energy requirement is the reuptake of Ca^{++} by the sarcoplasmic reticulum (SR), via a Ca^{++} ATPase. The other involves restoring myosin to its precontracted state by binding ATP. Thus, muscle contraction-relaxation is a process that consumes vast amounts of high-energy phosphate under exercise conditions. To meet this requirement, muscle not only stores glycogen and fat, but is a "consumer" of all available fuels (particularly glucose, glycogen, fatty acids, and ketones) except lactate, which it returns to the liver for gluconeogenesis.

Thus, in an overview, the process by which a simple command originating in the brain is converted into a muscular contraction is rather complicated and energy-costly. Dependence on the nervous system for its "marching orders" renders the musculature vulnerable to many adverse effects on central and peripheral nerves. In addition, the very flexibility that the muscle cell exhibits for fuel utilization can become a major liability if one of its preferred substrates (glucose, glycogen, or fatty acids) cannot be used because of an inborn error in one of the enzymes needed for its metabolism. Finally, in most discussions about muscle disease, the role of muscle protein as a vital metabolic fuel reservoir for the entire body is overlooked. We have mentioned this point in many different contexts throughout this book, but raise it here to remind the reader of its importance in nutritional homeostasis.

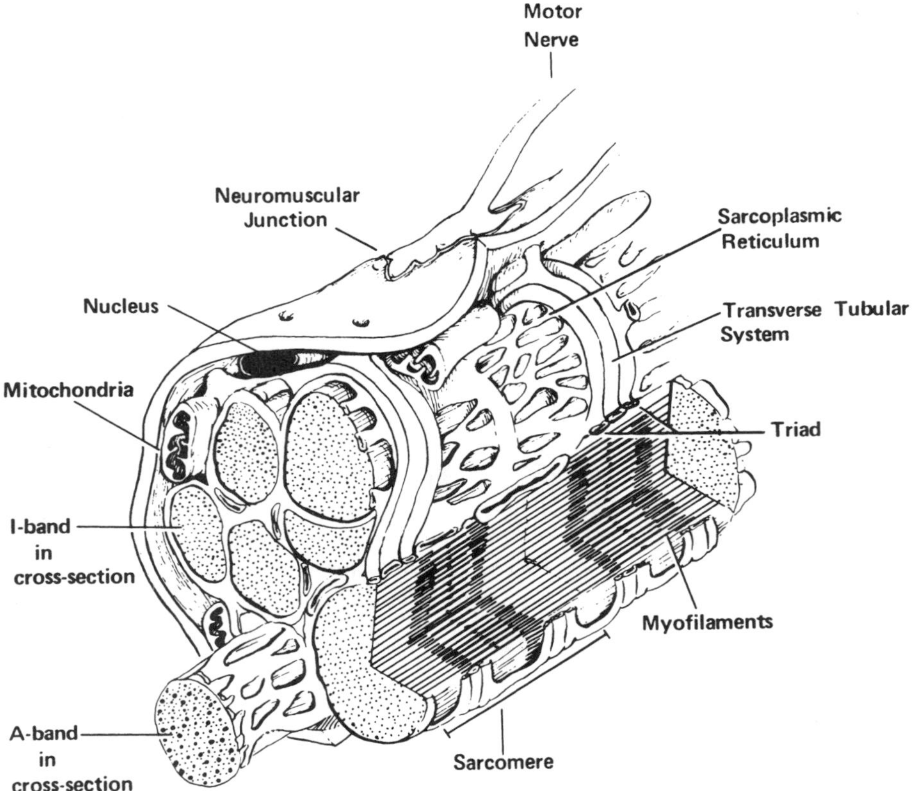

Figure 25.1. Skeletal muscle cell. The axonal terminus at the neuromuscular junction is the initiating factor in control of muscle contraction. Propagation of the impulse to the contractile myofilaments takes place through the extensive sarcoplasmic reticulum and T-tubules, with the final event being the conversion of the electrical impulse into mechanical movement. Reprinted with permission from Lieber RL. Skeletal Muscle Structure and Function. Baltimore: Williams & Wilkins, 1992: 17.

STRUCTURE AND FUNCTION

Neuromuscular Transmission

The neuromuscular junction is the point at which the descending neural impulse (either from spinal cord or anterior horn cell) is transferred to muscle for further propagation and membrane depolarization. This synaptic connection is termed the "motor end-plate," and transfer of the neural impulse is effected, as elsewhere in the nervous system, via chemical neurotransmitter substances. Although many neurotransmitters are used in the nervous system, in the case of muscle, the neurotransmitter substance is acetylcholine, synthesized and stored as vesicles in the specialized axon termini. Receptor sites on the sarcolemma, or muscle fiber membrane, represent specialized loci which surround the axon termini as shown schematically in Figure 25.2. A separation of charge across the plasma membrane creates a resting potential of about -70 mV on the inside of the membrane. A neural impulse resulting in release of acetylcholine causes a rapid change of potential difference, abolishing the negative potential and actually creating a positive potential of $+50$ mV due to depolarization. This rapid change in membrane potential is due to markedly increased sodium entry into the cell. Shortly thereafter, the sodium channels close and potassium channels open, with movement of potassium to the outside thereby restoring the resting membrane potential. The duration of this "action potential" is approximately one millisecond. When muscles

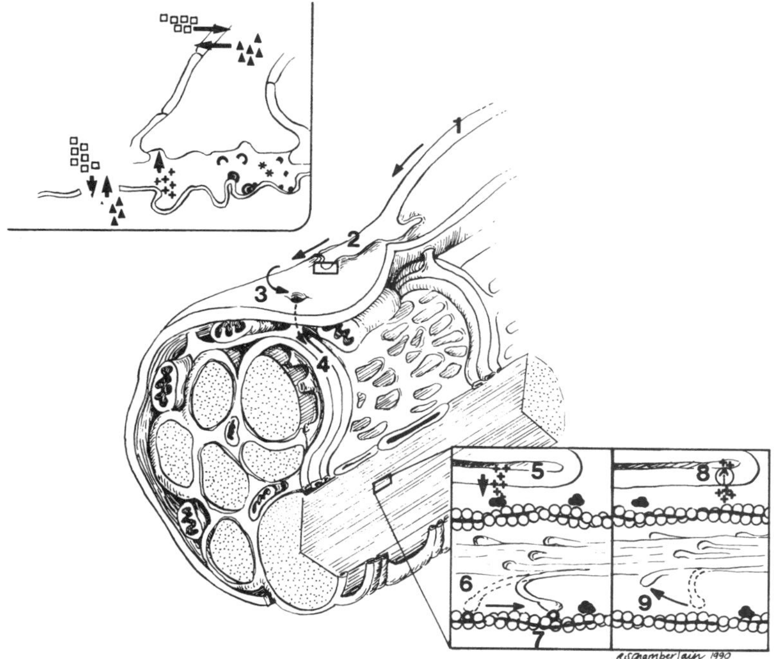

Figure 25.2. Process of coupling of nerve transmission to mechanical contraction. (1) Conduction of action potential (AP) along the axon (squares = Na^+ ions entering nerve, triangles = K^+ ions leaving nerve); (2) Transmission of nerve impulse to muscle fiber across neuromuscular junction (crosses = Ca^{++} ions entering nerve ending, semicircles = acetylcholine, * = acteylcholinesterase); (3) AP travels along fiber surface; (4) AP conducted deep into the fiber via the T-tubules; (5) Ca^{++} (crosses) released from sarcoplasmic reticulum for activation of actin filament; (6,7) Cross-bridges produce force and filament sliding; (8) Ca^{++} pumped into sarcoplasmic reticulum; (9) Cross-bridge relaxation due to lack of Ca^{++} filament activation. Reprinted with permission from Lieber RL. Skeletal Muscle Structure and Function. Baltimore: Williams & Wilkins, 1992: 50.

are used in voluntary activity, nerve impulses arrive at the neuromuscular junction at rates approaching 50 per second, each one eliciting an action potential which results in a contraction.

Through the mechanism outlined above, the message initiated at the level of the central nervous system is transmitted, in the same electrochemical "language" to the muscle. Acetylcholine release is facilitated by calcium and inhibited by high concentrations of magnesium. Neurotoxins, such as botulinum toxin also inhibit acetylcholine release. Exogenous stimuli, such as electrical shock, can also cause depolarization. Sodium channels may be blocked by a powerful neurotoxin, tetrodotoxin, which causes paralysis. In fact, this toxin helped establish the pivotal role of sodium channels in propagation of the action potential.

Coupling of Electrochemical to Mechanical Events

Obviously, for there to be movement, membrane depolarization must be transduced into mechanical contraction of muscle fibers. The mechanism for energy transduction is only partially understood. As mentioned earlier, the sarcolemmal depolarization phenomenon is propagated throughout the cell by means of the transverse, or "T-" tubules. It is thought that an accompanying influx of calcium from the extracellular to the intracellular space, distributed by the T-tubules, provokes a further release of calcium from the sarcoplasmic reticulum. How this provocation actually occurs remains unelucidated. Beyond this, the question remains as to how the extracellular calcium, now within the sarcoplasm, is removed to prevent con-

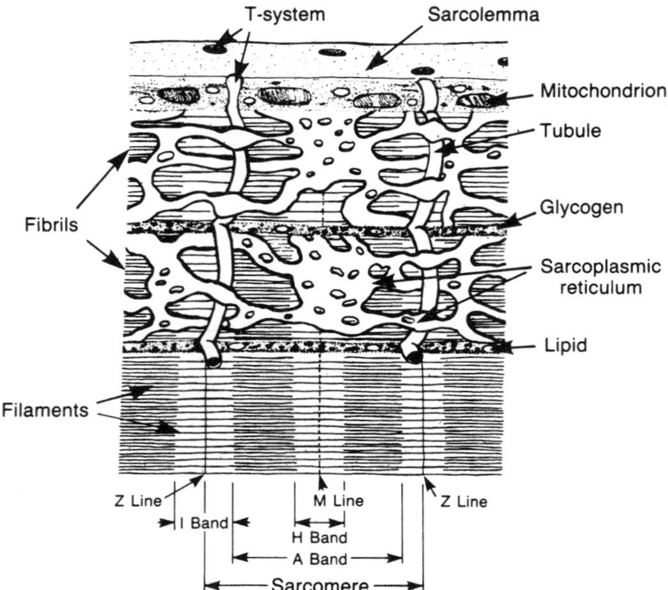

Figure 25.3. Skeletal muscle fiber. The basic elements are the myofilaments, grouped together into fibrils. Multiple fibrils, together with nuclei, mitochondria, and an extensive tubular system, surrounded by a specialized cell membrane (sarcolemma), constitute the typical skeletal muscle fiber. The varying densities of a fibril under the electron microscope are direct results of the molecular arrangements of the muscle proteins actin and myosin. Reprinted with permission from McCarty DJ, Koopman WJ. Arthritis and Allied Conditions: A Textbook of Rheumatology. 12th ed. Baltimore: Williams & Wilkins, 1993: 1896.

tinuous accumulation with repetitive neuromuscular transmissions.

Mechanical Contraction

Echoing a fundamental theme of living creatures, the structure of muscle is largely a reflection of its function. Thousands of fibers run longitudinally for varying lengths to compose a muscle (Figure 25.3). These fibers consist of multinucleated cells of which their length may reach 4 cm, with a diameter varying from 10 to 100 μm. Within each muscle cell cytoplasm (sarcoplasm), there are, in addition to organelles typical of all cells, myofibrils. These are the contractile elements composed of the proteins actin and myosin, in association with the proteins that modulate their interactions, troponin and tropomyosin (Table 25.1).

When muscle is relaxed, myosin has bound to it both a phosphoryl group and at a separate site, adenosine diphosphate (ADP). Actin, the other contractile protein of the myofilament, is bound to tropomyosin, when it is in the relaxed state (Figure 25.4). The fourth protein of the contractile unit, troponin, has three subunits: one subunit binds to tropomyosin, another binds to Ca^{++}, whereas the third (I) undergoes a conformational change that regulates the interaction of actin and myosin by affecting the location of tropomyosin. In this arrangement, tropomyosin is physically interposed between the actin and myosin molecules. This physical relationship ensures that myosin and actin cannot interact with each other. But when calcium levels increase in the region of the contractile proteins, calcium binds to the troponin "C" subunit and the troponin-actin association is severed. This, in turn, removes the interposed tropomyosin molecule, now permitting interactions between actin and myosin. The troponin-tropomyosin complex, therefore, appears to function both as a circuit breaker and a means of information transfer (Table 25.1). With tropomyosin out of the way, cross-bridges form between the actin and myosin filaments, which slide past one another, the physical movement producing what is perceived as a contraction. Should repolarization be interrupted because of persistence of acetylcholine at the end-plate, paralysis ensues.

Adenosine triphosphate (ATP) furnishes the energy for contraction and must be constantly replenished. Phosphocreatine serves as the immediate source to rephosphorylate ADP through the action of the enzyme creatine kinase. Ultimately, oxidative phosphorylation furnishes most of the ATP required. Before relaxation can be accomplished, allowing the actin and myosin filaments to return to their precontracted position, the calcium that triggered contraction must again be seques-

Table 25.1. Myofibrillar Proteins

PROTEIN	M.W.	PHYSICAL AND CHEMICAL CHARACTERISTICS	LOCALIZATION	FUNCTION
Myosin	470,000	Shaped like golf clubs Shaft—light chain Head—heavy chain Composed of 6 polypeptides	Thick filament (A band)	Head is the crossbridge—contains myosin ATPase activity Contraction
Actin	42,000	Globular—55Å in diameter "like strings of beads in a necklace"	Thin filament (I band)	Contraction
Tropomyosin	35,000	Two α-helical chains in a linear coil Covers 7 actin molecules 450Å long and 20Å in diameter	Thin filament	Regulation of actin-myosin interaction
Troponin	78,000	Globular with three subunits	Thin filament	T subunit binds tropomyosin C subunit binds Ca^{2+} I controls interaction of actin and myosin through position of tropomyosin

tered in the sarcoplasmic reticulum. As might be expected, calcium reaccumulation is an energy-requiring process; it is the absence of ATP that accounts for the contracted state of muscle in rigor mortis. Rigor sets in for two reasons. First, ATP is needed to power the Ca^{++}-ATPase that removes Ca^{++} from the myofibrils. Second, as noted, for myosin to relax it must bind ATP—not ADP and Pi.

Energy Supply

In contrast to the mature erythrocyte, a muscle cell is richly endowed with mitochondria. Nonetheless, muscle is a major producer of lactate as are red cells. Although muscle is able to use glucose, glycogen, fatty acids, and ketones to fuel contraction, it is not endowed with the terminal enzyme of gluconeogenesis, glucose-6-phosphatase, required for release of free glucose. Hence, although muscle can extract more energy than a red cell from a mole of glucose because of its ability to carry out oxidative phosphorylation, under stress conditions (exercise), muscle becomes a net producer of lactate. This lactate is released into the blood and conveyed either to the liver for conversion to glucose or to other tissues for conversion to pyruvate and further oxidative metabolism. Under sustained submaximal exercise, muscle turns to lipid as a fuel source, utilizing intrinsically stored fat or free fatty acids from body stores.

Entry of long-chain free fatty acids into mitochondria depends upon activation to acyl-CoA esters in the cytoplasm, with subsequent conversion of acyl-CoA to acyl-carnitine (Figure 25.5). Only in the acyl-carnitine form can the fatty acyl moiety cross the mitochondrial membrane, following which it is reconverted to acyl-CoA and subjected to β-oxidation. Without exaggeration, carnitine plays the pivotal role in the ability of muscle to extract energy from lipid; deficiency of carnitine, for any reason, will decrease submaximal exercise tolerance by reducing the ability to use fatty acids.

Finally, because of the central role of electron transport in the production of ATP production, impairment of electron transport by inherited or acquired mechanisms will also have adverse consequences on muscle function. In summary, as we consider disorders of muscle, many factors must be weighed. First, neurologic transmission must be intact to the affected muscle, because muscle dysfunction may result from neural dysfunction. Next, function of the neuromuscular unit must be assessed, with special consideration given to interference by pharmacologic agents with its function. Electrolyte abnormalities must also be assessed because each can be associated with weakness. The ability of muscle to produce lactate can be assessed with an ischemic exercise test, a convenient measure of the integrity of muscle glycogenolysis and glycolysis. Determination of normal car-

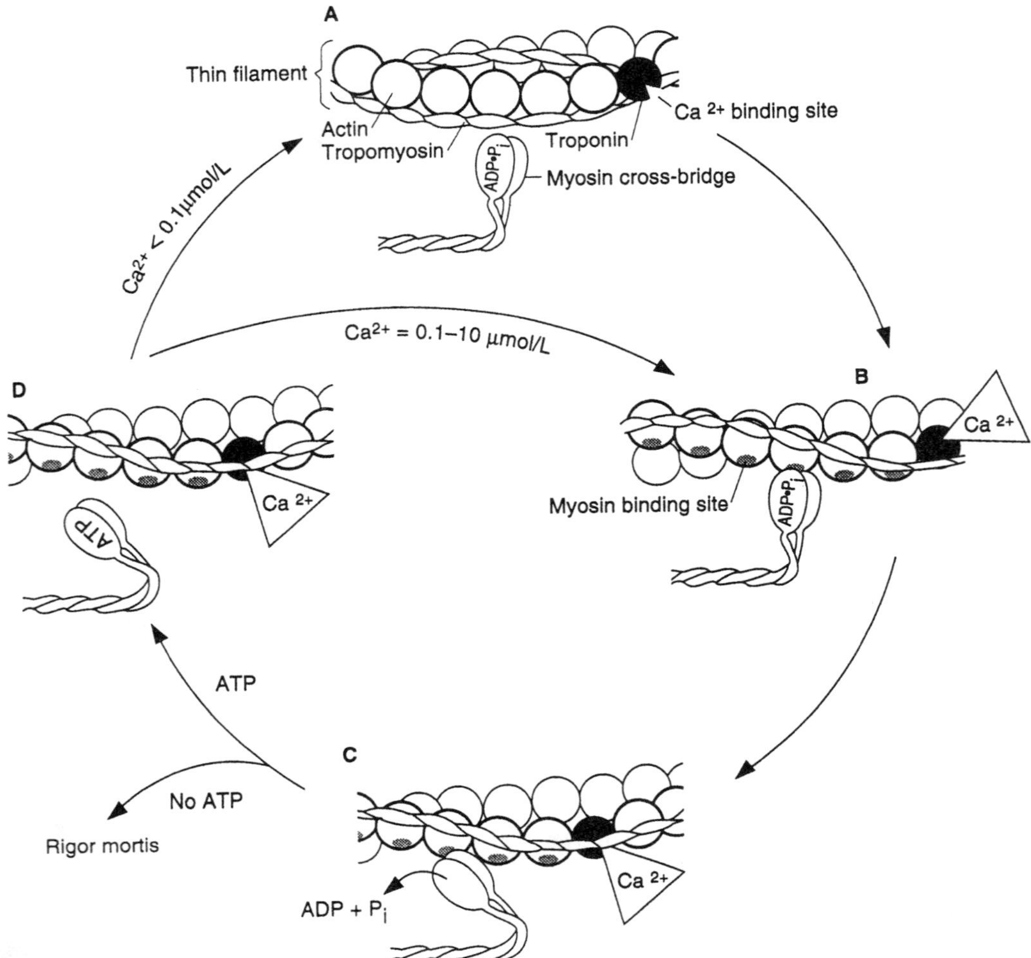

Figure 25.4. Mechanical events of muscle contraction. (A) Orientation of contractile components at rest. (B) Ca^{++}, released from the sarcoplasmic reticulum, binds to troponin causing the latter to undergo a conformational change. This change exposes the myosin binding site of actin, and permits myosin-actin binding with beginning of the cross-bridge cycle; (C) Cleavage of ATP to ADP + Pi provides the energy for "bending" of the cross-bridge, with consequent sliding of the thin filament over the thick filament and release of ADP + Pi; (D) Regeneration of ATP provides the energy for detachment and resumption of the upright posture of the cross-bridge. If Ca^{++} remains high, the cycle B-D cycle continues with further contraction; alternatively, the Ca^{++} is pumped out and state A is assumed by the elements. If ATP cannot be regenerated, as in death, mechanical contraction is irreversible, accounting for the state known as rigor mortis. Reprinted with permission from Bullock J, et al. Physiology. 3rd ed. Baltimore: Williams & Wilkins, 1995: 39.

nitine levels will at least ensure that fatty acid transport is not limited by carnitine unavailability. Further biochemical investigation of muscle generally requires biopsy, which permits histochemical, enzymatic, and molecular genetic examinations, all of which provide important clues in diagnosis of many primary muscle disorders.

MUSCULAR DISORDERS

Muscle disease presents in one of three ways, although some disorders manifest features of more than one syndrome. The first mode of presentation involves the insidious onset of progressive muscle weakness. The muscular dystrophies epitomize

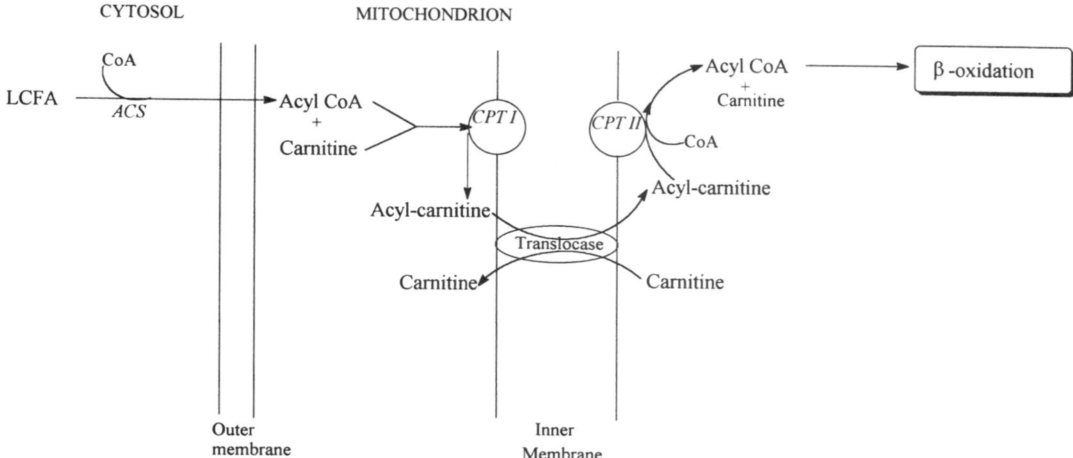

Figure 25.5. Mitochondrial transport and metabolism of fatty acids. Short and medium chain fatty acids reach the mitochondrial matrix without special mediators, where they enter β-oxidation and are converted to energy. Long chain fatty acids, by contrast, require activation within the outer mitochondrial membrane, becoming converted to fatty acyl CoA compounds by the enzyme acylCoA synthase (ACS). FACoA is transformed to FA-carnitine at the inner mitochondrial membrane by carnitine palmitoyltransferase (CPT I), the FA-carnitine then being transported through the inner membrane by acyl-carnitine translocase. At the matrix surface, the FACoA is resynthesized by CPT II for entry into β-oxidation and the free carnitine released in the exchange exits the matrix by means of the translocase.

this presentation, but it may also be seen in inflammatory, toxic, and endocrinologic conditions. A second pattern, one most associated with defects in substrate utilization or impairment of energy harvesting pathways, is exercise intolerance. Cramps often punctuate these episodes of muscle failure with the stress of sustained exercise. Finally, some muscle diseases present with sudden onset of paralysis, caused by a defect in the contractile mechanism. We will describe examples from each of these categories, emphasizing recent advances in our understanding of the mutations and defective protein products resulting from those mutations.

The Muscular Dystrophies

There are several forms of muscular dystrophy, each with important distinguishing features (Table 25.2). By definition, all are intrinsic diseases of the muscle fiber. The most common form, Duchenne muscular dystrophy (DMD), has an incidence of approximately 1:4000. DMD is transmitted as an X-linked trait, so that clinically affected individuals are male, although about 8% of carrier females may show clinical symptoms, as well. Because affected males generally die in the second decade, it is rather remarkable that the disease is so frequent. In fact, approximately one-third of all new cases represents a new mutation, or one in which the mutant gene has not been maternally transmitted.

More than a decade ago, before development of current molecular diagnostic capabilities, it was postulated that the pathogenetic basis for DMD resided in a membrane abnormality. In fact, little more than 5 years ago, application of these newer molecular techniques led to discovery of a deficient gene product, *dystrophin*, and localization of the normal protein within the sarcolemma. Dystrophin is a large molecule which is normally present in very small amounts in the transverse tubule system responsible for propagating the depolarization wave into the interior of the sarcomere. Dystrophin is believed to function in muscle much in the way spectrin does in the red blood cell cytoskeleton; that is, dystrophin stabilizes the membrane system and cytoskeleton. Given the countless times muscles contract, it is believed that absence of this stabilizing effect conferred by dystrophin hastens breakdown of muscle itself. This view is supported by the necrosis of muscle and

Table 25.2. Variants of Muscular Dystrophies

	DUCHENNE'S	FACIOSCAPULO-HUMERAL	LIMB GIRDLE	OCULO-PHARYNGEAL	MYOTONIC DYSTROPHY
Onset	Usually before age 3 years	Late childhood or adolescence	20–45 years	Late adult life	Childhood to adulthood
Genetics	XLR	AD	AR	AD	AD
Muscle groups	Pelvic and shoulder muscles, face usually spared	Facial and shoulder muscles	Proximal limb muscles	Levator palpebrae, pharyngeal lesser extent, facial, extraocular muscles	Facial, trunk, diaphragm, neck, smooth muscle ±
Symptoms and signs	Abnormal gait, fall frequently, difficulty climbing stairs, Gower's sign, pseudohypertrophy in most; unable to walk by end of first decade, never able to run; contractures	Cannot close eyes completely, cannot whistle, hands and feet spared, pseudo-hypertrophy uncommon, contracture rare	Pseudohypertrophy uncommon; feet, hands, and face uninvolved	Ptosis, myopathic facies, no myotonia	Myotonia, ptosis, frontal balding, hypogonadism
Cardiac involvement	Minor arrhythmias, hypertrophy	EKG changes	No	No	Arrhythmias, heart block, heart failure
Progression	Steady deterioration	Slow	Slow with long remissions, progresses more rapidly than facioscapulo-humeral	Slow	Slowly disabling
Prognosis	Rarely survive beyond 20 years	Good, occasionally severe disability, normal life span	Disability and death by 40 to 50 years	Usually normal life span	

replacement with connective tissue seen in DMD. There is evidence for a frameshift mutation in DMD resulting in total absence of dystrophin. A different mutation in Becker's muscular dystrophy results in reduced levels of dystrophin, which may account for the milder clinical phenotype in this condition.

Clinically, DMD is characterized by onset of progressive muscle wasting, usually by age 3 years. Earlier, there may a gait abnormality, accompanied by frequent falling. Although there is underlying progression of muscle wasting, this may be missed because of the phenomenon called pseudohypertrophy, which is due to replacement of muscle by fibrous tissue and fat. On occasion, affected children may look like "little Hercules," appearing muscular far in excess of their age and actual strength. Attention is often drawn to their weakness by the difficulty a child with DMD exhibits on attempting to stand from a sitting position (Gower's sign). Once clinically evident, the disease is usually rapidly progressive, rendering the child wheelchair bound before age 10 years. There is a disproportionately high incidence of associated mental deficiency among affected individuals which presently remains unexplained. Eventually, respiratory failure or pneumonia claims these patients, late in adolescence.

Serum creatine kinase (CK) in affected males is dramatically increased above normal and provides helpful diagnostic information which can now be definitively confirmed by studies using molecular techniques. Serum CK levels in carrier females are intermediate between the affected male and normal, as one would expect in X-linked disease. It is worthwhile noting again, however, that a substantial number of DMD patients represent new mutations. There is no treatment presently available, although rapid advances are being made in gene isolation and cloning which makes gene transfer a viable possibility in the near future.

Myotonic Dystrophy—Disorders of the Contractile Mechanism

Myotonia is characterized by repetitive firing of the muscle membrane associated with an inability to relax the muscle. For instance, myotonia can be elicited by percussing the thenar eminence. In the past, several different disorders were classified together on the basis of sharing myotonia as a feature of the clinical picture. Now it is clear that these disorders are the result of different mutations that affect different proteins. For instance, abnormalities of the sodium channel in muscle causes hyperkalemic periodic paralysis and paramyotonia congenita, whereas a defective protein kinase is at the root of myotonic dystrophy, and abnormal chloride channels underlie both the autosomal dominant (AD) and autosomal recessive (AR) forms of myotonia congenita. Consequently, there is a dramatic heterogeneity of the protein affected despite the similarity of some of the clinical features in these different disorders.

Separate and distinct ion channels for Na^+, Cl^-, and K^+ are embedded in the membranes of excitable cells. Sodium movement into the muscle cell sparks the onset of the action potential whereas potassium movement through specific channels brings about repolarization. Still other channels for chloride can bring about hyperpolarization of the muscle cells. For many years, it has been known that the myotonic syndromes were disorders of muscle membrane excitability because symptoms were not affected either by local nerve block or blockade of the neuromuscular junction by curare. In addition, studies of muscle tissue from patients with hyperkalemic periodic paralysis and paramyotonia congenita have revealed an abnormally large Na^+-ion conductance, which can be abrogated by the potent Na^+ channel blocking agent, tetrotoxin, further incriminating the Na^+ channel.

Muscle cells from patients with myotonic dystrophy have a lower-than-normal resting potential with normal K^+ conductance, but abnormal (heightened) Na^+ conductance. Yet, molecular diagnostic studies have shown that the product of the myotonic dystrophy gene is not the Na^+ channel itself. Current theory implicates a cAMP-dependent protein kinase as the modulator of the function of the Na^+ channel.

Unlike DMD, which principally affects young males, myotonic dystrophy is the most common form of muscular dystrophy in adults, with an incidence of 1:8000. Myotonic dystrophy is transmitted as an autosomal dominant trait, another important distinctive feature of its clinical presentation. As in DMD, modern techniques have resulted in a probe which can directly identify the mutation responsible for myotonic dystrophy—expansion of a C-T-G triplet on chromosome 19q. This expansion appears to increase in successive generations, correlating with the clinical pattern of increasing severity of disease in successive generations.

In the true adult form of myotonic dystrophy, the molecular defect resulting from the genetic mutation is deduced to be in a protein with homology to a cAMP-dependent protein kinase. It has been named *myotonin-protein kinase*. Electrophysiologic data point to abnormalities in the membrane which produce a lowered resting potential perhaps attributable to altered ionic conductance. It is possible that the genetically altered protein kinase normally plays a role in modulating ion channel function through phosphorylation, and that the mutated protein kinase cannot exert its intended action. Several different lines of experimental evidence would fit quite neatly with such an explanation. Because the clinical phenotype of myotonic dystrophy extends to many organs beyond the muscle (see below), a mechanism involving defective ionic channel modulations due to abnormal protein kinase activity would be consistent with this aspect of the disease, as well. Recently, three patients were reported who manifest many of the features of myotonia but did not have the CTG repeat on chromosome 19. It has not yet been determined whether they have another mutation that affects the myotonin-protein kinase.

As noted, "myotonia" is defined as the delayed relaxation of a muscle following a contraction. Electrophysiologic studies reflect these clinical findings demonstrating a rapid depolarization followed by delayed repolarization. Thus, affected individuals frequently present with symptoms referable to neuromuscular function, chiefly weakness and often stiffness with eventual atrophy of the affected muscles. It should not be forgotten that other muscle, in particular that of the gut and heart, can be affected. As a consequence, swallowing difficulties and cardiac arrhythmias are not uncommon, with swallowing dysfunction representing a major threat to life when present in conjunction with diaphragmatic dysfunction. Ptosis is frequent, in addition to involvement of the eye itself with formation of cataracts. There is often endocrine involvement, most prominent in males due to testicular tubular degeneration and marked frontal balding. A significant proportion of patients show personality changes and marked somnolence. The variable severity of each aspect of the clinical presentation can complicate diagnosis, especially because many patients are unaware of the fact that their painless muscle stiffness is abnormal. Therefore, clinical suspicion must be high, particularly because the disorder is so common. Early diagnostic suspicion can be heightened by demonstration of abnormalities in rapid and repetitive muscular activity, such as in grip.

Electromyography is useful in clarifying the diagnosis of myotonic dystrophy. Symptomatic myotonia may improve with procainamide or phenytoin. The tendency to cardiac arrhythmias may necessitate insertion of a pacemaker. In the absence of definitive therapeutic modalities, prenatal diagnosis assumes paramount importance. This has been reported, and should be considered in any pedigree where myotonic dystrophy has been identified, especially because the age of clinical onset in affected adults can be so variable.

Perhaps nowhere in medicine are the advantages and hazards of our advances in molecular medicine better illustrated than in the study of the muscular dystrophies and myotonic dystrophy. It is clear that molecular diagnostic techniques have permitted access to the defect at the most fundamental level—that of DNA. It is now possible to define the specific molecular defects in both DMD and myotonic dystrophy. Yet, in neither case are we entirely able to extrapolate from this information a cogent explanation for the abnormal processes underlying the clinical presentations. Most significant of all, even these most highly refined diagnostic tools are of no use whatever unless the physician suspects the presence of one of these disorders. Thus, in the final analysis, no laboratory test is ever likely to usurp the role of the clinician in the diagnostic process.

Episodic Muscle Weakness—The Periodic Paralyses

In contrast to the disorders discussed above, certain disorders of muscle function manifest fluctuating weakness, so that between attacks, the individual is normal or near normal. Pre-eminent among these are the periodic paralyses and myasthenia gravis. There are several forms of periodic paralytic disorders (Table 25.3), all of which share certain features, which should suggest the category of disorder to the physician. Strikingly, paralysis occurs when exercise is followed by complete rest and can be aborted by continued mild exercise. During attacks, decreased tendon reflexes occur and return to normal during intercurrent periods. Cold is the primary provocative environmental factor.

It is well known that secondary causes of hypokalemia and hyperkalemia, from wastage and retention of potassium respectively, are associated with abnormalities in neuromuscular function. In these secondary causes, the serum K^+ always fall outside of the normal range (3.5 to 5.5 mEq/L). In the primary periodic paralyses, however, the defect resides in the muscle membrane, thus permitting attacks with the K^+ level in the normal range. The lesion in hyperkalemic periodic paralysis appears to be impaired function of the sodium channel, whereas the lesion in the other forms has not been defined. In all forms of periodic paralysis, the muscle membrane nevertheless becomes inexcitable resulting in the episodes of paralysis.

In one patient with hyperkalemic periodic paralysis, a single base change in the gene for the sodium channel caused a methionine-to-valine substitution. Cells from this patient were grown in culture and examined by patch-clamp methods. When K^+ was elevated in the culture medium, some of the Na^+-channels in the patient's cells did not behave normally. Specifically, although these channels opened when the membrane was depolarized, they failed to close (as normally they should) at the end of the repolarization cycle. The result of some of the Na^+-channels remaining

Table 25.3. Variants of the Periodic Paralyses

	HYPOKALEMIC	HYPERKALEMIC (ADYNAMIA EPISODICA HEREDITARIA)	PERIODIC PARALYSIS WITH CARDIAC ARRHYTHMIA	SODIUM-RESPONSIVE
Age of onset	7–21 years	First decade	5–20 years	First decade
Genetics	AD	AD	?	AD
Clinical features	Fluctuating periods of normal strength alternating with flaccid paralysis lasting hours to days. Cold or rest after exercise precipitates attacks, whereas continuation of mild exercise may prevent or abort attacks.			
	Oliguria	Myalgias		
Duration	Usually several hours (may last 4 days)	1–2 hours	2–3 days	Days to weeks
Time of day	Paralyzed on awakening	Any time	Usually on awakening but can be any time	On awakening if N.P.O.
Severity	Complete quadriplegia frequent; muscles of respiration usually spared	Weakness of facial muscles; no respiratory involvement	Incomplete paresis; death from cardiac arrhythmias	Quadriplegia; respiratory muscles affected mildly
Precipitating factors	Exercise followed by rest, high CHO meal, alcohol, salt, trauma, psychological stress	Exercise followed by rest, fasting, cold (paramyotonia); K rich food and drink	Exercise followed by rest, high sodium intake; premenstrual state	Usually exercise followed by rest; may occur at rest, however; alcohol; psychological stress
Treatment	Potassium salts	Epinephrine, calcium	Glucose and K^+; quinidine	Sodium
Prevention	Low sodium, high K diet, acetazolamide	Frequent CHO ingestion, inhalation of salbutamol at first sign of weakness	High CHO/K^+ diet	High Na^+ diet

open is to allow excess Na^+ ions to enter the cell, preventing the cell from repolarizing and generating another action potential. The consequence of refractory depolarization is muscle paralysis.

Metabolic Myopathies—Exercise Intolerance and Cramps

Glucose (derived from muscle glycogen) and fatty acids serve the varying needs of muscle. During sedentary conditions, fatty acids provide for the preponderance of energy requirements. However, when muscles are stressed to the point of maximal exertion, glycogen provides the energy needs in this relatively hypoxic setting. Because of limitation of both glycogen stores and the capacity for gluconeogenesis, prolonged exercise (which is submaximal by definition) forces the carbohydrate muscle economy to give way to a lipid-based one.

Intracellular glycogen is the main carbohydrate fuel for muscle, being especially important for endurance exercise. In fact, it has long been known that trained athletes can fill up their muscles with glycogen by exercising to exhaustion and then ingesting large amounts of carbohydrate for several days. However, lipids, predominantly in the form of fatty acids and ketones, are the dominant fuel for muscle at rest and during prolonged light to moderate exercise. Because of the limitation of glycogen stores in muscle, when exercise is prolonged beyond 40 minutes, fatty acids increasingly support the muscle's energy needs. Indeed, greater reliance on fatty acids and ketones, formed in liver, characterizes the adaptation of muscle to exercise as well as to starvation.

Muscle is the site of various inborn errors involving either carbohydrate or lipid metabolism. Chief among this group, summarized in Table 25.4, are the glycogen storage diseases II, III, and V which are considered in Chapter 11. A brief discussion of the others which include glycolytic defects, lipid metabolic defects, and disorders of

Table 25.4. Glycogen Storage Diseases Affecting Muscle

TYPE	ENZYME AFFECTED	CLINICAL FINDINGS	TREATMENT
II (Pompe's)	Lysosomal α-glucosidase (acid maltase)	Infantile-hypotonia, cardiac failure, death by age 2 years Juvenile—late onset myopathy Adult—progressive muscle weakness	No effective treatment
III	Amylo-1,6-glucosidase Debrancher enzyme	Fasting hypoglycemia Myopathy with pain Cramps, myoglobinuria on exercise	Frequent feeding High carbohydrates, high protein Avoid strenuous exercise
V (McArdle's)	Muscle phosphorylase	Strenuous exercise induces pain, cramps, and myoglobinuria. No rise in blood lactate after ischemic forearm exercise test	Avoid strenous or prolonged exercise
VII	Phosphofructokinase	Similar to Type V	Same as for Type V

the electron transport chain is warranted as a means to underscore the importance of various fuels and pathways to power muscular activity.

The paradigm of inherited metabolic disorders of muscle is muscle phosphorylase deficiency (McArdles' disease). Bereft of muscle phosphorylase, such patients are unable to use muscle glycogen for energy and must depend instead on blood glucose (which is not as good a source of energy for muscle as glycogen) and on fatty acids. A hallmark of this disorder and those of the glycolytic pathway (see below) is the inability to produce lactate with ischemic exercise.

Phosphofructokinase (PFK) is an enzyme central to regulation of the glycolytic pathway by which glucose, galactose, and fructose enter the mainstream of carbohydrate metabolism to generate chemical energy (Figure 25.6). All three hexoses are eventually converted to fructose-6-phosphate; addition of a second phosphate moiety to form fructose-1,6-bisphosphate through the action of PFK is the step in glycolysis immediately proximal to the aldolase-mediated cleavage to triose-phosphate compounds. The reaction mediated by PFK is irreversible, so that fructose-6-phosphate can be generated only from the bisphosphate through action of an independent enzyme, fructose-1,6-bisphosphatase. Thus, the molecular characteristics of the two enzymes (Km, Vmax), as well as substrate concentrations, pH, etc, are the major determinants of control of glycolysis at this point in the pathway. From this it is clear that a deficiency of PFK activity would substantially disequilibrate the balance of metabolites, and hence the control of the pathway. The net effect of a PFK deficiency is to slow the rate of glycolysis beyond formation of fructose-6-phosphate and decrease the production of pyruvate and lactate from hexose substrates. Consistent with the essential role of glycolysis in generation of energy for muscular contraction, affected individuals experience cramping with exercise. By all odds, the myoglobinuria, which is typical of this group of disorders, strongly suggests that the sarcomere is highly dependent upon glycolysis for structural, as well as biochemical integrity, because the presence of myoglobin points to a membrane leak. It is noteworthy, that feeding carbohydrate to patients with PFK deficiency aggravates onset of fatigue because the effect of carbohydrate is to lower the plasma fatty acid levels and decrease formation of ketones, which thus deprives muscles of its major alternative fuels. Additional findings include a predisposition for gout, the basic pathophysiologic mechanism for which has been discussed under the section on hereditary fructose intolerance in Chapter 11, and hemolytic anemia. The latter is also not surprising, because the erythrocyte is totally dependent upon glycolysis for energy production and cellular integrity.

The other defects of glycolysis are similar to PFK in their clinical presentations. Inheritance of these defects is autosomally recessive, with the exception being deficiency of phosphoglycerate kinase (PGK) which is transmitted as an X-linked trait. PGK catalyzes a reversible interconversion of 1,3-diphosphoglycerate to 3-phosphoglycerate, with net production of 2 moles ATP/mole glucose.

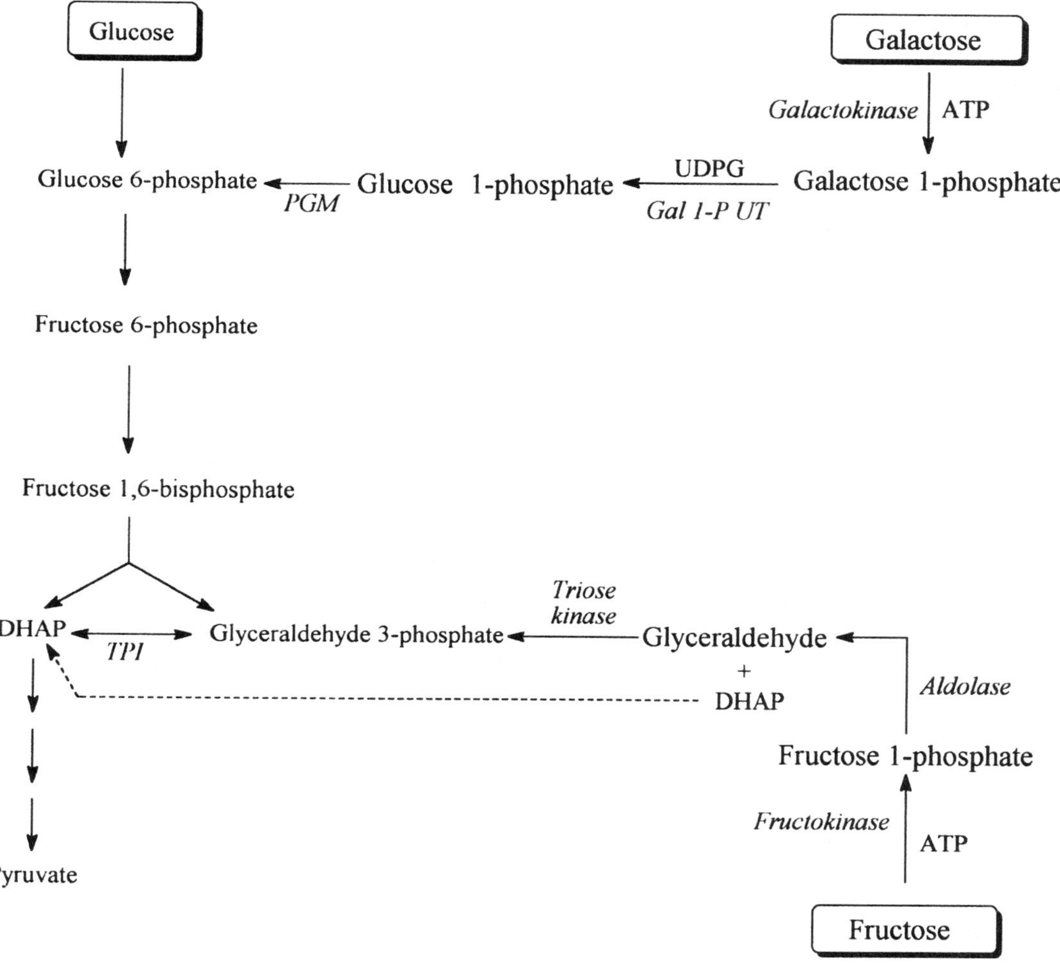

Figure 25.6. Scheme of glycolysis showing the point of entry of galactose and fructose into the glycolytic pathway. Phosphofructokinase catalyzes the conversion of fructose 6-phosphate to fructose 1,6-bisphosphate.

As an X-linked trait, one anticipates that affected males would have very low PGK in tissues throughout the body and experience severe clinical manifestations. Indeed, this is the case, with reported levels of 0.1% to 5% of control in brain, skeletal muscle, liver, and heart from a male patient at autopsy. Thus, in addition to the cramping and myoglobinuria in common with other disorders of glycolysis, there are neurologic manifestations and a relatively severe hemolytic anemia with periodic crises.

Another glycolytic enzyme disorder is triose phosphate isomerase (TPI), which catalyzes interconversion of dihydroxyacetone phosphate and glyceraldehyde-3-phosphate. Key to understanding the pathogenesis of this disorder is the fact that, although both of these triose fragments are normally produced in glycolysis from cleavage of fructose-1,6-bisphosphate, only glyceraldehyde-3-phosphate can be further metabolized via glycolysis. Thus, a deficiency of TPI activity leads to accumulation of DHAP to levels as high as 40 times normal in red cells. The defect is transmitted as an autosomal recessive trait, and the molecular abnormality appears in many tissues, including brain, as well as muscle. Indeed, affected individuals experience very severe neurologic dysfunction which, oddly, spares the cerebral cortex so that intellect is preserved. Death generally is due to sudden cardiac arrhythmias.

By contrast, deficient lactate dehydrogenase activity has been demonstrated in a kindred which experienced myopathic symptoms without hemolysis. NADH oxidation was relatively unaffected, presumably because of many other compensatory pathways for NAD^+ generation within the cell. Although it is likely that excess pyruvate is released from the red cell and metabolized elsewhere, it is unclear why the same would not be true of the sarcomere. The most reasonable speculation is that the rate of production in the sarcomere, much greater than that in erythrocyte, exceeds the diffusion capacity of the sarcolemma. An accumulation of pyruvate in any cell would be expected to cause a pH shift, in turn, affecting many other enzyme systems and possibly leading to a clinical myopathy.

Defects of Carnitine and of Fatty Acid Metabolism

We have pointed out that fatty acids are used preferentially by muscle at rest, during fasting, and when exercise is prolonged but of low to moderate intensity. Fat deposits proximate to muscle serve as one of the major sources of these fats. Although it is true that short chain fatty acids pass through the mitochondrial membrane easily, long chain fatty acids must form a covalent linkage with carnitine to enter the mitochondria where they undergo β-oxidation. Carnitine (3-hydroxy,4-N-trimethylaminobutyric acid) is synthesized in liver and kidney, but the preponderance of body stores (98%) are localized in skeletal and cardiac muscle. Another group of inborn errors that lead to clinical disorders of muscle function are defects involving fatty acid oxidation and carnitine metabolism. Defects in fatty acid oxidation can be anticipated with abnormalities in carnitine production or transport. One such scenario is primary carnitine deficiency, which can be subcategorized as systemic and myopathic. Systemic carnitine deficiency does not have myopathic findings, its chief clinical manifestations being those of Reye's syndrome with weakness and liver failure. Suffice to say that any decrease in carnitine, no matter in what tissue, is liable to reduce the capacity for β-oxidation, and with it the formation of ketones, as a consequence of decreased transport of fatty acid into the mitochondrion. In the case of myopathic carnitine deficiency, there is a marked clinical weakness after prolonged fasting causes exhaustion of muscle glycogen stores and a variable accumulation of lipid within muscle tissue. Although impaired uptake of carnitine by muscle has been postulated as a basis for the disorder, this has so far been demonstrated only in a single patient. The etiology of the primary systemic deficiency would logically be expected to derive from a synthetic defect, although this has not yet been reported. In any case, the inability of the muscle of such patients to derive energy from fatty acids and the resulting clinical symptoms underscores the importance of lipid metabolism in normal muscle function.

No less important than deficiency of carnitine in muscle as the basis for myopathy, is an additional entity, caused by deficiency of carnitine palmitoyltransferase (CPT), which also causes significant myopathy. Exercise intolerance after fasting, myalgias, episodic cramps, and myoglobinuria characterize the attacks, although myoglobinuria is rare before adolescence. In contrast to the defects in glycogenolysis or glycolysis, contractures do not occur with brief maximal exercise. Distinguishing this disorder from the carbohydrate defects is the finding that serum lactate rises in association with ischemic exercise. Prolonged fasting results in a rise in serum CK and myoglobinuria, commonly but not uniformly associated with an inability to mobilize ketones. One can anticipate that the block in ketogenesis will exacerbate the already restricted ability to utilize metabolic fuel in energy production. Patients with CPT deficiency should avoid prolonged exercise and eat carbohydrate rich diets, taking pains not to skip meals.

Mitochondrial Myopathies

The final common pathway for the generation of the major part of the ATP formed in the cell is the mitochondrial respiratory chain. The electron transport chain is divided into five complexes that are integral components of the inner mitochondrial membrane. Notably, some of the protein subunits of these complexes are encoded by mitochondrial DNA (mt DNA), a double stranded circular unit with 16,569 bp. For instance, complex I (NADH-coenzyme Q reductase) comprises 26 different

Table 25.5. Mitochondrial Myopathies*

Defects of the Electron Transport Chain
- Complex I (NADH-CoQ oxidoreductase) deficiency—2 forms: 1) myopathy with exercise intolerance; 2) encephalomyopathy with muscle, eye, and auditory defects
- Complex II (succinate-CoQ oxidoreductase) deficiency—infantile onset, encephalomyopathy
- Complex III (CoQ—cytochrome C oxidoreductase) deficiency-myopathy, encephalomyopathy with retinal degeneration and hearing loss
- Complex IV (cytochrome C oxidase) deficiency—myopathy, Leigh's syndrome: mental retardation, brainstem abnormalities, seizures

Other Mitochondrial Myopathies
- MERRF—*m*yoclonus, *e*pilepsy, *r*agged *r*ed muscle *f*ibers, lactacidemia
- MELAS—lactacidemia, encephalopathy with stroke like attacks and vomiting, dementia
- Kearns-Sayre syndrome—retinitis pigmentosa, heart block, opthalmoplegia, ataxia, lactacidemia

Pyruvate Dehydrogenase Complex Deficiency
- Lactacidemia, encephalopathy, movement disorders, neuropathy

* These disorders usually manifest weakness of limb and muscle under control of cranial nerves, inability to sustain activity, and lactic acidemia.

proteins, seven of which are encoded by mtDNA with the remainder encoded by the more familiar nuclear genes.

Although there are now numerous defects associated with these complexes (Table 25.5), from a clinical point of view, there are only two modes of presentation: a myopathic form and another encephalomyopathic form that may also involve other tissues. Patients suffering from the myopathic form show generalized muscle weakness including those under the control of cranial nerves, easy fatigability, and lactacidemia. Definitive diagnosis requires assay of the components of the respiratory chain.

Inflammatory Myopathies of Unknown Etiology—Polymyositis

Although many disorders affect muscle secondarily, a common example being electrolyte disorders, except for those already discussed, there is only a single entity remaining that can be considered primary to muscle. This is the disease called polymyositis, which is an inflammatory disorder of skeletal muscle occurring in approximately 1/200,000 persons annually. Although the cause is unknown, pathogenesis of the disorder is commonly attributed to autoimmunity. Affected muscle shows simultaneous degeneration and regeneration, partial necrosis of a fiber with macrocytic phagocytosis, infiltrate of mononuclear cells, and areas of atrophy and fibrosis.

Symptomatology is dominated by weakness of the proximal musculature, which tends to be symmetrical and to spare the face, in contrast to the myotrophic disorders. In polymyositis unassociated with malignancy, there is a preponderance of female cases, and there is a bimodal age distribution, the peaks being at 12 and 50 years. Of those unassociated with malignancy, about 50% will spontaneously regress with restoration of normal strength. The other half may do poorly, with death resulting from aspiration or cardiac arrhythmias. Treatment with steroids, as in many other suspected autoimmune disorders, is the therapy of choice, although controlled studies are lacking to demonstrate efficacy.

SUGGESTED READINGS

GENERAL

Elliott GF, Worthington CR. How muscle may contract. Biochim Biophys Acta 1994;1200:109.

Engel AG, Franzini-Armstrong C, eds. Myology: basic and clinical. 2nd ed. New York: McGraw-Hill, 1994.

Keynes RD, Aidley DJ. Nerve and muscle. 2nd ed. Cambridge: Cambridge University Press, 1991.

Schneider MF. Control of calcium release in functioning skeletal muscle fibers. Annu Rev Physiol 1994;56:463.

MUSCULAR DYSTROPHIES

Ahn AH, Kunkel LM. The structural and functional diversity of dystrophin. Nature Genetics. 1993;3:283.

Busby KM. The muscular dystrophies. Baillieres Clin Neurol 1994;3:407.

Dubowitz V. The muscular dystrophies. Postgrad Med J 1992;68:500.

Fabbrizio E, Pons F, Robert A, et al. The dystrophin superfamily. J Muscle Res Cell Motil 1994;15:595.

Iannaccone ST. Current status of Duchenne muscular dystrophy. Pediatr Clin North Am 1992;39:879.

Karpati G. Recent developments in the biology of dystrophin and related molecules. Current Opinion in Neurology and Neurosurgery 1992;5:615.

Kunkel LM, Hoffman EP. Duchenne/Becker muscular

dystrophy: a short overview of the gene, the protein, and current diagnostics. Br Med Bull 1989;45:630.
Miller G, Wessel HB. Diagnosis of dystrinopathies: review for the clinician. Pediatr Neurol 1993;9:3.

MYOTONIC DYSTROPHY AND PERIODIC PARALYSIS

Cannon SC, Brown RH Jr, Corey DP. A sodium channel defect in hyperkalemic periodic paralysis: potassium-induced failure of inactivation. Neuron 1991;6:619.
Fishbeck KH. The mechanism of myotonic dystrophy. Ann Neurol 1994;35:255.
Fontaine B, Khurana TS, Hoffman EP, et al. Hyperkalemic periodic paralysis and the adult muscle sodium channel α-subunit gene. Science 1990;250:1000.
Fu Y-H, Friedman D, Richards S, et al. Decreased expression of myotonin-protein kinase messenger RNA and protein in adult form of myotonic dystrophy. Science 1993;260:235.
Harley HG, Rundle SA, Reardon W, et al. Unstable DNA sequence in myotonic dystrophy. Lancet 1992;339: 1125.
Hoffman EP, Spier SJ. Sodium channelopathies: dramatic diseases caused by subtle genetic changes. News in Physiologic Science 1993;8:38.
Mahadevan M, Tsilfidis C, Sabourin L, et al. Myotonic dystrophy mutation: an unstable CTG repeat in the 3" untranslated region of the gene. Science 1992;255: 1253.
Ptacek L, Johnson KJ, Griggs RC. Genetics and physiology of the myotonic muscle disorders. N Engl J Med 1993; 328:482.
Shelbourne P, Davies J, Buxton J, et al. Direct diagnosis of myotonic dystrophy with a disease-specific DNA Marker. N Engl J Med 1993;328:471.
Thornton CA, Griggs RC, Moxley RT III. Myotonic dystrophy with no trinucleotide repeat expansion. Ann Neurol 1994;35:269.

METABOLIC MYOPATHIES

Brumback RA, Feeback DL, Leech RW. Rhabdomyolysis in childhood. Pediatr Clin North Am 1992;39:821.
Haller RG, Lewis SF. Glucose-induced exertional fatigue in muscle phosphofructokinase deficiency. N Engl J Med 1991;324:364.
Hirano M, Pavlakis SG. Mitochondrial myopathy, encephalopathy, lactic acidosis, and strokelike episodes (MELAS): current concepts. J Child Neurol 1994;9:4.
Lazyer RB. Muscle metabolism during fatigue and work. Ballieres Clin Endocrinol Metab 1990;4:441.
Luft R. The development of mitochondrial medicine. Proc Natl Acad Sci U S A 1994;91:8731.
Rustin P, Chretien D, Bourgeron T, et al. Biochemical and molecular investigations in respiratory chain deficiencies. Clin Chim Acta 1994;228:35.
Shoffner JM, Wallace DC. Oxidative phosphorylation diseases and mitochondrial DNA mutations: diagnosis and treatment. Annu Rev Nutr 1994;14:535.
Trijbels JMF, Scholte HR, Ruitenbeek W, et al. Problems with the biochemical diagnosis in mitochondrial (encephalo-)myopathies. Eur J Pediatr 1993;152:178.
Tsujino S, Shanske S, DiMauro S. Molecular genetic heterogeneity of myophosphorylase deficiency (McArdle's disease). N Engl J Med 1993;329:241.
Wallace DC. Mitochondrial DNA sequence variation in human evolution and disease. Proc Natl Acad Sci U S A 1994;91:8739.

chapter **26**

Diseases of the Nervous System

The nervous system controls and regulates every mental and physical activity. It controls all movement, thought, and feeling, permitting concrete and abstract thought, even the ability to reason. In fact, the essence of brain function is to be aware that we are aware. One's level of alertness is a function of the central nervous system and when the brain is severely injured or when vital centers are compressed, loss of consciousness (coma) may ensue. Coma is the opposite of alertness and is reflected by the patient's inability to respond to any stimulus including pain.

Brain function is so enormously complex that modern science has hardly been able to go beyond descriptive accounts. Although neurophysiologists have made substantial progress toward an understanding of the transmission of nervous impulses, this has so far led to no insight whatever into explaining rational thought and personality differences between individuals. It is important to recognize that the brain, unlike all other organs, functions at two levels: one is as the macroprocessor for all sensory input and motor function, whereas the other is as the repository of those attributes (memory, emotion, rationality) that are uniquely human characteristics. The nature of the interface between these two functions may be the determinant of an individual's "personality." Thus, an abnormality in one component may be expected to alter the interface as, for example, in the depression so often seen in patients with Parkinson's disease. It could reasonably be stated that the traditional disciplinary division of the nervous system between neurology, neurophysiology, psychiatry, and psychology underscores the vast gap between understanding nerve impulse transmission and understanding the state of "being human."

This said, we should acknowledge that our ignorance permits us to cover the subject, by dividing it into neuropathologic conditions that have identifiable abnormalities of structure and/or function, and those which affect mentation. The group affecting mentation results in psychiatric disorders, mental retardation, or both. In some cases, particularly those diseases with documented genetic etiologies, nerve structural/functional abnormalities, and mental dysfunction merge. Yet, in almost all instances, the sequence of events causing impaired mentation remain completely elusive. Thus, unlike disorders such as glycogen storage disease, Type I (glucose-6-phosphatase deficiency), in which the functional abnormalities can be understood as stemming from the specific biochemical defect (see Chapter 11), it is impossible at present to explain the basis for the mental retardation of classic phenylketonuria, despite our considerable insight into the molecular defect.

To an extent, all categories of neurologic disorders are somewhat artificial because more than one aspect of brain function may be affected. Nonetheless, in an attempt to minimize artificial separations, we have taken pains to underscore nervous system disorders that affect only the macroprocessing function for sensory and motor input and those that affect both nerve function and the intellectual capacity. To emphasize this point further, we have preceded discussion of each entity with a scale indicating roughly where, between these two extremes, the disorder falls. We have done this while following a traditional approach by class of disorder or by anatomic location. At the same time, we have discussed mental retardation as an entirely separate entity, thereby acknowledging the likelihood that many hitherto unrecognized processes may cause or contribute to mental retardation. Of course, the vast array of nervous system disorders has compelled us to be both selective and brief in our coverage.

NORMAL NERVOUS SYSTEM FUNCTION

We use the term "macroprocessor" to describe the brain, with the intent both to emphasize its role as the centerpiece of the nervous system as well as to communicate the concept that there are also "microprocessors" (sensory receptors) strategically placed throughout the peripheral nervous system. An additional facet to this conceptualization is the implicit assumption that the macroprocessor must receive inputs from and generate outputs to all other parts of the nervous system. The almost unbelievably painstaking efforts of neuroanatomists over the past two centuries has established the anatomic basis for this concept. Indeed, on the basis of what we now know about the anatomy of the central nervous system, it would be fair to say that virtually no message traveling through it escapes the notice of the normal brain.

The human central nervous system receives, processes, and transmits an avalanche of independent signals simultaneously without interference. There are between 10^{11} and 10^{12} neurons, each neuron receiving information at its dendrites and cell body. What is particularly impressive is that most nerve cells have many dendrites that dramatically increase the number of inputs a particular neuron may receive. In fact, many neurons receive 10,000 or so axonal outputs, and cells in the cerebellum may receive inputs from as many as 200,000 axons. Most astounding of all, the central nervous system has the capacity for memory and imagination, two processes that are presently beyond the ability of neural science to explain.

Signaling Function of the Nervous System: The Nerve Impulse

Although a transmembrane potential difference (negative inside) exists across the membrane of all cells, only neurons (and a few other specialized cells) are *electrically excitable*. Such electrical excitability refers to the ability of the membrane to propagate an electrical signal, called the nerve impulse or action potential, for substantial distances down the length of the axon and is the means by which all messages are transmitted to the nerve terminal. At the synapse, the region of contact between a nerve terminal and the next nerve in line, the electrical signal is converted to a chemical one, mediated by a neurotransmitter which triggers onset of another electrical signal. Thus, both electrical and chemical signals figure prominently in the transmission of information within the nervous system.

What features account for the electrical excitability of neurons? Specialized selective ionic channels set excitable cells apart from other cells that, although they are polarized, are unable to propagate an electrical signal. To understand how neurons differ from other cells, we must first examine the genesis of the resting membrane potential manifested by all cells and then consider the special properties of nerve cells.

Unequal Ion Distribution Across the Cell Membrane of All Cells Accounts for the Resting Membrane Potential

As was discussed in the chapter on fluid and electrolytes, the extracellular and intracellular fluids differ in their content of Na^+ and K^+. Extracellular $[Na^+]$ is 30 to 40 times higher than the K^+ concentration, whereas the reverse exists within the cell. Of course with appropriate counterions (Cl^-, HCO_3^-, proteinate$^-$), electroneutrality is preserved on either side of the membrane, as is osmolality.

Because membranes are lipophilic, ions, which are hydrophilic, can make their way across the membrane only through protein channels embedded in the membrane. These channels permit a modest leakage of ions down their concentration gradients. Pre-eminent among such passive channels is one for K^+ that permits some K^+ to exit the cell. This ΔK^+ will ever so slightly change the balance of charges deployed on either side of the plasma membrane: the inside will become slightly negative (ca. −75 mV) whereas the external face of the plasma membrane will become slightly positive. It is this unequal distribution of ions that generates the resting transmembrane potential of the plasma membrane (Figure 26.1).

The Nerve Cell Membrane

In the case of the nerve cell, in addition to being permeable to K^+, the neuron is also endowed with Na^+ channels, which confer permeability to Na^+ (at a level lower than conferred by K^+ channels

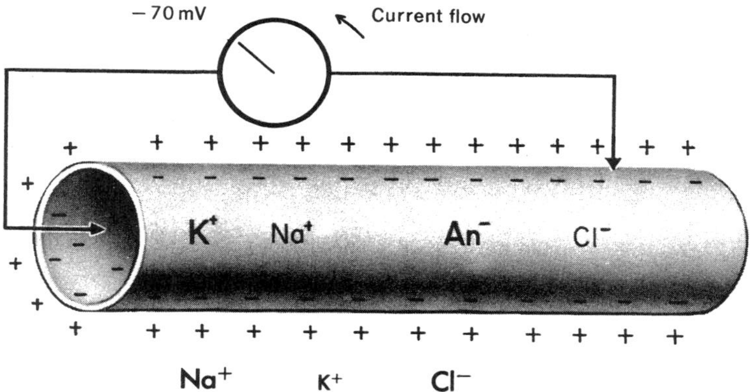

Figure 26.1. Resting potential of the neuron. The major extracellular ions are, of course, Na^+ and Cl^-, whereas those within the cell are K^+ and protein (An^-). There is a large cationic concentration gradient across the membrane, which is highly lipophilic and permits ionic transfer only through nongated open channels. The cationic gradient is sustained and regenerated by means of a Na^+-K^- ATPase pump, and is thus energy-requiring in nature. This energy expenditure results in an electrochemical gradient across the membrane at rest of −60 to −70 mV. Reprinted with permission from Noback CR, Strominger NL, Demarest RJ, et al. The Human Nervous System: Structure and Function. 5th ed. Baltimore: Williams & Wilkins, 1996: 33.

for K^+). Because Na^+ ions can enter the cell, the membrane potential of the neuron will be slightly less negative (−60 mV) than the membrane potential found in other cells devoid of Na^+ permeability. Of course, left to its own devices, this constant leak of K^+ and Na^+ eventually would dissipate the membrane potential. To ensure that this does not occur, a Na^+/K^+ ATPase is deployed in the cell membrane, pumping Na^+ out of the cell in exchange for K^+, in a ratio of Na^+:K^+ of 3:2, using adenosine triphosphate (ATP) to power this exchange process. Notably, about 50% of the total energy expenditure of the brain is accounted for by the activity of this pump mechanism.

Neuronal Excitability

Nerve cells, being electrically excitable, can be depolarized (the membrane potential becoming less negative to ca. −45 mV) and can also be hyperpolarized (the potential becoming more negative ~ −90 mV). When a nerve cell is stimulated by a current or excitatory neurotransmitter, the membrane potential decreases to −45 mV and this depolarization triggers the action potential (Figure 26.2). This phenomenon is the overt manifestation of excitability and the means by which nerves transmit information down their axons. Depolarization is the result of increased permeability to Na^+ through gated Na^+ channels, distinct from the passive Na^+ channels noted above. Repolarization of the membrane to the resting state is effected by closing the Na^+ channels followed by the leaking of K^+ out of the cell through the same passive K^+ channels that contributed to generating the resting membrane potential in the first place. Na^+ gated channels belong to a class of transmembrane proteins called *voltage-sensitive ion channels*.

When a nerve is stimulated, the membrane potential decreases from its resting level of −60 mV to the threshold potential of −45 mV, and prompts the voltage-sensitive Na^+ channels to open. This, in turn, causes the membrane potential actually to become positive (+30 mv) and triggers a wave of depolarization to propagate down the axon. This process is briefly self-perpetuating since as Na^+ enters the cell, adjacent regions of the axonal membrane depolarize, causing still more Na^+ channels to open. Whereas at rest the nerve cell membrane is normally more permeable to K^+ than to Na^+, when the Na^+ gates open during propagation of the action potential, the membrane permeability to Na^+ transiently increases 600-fold.

Only a minute fraction of the Na^+ and K^+ ions situated close to the membrane need cross the

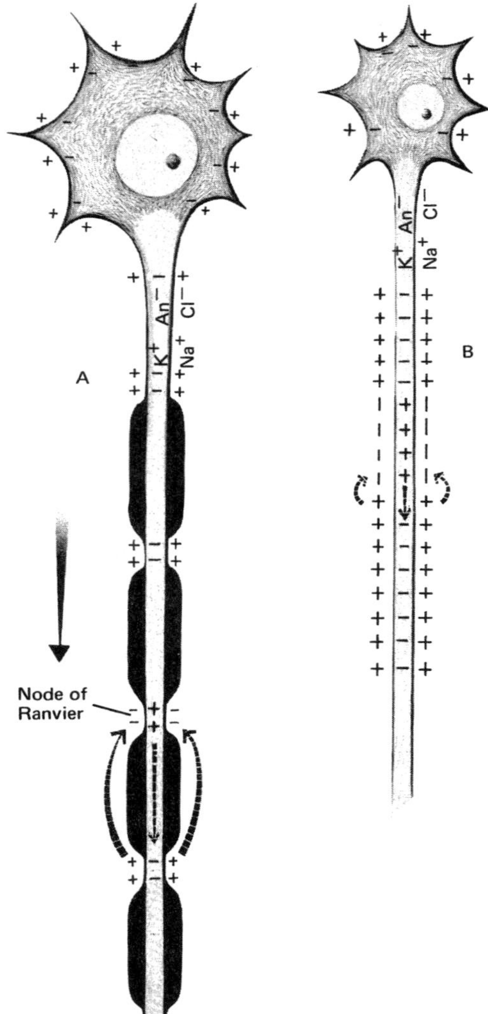

Figure 26.2. Action potential of the myelinated (A) and unmyelinated (B) neuron. The large, solid arrows indicate the direction of propagation of the impulse, away from the nerve body. The dashed arrows indicate the direction of current flow. The minus (−) signs within the boundaries of the neuronal membrane indicate the electrochemical negativity relative to the positive (+) extracellular fluid environment. Note the "jumping" of the impulse from node to node (saltatory conduction) in (A), in contrast to the continuous pattern of depolarization in the unmyelinated axon (B). Reprinted with permission from Noback C, Strominger NL, Demarest RJ, et al. The Human Nervous System: Structure and Function. 5th ed. Baltimore: Williams & Wilkins, 1996: 35.

membrane to spark the wave of depolarization and subsequent repolarization. If the number of Na^+ ions entering the cell causes depolarization to the threshold (−45 mV), an action potential is evoked. A stronger depolarizing stimulus will not increase the strength of the action potential. Accordingly, the action potential is an *all or none phenomenon*.

Synapses

As in all electrical circuitry, there are "terminals" at which the impulse can be arrested, redirected, or relayed. In the nervous system, such terminals are called *synapses* or, in the case when the message has reached a muscle, the *neuromuscular junction* (see Chapter 25). Synapses are interposed between the end of one axon and the nerve body of the next nerve cell in sequence. As noted, transmission of the impulse at the synapse is converted from one electrical in nature to one that is chemical. The latter, in turn, initiates another electrical response in the next fiber in line (Figure 26.3). A synaptic signal may be excitatory or inhibitory in nature, and is transmitted by substances known as neurotransmitters. These agents include acetylcholine, norepinephrine, dopamine, gamma-aminobutyric acid, and other compounds such as specific α-amino acids, most particularly glutamine and glycine.

Neurotransmitters are stored in vesicles localized at the synaptic cleft on the presynaptic side of the membrane. Release is by exocytosis, a process engendered by local increase of Ca^{++} ions. Upon release of neurotransmitter, it enters the synaptic cleft where it is bound to a receptor on the postsynaptic membrane. Reception of information at the postsynaptic site then initiates a change in membrane permeability which propagates the wave of depolarization. Removal of the transmitter substance occurs by re-uptake, enzymatic breakdown or diffusion. Because a given neuron can be subjected to the neurotransmitter influence of many hundreds to thousands of nerve inputs, it is the sum total of depolarizing and hyperpolarizing transmitter effects that will determine whether the neuron propagates a wave along its own axon or whether such propagation ceases. Although this is a rather simplistic view of the actual process, it suffices to convey a picture of the complexity of

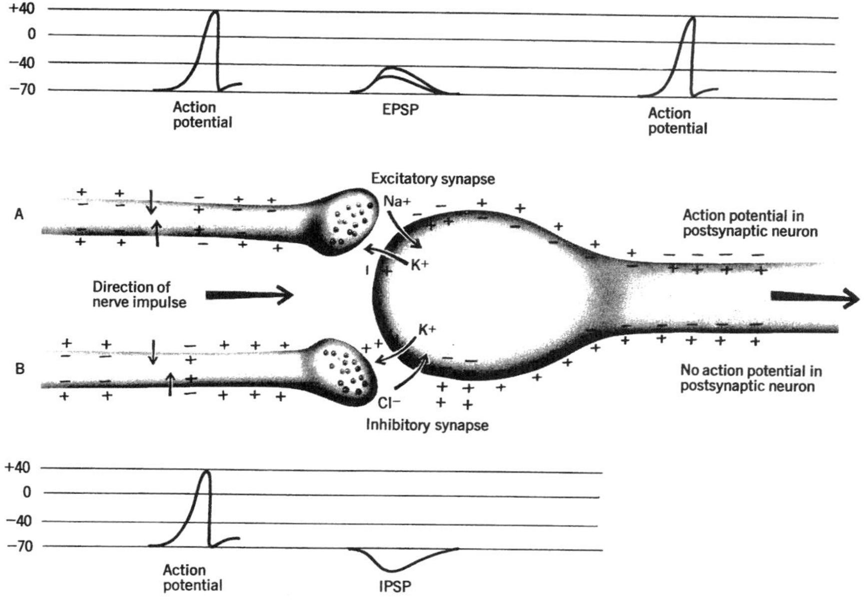

Figure 26.3. Synaptic transmission. (A) In excitatory transmission, arrival of the axonal impulse generates an excitatory postsynaptic potential (EPSP) in the postsynaptic neuron, leading to generation of a new action potential (depolarization), as shown in the top panel. (B) Inhibitory transmission at the synapse leads to generation of an inhibitory postsynaptic impulse (IPSP), which causes hyperpolarization, as shown in the lower panel, preventing formation of a new action potential. Reprinted with permission from Noback C, Strominger NL, Demarest RJ, et al. The Human Nervous System: Structure and Function. 5th ed. Baltimore: Williams & Wilkins, 1996: 37.

millions of such neurons, each subject to multiple influences, all coordinated in action or inaction to produce voluntary movement, or other responses. It is the question of how such a process can be translated into rational thought or emotion that continues to completely elude neuroscientists.

Myelination Accelerates Impulse Transmission By Saltatory Conduction

Finally, there is the issue of how the waves of depolarization traveling along axons are protected from the interference of adjacent fibers in a nerve bundle. In general terms, the nerve fiber is protected by its own insulating material, called *myelin*, an envelope synthesized by glial cells that surround the fiber. Because the electrical nature of neural conduction derives from changes in ion permeability, it is to be expected that myelin as an insulating material would be composed of relatively ion-impermeable material. In fact, human myelin consists of 70% lipid, the bulk of which is cholesterol, galactolipid, and phospholipid. By way of comparison, erythrocyte membrane contains approximately 35% lipid, a fact that underscores the specialization of the Schwann cells from which myelin is generated. Schwann cells are found in the peripheral nervous system and correspond to the supporting glial cells of the central nervous system. Glial cells constitute about 50% of the volume and 90% of the total cell number of the human central nervous system, and are strikingly different from neuronal cells because they retain the ability to divide and proliferate. It goes without saying that those cells that elaborate the insulation take no active part in impulse conduction.

Myelin is a very efficient insulator, but the myelin covering is interrupted at 1 mm intervals by bare areas called the *nodes of Ranvier* (Figure 26.2). It is at these nodes that the all important voltage-dependent Na^+ channels are concentrated. Deployed at that location, the Na^+ channels make it possible for the action potential to jump from node to node, greatly increasing the rate of transmission. Because the action potential jumps, this phenomenon is called *saltatory conduction*.

During saltatory conduction, electrical current flows, both through the surrounding extracellular fluid as well as the axoplasm of the neuron, but only at the nodes of Ranvier. Not only does saltatory conduction increase conduction rates, but by limiting repolarization to the nodes, it decreases the cost in ATP.

From this brief description of the importance of myelin to normal neural function, it should be clear that abnormalities involving myelin will have major functional ramifications, which we will examine later in this chapter.

DYSFUNCTION OF THE NERVOUS SYSTEM

Seizures

Epilepsy is expressed clinically in multiple ways, with paroxysms of motor, sensory, or psychic attacks being the most common manifestations. In many seizures, consciousness is lost, occurring in association with convulsive movements and psychological manifestations. As we will see, many seizures affect cognitive perceptions (complex partial seizures) but do not produce the abnormal movements that are the hallmark of the more well-known generalized tonic-clonic seizure (grand mal) that afflicted Julius Caesar, Alexander the Great, and countless others. Normal brain activity is marked by unsynchronized firing of neurons, the depolarization wave thus generated being channeled through a specific neural pathway to achieve a specific effect. In contrast, a seizure is due to the paroxysmal depolarization of neurons that become activated in a hypersynchronized fashion. These synchronous paroxysms, if limited only to electrical transmission, give rise to a "seizure pattern" seen by electroencephalogram. However, if the impulses are transmitted across synapses or neuromuscular junctions, they are translated into clinically detectable convulsions. As a consequence, abnormalities in EEG tracings may be found in individuals who have never experienced a convulsion. Conversely, an acute event such as hypoglycemia, which can cause instantaneous neuronal misfiring, may produce no abnormality in EEG pattern.

Various metabolic abnormalities including hyponatremia, hyperkalemia, hypocalcemia, hypoxia, hypoglycemia, hyperthermia, and alkalosis, can cause seizures. Interference with energy metabolism occurs not only in hypoxia and hypoglycemia but also in disorders of the respiratory transport chain. Such aberrations in energy coupling can cause seizures by interfering with the restoration of the normal resting potential.

Distortions of brain anatomy, on a congenital or acquired basis, can set up the conditions under which seizures may occur. It is noteworthy that penetrating head injuries, for example, suffered in time of war, may not be associated with seizures until many years have elapsed. This suggests that the reparative process, with its attendant scar formation, may be a contributory factor in seizure formation.

THE DEPOLARIZING SHIFT AND SEIZURES

A characteristic EEG finding during a seizure is the presence of spikes or sharp waves, which are fleeting, lasting only 20 to 70 milliseconds. In animals, simultaneous intracellular recordings during a seizure show a *depolarizing shift* (DS) that reflects an excitatory synaptic event. The DS is generated by opening of ion channels in the neuronal membrane causing localized extracellular $[Ca^{++}]$ to decrease, followed by an increase in extracellular $[K^{+}]$. It is believed that the DS sets up repetitive neuronal firing causing release into the extracellular space of a great deal of glutamate (the main excitatory neurotransmitter). This flooding of neurons by glutamate is likely to contribute to the hypersynchronous wave of excitation.

The hypersynchronous activity of the neurons participating in generation of a seizure contrasts sharply with the unsynchronized neuronal activity of the normal brain. This normal activity is not disorganized but it is distinct from the unusual level of synchronization of neurons just before and during a seizure. Unsynchronized activity rests on sequential processing of excitatory and inhibitory influences on the myriad neurons of the brain. Hypersynchronized activity, by contrast, depends on simultaneous activation and is manifestly abnormal.

Abnormal circumstances, including interference with normal ion channel function changes in the inhibitory or excitatory neurotransmitter levels or neurotransmitter receptor function, and decreased availability of glucose or oxygen can trigger a seizure by organizing the neurons to fire in a hypersynchronous manner. It is important to recognize that although previous injury that distorts neuronal or glial anatomy may set up an abnormal focus of activity, the normal brain is apparently always poised to develop a seizure (even if only transiently) if the right provocation obtains.

Several workers in the field advance the notion that the generation of a seizure is an outgrowth of normal brain function, because adaptation to change with experience is a vital facet of the brain. In this view, the tendency for hyperexcitability and hypersynchrony are but two manifestations of the wider phenomenon termed neuronal plasticity. Furthermore, cortical areas are at once the site from which epileptic foci arise and the region of the brain most capable of changing its functions as a result of new information received from the environment.

Certain other regions of the brain, in particular parts of the limbic system (hippocampus, entorhinal, and piriform cortices), are prone to become hyperexcitable. There are some neurons in these regions that normally are capable of generating bursts of discharges. These cells, of which there are only a few, are endowed with Ca^{++} channels that remain open while the membrane is depolarized.

For an individual with normal brain function to have a seizure, something vital to brain function, for instance, glucose availability, must be severely compromised. In contrast, subjects suffering from epilepsy have suffered a previous neuronal injury that has impaired normal brain anatomy or brain physiology so that without unusual provocation spontaneously they have a seizure.

In subjects with various forms of epilepsy, hypersynchrony of neural discharge is achieved because local excitatory circuits are reinforced. This tendency to seize is probably also fed by a loss of normal inhibitory mechanisms so that neural discharges radiate to more remote neurons. These remote neurons now fire in unison further reinforcing the hypersynchrony. When enough neurons are firing together, they exceed a threshold, overcoming offsetting inhibitory influences. If to this we add the evidence that current in the brain may flow through the extracellular space circumventing the normal synaptic route, we see yet another factor that may contribute to epileptogenesis.

Because glial cells take up K^+ from the extracellular space, defending the normal extracellular ion concentration upon which the generation of the resting potential depends, the gliosis that occurs after some neural injuries may also contribute to epileptogenesis. Once the excitation spreads to the surrounding cortex or to the other side of the brain a seizure will ensue. Depending on the region of the brain giving rise to the seizure activity, the attack will be expressed as a motor, sensory, or psychomotor phenomenon. We will now examine the various seizure types in terms of their manifestations and site of origin.

SEIZURE PATTERNS

From the point of view of therapy, and in the absence of detailed knowledge of the root cause of the various kinds of seizures, classifying seizures by clinical manifestations makes good sense. In this clinical classification, there are two general types of seizures: partial and generalized. Partial or focal seizures begin locally and when consciousness is retained are called simple, complex when consciousness is impaired. Simple partial seizures are next classified by clinical manifestations: motor, sensory (visual, auditory), autonomic (smell or taste sensations), or psychic. Psychic symptoms are the most varied and may take the form of inappropriate familiarity with an unknown place (deja vu) or unfamiliarity with a known place (jamais vu). Still other manifestations include sensory hallucinations and sometimes fear or euphoria.

Complex partial seizures are associated with distortions of consciousness, but may be preceded by an aura. Some attacks begin with *automatisms*, such as lip-smacking, pacing, and mumbling, which progress to seemingly more purposeful activity, but with sustained memory loss after the attack.

To the lay public, the most familiar and alarming type of seizure is the *generalized* convulsive (tonic-clonic or grand mal) attack. Less well known, but common in the pediatric age group, is the generalized nonconvulsive seizure, the absence or petit mal attack. Generalized tonic-clonic seizures may begin without warning, but in more than half there is an experience (aura) that precedes the attack and that will be recalled after the seizure, whereas the seizure itself will not. The aura may help pinpoint the region of the brain sparking the seizure activity.

Absence attacks are brief and, were it not for their frequency (up to 100/d) and consequent interference with school performance and other activities, they might be dismissed as mere daydreaming. In a high percentage of subjects, hyperventilation will trigger such an attack with vacant stare often accompanied by lipsmacking and rhythmic blinking, that lasts for 5 to 10 seconds.

Coma

Coma is the most severe form of depressed consciousness representing the end of a spectrum of clinical states that also includes inattention, confusion, and stupor. As these states reflect increasing degrees of impaired consciousness, patients may manifest any or all of these clinical states during the course of an illness. A comatose patient cannot be awakened by any stimulus to interact with his environment, whereas a stuporous patient may be roused briefly by a noxious stimulus. Both coma and stupor are distinctly abnormal and may be caused by one of three general abnormalities: (*1*) depressed metabolic function of the cerebral hemispheres; (*2*) defective brainstem arousal system; and (*3*) impairment of activity of the reticular activating system by an expanding mass that displaces the brain. Metabolic causes rest on interference with the ceaseless dependence of the brain for oxygen and glucose and on the normal function of metabolic pathways for extracting energy from substrates. Anatomic causes result from compression or destruction of vital brain centers.

DIFFUSE CEREBRAL HEMISPHERIC FAILURE

When the function of the brain stem or of both cerebral hemispheres is depressed, consciousness is lost. The most common causes for bilateral failure are metabolic and toxic encephalopathies: Over 50% of patients presenting in coma have suffered a drug-induced or metabolic encephalopathy. Examples of metabolic encephalopathy include severe hypoglycemia, hyperammonemia, acidosis, alkalosis, electrolyte abnormalities, hepatic encephalopathy, and severe hypoxia, whereas toxic encephalopathy is best exemplified by drug toxicity. Drugs associated with coma, as a result of overdose, are listed in Table 26.1.

Hypothermia (<32°C)is itself a cause of coma, but also may be associated with thiamine deficiency (Wernicke's encephalopathy), hypoglycemia, hypothyroidism, and drug overdose. Again, overdose of sedatives or opiates is probably the most common cause of hypothermia. When hypothermia occurs in a patient with sepsis this is a particularly ominous sign.

BRAINSTEM FAILURE

Brainstem function, especially that of the ascending reticular activating system, can be sufficiently compromised to result in coma with a cerebrovascular accident involving the basilar artery, hemorrhage into the pons, or compression of the brainstem by an expanding posterior fossa tumor.

COMPRESSION OF VITAL CENTERS BY DISPLACEMENT OF BRAIN STRUCTURES

When a space-occupying lesion, 30 to 60 cc. in volume, occurs in the cerebral hemispheres, the additional volume in the nonexpansile cranial vault requires that some other part of the brain shift its position. If the diencephalon is the structure that must move, a modest horizontal displacement of 3 to 5 mm is associated with drowsiness, whereas a greater displacement will cause stupor or coma. Space-occupying lesions that regularly cause such displacement are tumors, intracranial hemorrhage, and subdural hematomas. Structural lesions that impair consciousness can be localized by assessing the level of consciousness, respiratory pattern, pupil reactivity, pattern of extraocular movement, and motor responses to noxious stimuli. Armed with this information, the examiner can determine what level of the brain is involved and whether a supratentorial lesion is impinging on midbrain and lower brainstem centers.

Infectious Disease

An outstanding example of selective "macroprocessor" malfunction is found in the case of poliomyelitis. Polio, once dreaded as a cause of permanent motor paralysis and frequent death, has been rendered a minor public health problem through the combined efforts of Jonas Salk and Albert

Table 26.1. Drugs Associated With Coma

SUBSTANCE	ASSOCIATED SYMPTOMS AND SIGNS	DIAGNOSIS	SPECIFIC ANTIDOTE
Morphine Methadone Hydromorphone Meperidine Oxycodone Heroin Levorphanol	Hypotension Hypothermia Apnea Pinpoint pupils	Urine screen Rapid response to Naloxone	Naloxone
Ethanol Barbiturates Benzodiazepines Chloral hydrate Ethchlorvynol Glutethimide Meprobamate Methaqualone	Hypothermia Hypotension Hypotonia Pupils reactive	Blood levels	None
Amphetamines Cocaine Methylphenidate	Hyperactive Paranoid, pupils dilated, hypothermia, seizures	Blood levels	None
Lithium MAO inhibitors Phenothiazines Tricyclics	Lethargy (with Li+), agitation, seizures	Blood levels	None

N.B. This table is not intended to provide inclusive toxicity information, but only to communicate general detail.

Sabin. Poliovirus, although it gains entry through the alimentary canal, must undergo systemic spread and replication before attacking the central nervous system. This attack is entirely specific for the motor neurons of the brain stem and spinal cord, the infected cells undergoing degeneration. Loss of these neurons eventually leads to atrophy of their corresponding muscle groups, resulting in the flaccid paralysis characteristic of the disease. There is no case of poliomyelitis on record, despite the huge number of people affected in the past, in which mentation was impaired by the viral onslaught.

The number of infectious diseases that adversely affect the motor/sensory and intellectual functions of the central nervous system are legion. These include those of viral, bacterial, and fungal etiologies, some common and some very rare. Virtually all have in common systemic symptoms such as fever, lethargy, etc, chiefly due to the fact that they are systemic diseases in the true sense of the term. Thus, although the central nervous system effects of infectious disease in general are often of the greatest concern clinically, they are usually secondary to a more generalized infection. With the caveat that disorders of unknown etiology, such as multiple sclerosis, may ultimately turn out to be viral in nature, very few infectious agents have a selective propensity for the central nervous system.

As poliomyelitis is the paradigm of infection affecting the macroprocessor motor/sensory function, rabies could be considered its equivalent with respect to all major functions of the central nervous system. Fortunately very rare, the clinical picture caused by infection with rabies virus is the stuff from which nightmares are created. Following acquisition of infection, usually from the bite of a rabid animal, the virus invades skeletal muscle cells where it replicates and attaches to motor end plates. Unless the virus can be killed by host resistance factors prior to this stage, the virus becomes shielded from immunologic response and travels passively along motor nerve axons throughout the quiescent or incubation phase. By way of this route, it eventually reaches the complex area of the brain called the limbic system with connections throughout the cerebral cortex as well as the autonomic and endocrine systems. At this point, the patient manifests the prodromal stage, with systemic complaints such as headache, fever, and mood changes, all of which rabies infection shares with most other such etiologic agents. As the prodrome continues, the virus travels along the efferent nerves to distal nerve endings in most organs and the salivary glands, in particular.

Onset of the acute neurologic phase coincides with the true clinical manifestations of rabies infection. These generally take one of two courses, either the "furious rabies" or the "paralytic rabies" pattern. Furious rabies includes the nightmare complex of agitation, seizures, disorientation, hallucinations, and violent hydrophobia. Fluid ingestion induces painful muscle contractions of the pharynx and larynx, which lead the patient to violent avoidance of liquids, mimicking the behavior of a wild animal. These violent episodes can be induced by a variety of other sensory stimuli, the classic one being aerophobia, in response to the feeling of air blowing across the skin. In the paralytic form, there is predominance of an ascending, symmetrical paralysis culminating in respiratory failure. Both forms ultimately result in coma and death, "furious" rabies disappearing when the virus reaches the neocortex. The final phase is virtually identical to that due to many other causes of encephalitis.

Immunologic and inflammatory responses are not seen until after onset of the acute neurologic stage. A rather odd feature of the neuropathologic findings is the relative lack of degenerative changes, particularly in light of the striking severity of the clinical encephalopathy. Gray matter and spinal cord are the chief areas of congestion and inflammatory changes, but even these are frequently mild in comparison to what is seen in less impressive clinical disease of other etiologies. Perhaps the answer lies in the biochemical transformation occurring in infected neurons, directed by the viral RNA. However, until we are better informed as to what these are, these observations will remain unexplained.

Vascular Diseases

Brain metabolic activity proceeds at an astonishingly high fixed rate when one considers that the brain weighs only 1.3 kg and yet consumes 20% of the oxygen used by the individual. And of course, although the brain does not perform work in the sense that muscle does, it carries out an enormous amount of electrical activity, propagating action potentials down innumerable axons. A vital component of this electrical work is the activity of the Na^+-K^+ ATPase. Additional contributions to neuronal energy expenditure are axonal transport of proteins and synthesis of neurotransmitters. It is thus plain to see that the brain has prodigious and relentless energy requirements. Accordingly, any interference with either the blood supply or delivery of O_2 will have prompt and often devastating consequences for brain function. Such events are called strokes or *cerebrovascular accidents* and are the third most frequent cause of death among adults in developed countries and a major cause of permanent disability in those who survive. It follows that, at least at present, it is much more desirable to prevent a stroke than it is to treat its consequences. An individual who survives a stroke may be left imprisoned in a functionless, speechless existence which can be devastating.

CEREBRAL BLOOD FLOW

Normally, the brain receives about 800 ml/minute of blood, which represents 20% of the cardiac output. Because the brain must defend itself against regional and global acidosis and hypoxia, the baroreceptor reflexes of the systemic circulation are not sufficient to modulate blood flow to the specific regions of the brain. Instead, in the brain, control is local and is exquisitely responsive to changing metabolic conditions, especially as reflected by lactate and CO_2. This local control is termed *autoregulation* and as might be expected, acidosis and hypoxia trigger local vasodilation, enhancing delivery of blood to the affected region. Unfortunately, in a patient who has suffered a ce-

Table 26.2. Effects of Decreasing Levels of Cerebral Perfusion

Normal blood flow 52 ml/100 g tissue/minute
Symptoms begin when perfusion falls to 25–30 ml/100 g tissue/minute
Brain electrical activity ceases at 18 ml/100 g tissue/minute
Na^+, K^+-ATPase fails due to inadequate ATP when perfusion is <10 ml/100 g tissue/minute

K^+ leaks out of neurons
Ca^{2+} accumulates within the cell → neuronal injury
Intracellular lactic acidosis occurs
Cell death ensues within 3–4 hours

rebral vascular accident, or severe head trauma with hemorrhage, the protective autoregulatory system becomes inoperative. This is most unfortunate because it is just such patients who are most in need of the ability to respond to acidosis and hypoxia.

So exquisitely sensitive is the brain to ischemia (oxygen deprivation, hypoglycemia, and buildup of metabolic waste products) that irreversible injury begins within 4 to 8 minutes of cessation of blood flow. The functions compromised by increasing interference with blood flow to the brain are listed in Table 26.2. Areas of the brain that are totally deprived of oxygen are referred to as the *ischemic core*. This core is usually surrounded by a larger region that receives some blood from collateral circulation. This partially perfused area is known as the *ischemic penumbra*, and neurons in this region may recover from the insult. Obviously, deprivation of oxygen leads to collapse of oxidative phosphorylation resulting in lactate accumulation and from the lack of ATP to drive the Na^+-K^+, edema formation. Ca^{++} levels increase within neurons, activating protease and xanthine oxidase, the latter paving the way for generation of highly destructive free radicals. Activation of phospholipases, also instigated by influx of Ca^{++}, leads to dismantling of membrane phospholipids, causing considerable damage, if not death, of the affected cells.

GLUTAMATE EXCITOTOXICITY

Although cells in the ischemic core suffer death from the chain of events noted previously, neurons that are partially nourished by collaterals appear to suffer damage from the effects of release of glutamate and other excitatory neurotransmitters. In strokes and many neurodegenerative disorders, glutamate receptors are flooded by glutamate released from damaged cells.

When glutamate binds at one type of glutamate receptor, (the so-called N-methyl-d-aspartate or NMDA receptor), it causes ionic channels for Na^+ and Ca^{++} to open permitting an influx of these two cations into the neuron. This influx of Na^+ and Ca^{++} has two untoward effects. First, Na^+ entry, along with Cl, causes osmotic swelling, and second Ca^{++} influx triggers a chain of noxious events within the cell that results in death of postsynaptic neurons. Consequences of increasing intracellular Ca^{++} include activation of phospholipases, proteases, phosphatases, and endonucleases. These enzymes can dismantle cellular structural elements and cause fragmentation of DNA. To make matters worse, superoxide ions form during reperfusion leading to formation of more powerful toxic free radicals. To some extent, glial cells may mitigate these effects of glutamate by acting as a sink for the excess glutamate liberated.

At present, it is baffling as to why neurons are so vulnerable to glutamate, because it is the dominant excitatory neurotransmitter. Fortunately, although there is no ready answer to this enigma, it is possible to ameliorate the effects of glutamate excitotoxicity by administering antagonists that interfere with the action of glutamate at the NMDA receptor. The most effective of such agents are those that modulate binding of glutamate rather than those that act as competitive inhibitors. By not directly competing for these receptor sites, these agents do not block neurotransmission in regions of the brain not affected by ischemia. Three such agents are flebamate, nimodipine, and riluzole.

MECHANISMS CAUSING STROKE

Hypertension, diabetes, and hyperlipidemia are all major contributing factors to the development of *atherosclerosis*. As is well known, atherosclerosis is the major cause of thromboembolic phenomena, either thrombi or emboli having the capability of occluding vital cranial arteries.

Mitigating complete cessation of blood flow to a region of the brain is the effect of collateral circulation, which is sometimes so effective as to offset a narrowing of the vessel lumen of up to 90%. Strokes caused by thrombi often progress in a stepwise or discontinuous fashion with the deficit evolving over 24 to 48 hours. In contrast, an embolic stroke, most often arising from the heart, presents with a sudden loss of function—a loss that does not worsen over the ensuing hours as with a thrombus. Often overlooked, almost 60% of patients who develop a thrombotic stroke suffer a prior *transient ischemic attack* (TIA), an attack that is a harbinger of a more serious vascular event.

Degenerative Diseases

Although the category of degenerative diseases generally involves effects on mental capacity, there are certain neurodegenerative diseases that affect the "macroprocessor" only. Perhaps the most familiar of these are Friedreich's ataxia and amyotrophic lateral sclerosis ("Lou Gehrig" disease). In both disorders, mentation is left intact, whereas motor function is severely impaired.

Friedreich's ataxia is inherited as an autosomal recessive trait, with an estimated carrier frequency of approximately 1/100. The biochemical defect caused by the gene mutation has not been identified, but appears to be carried on chromosome 9. Whatever the biochemical etiology, it is clearly not confined to the central nervous system, because there is a close association with diabetes mellitus in 20% or more of these patients, and the major cause of death is cardiac failure. Clinical onset is in childhood or early adolescence, the first symptoms being associated with ataxia. In general, the neurologic progression of the disease mirrors progressive degenerative changes in the lateral corticospinal tracts and the dorsal and ventral spinocerebellar tracts. These are accompanied by degeneration of Purkinje cells in the cerebellum, and occasionally in certain cranial nerve nuclei, as well.

In Friedreich's ataxia, the ataxia and incoordination do not primarily result from a lesion in the cerebellum, but rather from loss of vital proprioceptive information that would normally feed into the cerebellum through the dorsal and ventral spinocerebellar tracts and Clarke's column (posterior spinocerebellar tract). Deprived of this proprioceptive information from muscle tendons and joints, the patient experiences jerky, clumsy movements in association with intention tremor. Other findings in Friedreich's ataxia that establish the diagnosis are the presence of clubfeet, kyphoscoliosis, and absent deep tendon reflexes (DTRs) in the legs. Over time, loss of ambulation and a hypertrophic myocardopathy develop, the cardiac abnormality generally causing death through initiation of a supraventricular arrhythmia and congestive heart failure. No treatment is available, and life-expectancy is usually confined to less than 40 years.

Amyotrophic lateral sclerosis is a sporadic disorder, occurring in the adult population aged 30 years or more, with an estimated incidence of 1/100,000. Rare reports of an autosomal dominant inheritance pattern in families exist, but the vast majority of cases occur randomly in the population. Lesions and clinical findings of amyotrophic lateral sclerosis are confined to the voluntary motor system with involvement of both upper and lower motor neurons, including motor nuclei of the cranial nerves. Clinically, the predominant findings in amyotropic lateral sclerosis are gait instability, limb weakness, dysarthria, and dysphagia associated with painful muscle cramps and fasciculations. Despite the eventual involvement of cranial nerve nuclei, resulting in tongue atrophy, swallowing difficulties, drooling of saliva, and unintelligible speech, mentation is left virtually untouched. It is this preservation of mental function in both of these mysterious disorders that renders them so frightening to affected individuals—together with their grim prognosis, patients can anticipate observing and being fully aware of their relentless deterioration and demise. Nevertheless, physical therapy, physical aids to compensate for the profound muscle weakness, electronic means to aid communication, and support and compassion by caregivers can help sustain patients and their families. A team approach is clearly needed to give these patients the support they require.

Several studies have implicated abnormal accumulations of glutamate in the central nervous system in the pathogenesis of amyotrophic lateral sclerosis (ALS). One such study demonstrated regionally selective decreased uptake of glutamate by synaptosomes prepared from spinal cords and motor cortex of patients succumbing to ALS. This glutamate transport defect was not found in synaptosomes from patients dying of Alzheimer's or Huntington's, or in subjects who had no evidence of neurologic disease. In support of a role for glutamate is the evidence that inhabitants of Guam who ingest the indigenous cycad palm excitotoxin β-N-methylamino-L-alanine develop a degenerative disorder virtually indistinguishable from ALS.

Recently, the glutamate antagonist, riluzole, was administered to a group of patients with ALS with the unexpected result that patients with a preponderance of bulbar symptoms seemed to improve, whereas those with lower motor symptoms did not. Unfortunately, the duration of symptomatic improvement was not sustained, the disease resuming its downhill course within 12 to 21 months. An editorial on this paper raised several probing questions about why improvement should occur in one subset of patients but not the other. If bulbar and limb-onset ALS are the same disease, the findings published in this study are baffling.

Demyelinating Disease

The chief representative of this group of demyelinating disorders is multiple sclerosis (MS), a disease of unknown etiology which has an approximate prevalence in North America and Europe of 60/100,000 people. Current wisdom holds that the disease is one of autoimmunity developed as a consequence of viral infection, although this remains far from conclusive. There is reasonable evidence for an association between certain HLA haplotypes (DR2 in North American and European populations), and a 50% concordance rate among twins further supports the possibility of genetic susceptibility. Whether this susceptibility relates to the triggering infection or to regulating the subsequent immune response is at present unknown. Onset can occur from adolescence to middle age, but the average patient presents from 30 to 35 years. Pathologically, MS is marked by inflammation, demyelination (usually in a patchy distribution), and scarring.

Early clinical diagnosis can be difficult, due to the fact that distribution of lesions in the brain is so often widespread and disparate from patient to patient. In fact, one of the characteristics of MS is the diversity and multiplicity of clinical manifestations and their waxing and waning with time. The most likely presenting findings include weakness in a lower extremity with clumsiness or a tendency to stumble when walking, paresthesia, and optic neuritis resulting in unilateral blindness. All myelinated fibers within the central nervous system are at risk, yet there is a randomness to the pattern which has defied explanation. Some myelin may be only partially destroyed, whereas other nerve fibers may be laid bare; lesions vary from a millimeter to several centimeters in length. Because saltatory conduction depends on an intact myelin membrane, when it is disrupted, nerve conduction is slowed or blocked entirely. Within the lesion, attempts at remyelination can be identified, accompanied by astrocytic infiltration and scar formation.

No specific laboratory methods exist for diagnosis, which usually requires exclusion of other entities and observation over time. Magnetic resonance imaging (MRI) of brain or spinal cord may reveal the presence of multiple (often subclinical) lesions because the recurrent nature of the symptoms leads inevitably to the diagnosis of MS. Life span is reduced, death from secondary infection generally occurring within 30 to 35 years of diagnosis. Two agents, β-interferon and copolymer I, have shown promise in arresting the progress of MS and are now the targets of multicenter blinded clinical trials. Copolymer I is a random linear polymer of alanine, glutamatic acid, lysine, and tyrosine with a mass of 23 KDa. It appears to share cross reactivity with myelin basic protein (MBP), perhaps acting by inducing immunologic tolerance to MBP.

Movement Disorders

Movement requires, in addition to the obvious participation of muscles, bones, and joints, participation of various sensory systems and higher neural centers (cerebral cortex, cerebellum, and basal ganglia) to plan and coordinate voluntary movements like walking, running, or playing a sport or a musical instrument to name but a few. Sensory inputs are used by higher centers to ensure that the individual maintains his balance during various acts. This requires receipt of information from proprioceptive centers that apprise the central nervous system of position of limbs in space. The cerebellum and basal ganglia provide inputs to the thalamus that pass up to the cerebral cortex providing necessary information to maintain balance and coordinate movement. Anyone who has picked up an empty container expecting it to be full, will appreciate the role of the central nervous system in motor control.

In reaching for something, for instance, sensory input is vital to ensuring that the trajectory of the arm and hand are on target, thus avoiding "past pointing." Overshooting or past pointing is associated with cerebellar defects. Although visual cues can compensate for abnormalities in the function of the cerebellum and basal ganglia, when the eyes are closed, the defects in motor control become evident.

CEREBELLUM

The province of the cerebellum is to ensure performance of smooth accurate movements. This region of the brain carries out this overall function by comparing commands to initiate an act with actual performance as reflected by information about limb position and velocity. In so doing, the cerebellum sees to it that ongoing movements are smoothly executed, and that desired targets are reached precisely. This role can best be appreciated by considering the effects of lesions of the cerebellum. Such lesions impair both balance and the normal close coordination between limb and eye movements. At rest, patients with cerebellar lesions evince no symptoms, but as soon as they move, abnormalities become readily apparent. One symptom is *ataxia* in which the patient suffers from movements that are not coordinated in range, speed, direction, or strength. In consequence, such individuals sway or stagger, manifesting robotlike movements, because complex acts are executed in a stepwise fashion rather than in the normal fluid or "seamless" manner. Another symptom is *dysmetria* or past pointing in which the affected individual cannot home in on the desired target without first missing. Still another manifestation of cerebellar dysfunction is *dysdiadochokinesia*, the inability to perform rapidly alternating movements such as rapidly turning over one's hand back and forth. The last is *action tremor*, an oscillation of the extremity manifest only when movement is attempted, so that unlike the tremor of Parkinson's disease, it does not appear at rest. Because of these symptoms, patients with cerebellar disease must consciously "think out" the movements of a limb. This contrasts sharply with the normal situation in which we are unaware of how we carry out most of our movements once they have been initiated.

BASAL GANGLIA

Working in concert with the cerebellum, the basal ganglia are primarily concerned with planning and executing complex motor acts. The basal ganglia seem to be the dominant factor in regulating how rapidly movement is initiated and appear as well to play a major role in making possible simultaneous acts such as steering a car while working the clutch with one's feet. The basal ganglia consist of five subcortical nuclei that interconnect extensively (Figure 26.4): the caudate nucleus, putamen, globus pallidus, subthalamic nucleus, and the substantia nigra. Furthermore, the basal ganglia receive inputs from and deliver output to the

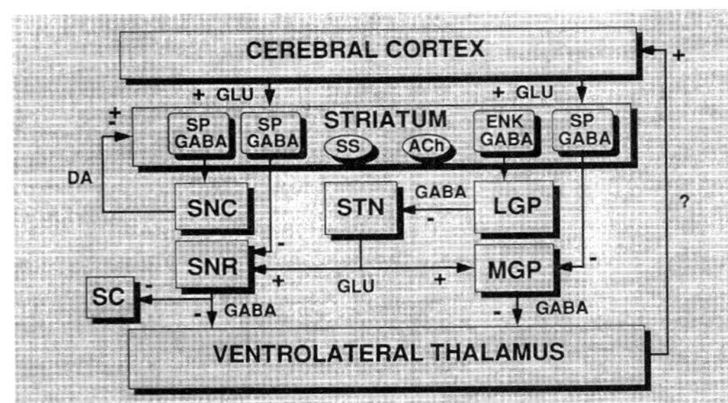

Figure 26.4. Diagram of basal ganglia motor pathways. Arrows denote the direction of impulse flow, whereas + and − indicate the respective excitatory and inhibitory nature of the extensively interrelated neurotransmitter response. ACh = acetylcholine; DA = dopamine; ENK = enkephalin; GABA = γ-aminobutyric acid; GLU = glutamic acid; LGP = lateral globus pallidus; MGP = medial globus pallidus; SC = superior colliculus; SNC = substantia nigra pars compacta; SNR = substantia nigra pars reticulata; SP = substance P; SS = somatostatin; STN = subthalamic nucleus. Reprinted with permission from Jankovic J, Tolosa E. Parkinson's Disease and Movement Disorders. 2nd ed. Baltimore: Williams & Wilkins, 1993: 2.

association cortex and limbic systems underscoring the fact that the basal ganglia participate in functions other than motor control.

The characteristic feature of disorders of the basal ganglia is the presence of abnormal involuntary movements. Such movements include *tremors* (rhythmic oscillating movements), *chorea* (abrupt, dancing limb movements), *athetosis* (slow, writhing movements), and *ballism* (intense, violent flailing movements of the limbs). These abnormal movements are believed to reflect a *release* phenomenon, that is, the expression of movements that are normally suppressed because of inhibition from higher centers. With damage to the basal ganglia and consequent cessation of inhibitory input, these more primitive movements are overtly expressed. In addition, as we will see when discussing the akinesia of Parkinson's disease, difficulty in initiating movement is also a striking feature of basal ganglia disease, the symptom stemming from interruption in dopamine input from the basal ganglia and other centers.

MAJOR NEUROTRANSMITTERS OF THE BASAL GANGLIA

The most familiar member of this group of basal ganglia disorders is Parkinsonism, in which the

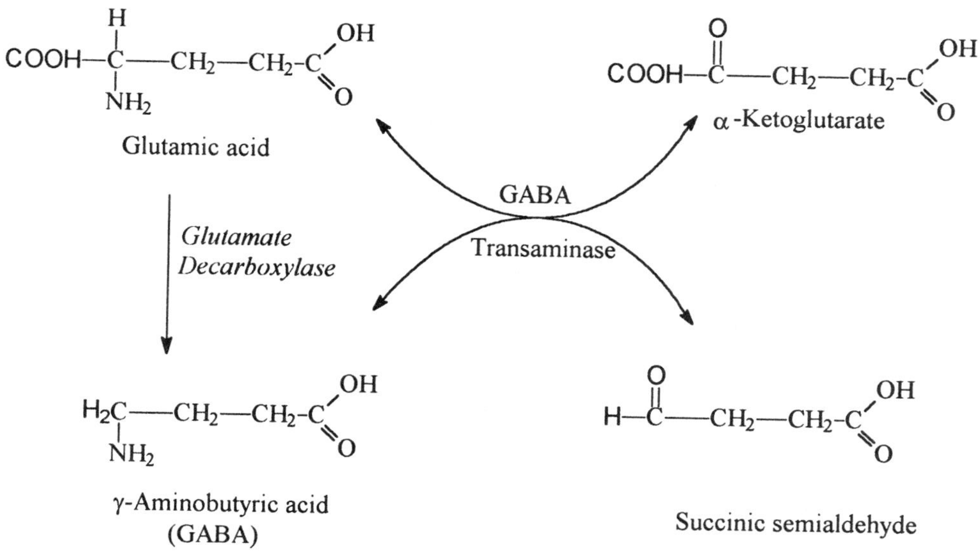

Glutamic acid

α-Ketoglutarate

GABA Transaminase

Glutamate Decarboxylase

γ-Aminobutyric acid (GABA)

Succinic semialdehyde

Figure 26.5. Synthesis of γ-aminobutyric acid (GABA). This reaction is of critical importance to the normal function of the central nervous system. Note that conversion of glutamate to GABA results in transformation of an excitatory to an inhibitory neurotransmitter.

movement disorder is characterized by tremor at rest, rigidity, bradykinesia (generally slow movements) and loss of postural reflexes. As we have seen, the regions of the brain involved, the basal ganglia, serve as vital centers for coordination of posture, walking, and other movements that are purposeful but relatively automatic in nature. The basal ganglia are chiefly responsible for the relay of messages within the central nervous system, as distinct from the pyramidal tracts, which conduct messages from the brain into the periphery.

The caudate and putamen are collectively known as the striatum and are the "reception center" for signals sent from the entire cerebral cortex and the thalamus to the extrapyramidal tract. The inflowing signals are chiefly mediated by the excitatory neurotransmitter *glutamate*. Neural output from the striatum runs to the globus pallidus and to the substantia nigra. In both cases, messages are mediated via the neurotransmitter *γ-aminobutyric acid* (GABA). Within the globus pallidus, there is interneuronal transmission by way of glutamate, while GABA subserves this function within the substantia nigra. GABA synthesis arises from two sources (Figure 26.5), the decarboxylation of glutamate through the action of glutamate decarboxylase, and the pyridoxine-dependent transamination of succinic semialdehyde, generated from succinate through the action of succinic acid semialdehyde dehydrogenase. Because both glutamate and succinate are generated from α-ketoglutarate, intact operation of the Krebs cycle is critical to normal GABA formation. It is worth noting that inborn defects of glutamate decarboxylase and both the succinate dehydrogenase and semialdehyde transaminase have been described in humans. Unlike glutamate, which is an excitatory neurotransmitter, GABA is considered an inhibitory neurotransmitter.

The output from the globus pallidus and the substantia nigra runs chiefly to the thalamus and the striatum. Joint output from both the globus pallidus and substantia nigra to the thalamus are mediated by GABA, the messages relayed from there going to the prefrontal cortex, the major origin of the pyramidal tracts. With particular relevance to the genesis of the defect in Parkinson's disease, transmission from the substantia nigra to the striatum is selectively mediated by dopamine, an inhibitory neurotransmitter. Dopamine synthesis (Figure 26.6) derives from tyrosine.

In essence, then, the chief inhibitory neurotransmitter influence on the striatal structures is dopamine, produced by the substantia nigra. Any

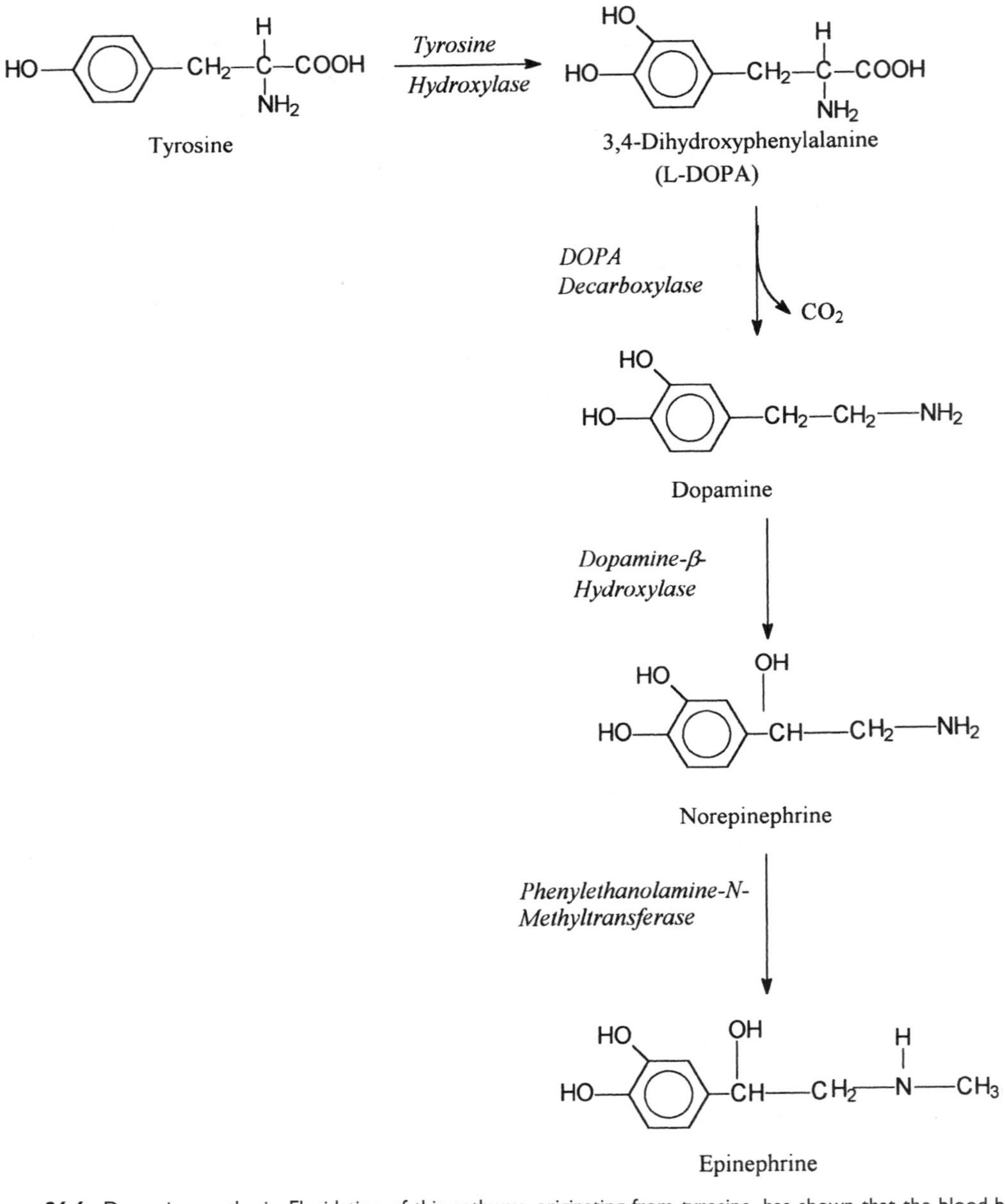

HO–C₆H₄–CH_2–CH(NH_2)–COOH
Tyrosine

Tyrosine Hydroxylase →

(HO)₂C₆H₃–CH_2–CH(NH_2)–COOH
3,4-Dihydroxyphenylalanine
(L-DOPA)

DOPA Decarboxylase ↓ CO_2

(HO)₂C₆H₃–CH_2–CH_2–NH_2
Dopamine

Dopamine-β-Hydroxylase ↓

(HO)₂C₆H₃–CH(OH)–CH_2–NH_2
Norepinephrine

Phenylethanolamine-N-Methyltransferase ↓

(HO)₂C₆H₃–CH(OH)–CH_2–N(H)–CH_3
Epinephrine

Figure 26.6. Dopamine synthesis. Elucidation of this pathway, originating from tyrosine, has shown that the blood-brain barrier is impervious to dopamine, while permitting small amounts of L-DOPA to cross. Although this information has led to the successful use of synthetic 3,4-dihydroxyphenylalanine(L-DOPA) in treatment of Parkinson's disease, it is clear that the decarboxylase reaction in Parkinson's disease patents does not take place in the substantia nigral dopaminergic cells, which is the normal site of the conversion. Further transformation of dopamine leads to production of epinephrine and norepinephrine, which have limited but important neurotransmitter roles in the central nervous system.

Table 26.3. Etiologies of Parkinsonism

1. Primary
   Parkinson's disease (Idiopathic)—insidious onset, unrelated to other disease, drugs, or injury
2. Secondary
   Association with disease and/or injury
   a. Drugs—characteristic of reserpine, phenothiazines, and butyrophenones; onset is frequently sudden; condition typically refractory to levodopa; drug withdrawal leads to remission
   b. Infection—typically post-encephalitic by months to years; associated with Coxsackie and western equine encephalitis viruses; treatment requires relatively small doses of levodopa
   c. Vascular—may appear after stroke, usually a result of multiple striatal infarcts which are demonstrable by radiologic imaging; patients typically have a gait disturbance without tremor or characteristic facies; levodopa refractory
3. Associated with complex multisystem disease
   a. Alzheimer's disease—occasional patients are seen with pathologic features of both disorders
   b. Progressive supranuclear palsy (PSP)—tremor is rare; all vertical eye movements are restricted in PSP
   c. Striatonigral degeneration—rare, progresses to include cerebellar ataxia
   d. Wilson's disease—includes renal tubular aminoaciduria, diagnosed by serum ceruloplasmin and hepatic copper levels, definitively treatable with D-penicillamine

interruption in this pathway will substantially reduce any modulatory input from the basal ganglia into the excitatory (glutamate-mediated) transmission arriving from the cortex at the level of the striatum. Indeed, there is a well-documented relationship between lesions of the substantia nigra and movement abnormalities associated with parkinsonism. Moreover, certain drugs, such as reserpine, which deplete dopamine, produce the same effect. Thus, the clinical movement disorder created by dopamine paucity is generally termed Parkinson's disease, whereas those caused by other etiologies (Table 26.3) are referred to as "parkinsonism."

PARKINSON'S DISEASE

Classic Parkinson's disease is caused by premature degeneration of the dopaminergic neurons of the substantia nigra, with consequent loss of the ability to generate dopamine. A current hypothesis of the role of dopamine in basal ganglia function posits that there are two major pathways through the basal ganglia and that while each pathway receives significant dopaminergic input, each is affected differently by that input. One pathway, dubbed the *direct* pathway proceeds from the striatum to the medial globus pallidus and substantia nigra. Dopamine facilitates the direct pathway, releasing inhibition of thalamic nucleic. By stimulating cortical activity, the direct pathway thereby instigates movement.

The other pathway, called the *indirect* pathway, travels through the striatum to the lateral globus pallidus and subthalamic nucleus. Dopamine inhibits the indirect pathway with the result that, under normal circumstances, unwanted or abnormal movements are suppressed. But in Parkinson's disease, there is wholesale loss of dopaminergic neurons. Consequently, the influence of the direct pathway to instigate movement is suppressed leading to akinesia, whereas the influence of the indirect pathway to suppress unwanted movements becomes so potent that the patient now has difficulty carrying through movements once they are initiated.

Difficulty initiating a movement is manifested as akinesia, whereas slowness in carrying out movements is manifested as bradykinesia. The shuffling gait so characteristic of Parkinson's disease is testament to the pervasive bradykinesia in this disorder. Although the term bradykinesia implies slowness of movement, within this slowing of gross motor activity, there is actually a subset of hyperkinetic movements. These include a tremor at rest, most marked in the distal extremities, and the classic "cog-wheel" rigidity of gross motor movements, which is consistent with the increased tone of the muscle groups involved. Thus, a closer look at the abnormalities of movement in Parkinson's disease points to a direct relationship between the abnormal movements and a decrease in the elaboration of the inhibitory neurotransmitter—dopamine.

Attempts at dopamine replacement therapy for Parkinsonism failed, because dopamine, unlike the neurotransmitter glutamate (eg, "Chinese restaurant syndrome") does not cross the blood-brain barrier. However, a treatment breakthrough took place when it was discovered that limited amounts of DOPA enter the brain, and are decarboxylated to dopamine. Although the specific site of this decarboxylation is not known, it is clear that it is not the dopaminergic neurons of the substantia nigra. It is postulated that the reaction takes place in neighboring neurotransmitter-generating cells, and that the dopamine thus synthesized reaches the appropriate neural pathways by diffusion. Many factors impinge on the success of this treatment modality, including the presence of peripheral DOPA-decarboxylase activity, relatively low permeability of the blood-brain barrier to DOPA and the overall continued reduction of decarboxylase activity in the basal ganglia. Peripheral decarboxylase activity can be inhibited by use of the structural analogue, carbidopa, permitting reduction of the administered DOPA dosage. The limited quantities of DOPA reaching the brain and the nonspecific sites of decarboxylation suggest that, in the face of the therapeutic benefit, dopamine receptors remain intact and may even be either increased in number or sensitivity. Although significant problems remain in the treatment of Parkinson's disease, the success of DOPA therapy stands as a monument to the marriage of neurochemical research with clinical neurology.

The incidence of all forms of parkinsonism in the United States is impressive, with an estimated 50,000 new cases appearing per year. The majority of these are classic Parkinson's disease, which has an increasing incidence with age, the peak occurring at 75 years. There is a predominance of cases in males over females, in a ratio of 3:2. The etiology of the basal ganglia degeneration is unknown, but twin studies have shown a lack of concordance, indicating that genetic factors do not play a major role.

HUNTINGTON'S DISEASE

Huntington's disease is an entity that has been the subject of intense scrutiny by scientists and the popular press in recent years. Long known to be an inherited disorder with an autosomal dominant pattern, until recently it was not possible to predict which of an affected person's progeny was at risk for the gene. Thus, each child has a 50% chance of inheriting such a gene with its attendant clinical manifestations. Full-blown Huntington's disease is marked by a characteristic triad of dementia, chorea, and behavioral abnormalities. Given the peak age of onset at 40 years, most children at risk already were born before the parent became affected, and were forced to witness their parent's clinical decline into dementia. For these progeny, their existences were a lifetime of agony because of uncertainty over their own destinies. For these and other reasons, research scientists actively pursued the abnormal gene, finally showing a strong linkage to a G8 clone on chromosome 4. However, the distance between the putative Huntington's disease gene and the G8 locus is such that there is an incidence of recombination of about 5%. Recombination will render the probe for G8 useless in detection of the mutant gene in at least 5% of patients, translating itself into a 5% rate of false reassurance that a family member of an affected individual is not carrying the gene. Very recently, it was announced that the gene itself has been located. It is now clear that at the 5′ end of the gene, which is 210 Kb in length, the codon CAG is repeated between 11 to 24 times in normals, whereas the Huntington's disease mutation consists of from 42 to 86 repeats. At this time, the nature of the protein coded for by the gene is not known. Thus, the biochemical consequence of mutation cannot be specified. Nonetheless, mapping of the specific gene can be expected to lead rapidly to a very simple and foolproof method of detection without regard to recombinants of a marker gene. In cases that are identifiable by genetic probing, many other moral dilemmas present themselves. For example, what are the implications of Huntington gene detection in a healthy 20-year-old with respect to the impact of such information on future life quality?

Despite the many problems created by gene detection techniques, the power to understand the biochemical abnormalities deriving from presence of the gene are almost within our grasp. We may soon know why neurons, predominantly in the striatum and the cerebral cortex, involute and are replaced by glial cell proliferation. At the moment, we understand only at the level of neurochemistry that there is a consistent loss of GABA and glutamic acid decarboxylase in the basal ganglia. This state parallels the deficiency of this enzyme in genetic defects described in infants, as in glutaric aciduria, Type I. The movement disorder, which is characterized by chorea and dystonia, is strikingly similar in these two disorders, and the striatum is the focus of the neuropathologic damage in each. However, although the pathophysiologic effects on movement in glutaric aciduria derive from secondary inhibition of glutamic acid decarboxylase, the striatal involution in Huntington's disease remains unexplained. Beyond loss of GABA-ergic neurons, there is a decline in specific cholinergic neurons in the striatum as well. An additional factor in Huntington's disease is so-called *glutamate excitotoxicity*, caused by sustained increases in glutamate which result in neuronal death. When glutamate levels remain elevated in brain, Ca^{++} influx is dramatically increased activating both Ca^{++} dependent proteases and phospholipase A_2 which releases arachidonic acid from cell membranes. Arachidonate is precursor to eicosanoids, thromboxanes, and leukotrienes—all of which have been implicated in inflammation. Taken together, these glutamate-mediated effects cause death of neurons.

Recently, a hypothesis has been put forward to explain how the abnormal number of repeated CAG trinucleotides in Huntington's disease and several other neurodegenerative diseases lead to neuronal death. It has been suggested that the CAG repeats in both normal individuals and patients with Huntington's disease are translated into a string of glutamine residues situated at the amino terminus of the protein. The amino terminus, including the polyglutamine residues, may function as a signal sequence directing the protein to its intended intracellular site. Extra glutamine residues in Huntington's disease, occurring as a result of the abnormal number of repeats might be cleaved and, if not degraded, could exert neurotoxic effects. One possible avenue of toxicity would be to mimic the action of polyamines that have excitotoxic properties, sparking the cascade of effects discussed with glutamate excitotoxicity. At present, this hypothesis is an interesting speculation.

Emotional disturbances in Huntington's disease are very common and are considered a second member of the diagnostic triad. These may actually precede motor changes, but isolated emotional problems such as personality changes, impulsiveness, paranoia, and depression are so common in the general population that they offer little ground for suspicion in themselves. Further progression of the disease to include cognitive defects, such as loss of recent memory, loss of organizational skills, and true intellectual deficits completes the clinical triad. The full-blown disease, combining the motor deficits leading to loss of ambulation with the independent and secondary emotional disturbances and the intellectual deficits, creates an individual who is totally dependent and, therefore, often intolerable to their families.

It is estimated that Huntington's disease is present in 4 to 8/100,000 individuals. It occurs equally in both sexes and incomplete penetrance of the gene has not been described.

Treatment is largely symptomatic. Reserpine is useful for its dopamine-depletion effect at the presynaptic site and generally produces a decrease in choreiform movements. Tricyclic antidepressants and antipsychotic agents are useful in treatment of the emotional and intellectual deficits.

To summarize, Huntington's Disease and Parkinson's disease represent polar opposites of the effects of lesions of the basal ganglia. In Huntington's disease, there are abnormal movements and dementia associated with decreased signal output from the basal ganglia, whereas in Parkinson's disease, there is increased signal output causing tremor, rigidity, and bradykinesia. The final common pathway for expression of these varying inputs as clinical disease is believed to be through the subthalamic nucleus.

Dementias

As a group, the dementias all cause permanent impairment of memory, attention span, and ability to think abstractly and plan future actions, all occurring in an individual who at one time enjoyed normal or near normal intellectual function. Thus, the dementias are distinguished from mental retardation, because with mental retardation, normal intellectual function either is not attained or rapidly regresses. It follows that mental retardation is an affliction of the young developing brain, with clinical presentation in the first few years of life.

Even in normal adults, demise of nerve cells is believed to occur beginning at around age 30 years, so that by age 70 years, a significant loss of neurons is typical. Yet, most elderly individuals do not suffer from dementia, although because of the decrease in the number of neurons, older people are more susceptible to the neurotoxic effects of various drugs, notably the psychotropic drugs. These drugs include barbiturates, benzodiazepines, phenothiazines, antidepressants, MAO inhibitors and anticholinergics, as well as ethanol, glucocorticoids, and cardiac glycosides.

The major causes of true dementia are Alzheimer's disease and multiple strokes or infarcts. Alzheimer's disease, the most common form of dementia in the elderly, is characterized by severe memory loss, loss of reasoning and arithmethic abilities, and episodes of confusion. Eventually, most patients become unable to care for themselves, suffering from widespread failure of all cognitive functions. Because Alzheimer's disease is so prevalent there is, understandably, great interest in determining the root cause in order to prevent this devastating condition—one that exacts such a terrible personal toll and accounts for billions of dollars in health-care costs.

From a neuropathologic viewpoint, the most striking lesions in Alzheimer's disease are the β-amyloid plaques (senile plaques) and neurofibrillary tangles. Plaques consist of a core of amyloid protein surrounded by abnormal cell processes and dead or dying neurons and glial cells. Although these two findings are characteristic of Alzheimer's disease, they are found in other degenerative brain disorders. Moreover, they are found in small numbers in brains of individuals who do not suffer from dementia.

The amyloid core is composed of a small fragment of about 40 amino acids, cleaved from a much larger precursor containing 695 amino acid residues. This fragment is termed the β-amyloid precursor in recognition of its β-pleated sheet structure (see Chapter 1). It is interesting that the precursor protein is encoded on chromosome 21 and even more notable that patients with Down syndrome (Trisomy 21) precociously develop the β-amyloid deposits characteristic of Alzheimer's disease. In fact, there is one form of Alzheimer's that is inherited, being associated with a defect on chromosome 21. We must emphasize, however, that most cases of Alzheimer's disease are not inherited, and furthermore, that other inherited forms have been associated with defects on chromosomes other than 21.

Although the deposition of β-amyloid protein (β-APP) is a factor in the pathogenesis of Alzheimer's disease, it is not clear whether this accumulation is the direct biochemical cause. Much remains to be learned about the normal function of the β-APP, but significant homology with serine protease inhibitors suggests that one of its roles may be to modulate activity of extracellular serine proteases, perhaps during differentiation. Whatever its physiologic function, in Alzheimer's disease, over years, there is considerable accumulation of the peptide fragment (amyloid β-peptide) with associated effects on axons and dendrites. One aspect of this association may be the binding of amyloid β-peptide to serine protease inhibitor receptors, hampering their ability to remove extracellular proteases. Unchecked action of extracellular proteases could cause damage to neurons, just as α_1-antitrypsin deficiency permits unrestrained activity of proteases in lung.

Neurofibrillary tangles (NFTs) are also found in brains of patients dying with Alzheimer's disease. These NFTs are bundles of fibers found within neuronal cell bodies. They are made of an abnormally phosphorylated protein called tau, which is one of the microtubule associated proteins (MAPs). MAPs are important in stabilizing microtubules, serving also to modify microtubules so as to provide a site of attachment on the microtubules to adjacent cell structures.

NFTs consist of pairs of twisted filaments, called paired helical filaments (PHFs), that derive from the region of the tau protein that binds to microtubules (Figure 26.7). Also associated with NFT is the protein ubiquitin, which is thought to have a role in nonlysosomal degradation of proteins. Some workers believe that PHF formation is a secondary event coming after damage to the cytoskeleton of neuronal cell bodies, whereas others believe they are central to the pathogenesis of Alzheimer's disease. This controversy represents just one of the unsolved puzzles of this devastating dementia. Other puzzles include the normal function of APP, the relationship of age-related changes in brain to those changes associated with Alzheimer's disease, the process responsible for the abnormal phosphorylation of the tau protein, and whether the mitochondrial enzyme changes observed in Alzheimer's disease are primary or secondary to the neuronal degeneration. Because of the great interest that attaches to Alzheimer's disease, the next few years should witness dramatic strides in understanding the enigma of Alzheimer's disease.

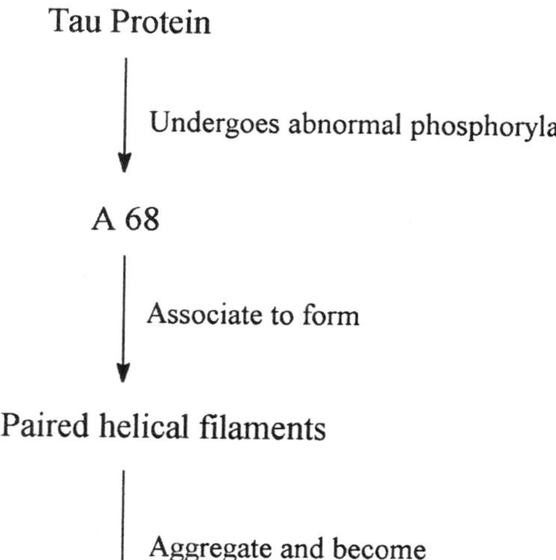

Figure 26.7. The formation of neurofibrillary tangles. These structures, found in brains of patients afflicted with Alzheimer's disease, are formed from normal, microtubule associated protein (Tau protein) which undergoes abnormal phosphorylation. It is unclear as to what role these structures play in pathogenesis of Alzheimer's disease, and what accounts for the abnormal phosphorylation process.

Metabolic Disorders

In this section, we have limited discussion solely to inborn errors that originate from an enzyme defect predominantly expressed in the central nervous system. We do this because many other entities can wreak devastation upon an individual's nervous system. The scope of these secondary causes is so broad, including heavy metals, medications, other inborn errors of metabolism (apart from neurodegenerative disorders), and the like, that they cannot be adequately covered in a discussion of this length.

Neurodegenerative disorders constitute an extensive group including those that are primarily hereditary in nature. Complete discussions of these entities involve a total of 1500 out of 3000 pages in the key reference book in the field, obviously beyond the scope of this text. It is worth noting, as well, that most of the remaining 1500 pages are occupied by discussion of hereditary disorders that secondarily result in encephalopathic and intellectual changes. Despite all of this information, what is still lacking is a unifying biochemical explanation for the relationship between the genetic defect and the deterioration of mental capacity that ensue. This is true for both the primary and the secondary neurodegenerative disorders.

Many of these disorders are the result of a defect in a specific lysosomal enzyme. With the availability of prenatal diagnosis for many of these storage diseases, the birth of an unaffected infant can be ensured. In evaluating an infant or child suspected of having a neurodegenerative storage disease, one should determine if the process is acute or chronic, static or progressive. A degenerative disease may evolve rather insidiously over a protracted period of time ranging from months to years. If the history suggests a delay in or failure of the acquisition of developmental milestones, progressive deviation from the normative curves, or regression of previously attained milestones, the physician should be alerted to the possibility of a neurodegenerative disorder.

PATHOGENESIS OF MENTAL DYSFUNCTION IN LYSOSOMAL STORAGE DISEASES

Two general consequences of accumulation of undegraded cell constituents appear to bear upon the pathogenesis of mental dysfunction in the lysosomal storage diseases. Cell dysfunction and cell death occur at some point when storage exceeds a critical threshold. Although that threshold has not been established, it must relate to the disruption of cellular components, as well as possible toxic effects of some of the "detergent-like" glycosphingolipids that accumulate.

An additional factor in the mental dysfunction relates to distortion of the intricately laid out neuronal geometry of the central nervous system. This geometry must be fundamental to the myriad connections that underlie the integrated development and functioning of the nervous system. Abnormal, very large neuronal processes termed meganeurites form as a response to accumulation of undigested cell constituents in neurons. These meganeurites are often larger than the parent cell body and with their multiple spines ramify in a haphazard fashion, forming aberrant contacts with other neurons, dendrites, and meganeurites. In this way, they have a profoundly deleterious effect on the normal "wiring diagram" of the brain.

Metachromatic Leukodystrophy

As a representative of this large group of lysosomal storage diseases, we have selected metachromatic leukodystrophy (MLD) for discussion. This disorder derives its name from the original description of an adult with general paresis whose nervous system showed metachromatic staining properties. Later, it was discovered that various tissues, such as kidney, liver, gallbladder, and retina among others, also exhibit metachromasia in affected patients. At the present time there are seven clinical entities categorized as different forms of MLD, five of which represent deficiency of the lysosomal enzyme arylsulfatase A. Deficiency of this enzyme results in defective catabolism of many sulfolipids, causing accumulation of partially degraded material in the lysosome. A principal substrate for the enzyme in vivo is cerebroside sulfate, an important membrane component of the myelin sheath.

Membrane sulfolipids, because of their polar side groups, possess both hydrophilic and hydrophobic properties. The importance of such dual affinities to the overall interaction of the cell membrane with the internal and external milieu cannot be overstated. Cerebroside sulfate, in particular, is known to be linked to basic proteins at the surface of the myelin sheath membrane through ionic interactions. There is also a correlation between the quantity of cerebroside sulfate present in the membrane and the Na^+-K^+ ATPase activity; exposure of such a membrane to arylsulfatase A results in decreased ATPase activity. The implications of disruptions in this sulfolipid homeostatic system for maintenance of ionic gradients, as well as the ability to conduct neural impulses are enormously far-reaching, and involve tissues outside of the nervous system as well. Within the nervous system, sulfolipids are implicated in function of β-endorphin and GABA, and possibly serotonin receptor sites. Alterations of sulfolipid homeostasis would be expected to affect binding capacities of these receptor sites within the central nervous system, with consequent major disruptions in function.

Given the implications of an abnormality in sulfolipid homeostasis, it is fortunate that all forms of MLD together occur with an overall incidence of approximately 1:100,000. Clinically, all forms of MLD present themselves with the features of a neurodegenerative disease, due chiefly to a process of demyelination. The major distinguishing feature of the various forms is the age of onset (Table 26.4), the duration of the clinical course correlating positively with this factor. Histopathologic findings in MLD correlate with the neurophysiologic findings. There is demyelination in both the central and peripheral nervous systems, together with metachromatic granules bounded by lysosomal membranes. The chemical composition of these granules is largely sulfolipid, together with cholesterol and phospholipid. Whereas sulfatides comprise 4% or less of normal cerebral white matter dry weight, in infantile MLD they are increased to more than 10%. The granules are found throughout the central nervous system, within macrophages, oligodendrocytes and free within the tissues. Location of the granules is not confined to areas of obvious destruction of the myelin sheath. This destruction is widespread, in severe areas progressing to cavitation and spongy degeneration, and the entire white matter of the brain is markedly decreased in mass. Cortical neurons are spared, although their axons are frequently denuded of myelin altogether. The cerebellum atrophies, with marked reduction in numbers of Purkinje cells.

Neurophysiologic changes, as stated, parallel

Table 26.4. Clinical Phenotypes of Metachromatic Leukodystrophy

PHENOTYPE	AGE AT ONSET	CLINICAL FEATURES	DURATION OF ILLNESS
Late infantile	24–48 months	Developmental delay, speech and motor delay, eventual seizures, quadriparesis	Several months to a few years
Early juvenile	4–6 years	Ataxia, abnormal posture, optic atrophy, quadriparesis	10–20 years
Late juvenile	6–12 years	Abnormal cognition, ataxia, long-tract signs, extrapyramidal signs, quadriparesis	10–20 years
Adult	>16 years	Dementia, psychosis, ataxia, incontinence, quadriparesis	Several decades

the pattern of histopathologic events. Electroencephalographic patterns become abnormal, sometimes earlier than the clinical onset of symptoms. Nerve conduction velocity decreases in both sensory and motor pathways. Brainstem auditory evoked response indicates delayed conduction in auditory nerve and brainstem, and may precede nerve conduction abnormalities. Visual evoked response may also be abnormal.

To a significant degree, the age of onset will determine the nature of the clinical presentation. Obviously, for example, when speech is developing at age 1 to 2 years, clinical onset at that time will result in delay or failure of acquisition of speech. However, after full development of speech by 4 to 6 years, one would expect changes in an established pattern. In all MLD other than the congenital form, the overall clinical picture involves impairment of locomotion, ataxia and general regression of whatever stage of development has been reached at onset. As with most clinical categorizations, there is a vast degree of heterogeneity within each group. In general, however, the earlier the age of onset the more rapid and severe the progression. Irrespective of the form, all cases of MLD progress eventually to a state of severe intellectual deficit, and from there to a final, vegetative state.

A key, unanswered question regarding pathogenesis of MLD is what relationship exists between a deficient catabolic enzyme and normal synthesis of the substrate for this enzyme? A simple possibility would be that sulfolipid granule accumulation is detrimental to cellular metabolism. If this were the case, it would be reasonable to expect that the rate of accumulation would determine the age of clinical onset, and that this rate would be related to degree of residual enzyme activity. This, however, has not been demonstrated, the degree of arylsulfatase A deficiency being equally profound in both the infantile and adult-onset forms of MLD. A more reasonable hypothesis, based on classic enzyme theory, is the product inhibition of the microsomal synthetic enzyme, sulfotransferase, the normal product of which is cerebroside-3-sulfate. This possibility remains untested. A third possibility is that sulfatide is recycled in turnover of myelin, a process which requires partial degradation of the sulfolipid which, in MLD cannot proceed through the initial catabolic step. This, too, remains unexamined. Thus, although we understand a great deal about the enzyme defect, we lack important information regarding its relationship to pathogenesis of the disease. Without this knowledge, no rational therapeutic means exist with which to counter the devastating effects of MLD, nor any other disease entity falling into this category.

MENTAL RETARDATION

Mental retardation is considered to be a nonprogressive intellectual deficit that occurs before age 18 years. Thus, it differs from dementia, in which intellectual function is lost by an adult who had been functioning normally. Because of the potential for harm to the individual and to the family, it is imperative that a diagnosis of mental retardation, particularly when mild, be carefully documented. This usually requires a longitudinal approach to diagnosis. Although the diagnosis of mental retardation in an older child may be obvious, it may not be so obvious in the infant and young child. In the young child, tracking acquisition of developmental milestones is an important aspect of evaluation, and the revised Denver Developmental Screening Test has been refined to improve its predictive value in case finding. IQ testing is a key component of evaluation of children suspected of mental retardation, but it is vital to remember that human beings possess many intelligences, and that IQ is inadequate to describe the full gamut of human behavior. In addition, it is a mistake to allow only one measurement to label a child for life, foreclosing on any reasonable hopes for a productive life within the realm of their total capabilities. Even so, if a professionally administered battery of IQ tests reveals a score more than 2 standard deviation (SD) below the norm, this is strong evidence for serious impairment of some cognitive functions. Many such individuals can lead productive lives, and so it becomes essential to give realistic hope and options to parents who must cope with this diagnosis—an emotional task akin to being told that one has cancer.

As enormous and diverse as causes of mental retardation are, certain broad categories can be very briefly mentioned. Severe mental retardation is frequently the result of a process that begins in utero, including chromosomal abnormalities of which Down syndrome and Fragile X syndrome are the most common. Inborn errors, endocrinopathies, congenital anomalies, hypoxic injury, and teratogens are also important causes of severe mental retardation. However, mild mental retardation is not typically associated with the many obvious clinical conditions that result in severe mental retardation. It is practically self-evident that any infection or hypoxic event resulting in structural damage to critical areas of the cerebral cortex will often lead to intellectual impairment. Age plays an important role in recovery, as do other many unknown factors. There is a plasticity of the developing nervous system that can contribute to recovery; however, in the fully developed brain, loss of certain functions can be gradually assumed by other areas of the brain. Although we can describe these differences phenomenologically, science is presently unable to define any of the underlying mechanisms.

Careful consideration of the development of the human brain leads to some vital points—chronic insult is more likely to result in permanent deficit in the immature than the fully developed brain, although the timing of initiation of the insult may play an important part in determining the nature of the deficit. For example, the infant born with phenylketonuria, if treated early suffers no significant ill effect with respect to intellect. The same child, recognized and treated late, may be speech-impaired with significant intellectual deficit, yet continue to develop on treatment. If treatment is withheld for years, such a child will be irretrievably impaired and probably institutionalized for life. In contrast to these scenarios, a genetically normal infant born to an untreated phenylketonuric mother, will almost certainly be unalterably mentally retarded. Thus, we would be forced to conclude that in utero exposure to high phenylalanine levels irreparably damages the developing nervous system, whereas the same level of exposure postnatally must be much more extensive to achieve the same result.

The previous example leads us to consider the inborn errors of metabolism as causes for mental retardation. We will sweep aside those of this group in which direct central nervous system involvement is an integral part (Table 26.5), because we already have said that structural damage will have obvious implications for function. Having done this, we are left with a metabolically diverse group of disorders in which there is usually an identifiable elevation in one or more metabolites. However, it is important to avoid the simplistic notion that "toxic" metabolites are the direct cause of the abnormal intellectual function. Given the complexity of metabolic regulatory mechanisms such as feedback or product inhibition or allosterism, there are alternative possibilities:

1. A direct toxicity or lethality toward brain cellular elements, mediated by an inhibitory effect of the high levels of intermediates proximal to the defect upon one or more critical metabolic pathways;
2. An indirect toxicity or lethality, mediated by deficient synthesis of compounds distal to the defect necessary for normal synthetic or regulatory metabolic pathways;
3. A combination of 1 and 2 to varying degrees.

There is a high likelihood that any given inborn error resulting in cerebral dysfunction exerts its effects through a combination of direct and indirect toxicity.

Many factors complicate our ability to understand the chemistry and physiology of the brain. Measurements of circulating metabolites, for example, do little to clarify levels of these compounds in brain tissue. Metabolite levels within brain tissue itself are distributed unevenly between cellular and interstitial compartments. The brain is an enormous organ with numerous cell types of vastly different functions and located in topographically distinct sites. Beyond these problems, there are the difficulties in tracing the course of afferent and efferent transmissions. In rat brain, for example, each neuron is engaged in several hundred to over 20,000 synapses, with an estimated neuron population of 150,000,000. The human brain weighs roughly 700 times more than the rat brain! Additional detriments to our understanding include incomplete information regarding the presence and location in brain of well-described enzyme pathways in other organs, or the reverse-pathways which may be uniquely expressed in brain tissue. Recording of EEG and nerve conduction velocities in afflicted patients

Table 26.5. Disorders Associated with Mental Retardation

Amino Acid Disorders
- Carnosinemia (3)*
- Gamma-glutamyl transpeptidase deficiency
- Hartnup disease (4, 5, 7)
- Histidinemia (4)
- Homocystinuria (cystathionine-β-synthase) (3–5, 7)
- Hydroxylysinemia (α-aminoadipic aciduria) (3)
- Hyper-β-alaninemia (3)
- Hyperleucinemia (3–5)
- Hyperlysinemia, episodic (3, 4)
- Hyperlysinemia, persistent (3, 7)
- Hypervalinemia (1, 4, 5)
- Lysinuric protein intolerance (3, 4, 6, 7)
- β-Mercaptolactate cysteine disulfiduria (3)
- Methionine malabsorption syndrome (2, 3, 7)
- Nonketotic hyperglycinemia (1, 3, 4)
- Pipecolic acidemia (4–6)
- Phenylketonuria (phenylalanine hydroxylase) (3–5, 7)
- Tyrosine amino transferase deficiency (5, 7)
- Tryptophanuria (4, 7)

Organic Acidemias
- Glutaric aciduria (2)
- Isovaleric acidemia (1, 2, 3)
- β-Ketothiolase deficiency (2, 3)
- Maple syrup urine disease (1, 2, 3)
- Methylmalonic aciduria (1, 2, 3)
- Propionic acidemia (1, 2, 3)
- Pyroglutamic aciduria (2, 4)
- Pyruvate carboxylase deficiency (2)
- Pyruvate dehydrogenase deficiency (2, 4)

Urea Cycle Defects
- Argininosuccinic aciduria (3, 4, 6, 7)
- Carbamyl phosphate synthetase deficiency (3)
- Citrullinemia (3, 4)
- Hyperargininemia (3, 4, 6)
- Hyperornithinemia (3)
- Hyperornithinemia, hyperammonemia, and homocitrullinuria (3)
- Ornithine transcarbamylase deficiency (3)

Carbohydrate Disorders
- Galactosemia (5, 6)
- Glycogen storage diseases (3, 6)
- Glycogen synthetase deficiency (3)
- Hypoglycemia (3)
- Leigh's syndrome (2, 3, 7)

Neurodegenerative Disorders

Mycopolysaccharidoses
- β-Glucuronidase deficiency (5, 6)
- Hunter's syndrome (5–7)
- Hurler's syndrome (5–7)
- Mucolipidoses (see Chapter 32)
- Mucopolysaccharidosis VIII (6)
- Sanfilippo's syndrome (3–7)

Sphingolipidoses and Lipid Disorders
- Abetalipoproteinemia (4, 5)
- Gaucher's disease (5–7)
- GM_1 gangliosidosis (5, 6)
- Krabbe's disease (3, 4)
- Metachromatic leukodystrophy (4, 5)
- Niemann-Pick disease (3–7)
- Tay-Sachs disease (3–5)

Defect Unknown
- Alexander's disease
- Ceroid lipofuscinosis (3–6)
- Neuronal-axonal dystrophy (3)
- Schilder's disease (5)

Other
- Ataxia-telangiectasia (4, 5, 7)
- Cretinism (5, 7)
- Familial dysautonomia (5)
- Formiminoglutamic aciduria (4)
- Hypophosphatasia (late manifestation of oxycephaly) (3, 4)
- Lesch-Nyhan syndrome (4)
- Lowe's syndrome (5)
- Menkes' disease (3, 7)
- Myotonic dystrophy (5)
- Neonatal hyperbilirubinemia (3, 4)
- Nephrogenic diabetes insipidus
- Pseudo hypoparathyroidism (5)

* Associated findings; 1—catastrophic presentation in the neonate; 2—derangements of acid-base balance; 3—seizures; 4—other neurologic; 5—eye findings; 6—visceromegaly; 7—skin and/or hair findings.

provides virtually no insight into the basic molecular mechanisms at work. It would appear that only through painstaking molecular studies, involving distinct metabolic pathways in each pathologic state will we eventually come to a better understanding of these mechanisms. It is devoutly to be hoped that the human race survives long enough to achieve this and that, once it does, we will have arrived at the point where we can use the information to grasp the meaning of "intelligence" and "personality."

SUGGESTED READINGS

GENERAL

Adams RD, Victor M. Principles of neurology. 5th ed. New York: McGraw Hill, 1993.

Eisen JS. Development of motoneuronal phenotype. Annu Rev Neurosci 1994;17:1.

Guberman A. An introduction to clinical neurology. Boston: Little, Brown & Co, 1994.

Hockfield S, Kalb RG. Activity-dependent structural changes during neuronal development. Curr Opin Neurobiol 1993;3:87.

Hopkins A. Clinical neurology: a modern approach. Oxford: Oxford University Press, 1993.
Horn JP. The heroic age of neurophysiology. Hosp Pract 1992;27:65.
Keynes R, Krumlauf R. Hox genes and regionalization of the nervous system. Annu Rev Neurosci 1994;17:109.
Oppenheim RW. Cell death during development of the nervous system. Annu Rev Neurosci 1991;14:453.
Rowland LP, ed. Merritt's textbook of neurology, 9th ed. Baltimore: Williams & Wilkins, 1995.
Snider WD. Functions of the neurotropins during nervous system development: what the knockouts are teaching us. Cell 1994;77:627.
Sudarsky L. Pathophysiology of the nervous system. Boston: Little, Brown & Co, 1990.
Timiras PS, Privat A, Giacobini E, et al. Plasticity and regeneration of the nervous system. Adv Exp Med Biol 1991;296:1–352.

NERVOUS SYSTEM FUNCTION

Dagani F, D'Angelo E. Glutamate metabolism, release, and quantal transmission at central excitatory synapses: implications for neural plasticity. Funct Neurol 1992;7:315.
D'Angelo E, Rossi P. Excitatory amino acid regulation of neuronal functions. Funct Neurol 1992;7:145.
Davies RW, ed. Life and death in the nervous system. Proceedings of the Robertson Symposium. Prog Neurobiol 1994;42:283.
Furuichi T, Kohda K, Miyawaki A, Mikoshiba K. Intracellular channels. Curr Opin Neurobiol 1994;4:294.
Greenberg DA, Chan J, Sampson HA. Endothelins and the nervous system. Neurology 1992;42:25.
Hille B. G Protein-coupled mechanisms and nervous signaling. Neuron 1992;9:187.
Hille B. Ionic channels of excitable membranes. 2nd ed. Sunderland, MA: Sinauer Associates, 1992.
Joe EH, Angelides KJ. Clustering and mobility of voltage-dependent sodium channels during myelination. J Neurosci 1993;13:2993.
Siegel GJ, Agranoff BW, Albers RW, Molinoff PB, eds. Basic neurochemistry. 5th ed. New York: Raven Press, 1994.
Strange PG. Brain biochemistry and brain disorders. Oxford: Oxford University Press, 1992.

SEIZURES

Engel J Jr, Starkman S. Overview of seizures. Emerg Med Clin North Am 1994;12:895.
Jagoda A. Nonconvulsive seizures. Emerg Med Clin North Am 1994;12:963.
Lothman EW. Basic mechanisms of the epilepsies. Current Opinion in Neurology and Neurosurgery 1992;5:216.
Morrell MJ. Differential diagnosis of seizures. Neurol Clin 1993;11:737.
Mandel G. Sodium channel regulation in the nervous system: how the action potential keeps in shape. Curr Opin Neurobiol 1993;3:278.
Partridge LD, Muller TH, Swandulla D. Calcium-activated non-selective channels in the nervous system. Brain Res Brain Res Rev 1994;19:319.
Shin C, McNamara JO. Mechanisms of epilepsy. Annu Rev Med 1994;45:379.
So EL. Update on epilepsy. Med Clin North Am 1993;77:203.
Wyllie E, ed. The treatment of epilepsy: principles and practice. Philadelphia: Lea and Febiger, 1993.

COMA

Bates D. The management of medical coma. J Neurol Neurosurg Psychiatry 1993;56:589.
Griggs RC, Satran R. Metabolic encephalopathy. In: Rosenberg RN, ed. Comprehensive neurology. New York: Raven Press, 1991:525.
Medical aspects of the persistent vegetative state (2). The multi-society task force on PVS. N Engl J Med 1994;330:1572.

INFECTIOUS DISEASE

Bruno RL, Frick NM, Cohen J. Polioencephalitis, stress, and the etiology of post-polio sequelae. Orthopedics 1991;14:1269.
Charlton KM. The pathogenesis of rabies and other lyssaviral infections. Recent studies. Curr Top Microbiol Immunol 1994;187:95.
DeLouvois J. Acute bacterial meningitis in the newborn. J Antimicrob Chemother 1994;34(suppl A):61.
Groleau G. Rabies. Emerg Med Clin North Am 1992;10:361.
Hemachuda T. Human rabies: clinical aspects, pathogenesis, and potential therapy. Curr Top Microbiol Immunol 1994;187:121.
King AA, Turner GS. Rabies: a review. J Comp Pathol 1993;108:1.
Johnson RT. The virology of demyelinating diseases. Ann Neurol 1994;36(suppl):S54.
Ren R, Racaniello VR. Poliovirus spreads from muscle to the central nervous system by neural pathways. J Infect Dis 1992;166:747.
Tsiang H. Pathophysiology of rabies virus infection of the nervous system. Adv Virus Res 1993;42:375.

VASCULAR DISEASES

Caplan LR. Stroke—a clinical approach. 2nd ed. Stoneham, MA: Butterworth-Heinemann, 1993.

Coull BM, Clark WM. Abnormalities of hemostasis in ischemic stroke. Med Clin North Am 1993;77:77.
Garcia JH, Ho KL. Pathology of hypertensive arteriopathy. Neurosurg Clin N Am 1992;3:497.
Matchar DB, McCrory DC, Barnett HJM, Feussner JR. Medical treatment for stroke prevention. Ann Intern Med 1994;121:41.
Moulin F, Crepin-Leblond T, Chopard JL, Bogousslavsky J. Hemorrhagic infarcts. Eur Neurol 1994;34:64.
The Dutch TIA trial study group: predictors of major vascular events in patients with a transient ischemic attack or nondisabling stroke. Stroke 1993;24:527.
Strangaard S, Paulson OB. Pathophysiology of stroke. J Cardiovasc Pharmacol 1990;15(suppl):S38.
Weaver JP, Fisher M. Subarachnoid hemorrhage: an update of pathogenesis, diagnosis and management. J Neurol Sci 1994;125:119.

DEGENERATIVE DISEASES

Bensimon G, Lacomblez L, Meininger V, et al. A controlled trial of riluzole in amyotrophic lateral sclerosis. N Engl J Med 1994;330:585.
Brown RH Jr. Amyotrophic lateral sclerosis: recent insights from genetics and transgenic mice. Cell 1995; 80:687.
Lowe J. New pathological findings in amyotrophic lateral sclerosis. J Neurol Sci 1994;124(suppl):38.
Rowland LP. Riluzole for the treatment of amyotrophic lateral sclerosis—too soon to tell? N Engl J Med 1994;330:636.
Rowland LP. Amyotropic lateral sclerosis: human challenge for neuroscience. Proc Natl Acad Sci U S A 1995;92:1251.
Smith RG, Appel SH. Molecular approaches to amyotrophic lateral sclerosis. Annu Rev Med 1995;46: 133.
Tolosa E, Berciano J. Choreas, hereditary and other ataxias, tics, myoclonus, and other movement disorders. Curr Opin Neurol Neurosurg 1993;6:358.

MULTIPLE SCLEROSIS

French-Constant C. Pathogenesis of multiple sclerosis. Lancet 1994;343:271.
Giang DW, Grow VM, Mooney C, et al. Clinical diagnosis of multiple sclerosis. The impact of magnetic resonance imaging and ancillary testing. Rochester-Toronto Magnetic Resonance Study Group. Arch Neurol 1994;51:61.
Hartung H-P. Immune-mediated demyelination. Ann Neurol 1993;33:563.
Mitchell G. Update on multiple sclerosis therapy. 1993;77: 231.
Weinshaker BG. Natural history of multiple sclerosis. Ann Neurol 1994;36(suppl):S6.

PARKINSON'S AND HUNTINGTON'S DISEASES

Calne DB. Treatment of Parkinson's disease. N Engl J Med 1993;329:1021.
Cha J-H, Dure LS IV. Trinucleotide repeats in neurologic diseases: an hypothesis concerning the pathogenesis of Huntington's disease, Kennedy's disease, and spinocerebellar ataxia type I. Life Sci 1994;54:1459.
Goldberg YP, Telenius H, Hayden MR. The molecular genetics of Huntington's disease. Curr Opin Neurol 1994;7:325.
Griffiths PD, Perry RH, Crossman AR. A detailed anatomical analysis of neurotransmitter receptors in the putamen and caudate in Parkinson's disease and Alzheimer's disease. Neurosci Lett 1994;169:68.
Gusella JF. Huntington's disease. Adv Hum Genet 1991; 20:125.
Gusella JF, MacDonald ME, Ambrose CM, Duyao MP. Molecular genetics of Huntington's disease. Arch Neurol 1993;50:1157.
Hallett M. Physiology of basal ganglia disorders: an overview. Can J Neurol Sci 1993;20:177.
Harper PS. Editorial: a specific mutation for Huntington's disease. J Med Genet 1993;30:975.
Jankovic J, Tolosa E, eds. Parkinson's disease and movement disorders. 2nd ed. Baltimore: Williams & Wilkins, 1993.
Kopin IJ. The pharmacology of Parkinson's disease therapy: an update. Annu Rev Pharmacol Toxicol 1993;32:467.
Marsden CD. Parkinson's disease. Postgrad Med J 1992; 68:538.
Marsden CD. Parkinson's disease. J Neurol Neurosurg Psychiatry 1994;57:672.
Parkinson's disease: diagnosis and therapy. Proceedings of a satellite symposium to the 2nd International Congress of Movement Disorders. Neurology 1993; 43(suppl):S1.
Purdon SE, Mohr E, Ilivitsky V, Jones BD. Huntington's disease: pathogenesis, diagnosis and treatment. J Psychiatry Neurosci 1994;19:359.
Sutherland GR, Richards RI. Dynamic mutations on the move. J Med Genet 1993;30:978.
The Huntington's Disease Collaborative Research Group. A novel gene containing a trinucleotide repeat that is expanded and unstable on Huntington's disease chromosomes. Cell 1993;72:971.

DEMENTIAS

Bennett DA, Evans DA. Alzheimer's disease. Dis Mon 1992;38:1.
Cordell B. β-amyloid formation as a potential therapeutic target for Alzheimer's disease. Annu Rev Pharmacol Toxicol 1994;34:69.
Hardy J. Alzheimer's disease. Clinical molecular genetics. Clin Geriatr Med 1994;10:239.

Lamour Y. Alzheimer's disease: a review of recent findings. Biomed Pharmacother 1994;48:312.

Lee VM-Y, Trojanowski JQ. The disordered neuronal cytoskeleton in Alzheimer's disease. Curr Opin Neurobiol 1992;2:653.

McKeith IG, Fairbairn AF, Perry RH, Thompson P. The clinical diagnosis and misdiagnosis of senile dementia of lewy body type (SDLT). Br J Psychiatry 1994;165: 324.

Norstedt C, Lannfelt L, Winblad B. Editorial. Alzheimer's disease: a molecular perspective. J Intern Med 1994; 235:195.

Price DL, Sisodia SS. Cellular and molecular biology of Alzheimer's disease and animal models. Annu Rev Med 1994;45:435.

Rosenberg RN. A causal role of amyloid in Alzheimer's disease: the end of the beginning. Neurology 1993;43: 851.

Roth ME. Advances in Alzheimer's disease. A review for the family physician. J Fam Pract 1993;37:593.

METABOLIC DISORDERS

Aicardi J. The inherited leukodystrophies: a clinical overview. J Inherit Metab Dis 1993;16:733.

Gieslemann V, Zlotogora J, Harris A, et al. Molecular genetics of metachromatic leukodystrophy. Hum Mutat 1994;4:233.

Heinisch U, Zlotogora J, Kafert S, Gieselmann V. Multiple mutations are responsible for the high frequency of metachromatic leukodystrophy in a small geographic area. Am J Hum Genet 1995;56:51.

Rapola J. Lysosomal storage diseases in adults. Pathol Res Pract 1994;190:759.

Scriver CS, Beaudet AL, Sly WS, Valle D, eds. The metabolic and molecular bases of inherited disease. 7th ed. New York: McGraw-Hill, 1995.

MENTAL RETARDATION

Batshaw ML. Mental retardation. Pediatr Clin North Am 1993;40:507.

First LR, Palfrey JS. The infant or young child with developmental delay. 1994;330:478.

Schaefer GB, Bodensteiner JB. Evaluation of the child with idiopathic mental retardation. Pediatr Clin North Am 1992;39:929.

Thapar A, Gottesman II, Owen MJ, et al. The genetics of mental retardation. Br J Psychiatry 1994;164:747.

Trembath RC. Genetic mechanisms and mental retardation. Journal of the Royal College of Physicians-London 1994;28:121.

Index

Note: Page numbers in *italics* indicate illustrations; numbers followed by "t" indicate tables.